Best
Restaurants
1998

Produced by:
AA Publishing

Maps prepared by:
the Cartographic Department of
The Automobile Association
Maps © The Automobile Association 1997

Restaurant assessments and rosette awards are based on reports of visits carried out anonymously by the AA's Hotel and Restaurant Inspectors.

Editor: Elizabeth Carter

Restaurant descriptions have been
contributed by the following team of writers:
William Boden, David Hancock, Catey Hillier,
Clarissa Hyman, Julia Hynard, David Mabey

Photograph of Toby Hill p20 © Tom Stockill

Cover illustration by:
Sue Climpson, Whitchurch, England

Typeset by:
Anton Graphics, Andover, England

Printed and bound by:
Gráficas Estella, SA, Navarra, Spain

Published by:
AA Publishing, which is a trading name of Automobile Association Developments Limited whose registered office is Norfolk House, Priestley Road, Basingstoke, Hampshire RG24 9NY
Registered number 1878835.

AA Ref 59925

ISBN 0 7495 1684 4

Contents

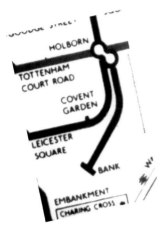

RESTAURANTS

HOW TO USE THIS *guide*

Every restaurant in this Guide has had at least one anonymous meal visit from an AA inspector. Many, especially at the higher award levels, have been visited more than once by different inspectors at different times. AA inspection visits are anonymous; no favours are accepted; no charge is made for entries in this Guide.

All the entries in this year's Guide have been written from reports filed by AA inspectors. Although our inspectors are a highly trained and very experienced team of professional men and women, it must be stressed that the opinions expressed are only opinions, based on the experience of one or more particular occasions. Assessments are therefore to some extent necessarily subjective. AA inspectors are experienced enough to make a balanced judgement, but they are not omniscient.

SAMPLE ENTRY (fictitious)

1. BRISTOL, The Restaurant   2.   3.   4.

5. **DIRECTIONS:** City centre

6. The Street XY21 1AB

7. **MAP 3:** ST57

8. **TEL:** 0111 2345678   **FAX:** 0111 3456789

9. **CHEF:** John Brown

   OWNERS: John & Mary Brown

10. **COST:** *Alc* £26.50, fixed-price L £11.50 (2 courses)/D £22. H/wine £9.75. ☺

11. **TIMES:** Noon-last L 2pm/7pm-last D 10pm. Closed L Sat, Sun, Mon, 1 wk Easter, 1 wk summer, 10 days Xmas, Bhs

12. **ADDITIONAL:** Bar meals; Sunday L; Children welcome; ❹ dishes

13. **SEATS:** 40. Private dining room 26. Jacket & tie preferred

14. **SMOKING:** No smoking in dining room

15. **ACCOMMODATION:** 3 en suite

16. **CREDIT CARDS:**

1. The Guide's entries are divided into sections. London restaurants are listed alphabetically by name (but see also the hotels featured on page 157). In the rest of Britain, establishments are listed in country and county order, by town, and then alphabetically within that town. There is also an index by establishment name.

2. **NEW** indicates an entry new to the Guide this year

3. indicates a waterside location

4. ❀ is the Guide's rosette award for cooking quality. Every restaurant included has been awarded one or more rosettes, up to a maximum of five. See page 8 for a clear explanation of how they are graded.

5. Directions are given wherever they have been supplied by the proprietor.

6. The establishment's address and postcode

7. The map number. In the London section, each restaurant has a map reference number to help locate its approximate position on the Central or Greater London maps on pages 825-827. In the remainder of the Guide, the map references refer to the 16 pages of maps of Britain starting on page 828. First is the map page number, followed by the National Grid Reference. To find the location, read the first figure across and the second figure vertically within the lettered square.

8. The establishment's telephone number, including its STD code.

9. The names of the chef(s) and owner(s). These are as up-to-date as we could make them at the time of going to press, but changes in personnel often occur, and may affect both the style and the quality of the restaurant.

10. *Alc* is the cost of a meal for one person, including coffee and service but not wine. Fixed-price lunch and dinner menus come next. If these meals have more or less than three courses we have indicated this. The cost of the house wine or one of the cheaper wines on the list follows. Prices quoted are a guide only, and are subject to change without notice. ☺ indicates where restaurants have told us they offer dinner for under £25 a head (excluding wine).

11. The times of the first and last orders for meals, and the days of the week the restaurant is closed, together with seasonal closures. Note that opening times are liable to change without notice.

12. In addition to meals in the restaurant, bar meals are served at lunch and/or dinner; Sunday lunch is served; Children are welcome, any age limitations are specified; 🍃 indicates where a vegetarian choice is always offered on a menu. Almost all restaurants featured will prepare a vegetarian dish or accommodate a special diet if given prior notice, but even where a symbol appears by an entry it is wise to check with the establishment first.

13. The number of seats in the restaurant. Not all restaurants will take private parties, the number given is for the maximum number of people in a party. Jacket and tie are preferred in a few restaurants, and this is specified.

14. Establishments that do not allow smoking in the dining room may allow it elsewhere, in a lounge bar, for instance. If you are a smoker, it is worth checking beforehand.

15. Accommodation is also available.

16. The credit cards accepted by the establishment.

- Mastercard
- American Express
- Visa
- Delta
- Diners
- Switch

TELEPHONE FOR DIRECTIONS
appears where an establishment has not supplied us with current details.

SIGNATURE DISHES
appears at the end of the main entry, supplied by chefs from establishments with three or more AA Rosettes. Some entries do not show signature dishes either because the chef has chosen not to give them or the establishment was a late appointment.

AA ℛOSETTE AWARDꞨ

𝒪ne rosette denotes simple, carefully prepared food, based on good quality, fresh ingredients, cooked in such a way as to emphasise honest flavours. Sauces and desserts will be home-made and the cooking will equate to first-class home cooking.

Two rosettes denote cooking that displays a high degree of competence on the part of the chef. The menus should include some imaginative dishes, making use of very good raw ingredients, as well as some tried and tested favourites. Flavours should be well balanced and complement or contrast with one another, not over-dominate.

French Garden - *the very latest in Villeroy & Boch's House & Garden Collection reflecting the warmth of the summer with colourful ripe fruits bordered with pale yellow bands and green fluted edging.*

Only about ten percent of the restaurants receiving rosette awards will achieve high enough standards of cooking, presentation of dishes and service to merit the AA's top awards of three, four and five rosettes.

Only cooking of the highest national standard receives three or more rosettes. Menus will be imaginative; dishes should be accurately cooked, demonstrate well-developed technical skills and a high degree of flair in their composition. Ingredients will be first-class, usually from a range of specialist suppliers, including local produce only if its quality is excellent. Most items – breads, pastries, pasta, petits fours – will be made in the kitchens, but if any are bought in, for example, breads, the quality will be excellent.

At this level, cuisine should be innovative, daring, highly accomplished and achieve a noteworthy standard of consistency, accuracy and flair throughout all the elements of the meal. Excitement, vibrancy and superb technical skill will be the keynotes of a chef's style.

Five rosettes is the supreme accolade, made to chefs at the very top of their profession. This award recognises superlative standards of cuisine at an international level, evident at every visit in every element of the meal. Creativity, skill and attention to detail will produce dishes cooked to perfection, with intense, exciting flavours in harmonious combinations and faultless presentation. Menus may be innovative or classical, and may use luxury ingredients like lobster, truffles, foie gras, etc. often in unexpected combinations and with secret ingredients that add an extra dimension of taste and interest to the entire range of dishes.

VILLEROY & BOCH

*R*osettes, ranging from one up to five, are awarded by the AA for culinary excellence, and an explanation of the levels is given opposite. Tableware designers and manufacturers Villeroy & Boch provide specially designed award plates to all the restaurants in this guide, but the index below lists only the highest rated restaurants. It is illustrated with photoraphs of designs which you may see either when dining out or on sale in the china departments of many of Britain's best stores. Full details of all the restaurants listed will be found in the directory.

LONDON

AUBERGINE,
11 Park Walk, SW10
☎0171 352 3449
CHEZ NICO
AT NINETY PARK LANE, W1
☎0171 409 1290
LE GAVROCHE,
43, UPPER BROOK STREET, W1
☎0171 408 0881
LE MERIDIEN PICCADILLY,
21, PICCADILLY, W1
☎0171 734 8000
LA TANTE CLAIRE,
68, ROYAL HOSPITAL ROAD, SW3
☎0171 352 6045

ENGLAND

BERKSHIRE
L'ORTOLAN,
CHURCH LANE, SHINFIELD
☎01734 883783
DEVON
GIDLEIGH PARK,
CHAGFORD ☎01647 432367
OXFORDSHIRE
LE MANOIR AUX QUAT' SAISONS,
GREAT MILTON
☎01844 278881

SCOTLAND

HIGHLAND
ALTNAHARRIE INN,
ULLAPOOL
☎01854 633230

LONDON

BIBENDUM,
MICHELIN HOUSE, SW3
☎0171 581 5817
THE CAPITAL,
BASIL STREET, KNIGHTSBRIDGE, SW3
☎0171 589 5171
THE RITZ,
150, PICCADILLY, W1
☎0171 493 8181

ENGLAND

BERKSHIRE
WATERSIDE INN,
FERRY ROAD, BRAY
☎01628 20691
BRISTOL
RESTAURANT LETTONIE,
9, DRUID HILL, BRISTOL
☎0117 968 6456
BUCKINGHAMSHIRE
CLIVEDEN HOTEL,
TAPLOW
☎01628 668561
CUMBRIA
MICHAEL'S NOOK,
GRASMERE
☎015394 35496
GLOUCESTERSHIRE
LE CHAMPIGNON SAUVAGE,
24, SUFFOLK ROAD, CHELTENHAM
☎01242 573449

HAMPSHIRE
GORDLETON MILL,
SILVER STREET, HORDLE, LYMINGTON
☎01590 682219
LANCASHIRE
PAUL HEATHCOTE'S RESTAURANT,
104-106 HIGHER ROAD, LONGRIDGE
☎01772 784969
LINCOLNSHIRE
WINTERINGHAM FIELDS,
WINTERINGHAM
☎01724 733096
RUTLAND
HAMBLETON HALL,
OAKHAM ☎01572 756991
SOMERSET
HOMEWOOD PARK,
HINTON CHARTERHOUSE
☎01225 723731
CASTLE HOTEL,
CASTLE GREEN, TAUNTON
☎01823 272671

Adeline - *evokes country style with light, fresh colours and small naively depicted flowers. Traditional style complimented by contemporary shape.*

LONDON

EC1

MAISON NOVELLI,
29, Clerkenwell Green,
☎0171 253 0994
TATSUSO RESTAURANT,
32, Broadgate Circle,
☎0171 638 5863

EC2

SEARCY'S BRASSERIE,
Library Floor, Barbican Centre,
Silk Street,
☎0171 588 3008

EC4

CITY RHODES RESTAURANT,
1, New Street Square,
☎0171 583 1313

NW1

ODETTES,
130, Regents Park Road,
☎0171 586 5486

SW1

AUBERGE DE PROVENCE
41, Buckingham-Gate,
☎0171 821 1899
LE CAPRICE,
Arlington House, Arlington
Street, ☎0171 629 2239
HALKIN HOTEL,
Halkin Street,
☎0171 333 1000
THE LANESBOROUGH,
Hyde Park Corner,
☎0171 259 5599
L'ORANGER,
5, St James's Street,
☎0171 839 3774
SHERATON PARK TOWER,
101, Knightsbridge,
☎0171 235 8050
SIMPLY NICO,
48A, Rochester Row,
☎0171 630 8061
THE SQUARE,
32, King Street, St James's,
☎0171 839 8787
VONG,
The Berkeley, Wilton Place,
☎0171 235 1010
ZAFFERANO,
15, Lowndes Street,
☎0171 235 5800

SW10

THE CANTEEN,
Harbour Yard, Chelsea Harbour,
☎0171 351 7330

SW13

RIVA,
169, Church Road, Barnes,
☎0181 748 0434

SW17

CHEZ BRUCE,
2, Bellevue Road,
☎0181 672 0114

SW3

CHAVOT,
257-259 Fulham Road,
☎0171 351 7823

Eden - *visions of spring in your own private paradise, where beautiful china does not have to be forbidden fruit!*

DAPHNE'S,
110-112 Draycott Avenue,
☎0171 584 4257
TURNERS,
87-89 Walton Street,
☎0171 584 6711

SW7

HILAIRE,
68, Old Brompton Road,
☎0171 584 8993

W1

ALASTAIR LITTLE SOHO,
49 Frith Street,
☎0171 734 5183
ATELIER,
41 Beak Street,
☎0171 287 2057
CAFE ROYAL GRILL ROOM,
68, Regent Street,
☎0171 437 9090
THE CONNAUGHT,
Carlos Place
☎0171 499 7070
THE CRITERION,
224 Piccadilly
☎0171 930 0488
THE DORCHESTER,
Park Lane ☎0171 629 8888
FOUR SEASONS HOTEL,
Hamilton Place, Park Lane,
☎0171 499 0888
HOTEL INTER-CONTINENTAL,
1, Hamilton Place, Hyde Park
Corner, ☎0171 409 3131
**THE LONDON HILTON
ON PARK LANE,**
22 Park Lane ☎0171 493 8000
L'ODEON,
65, Regent Street,
☎0171 287 1400
PIED A TERRE,
34, Charlotte Street
☎0171 636 1178
QUO VADIS,
26-29 Dean Street
☎0171 437 9585

W11

HALCYON HOTEL,
81, Holland Park
☎0171 727 7288

LEITH'S,
92, Kensington Park Road
☎0171 229 4481

W14

CHINON,
23, Richmond Way
☎0171 602 5968

W6

RIVER CAFÉ,
Thames Wharf Studios,
Hammersmith ☎0171 381 8824

W8

CLARKE'S,
124, Kensington Church Street
☎0171 221 9225

WC2

NEAL STREET RESTAURANT,
26, Neal Street
☎0171 836 8368
THE IVY,
1, West Street, Covent Garden
☎0171 836 4751
THE SAVOY,
The Strand ☎0171 836 4343

ENGLAND

BEDFORDSHIRE

FLITWICK MANOR,
Church Road, Flitwick
☎01525 712242

BERKSHIRE

THE FAT DUCK,
High Street, Bray
☎01628 580333
FREDRICK'S HOTEL,
Shoppenhangers Road,
Maidenhead
☎01628 635934
ROYAL OAK HOTEL,
The Square, Yattendon
☎01635 201325

BRISTOL

HARVEYS RESTAURANT,
12, Denmark Street, Bristol
☎0117 927 5036

BUCKINGHAMSHIRE

HARTWELL HOUSE,
OXFORD ROAD, AYLESBURY
☎01296 747444

CAMBRIDGESHIRE

MIDSUMMER HOUSE,
MIDSUMMER COMMON, CAMBRIDGE
☎01223 369299

CHESHIRE

CRABWALL MANOR,
PARKGATE ROAD, MOLLINGTON,
CHESTER ☎01244 851666
THE CHESTER GROSVENOR,
EASTGATE, CHESTER
☎01244 324024
NUNSMERE HALL,
TARPORLEY ROAD, OAKMERE,
SANDIWAY ☎01606 889100

CORNWALL

PENNYPOTS,
MAENPORTH BEACH, FALMOUTH
☎01326 250251
WELL HOUSE HOTEL,
ST KEYNE, LISKEARD
☎01579 342001
THE SEAFOOD RESTAURANT,
RIVERSIDE, PADSTOW
☎01841 532485
ST MARTIN'S ON THE ISLE,
LOWER TOWN, ST MARTIN'S
☎01720 422092

CUMBRIA

SHARROW BAY,
HOWTOWN ☎017684 86301
**RAMPSBECK COUNTRY HOUSE
HOTEL,**
WATERMILLOCK ☎017684 86442
GILPIN LODGE,
CROOK ROAD, WINDERMERE
☎01394 88818
HOLBECK GHYLL,
HOLBECK LANE, WINDERMERE
☎015394 32375

DERBYSHIRE

FISCHER'S BASLOW HALL,
CALVER ROAD, BASLOW
☎01246 583259
THE OLD VICARAGE,
RIDGEWAY MOOR, RIDGEWAY
☎01142 475814

DEVON

HOLNE CHASE HOTEL,
TWO BRIDGES ROAD, ASHBURTON
☎01364 631471
CARVED ANGEL,
2, SOUTH EMBANKMENT, DARTMOUTH
☎01803 832465
THE HORN OF PLENTY,
GULWORTHY
☎01822 832528
ARUNDELL ARMS,
LIFTON ☎01566 784666
CHEZ NOUS,
13, FRANKFURT GATE, PLYMOUTH
☎01752 266793
WHITECHAPEL MANOR,
SOUTH MOLTON
☎01769 573377
POPHAMS,
CASTLE STREET, WINKLEIGH
☎01837 83767

DORSET

SUMMER LODGE,
EVERSHOT ☎01935 83424
STOCK HILL HOUSE,
STOCK HILL, GILLINGHAM
☎01747 823626

GLOUCESTERSHIRE

BUCKLAND MANOR,
BUCKLAND, BROADWAY
☎01386 852626
81 RESTAURANT,
81 THE PROMENADE, CHELTENHAM
☎01242 222466
THE GREENWAY,
SHURDINGTON, CHELTENHAM
☎01242 862352

LOWER SLAUGHTER MANOR,
LOWER SLAUGHTER
☎01451 820456
THE CLOSE HOTEL,
8, LONG STREET, TETBURY
☎01666 502272
THORNBURY CASTLE,
CASTLE STREET, THORNBURY
☎01454 281182
LORDS OF THE MANOR,
UPPER SLAUGHTER
☎01451 820243

GREATER MANCHESTER

JUNIPER,
21, THE DOWNS, ALTRINCHAM
☎0161 929 4008
NORMANDIE HOTEL,
ELBUT LANE, BURY
☎0161 764 3869

HAMPSHIRE

LE POUSSIN,
THE COURTYARD, BROCKENHURST
☎01590 623063
36 ON THE QUAY,
47 SOUTH STREET, EMSWORTH
☎01243 375592
THE THREE LIONS,
STUCKTON, FORDINGBRIDGE
☎01425 652489
CHEWTON GLEN HOTEL,
CHRISTCHURCH ROAD, NEW MILTON
☎01425 275341
THE DEW POND RESTAURANT,
OLD BURGHCLERE
☎01635 278408
OLD MANOR HOUSE,
21, PALMERSTON STREET, ROMSEY
☎01794 517353

HERTFORDSHIRE

MARRIOTT HANBURY MANOR,
WARE ☎01920 487722

KENT

EASTWELL MANOR,
BOUGHTON LEES, ASHFORD
☎01233 219955
WALLETT'S COURT,
ST MARGARETS-AT-CLIFFE, DOVER
☎01304 852424
READ'S RESTAURANT,
PAINTERS FORSTAL, FAVERSHAM
☎01795 535344
SANDGATE HOTEL,
THE ESPLANADE, FOLKESTONE
☎01303 220444

LANCASHIRE

NORTHCOTE MANOR,
LANGHO ☎01254 240555

LINCOLNSHIRE

HARRY'S PLACE,
17, HIGH STREET, GREAT GONERBY,
GRANTHAM
☎01476 561780

NORFOLK

MORSTON HALL,
BLAKENEY ☎01263 741041
ADLARD'S RESTAURANT,
79, UPPER ST GILES STREET, NORWICH
☎01603 633522

*Switch 3 - one of Villeroy & Boch's most popular 'mix and match' casual tableware
collections - it's young and modern - perfect for informal eating and
relaxed entertaining.*

OXFORDSHIRE

LOVELLS AT WINDRUSH FARM,
MINSTER LOVELL
☎*01993 779802*
BEETLE & WEDGE,
FERRY LANE, MOULSFORD
☎*01491 651381*

SHROPSHIRE

MERCHANT HOUSE,
62, LOWER CORVE STREET, LUDLOW
☎*01584 875438*
OAKS RESTAURANT,
17, CORVE STREET, LUDLOW
☎*01584 872325*

SOMERSET

MOODY GOOSE,
7A KINGSMEAD SQUARE, BATH
☎*01225 466688*

SUFFOLK

HINTLESHAM HALL,
HINTLESHAM
☎*01473 652334*

SURREY

PENNYHILL PARK,
LONDON ROAD, BAGSHOT
☎*01276 471774*
FLEUR DE SEL,
23/27 LOWER STREET, HASLEMERE
☎*01428 651462*
MICHELS',
13 HIGH STREET, RIPLEY
☎*01483 224777*

SUSSEX, EAST

RÖSER'S RESTAURANT,
64, EVERSFIELD PLACE,
ST LEONARDS-ON-SEA
☎*01424 712218*

MANLEYS RESTAURANT,
MANLEYS HILL, STORRINGTON
☎*01903 742331*

TYNE & WEAR

21 QUEEN STREET,
QUAYSIDE, NEWCASTLE UPON TYNE
☎*0191 222 0755*
VERMONT HOTEL,
CASTLE GARTH, NEWCASTLE UPON
TYNE ☎*0191 233 1010*

WARWICKSHIRE

MALLORY COURT HOTEL,
HARBURY LANE, BISHOIP'S
TACHBROOK, ROYAL LEAMINGTON SPA
☎*01926 330214*

WEST MIDLANDS

SWALLOW HOTEL,
12, HAGLEY ROAD, FIVE WAYS,
BIRMINGHAM ☎*0121 452 1144*
NUTHURST GRANGE,
HOCKLEY HEATH ☎*01564 783972*
NEW HALL,
WALMLEY ROAD, SUTTON COLDFIELD
☎*0121 378 2442*

WIGHT, ISLE OF

GEORGE HOTEL,
QUAY STREET, YARMOUTH
☎*01983 760331*

WILTSHIRE

MANOR HOUSE HOTEL,
CASTLE COMBE
☎*01249 782206*
LUCKNAM PARK,
COLERNE ☎*01225 742777*
HOWARD'S HOUSE HOTEL,
TEFFONT EVIAS, SALISBURY
☎*01722 716392*

WORCESTERSHIRE

THE LYGON ARMS,
BROADWAY ☎*01386 852255*
CROQUE-EN-BOUCHE,
221 WELLS ROAD, MALVERN
☎*01684 565612*
OLD SCHOOLHOUSE,
SEVERN STOKE
☎*01905 371368*

YORKSHIRE, SOUTH

SMITH'S OF SHEFFIELD,
34, SANDYGATE ROAD, SHEFFIELD
☎*0114 2666096*

YORKSHIRE, NORTH

MIDDLETHORPE HALL,
BISHOPTHORPE ROAD, YORK
☎*01904 641241*

YORKSHIRE, WEST

RESTAURANT NINETEEN,
19 NORTH PARK ROAD, BRADFORD
☎*01274 492559*
BOX TREE RESTAURANT,
35/37 CHURCH STREET, ILKLEY
☎*01943 608484*
POOL COURT AT 42,
44 THE CALLS, LEEDS
☎*0113 224 4242*
RASCASSE,
CANAL WHARF, LEEDS
☎*0113 244 6611*

Perugia - *soft translucent colours of blue and green featuring vases of pink tulips on white and pale yellow backgrounds.*

Villeroy & Boch

ROYAL CRESCENT,
16 ROYAL CRESCENT, BATH
☎*01225 823333*
HUNSTRETE HOUSE HOTEL,
HUNSTRETE ☎*01761 490490*
CHARLTON HOUSE HOTEL,
CHARLTON ROAD, SHEPTON MALLET
☎*01749 342008*
STON EASTON PARK,
STON EASTON
☎*01761 241631*
WHITE HOUSE HOTEL,
LONG STREET, WILLITON
☎*01984 632306*

HORSTED PLACE,
LITTLE HORSTED, UCKFIELD
☎*01825 750581*

SUSSEX, WEST

GRAVETYE MANOR,
EAST GRINSTEAD
☎*01342 810567*
SOUTH LODGE HOTEL,
BRIGHTON ROAD, LOWER BEEDING
☎*01403 891711*
ANGEL HOTEL,
NORTH STREET, MIDHURST
☎*01730 812421*

CHANNEL ISLES

JERSEY

JERSEY POTTERY,
GOREY ☎ *01534 851119*
LONGUEVILLE MANOR,
ST SAVIOUR ☎ *01534 25501*

IRELAND

BELFAST

DEANES,
38/40, HOWARD STREET, BELFAST
☎ *01232 560000*
ROSCOFF,
7 LESLEY HOUSE, SHAFTESBURY
SQUARE, BELFAST ☎ *01232 331532*

DOWN

SHANKS,
THE BLACKWOOD, CRAWFORDSBURN
ROAD, BANGOR ☎ *01247 853313*

DUBLIN

PATRICK GUILBAUD RESTAURANT,
DUBLIN ☎ *003531 764192/601799*
THORNTON'S RESTAURANT
DUBLIN ☎ *003531 454 9067*

SCOTLAND

ABERDEENSHIRE

DARROCH LEARG,
BRAEMAR ROAD,
BALLATER ☎ *013397 55443*

ARGYLL & BUTE

ISLE OF ERISKA,
ERISKA ☎ *01631 720371*
AIRDS HOTEL,
PORT APPIN ☎ *01631 730236*

DUMFRIES & GALLOWAY

KIRROUGHTREE HOUSE,
MINNIGAFF, NEWTON STEWART
☎ *01671 402141*
KNOCKINAAM LODGE,
PORTPATRICK ☎ *01776 810471*

DUNBARTONSHIRE, WEST

CAMERON HOUSE HOTEL,
BALLOCH
☎ *01389 755565*

EDINBURGH, CITY OF

ATRIUM,
CAMBRIDGE STREET, EDINBURGH
☎ *0131 228 8882*
MARTINS RESTAURANT,
70 ROSE STREET NORTH LANE,
EDINBURGH ☎ *0131 225 3106*
THE SHERATON GRAND HOTEL,
1, FESTIVAL SQUARE, EDINBURGH
☎ *0131 229 9131*

FIFE

CELLAR RESTAURANT,
24, EAST GREEN, ANSTRUTHER
☎ *01333 310378*
OSTLERS CLOSE,
BONNYGATE, CUPAR
☎ *01334 655574*
BOUQUET GARNI,
51, HIGH STREET, ELIE
☎ *01333 330374*

Switch Plantation - *inspired by tropical plantations and colonial style, fruit and dot motifs are complemented by bold terracotta borders and yellow rattan bands.*

THE PEAT INN,
PEAT INN ☎ *01334 840206*

GLASGOW, CITY OF

ONE DEVONSHIRE GARDENS,
GLASGOW ☎ *0141 339 2001*

HIGHLAND

ARISAIG HOUSE,
BEASDALE, ARISAIG
☎ *01687 450622*
INVERLOCHY CASTLE,
TORLUNDY, FORT WILLIAM
☎ *01397 702177*
HARLOSH HOUSE,
HARLOSH, ISLE OF SKYE
☎ *01470 521367*
THE CROSS,
TWEED MILL BRAE, KINGUSSIE
☎ *01540 661166*

LOTHIAN, EAST

LA POTINIERE,
MAIN STREET, GULLANE
☎ *01620 843214*
CHAMPANY INN,
LINLITHGOW ☎ *0150683 4532*

PERTH & KINROSS

THE GLENEAGLES HOTEL,
AUCHTERADER ☎ *01764 662231*
KINLOCH HOUSE,
BLAIRGOWRIE ☎ *01250 884237*
KINNAIRD,
DUNKELD ☎ *01796 482440*
NEWMILN COUNTRY HOUSE HOTEL,
NEWMILN ESTATE, PERTH
☎ *01738 552364*

STIRLING

BRAEVAL,
ABERFOYLE ☎ *01877 382711*

WALES

CEREDIGION

YNYSHIR HALL,
EGLWSFACH ☎ *01654 781209*

CONWY

TAN-Y-FOEL,
CAPEL GARMON, BETWS-Y-COED
☎ *01690 710507*
THE OLD RECTORY,
LLANSANFRAID GLAN CONWY, CONWY
☎ *01492 580611*
BODYSGALLEN HALL,
LLANDUDNO
☎ *01492 584466*
ST TUDNO,
PROMENADE, LLANDUDNO
☎ *01492 874411*

DENBIGHSHIRE

TYDDYN LLAN,
LLANDRILLO ☎ *01490 440264*

GWYNEDD

PLAS BODEGROES,
NEFYN ROAD, PWLLHELI
☎ *01758 612363*
HOTEL MAES Y NEUADD,
TALSARNAU
☎ *01766 780200*

MONMOUTHSHIRE

WALNUT TREE INN,
LLANDDEWI SKYRRID
☎ *01873 852797*
CROWN AT WHITEBROOK,
WHITEBROOK
☎ *01600 860254*

POWYS

CARLTON HOUSE,
DOLYCOED ROAD, LLANWRTYD
☎ *01591 610248*
LLANGOED HALL,
LLYSWEN ☎ *01874 754525*

SWANSEA

FAIRYHILL,
REYNOLDSTON. SWANSEA
☎ *01792 390139*

VILLEROY & BOCH

250TH ANNIVERSARY

Bound to Tradition - Committed to Progress

1748 - 1998

For 250 years, this highly esteemed company has devoted itself to dining culture and, in the history of European porcelain, the name of Villeroy & Boch holds a unique position. A thousand mile journey always begins with a single step. For Villeroy & Boch, that step was the establishment of a ceramics factory by Francois Boch in Audun-le-Tiche, Lorraine, in April 1748. Just a few decades later, the enterprise counted among the finest in Europe and having expanded into Germany, the Boch company merged with a local rival, Nicolas Villeroy.

In 1843, Villeroy & Boch jointly founded a factory to cope with the demand for their high quality tableware and now the company is Europe's largest manufacturer of ceramic products.

The company owe their leading position today to their outstanding achievement at both design and production levels. Working with major international artists and designers, Villeroy & Boch illustrate their commitment to excellence and design.

Villeroy & Boch are a European company with branches throughout the world. Their factories situated in Germany, France and Luxembourg make them ideally equipped for the millennium, whilst still upholding the tradition established by the company over the last 250 years.

Julie - simplistic floral designs contained within colourful geometric borders evoke a summer mood.

FOR FURTHER INFORMATION AND STOCKISTS PLEASE CONTACT:
VILLEROY & BOCH (UK) LIMITED
TELEPHONE 0181 881 0011. FAX 0181 871 1062

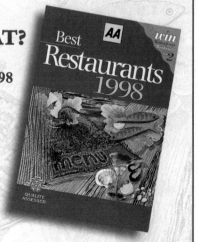

AA Hotel Booking Service

The AA Hotel Booking Service - Now AA Members have a free, simple way to find a place to stay for a week, weekend, or a one-night stopover.

Are you looking for somewhere in the Lake District that will take pets; a city-centre hotel in Glasgow with parking facilities, or do you need a B & B near Dover which is handy for the Eurotunnel?
The AA Booking Service can not only take the hassle out of finding the right place for you, but could even get you a discount on a leisure break or business booking.

And if you are touring round the UK or Ireland, simply give the AA Hotel Booking Service your list of overnight stops, and from one phone call all your accommodation can be booked for you.

Telephone 0990 050505
to make a booking.
Office hours 8.30am - 7.30pm
Monday - Saturday.

Full listings of the 7,920 hotels and B & Bs available through the Hotel Booking Service can be found and booked at the AA's Internet Site:

http://www.theaa.co.uk/hotels

There's a huge variety of wine lists facing the restaurant goer, from punchy examples of how to get an ample choice onto two sides of A4 to tightly scripted tomes that require an encyclopaedic knowledge of the customer.

WHAT makes a GOOD *wine* LIST

Obviously, lists do relate to the size of the establishment, and big lists have the advantage of offering a wide variety, but our inspectors' feel, increasingly, that sheer volume does not serve much purpose. Some are just catalogues of the contents of the cellar, regardless of whether the wine is ready for drinking or not. And, on a long list of pricey wines, that increases the opportunity for the unwary customer to make an expensive mistake as the cheaper wines will be the poor vintages or the first growths that are too young to be drunk at the moment.

However, a growing number of establishments offer a selection of house recommended wines at the beginning of their list, and that is to be applauded, and used.

But what should we be looking for in a good wine list? Here are a few guidelines:

+ *Are there exciting things under £20? It is easy to find exciting wines at the expensive end of the scale - but not everyone has the budget.*

+ *Are there wines of character? In other words, something other than what is found on supermarket shelves.*

+ *Do native growths from around the world feature? These are reasonably priced with Spain and Italy current favourites.*

+ *Are there some good example clarets? There were three great years at the turn of the decade - 88, 89, 90 - of these, the petits châteaux are now drinking well at under £20. A good wine list should include some petits châteaux from these years.*

+ *Is the list clearly laid out and the annotation informative?*

It is, perhaps, stating the obvious that exciting wine lists are those that present the customer with real choice and offer some help.

Wine list of THE year

This year AA Best Restaurants have chosen several establishments for the award of Wine List of the Year. As we studied the lists that poured into the Best Restaurant office earlier this year, it became apparent that there were some outstanding wine lists scattered about the country, making it difficult to pick out any single one for an overall best award. We were spoilt for choice and felt that regional awards best reflected the strong wine lists that made up our short list. As with our first award last year, we took the view that content, advice, value for money and a certain awareness and comprehension of how the wine market is changing, and which countries or areas are producing exciting, good value wines, were the key areas to single out for recognition.

SCOTLAND

BALLATER,
Darroch Learg Hotel 🏵🏵🏵
Enthusiastically and irreverently annotated, there is a pleasing emphasis on wines that are within the reach of ordinary mortals. Bordeaux, in particular, boasts some cracking examples from the end of the 80s, astutely selected from the best of the lesser estates. No-one should begrudge £19.10 for the finesse and depth of a 1990 Château Liversan, or an extra £1.50 for Château Marbuzet 1988. Similar philanthropy distinguishes the rest of a wide-ranging list with a generous selection of half-bottles being the icing on the cake.

WALES

WHITEBROOK,
Crown at Whitebrook 🏵🏵🏵
This really useful wine list benefits from the tireless and informative annotation of Roger Bates. Coverage is extensive and very well chosen with some truly remarkable pricing. Bordeaux offers good drinking with Château Fourcas Hosten 89/90 at £19.95, plus a strong selection of halves. Gaston Hochar's intense Château Musar 1989 at £17.95 from Lebanon and the rich, opulent Meerlust Rubicon from South Africa at £19.50 are just two other notable examples.

LONDON

River Café 🏵🏵🏵
This is a splendidly chauvinist wine list, and (Champagne apart) entirely Italian and unfailingly well chosen. Tuscany takes the tapioca, with Chianti from Isole e Olena and Brunello di Montalcino from Argiano at moderate prices, although Allegrini's hedonistic 1990 Amarone Classico Della Valpolicella at £33 is a Veneto heavyweight of thumping good value. An impressive list of dessert wines takes in two Vin Santos, and a red grape Recioto Classico della Valpolicella 93 from Allegrini (£25.50) to go with cheese.

HEART OF ENGLAND

SHROPSHIRE, WORFIELD,
Old Vicarage 🏵🏵🏵
Adventurous, balanced and democratically priced, this wine list has much to commend it. For once, Bordeaux can be approached with confidence offering ready to drink vintages from quality producers at exemplary prices – Château de Gaillat 90 at £20, for example. Similar virtues are apparent across the globe with selections displaying verve, imagination and generosity throughout. From Piedmont a rare Ruche di Castagnole Monferrato 93 at £20.45, from South Africa, Lemberg Sauvignon Blanc 95 at £15.95. Not much is above £30.

NORTH OF ENGLAND

CHESHIRE, CHESTER,
Chester Grosvenor 🏵🏵🏵
A tremendous wine list with something on every page. It's well set out with some of the lesser known wines explained in depth. Particularly impressive is a page of reserve vintage Burgundies dating from the 50s, with prices up to £500. The Sommeliers Selection offers a clutch of interesting wines with a broad price span to suit all pockets - Cuvée Signee St Chinian a stunning wine (£19.50), spicy, vibrant Viognier, Dom St Hilaire (£19). France is covered in depth with extensive representation from the major growing areas and in many vintages.

SOUTH OF ENGLAND

SOMERSET, WILLITON,
White House Hotel 🏵🏵🏵
An interesting and well balanced list that makes compulsive reading; informative without being high-brow it inspires enthusiasm. Lest you are not lured into the main list, two pages of particularly interesting wines have been picked out, half of them are under £25, with the Australian Barossa Valley Semillon 94, from Peter Lehmann £13, and a 92 Tinto Pesquera: Cosecha Especial, from Ribera del Duero, £18, outstanding value. There's a strong Rhône section with wines from Robin Yapp - where wines carry higher price tags but are well worth it.

CHEFS'
chef
of *THE*
YEAR

'Winning the AA Chefs' Chef of the Year was the ultimate compliment', was how Gordon Ramsay viewed winning our first Chefs' Chef award. But who would be Chefs' Chef for 1998? Once again we asked the 1800 AA Rosetted chefs to vote for their choice and the nominations poured in. Chefs' Chef of the Year is the result of a magnificent response from chefs across the country.

CHEFS' CHEF OF THE YEAR 1998

JEAN-CHRISTOPHE NOVELLI
Chef/proprietor, Maison Novelli
❀❀❀, *London*

Rumours started coming out of Devon in 1989, of the young Frenchman who was cooking incredible food at a pub owned by Keith Floyd. Gordleton Mill in Hampshire saw the first accolades, doors opened in London, and time spent at the Four Seasons Hotel, where he earned five AA Rosettes, established Jean-Christophe Novelli as one of the most exciting young chefs on the British scene. The overwhelming urge to own his place resulted in Maison Novelli, which opened in the summer of 1996 to great acclaim, closely followed by Novelli W8, in the spring of 1997, and Novelli EC1, the brasserie next door to the now flagship Maison Novelli; it is a rapidly growing empire, interwoven by TV and consultancy work. Jean-Christophe may not be seen in the kitchen these days, he takes a more 'Papal role' in the words of one inspector, but the stimulating menus and vibrant food have all the Novelli hallmarks. There's a signature dish of cassoulet terrine, another of pig's trotter (one for each day of the week), both of which drew superlatives from our inspectors. Jean-Christophe Novelli is firmly at the helm, with a highly motivated, dedicated crew behind him.

RICK STEIN
Chef/proprietor, The Seafood Restaurant 🏵🏵🏵, *Padstow*

To be sandwiched between the two young bloods of the British culinary scene is a fitting compliment to the self-taught Rick Stein. Along with Shaun Hill and Simon Hopkinson, his culinary pioneering in the 80s set the stage for the wilder talents of Novelli and Ramsay. Influenced by that earlier food revolutionary, George Perry Smith, and by the cookery books of Jane Grigson, Elizabeth David and Anton Mossiman, Stein has virtually single-handedly raised the awareness of fish in this country; note the popularity of his TV show, one of the most talked about food programmes in a bumper crop. The Seafood Restaurant is booked up weeks in advance.

GORDON RAMSAY
Chef/proprietor, Aubergine 🏵🏵🏵🏵🏵 *London*

Gordon Ramsay is considered one of our most inventive chefs. The ex-professional footballer (Glasgow Rangers) trained hard with the best: three years with Marco Pierre White at Harvey's, then Albert Roux at Le Gavroche, plus time in Paris with both Guy Savoy and Joël Robuchon. With such an impressive CV it is no wonder that when Aubergine opened in 1994, it hit the ground running. A second restaurant, L'Oranger, and a book, have followed swiftly, consolodating Ramsay's position in the vanguard of new British cooking. Guy Savoy remains the chef who inspired him the most, for 'his extreme lightness, very little cream and butter'. *Le French Rivière*, by Alain Ducasse is his cookery book of choice.

FIVE *chefs* WORKING on the *Waterside*

GUNN ERIKSEN, Altnaharrie Inn, Ullapool ⊛⊛⊛⊛⊛
One of the top women chefs in Britain, and by far the most individualistic, Gunn Eriksen has always followed her own instincts, developed her own ideas; she owes allegiance to no one. In her time young sparks have flared and turned into gastro-businessmen, but she remains in her remote kitchen dedicated to her craft. A trip to Altnaharrie requires planning, and time – the isolated setting on Loch Broom makes it one of the few gastronomic adventures left in Britain – the cooking more than lives up to the stunning location.

TOBY HILL, Gordleton Mill, Hampshire ⊛⊛⊛
Franco Taruschio and Raymond Blanc are both individualists, and their respective influence on the young Toby Hill, when he worked in their kitchens, has shaped this rising star. In the timeless, watery setting of Gordelton Mill, ideas are worked at, built up over time – simplicity and the importance of seasonal produce is stressed. He looks to John Burton-Race and Marco Pierre White for what they've done for British cooking, hangs out with Gordon Ramsay, but the dishes are his own.

SAMUEL GICQUEAU, Sandgate Hotel, Folkestone ⊛⊛⊛
A classical training in France, then a couple of years with Raymond Blanc at Le Manoir aux Quat' Saisons, has given depth to this young chef's considerable talent. *Larousse Gastronomique* is his bible, Escoffier is dipped into for the basics, but Samuel Gicqueau aims not to produce complicated dishes but to stay with basic ingredients and natural flavours. Influences, absorbed over the years, have found fruition in the Sandgate Hotel, overlooking the English Channel, which opened in late 1995 to much acclaim.

JOYCE MOLYNEUX, The Carved Angel, Dartmouth ⊛⊛⊛
George Perry Smith, the father of modern British cooking, remains her most important influence, but the British restaurant scene would be very different today without its first lady, Joyce Molyneux. She promoted the works of Jane Grigson and Elizabeth David, and her own influence has been strongly acknowledged by too many chefs to list here. Now semi-retired (just three sessions a week), her harbourside restaurant remains a mecca for those wishing to see what freshness, simplicity and seasonality are all about.

KEVIN VINER, Pennypots, Falmouth ⊛⊛⊛
For a civilian chef from the Royal Military Academy at Sandhurst, Kevin Viner has come a long way. He cites that supreme perfectionist Nico Ladenis, for whom he once worked, as one of the major influences on his style, although Pierre Koffmann comes in for praise too. Pennypots is nearly ten years old, and a relocation in 1996 to a secluded cove just outside Falmouth proved a seamless move, with the kitchen barely missing a beat in preparing the deceptively simple repertoire of fresh local produce, especially fish and shellfish.

THE
master
chefs
of

Gourmet Club

GREAT BRITAIN

The membership list of The Master Chefs of Great Britain reads as a roll-call of chefs who have one common goal – to produce the highest quality food using the best ingredients. They may not all be household names, for many are chef-patrons who have little time to spend on anything other than running the kitchen, but they do produce excellent food. Indeed, this is doubly apparent when one leafs through AA Best Restaurants to see what AA inspectors have said.

For the chef...

This quest for excellence is reflected in the aims and activities of the association that was established in 1980 as a forum for the exchange of ideas between many of Britain's leading chefs.

Raising the profile of Britain's quality food producers, through meals in this country and abroad, coupled with demonstrations using British produce, is important to all chefs.

Membership is by invitation, or chefs may write to the chairman, enclosing their curriculum vitae, and their application goes before the Executive Committee.

The association works with other industry bodies to assist in the running of competitions and initiatives, and their Annual General Meeting and Luncheon attracts guests from the whole of the food industry.

For the person who enjoys food...

The association's aims are reflected in a quarterly magazine, The Master's Table, which brings together chefs, leading food and wine writers, and industry figures, to provide articles that are both informative and entertaining. Besides being available in the hotels and restaurants, the magazine can be obtained through subscription (£15 per annum including P&P) and has a growing readership in this country and abroad.

In addition, the association runs a Gourmet Club (joint annual membership £45 per annum), which holds events throughout the British Isles. These bring together the food interested public, chefs and suppliers, not just to experience great food and wine but, hopefully, to learn a little about what goes on behind the scenes.

Benefits of the Gourmet Club include:

✦ *A free annual subscription to the Master's Table magazine, a quarterly 88 page, full colour glossy magazine that contains articles from leading food and wine writers and a host of recipes from the Master Chefs.*

✦ *Complimentary access to the Fine Food Club with over 1000 small quality food producers on its data base, and the resources to source and send out speciality produce to both gourmets and the chef.*

✦ *There is always a selection of quality wine and product offers available to members through the Gourmet Club News pages in the magazine, as well as Reader Offers and Competitions for such things as wines, books, and even the odd weekend away.*

✦ *Many of the chefs hold cookery courses both at their hotels and restaurants and at venues around the country, and some give special tuition rates.*

✦ *A cornucopia of benefits at selected member establishments, aimed at people who are interested in food and wine. It could be a discount, or you might find yourself on a tour of the wine cellar or kitchen, or eating a specially prepared dish.*

For the future...

Under the Presidency of the Earl of Bradford, a growing membership ensures that the organisation remains pro-active working within the industry and consumer markets to ensure that British chefs and produce are recognised world-wide. Training initiatives remain high on the agenda, and it is recognised by the members that young chefs must be given a classical grounding from which to move on and create new and innovative dishes.

For further information about the membership criteria of The Master Chef's of Great Britain, their Gourmet Club and magazine, The Master's Table, call or fax 01491 872900 or write to:

THE MASTER CHEFS OF GREAT BRITAIN, CHAIRMAN'S OFFICE, BEAR COTTAGE, READING ROAD, GORING-ON-THAMES, OXON, RG8 0ET

---

or simply fill in form below

The Master Chefs of Great Britain

NAME. . . . .

ADDRESS . . . .

. . . .

TELEPHONE NUMBER . . . . FAX NUMBER . . . .

I would like to join The Master Chefs of Great Britain Gourmet Club. ☐

ANNUAL JOINT MEMBERSHIP £45 PER ANNUM.

I would like to subscribe to The Master's Table magazine at the annual subscription rate of £15 inc P&P ☐

Please send me details of various levels of 'chef membership' of The Master Chefs of Great Britain. ☐

Please make all cheques payable to The Master's Table Ltd

Please return this form to:

THE MASTER CHEFS OF GREAT BRITAIN, CHAIRMAN'S OFFICE, BEAR COTTAGE, READING ROAD, GORING-ON-THAMES, OXON RG8 0ET

LONDON

Abingdon

Conversion has turned this corner pub in a well-heeled residential Kensington street into a light, airy modern bistro with up-to-the-minute cooking to match. From an early summer menu that took in a simple asparagus vinaigrette, puff pastry tart of chicken livers and shallots in balsamic dressing, pan-fried loin of tuna with tomatoes, olives and artichokes and grilled pavé steak with béarnaise sauce and pommes frites, our inspector plumped for an excellent duck leg confit with celeriac remoulade. This was followed by deeply flavoured pan-fried breast of chicken, with carrots, courgettes and a yogurt and mint dressing, then vanilla crème brûlée with summer berries. 'Well balanced and thoughtfully chosen flavours' was the succinct summing up. Service by casually dressed staff is informal but attentive. The short, fashionable wine list offers a good selection by the glass and is very reasonably priced.

Directions: Nearest Tube, High Street Kensington.

54 Abingdon Road W8
Map GtL: C3
Tel: 0171 9373339
Fax: 0171 7956388
Chef: Brian Baker
Owner: My Kinda Town Ltd
Cost: Alc £24, fixed-price L £9.95 (2 courses). ☺ H/wine £9.25
Times: Noon-last L 2.30pm (3pm Sat, Sun)/6pm-last D 11pm (10.30pm Sun). Closed 25-26 Dec, 1 Jan
Additional: Sunday L; Children welcome; ✪ dishes
Seats: 45
Smoking: No pipes and cigars
Credit cards: ▬ ▦ ▦ ▅ ▢

The Academy

Created out of four Georgian town houses in Bloomsbury, not far from the British museum, The Academy has a great individual feel. The dining room may be in the basement, but windows into the street-side well let in a good amount of natural light, and the decor is an appealing modern, clean-cut style. The menu is very Mediterranean with a few exotic flourishes such as shiitake mushrooms, satay sauce and pak choi. At a summer dinner, Mediterranean fish soup (made from several different species of fish) came with all the trimmings, was followed by good duck breast with cracked pepper, Cassis jus, fondant potatoes and new seasons carrots, and finished with lemon tart.

Directions: Five minutes walk from Oxford St, Tottenham Court Road Tube, Goodge St

17-21 Gower Street WC1E 6HG
Map: D4
Tel: 0171 6367612
Fax: 0171 6363442
Chef: John O'Riordan
Owner: Alan Rivers
Cost: Alc £22.50. ☺ H/wine £9.50.
Times: Noon-last D 10.45pm. Closed L Sat, Sun
Additional: Bar food; Children welcome; ✪ dishes
Seats: 70. Private dining room 15
Smoking: Air-conditioning
Accommodation: 48 en suite
Credit cards: ▬ ▦ ▦ ▅ ▢ ▢

L'Accento ✿

Rustic Italian restaurant specialising in robust regional dishes. Cooking is fresh with bold flavours evident in such choices as linguine of lobster with tomatoes and herbs, baked red mullet with sage and Parma ham and pan-fried calves' liver with balsamic vinegar. Friendly staff.

Additional: Children welcome; ✪ dishes
Smoking: No pipes or cigars; air-conditioning
Credit cards: ▬ ▦ ▦ ▅ ▢ ▢

Directions: Nearest tube stations Bayswater and Queensway

16 Garway Road W2 4NH
Map GtL: C3
Tel/Fax: 0171 2432201
Chef: Enrico Sartor
Cost: Alc £25, fixed-price L&D £11.50. ☺ H/wine £9.
Times: Last L 2.30/last D 11.30pm

Adams Café ❀

King of couscous, Abdel Boukraa, delivers the real thing in all its forms in this fun-loving café. His short menu also extends to harira (Moroccan vegetable and chick pea soup), ojja (ratatouille baked with an egg in the middle) and tajines. Flavours are authentic, prices are low, and there are some gutsy North African wines and digestif wines to boot.

Credit cards: �◼ ▨ ▨ ▨ ▨

Directions: Nearest Tubes – Shepherd's Bush and Hammersmith

77 Askew Road W12 9AH
Map GtL: C2
Tel/Fax: 0181 7430572
Chef: Abdel Boukraa
Owners: Abdel & Frances Boukraa
Cost: *Alc* £14. H/wine £7.50. ☺
Times: D only, 7pm-11pm. Closed 25-26 Dec
Additional: Children welcome; ❧ dishes

Alastair Little ❀❀

The eponymous Mr L opened this modest offshoot of his West End trend-setter in 1996 and, true to form, the simple shop conversion bears all his trademarks: tables are closely packed and the walls are stark white, with only a vast embossed letter 'a' to provide relief. Like the decor, the short menu is pared down to the bare essentials – raw salmon with ginger dressing, lamb's tongues with parsley salad – but the results on the plate are multi-dimensional. Chef Toby Gush follows the Little philosophy of keeping it simple, while allowing flavours full rein. Foie gras, pork and Agen prune terrine is a gutsy, rustic interpretation, while light fluffy quenelles of conger eel come with red wine, flat onions and bacon. Among the main courses, unctuous slow-roasted belly pork with arrocina beans, swede and thyme is real comfort food for the 90s, and poached skate wing sits happily with lentils, roast fennel and a powerful minty salsa verde. As for desserts, there might be tongue-tingling lemon tart, pizza di noci e canditi, or tutti frutti and chocolate chip ice cream. The wine list crams a lot of interest into a small space.

Directions: From Ladbroke Grove Tube station turn R, Lancaster Road is 1st R

136A Lancaster Road W11 1QU
Map: C2
Tel: 0171 2432220
Fax: 0171 7924504
Chef: Toby Gush
Owners: Alastair Little, Mercedes André-Vega, Kirsten Tormod Pedersen
Cost: *Alc* £27, fixed-price L £20/D £25. H/wine £13
Times: 12.30pm-last L 2.30pm (3pm Sat)/7pm-last D 11pm. Closed Sun
Additional: Children welcome
Seats: 42
Credit cards: ▬ ▨ ▨ ▨

Alastair Little Soho ❀❀❀

Soho minimalism has taken on a new, softer look at Alastair Little's original stamping ground, but the interior is as uncluttered as ever – one artistic vase of flowers representing the sum total of extraneous decoration. The daily changing menu offers great value for money, with a choice ranging from the Mediterranean inspired black mushroom risotto to sliced pork salad Chinese-style amongst starters, and grilled vegetable lasagne with buffalo mozzarella and truffled breast of chicken with creamed leeks amongst the main courses. Although the inspiration is eclectic, Little's first love remains Italy, and it is from that source he has developed a style of cooking that has influenced a generation of chefs. The grand master of simplicity, flavour and texture, his food remains as fresh as ever and the respect shown for ingredients does not falter. Lightness of touch is second nature – an intense salsa verde with poached shin of tip-top beef could easily have dominated the whole dish, instead it balanced perfectly, melting into the bouillon to create a further dimension of taste. Root vegetables were well timed, although the leeks and onions were perhaps too al dente for the nature of the dish. No problems, however, with a richly satisfying starter of brawn with truffled French beans and pickles; a homage to Jane

49 Frith Street W1V 5TE
Map: D4
Tel: 0171 7345183
Chef: Alastair Little
Owners: Alastair Little, Kirsten Tormod Pederson, Mercedes André-Vega
Cost: Fixed-price L £25/D £30. H/wine £12
Times: Noon-last L 3pm/6pm-last D 11pm. Closed L Sat, Sun, Bhs
Additional: Children welcome; ❧ dishes
Seats: 35. Private dining room 20 max
Smoking: Air-conditioning
Credit cards: ▬ ▨ ▨ ▨ ▨

Directions: Nearest Tubes: Leicester Square, Tottenham Court Road.

Grigson, it was light, barely held together by the gelatine and with a fresh flavour and a soft texture offset by the crunchy relish. Other typical seasonal dishes (in this case spring) were nettle soup, baby artichoke risotto, hot soused mackerel with sweet and sour onions, baked sea trout with herb dressed sorrel, roast pigeon and Umbrian lentils, rhubarb trifle and an Anglo-Italian panettone bread and butter pudding. Do not pass on the bread – the focaccia and wholemeal poppy are superb. The punchy wine list is a good example of how to get an ample choice of well-sourced wines onto two sides of A4. Pricing is moderate and although there is little age, there is much that is food friendly.

Alba Restaurant

You could almost believe you were in Italy, such is the feel and look of this modern, spacious restaurant serving regional Italian food. Sip an *aperitivo della casa* (Aperol and white wine) or a Bellini whilst choosing from a menu that includes salad of raw artichoke hearts and Parmesan shavings, fresh pasta with a rich chicken liver sauce, grilled red mullet with a spicy tomato sauce, and veal escalopes with porcini mushroom sauce. Breast of duck in a sweet and sour sauce, rabbit braised with olives and polenta, and asparagus with Fontina cheese fondue are some of the dishes less frequently found outside Italy. Vegetarians do well with Swiss chard, free-range eggs, Parmesan and balsamic vinegar. An authentic shot of espresso is just the job to follow almond nougat ice cream cake or pannacotta, although there are cappuccinos and Italian hot chocolate as well as a large selection of grappas.

Directions: 100 yards from entrance to Barbican Arts Centre; 3 mins walk from Barbican Station.

107 Whitecross Street EC1
Map: F4
Tel: 0171 5881798
Chef: Armando Liboi
Owner: Rudi Venerandi
Cost: *Alc* £25, fixed-price D £13.40. ☺ H/wine £10.90.
Times: Noon-last L 3pm/6pm-last D 11pm. Closed Sat, Sun, Xmas, Bhs
Additional: Bar meals L; Children welcome; ✇ dishes
Seats: 60. Private dining room 40
Smoking: No-smoking area; air conditioning
Credit cards: 🗖 🗖 🗖 🗖 🗖 🗖

Al Bustan

Greenery – the name means garden in Arabic – fills this elegant, formal Lebanese restaurant. Meze of little spicy sausages, and baby aubergines with pine nuts, garlic and spices have been praised, as has a dish of boneless grilled chicken with garlic sauce. Raw meat dishes and Lebanese bread-and-butter pudding are an acquired taste.

Additional: Sunday L; Children welcome; ✇ dishes.
Smoking: Air-conditioned.
Credit cards: 🗖 🗖 🗖 🗖 🗖 🗖

Directions: Behind Carlton Tower Hotel, off Lowndes Street.

Motcomb Street
SW1X 8JU
Map: B2
Tel: 0171 235 8277
Fax: 0171 235 1668
Chef: Inam Atalla
Owners: Mr & Mrs Atalla
Cost: *Alc* £20, fixed-price L £13/D £18. ☺ H/wine £11.
Times: Noon – last D 11pm. Closed Xmas

Alfred

Jellied oysters, white wine, samphire and sea kale, braised belly of pork, root vegetables and thyme mashed potatoes, roast ling, mussels, leeks and spinach, and Sussex pond pudding with vanilla custard are some of the resolutely British-inspired dishes served at this unpretentious but popular restaurant. There may be new blood in the kitchen but the cooking remains as assured as ever. Traditional ideas continue to get a modern lift, as in juniper-cured salmon with lemon oil, herbs and courgette cream, for example, or steamed gurnard with orange oil, fennel and spring onions. Freshness of flavour was

245 Shaftesbury Avenue
WC2 8EH
Map: D3
Tel: 0171 2402566
Fax: 0171 4970672
Chef: Trevor Blyth
Owner: Fred Taylor
Cost: *Alc* £23, Fixed-price L&D £12.95. ☺ H/wine £9.50.
Times: Noon-last L 3.30pm/6pm-last D 11.30pm. Closed Sun, L Sat, Xmas, Bhs

the keynote at a winter inspection lunch: ham and pea soup based on a well-made basic stock, freshly cooked toad-in-the-hole served with excellent mashed potatoes, French beans and red cabbage, light sticky toffee pudding. Bread, baked on the premises, and Milleens Irish cheese served with quince preserve show sound attention to small details.

Directions: Close to Shaftesbury Theatre

Alounak ✿

Additional: Children welcome; ❹ dishes
Seats: 60. Private dining room 20
Smoking: No pipes and cigars; air-conditioning
Credit cards: ▆ ▆ ▆ ▆ ▆ ▆

44 Westbourne Grove W2
Map GtL: C3
Tel: 0171 229 4158/0416
Telephone for details

Diminutive, popular neighbourhood restaurant specialising in Persian cooking. Sit in cramped surroundings and enjoy houmus, chelo kebab with saffron rice or one of the daily specials, as well as splendid 'taftoon' (unleavened bread cooked in a tandoor). Drink traditional, yogurt-based 'dogh' or black tea, otherwise bring-your-own wine.

Directions: Nearest Tube – Notting Hill Gate

L'Altro Restaurant ✿✿

This modern Italian restaurant has now expanded into a London chain, with two branches in Chelsea and others in Hampstead and Soho. The Notting Hill original has rustic decor, wrought ironwork, tiled floors and distressed plaster walls. An abundance of trompe l'oeil effects may make you think you are sitting back in the old country. A lengthy *carte* needs serious study – roasted quail with polenta and lentils, sautéed spinach, Luganica sausage and wild mushrooms, and ravioli of salmon and dill with burnt butter pesto and pine nuts catch the eye amongst the starters. Main courses stick to an uncluttered basic repertoire – grilled monkfish with spinach and lemon, whole roast baby chicken with garlic and chillies, osso buco milanese. Fish and seafood predominate – a grilled seafood platter comprises langoustines, tiger prawns, clams and half a lobster, lemon sole is served with pesto, sauce vierge and topped with crispy zucchini. As well as a good choice of Italian cheeses, there are desserts such as panettone tiramisu with cinnamon spiced figs.

210 Kensington Park Road
Notting Hill W11 1NR
Map GtL: C3
Tel: 0171 7921066
Fax: 0171 792 1077
Chef: G Vella
Owner: Arty Restaurants Ltd
Cost: *Alc* £25, fixed-price L £9.95/D £10.95. ☺ H/wine £9.50.
Times: 11.30am-last L 3.30pm/6.30pm-last D 11.30pm
Additional: Sunday L; Children welcome; ❹ dishes
Seats: 45.
Smoking: Air-conditioning
Credit cards: ▆ ▆ ▆ ▆ ▆ ▆

Directions: Nearest tubes Ladbroke Grove/Notting Hill Gate, straight down Kensington Park Road to Westbourne Park Road end, opposite health centre

Al San Vincenzo ✿✿

Family-run Italian restaurant with simple, stylish decor and an understated atmosphere. The seasonal menu lists some enticing dishes such as smoked goose breast with mostarda di Cremona, pasta tubes with young broccoli leaves, Parmesan and Pecorino cheeses (a little spicy, is how it is charmingly described), haunch of venison with quince sauce and thin slices of capon with wild mushrooms. Other exciting main courses include deep-fried eels with raddichio di Treviso, and pig's trotters with zampone sausage and lentils. Even pork chops get a twist by being marinated in oil and chilli, then grilled and served with zucchini alla scapece. Authenticity is sustained in the dessert menu – *semifreddo al cioccolato, baba al limoncello con panna*, Vino Santo with biscotti, plus Italian farmhouse unpasteurised cheeses.

30 Connaught Street W2 2AF
Map: B3
Tel: 0171 2629623
Chef: Vincenzo Borgonzolo
Owners: Vincenzo & Elaine Borgonzolo
Cost: *Alc* £35. H/wine £11
Times: 12.30pm-last L 2pm/7pm-last D 10pm. Closed L Sat, Sun, 25-26 Dec
Seats: 24
Smoking: No pipes and cigars
Credit cards: ▆ ▆ ▆

Directions: 2nd left in Edgware Road, from Marble Arch

Anglesea Arms ❀❀

Smoky, bare-boarded and fashionably frayed around its gentrified edges, the large, L-shaped pub dining-room spreads out into the bar when busy. The blackboard menu changes twice daily, with dishes available either as starters or main courses. Although short, the choice of modern British-cum-Mediterranean dishes is appealing and well balanced, ranging from steak and oyster to spring rolls. Gutsy tasting rillettes of tuna and lobster were packaged in filo and served on a bed of sesame oiled green leaves; these were followed by a rather busy confection of fresh home-made flat pasta, beetroot, grated horseradish, mustard fruits and pieces of braised rabbit and pigeon, which almost, but not quite, succeeded in welding together the disparate nature of its component parts. Nonetheless, talent and flair in the kitchen is unmistakable, and overall this is a great pub with really good food, atmosphere and wines – and service which has sharpened up considerably since last year's guide entry.

Directions: Off Goldhawk Road; nearest Tube – Goldhawk Road, Ravenscourt Park

35 Wingate Road W6
Map GtL: C3
Tel: 0181 7491291
Chef/Owner: Dan Evans
Times: L from 12.30pm/D from 7.30pm
Additional: Bar food; Sunday L; Children welcome; ❧ dishes
Seats: 40
Credit cards: None

Anna's Place ❀❀

The eponymous Anna has been persuading Londoners of the pleasures of Swedish cooking for over 20 years now. The formula remains unaltered, but why fix something if it ain't broke? First courses are based on a selection of marinated herrings, home-cured salmon, daily soups and weekly special starters; fish dishes depend on that day's market, but may also include red sea bream with dill and anchovy sauce. Meat dishes change weekly, as do various specials, but one popular main course is roast shank of pork with tomato marmalade and match stick potatoes. Look out for unusual ingredients such as marinated venison with a lingonberry vinaigrette. Enjoy a few Akvavits, Swedish vodkas or special cocktails, then try pronouncing one of the puddings – or simply point and ask for an explanation.

Directions: Left off Balls Pond Road into Mildmay Park. On the corner of Newington Green, Bus 73, 171, 141 to Newington Green

90 Mildmay Park N1 4PR
Map GtL: D3
Tel: 0171 2499379
Chef: Patrick Schyum
Owner: Anna Hegarty
Cost: *Alc* £20. H/wine £8.95. ☺
Times: 12.15pm-last L 2.15pm/7pm-last D 9.45pm. Closed Sun, Mon, Aug, 2 wks Xmas, 2 wks Easter
Additional: Children welcome; ❧ dishes
Seats: 42
Credit cards: None

Apprentice Restaurant ❀

Part of the Butlers Wharf Chef School – eat here (at moderate prices), to spot the stars of the future. Converted from an old spice warehouse, an open-plan kitchen delivers a stream of dishes, largely in the modern European style. Chargrilled squid salad with tomato, orange and chilli dressing, braised lamb shank with pesto mash and green beans and warm berry pavlova are typical of the choice.

Times: Last L 1.15pm/last D 8.30pm. Closed Sat, Sun, Bhs, 20 Dec-5 Jan
Additional: Children welcome; ❧ dishes
Smoking: No-smoking area; air-conditioning
Credit cards: ▅▅ ▆▆ ▫

Directions: On S side of river, two minutes from Tower Bridge; nearest Tubes – Tower Hill and London Bridge

31 Shad Thames SE1 2YR
Map: G3
Tel: 0171 234 0254
Fax: 0171 403 2638
Chef: Gary Witchalls
Cost: *Alc* £21, fixed-price L £9.50/D £17.50. ☺ H/wine £8.95

Arcadia ❁

Two macaws, Sally and Stanley, add to the unique charm of Arcadia, a pleasant restaurant just round the corner from Kensington High Street. Modern dishes such as grilled salmon with pear and potato risotto, and baked sea bream with tagliatelle and sage capponata are typical of the short carte.

Kensington Court 35 Kensington High Street W8 5EB
Map GtL: C3
Tel: 0171 937 4294
Chef: Ian Loynes
Owner: A V Garcia-Quiros
Cost: *Alc* £20, fixed-price L £15.95/D £13.75. ☺ H/wine £10.95
Times: Last L 2.30pm/D 11pm. Closed Sat L, 25 Dec
Additional: Sunday L; Children welcome; ❹ dishes
Credit cards: ▬ ▬ ▬ ▨ ◨

Directions: From High Street Kensington Tube turn R, take 3rd turning on L. Signed path leads to Kensington Court

Les Associés ❁❁

This little front room of a restaurant is dedicated to the art of fine French cuisine. Despite the cramped dining area, there is a buzz in the evenings when discerning clientele eagerly devour the contents of the platters emerging from the kitchen. The short *carte* changes every two months or so and there are always a number of daily specials. Certain special dishes, such as bouillabaisse, can be ordered in advance. Fish soup is always a popular choice, but other starters might include delicious warm skate salad with caper sauce, or snails, mushrooms and shallots in garlic and parsley cream sauce. The fish of the day might be cooked in a parcel with fresh foie gras; other main courses might include chicken with cabbage and carrot sauce, sautéed pork with prunes, or a pot au feu made with duck. Finish with either a plated selection of desserts or cheese. Service is thoroughly professional, and the waiters work at a tremendous pace. Reservations are a must.

Directions: Nearest Tube – Finsbury Park

172 Park Road N8 8JT
Map: B5
Tel: 0181 3488944
Chef: Mark Spindler
Owner: Dominique Chéhère
Cost: *Alc* £21, fixed-price L £10.50. H/wine £9.80
Times: Noon-last L 2pm/7.30pm-last D 10pm. Closed L Sat, Mon
Additional: Sunday L; No children under 6; ❹ dishes
Seats: 40
Smoking: No-smoking area
Credit cards: ▬ ▬ ◨

Atelier ❁❁❁

Canaletto once had a studio here and the soft terracotta walls are lined with paintings – although not by the man himself. The visual impact is emphasised by the stunning cover plates on each table which shine with the springtime colours of fruit and vegetables in relief. Clean, light and inviting is the message. Stephen Bulmer works to a bright modern French menu with some oriental influences; dishes change every few weeks and there's also the option of a set menu that might take in vichyssoise, pan-fried trout with a fricassée of frog's legs and mustard mash, and chocolate marquise with caramel and chocolate sauces. (It's worth noting that prices are reduced if you eat before 8pm). The arrival of a new pastry chef has raised the quality of breads and pâtisserie, allowing Stephen to focus on the core of his repertoire. To start, our inspector went for a beautifully constructed tian of aubergine with layers of

41 Beak Street W1R 3LE
Map: C3
Tel: 0171 2872057
Fax: 0171 2871767
Chef: Stephen Bulmer
Owners: Joanna Shannon, Stephen Bulmer
Cost: *Alc* £27.50, fixed-price L&D £19.50. ☺ H/wine £13.25
Times: Noon-last L 2.30pm/6pm-last D 10.45pm. Closed L Sat, Sun, Xmas wk, Bhs
Additional: Children welcome; ❹ dishes
Seats: 45. Private dining room 16
Smoking: No pipes & cigars
Credit cards: ▬ ▬ ▬ ▨ ◨ ◨

Atelier

tomato, fresh pesto, rouille and tapenade with baby mozzarella cheeses sitting atop each mound. Then came monkfish tail with vegetable spaghetti served with a crab dumpling spiked with lemon grass, coriander and ginger. Bulmer also roasts chump of lamb and serves it with dauphinoise potatoes, carrot purée, green beans and rosemary jus, as well as serving chicken breast with asparagus, morels, wild and basmati rice, coupled with a chive-speckled sherry sauce. Read the menu descriptions and you know exactly what is going to arrive on the plate. Caramelised banana mille-feuille with pistachio parfait is a typically impressive dessert, otherwise expect hot chocolate sponge with Chantilly cream or orange and pink grapefruit terrine with passionfruit coulis. The short wine list is arranged in ascending order by price. Essentially French, with liberal dabs of New World, the approach is somewhat confusing although a proportionally good choice of wines by the glass is something of a virtue.

Directions: From Piccadilly Tube go north up Regent Street. Beak Street is on the right

Athenaeum Hotel ✿✿

116 Piccadilly
W1V 0BJ
Map: C3
Tel: 0171 4993464
Fax: 0171 4931860
Chef: David Marshall
Cost: *Alc* £28.35, fixed-price L&D £21.90 (2 courses). H/wine £13.95
Times: 12.30pm-last L 2.30pm/6pm-last D 11pm. Closed L Sat, L Sun, Bhs

'Super hotel, I'd like to check-in here for at least a month', sighs an inspector of this elegant hotel overlooking Green Park. The achievement of a warm, relaxed atmosphere as well as high levels of service is no mean feat, and the same high standards carry through to the restaurant, Bullochs, where imagination and sound technical skills are very much in evidence. At a May dinner great breads – raisin and walnut, tomato and herbs, and olive – preceded a 'delicious' langoustine risotto in a 'wafer-fine' Parmesan basket. Beautifully fresh and succulent seared yellow tuna with an assorted bean dressing followed, accompanied by a spicy coriander dressing, an idea that showed good clean flavours working well together. Tarte Tatin for dessert was excellent, as was the selection of cheeses that came with walnut bread.

Directions: Hyde Park Corner/Green Park on Piccadilly

Additional: Children welcome; 🍴 dishes
Seats: 55. Private dining room 16
Smoking: No-smoking area; air-conditioning
Accommodation: 156 en suite
Credit cards: 🂠 🂡 🂢 🂣 🂤 🂥

Atlantic ✿✿

To queue up in a windswept, grimy street off Piccadilly Circus just to have your reservation checked, is perhaps not the best start to an evening, but once you've descended the imposing, sweeping staircase, taken in the marble pillars, ornate ceiling and large circular bar, things start to look up. This is a young place, brash and lively, with crowds clustering round the American-style bar. In full swing, the noise levels are high. The menu is extensive with most dishes originating from a modern pan-European stable, such as pan-fried fillet of salmon on choucroute with smoked bacon and juniper and roast best end of lamb with a mustard crust, aubergine tart and rosemary lamb sauce. At inspection, crab and lettuce spring rolls with a hot and sour, pineapple and green peppercorn sauce, preceded a main course of tournedos of beef with foie gras and Périgord truffle with Madeira jus, spinach and a light potato pancake. Chargrilling is a popular technique – squid comes with couscous, tomato, coriander and houmus. Tournedos Rossini evokes the great ocean liner era at the earlier part of the century when The Atlantic was built.

Directions: Just off Piccadilly Circus

20 Glasshouse Street W1
Map: D3
Tel: 0171 7344888
Fax: 0171 7343609
Chefs: Stephen Terry, Martin Dickinson
Owner: Oliver Peyton
Cost: Alc £25. Fixed-price L £14.90. ☺ H/wine £11.50.
Times: Noon-last L 3pm/6pm-last D midnight. Closed L Sat, L Sun, Bhs D.
Additional: Bar food. Children welcome. 🍴 dishes.
Seats: 180. Private dining room 60
Smoking: Air-conditioning
Credit cards: 🂠 🂡 🂢 🂣 🂤

Auberge de Provence, St James Court Hotel ✿✿✿

The location may be tourist London (Buckingham Palace is nearby), but the team behind this restaurant have managed to conjure up something akin to a French auberge. This is the English outpost of the award winning L'Oustaù de Baumanière in Provence, from where Jean-André Charial acts as consultant, although chef Bernard Briqué is allowed to go his own way. The connection is enduring and meaningful; decor and food are in

41 Buckingham Gate SW1E 6AF
Map: D2
Tel: 0171 8211899
Fax: 0171 6307587
Chef: Bernard Briqué
Owner: St James Court Hotel
Cost: Alc £29.50, fixed-price L £22.50/D £29.50. H/wine £13.50
Times: 12.30pm-last L 2.30pm/7.30pm-last D 11pm. Closed Sat L, Sun, 1wk Jan, 2 wks Aug
Additional: Children welcome; 🍴 dishes
Seats: 75
Smoking: No-smoking area, air-conditioning
Credit cards: 🂠 🂡 🂢 🂣 🂤

Directions: Off Victoria Street, close to St James's Park Tube station

sympathy. In a setting that has rustic overtones with an arched wall, hidden light and a cart loaded with dried flowers, the kitchen delivers a version of French provincial cooking that has both authenticity and refinement. Soupe de poissons de roche is the real thing, with croûtons, saffron rouille and cheese silver-served into the soup. Luxuries abound throughout the repertoire: ultra-thin ravioli filled with foie gras and served with a frothy truffle jus, terrine of lobster with leeks, neat tournedos of monkfish wrapped in bacon with a mélange of sweet peppers, baby asparagus and herbs. By contrast, pissaladière and roast corn-fed chicken with braised vegetables and tarragon strike a more gutsy note. French cheeses are dispensed from 'le chariot' and a line-up of impeccably wrought desserts could include first-rate feuilleté of winter fruits, pancakes filled with hot Grand Marnier soufflé, and an architecturally stunning pyramid of coconut mousse with passionfruit coulis. Service is silky smooth, attentive and friendly.

Signature dishes: Salade baussenque; filet de loup de mer au basilic; saddle of lamb with courgette and tapenade flan; noisettes of venison with cranberries and three purées.

Aubergine   ✿✿✿✿✿

11 Park Walk SW10
Map: A1
Tel: 0171 3523449
Fax: 0171 3511770
Chef/Owner: Gordon Ramsay
Cost: Fixed-price L £24/D £45.
H/wine £15
Times: 12.15pm-last L 2.30pm/7pm-last D 10.45pm. Closed L Sat, Sun,
2 wks Xmas, 1st 2 wks Aug
Additional: ✿ dishes
Seats: 45
Smoking: No pipes and cigars;
air-conditioning
Credit cards: ▬ ▬ ▬ ▬ ▣ ▢

Directions: Fulham Road. 2nd road L after MGM cinema

Thank goodness Gordon Ramsay's career as a professional footballer was short lived for he would not now be cooking some of the most exciting food this country has to offer. However, the standards, consistency and sheer genius of Gordon's cooking mean that he is firmly playing in the restaurant premier division. Over the past year or so what once erred on the side of bold, catchy and energetic, has reached new heights. Today the strokes of genius are more subtle, the cooking more assured than ever, and there's a thoughtful consistency. Gordon describes his style as 'modern and light French cooking', and indeed, the bargain lunch menu is irritatingly written in French, but it is worth having to ask for a translation. We relished every sip of an intense, frothy cappuccino of langoustines and lentils. A perfectly cooked main course, a collection of fish – bass, salmon, brill, and scallops – sat on a jus infused with five spice. A top notch tarte Tatin concluded a most noteworthy meal. The description of the dishes which appear on the fixed-price dinner menu (in English) sound suitably enticing; our inspectors reports read superlative after superlative. Of particular note was a terrine of bouillabaisse, beautifully balanced and moist – a real slice of Marseilles in land-locked Chelsea! A main course of Bresse pigeon poached in a bouillon of ceps, a ravioli of wild mushrooms with sauce foie gras was characteristically tender and the sauce suitably light and complex. To take your taste buds to new heights we recommend the menu prestige – seven tiny taster courses provide a culinary journey through a repertoire that has seen Gordon's cooking rise to superstar status. From the famous cappuccino of haricots blancs with sauté girolles and grated truffle, to fillet of halibut poached in court bouillon with a velouté of broad beans, we experienced exceptional textures and flavours along the way. If you choose three miniature crème brûlées rather than French cheeses, don't bet on guessing the different flavours as infusions of herbs and spices are used in this unusual dessert. Mainly French waiting staff provide impeccable service in what is quite a modern setting: line rag-rolled walls, bold paintings and trendsetting floral displays abound. Those looking for top class Bordeaux and Burgundy will not be disappointed but the wine list is distinguished more by intrepid selections from Alsace, Rhône and the Loire. Keep an eye out for Léon Beyers crisp, rich Pinot Blanc at £18, the heady Côtes du Rhône Villages Rasteau from Domaine St Gayan at £24, and the intense Savennières Roches au Moines from Soulez at £23. All offer bags of character at sensible prices.

Signature dishes: Foie gras served three ways with an Earl Grey consommé; filet of John Dory with crushed new potatoes and confit tomatoes with beignets of langoustines; Bresse pigeon poached in a bouillon of ceps, a ravioli of wild mushrooms, sauce foie gras; cappuccino of haricots blancs with sauté girolles and grated truffle.

Au Jardin des Gourmets ❀❀

5 Greek Street W1V 5LA
Map: D4
Tel: 0171 4371816
Fax: 0171 4370043
Chef: Vincent Hiss
Owner: Novoport Group Ltd
Cost: *Alc* £30, fixed-price L/D £16.50 (2 courses). ☺ H/wine £9.75.
Times: Noon-last L 2.30pm/6pm-last D 11.15pm. Closed L Sat, Sun, Bhs
Additional: Children welcome; ◑ dishes
Seats: 50. Private dining room 8-50
Smoking: No-smoking area; air-conditioning
Credit cards: ▆ ▆ ▆ ▆ ▆ ▆

Since the demise of The Boulestin, this fine old establishment lays claim to being London's oldest French restaurant. Established in 1931, it still clings to its past although things are beginning to change: dining now takes place in the elegant first-floor terrace restaurant with windows overlooking the Soho streetlife, and the place is now owned by a Russian company who also import smoked sturgeon and caviar – so if you crave a spoonful of Oscietra and a glass of champagne, you won't be disappointed. The *carte* is written in French with English translations and the kitchen rolls out a few classics while keeping its pulse on the mood of the times. A recent inspection began delicately with a layered crab gâteau provençale served with a light, well flavoured lobster sauce vinaigrette. Next came slices of tender lamb fillet with young

herbs bedded on couscous with vegetables that had balance as well as contrast. To finish, there was a trio of apple desserts – featuring a light crisp sorbet, a charlotte and a dumpling accompanied by a fruit coulis. The wine list is a magnificent tome running to 400 bins with heavyweight Burgundies and glorious clarets dating back to the 1940s.

Directions: Near Soho Square and Oxford Street; nearest Tube – Tottenham Court Road.

The Avenue

Interior with minimal design and maximum impact, courtesy of an eminent US architect whose mission was to bring New York style to London, and modern British cooking with Mediterranean influences, are the key features of this expansive 200 seat restaurant. The Avenue operates a fixed-price lunch menu with *carte* only at dinner, plus good value pre- and post-theatre menus. Snacks can be ordered from the long, uplit bar. During our visit on a midweek evening, the noise and buzz was considerable; service however was confident, yet caring. A starter of cured salmon with French bean and artichoke salad and shallot vinaigrette was well balanced. Roast cod, extremely moist and flaky with a crunchy tomato and bean salad, went down well, and vacherin of spiced pears with ginger ice cream, and sticky toffee pudding with honey ice cream and butterscotch sauce, both proved good desserts. An interesting selection of wines are arranged by grape variety, plus there's a large number sold by the glass.

7-9 St James's Street SW1
Map: C3
Tel: 0171 3212111
Fax: 0171 3212500
Chef: Dean Carr
Owner: Moving Image Restaurants Ltd
Cost: *Alc* £27.05, fixed-price L £19.50. ☺ H/wine £12.50.
Times: Noon-last L 3pm (3.30pm Sun)/6pm-last D midnight (12.30am Fri, Sat).
Additional: Bar food; Children welcome; ✿ dishes
Seats: 180
Smoking: Air-conditioning
Credit cards: 💳 💳 💳 💳 💳

Directions: Green Park Tube, R past The Ritz, R into St. James's Street

Ayudhya Thai Restaurant

14 Kingston Hill
Kingston-upon-Thames KT2 7NH
Map GtL: B2
Tel: 0181 5495984/5465878
Chef/Owner: Ms Somjai Thanpho
Cost: *Alc* £18.50. H/wine £8.75. ☺
Times: Noon-last L 2.30pm/6.30pm-last D 11pm. Closed Mon, 25-26 Dec, Easter Sun, Bhs
Additional: Children welcome; ✿ dishes
Seats: 82. Private dining room 22
Smoking: No-smoking area
Credit cards: 💳 💳 💳 💳 💳 💳

Ayudhya (named after the ancient capital of Siam) occupies three floors in well-heeled Kingston and it creates a suitably authentic atmosphere with wooden carvings, artefacts, pictures and even a little Buddhist shrine in one corner. The menu of around 90 dishes is clearly laid out, well described and succeeds in covering all the main departments of the cuisine. Familiar satays, soups, spicy salads (green mango with minced pork, for example), curries and stir-fries show up well and the kitchen also has a few more unusual specialities up its sleeve. *Hoy Jaw* is a 'Southern Snack' consisting of minced prawn, crab and pork steamed in a beancurd wrapper then deep fried, while *paht pak boong* is stir-fried Thai water spinach (aquatic morning glory) with black bean sauce. Also worth noting is the restaurant's special version of fried rice which includes smoked frankfurters and squid along with the more usual bits and pieces. Jasmine tea or Singha Thai beer are appropriate tipples.

Directions: 0.5 mile from Kingston town centre on A308, and 2.5 miles from Robin Hood Roundabout at the junction of A3

Babur Brasserie ❀❀

119 Brockley Rise Forest Hill
SE23 1JP
Map GtL: D2
Tel: 0181 2912400/4881
Chef: Enam Rahman
Owner: Babur Ltd
Cost: *Alc* £13.75. H/wine £7.95 ☺
Times: Noon-last L 2.15pm/6pm-last D 11.15pm. Closed L Fri, 25-26 Dec
Additional: Sunday buffet; Children welcome; ◑ dishes
Seats: 56
Smoking: No-smoking area
Credit cards: 〓 ▤ ▨ ⇥ ⇥ ▣ ⌐

A large Indian tiger hangs over the doorway of this small, genuinely friendly restaurant. Run by two brothers, service is helpful and attentive with plenty of advice on hand to guide newcomers through the colourful menu. Home-made yoghurt is used to marinade tandoori tikka chicken, and appears, butter yellow and herb-flavoured, in a jug at the table. The quality of the raw ingredients is evident in dishes such as *sali jardaloo*, lamb with apricot and honey with a fried potato topping for textural contrast. *Chingri meerchi* are tiny prawns tossed in shredded green chillies, ginger, garlic and spring onions, finished with fresh tomato and coriander; heat-seekers will enjoy a fiery but excellent tuna buchao made with bonnet and Goan red chillies. A vegetable dish, *oonbhariu*, inventively combined bananas, sweet potato, aubergine, shallots, lovage seeds and cumin with puréed asafoetida. Details are not skimped – real saffron colours the basmati rice in *pillao chawal*, poppadums arrive with thin mango sauce, fresh salad and hot chilli chutney, and nan is flavoured with grated carrot and ground garlic.

Directions: 5 mins walk from Honor Oak BR Station, where parking is available

Bahn Thai ❀❀

21a Frith Street W1V 5TS
Map: D4
Tel: 0171 437 8504
Fax: 0171 439 0340
Chef: Mrs Pen Squires
Owner: Philip Harris
Times: Noon-last L 2.45pm (12.30pm Sun)/6pm-last D 11.15pm (10.30pm Sun). Closed Bhs, Xmas, Easter

One of the first of London's Thai restaurants and head chef, Mrs Pen Squires, has been here since the beginning in 1982. The small ground floor room is used for lunch and early, quick dinners, with the larger first floor room, with its greenery hung 'roofs', the main place at night. The longish menu offers lots of preliminary notes about Thai dining with various symbols denoting heat. Dishes are well differentiated with good, clear

Bahn Thai

Additional: Sunday L; Children welcome; dishes
Seats: 120. Private dining rooms
Smoking: No smoking establishment; air-conditioning
Credit cards: ▆ ▆ ▆ ▆ ▆ ▆

flavours. Dim sum was home-made with a well flavoured filling 'not just the usual bland mince', crab cake, made with Blue Swimming crab and pork, came in a crab shell, marinated duck was served with pickled ginger and soy sauce, and both wok-fried prawns and garlic, pepper and coriander paste and green chicken curry were particularly good, a great mix of textures and flavours.

Directions: Halfway between Leicester Square & Tottenham Court Road tube stations, opposite Ronnie Scott's jazz club

Baileys Hotel ❀ NEW

See *Where London Meets* page 157

Bank Restaurant ❀❀ NEW

The success of this dynamic, colourful new restaurant, on the edge of theatre land, is evident from the huge volume of people passing through the spacious, ultra-modern interior. Slanted sheets of hardened glass (all 17.5 tons of it) hang from overhead panels, tables are well-spaced with red tub chairs, and walls are painted in strong pastel shades with the odd pillar in a bolder red. There's a real buzz in the air. Speed is the key to a rapid turnaround in tables, both from the hard-working waiting staff and the energetic crew in the open-view kitchen. The 'liberated French' menu, under the overall guidance of Christian Delteil, is vibrant and stimulating, with something for all tastes. Smoked haddock, wild garlic and ricotta tart, fried chicken and shrimp nam rolls with a spicy dip, and seared rare spiced tuna excitingly paired with mango and tomato salad all made great first courses. Caramelised scallops, flavoured with lemon grass, could have been finished off better, but worked well with celeriac purée; herb-roasted rabbit, with field mushrooms and mustard sauce, and red curried guinea fowl with Thai creamy coconut sauce both were just the ticket. Puddings turned out to be the weakest link – a rhubarb and orange sablé with mascarpone ice cream had a lovely sweet-sharp balance of flavours, but a sticky toffee pudding was not the best example of the genre. The wine list is comprehensive, reasonable value and user-friendly (listed by wine qualities).

Directions: Nearest Tube – Holborn. On Aldwych opp Bush House

1 Kingsway WC2B 6XF
Map: E4
Tel: 0171 3799797
Fax: 0171 3799014
Chef: Christian Delteil
Owners: Tony Auan, Jeremy Ormerod, Ron Truss, Christian Delteil, Eric Garnier
Cost: *Alc* £35, fixed-price L&D £16.50. ☺ H/wine £11.
Times: Noon-last L 3pm/5.30pm-last D 11.30pm
Additional: Bar meals; Sunday L; Children welcome; dishes
Smoking: Air-conditioning
Credit cards: ▆ ▆ ▆ ▆ ▆

Bardon Lodge Hotel

See Where London Meets page 157

Basil Street Hotel

See Where London Meets page 157

Belgo Centraal

Reservations are preferable to dining in the beer hall, where it's first come, first served, and seating is on benches at communal tables. You descend by metal freight elevator to be greeted by waiters dressed as Trappist monks. Try mussels any number of ways with pommes frites and mayonnaise, plus the Belgian national dish, waterzoi à la gantois.

Additional: Café menu 3pm-5.30pm; Children welcome;
⚫ dishes
Seats: 426. Private dining rooms 25, 35
Smoking: No pipes and cigars; air-conditioning
Credit cards: ▬ ▬ ▬ ▬ 💳 💳

Directions: Nearest Tube – Covent Garden

50 Earlham Street WC2 9HP
Map: D4
Tel: 0171 8132233
Fax: 0171 2093212
Chef: Richard Coates
Owners: Denis Blais, André Plisnier
Cost: *Alc* £25, fixed-price L £5 (1 course)/D £12.95 (2 courses). ☺ H/wine £8.95.
Times: Noon-11.30pm (10.30pm Sun). Closed 25 Dec

Belgo Noord

The ideas get wackier and the marketing keeps going up a notch. A lunch special is called the 'Psycho Plateau' (mussels espagnole or escargot with frites, mayo and beer), but it's all clean, loveable fun. The railway station-cum-European brewery eating-hall interior and waiters dressed as Trappist monks might have lost some of their novelty value, but moules mania is as strong as ever; one special deal is an all-the-mussels-you-can-eat offer between 6pm and 7.30pm Monday-Friday. There are other Belgian favourites to try, some of which feature the other house speciality – beer. Shank of lamb is braised in De Koninck beer with flageolet beans and *stoemp* (Belgian mash), wild mushrooms are stewed in Orval beer, in a light puff pastry case topped with Orval Trappist cheese, and cod is baked with a basil crust on a white beer and oyster cream. Other main courses include freshly grilled lobster, and Belgian endives wrapped in Ardennes ham with cheese and béchamel au gratin.

Directions: Nearest Tube – Chalk Farm or Camden Town. Opposite the Roundhouse

72 Chalk Farm Road NW1 8AN
Map GtL: C3
Tel: 0171 2670718
Fax: 0171 2844842
Chef: Richard Coates
Owners: Denis Blais & André Plisnier
Cost: *Alc* £25, fixed-price L £5 (1 course)/D £12.95 (2 courses). ☺ H/wine £8.95.
Times: Noon-last L 3pm/6pm-last D 11.30pm. Sat Noon-11.30pm (10.30pm Sun). Closed 25 Dec
Additional: Children welcome;
⚫ dishes
Seats: 140
Smoking: No pipes and cigars; air-conditioning
Credit cards: ▬ ▬ ▬ ▬ 💳 💳

Belvedere

The Belvedere offers a great location, situated in the calm tranquillity of Holland Park, just minutes away from the bustle of Kensington and Notting Hill. The light, bright, airy restaurant is set on two floors, and offers a seasonally changing *carte* that is thoroughly steeped in modern, fashionable ideas. This was evident at a meal in April, when our inspector kicked off with duck liver terrine with fennel and parsley oil, followed by a baked sea bass on a bed of couscous with cheese and bacon mash. Other main courses could include roast saddle of lamb stuffed with forest mushrooms and served with a pearl

Abbotsbury Road
Holland Park W8 6LU
Map GtL: C3
Tel: 0171 6021238
Fax: 0171 6104382
Chef: Duncan Wallace
Owners: Mr J Gold, Mr W Ofner
Cost: *Alc* £22.50. H/wine £10.50. ☺
Times: Noon-last L/7pm-last D 10pm. Closed D Sun, 25 Dec, 1 Jan
Additional: Sunday L;
Children welcome; ⚫ dishes

barley risotto, roast guinea fowl wrapped in bacon with a lentil cassoulet, and blackened tuna steak with salsa verde. Desserts include red berry trifle in a brandy snap basket with raspberry custard, chocolate marquis with a pistachio nut sauce, and pear and almond tart with ginger ice cream. Service is efficient and attentive.

Directions: On Kensington High Street side of Holland Park. Nearest Tube – Holland Park

Seats: 132
Smoking: Air-conditioning
Credit cards: ▆ ▆ ▆ ▆ ▆ ▆

The Bengal Clipper ❀❀

The stiffly starched uniforms of the staff give an air of imperial hauteur to this airy, modern restaurant, hung with vibrant, modern Indian paintings, and located in a former spice warehouse by the Thames, The short menu, however, is not overpriced and there is much of interest. Karkra chop, for instance, was a well-flavoured patty of minced crab meat with mashed potato and Goan spices, served with a sweet and sour sauce. Our inspector followed this with stuffed *murgh masala*, breast of chicken stuffed with apricots, potato, onion and almonds, cooked in yogurt and served with a freshly made mild curry sauce. Other dishes listed under the heading of 'India's Most Remarkable Dishes' are *hass vindaloo*, off-the-bone duckling served in a thick and tangy sauce, and lamb pasanda, a North Indian speciality of marinated lamb cooked in cream, cashew nuts and freshly ground ginger. Extras are good – dry cooked spinach with aniseed and garlic, pilau rice, pershwari nan and poppadums with home-made chutneys all helped the meal along.

Directions: By Tower Bridge, nearest Tube – Tower Hill

Butlers Wharf
SE1 2YE
Map GtL: D3
Tel: 0171 3579001
Fax: 0171 3579002
Chef: Azam Khan
Owners: Mr Chowdhury
Cost: *Alc* £25, fixed-price L £9.75/D £28. ☺ H/wine £8.95.
Times: Noon-last L 2.45pm/6pm-last D 11.15pm
Additional: Sunday L; Children welcome; ♦ dishes
Seats: 170
Smoking: Air-conditioning
Credit cards: ▆ ▆ ▆ ▆ ▆ ▆

Bentley's ❀❀

A popular seafood restaurant (established in 1916) that is proudly English in its setting – chandeliers, oil paintings and lots of marble. The oyster bar offers more informality. The menu takes in traditional fish and chips, Dover sole and salmon and haddock fishcakes with tarragon sauce, but is in tune with modern ideas offering the likes of spaghetti of lobster and clams with gremolata, and seared scallops with lentil pilaff. Bouillabaisse, fillet of haddock, poached egg and new potatoes with a strong mustard sauce and spinach, and chocolate mille-feuille filled with fresh raspberries and cream

11-15 Swallow Street
W1R 7HD
Map: C3
Tel: 0171 7344756
Fax: 0171 2872972
Owner: O Owide
Times: Noon-11.30pm.
Closed Sun, 25-26 Dec
Additional: Bar food; Children welcome; ♦ dishes
Seats: 70. Private dining room 14
Smoking: Air-conditioning
Credit cards: ▆ ▆ ▆ ▆ ▆ ▆

with raspberry coulis and sauce anglaise made up one well-reported meal.

Directions: Nearest Tube – Piccadilly Circus. Swallow Street links Regent St & Piccadilly and is opposite St James's Church on Piccadilly

The Berkeley ❀❀

The old world of civilised courtesies and polished style seems to linger on in this upper-crust Belgravia venue overlooking Hyde Park. Here is a place where you can take tea amid magnificent arrangements of flowers in one of the lounges, or dine in the classy intimacy of the main restaurant. Staff go through their paces with tutored professionalism and discretion. The cooking has its roots in the classical French tradition, although the kitchen tries to lighten up the mood here and there. Starters might feature a salad of langoustines, artichokes, sweet potatoes and herbs or terrine of foie gras, celeriac and leek with truffled brioche, while main courses could range from poached fillet of brill with spring onion, potato purée, chicory and a grain mustard sauce, to breast and confit of Blackleg chicken with crayfish risotto and basil bouillabaisse, or cassoulet of French duck with haricot beans and a herb crust. A decent clutch of wines by the glass kick off the heavyweight list.

Directions: 200 yds from Hyde Park Corner. Nearest Tube – Hyde Park Corner

Wilton Place SW1X 7RL
Map: B2
Tel: 0171 2356000
Fax: 0171 2354330
Chef: Andrew Turner
Owner: The Berkeley
Cost: Alc £26, fixed-price L £22.50/D £26 (3 courses). H/wine £16.50
Times: 12.30pm-last L 2pm/6.30pm-last D 10.30pm.
Additional: Bar meals L; Children welcome; ❀ dishes
Seats: 70. Private dining room 180. Jacket and tie preferred
Smoking: Air-conditioning
Accommodation: 157 en suite
Credit cards: ▬ ▬ ▬ ▣

The Berkshire ❀

See Where London Meets page 157

Bibendum ❀❀❀❀

Map: A1
Tel: 0171 5815817
Fax: 0171 8237925
Chef: Matthew Harris
Owners: Sir Terence Conran, Paul Hamlyn, Simon Hopkinson, Graham Williams
Cost: Alc £55, fixed-price L £28. H/wine £9.50
Times: 12.30pm-last L 2.30pm/7pm-last D 11.30pm. Closed Xmas
Additional: Sunday L; Children welcome; ❀ dishes
Seats: 72
Smoking: Air-conditioning
Credit cards: ▬ ▬ ▬ ▰ ▣ ▯

Directions: Nearest Tube: South Kensington

'Small wonder that the Michelin man has a grin as broad as his girth', quipped an inspector. The building is an absolute dream – an irresistible oyster bar for light meals on the ground floor, then up the staircase to the main dining room with its magnificent stained glass windows allowing light to stream through. The atmosphere fairly fizzes with life, tables are often turned round three times in a session and – needless to say – you need to book weeks ahead. It may seem frenetic, but there's also a degree of privacy about the lay-out and staff provide just the right kind of service to suit the setting. What the kitchen offers is, arguably, the best brasserie food of its kind in the capital. Matthew Harris heads a brigade of six and they work to a philosophy of exact simplicity 'with knobs on'. Part of the secret is canny buying and attention to detail – witness the wonderfully oily green and black olives and the baguettes, which are as close to France as you can get. The menu is shot through with great combinations: open chicken liver ravioli with lemon cream and gremolata, brilliant grilled pigeon with 'deceptively yielding' leek stalks and a zingy three-dimensional jus suffused with truffle oil, and braised oxtail with red wine, cinnamon prunes and saffron risotto, to name but three. But there's also earthy revivalism in dishes such as faggots and mash, mushrooms on toast, coq au vin and deep-fried plaice and chips. Desserts go all the way – blood orange fool with sesame cookies, passionfruit cream pot with sablé biscuits and a glorious tart of the finest feuilleté pastry and thin slices of gentle tasting apples neatly arranged in a circle, not to mention lusciously creamy ice creams. Perfect chocolate truffles and faultless espresso round things off with real style.

A wine list of extraordinary depth. Naturally, Bordeaux is particularly well served with exhaustive lists of great names from distinguished vintages. The ambition does not end in claret however, there are awe inspiring selections from the rest of the world; for just over £20 one can choose from a legion of fine examples. An impressive array of half-bottles is a fitting close to a remarkable *carte*.

Signature dishes: crab vinaigrette with herbs; poached wild salmon with peas, asparagus and tarragon; roast grouse with bread sauce, port and redcurrant jelly.

Bice ✿✿

Born in Milan, but now with siblings scattered everywhere from Beverley Hills to Tokyo. The Mayfair branch – in keeping with its brothers and sisters – offers glitzy 1920s decor with an abundance of wood and mirrors, and a menu that follows a well-tried pattern. Some dishes, such as risotto alla milanese and tiramisu della Bice are common to all branches, others vary to keep the chefs interested. Fresh pastas, made with lots of egg, are reliably good; our inspector's quadrucci (little squares) with artichoke hearts and slices of asparagus was sound. Meat and fish are also well represented by, say, pan-fried duck breast with a sauce of apples and pine kernels or grilled sea bass with rocket salad and braised lentils. Ricotta and pistachio tart with rich chocolate sauce is a good way to finish. Business lunches are paced for those living in the fast lane.

Directions: Off Piccadilly, near Old Bond Street; nearest tube Green Park

13 Albermarle Street W1X 3HA
Map: C3
Tel: 0171 4091011
Fax: 0171 4930081
Chef: Antonello Tagliabue
Owner: Jolanda Ruggeri
Cost: *Alc* £35, fixed-price L £20 (2 course). H/wine £15
Times: 12 noon-last L 2.45pm/7pm-last D 11pm. Closed Sun, Sat L
Additional: Bar meals L; Children welcome; ✿ dishes
Seats: 90. Private dining room 25
Smoking: Air-conditioning
Credit cards: ▬ ▬ ▬ ▬ ▣ ▢

Big Night Out ✿✿

Despite the name (or maybe it's ironic?), the setting is plain and simple with an equally unassuming and informal atmosphere. Attentive and friendly staff guide the diner through a range of interesting dishes that are freshly prepared and have good strong flavours. The style is broadly Mediterranean. Succulent, seared scallops came with tarragon-flavoured butter, although the rocket garnish was a little tired

148 Regents Park Road NW1 8XN
Map GtL: C3
Tel: 0171 5865768
Fax: 0171 5860943
Chefs: Richard Coates, Ahmed
Owners: Richard Coates, Jeton Sadiku
Cost: *Alc* £17.50, fixed-price L £7.95/£9.95/D £11.50/£14. H/wine £9.50

looking. Fresh roasted poussin was saved from blandness by a robust rosemary and balsamic vinegar, and served on a bed of crisp, baby spinach leaves. A dessert of tiramisu was very moist, with lots of delicious flavour. Espresso coffee is good and strong.

Directions: Near Primrose Hill, 750yds from Chalk Farm tube station, on L going N

Times: Noon-last L 2.45pm (Fri, Sat, Sun only)/7pm-last D 10.30pm (Tue-Sat)
Additional: Children welcome; dishes
Seats: 36. Private dining room 30
Smoking: Air-conditioning
Credit cards: ■ ▆ ▆ ▆

Bistro 190 ❀❀

'No booking unless you are a member, so wait for a table in the bustling bar; very informal atmosphere, cosmopolitan crowd with quite a few lone diners stopping in for one course; almost bohemian-style, sparse wooden tables, tumblers for wine like some backwoods French café, eclectic collection of pictures and ornaments'. So ran one inspector's notes on this popular South Kensington hang-out. Food is Mediterranean-peasantish bistro dishes along the lines of roast vine tomato tart, Bocconcini mozzarella and pesto, saddle of rabbit stuffed with spicy Italian sausage on braised butter beans (real Tuscan-style peasant cooking with flavours as robust as campfire as it sounds), and still steaming steamed chocolate pudding with orange sauce. This is straightforward, gutsy stuff. The wine list has some exciting, good value French bins.

Directions: Hyde Park end of Queen's Gate

190 Queen's Gate SW7 5EU
Map: A1
Tel: 0171 5815666
Fax: 0171 5818172
Chef: Mark Emberton
Cost: *Alc* £21
Times: 7am-12.30am.
Closed 25-26 Dec
Additional: Children welcome; dishes
Seats: 60
Credit cards: ■ ▆ ▆ ▜

Bistro Soho ❀

Lively Soho restaurant with an eclectic menu that embraces Galway oysters, Dover sole meunière, mezze, duck pastilla with fig chutney, and couscous. French brasserie staples take in jambon persillade, or there could be grilled onglet with shallots and mash. Young, on-the-ball service tries hard. Simple decor.

Additional: Children welcome; dishes
Seats: 90. **Credit cards:** ■ ▆ ▆ ▜ ▆ ▆

Directions: Nearest Tube: Tottenham Court Road

63 Frith Street W1V 5TA
Map: D4
Tel: 0171 7344545
Fax: 0171 2871027
Chef: James Kirby
Owners: Mr & Mrs Condou
Cost: H/wine £8.75. ☺
Times: 12.15pm-last L 2.30pm/6pm-last D 11.45pm. Closed L Sat, Sun

The Blenheim ❀

21 Loudoun Road NW8 0NB
Map GtL: C3
Tel: 0171 625 1222
Fax: 0171 328 1593
Chef: Peter Caldwell
Owner: Café Med Ltd
Cost: *Alc* £20. H/wine £9.20. ☺
Times: Noon-11.30pm.
Closed 25 Dec
Additional: Children welcome; dishes
Smoking: No-smoking area; no pipes & cigars; air-conditioning
Credit cards: ■ ▆ ▆ ▜ ▆ ▆

Corner pub-turned-restaurant with terrace for summer eating. The bright, uncomplicated menu features two sorts of Caesar salad,

mixed mushroom risotto, grilled tuna niçoise and steak, mustard
aïoli and fries. The chargrill is used for salmon fillet with warm
potato salad and salsa verde. Chocolate nemesis and clotted cream
sounds a suitable way to bow out.

Directions: Nearest Tube St John's Wood

Bluebird

Conran empire newcomer that continues the theme of great
design coupled with accessible yet subtly innovative food.
The Kings Road Gastrodome, as it is billed, features a host of
food related outlets, all of which sell fabulous-looking high
quality goods with prices to match. Converted from a garage
(where the famous eponymous vehicle was built) the
cathedral-like restaurant is full of natural light; kite-inspired
sculptures by Richard Smith quiver gently overhead. The
centrepiece of the open-plan kitchen is a huge wood-burning
oven, otherwise there are three main focal points – the
stainless steel and granite bar, a crustacea bar and the windows
overlooking the ground floor foodmarket. Dishes from the
rotisserie include suckling pig stuffed with a sage-based
stuffing, served with cassoulet-style beans in tomato sauce.
Pudding could be a super rhubarb ice cream with rhubarb and
ginger compote.

350 Kings Road SW3 5UU
Map: B1
Tel: 0171 5591000
Fax: 0171 5591111
Chef: Michael Moore
Owner: Conran Restaurants
Cost: Alc £35, fixed-price L & pre-
theatre D £14.50. H/wine £11.75
Times: Noon-3.30pm/6pm-11pm (Sun
10pm)
Additional: Bar meals L; Sat/Sun
brunch (11am-4.30pm); Children
welcome; dishes
Seats: 288. Private dining room 20
Smoking: Air-conditioning
Credit cards:

Directions: Nearest Tube – Sloane Square

Blue Print Cafe

The Design Museum Shad Thames
Street SE1 2YD
Map: G3
Tel: 0171 3787031
Fax: 0171 3578810
Chef: Jeremy Lee
Owner: Conran Restaurants.
Cost: Alc £38. H/wine £14.95. ☺
Times: Last L 3pm (3.30pm Sun)/last
D 10.30pm. Closed D Sun
Additional: Sunday L; Children
welcome; dishes.
Credit cards:

Busy bistro-cum-brasserie with vibrant atmosphere, cosmopolitan
clientele. Great Thames views from much-in-demand window seats.
Ambitious cooking offers the likes of chilli bean broth with shell fish
and basil, calves' liver with melted onion and sage, bourride of cod,
and petit pot au chocolat.

Directions: SE of Tower Bridge, on mezzanine of the Design
Museum

Bombay Bicycle Club

The Club, after which this restaurant is named, was a gathering
place in the northern part of the Indian sub-continent where
colonial officers used to meet and catch up on the local gossip.
There's a deliberately westernised feel to the high-ceilinged

95 Nightingale Lane SW12
Map: G3
Tel: 0181 6736217
Fax: 0181 6739100
Chef: BJ Gurung
Cost: Alc £24. H/wine £9.90. ☺

dining room in this Grade II listed building: casually dressed staff serve in friendly fashion, the mood is bright and airy with some attractive floral displays adding a splash of colour. The menu is predominately North Indian and it's an accessible blend of familiar tandooris and curries with a few more esoteric items. Our inspector chose *gosht kata masala* (tender braised lamb cooked with onions, ginger and garlic) *murgh mangalore* (chicken with an unusual sauce flavoured with aniseed and cardamom), and *gosht kalia* in a thick yogurt sauce loaded with methi. Incidentals such as kebabs, freshly cooked nan and pilau rice cooked to the kitchen's own recipe are well up-to-the mark.

Times: D only, 6.30pm-last D 11pm. Closed D Sun
Additional: Children welcome; ◑ dishes
Seats: 80. Private dining room 24
Credit cards: ▨ ▨ ▨ ▨ ▨ ▨

Directions: Nearest Tube – Clapham South

Bombay Brasserie ❀❀

Fashionable, cool and classy, this deluxe brasserie conjures up a vision of Raj splendour in South Kensington. Paddle fans revolve in the grand, high-ceilinged dining room, luxuriant palms and tropical plants fill the magnificent conservatory. Service comes with plenty of formality. The menu is a cook's tour of the sub-continent, taking in Bombay roadside snacks, Goan fish dishes spiked with coconut and chillies, tandooris from the North West Frontier, Kashmiri kormas and fruity Parsee specialities. Appetisers are particularly interesting: *ragara pattice* (a potato cake stuffed with spicy yellow gram) comes with a quartet of chutneys – a dish 'as colourful as a Mediterranean painting', noted our inspector. Chicken tikka kalimiri has also been good, while lamb chops with ginger and green herbs highlight the quality of the ingredients to telling effect. Vegetables such as *palak makki* (puréed spinach with baby corn) are fine, as are breads. Lunch is a multi-dish buffet. Chaas, lassi and Kingfisher beer suit the food, otherwise there's a short international wine list.

Courtfield Close SW7 4UH
Map: A1
Tel: 0171 3704040
Fax: 0171 8351669
Chef: Udit Sarkhel
Owner: Taj International Hotels
Cost: Alc (D only) £30, buffet L £14.95. ☺ H/wine £11.75.
Times: 12.30pm-last L 3pm/7.30pm-last D midnight. Closed 25-26 Dec
Additional: Sunday L buffet; Children welcome L only; ◑ dishes
Seats: 180
Smoking: No-smoking area; No pipes; air-conditioning
Credit cards: ▨ ▨ ▨ ▨ ▨

Directions: Opposite Gloucester Road tube adjacent to Bailey's Hotel

Boyd's Restaurant ❀❀

The name remains, but a new chef/proprietor in the shape of Maria Zarari has taken up residence in this rather intimate conservatory-style restaurant on two levels. With Kensington Place and Sally Clarke's a stone's throw away, the local competition is fierce, but the kitchen knows what it's at and goes about its business with keen enthusiasm. Classic dishes such as a crêpe of wild mushrooms and Gruyère with flavoursome red pepper coulis, or grilled halibut with asparagus and chive hollandaise are handled with confidence, but there is also a modish Mediterranean imprint here and there. Loin of swordfish is served with roast tomatoes, garlic and black olives en papillote, while medallions of monkfish and Parma ham receive a creamy pesto sauce. Away from fish, the menu also promises baked black pudding with apple and cider sauce, sautéed calves' liver and sweetbreads with foie gras sauce, and seared saddle of venison with redcurrant sauce. Chocolate bread-and-butter pudding makes for a novel dessert.

135 Kensington Church Street W8 7LP
Map GtL: C3
Tel: 0171 7275452
Fax: 0171 2210615
Chef/Owner: Maria Zarari
Cost: Alc £30, fixed-price L £15. ☺ H/wine £11.95.
Times: 12.30pm-last L 2.45pm/7pm-last D 10.45pm. Closed Sun, Xmas, Easter, Bhs
Additional: No children under 7; ◑ dishes
Seats: 40. Private dining room 10
Smoking: Air-conditioning
Credit cards: ▨ ▨ ▨ ▨ ▨

Directions: Nearest Tube – Notting Hill Gate. 2 blocks south

The Brackenbury

'I fell in love with this diminutive little place tucked away down a residential side street off Goldhawk Road', confessed our inspector. The emphasis is on 'sunny food, simply prepared without too much fuss', and locals flock here, creating a relaxed, lively atmosphere. Mediterranean influences shone through in a meal that opened with grilled flat bread with aubergine, mint and crème fraîche, with tomatoes, young dandelion leaves and a sharp, vinegary dressing, then went on to a fillet of grey mullet, pan-fried, and served with tomatoes, basil, braised fennel and wilted spinach, and finished with cherry custard tart. The short wine list has most bottles coming by the glass as well, and fairly spans the globe.

Additional: Sunday L; Children welcome; ◔ dishes
Seats: 55
Smoking: No pipes or cigars
Credit cards: ▆ ▆ ▆ ▆ ▆

Directions: Off Goldhawk Road. Nearest tubes Hammersmith & Goldhawk Road

129 Brackenbury Road W6 0BQ
Map GtL: C3
Tel: 0181 7480107
Fax: 0181 7410905
Chefs: Garrett O'Brien, Marcia Chang-Hong
Owners: Nick Smallwood, Simon Slater
Cost: Alc £20-£25. H/wine £9.25. ☺
Times: 12-30pm-last L 2.45pm/7pm-last D 10.45pm. Closed L Sat, D Sun, L Mon, Bhs, 10 days Xmas

Britannia Hotel

Smartly presented hotel, prominently placed on the south side of Grosvenor Square, just a stone's throw from the American Embassy. There are two restaurants here, both worth exploring. The Japanese restaurant, a subterranean cave-like establishment with exposed walls (so unlike the general minimalist setting loved of most of London's Japanese restaurants), is a hugely popular place, full of Japanese suits 'often being entertained by their American counterparts'. Booking is essential. Menus are mostly based on set dinners of approximately six small courses built around the main ingredient which could be tempura or sashimi, for example. Chicken yakitori, dobin-mushi, buta-kanani – steamed pork belly with ginger – crisp tempura, and sushi formed the components of one well reported meal. As a complete contrast, the French-style Adams restaurant offers ambitious modern British cooking. An inspection lunch produced lamb fillet terrine with cranberry, mint and onion chutney, sole with pistachio soufflé and creamy seafood sauce, and crème brûlée from the dessert trolley.

Directions: Nearest Tubes – Bond Street, Green Park

Grosvenor Square W1A 3AN
Map: C3
Tel: 0171 6299400 ext 7807
Fax: 0171 6297736
Chef: Neil Gray
Owner: Millenium Hotels
Cost: Alc £28, fixed-price L £25/D £23. H/wine £14.95
Times: Last L 2.30pm/last D 9.30pm. Closed L Sat, Sun, 3 wks Aug
Additional: Sunday L; Bar meals; Children welcome; ◔ dishes
Smoking: Air-conditioning
Accommodation: 318 rooms
Credit cards: ▆ ▆ ▆ ▆ ▆ ▆

Brown's 🍴🍴

Albemarle Street,
Dover Street W1X 4BP
Map: C3
Tel: 0171 4936020
Fax: 0171 4939381
Chef: Alan Maw
Cost: *Alc* £40, fixed-price L £24.50/D
£29. ☺ H/wine £18.
Times: 12.30pm-last L 2.15pm/6pm-
last D 10pm. Closed L Sat
Additional: Sunday L; Children
welcome; 🍴 dishes
Seats: 80. Private dining room 8-70.
Jacket and tie preferred
Smoking: No-smoking area; no pipes;
air-conditioning
Accommodation: 118 en suite
Credit cards: ▨ ▨ ▨ ▨ ▨ ▨

Directions: Main entrance in
Albemarle Street, off Piccadilly.
Nearest tubes – Piccadilly Circus,
Green Park

This stylish and much loved deluxe town-house hotel provides
welcome relief and serves as a haven from the frenetic pace of
the West End. 'The Restaurant at Brown's' is a room of quality
with its wood panelling, floral displays and well-spaced tables
and civilised atmosphere. New chef Alan Maw (ex-Hartwell
House and The Savoy) has settled in well and his weekly
changing menus provide a sound balance of traditional
Brown's favourites (a roast of the day, grilled calves' liver and
bacon, Dover sole meunière) plus those in the modern idiom.
Recommended dishes from recent meals have included
marinated raw tuna speckled with sesame seeds and served
with a citrus dressing, and an intriguing dish of rabbit
presented attractively in different ways – little cutlets, stuffed
saddle and glazed leg with a mustard sauce, caramelised
shallots and lentils. Desserts range from nougat parfait with
caramel sauce to glazed almond and apricot tart. The wine list
does not quite match the serious intent of the cooking.

Buchan's 🍴🍴

62-64 Battersea Bridge Road
SW11 3AG
Map GtL: C2
Tel: 0171 2280888
Fax: 0171 9241718
Chef: Jane Melia
Owner: Anthony Brown
Cost: *Alc* £25, fixed-price L £7.50 (2
courses). ☺ H/wine £9.50.

There's been a change of ownership and chef at this friendly
and informal Scottish/French restaurant, but the cooking
remains much as before. Thick slices of wholemeal and white
bread come with a dish of salted butter, followed perhaps by
a well-constructed skate and artichoke terrine, with moist,
good-flavoured fish. Our inspector chose as a main course the
plat du jour, tender leg of lamb with a fine rosemary and red
wine sauce, served with small roast tatties and fresh leaf

spinach. Dessert was particularly enjoyable – white chocolate mousse on a crunchy nut and fruit base with a good raspberry coulis.

Credit cards:

Directions: 200 yards S of Battersea Bridge. Nearest tube stations: Sloane Sq or South Kensington

Butlers Wharf Chop House ⊛⊛

This is the food world's answer to the *Last Night of the Proms:* flag-wavingly British, noisy and a great bash. The setting is part of the Conran complex, with Tower Bridge looming close by, and it is exactly the kind of place where you can indulge in that current fashion leader, fish and chips with mushy peas. If that doesn't take your fancy, then consider other re-invented constructions such as fillet of sole with viper's grass, artichokes and rosemary, and pan-fried fillet of beef with braised oxtail, parsnip and brown ale sauce. Menus are peppered with judiciously sourced regional produce: Loch Fyne herrings, Eastbrook Farm organic pork chops – which are grilled and served with apple and sage. Desserts prove that Britannia still rules – here you will find a splendid baked rhubarb and custard tart.

Directions: On river front, on SE side of Tower Bridge

Byron's Restaurant ⊛

Youthful and enthusiastic team operating in a simply furnished but elegantly themed town-house restaurant. The attitude is switched on and ambitious. Blast-from-the-past chicken liver parfait with melba toast vies for attention with modish prawn won ton soup, and breast of English duck comes with red onion, spinach and walnut oil.

Seats: 50
Smoking: No pipes
Credit cards: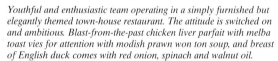

Directions: Nearest tube stations Hampstead, Belsize Park

Cadogan Hotel ⊛⊛

In Edwardian times, Oscar Wilde and Lillie Langtry were regular visitors to the hotel, and the building has been refurbished with good feeling for that period. The dinner *carte* is short but well balanced, and displays a classy simplicity with dishes such as cream of lobster and morel soup, salad of haricot beans and boudin of foie gras, roast rack of lamb with braised white beans, pancetta and rosemary, and baked sea bass with a confit of potato, marinated peppers and mushroom oil. Grilled fillets of Dover sole are given a suitably fin de siècle look with a fricassée of lobster and Sauternes sauce but, as the menu points out, grilled Dover sole, fillet steak and ice creams are always available. For those, however, who agree with Mr Wilde on the subject of temptation, there is always hot caramel soufflé with banana and peanut brittle ice cream.

Directions: Nearest tubes – Sloane Square & Knightsbridge

Times: Noon-last L 2.45pm/7pm-last D 10.40pm. Closed Good Fri, Easter Mon, 26 Dec
Additional: Bar food; Sunday L; Children welcome; ⑤ dishes
Seats: 75. Private dining room 50
Smoking: Air-conditioning

The Butlers Wharf Building
36e Shad Thames SE1 2YE
Map: D3
Tel: 0171 4033403
Fax: 0171 4033414
Chef: Henrik Iverson
Owner: Conran Restaurants
Cost: *Alc* £36; fixed-price L £22.75.
☺ H/wine from £13.95.
Times: Noon-last L 2.45pm/6pm-last D 10.30pm. Closed L Sat,D Sun
Additional: Bar food;
Children welcome; ⑤ dishes
Seats: Restaurant 114
Smoking: Air-conditioning
Credit cards: ▇ ▇ ▇

3a Downshire Road NW3
Map GtL: C4
Tel: 0171 435 3544
Fax: 0171 431 3544
Chef: Jonathan Simon Coxon
Owners: Dalgreave (Byron) Ltd
Cost: *Alc* £25, fixed-price L £10.95 (3-courses). ☺ H/wine £9.95
Times: Last L 2.30pm (Sun 3.30pm)/last D 11pm (Sun 10pm)
Additional: Sunday L;
No children under 8; ⑤ dishes

75 Sloane Street SW1X 9SG
Map: B2
Tel: 0171 2357141
Fax: 0171 2450994
Chef: Graham Thompson
Owner: Historic House Hotels
Cost: *Alc* £37.50, fixed-price L £17.90/D £25.50. H/wine £13.50
Times: 12.30pm-last L 2pm/5.30pm-last D 9.45pm. Closed L Sat
Additional: Bar meals; Sunday L; No children under 10; ⑤ dishes
Seats: 36. Private dining room 32. Jacket and tie preferred
Smoking: No pipes & cigars; air-conditioning
Accommodation: 65 en suite
Credit cards: ▇ ▇ ▇ ▇ ▇

Café des Arts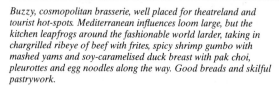

*A relaxed, informal bistro-style restaurant, with some of
Hampstead's oldest architecture. Recommended dishes from the
short menu include roast venison and Guinness sausages with
buttered leeks, fillet of red mullet with teriyaki glaze and noodles,
and pan-fried chicken breast with porcini torte.*

Smoking: No-smoking area; no cigars or pipes
Credit cards: ■ ■ ■ ■ ■ ■

Directions: Middle of Hampstead High Street, next door to Post
Office. Nearest tube – Hampstead

82 Hampstead High Street NW3
Map GtL: C4
Tel: 0171 435 3608
Chef: Jerri Norckett
Owner: Brian Stein
Cost: *Alc* £18, fixed-price L £5/D
£7.95. ☺ H/wine £9.50.
Times: Last L 4pm/D 11.30pm (noon-
11pm Sun). Closed 25-26 Dec
Additional: Sunday L; Children
welcome; ◗ dishes

Le Café du Jardin NEW

*Buzzy, cosmopolitan brasserie, well placed for theatreland and
tourist hot-spots. Mediterranean influences loom large, but the
kitchen leapfrogs around the fashionable world larder, taking in
chargrilled ribeye of beef with frites, spicy shrimp gumbo with
mashed yams and soy-caramelised duck breast with pak choi,
pleurottes and egg noodles along the way. Good breads and skilful
pastrywork.*

Smoking: Air-conditioning
Credit cards: ■ ■ ■ ■ ■ ■

Directions: On the corner of Wellington Street and Tavistock
Street. Nearest Tube – Covent Garden

28 Wellington Street WC2E 7BD
Map: D3
Tel: 0171 8368769/8760
Fax: 0171 8364123
Chef: Steven Nash
Owners: Robert Seigler,
Tony Howorth
Cost: *Alc* £23.50, fixed-price L&D
£13.50. ☺ H/wine £8.95
Times: Noon-3pm/5.30pm-midnight.
Closed 25-26 Dec
Additional: Sunday L; Children
welcome; ◗ dishes.

Le Café du Marché NEW

*Popular French restaurant and bar featuring typical brasserie dishes
such as fish soup, jambon persillé, daube de boeuf and chicken
ballotine with smoked bacon. There are daily plats du jour and the
classic range of desserts includes tarte aux fruits and crème caramel.*

Additional: No children under 5; ◗ dishes
Smoking: No pipes; air-conditioning. **Credit cards:** ■ ■ ■ ■

Directions: Nearest tube – Barbican. Charterhouse Mews is off
Charterhouse Sq

Charterhouse Mews Charterhouse
Square EC1M 6AH
Map: E5
Tel: 0171 6081609
Chef: Simon Cottard
Owner: CK Graham-Wood
Cost: Fixed-price D £21.50. ☺
H/wine £8.50.
Times: Last L 2.30pm/6pm-last D
10pm. Closed L Sat, Sun, Xmas,
Easter, Bhs

Café Fish

A busy, bustling seafood restaurant with a lively atmosphere.
The main attraction is, of course, fresh fish, whether it's roasted
baby turbot with artichoke and mushrooms in a light port
sauce, steamed fillet of trout with shredded Thai vegetables,
lemon grass and lime leaves, or deep-fried haddock with
mushy peas. Speciality main courses might include pan-fried
fillet of sea bass with scallops, creamed leeks and almondine
potatoes, baked monkfish with smoked bacon, mushrooms and
spinach, served on a potato galette, and half a lobster served
with white wine sauce and glazed with Parmesan. For starters
look out for Mediterranean fish soup with rouille, Gruyère
cheese and croûtons, and grilled Brittany sardines with tomato,
olive and herb tapenade. The short wine list covers bottles
from around the world, and are well chosen to complement the
restaurant's fish dishes.

39 Panton Street Haymarket
SW1Y 4EA
Tel: 0171 930 3999
Chef: Andrew Magson
Owners: Groupe Chez Gerard
Cost: *Alc* £28. H/wine £8.95 ☺
Times: Noon-last L 3pm/5.45pm-last
D 11.30pm. Closed L Sat, Sun, D Bhs
Additional: Children welcome;
◗ dishes
Seats: 90
Smoking: No-smoking area; no pipes
or cigars; air-conditioning
Credit cards: ■ ■ ■ ■ ■

Directions: Nearest tube Piccadilly
Circus. Off the Haymarket

Café Royal Grill Room

68 Regent Street W1R 6EZ
Map: C3
Tel: 0171 4379090
Fax: 0171 4397672

Chef: Herbert Berger

Owner: Granada plc (Forte Division)
Cost: *Alc* £44, fixed-price L £25/D
£39. H/wine £16.50
Times: Noon-last L 2.30pm/6pm-last
D 10.30pm. Closed L Sat, Sun, 26-30
Dec, Bhs
Additional: No children under 6;
👶 dishes
Smoking: No pipes; air-conditioning
Credit cards: 🔲 🔲 🔲 🔲 🔲 🔲

There can be few more glamorous or breathtakingly
sumptuous dining rooms than this tribute to Victorian
extravagance. The matt gilding, mirrors, cherubs, sensual
statues and plush red velvet never fail to impress and they
provide a spectacular – but also intimate – setting for Herbert
Berger's cooking. While new trends wax and wane, he stays
steadfastly with the traditions of the old-school of French
cuisine, although there are signs that he occasionally wants to
keep up with the youngbloods. Technical accomplishment and
sheer classical style are what stand out. It goes without saying
that the kitchen never shirks from foie gras and truffles. Daily
changing lunch and dinner menus back up a *carte* which is
rooted in dishes that are preserved intact for regular palates.
Here are roast rack of lamb with truffled potatoes, sea bass
baked in sea salt, and suprême of free-range chicken with
young leeks, morels and vin jaune, as well as a mightily
impressive breast and confit of Barbary duck served with
lentils, thyme, smoky bacon and glazed onions, plus a
wonderful, flawlessly textured slice of duck liver. Lighter
contemporary ideas generally surface among the starters:
pressed skate terrine with pickled vegetables, capers and
tarragon surrounded by an olive oil sauce or a salad of lobster,
asparagus and Jerusalem artichokes with ginger vinaigrette, for
example. The signature dessert of hot almond and apple
pithiviers with blackberry coulis makes an eye-catching finale,
and intense espresso comes with top-notch petits fours. Service
is slick and dapper. Berger also oversees culinary proceedings
in the bustling, pacey brasserie adjoining the restaurant. The
lengthy wine list features, not surprisingly, a wide range of
Champagnes and extensive Bordeaux and Burgundies. The
Bordeaux are listed according to vintage and, although on the
pricey side, some good drinking is to be had in the younger
vintages. Ch Maucaillou – Moulis 88 is well priced at £35.
Bahans-Haut-Brion '85, the second wine of Ch Haut-Brion, at
£45. Jadot features strongly in the Burgundy section. A
regional selection of six wines are good value, all under £20.
  Signature dishes: Seared sea bass with fennel, sun-dried
tomatoes and saffron; carpaccio of tuna and scallops with
oriental spices, black radish and lime; pithiviers of apples and
almond with blackberry coulis; tournedos of Angus beef with
parsnip gratin, foie gras and truffles.

Directions: End of Regent Street, near Piccadilly Circus

Canal Brasserie

*Open weekday lunchtimes for moderately priced food with a
fashionable air. Located amongst a complex of faceless office
buildings it serves as an unofficial canteen for nearby media
workers. Daily dishes take in Malaysian chicken salad, and
blackened pork fillet with sweet potato mash, tomato and chilli salsa.*

Additional: Bar food L; Children welcome; 🍴 dishes
Credit cards: ▆▆ ▆▆ 🔫 🄲

Directions: Turn right at the top of Ladbroke Grove, just before
bridge crossing canal, 300 yds on L inside Canalot Studio
building

Canalot Studios 222 Kensal Road
W10 5BN
Map GtL: C3
Tel: 0181 9602732
Fax: 0181 9691863
Chef: Gary Farquarson
Owner: Antony Harris
Cost: *Alc* £20.
Times: L only, noon-3.30pm.
Closed Sat, Sun

Cannizaro House

West Side
Wimbledon Common
SW19 4UE
Map GtL: C2
Tel: 0181 8791464
Fax: 0181 8797338
Chef: Christopher Harper
Cost: *Alc* £35, fixed-price L £21.50 (2
courses)/D £25.75. H/wine £16.95.
Times: Noon-2pm/7pm-10pm
Additional: Sun L; 🍴 dishes
Seats: 45. Private dining room 2-100
Smoking: No-smoking area; no pipes
and cigars
Accommodation: 46 en suite
Credit cards: ▆▆ ▆▆ ▆▆ 🔫 💷 🄲

An ornamental lake, quiet woodland walks and sweeping
lawns surround this graceful Georgian mansion on Wimbledon
Common. The two *cartes*, seasonal and daily, sound as elegant
as the fine dining-room looks. Most of the dishes are modern
Anglo-French combinations, but there are a few classic
inclusions, such as steak au poivre and crêpes suzette flambéd
at the table, and grilled Dover sole with asparagus and
hollandaise sauce. Otherwise choose rosette of caramelised
scallops with crisp leeks, monkfish braised in a rosemary and
saffron stock with button onions and smoked bacon, best end
of lamb with creamed polenta and balsamic reduction, and
warm 'bonbons' of doughnuts filled with fresh fruits. An
oriental touch is evident in roasted salmon with ginger, basil
and soya sauce, and some original ideas include blackened veal
pancetta with creamed potatoes and roasted carrots, and
slightly smoked pheasant breast with horseradish cream and
pickled oyster mushrooms.

Directions: From A3 (London Rd) Tibbets Corner, take A219
(Parkside) right into Cannizaro Rd, then R into West Side

The Canteen

According to the management, the word 'canteen' used to
mean a gambling house as well as a place for institutional
eating – hence the playing card motifs which are stamped on
everything from chairs and walls to menu covers. One of the
attractions of this high-profile address is its setting by the

Harbour Yard,
Chelsea Harbour
SW10 0XD
Map GtL: C2
Tel: 0171 3517330
Fax: 0171 3516189
Chef: David Ali

The Canteen

Owners: Michael Caine, Claudio Pulze
Cost: Alc £27, fixed-price L £19.50. H/wine £14
Times: Noon-last L 3pm/6.30pm-last D 11pm. Closed L Sat, D Sun, Xmas, Bhs
Additional: Sunday L; Children welcome; ❹ dishes
Seats: 120
Smoking: No pipes, air-conditioning
Credit cards: ▆▆ ▆▆ ▆▆ ◥ ◖

harbour, and it's worth trying to sit in the window overlooking the water. The kitchen has developed a style based on studied precision and technical accuracy; it's a laid back approach that promises great flavours without too much in the way of firecrackers. Two dishes sampled during an inspection sum up perfectly what is going on. First, a delicate open lasagne with layered wafers of in-house pasta and ultra-sweet, spiced mussels topped with deep-fried seaweed to provide crunch, surrounded by a gently aromatic sauce of mollusc liquor and coconut cream. Secondly, 'leaves' of tender pink roast rump of lamb bedded on sweet red peppers with olives and an astonishingly fresh pesto and red wine jus 'as if a Mediterranean stew had been disassembled and carefully rearranged into its component parts'. All courses on the *carte* are equally priced (apart from a few supplements) and the repertoire embraces such carefully considered ideas as risotto of butternut squash, mascarpone and coriander, sauté of monkfish with creamed peas, bacon and champ potatoes, and roast corn-fed chicken and buttered spinach with a fricassée of artichokes and olives. Desserts herald such French-inspired delights as cadeau of chocolate with cherry sauce or a heavenly confection of summer fruit in a perfectly constructed champagne jelly – 'as if the fruits had been preserved in amber', noted our inspector. Smart, cosmopolitan staff provide efficient, unobtrusive service.

Signature dishes: Roquefort and endive salad with honey and mustard dressing; macaroni of lobster, baby spinach and morels; sirloin of beef with parsnip puree, pommes fondant and roasted garlic; tarte Tatin of pears.

Directions: Off Kings Road, Chelsea. Nearest tube Earls Court; Fulham Broadway

Cantina del Ponte ✦

Part of the Conran complex at Butlers Wharf with great views over Tower Bridge. The decor is sunny Med and the menu follows suit. Cotechino and Italian sausage with lentils and salsa verde or grilled lemon sole with mussels are typical dishes; pizzas and pastas show up well and there is panettone bread and butter pudding to finish.

Times: Last L 2.45pm/D 10.45pm Closed D Sun, Good Friday, 2 days Xmas
Additional: Sunday L; Children welcome; ❹ dishes
Credit cards: ▆▆ ▆▆ ▆▆ ▆▆

Directions: SE side of Tower Bridge, by riverfront

The Butlers Wharf Building 36c Shad Thames SE1 2YE
Map GtL: G3
Tel: 0171 403 5403
Fax: 0171 403 0415
Chef: Mark O'Brien
Owners: Conran Restaurants
Cost: Alc £30. H/wine £13.95

The Capital ❀❀❀❀

Basil Street Knightsbridge SW3 1AT
Map: B2
Tel: 0171 5895171
Fax: 0171 2250011
Chef: Philip Britten
Owner: David Levin
Cost: *Alc* £55, fixed-price L £25/D £55 (7 courses), H/wine £14.50
Times: 12.30pm-last L 2.30pm/7pm-last D 11.15pm
Additional: Sunday L; Children welcome; ❀ dishes
Seats: 44. Private dining rooms 22. Jacket and tie preferred
Smoking: No pipes and cigars in dining room; air-conditioning
Accommodation: 48 en suite
Credit cards: ▬ ▨ ▨ ▨ ▨ ▨

This small but perfectly formed hotel, fifty convenient yards from Harrods, attracts a loyal clientele – one of the main attractions is some of the best food in town, served in a decorous, elegant setting. Philip Britten pulls off a clever balancing act, the food is eye-catching without overstepping the mark, imaginative but not the gastronomic equivalent of a fashion victim, deft in technique yet seemingly apparently effortless. He has unobtrusively set standards few others have matched, and his cooking still displays a vibrant freshness and clarity of flavour; technical excellence underpins every idea. As well as the *carte*, there are two set sampler menus – Temptation' and 'Seduction' – of seven and nine (small) courses each, which represent great value for the enthusiastic diner as they cost little more than choosing a full meal from the *carte*. First course jellied consommés arrive in two small glass cups, topped with light, creamy vegetable purée, risotto of foie gras and roasted shallots with Madeira and rosemary is smooth, soft and luxuriant, and three vegetable crème brûlée make you wonder why no one has thought of this before. Fish dishes include a light lobster mousse in a broth of lime leaves and mussels, langoustines tenderised in olive oil and tarragon with asparagus and a lemon compote, and red mullet on distinctive olive pasta with strips of grilled pepper and the rich sharpness of balsamic vinegar. Ingredients are paramount – marinated rare-breed pork is sauced with ceps and caramelised apples, pot-roasted rabbit with Serrano ham and sage dumplings. Orientalism is intelligently incorporated into the repertoire – baked sea bass is cooked in black bean sauce with coriander and saffron cream, honey-roasted duck breast is presented on a stir-fry of noodles and ginger with a plum sauce. Amongst a choice of desserts, such as blueberry and hazelnut tart with a praline ice-cream and banana and pistachio soufflé with butterscotch, raspberry soup with flavoured mousses stands out for originality and intensity of flavour. Lunch is also a good way of becoming acquainted with Britten's cooking at non-frightening prices – deceptively simple dishes include pasta with truffles, seafood nage with lime leaf, saffron and dill, salt beef, carrots and turnips sauced with rosemary, and rhubarb crumble with custard. Service is impeccably formal and suave. David Levin's interests extend to his own Loire vineyard and nestling in a wine list of some depth are Le Vin de Levin both blanc and rouge at the worth-a-try-price of £14.50. A thorough selection of clarets will repay consideration, with some top quality examples at restrained mark-ups, quite a few being available in halves

Directions: Between Harrods and Sloane Street, nearest Tube – Knightsbridge

Le Caprice ❀❀❀

Le Caprice attracts an interesting mix of people, but there's a general uniform look of designer jeans, designer sunglasses, loafers and air kissing. A very efficient hostess keeps the social ball rolling, chatting to regulars and keeping taps on the bustling but slick service. The decor is timeless with lots of white walls, black and chrome plus large black and white photographs of celebrities. Diners can also eat at the stylish high bar. Risotto nero made a perfect first course, intensely flavoured, perfectly cooked and deliciously creamy. Fillet of brill displayed true class, with superbly fresh fish pan-fried with tarragon mashed potatoes, served with fresh peas à la crème. The high standard was maintained with a dessert of cherry pie which had good, slightly tart filling, a sweet crust and a blob of soured cream. Details, such as large hunks of granary and French bread and richly flavoured espresso all hit the spot. A good, concise wine list includes about ten available by the glass, some good halves and a few classic Burgundies and Clarets – and, surprisingly for this part of town, doesn't make the credit card wince in pain. Both Le Caprice and its younger sibling, The Ivy, have certainly mastered the art of a concise wine list that has something for everyone and is still interesting. Surprisingly reasonable with a good number of halves (all available by the glass). Over half the wines on the list are under £25.

Signature dishes: Crispy duck and watercress salad; iced plum tomato basil and mozzarella soup; risotto butternut squash; ham hock with caper sauce.

Directions: Nearest Tube: Green Park. Arlington St runs beside the Ritz, Le Caprice is at the end

Arlington Street SW1A 1RT
Map: C3
Tel: 0171 6292239
Fax: 0171 4939040
Chefs: Mark Hix, Kevin Gratton
Owners: Christopher Corbin, Jeremy King
Cost: *Alc* £35. H/wine £9.50. ☺
Times: Noon-last L 3pm/6pm-last D midnight. Closed D 24 Dec, 25-26 Dec, 1 Jan
Additional: Sunday brunch; Children welcome; ❸ dishes
Seats: 70
Smoking: Air-conditioning
Credit cards: ▉ ▉ ▉ ▉ ▣ ▣

Caraffini ❀❀

Having run the front of house at nearby Como Lario for countless years, the eponymous Paulo C. clearly has hospitality running through his veins. When he opened his own boisterous, up-tempo trattoria he infused it with every ounce of Italian camaraderie he could muster. Customers come here to enjoy the vitality of the place and to sample the kind of dishes that seem to have gone out of fashion since the culinary renaissance – or perhaps they were never 'in'. The menu is peppered with classics, such as tagliatelle with smoked salmon, seafood risotto, escalope of veal with lemon sauce and calves' liver with sage, although the kitchen also tries to keep pace with the times by offering the likes of bresaola and Pecorino cheese with extra virgin olive oil, pan-fried squid with peas and black olives, and chicken breast sliced into strips and cooked with pine kernels, sultanas and balsamic vinegar. Three dozen wines promise an oenophilic trip around the regions of Italy.

Directions: Nearest Tube – Sloane Square

61-63 Lower Sloane Street SW1
Map: B2
Tel: 0171 2590235
Chef: Marcelino Tome
Owners: Paolo Caraffini, Frank di Rienzo
Cost: *Alc* £27. H/wine £8.95. ☺
Times: 12.15pm-last L 2.30pm/6.30pm-last D 11.30pm. Closed Sun, Bhs
Additional: Children welcome; ❸ dishes
Seats: 70
Smoking: Air-conditioning
Credit cards: ▉ ▉ ▉ ▉ ▣

The Cavendish ❀❀

On one of the oldest hotel sites in London, just a stone's throw from the delectations of Fortnum & Mason, The Cavendish now puts on an up-to-the-minute face. The Sub Rosa Bar hums with a clubby atmosphere, but pride of place goes to the 81 Restaurant on the first floor. Tapas snacks are served at the

81 Jermyn Street
SW1Y 6JF
Map: D3
Tel: 0171 9302111
Fax: 0171 8392125
Chef: Andy Shortman
Owner: The Cavendish Hotel

The Cavendish

Cost: *Alc* £22, fixed-price L £13. ☺
H/wine £13.95.
Times: Noon-last L 2.30pm/6pm-last
D 10.30pm
Additional: Sunday L; Bar meals;
Children welcome; dishes
Seats: 81
Smoking: No-smoking area; air-
conditioning
Accommodation: 255 en suite
Credit cards: 🆑 🆑 🆑 🆑 🆑 🆑

Directions: Nearest Tubes – Green
Park and Piccadilly Circus

counter, a live guitarist often fingers the strings and the menu
is sun-blessed Mediterranean with vibrant Spanish overtones.
Start with parfait of sweet bell peppers garnished with
chargrilled asparagus, or a light broth with diced vegetables
and chorizo ravioli. Main dishes are full of dark-hued flavours:
baked sea bass with roasted baby fennel and Manchengo
potatoes; pan-fried fillet of beef with fondant potatoes, tomato
and artichoke salsa; mixed shellfish with saffron risotto and
fried leeks. As a finale, try warm fig tart with nougat ice cream.
The wine list has a fair geographical spread and there's a
decent selection by the glass.

Caviar House ❀❀ NEW

Anyone with a weakness for champagne and caviar can soon
over-indulge, sampling a range of over half a dozen different
fish eggs, classically served with blinis, sour cream and Jersey
potatoes. The dining room has sufficient style to match this
high living, with unique chandeliers made from ostrich
eggshells, water sculptures created from soft French limestone,
and mosaics and toilets designed by footwear designer Manolo
Blahnik (shoes to loos, as it were). The set menu is more
accessibly priced, but does not include caviar; in the interests
of research our inspector felt duty bound to have a little
Sevruga, but was frankly disappointed by the excessive salt
level. Terrine of foie gras, on the other hand, was superb, not
too firm, but smooth and silky on the tongue, as was a ravioli
of wild mushrooms with mushroom sabayon and truffle jus,
and fillet of beef with sweetbreads, kidney and a ginger lime
sauce. A gratin of scallops and lobster served the latter
crustacean better than when it was served grilled with parsley
and garlic butter. Tropical fruit soup with mango sorbet will
refresh any flagging taste buds.

161 Piccadilly W1V 9DF
Map: C3
Tel: 0171 4090445
Fax: 0171 4931667
Chef: Masayuki Hara
Owners: Caviar House
Cost: *Alc* £35, fixed-price L £19.50 (2
courses)/D £42 (6 courses). ☺
H/wine £11.50
Times: Noon-last L 3pm/7pm-last D
10pm. Closed Sun, 25-26 Dec, 1 Jan
Additional: Children welcome;
 dishes
Seats: 35
Smoking: Air-conditioning
Credit cards: 🆑 🆑 🆑 🆑 🆑 🆑

Directions: Nearest tube: Green Park

Cecconi's ❀

*Plush venue catering for gilded palates. The menu might be
described as latter-day trattoria, with a generic undercurrent and the
emphasis on freshness and simplicity. Pasta and veal show up on the
menu, tiramisu puts in an appearance on the sweet trolley. Prices
may seem intimidating, but this is, after all, Burlington Gardens W1.*

5a Burlington Gardens W1X 1LE
Map: C3
Tel: 0171 434 1509
Fax: 0171 494 2440
Telephone for details

Directions: Nearest Tubes – Green Park, Piccadilly Circus

Chapter One

Don't let the mock Tudor exterior or the location of this 120 seater – at the junction of several trunk roads – put you off. Minimal decor, primary colours plus plenty of mirrors replicate the interiors of some of the newer equally large, central London restaurants. The cooking parallels West End flavours and ingredient combinations too: escabeche of mackerel, Parmesan cracking; poached hen's egg, spinach, bubble and squeak, sauce mousseline; salad of trotters, black pudding, sauce gribiche. On a recent lunch visit our inspector praised the starter and pudding from the fixed-price business lunch – saffron herb risotto topped with crisp vegetable beignets, with a chive butter, and hot berry soufflé accompanied by an intense passionfruit sorbet. Service lacked warmth, and was not that speedy. A compact wine list offers adequate choice from around the world, including ten house wines.

Directions: At junction of A21 and A232

Locksbottom
Farnborough Common BR6 8NF
Map GtL: E1
Tel: 01689 854848
Fax: 01689 858439
Chef: John Wood
Cost: Alc £24.50, fixed-price L £19.50
Times: Noon-last L 2.30pm (4pm Sun)/6.30pm-last D 11pm
Additional: Sunday L; Children welcome; dishes
Seats: 120. Private dining room 60
Smoking: No-smoking area; air-conditioning
Credit cards: ▆ ▆ ▆ ▆ ▆ ▆

Chavot

It's sometimes hard to keep pace with the transfers and comings-and-goings that seem to be de rigueur in the London restaurant scene of the 90s. A new regime has moved in here: the owners of Le Café du Jardin in Covent Garden have teamed up with Eric Chavot, who moved from his much lauded Interlude de Chavot in February 1997. The dining room is virtually unchanged, with its muted coloured walls, polished floors and some unusual objects d'art and vibrant pictures lifting the mood. Devotees of the Interlude will recognise many of the signature dishes that are peppered throughout the short carte. Melt-in-the-mouth roasted scallops are served with mustard oil and horseradish potatoes, while oven-roasted leg of rabbit is stuffed with a squid and barley risotto that provides a rustic but sophisticated edge. This is bold, powerful cooking with true clear flavours and extraordinary depth, but also lightness when it is needed. Elsewhere you might come across red mullet fillet with spiced aubergine, chump of lamb on polenta and couscous, and venison cutlet with braised cabbage. Set menus are in similar vein, although conceptions tend to be simpler: lobster ravioli with red onion vinaigrette, and pan-fried brill on a confit of roasted red and yellow peppers, for example. Desserts are out of the top-drawer. Our inspector sampled a geometrically dazzling three-dimensional pyramid enclosing a tangy citrus terrine accompanied by witty chocolate samosas, as well as a beautifully delicate apple tarte that highlighted the quality of the pastry work behind the scenes. The wine list is quite short but prices are keen and there is some good drinking especially from the New World.
Signature dishes: Snail raviolo with garlic cream and pestou; chargrilled wild salmon with niçoise garnish; leg of rabbit stuffed with squid and barley risotto; foie gras with a tarte Tatin of endive.

257-259 Fulham Road SW3 6HY
Map: A1
Tel: 0171 3517823
Fax: 0171 3764971
Chef: Eric Crouillere-Chavot
Owner: Robert Seigler, Tony Howorth, Eric Crouillere-Chavot
Cost: Alc £38, fixed-price L £22.50. H/wine £14.50
Times: Noon-last L 2.30pm/7pm-last D 11pm (10pm Sun). Closed L Sat, Sun, 1 wk from 24 Dec
Additional: Children welcome; dishes
Seats: 80. Private dining room 15
Smoking: No pipes or cigars; air-conditioning
Credit cards: ▆ ▆ ▆ ▆ ▆ ▆

Directions: Close to junction of Fulham Rd and Old Church St

Chelsea Hotel

'It is an understatement to say that this is a very fashion-conscious part of town', observes an inspector of the modish Chelsea Hotel, surrounded by a wealth of designer stores and haute couture houses. Bruno Loubet has teamed-up with

17 Sloane Street Knightsbridge
SW1X 9NU
Map: B2
Tel: 0171 2354377
Fax: 0171 2353705
Chef: Bruno Loubet

Swedish Baron Otto Stromfelt to form Bruno and the Baron, a company that is responsible for all the food served at the hotel. Early reports have centred around lunch, which brings three menus: one deliberately light 'Menu de Jardiniere'. built around vegetables, herbs and fruit 'which would please any cellulite-hiding Versace-clad thigh', the set menu, very reasonably priced with modern brasserie theme, and the *carte* with the Loubet 'works'. Meals have included smoked mackerel and aubergine terrine, grilled tuna steak with spring onion risotto, and a perfect ginger crème brûlée, whilst sardine spring roll with wood-roasted tomatoes and raw fennel salad preceded a Loubet signature dish of roast scallops and black pudding with mash, garlic cream and parsley coulis, and dessert of apple compote in apple tea jelly with Calvados sabayon.

Directions: Two minutes from Knightsbridge tube

Owners: The Chelsea Hotel
Cost: *Alc* £25, fixed-price L £14.50.
☺ H/wine £12.50.
Times: Noon-last L 2.30pm/6pm-last D 10.30pm. Closed D Sun
Additional: Sunday L; Bar meals; Children welcome; ◑ dishes
Seats: 80 – 90
Smoking: Air-conditioning
Accommodation: 224 en suite
Credit cards: ■ ■ ■ ■ ■ ■

The Chesterfield Hotel

The discreet and exclusive atmosphere is appropriate to the prestigious Mayfair address. The lobby is quietly elegant, with a marble floor, glittering chandelier and fluted pillars, there is a clubby bar and visitors can sit in an airy conservatory or in the more traditionally styled dining room. A short but modish dinner menu also includes some traditional favourites such as Dover sole, salmon hollandaise and fillet béarnaise. A starter of fish cakes on a bed of fresh baby spinach leaves with tomato and rosemary sabayon was chunky and full of flavour, although seared sea bass on cassoulet with pancetta and oblongs of slightly sticky potato gnocchi, was not as exciting a dish as it sounded. On the other hand a mango summer pudding worked much better than our inspector imagined it would.

Directions: Nearest tube Green park. Bottom of Berkeley Square, on corner of Charles Street & Queen Street

35 Charles Street W1X 8LX
Map: C3
Tel: 0171 4912622
Fax: 0171 4091726
Chef: Stephen Henderson
Owners: Mr & Mrs Tollman
Cost: *Alc* £25, fixed-price L £12.50/ D £15.50. H/wine £13.75
Times: Noon-last L 2.15pm/6pm-last D 10.45pm. Closed L Sat
Additional: Bar food; Sun L; No children under 8; ◑ dishes
Seats: 60. Private dining room 4-60
Smoking: No-smoking area; air-conditioning
Accommodation: 110 en suite
Credit cards: ■ ■ ■ ■ ■ ■

Chez Bruce ❀❀❀

Stark white walls and linen, a distressed concrete ceiling with beams, and chairs that do not suit everyone's posterior are the setting for Bruce Poole's popular idiosyncratic style of modern European cooking. His ideas are imaginative, and ingredients superb. A starter of very rare grilled tuna, was served with a twist of pesto noodles and juicy, fruity roast tomatoes on the vine. The kitchen's gift for flavours and balance, and its considerable self-confidence was showcased in a main course of rare rump of lamb, thinly sliced over a bed of couscous, humous and spinach, altogether a rare delight of spices and sweetness, with merguez sausage adding a note of meatiness and garlic. A posh Black Forest gâteau restored our faith in this much maligned pudding – just huge black cherries with layers of sponge and chocolate, and not a bit of frothy cream in sight! Service comfortably straddles the middle ground between casual and formal, and the three-course menu is extremely good value for money at £25. A two page wine list (85 bins) with a good balance of European and New World wines, offers a dozen by the glass. A good price range as well, with something for all pockets – from Côtes de Gascogne at £10.50 to Ch Cos d'Estournel 85 at £90. Collines Rhodaniennes Syrah is good drinking at £14.50.
Signature dishes: Navarin of lamb with spring vegetables;

2 Bellevue Road Wandsworth Common SW17 7EG
Map GtL: C2
Tel: 0181 6720114
Fax: 0181 7676648
Chef/Owner: Bruce Poole
Cost: Fixed-price L £17.50/D £24.50. H/wine £10.50.
Times: Noon-last L 2pm/7pm-last D 10.30pm. Closed Sun D, 1 wk Xmas, Bhs
Additional: Sunday L; No children at D; ◑ dishes
Seats: 75. Private dining room 20
Smoking: No pipes or cigars; air-conditioning
Credit cards: ■ ■ ■ ■ ■ ■

roast wild salmon with asparagus and sauce vierge; roast pheasant with wild mushrooms, chestnuts and Madeira jus; pot au feu

Directions: 2 mins walk from Wandsworth Common (BR), 5 mins   from Balham Tube

Chez Max ❀❀

Chef Max wears its Gallic heart on its sleeve. The tricolour often flies outside, and menus from famed French restaurants line the walls of the basement dining room where the tables are bare and there are plenty of nooks and crannies. The impression may be of a bistro, but the cooking is a few notches above that. A daily changing 'Menu Vite' (Tues to Fri) offers 'quality food in half the time at half the price', otherwise the full repertoire is uncompromisingly French in tone. Ballotine of foie gras with haricot verts or ragout of wild mushrooms are typical starters, while main courses could range from navarin of lamb to magret of duck with braised chicory and orange sauce. Desserts include the equally patriotic tart au citron and Grand Marnier soufflé.

168 Ifield Road
SW10 9AF
Map: C2
Tel: 0171 8350874
Fax: 0181 9468301
Chef: Nigel Horton
Owners: Graham Thomson, Stephen Smith
Cost: *Alc* £26, fixed-price L £10/D £23.50. ☺ H/wine £11.50.
Times: Noon-last L 2.30pm/6.30pm-last D 11pm. Closed Sun, Mon, Xmas, 2 wks Aug, Bhs
Additional: Bar meals; Children welcome; ❹ dishes

Smoking: No pipes or cigars in dining room
Credit cards: ▪▪ ▪▪ ▪▪ ▪▪ ▪

Directions: Turn off the Fulham Road into Ifield Road, restaurant is 500yds on the L

Chez Moi ❀❀

'We carry on in much the same style...changing the menu frequently, except for a few faithfuls that have been on since we opened,' writes Richard Walton and Colin Smith of their long-established neighbourhood restaurant. Chez Moi has never been one for standing still, and by striving to be just that little bit different, has managed to keep a culinary edge throughout its thirty one years. The standard of cooking remains consistent, and the Orient is a favourite source of ideas with Thai chicken and Japanese-style scallops appearing on the menu alongside Moroccan tagines and confit of Gressingham duck legs. A May inspection lunch took in chicken and prawn dhosa with a mild curry sauce, rack of lamb à la diable, the meat coated in a tangy mixture of breadcrumbs, shallots, fines herbes, and served with boulangère potatoes and crisp cabbage with bacon and shallots, and finished with a tangy lemon tart.

1 Addison Avenue W11 4QS
Map GtL: C3
Tel: 0171 6038267
Fax: 0171 6033898
Chef: Richard Walton
Owners: Richard Walton, Colin Smith
Cost: *Alc* £27.25, fixed-price L £15. H/wine £9.75
Times: Noon-last L 2pm/7pm-last D 11pm. Closed L Sat, Sun, Bhs
Additional: Children welcome (no small babies); ❹ dishes
Seats: 45
Smoking: Air-conditioning
Credit cards: ▪▪ ▪▪ ▪▪ ▪▪ ▪ ▪

Directions: N side of Holland Park Avenue, opposite Kensington Hilton. Nearest Tube – Holland Park

Chez Nico at 90 Park Lane ❀❀❀❀❀

Park Lane is the classiest address in London, and Chez Nico is the classiest place on the block and, arguably, in London. His legions of loyal fans certainly consider a meal here to be a tremendous experience, one which acts as a benchmark for an infinite number of aspirant super-chefs. Book well ahead to

90 Park Lane
W1A 3AA
Map: B3
Tel: 0171 4091290
Fax: 0171 3554877
Chefs: Nico Ladenis, Paul Rhodes
Owners: Nico & Dinah-Jane Ladenis

make the most of dining in the elegant, spacious restaurant run with faultless French professionalism. Although the menu is lengthy, it is readable and refreshingly comprehensible, showing a clarity of concept only equalled by the kitchen's unflagging determination to keep to the standards of consistency and execution for which it is acclaimed. Nico himself is still captain of the ship, but Paul Rhodes is a tremendous second mate, fully steeped in the Ladenis philosophy and able to bring his own original input to the operation. Signature dishes are rightly retained on the *carte*, thus providing an opportunity for newcomers to sample stunning combinations such as warm salad of foie gras on toasted brioche with 'confied' orange zest or cep risotto, but ideas don't stand still and dishes are continually evolving. From the masterly canapés and choice of breads with Echiré butter at the beginning of the meal, to superb coffee and petits fours, the pace never falters, the delivery is never less than perfect. Langoustine soup is packed with crustacean intensity, a ballotine of quail is not only delightfully pretty to the eye but the pinkish flesh is as full of flavour as the small cake of chopped leeks and asparagus alongside. Escalope of sea bass is stunningly uncomplicated – simply plain but quite brilliant fish, the basil coulis just there to give contrast along with a delicious purée of olives. In between the principal courses come little palate-teasers such as a piece of marinated salmon with blini and caviar, a superb haricot bean salad, a lime sorbet made with champagne. Lemon tart with raspberry coulis is simply classic perfection. The platter of mini-desserts makes a memorable finale, that is if you can bear to forgo the superb choice of cheese. The wine list oozes class but is admirably unstuffy. Compilations of the great and the good from France are complemented by some imaginative selections from the New World and an abundance of halves.

Cost: *Alc* £67, fixed-price L £31/D £67
Times: Noon-2pm/7pm-11pm. Closed L Sat, Sun, 4 days Easter, 10 days Xmas, Bhs
Seats: 65. Private dining room 20. Jacket & tie preferred
Smoking: Air-conditioning
Credit cards: ▬ ▬ ▬ ▣

Directions: Next to Grosvenor House Hotel

Chinon Restaurant

A true neighbourhood restaurant, in a residential part of West London, run with great individual style by Jonathan Hayes and Barbara Deane. Their first love is France, and this is reflected in a room that has all the feel of a provincial French dining room; there is nothing mega or minimalist here – this is a small, simple, comfortably appointed place with a great view out over leafy gardens from an immense window. Simplicity is Jonathan Hayes hallmark. His hand-written menu is produce led, the very best available, which is prepared with enormous respect. Fresh flavours and textures are both paramount, presentation is stunning. Note a starter of mixed leaves and some half-dozen vegetable quenelles with an olive oil dressing. Another chef would have proffered a purée of the vegetables, but not here; each quenelle relied on texture – grated beetroot in one, a spaghetti of cucumber in another, diced potato, grainy chickpea. That same meal produced an excellent sautéed squid with pesto. Again the squid had been treated in different ways, the pesto separated into two components – a pungent green basil oil and the fine pesto added to a little heap of shredded squid. Ravioli of scallops with ginger cream was vibrant with flavour, the plate dotted with spanking fresh scallops, a raviolo sitting in the middle of the plate, really just a sheet of pasta draped over a heap of more scallops and corals. Desserts yielded a fine warm poached pear and frangipane tart with vanilla ice cream, and a superb selection of home-made sorbets. Excellent bread and espresso.

23 Richmond Way W14 0AS
Map GtL: C3
Tel: 0171 6025968/4082
Chef: Jonathan Hayes
Owners: Barbara Deane, Jonathan Hayes
Cost: Fixed-price D £15. H/wine £10.50
Times: D only, 7pm-last D 10.30pm.
Seats: 60
Smoking: No pipes and cigars; air-conditioning
Credit cards: ▬ ▬ ▬ ▣

Directions: Behind Olympia Exhibition Hall, round the corner to Sinclair Road, close to Kensington & Olympia Hiltons

The Chiswick ❀❀

Simplicity, matched with a certain urbane coolness, sets the tone. The menu takes its cue from the flavours of the moment and the value for money is reckoned to be excellent. An inspection dinner in March produced an ultra-light potato pancake with immaculately cooked pigeon breast, crisp French beans and light truffle oil, before tender neck fillet of lamb with artichoke bottoms, fresh peas and a mint flavoured jus. Elsewhere, you might encounter steamed mussels with curry cream and coriander, bourride of capon with saffron, and roast hake with fennel purée and tapenade. To finish, brioche bread and butter pudding has passed muster. A two-course early evening menu (available until 8pm) satisfies the famished with the likes of duck terrine and roast chicken leg with lentils and button onions. The wine list gives a big push to 50cl bottles, and the rest is an imaginative slate defined by bold flavours and fair prices.

Directions: On Chiswick High Road close to junction with Turnham Green Terrace. 3 mins walk from Tube station

131-133 Chiswick High Road W4
Map: B3
Tel: 0181 9946887
Chef: Ian Bates
Owners: Adam & Kate Robinson
Cost: Alc £22. Fixed-price L&D £9.50 (2 courses). ☺ H/wine £9.50.
Times: 12.30pm-last L 2.45pm/7pm-last D 11.30pm. Closed L Sat, D Sun, 3 days Xmas
Additional: Sunday L; Children welcome; ❹ dishes.
Seats: 90
Smoking: No pipes and cigars; air-conditioning
Credit cards: 🟦 🟦 🟦 🟦 🟦

Christophe's ❀❀

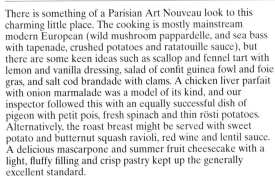

NEW

There is something of a Parisian Art Nouveau look to this charming little place. The cooking is mostly mainstream modern European (wild mushroom pappardelle, and sea bass with tapenade, crushed potatoes and ratatouille sauce), but there are some keen ideas such as scallop and fennel tart with lemon and vanilla dressing, salad of confit guinea fowl and foie gras, and salt cod brandade with clams. A chicken liver parfait with onion marmalade was a model of its kind, and our inspector followed this with an equally successful dish of pigeon with petit pois, fresh spinach and thin rösti potatoes. Alternatively, the roast breast might be served with sweet potato and butternut squash ravioli, red wine and lentil sauce. A delicious mascarpone and summer fruit cheesecake with a light, fluffy filling and crisp pastry kept up the generally excellent standard.

Directions: Nearest Tube – South Kensington. Go W down Fulham Road and take second L

7 Park Walk SW10
Map: A1
Tel: 0171 3498866
Fax: 0171 3498867
Chef: Graham Garrett
Owner: Christoph Brooke
Cost: Alc £22.50, fixed-price L £8.50/D £14.50. H/wine £9.95
Times: 12.30-last L 2.30pm/7.30pm-last D 11pm. Closed Sun, Xmas, Easter, Bhs
Additional: Children welcome; ❹ dishes
Seats: 62
Smoking: No pipes & cigars; air-conditioning
Credit cards: 🟦 🟦 🟦 🟦 🟦 🟦

Christopher's ❀❀

It's all change in this glitzy 'American Grill' housed in a grand building that was once a casino. A new café/bar has been moved to the basement, where the menu promises transatlantic snacks like shrimp wun tuns, Caesar salad and BLTs with crispy pancetta, plus (at weekends), brunch. Up a stone staircase is the lofty main dining room. Here a pin-striped clientele dreams of the Big Apple while checking out the all-American menu. What they get is unapologetically brash cooking, with big bold flavours fired out like shots from a six-gun. Typically punchy offerings might include sauté of wild mushrooms with Texas toast encircled by pungent barbecue sauce, and a tuna steak of 'Lone Star State proportions' with rose-tinted flesh and a balsamic dressing on a bed of crunchy curly kale. American ice creams, baked New York cheesecake and banana and pistachio pie provide a cheerleading finish. Espresso has a real kick, and the wine list naturally favours the U.S. Slick service does the business.

18 Wellington Street WC2E 7DD
Map: E3
Tel: 0171 2404222
Fax: 0171 2403357
Chef: Adrian Searing
Owner: Christopher Gilmour
Cost: Alc £30, fixed-price theatre D £15 (2 courses). ☺ H/wine £12.
Times: Noon-last L 3pm/6pm-last D 11.45pm. Closed Xmas
Additional: Bar food; Sunday L; Children welcome (in café); ❹ dishes
Seats: 100. Private dining room 60
Smoking: Air-conditioning
Credit cards: 🟦 🟦 🟦 🟦 🟦 🟦

Directions: 100 yards from the Royal Opera House; nearest Tube – Covent Garden

Churchill Inter-Continental

30 Portman Square W1A 4ZX
Map: B4
Tel: 0171 4865800
Fax: 0171 4861255
Chef: Idris Caldera
Owner: Churchill Inter-Continental
Cost: *Alc* £30, fixed-price L&D £23.
☺ H/wine £13.
Times: 12.30pm-3pm/6pm-11pm.
Closed L Sat
Additional: Sunday L; Children
welcome; ❸ dishes
Seats: 102
Smoking: No-smoking area;
air-conditioning
Accommodation: 435 en suite
Credit cards: ▆ ▆ ▆ ▆ ▆ ▆

Perched above Portman Square, Clementines has a Mediterranean feel, both in terms of the light, bright decor and the up-beat, imaginative cooking. Fish is a particular forte – spicy fillet of red snapper with lemon noodles, roasted halibut provençale with tomato and potato purée, and lobster ravioli with baby spinach all sound tempting, but there is also rack of lamb, couscous and smoked tomato confit, breast of guinea fowl, garganelli pasta with garden peas and pancetta, or tomato risotto with braised smoked bacon, French sausage and black pudding for meat eaters. Vegetarians can go for the lasagne of grilled vegetables, pesto and tomato sauce, and everyone can happily tuck into the chocolate tart with walnut brittle ice cream or lemon cream in a sweet ravioli with fruit berry sauce – those requiring low cholesterol or salt-free options, need only ask.

Directions: Close to Marble Arch, just off Oxford Street

Chutney Mary

535 King's Road
Chelsea SW10
Map GtL: C2
Tel: 0171 3513113
Fax: 0171 3517694
Chef: Hardev Singh Bhatty
Owners: Mr Ranjit Mathrani,
Mrs Namita Panjabi
Cost: *Alc* £32, fixed-price L £10.
H/wine £10.75

Large murals depicting the time of the Raj, and a beautiful conservatory with rustling palms and rattan chairs accurately suggest the colonial theme of this Anglo-Indian restaurant. Plenty of space too, spread over two floors with a separate bar. The style of cooking is more regional Indian, with just a few specialities. Staff are knowledgeable and the menu reads well; the heat of each dish is denoted by chilli symbols. Authentic chutneys are flown in from India. A test meal revealed sound

cooking skills: a platter of kebabs with minced chicken and lean lamb, and an excellent full bodied lamb curry flavoured with 18 individually roasted spices. Interesting puddings include a delicious carrot cake with a custard sauce. For something to drink, there is a carefully annotated wine list plus a range of beers and infusions.

Smoking: No-smoking area; no pipes and cigars; air-conditioning
Credit cards: ■ ■ ■ ■ ■ ■ ■

Directions: On corner of Kings Road and Lots Road; 2 mins from Chelsea Harbour, nearest Tube – Fulham Broadway

Times: 12.30pm-last L 2.15pm /7pm-last D 11.15pm. Closed D 25 Dec, 26 Dec
Additional: Bar food; Sunday L; Children welcome; ● dishes
Seats: 120. Private dining room 50

Cibo ❀❀

Fish cooked Italian-style is the speciality of this informal, popular neighbourhood restaurant. Most dishes depend on what's available from the market that day, although ever-popular choices include grilled baby squid with chilli peppers, and spaghetti with lobster. Monkfish, sea bream, baby octopus, sea bass, langoustines and prawns all have featured on a single late summer menu. Desserts include wobbly, creamy pannacotta, and wines come from all regions of Italy.

Directions: Russell Gardens is a residential area off Holland Road. Nearest tubes – Kensington (Olympia); Shepherds Bush

3 Russell Gardens W14 8EZ
Map GtL: C3
Tel: 0171 3712085
Fax: 0171 6021371
Telephone for details

City Miyama Restaurant ❀

Sushi and teppan-yaki specialities at this two floor, minimalist-style Japanese, plus special set meals served with rice, miso soup and pickles. Busiest at lunchtime when city types order the turbot grilled with salt, eel grilled with kabayaki sauce and beef teriyaki whilst charting the course of sterling against the yen.

Times: Last L 2.30pm/6pm-last D 9.30pm. Closed D Sat, Sun
Smoking: Air-conditioning
Credit cards: ■ ■ ■ ■ ■ ■ ■

Directions: South side of St Paul's churchyard, behind city information centre

Godliman Street EC4V 5BD
Map: F3
Tel: 0171 489 1937
Fax: 0171 236 0325
Chef: Isao Ebina
Owner: K Furuya
Cost: Alc £25, fixed-price L £20 (6 courses)/D £45 (7 courses). ☺
H/wine £12.

City Rhodes ❀❀❀

The decor is almost austere, mainly white, with the only splashes of colour in the Victor Pasmore prints on the walls and the yellow shirts of the waiters. It advertises itself as 'A Gardener Merchant Restaurant' but there is no doubt that Gary Rhodes is firmly in control. The formula is a shortish *carte* of some nine main courses, plus specials of the day; the successful ones get onto the next six-weekly changing *carte* ('and then onto TV and into a book'). On BBC days, head chef Wayne Tapsfield, who has been with Gary since the Greenhouse, ensures continuity of the exciting menu 'from which it was difficult to choose three dishes so I chose four'. That meal was hard to fault: sautéed artichoke with baby leeks and an egg yolk ravioli surrounded by a little balsamic dressing (the novel touch was the egg yolk which was still runny and mingled with the dish when the ravioli was breached), escalope

1 New Street Square EC4A 3BF
Map: E4
Tel: 0171 5831313
Fax: 0171 3531662
Chefs: Gary Rhodes, Wayne Tapsfield
Owners: Gardener Merchant
Cost: Alc £40. H/wine £11.50
Times: Noon-last L 2.45pm/6pm-last D 8.45pm. Closed Sat, Sun, Bhs
Additional: Children welcome; ● dishes
Seats: 96. Private dining room 12
Smoking: No pipes; air-conditioning
Credit cards: ■ ■ ■ ■ ■ ■

of salmon with black treacle, juniper and sherry dressing ('super flavours'), pigeon trotter – a pig's trotter stuffed with pigeon – with mashed potato and red onions, and baked fig tart with cinnamon ice cream. The keynote of the whole operation is well thought out combinations of flavours in dishes that contain nothing extraneous to their composition. The quality of the service matched the food too, the senior staff personable and able to communicate well with the predominantly business clientele and junior staff efficient and smiling.

Directions: Off Shoe Lane, behind International Press Centre

Claridges ✿✿

Brook Street W1A 2JQ
Map: C3
Tel: 0171 6298860
Fax: 0171 4992210
Chefs: John Williams, Emmanuel Renaut
Owner: Savoy Group
Cost: *Alc* £50, fixed-price L £29/D £38. H/wine £17.50
Times: 12.30pm-last 3pm/7pm-last D 11pm (1pm Sat)
Additional: Sunday L: Children welcome; ✦ dishes
Seats: 120. Private dining room 14. Jacket & tie preferred
Smoking: No pipes & cigars; air-conditioning
Accommodation: 197 en suite
Credit cards: ▬ ▬ ▬ ▬ ▣ ▣

As institutions go, this is one of the most distinguished. From the black and white marbled foyer to the liveried lift attendant, this quintessential grand hotel has provided a London address of style, discretion and total luxury for royals and ex-royals for almost 100 years. The Art Deco restaurant with its tall glass doors and elegant columns offers a classic Anglo-French *carte* of dishes such as lobster bisque with Armagnac, truffled foie gras terrine with fig chutney and Sauternes jelly, whole grilled Dover sole, and roast calves' sweetbreads with truffle and braised Savoy cabbage. A main course of breast of squab pigeon with potato tourte and port sauce was exceptionally tender, with a boldness of flavour well matched with a first-class sauce. The restaurant now offers a 'Fifty Nine Minute Lunch', based on a three-course fixed price menu, as well as a series of themed 'Musical Evenings' with dancing and dinner. Breakfasts include a special sausage menu, featuring ten of the best bangers in Britain.

Directions: At the corner of Brooks & Davies Street

Clarke's ✿✿✿

124 Kensington Church Street W8 4BH
Map GtL: C3
Tel: 0171 2219225
Fax: 0171 2294564
Chefs: Sally Clarke, Elizabeth Payne
Owner: Sally Clarke

Sally Clarke was one of the original Cal-Ital cooks in London; her elegant, split-level restaurant with dramatic red granite bar sticks to its guns, serving a no-choice dinner although there is more flexibility at lunchtime. The menu changes nightly and the week's list is available in advance. Breads, naturally, come from Sally Clarke's shop and jugs of freshly squeezed juices are a popular aperitif. A June dinner started with a large salmon fishcake with vine tomato sauce, well-flavoured if a touch lumpy, spinach and a little smoked salmon. Main course was succulent chargrilled chicken on skewers, served with a greengrocers display of asparagus, baby carrots, fresh peas, broad beans and lentils. Cheeses come with oatmeal biscuits and apple, dates or radishes. Lemon tart with whipped cream and candied zest was served with good espresso. A February night saw a typical menu of ricotta and thyme ravioli with roasted artichoke, Parmesan and rocket, followed by grilled squab pigeon with crostini of wild mushrooms, pine nuts and red wine glaze, plus a salad of celery, trevisse and young spinach, then pear, cranberry and blood orange brioche with spiced cream. Staff are smartly dressed and quite formal but a few more West Coast smiles would help. However, any wine list that begins with a selection by the glass is off to an encouraging start. A thoughtful range of French country wines offers interest and value for money, and a notable Californian selection is characterised by imagination and reasonable pricing.

Directions: Near Notting Hill Gate Tube station

Times: 12.30pm-last L 2pm/7pm-last D 10pm. Closed Sat, Sun, Xmas and summer breaks
Seats: 90
Smoking: No-smoking area; air-conditioning
Credit cards:

Coast Restaurant ❀❀

Busy, busy, busy and very noisy. This is a bright, airy space-age restaurant of pale green walls and utilitarian yellow chairs, set in a converted car showroom, and offering an inventive short menu that changes several times a year. Game terrine, for example is a 'crazy paving' of 10p-size meats with a morsel of foie gras and prunes, and a salad of baby gems that comes with lightly poached egg, crisp bacon fries, marinated anchovies, croutons, Caesar dressing, and is topped with generous shavings of Parmesan. Main courses include roasted cod served on spicy noodles and wok-fried squid and Asian greens, crispy roast sea bass with Jersey royals bound with sour cream and chives, and saddle of rabbit wrapped in herbs and Parma ham, and served with pan-fried polenta, grilled artichokes and corn stock. Blood orange trifle is an unusual dessert.

Directions: Nearest Tube – Green Park

Albemarle Street W1
Map: C3
Tel: 0171 4955999
Fax: 0171 4952999
Chef: Stephen Terry
Owner: Oliver Peyton
Cost: Alc £30. H/wine £12.50. ☺
Times: Noon-last L 3pm/6pm-last D 11.30pm. Closed Bhs
Additional: Sunday L; Children welcome; ♿ dishes
Seats: 150
Smoking: Air-conditioning
Credit cards:

The Collection ❀❀

The former fashion warehouse makes an alternative Sloane-hang-out to Mogens Tholstrup's other place, Daphne's (see entry). By day, the techno-chic neutral colour scheme of the upper-level restaurant is just the right backdrop for ladies-who-lunch. At night, the long, ground floor bar-cum-bistro can see some lively action. The kitchen, however, produces good-looking dishes, the emphasis firmly on the fusion of lightness with a fashionable eclecticism; ideas and influences are plucked from a global hat seemingly at will. Note an inspection lunch that took in fresh and accurately cooked clams in seaweed and miso broth, chargrilled baby squid with wasabi, lime and mint, chargrilled venison with tamarind soured cream dressing and a generous portion of sweet potato rolled in crushed cardamom, and grilled lamb with 'quinoa' salad, braised aubergine and

264 Brompton Road SW3
Map: B1
Tel: 0171 2251212
Fax: 0171 2251050
Chef: Chris Benians
Owner: Mogens Tholstrup
Cost: Alc £30. H/wine £11.50. (☺ Bistro only)
Times: Noon-last L 3pm/7pm-last D 11pm. Closed Sun, 23-31 Dec
Additional: Bistro menu (downstairs); Children welcome; ♿ dishes
Seats: 150 upstairs/80 downstairs
Smoking: Air-conditioning
Credit cards:

spiced yoghurt. Warm, very dark and dense chocolate pudding enclosing a layer of pistachio sauce finished the meal on a high note. Fair range of wines by the glass.

Directions: Nearest tube stations Brompton Cross and South Kensington

The Connaught ❀❀❀

One of the most discreet and reserved of London's great hotels, The Connaught was built in 1889 as a London home for the landed gentry. Today's clientele may be more cosmopolitan but the gentlemanly atmosphere still prevails. Both the Restaurant, with its highly polished wood panelling and the smaller, pale green Grill Room more or less share the same *carte* (written almost entirely in French without translation) of classic French dishes admirably realised by Michel Bourdin, but lunch sees some traditional English dishes offered. At dinner in the Restaurant our inspector was struck by the slightly old-fashioned style of service, with 'lamps' on the service trolleys, and dishes presented for approval at the table on silver platters before being served. Few places nowadays bother to roll a new tablecloth over the old one before dessert; even fewer do it so effortlessly that it does not disturb the conversation. The menu is laid out in classic Grand Hotel style and is full of appropriate garnishes; that there is a portrait of Escoffier in the kitchen says everything about the cooking. This is not a criticism, rather it is that Bourdin is keeping the flame of classic French cooking alive, and doing it very well in the process. Over the past year, to celebrate the Connaught's centenary, a number of highly celebrated guest chefs have worked alongside him, a tribute also to the esteem in which he is held by his peers. Amongst Bourdin's own dishes, his terrine Connaught particularly lives up to its great reputation – duck-based, moist, flavoursome and studded with wild mushrooms, pistachio nuts and squares of foie gras pâté. Desserts from a well-stocked, varied trolley, might include a good-looking bread-and-butter pudding, puff pastry raspberry band and a first-rate passion fruit and sponge gâteau.

Carlos Place W1Y 6AL
Map: C3
Tel: 0171 4997070
Fax: 0171 4953262
Chef: M Bourdin
Owner: The Savoy Group
Cost: £38.50, fixed-price L £25/D £35 (Grill Room), £55 (Restaurant)
Times: 12.30pm-last L 2.30pm/6.30pm-last D 10.45pm
Additional: Sunday L; Children welcome
Seats: 75 (Restaurant), 35 (Grill Room)
Smoking: No pipes; air-conditioning
Accommodation: 90 en suite
Credit cards: ■ ■ ■ ■

Directions: On corner of Mount Street and Carlos Place, between Bond Street and Hyde Park Corner Tube stations

Conrad International ❀

See Where London Meets page 158

The Cook House ❀ NEW

A tiny, lively BYO restaurant with a loyal following for the monthly-changing menu which may include pot-roasted pigeon with root vegetable 'mash', skate wing with lemon grass and Thai noodles, roasted smoked haddock with colcannon and braised lamb shank with sweet roasted aubergine and coconut rice.

Additional: Children welcome; ❹ dishes
Smoking: No pipes & cigars; air-conditioning
Credit cards: ■ ■ ■ ▢

Directions: Nearest Tube – Putney Bridge

56 Lower Richmond Road Putney SW15 1JT
Map GtL: C2
Tel: 0181 7852300
Chef: Tim Jefferson
Owners: Tim Jefferson, Amanda Griffiths
Times: D only, 7pm-11pm. Closed D Sun & Mon, 2 wks Aug
Cost: *Alc* £24. ☺

Copthorne Tara

See Where London Meets page 158

Coulsdon Manor Hotel

Coulsdon manor is a popular golfing, leisure and conference hotel. In the restaurant the price of the main course denotes the total cost of a four-course meal, and ranges from boned roasted quail filled with apple and black pudding mousse with steamed couscous and pistachio sauce at £25.50, to whole roasted lobster rubbed with garlic, ginger and Ricard oil and gratinated with crème fraîche at £39.50. An inspection meal kicked off with an admirable pressed terrine of duck confit and garden vegetables, but almost marred by excessive amount of rock salt sprinkled on top. This was followed by pan-fried calves' liver, a moist mound of sweet potato purée and a sauce effectively sharpened with lime juice. The 'Manor House Signature Chocolate Plate' comprises five individual chocolate desserts, including a good iced white chocolate soufflé with a tart raspberry coulis, and a warm dark chocolate tart.

Directions: M23 N until road becomes A23. At 2.5 miles, R after Coulsdon S Railway Station onto B2030 (Purley). Follow uphill 1 mile, L past pond, 0.5 mile, and turn R into Coulsdon Court Rd.

Coulsdon Court Road Croydon
CR5 2LL
Map GtL: D1
Tel: 0181 6680414
Fax: 0181 6680342
Chef: Robert Bird
Owner: Coulsdon Manor Hotel
Cost: *Alc* £33. Fixed-price L £15.95/D £20.95. ☺ H/wine £13.
Times: 12.30pm-last L 2pm/7pm-last D 9.30pm.
Additional: Bar food; Sunday L; Children welcome; ✪ dishes.
Seats: 120. Private dining room 150. Jacket and tie preferred
Smoking: No smoking in dining room
Accommodation: 35 en suite
Credit cards: ▆ ▆ ▆ ▆ ▆ ▆

The Cow Dining Room ✿✿ NEW

Situated above the Cow Saloon (where there is also good bar food), it is essential to book at this buzzing little place. Kick off with the house cocktail, prosseco with blood orange juice, as refreshing and straightforward as everything else here. There are no frills, either in terms of the decor or the food, but everything is freshly prepared and the menu changes daily. Bruschetta of crab was plentiful and full of flavour, served on good Italian bread with a drizzle of olive oil. Another starter of duck liver terrine with onion confit and brioche was equally successful, but the hit of the meal was the main course of roast skate with spicy aubergine salad – a fine piece of fish, with wilted dandelion leaves being the perfect foil to the slight sweetness of the rich aubergine mixture. Lemon curd tart was made with a good quality filling and a super crisp pastry shell. Service hits just the right note of capable amiability – not an easy job with such an eclectic mix of customers.

Directions: Nearest Tubes – Royal Oak, Westbourne Park, Queensway. 5 mins from Portobello Market

89 Westbourne Park Road
W2 5QH
Map GtL: C3
Tel: 0171 2210021
Chef/Owner: Francesca Melman
Cost: *Alc* £21. H/wine £9.50. ☺
Times: D only, 7pm-D 11.30pm. Closed D Sun
Additional: Sunday L (12.30pm-4pm); Children welcome; ✪ dishes
Seats: 35
Smoking: No pipes & cigars
Credit cards: ▆ ▆ ▆ ▆

The Criterion ❀❀❀

224 Piccadilly W1V 9LB
Map: C3
Tel: 0171 9300488
Fax: 0171 9308190
Chef: Peter Raffel
Owners: Marco Pierre White/Granada
Cost: Alc £28, fixed-price L £17.95.
☺ H/wine £12.50.
Times: Noon-last L 2.30pm/6pm-last
D midnight. Closed 25-26 Dec, 1 Jan
Additional: Sunday L;
Children welcome; ❀ dishes
Seats: 180
Credit cards: ▀ ▒ ▒ ▚ ▣ ▢

A setting right on Piccadilly Circus can have its disadvantages, but once through the crusties and hangers-on around Eros things begin to look up. The entrance is grand, the setting theatrical – high, gold studded ceilings, marbled walls, large pot palms, oriental rugs, huge lamps, and large Eastern-style paintings. 'Affordable glamour' was what Marco Pierre White was after, and this is what the customer gets. The food is very French brasserie, very simple, and very good; prices are not bad either. From a clearly laid out menu there is plenty of choice. Spaghetti of langoustine with rocket, or parfait of foie gras and chicken livers to start. Then a grilled lemon sole with winkles, deep-fried capers and jus Parisienne, perhaps, or roast rump of lamb boulangère, caramelised shallots, young vegetables and rosemary jus. Highlights of inspection meals have been a brilliant gazpacho of crab, tender calves' liver with sauce diable, and roast French chicken, properly garnished, and served with pomme fondant and haricot vert. Staff are smartly turned out though service can be a bit erratic. The precise wine list covers most bases and whilst taking few risks, doesn't put a foot wrong in terms of quality. Excellent producers are to be found across the continents, with Australia and New Zealand the places to look for some elegant examples under £30. A decent selection of half-bottles is bolstered by a good choice by the glass.
Signature dishes: Poached fillet of smoked haddock, new potatoes and chervil, grain mustard sauce; honey-roast pork 'oriental', braised pak choi, bitter sweet sauce.

Directions: Nearest Tube – Piccadilly

Crowthers ❀

481 Upper Richmond Road West
SW14 7PU
Map GtL: B2
Tel: 0181 876 6372
Chef: Philip Crowther
Owners: Philip & Shirley Crowther
Cost: Alc £23, fixed-price L £18.50/D
£23. ☺ H/wine £9.50.
Times: Last L 2pm/D 10pm. Closed L
Sat, Sun, Mon, 1 wk Aug, Xmas

A popular little restaurant, with an enthusiastic husband and wife team – Philip Crowther cooks and Shirley looks after guests. Typical main courses include pot roast loin of pork baked with orange and ginger, grilled breast of chicken with fresh egg noodles, and pan-fried wing of skate with black butter sauce.

Additional: Children welcome; ❀ dishes
Smoking: Air-conditioning
Credit cards: ▀ ▒

Directions: Train to Mortlake; train or tube to Richmond. Btw junction of Sheen Lane & Clifford Ave

Cucina ❀❀

45a South End Road
NW3
Map GtL: C4
Tel: 0171 4357814
Fax: 0171 4357815
Chefs: A Poole, A Baker
Owners: Vernon Mascarenhas,
A Poole, S Baker
Cost: Alc £18.50, fixed-price L £10/D
£15.95. ☺ H/wine £10.95.
Times: Noon-last L 2.30pm/7pm-last
D 11pm. Closed D Sun, Xmas
Additional: Sunday L;
Children welcome; ❀ dishes

In a parade of shops opposite Hampstead Heath, Cucina puts on a sophisticated face, with its stripped wood floors, sun-bleached orange walls and modern Italian chairs with asymmetric backs. The kitchen surfs boldly over the Pacific Rim, negotiating salad of soy-marinated pigeon with nashi pear, crispy prosciutto and mizuna leaves, and mussels steamed in massaman Thai curry and coconut broth with Thai basil, as well as chargrilled monkfish with wasabi beurre blanc and wild garlic leaves. There's also a Mediterranean undercurrent that surfaces in dishes such as roast chicken with chorizo, thyme and smoked plum tomatoes, salt-cured cod with lobster mash and gazpacho, or a garlic pizza of sautéed mixed mushrooms,

Cucina

Seats: 96
Smoking: No pipes or cigars; air-conditioning
Credit cards: 💳 💳 💳 💳 💳

wilted rocket and mascarpone. Desserts follow a similar route: warm Muscat and olive oil cake with lemon sabayon; bitter chocolate tart with Rocky Road ice cream. The wine list zips affordably around the world.

Directions: Opposite Hampstead BR station. Nearest Tube – Belsize Park or Hampstead

Dan's Restaurant ❀

A bright, informal restaurant with stripped pine floors, smart rear conservatory and splendid summer garden for alfresco dining. A recent inspection meal took in well cooked confit of duck with Oriental sauce, and a light lemon tart with blackcurrant coulis.

Additional: Sunday L; Children welcome; 🥄 dishes
Credit cards: 💳 💳 💳 💳

Directions: At Kings Road end of Sydney Street. Nearest Tube – South Kensington

119 Sydney Street SW3 6NR
Map: B1
Tel: 0171 3522718
Fax: 0171 3523265
Chef: Vincent Morse
Owner: Dan Whitehead
Cost: Alc £25, fixed-price L £10.95.
☺ H/wine £10.
Times: Last L 2.15pm/last D 10.15pm.
Closed D Sun, Xmas, New Year

Daphne's ❀❀❀

110-112 Draycott Avenue
SW3 3AE
Map: B1
Tel: 0171 5894257
Fax: 0171 5812232
Chef: Chris Benians
Owner: Mogens Tholstrup
Cost: Alc £30, fixed-price L £30/D £45. H/wine £11.50
Times: Noon-last L 3pm/7pm-last D 11.20pm. Closed Xmas
Additional: Sunday L; Children welcome; 🥄 dishes
Seats: 118. Jacket and tie preferred
Smoking: Air-conditioning
Credit cards: 💳 💳 💳 💳 💳 💳

'Why don't we have more Italians like this in London', mused an inspector. who was not at all fazed by the glitzy mood of this ever-so-fashionable restaurant. You come here to see and be seen, whether you are sporting a bald pate or a pony tail. The menu is tailored to the needs of just about everyone: groovy salads for the trim ladies-who-lunch, beefy chargrills for heartier appetites. A test meal began with calamari fritti – long strips of crisp deep-fried squid with a decent dipping sauce – before roast cod with fennel, wild mushrooms and spinach. The kitchen also does a good line in risottos; a version with masses of tiny brown shrimps was reckoned to be 'true comfort food for the restaurant weary'. Elsewhere, expect flash dishes such as carpaccio of tuna with fennel and Sevruga caviar, brill with girolles, and roast duck with squash, endive and baby onions. Desserts include polenta and lemon cake with stewed plums, almond and apricot tart and a wonderful concoction of puffy, semi-circular deep-fried ravioli stuffed with mascarpone and prunes, all accompanied by lemon ice cream. Service is swift, but don't expect much in the way of personal communication. Around a hundred wines are listed without annotation, and in this case there is some opportunity to make an expensive mistake. Not all selections are from the best sources and some will not yet be drinking at their best. The greatest reliability is to be found in the New World but elsewhere care is needed and advice should certainly be sought.

Directions: Jnc of Draycott Avenue & Walton Street, Brompton Cross. Nearest Tube – South Kensington

The Dorchester, Grill Room ❀❀❀

Park Lane W1A 2HJ
Map: C3
Tel: 0171 3176363
Fax: 0171 4090114
Chef: Willi Elsener
Owner: The Dorchester
Cost: *Alc* £40; fixed-price L £28/D £37 (4 courses). H/wine £19.50.
Times: 12.30pm-last L 2.30pm/6pm-last D 11pm (D Sun 7pm-10.30pm)
Additional: Sunday L; Children welcome; ❹ dishes
Seats: 81
Smoking: Air-conditioning
Accommodation: 244 en suite
Credit cards: ▉ ▉ ▉ ▉ ▉ ▉

This stately Park Lane hotel draws an international clientele, and the Grill Room, with its very traditional British menu, is modelled on an old Spanish palace. The walls are rough plastered, the chairs sumptuous leather, the ceiling is beautifully ornate with gold leaf galore, and rich tapestries and polished silver round off the picture. Although there's an impressive vegetarian menu, this is the place to eat meat, soundly sourced, superbly cooked, either in the old fashioned dishes of the day or carved from the trolley. Trolleys, indeed, appear to be a major feature of the service; there's the bread trolley with breads in many shapes, flavours and size, all expertly carved, the sweet trolley, and the silver domed carving trolley for the traditional roasts. An appetiser of bound smoked salmon and prawn served with lobster oil and squid ink, showed that Willi Elsener can have fun with modern combinations and ingredients, and this opened a well reported meal that took in crab cakes with ginger, and a 'superb' saddle of lamb stuffed with asparagus. Service is good, but on our visit in March, there were too many staff on duty with not enough to do; wine top up, for example, was over zealous.

Signature dishes: Traditional steak and kidney pie; oven-roasted escalope of beef with cracked wheat, tomato and herb crust; roast loin of lamb wrapped in Cumberland ham with cep mushrooms on a rice galette; Scottish wild salmon and chargrilled vegetable terrine served with spicy red radish cream.

Directions: Two-thirds of the way down Park Lane, fronting a small island garden. Nearest Tube – Hyde Park

The Dorchester, The Oriental ❀❀❀

Park Lane W1A 2HJ
Map: C3
Tel: 0171 3176328
Chefs: Willi Elsener, Simon Yung
Owner: The Dorchester
Cost: *Alc* £50, fixed-price L £28/D £37. H/wine £19.50
Times: Noon-last L 2.30pm/7pm-last D 11pm. Closed L Sat, Sun
Additional: Children welcome; ❸ dishes
Seats: 51. Private dining rooms 5-16
Smoking: Air-conditioning
Accommodation: 244 en suite
Credit cards: ■ ▨ ▨ ✈ ▨ ▨

The Oriental is on two floors. Downstairs is the bar, and a number of interesting looking private dining rooms (the Thai Room, the Chinese Room and the Indian Room); upstairs in the main restaurant. The decor is tastefully sumptuous, nothing shouts, it's calming, discreet and efficient, just like the staff who are immaculately turned out.

Traditional-classical Cantonese cooking by Simon Yung is first-class; there's a deftness to his dishes in terms of accuracy of cooking and of flavours. This was evident at a winter inspection lunch that opened with soft, boiled prawn and chicken dumplings with ginger and spring onion sauce of incredible balance and flavour, and went on to a 'wonderfully clear, clean' double boiled cabbage and black mushroom soup that was just 'flavour, flavour, flavour'. Then came one of Yung's signature dishes, deep-fried sole with black bean sauce and asparagus tips 'Oriental' style. This was beautifully presented – the fish had been rolled around the asparagus, and other spring vegetables, into little parcels, these were placed on the fish bone that was supported by a carved Chinese dragon at both ends, with the black bean sauce served in a separate bowl for dipping or pouring. Wines ranging from Pouilly Fuisse, Volnay, Nuit St Georges (Faiveley), to a Riesling, are helpfully recommended at the bottom of each of the exotic sounding set menus.

Signature dishes: Roasted Peking duck (served in two courses for between two and six people); stir-fried minced pigeon with bamboo shoots served in lettuce.

Directions: See Dorchester Grill Room (entry above)

Downstairs at
190 Queensgate

The menu continues squarely in a trendy, eclectic vein with lots of Mediterranean influences, a good match for the modern minimalist decor brightened by splashes of primary coloured abstract paintings. It reads excitingly, but the technical ability needed to bring off this style of ingredient-oriented food has been somewhat lacking of late. A classic of the genre, risotto nero was well textured, but sashimi should be left to the Japanese, otherwise you're likely to get the clumsily balanced and presented arrangement served here. A main course of roast poulet noir was rather spoilt by a sloppy pool of corn purée and the flavour of confit of vegetables muddled by being cooked in duck fat. Honey popcorn chocolate mousse sounded great, but what actually arrived was a chocolate mousse garnished with sweet popcorn.

190 Queensgate SW7 5EU
Map: A1
Tel: 0171 5815666
Owners: Simpsons of Cornhill
Telephone for details

Directions: Next to Gore Hotel on Queensgate; easy walking distance from South Kensington Tube station

Drones of Pont Street

1 Pont Street SW1
Map: B2
Tel: 0171 2596166
Fax: 0171 2596177
Chef: Jez Hill
Owner: Simpsons of Cornhill
Cost: *Alc* £35. Fixed-price L £9.95 (2 courses). ☺ H/wine £11.95.
Times: Noon-last L 3.30pm/7pm-last D 11.30pm. Closed 24-26 Dec
Additional: Sunday lunch; Children welcome; ❹ dishes.
Seats: 120; Private dining room 40
Smoking: Air-conditioning
Credit cards: ▬ ▧ ▨ ▧ ▨ ▨

This reincarnation of a 70s classic is now done out in the style of a Tuscan villa, with an enclosed domed garden area as a novel feature. Crowds pack the bar and the main dining area; there is even a grocer's next door. Flexibility is the name of the game and the menu changes monthly. Whether you want a plate of Rossmore rock oysters, some tapas, a burger with fries or even Sevruga caviar, the kitchen can oblige. In between, the style owes much to the Med, with bruschetta, risottos, and home-made pappardelle rubbing shoulders with tuna sashimi with nori rolls, duck confit and crab and coriander fishcakes. A recent inspection lunch kicked off with boneless grilled sardines with spinach and yoghurt salad, before roast rump of lamb with a leek and truffle gratin, rounded off with an excellent panettone and banana toffee pudding with a toffee sauce. The wine list has plenty of depth, with safe drinking from popular sources plus a few good-looking special tipples.

Directions: Nearest Tubes – Knightsbridge and Sloane Square

The Eagle

Popular dining pub media hang-out where tables are at a premium and the food is gutsy with strong Mediterranean influences. The menu of half-a-dozen main dishes is hand-scrawled on the

159 Farringdon Road EC1R 3AL
Map GtL: E5
Tel: 0171 837 1353
Chef: David Eyre
Owners: Michael Belben, David Eyre

blackboard, and could include the likes of spicy Italian sausages with braised butter beans threaded with spinach, and grilled swordfish steak with anchovies and pine nuts.

Directions: N end of Farringdon Road close to Mount Pleasant. Nearest tube: Farringdon

Cost: H/wine £8.50. ☺
Additional: Children welcome;
❸ dishes
Credit cards: None

Elena's L'Etoile

Elena Salvoni is the grande dame of Soho, and runs the show at this Soho landmark with motherly attention. The atmosphere is quite informal, with old wooden floorboards and pale ochre walls covered in black and white prints of actors; over a large part of its 100-years existence the place has thrived on an association with the film world. Alas, no such stars were visible on our lunchtime visit – just a busy mix of friends, business men, 'posh mothers and daughters'. The menu gives 'a fresh modern appeal' to many classic dishes and a full, rich, rounded chicken liver and wild mushroom parfait with a smooth, buttery texture, and translucently fresh, accurately cooked brill with horseradish and parsley crust, served on a generous portion of 'just cooked' spinach and a round of creamed potatoes, were both strongly endorsed. Quite a detailed wine list offers some six New World populars, but the remainder of the 50 or so wines, bar a token Chianti and Gewürztraminer, are French, with a lot of expensive white Burgundies.

Directions: Southside of Goodge Street, between Goodge Street and Oxford Street. Nearest Tube – Tottenham Court Road

30 Charlotte Street W1
Map: C4
Tel: 0171 6367189
Fax: 0171 6370122
Chef: Kevin Hopgood
Owners: The Restaurant Partnership plc
Cost: *Alc* £30.35. ☺ H/wine £10.95.
Times: Noon-last L 2.45pm/D 6pm-last D 11pm. Closed L Sat, Sun
Additional: Children welcome;
❸ dishes
Seats: 80. Private dining room 30
Smoking: No pipes
Credit cards: ▆▆ ▆▆ ▆▆ ▆▆ ▆▆ ▆

Ellington's ✿

A comfortable jazz-orientated restaurant with honest cooking and an interesting choice. Starters include toad-in-the-hole with shallot red wine gravy, and spicy crab cakes with avocado salsa, followed perhaps by calves' liver and bacon served on champ (spring onion and mashed potato).

Additional: Sunday L; Children welcome; ❸ dishes
Smoking: Air-conditioning
Credit cards: ▆▆ ▆▆ ▆

Directions: Opposite Chingford railway station

140 Station Road E4 6AN
Map GtL: E5
Tel/Fax: 0181 5245544
Chef: Karen Neish
Owners: Brian Hutchinson & Greg Simpson
Cost: *Alc* £20.75, fixed price L £5.95/D £19.50. ☺ H/wine £9.80.
Times: Last L 2pm/D 10pm. Closed D Sun, Mon

English Garden Restaurant

In terms of decor, The English Garden is almost two restaurants in one. The Marble Room mixes objets and antiques with contemporary art, whilst the conservatory-like Garden Room, on the ground floor, has a domed glass roof, Gothic-style rattan chairs and is filled with freshly cut flowers and pristine pot plants. The seasonal Spring menu offered a satisfying back-to-basics selection of dishes, from hot crab soufflé and rabbit terrine with sage jelly at one end of the meal, to rhubarb and cardamom ice cream and hot blackberry and apple charlotte with apple custard at the other. Main courses included a tender, well-flavoured saddle of hare with blackcurrants, as well as roast venison with beetroot and juniper berries, roast rump of lamb with turnip gratin and cod

10 Lincoln Street
SW3 2TS
Map: B1
Tel: 0171 5847272
Fax: 0171 5812848
Chef: Brian Turner
Owner: Roger Wren
Cost: *Alc* £28, fixed-price L £15.75 (3 courses). ☺ H/wine £11
Times: 12.30pm-last L 2.30pm (2pm Sun & Bhs)/7.30pm-last D 11.30pm (7pm-10pm Sun & Bhs).
Closed 25-26 Dec
Additional: Sunday L;
Children welcome; ❸ dishes

English Garden Restaurant

Seats: 55. Private dining
rooms 22 & 9
Smoking: No pipes in dining room;
air-conditioning
Credit cards: [symbols]

in a herb crust with saffron mash. The good value, set lunch
might start with devilled chicken livers on toast, followed by
white veal stew topped with sage dumplings, and end with a
well-chosen selection of English farmhouse cheeses.

Directions: Nearest tube – Sloane Square

The English House ✿✿

3 Milner Street SW3 2QA
Map: B1
Tel: 0171 5843002
Fax: 0171 5812848
Chef: David Clouston
Owner: Roger Wren
Cost: *Alc* £28, fixed-price L £15.75.
H/wine £11
Times: 12.30pm-last L 2.30pm (2pm
Sun & Bhs)/7.30pm-last D 11.30pm
(7pm-10pm Sun & Bhs). Closed 26
Dec
Additional: Sunday L; Children
welcome; ✿ dishes
Seats: 28. Private dining rooms 8-20
Smoking: No pipes in dining room
Credit cards: [symbols]

Tucked away in the heart of Chelsea, the chintzy English
House remains a pleasure to visit. The staff are most attentive
and the quintessential English cooking is a salutary reminder
that good food existed in these isles before we discovered
Chiantishire. Grilled pigeon breast garnished with bacon and
onions with a light but well-flavoured brown sauce opened our
inspector's meal on a high note, and the standard was
maintained with a main course of poached fillet of Dover sole
stuffed with a fluffy fish mousse and served with a saffron
sauce. other dishes might include, depending on the season,
cream of onion soup, mackerel pâté, roast duck with spiced
oranges and celeriac mash, grilled venison steak with Savoy
cabbage and roast rack of lamb with a herb crust. Old-
fashioned, proper puddings include apple and blackberry
steamed pudding, sticky toffee pudding and a baked rice
pudding with cinnamon fruits. alternatively, there is a good
choice of British farmhouse cheeses served with oatcakes.

Directions: Between South Kensington and Sloane Square Tubes

L'Escargot ❀❀

Firmly established on the Soho scene, L'Escargot has been around in a number of incarnations since 1927. These days the establishment is split between a bustling street level bistro and a quieter, more intimate restaurant on the first floor. Both offer spot-on French cooking with Mediterranean overtones. A mixture of innovative and traditional dishes feature on the mosaic-design menus: expect main courses such as terrine of guinea fowl with prunes d'Agen and chopped capers, fillet of venison with chestnuts, Savoy cabbage and sauce grand veneur, and saddle of rabbit with pearl barley risotto and sauce Sauternes. Desserts to watch out for include chocolate marquise with pistachio and caramel ice cream, brandy snaps served with prune and Armagnac ice cream, and Fourme d'Ambert cheese, accompanied by grapes and home-made walnut bread. The wine list is long and mainly French, although there is plenty of choice from the New World.

Greek Street W1V 5LQ
Map: D4
Tel: 0171 4376828
Fax: 0171 4370790
Chefs: Billy Reid, David Hawksworth
Owner: Jimmy Lahoud
Cost: Alc £24.45, fixed-price L £17.50 (Brasserie), £30 (1st floor)/D £23.45 (Brasserie), £38 (1st floor). ☺ H/wine £13.
Times: 12.15pm-last L 2.15pm/6pm-last D 11.30pm. Closed L Sat, Sun. 1st floor closed 25-26 Dec, 1 Jan, Aug
Additional: Children welcome; ⓐ dishes
Smoking: No pipes and cigars in dining room; air-conditioning
Credit cards: ▬ ▬ ▬ ▬ ▣ ▯

Directions: Nearest Tubes – Tottenham Court Rd, Leicester Sq

Fats ❀

An 'experience of paradise' is promised at this lively, fun hang-out with a Cajun/Creole/Caribbean accent. Spicy, deep fried salt fish balls, chicken jambalaya and seafood 'gambo' are typical dishes. Roti dishes and 'ground provisions' such as yam, dasheen and cassava also make an appearance.

178 Shirland Road
Maida Vale W9 3JR
Map: B3
Tel: 0171 289 3884
Telephone for details

Directions: Off Harrow Road, via Chippenham Road. Nearest Tubes: Warwick Avenue, Queen's Park, Kilburn Park, Westbourne Park

Fifth Floor Restaurant ❀❀

Arriving early at this stylish restaurant on the fifth floor of Harvey Nichols can be a mistake; the distractions on the way up can add significantly to the cost of the meal. Although coveted window tables in this smart environment are usually reserved for threesomes, the rear tables are much better placed to watch the air-kissers and suits-in-sunglasses in action. In the kitchen, Henry Harris draws inspiration from all corners of the world in his daily changing set-lunch and evening *carte*; dishes such as spinach and dolcelatte tart, deep-fried squid with potato salad and aïoli, and seared tuna with vermicelli noodles

Harvey Nichols
Knightsbridge
SW1X 7RJ
Map: B2
Tel: 0171 2355250
Fax: 0171 8232207
Chef: Henry Harris
Owner: Harvey Nichols & Co Ltd
Cost: Fixed-price L £22.50.
Times: Noon-last L 3pm (3.30pm Sat, Sun)/6.30pm-last D 11.30pm. Closed D Sun

Fifth Floor Restaurant

Additional: Bar food L; Sunday L;
Children welcome; 🍴 dishes.
Seats: 110
Smoking: No pipes; air-conditioning
Credit cards:

and spring onion salad. An inspection lunch began with an
inspired oriental combination of slow-braised belly of pork
with mussels and bok choy. Then came two plump pot-roasted
quails with pumpkin ravioli and crisp sage, followed by a
cherry parfait with shortbread and cherry compote. The 'Little
List' of wines has more than enough choice, and is sensibly
chosen to complement the food, whilst the 'Big List' is always
available for those wanting to impress.

Directions: Knightsbridge Tube. Entrance via Sloane Street

Foundation 🏵🏵 NEW

This is the latest addition to Harvey Nichols gastro-circus. As
the name suggests, Foundation is on the lower ground floor of
London's trendiest department store. A glistening blue-green
waterfall forms a dramatic backdrop for the 30-foot bar (where
light meals are served all day) and the decor is a mix of sleek
wooden floors and lightly polished concrete. On-the-ball staff
in black mandarin jackets serve efficiently. Seasonally changing
menus advertise the kind of cosmopolitan modern dishes that
have become the norm in the capital: simmered chicken
noodles, butternut squash risotto, rare grilled tuna with a green
bean and sweetcorn salsa and lime aïoli define the style. A real
'treat ' of a test meal began with a visually stunning timbale of
layered ratatouille with escabeche of red mullet and basil
mayonnaise embellished with slivers of carrot cut into flowers.
The main course was a salad of lobster, beetroot and cucumber
with cardamom and yogurt dressing, and proceedings
concluded with a spectacular mille-feuille of crisp pineapple
with an ultra-smooth coconut sorbet. The wine list includes a
plentiful selection by the glass.

Directions: Nearest Tube – Knightsbridge. Entrance off Seville
Street opposite The Sheraton Hotel

Harvey Nichols Seville Street
Knightsbridge SW1
Map: C3
Tel: 0171 2018000
Fax: 0171 2018080
Chef: Simon Barnett
Owners: Harvey Nichols
Cost: Alc £20, fixed-price L £16.50.
☺ H/wine £11.95
Times: Noon-3.30pm/6.30pm-last D
10.55pm. Closed D Sun
Additional: Sunday L; Bar meals;
Children welcome; 🍴 dishes
Seats: 180
Smoking: No-smoking area;
air-conditioning
Credit cards:

Four Seasons Hotel 🏵🏵🏵

Large picture windows overlook the hotel's gardens, so during
the day the dining room is filled with natural light. Chef Shaun
Watling does a good job with a style of cooking that adds a few
classical French touches to a seasonal modern European
repertoire. Quenelles of duck mousse were more akin to
rillettes, but with tomato chutney made for a fine appetiser,
followed, on our visit, by raviolone with wild mushrooms and a

Park Lane
W1A 1AZ
Map: C3
Tel: 0171 4990888
Fax: 0171 4931895
Chef: Shaun Whatling
Owner: Four Seasons Hotel
Cost: Alc £45, fixed-price L&D £48 (5
courses). ☺ H/wine £24

light parsley and truffle sauce. This excellent starter included a good variety of mushrooms, tender pasta, a frothy sauce with a real aroma of truffles and a garnish of deep-fried parsley. Our inspector then went on to grilled wild salmon on roasted vegetables with tarragon and mustard sauce. Dessert was a good cherry and chocolate tart with pistachio ice cream, with a clear chocolate flavour and thin, freshly cooked pastry. For such a suave setting, service has not always been as smooth as might be expected.

Signature dishes: Cutlets of new season lamb with goat's cheese soufflé, basil sauce. Baked sea bass with a herb crust on crushed potatoes with turmeric sauce; pan-fried foie gras with onion marmalade and old balsmaic reduction; spiced pear Tatin with cinnamon sorbet.

Directions: Nearest Tubes – Hyde Park Corner, Green Park. Set back from Park Lane in Hamilton Place

Times: 12.30pm-last L 3pm/7pm-last D 10.30pm
Additional: Sunday L; Children welcome; 🍴 dishes
Seats: 60. Jacket & tie preferred
Smoking: No pipes; air-conditioning
Accommodation: 227 en suite
Credit cards: ▬ ▬ ▬ ▬

The Fox Reformed ❀

Not so much a wine bar more a laid-back hang-out, with magazines and board games on tap. Whilst taking on the demon backgammon players, enjoy fishcakes with parsley sauce, calves' liver with sage and onion, and linguini with roast Mediterranean vegetables. Walled rear garden for warm weather eating.

Additional: Sunday L; Bar snacks; Children welcome; 🍴 dishes
Smoking: No-smoking area; air-conditioning
Credit cards: ▬ ▬ ▬ ▬ ▥

Directions: Opposite the junction with Woodlea Road

176 Stoke Newington
Church Street N16
Map GtL: D4
Tel/Fax: 0171 254 5975
Chef: Paul Harper
Owners: Carol & Robbie Richards
Cost: H/wine £8.25 ☺
Times: Last L 2.30pm/6.30pm-last D 10.30pm. Closed 25-26 Dec

Frederick's Restaurant ❀❀

A garden, patio and conservatory all help to make dining at this long-established restaurant a continuing pleasure. A two-course business lunch and early dinner menu is particularly good value at £12, with a choice of three dishes at each, and there is also a good Saturday lunch menu at £13.50, plus a 'kids' menu (chicken goujons with tomato sauce and chips). The main *carte* is very long, and reads like an index to modern British and French cooking – fresh tuna tartare with sour cream and blinis, house-smoked Barbary duck with chilli and mango chutney, roast cod fillet with white beans, cabbage and foie gras parfait, pan-fried calves' liver with colcannon and sweet and sour shallots. One advantage of the length is the choice it gives to vegetarians, such as salad of artichoke, French beans and trompette with a creamy mustard sauce, and pithiviers of spiced parsnips with roast onion and mint yogurt. All prices include service.

Directions: Nearest Tube – Angel, 2 mins walk to Camden Passage. Restaurant amongst the antique shops

Camden Passage N1 8EG
Map GtL: D3
Tel: 0171 3592888
Fax: 0171 3595173
Chef: Andrew Jeff
Owner: Louis Segal
Cost: *Alc* £25, fixed-price L&D £12 (2 courses). ☺ H/wine £11.95.
Times: Noon-last L 2.30pm/6pm-last D 11.30pm. Closed Sun, Bhs
Additional: Bar food; Children welcome; 🍴 dishes.
Seats: 130. Private dining rooms 18-28
Smoking: No-smoking area; air-conditioning
Credit cards: ▬ ▬ ▬ ▬ ▥ ▥

French House Dining Room ❀

A smart but informal Soho restaurant above the French House Pub – the unofficial 'headquarters' of the free French during the second World War. A lively modern British menu includes pan-fried duck livers with chick peas, poached chicken with ox tongue sausage and green sauce, and orange bavarois with fruit compote.

Additional: Bar meals L; Children welcome; 🍴 dishes
Credit cards: ▭ ▭ ▭ ▭ ▭

Directions: Above the French House pub. Nearest Tubes: Leicester Square, Tottenham Court Rd & Piccadilly Circus

49 Dean Street W1V 5HL
Tel: 0171 4372477
Fax: 0171 2879109
Chef: Margot Clayton
Owners: Margot Clayton, Melanie Arnold
Cost: *Alc* £20.25. H/wine £9.50. ☺
Times: 12.30pm-last L 3.15pm/6pm-last D 11.15pm. Closed Sun, Bhs

Friends Restaurant ❀

11 High Street Pinner HA5 5PJ
Map GtL: A4
Tel/Fax: 0181 8660286
Chefs: Terry Farr, Ben Denny
Owner: Terry Farr
Cost: *Alc* £26.50, fixed-price L £14.95/D £18.95. ☺ H/wine £9.55.
Times: Last L-2.15pm/D-10pm. Closed D Sun, Bhs
Additional: Sunday L; Children welcome; 🍴 dishes
Smoking: No pipes and cigars
Credit cards: ▭ ▭ ▭ ▭ ▭ ▭

Consistent modern cooking attracts the crowds to this 400-year-old timbered restaurant. In addition to good-value set menus, the seasonally-changing carte may list seafood chowder, followed by wild boar on a ragout of wild mushrooms, or brill with saffron and soy jus, with coffee and Marsala cheesecake to finish.

Directions: Follow A404 from Harrow. In the centre of Pinner

Fung Shing ❀❀

15 Lisle Street WC2
Map: D3
Tel: 0171 4371539
Fax: 0171 7340284
Chef: Mr Ly
Owner: Forum Restaurant Ltd
Cost: *Alc* £15. H/wine £10. ☺

Lisle Street is not exactly short of Chinese restaurants, but the family-run Fung Shing consistently remains one of the best. Seafood is a speciality, and it's worth splashing out on lobster with noodles or braised shark's fin. Carp is served in a

'superior' sauce or braised with ginger and spring onion, eel is cooked in a variety of ways including roasted with honey sauce and turbot is pan-fried with ginger and garlic sauce. Other relatively unusual ingredients include pigeon, venison, veal and tea-smoked silver pomfret. Braised suckling pig and abalone are geared to big spenders, but there are plenty of less pricey delicacies such as pan-fried wind-dried oysters with preserved pork, and stewed duck and yam hot-pot, plus sweet and sour spare-ribs and beef with cashew nuts for the less gung-ho. A few Chinese wines are amongst the short wine list, including *Shao Hsing*, served hot.

Directions: Nearest Tube – Leicester Square. Behind Empire Cinema

Times: Noon-last D 11.15pm.
Closed 24-26 Dec
Additional: Children welcome;
⍟ dishes
Seats: 115. Private dining room 25-40. Jacket and tie preferred
Smoking: Air-conditioning
Credit cards: ▆ ▆ ▆ ▆ ▆ ▆

Le Gavroche Restaurant

Moving downstairs from reception, through the lounge and into the dining room, there is little by way of sheer opulence, rather a quiet comfort, with half-round banquette seating and other chairs of equally relaxing proportions. Tables are perhaps a little too close together, restricting conversation to a murmur early on, increasing in volume as more diners appear. Service is like a well-oiled machine, smooth, unobtrusive, efficient. It can be formal, but when addressed, staff do open up and are to be applauded for adapting to diners' requirements. Water is topped up as if the waiters are on a commission scheme, yet no charge is made for this. This is Le Gavroche, now 25 years-old, and very much a London institution. Michel Roux jnr has trodden a careful path since taking over from his father, Albert, keeping well within Le Gavroche tradition of classic French cuisine, especially in the section 'Hommage à Mon Père'. Now exciting new ideas have been introduced, firmly rooted in the classic tradition, but accurately reflecting modern trends in dishes such as warm glazed oysters on red radish, grilled turbot on the bone with vegetables marinated in lemon and olive oil, and fillet of beef with cepes and glazed with Fontina cheese. Several meals taken this year have highlighted some memorable dishes: a rich and meaty duck neck sausage with pistachios and port jelly; a terrine of foie gras and celery and truffles showing good classic technique; pan-fried wild salmon with five spice sauce with just the right 'hit' of oriental flavour; an excellent medallion of veal on a bed of diced tomatoes and black olives, topped with thick, juicy asparagus. At another meal, veal 'osso buco' style with pasta and basil oil was similarly outstanding. Omelette Rothschild, vanilla flavoured crème brûlée and a selection of home-made sorbets and ice creams sum up desserts that lack the interest available elsewhere, but are well executed. The cheeseboard offers about 25 regional French cheeses, all in prime condition, and properly detailed by the waiter. Espresso is heart stoppingly good, but petits fours are not in the same class as the brilliant canapés. The set lunch is outstanding value.
Signature dishes: Asperges aux truffes et Parmesan; darne de saumon à la nage de petits legums; navarin d'agneau à la provençale; daube de boeuf à la ancienne.

Directions: From Park Lane, into Upper Brook Street (one way), restaurant is on R. Nearest Tube: Marble Arch

43 Upper Brook Street W1Y 1PF
Map: B3
Tel: 0171 4080881/4991826
Fax: 0171 4090939/4914387
Chef: Michel A Roux
Owner: Le Gavroche Ltd
Cost: *Alc* £80, fixed-price L £39/D £60. H/wine £20
Times: Noon-last L 2pm/7pm-last D 11pm. Closed Sat, Sun, Bhs,
Seats: 60. Private dining room 20. Jacket and tie preferred
Smoking: No pipes, cigars in lounge only; air-conditioning
Credit cards: ▆ ▆ ▆ ▆ ▆ ▆

Gay Hussar ❀

Still going strong after forty-five years, The Gay Hussar never changes. Good value, old-fashioned Hungarian cooking continues to draw the crowds. Popular dishes include roast duck with red cabbage, veal schnitzel with mushroom sauce and smoked goose with scholet. Drink Hungarian Bull's Blood to accompany any main dish.

Smoking: Air-conditioning
Credit cards: ▬ ▦ ▭ ◥ ▣ ▢

Directions: Off Soho Square. Nearest Tube – Tottenham Court Road

2 Greek Street W1V 6NB
Map: D4
Tel: 0171 4370973
Fax: 0171 4374631
Chef: Laszlo Holecz
Owners: Restaurant Partnership plc
Cost: *Alc* £25.30, fixed-price L £16.
☺ H/wine £10.
Times: Last L 2.30pm/D 10.45pm.
Closed Sun, Bhs
Additional: Children welcome;
❹ dishes

Gladwins ❀❀

It's lunch only at this light, colourful basement restaurant filled with foliage and greenery. The cooking takes a monthly voyage around the globe to return with dishes such as Cajun shrimp and papaya salad with Avery Island pepper dressing, fillets of red mullet, sea bass and trout with Thai hot, sour and sweet flavours, chicken scaloppini and lemon provençale tart. Familiar concepts are given a pacy spin – chargrilled rib steak is served with blackeye bean sauce and devilled tomato sauce, oriental duck breast with lime and mango, but there are also some dishes straight out of the *haute cuisine* handbook, such as a ballotine of lamb, beef and turkey layered with mushroom duxelles, bound in bacon and served on a wild mushroom jus. Stilton croustade with quince sauce and Scotch woodcock with anchovy toast and creamed scrambled egg, make good alternatives to desserts such as blackcurrant soufflé with berries. Mineral water is on the house.

Directions: Opposite Fenchurch Station, between Fenchurch Street & Eastcheap. Nearest Tube – Bank or Monument

Minster Court Mark Lane EC3R 7AA
Tel: 0171 4440004
Fax: 0171 4440001
Chef: Peter Gladwin
Cost: Fixed-price L £27 (2 courses).
H/wine £12.50
Times: L only, noon-last L 2.30pm.
Closed Sat, Sun, Bhs, 2 wks mid August
Additional: ❹ dishes
Seats: 120
Smoking: Air-conditioning
Credit cards: ▬ ▦ ▭ ◥ ▢

Gloucester Hotel ❀

See Where London Meets page 158

Gopal's of Soho ❀

Reliable, well regarded Indian restaurant offering a wide range of curry house staples alongside the more interesting selection from south India. A test meal featured wonderful Peschwari naan with almond paste and sultanas, succulent chicken cooked with hot green chillies in a coconut sauce, and lamb cooked in ginger, tomatoes, garlic and fresh coriander.

Directions: Nearest Tubes – Tottenham Court Road, Piccadilly Circus

12 Bateman Street W1V 5TD
Map: D4
Tel/Fax: 0171 4340840
Chef/Owner: N P Pittal (Mr Gopal)
Cost: *Alc* £16. H/wine £8.25. ☺
Times: Last L 2.30pm/D 11.15pm.
Closed 25-26 Dec
Additional: No children under 8;
❹ dishes
Smoking: Air-conditioning
Credit cards: ▬ ▦ ▭ ◥ ▢

Goring Hotel ❀❀

An elegant Edwardian hotel that maintains high standards of service, and has been personally run by the Goring family since 1910. The Dining Room restaurant is one of the last bastions of traditional British cooking in the capital – guests still flock

Beeston Place Grosvenor Gardens
SW1W 0JW
Map: C2
Tel: 0171 3969000
Fax: 0171 8344393
Chef: John Elliot

Goring Hotel

Owner: George Goring
Cost: Fixed-price L £23/D £32.
H/wine £17.50
Times: 12.30pm-last L 2.30pm/6pm-
last D 10pm. Closed L Sat
Additional: Sunday L; Bar meals;
Children welcome; ⬧ dishes
Seats: 60. 4 private dining
rooms (up to 50)
Smoking: No cigars or pipes
Accommodation: 76 en suite
Credit cards: ▆ ▆ ▆ ▆ ▆

here on Wednesdays for the hotel's spectacular steak and
kidney pie. However, not all dishes come from the past;
indeed, chef John Elliot takes an imaginative approach to
many classic ideas. Typical main courses could include braised
oxtail wrapped in Savoy cabbage, roast fillet of pork with wild
mushrooms and smoked bacon, fillet of Cornish mackerel with
potato crust, and roast monkfish with leeks and red wine
butter sauce. The airy restaurant is spacious without losing
intimacy; elegant yet not overpowering. In the evenings there's
a pianist. The extensive wine list, featuring a good choice of
premier cru classé Bordeaux, is personally selected by the
General Manager.

Directions: In central London behind Buckingham Palace.
Exit from Victoria tube station onto Victoria Street, turn L
into Grosvenor Gdns, cross Buckingham Palace Road,
75 yds turn L into Beeston Place

Granita 🌸🌸

Minimalist blonde wood is highlighted by blue and yellow
walls in this ultra-modern restaurant. A high zinc bar is
practically the only adornment in the long, narrow room –
tables are without cloths and fashionably lack side plates. Staff
wear black mandarin overshirts and trousers. The short but
considered menu is modern European with some oriental
influences. Starters might include Thai mackerel with ginger,
lemon grass, coriander, chilli and toasted peanuts, courgette
and basil soup, or fresh asparagus with boiled eggs, anchovy
and Parmesan shavings. Fillet of pan-roasted cod was perfectly
cooked with nicely crisped skin, served on a bed of wilted
spinach with delicious olive oil mash. Other choices that day
included tagliatelle with artichoke, pesto tarragon and flat
mushrooms or cornfed chicken, marinated, then chargrilled on
skewers and served with roasted aubergine, tomato, herb
gratin and wild rocket salad. A strawberry trifle rounded off a
meal of exceptional value for money.

Directions: Nearest Tube: Highbury & Islington, and Angel.
Opposite St Mary' s Church.

127 Upper Street Islington N1
Map GtL: D3
Tel: 0171 2263222
Fax: 0171 2264833
Chef: Ahmed Kharshoum
Owners: Ahmed Kharshoum,
Vikki Leffman
Cost: *Alc* £22, fixed-price L £11.95 (2
courses). ☺ H/wine £9.50.
Times: 12.30-last L 2.30pm/6.30pm-
last D 10.30pm. Closed Mon, L Tue,
2 wks Aug, Xmas, Easter
Additional: Sunday L;
Children welcome; ⬧ dishes
Seats: 72
Smoking: No pipes and cigars;
air-conditioning
Credit cards: ▆ ▆

Great Nepalese 🌸

*Familiar curries and tandoori dishes make up most of the menu, but
the Nepalese set lunch or dinner is a good way to sample some of the*

48 Eversholt Street NW1 1DA
Map: D5
Tel: 0171 388 6737
Chef: Masuk Miah

house specialities such as mutton curry, black lentils and potato, bamboo shoots and beans. Other interesting dishes include duck on the bone and mamocha or steam cooked meat pastries.

Owner: Mr GP Manandhar
Cost: *Alc* £15, fixed-price L&D £11.75 (2 courses). ☺ H/wine £6.95.

Times: Last L 2.30pm/6pm-last D 11.30pm. Closed 25-26 Dec
Additional: Children welcome; ◑ dishes
Credit cards: ▬ ▦ ▦ ▚ ▣

Directions: East side of Euston station

Greek Valley Restaurant ✿✿

130 Boundary Road NW8 0RH
Map GtL: C3
Tel: 0171 6243217
Fax: 0171 6244717
Chef: Peter Bosnic
Owners: Mr & Mrs Bosnic
Cost: *Alc* £11.50, fixed-price D £7.50 (2 courses, Mon-Thu). ☺ H/wine £7.50.
Times: D only, 6pm-midnight. Closed Sun
Additional: Children welcome; ◑ dishes
Seats: 62. Private dining room 32
Smoking: Air-conditioning
Credit cards: ▬ ▦

A small family restaurant that serves its local community well, with authentic Greek food and, in summer, tables outside. No frills but good, homely, straightforward cooking along the lines of fried kalamari, lamb kleftico, home-made sausages, creamy dips, and grilled flat mushrooms. Casseroles of lamb, chicken or vegetables are served with rice. Lamb souvla is marinated in red wine, lightly spiced with oregano and black pepper, and slowly grilled over charcoal, and chicken is cooked on skewers with peppers, onions and mushrooms. Baklava and kataifi are amongst a small selection of sweet and sticky desserts. Friday night is bouzouki night.

Directions: Nearest Tubes – Swiss Cottage, St John's Wood

Green Olive ✿✿

After setting out its stall as a bastion of French provincial cooking, this particular olive now has a gutsy peasant Italian flavour. The thrust of the menu owes much to Sardinian and Ligurian roots. Dishes are simple and straight to the point: grilled scallops are served on a bed of rocket; slices of pink duck breast sit on a pile of broccoli florets with an olive and mint sauce spiked with a hint of chilli. Elsewhere you might find black ravioli stuffed with monkfish, baked sea bream with onions and basil and Ligurian-style rabbit casserole. A dish of the eponymous oil is provided to dip your bread, and meals conclude with, say, chocolate and almond tart or 'crespelle' of apples with vanilla sauce. Like the food, the decor is unfussy but stylish: bare brick walls, bare boarded floors, rustic furniture, coarse fabric hanging at the windows.

5 Warwick Place W9
Map GtL: C3
Tel: 0171 2892469
Fax: 0171 2894178
Chef: Sandro Medda
Owner: Bijan Behzadi
Cost: Fixed-price L £12.50/D £21 ☺ H/wine £9.50.
Times: 12.30pm-last L 2.30pm /7pm-last D 10.45pm. Closed weekday L, 25-26 Dec, Easter Good Friday
Additional: Sunday lunch; Children welcome; ◑ dishes
Seats: 55. Private dining room 22
Smoking: No pipes or cigars; air-conditioning
Credit cards: ▬ ▦ ▦ ▚ ▣

Directions: Nearest Tube – Warwick Avenue

The Greenhouse Restaurant

Since Gary Rhodes' departure, The Greenhouse has been a restaurant with shifting fortunes. Changes in the kitchen and out-front have continued and consistency seems to have become a casualty along the way. That said, the place remains a popular venue – particularly at lunchtime when the business community comes in to do deals over food that has a strong, masculine English accent. Starting proceedings there might be warm smoked eel with bacon and new potatoes or, for Francophiles, ballotine of foie gras on lamb's lettuce and shallot salad. Main courses are a similar mix: roast saddle of lamb with braised onions, and confit of duck with braised lentils, artichokes, parsley and red wine for example. It should come as no surprise that desserts include an authentic version of bread-and-butter pudding, along with tarte Tatin and Sauternes crème caramel.

Directions: Behind Dorchester Hotel just off Hill St, nr Berkeley Sq.

27A Hay's Mews W1X 7RJ
Map: C3
Tel: 0171 4993331
Fax: 0171 4995368
Chef: Graham Grafton
Owner: David Levin
Cost: Alc £28. H/wine £12
Times: Noon-last L 2.30pm/7pm-last D 11pm. Closed L Sat, Xmas-New Year, Bhs
Additional: Children welcome; ✪ dishes
Seats: 110
Credit cards: ▩ ▩ ▩ ▩ ▩ ▩

Green's Restaurant & Oyster Bar

A busy, well-run restaurant with a strong clubby atmosphere brought about no doubt by the dark look of mahogany and leather booths and a strong male following. The menu offers a well balanced choice of fish and meat dishes, changes according to the season, and generally offers a traditional English-based repertoire, with modern touches. Native oysters, of course, as well as crab bisque, smoked cod's roe, and potted shrimps, with main courses of salmon fishcakes with tomato sauce, Dorset crab, bangers and mash with parsnip purée and port wine sauce, and calves' liver and bacon with mash and onion gravy. In a more up-to-date vein, excellent scallops, lightly grilled and served with a crisp rocket salad and a 'flavoursome' gazpacho dressing, opened a spring lunch. Prime quality noisettes of lamb followed, served on a bed of broad bean purée with a light smoked bacon jus. Puddings are limited to a few tarts, ice creams and sorbets; there's more custom here for the superb British cheeses from Paxton and Whitfield, and the selection of ports and dessert wines.

36 Duke Street SW1Y 6DF
Map: C3
Tel: 0171 9304566
Fax: 0171 4917463
Chef: Dean Peck
Owner: Simon Parker Bowles
Cost: Alc £30. H/wine £12 ☺
Times: Noon-last L 3pm/6pm-last D 11pm. Closed Sun (May-Aug), 25-26 Dec, 31 Dec
Additional: Bar meals; Children welcome; ✪ dishes
Seats: 70. Private dining room 24-36
Smoking: Air-conditioning
Credit cards: ▩ ▩ ▩ ▩ ▩

Directions: Opposite the Cavendish Hotel

Grosvenor House, Café Nico

Grosvenor House Park Lane W1A 3AA
Map: B3
Tel: 0171 4996363
Fax: 0171 4933341
Chef: Michael Glynn
Owners: Forte-Granada
Cost: Fixed-price L & D £29.50 H/wine £17.50
Additional: Bar food; Sunday L; Children welcome; ✪ dishes
Seats: 100. Private suites 20-120. Jacket and tie preferred
Smoking: Air-conditioning
Accommodation: 459 en suite
Credit cards: ▩ ▩ ▩ ▩ ▩

It's a large, strikingly light room, with massive windows facing onto the rush of Park Lane. Café Nico is on a split level with a balustrade on two sides separating off the lower level where there are also tables, and a bar counter with stools. As the name implies, Nico Ladenis, whose Chez Nico (see entry) is next door, takes more than just a passing interest in Grosvenor House Hotel's main restaurant; he creates the menus and supervises the kitchen. The fixed-price lunch and dinner menu offers a well-balanced selection of brasserie staples, from an excellent, simply grilled fillet of Dover sole with tartare sauce, best end of lamb with provençale vegetables, and old favourites such as fillet steak au poivre, to a contemporary reworking of the likes of crispy duck confit served here with oriental sauce and fresh orange. Crème brûlée with marinated fresh fruit vies with chocolate marquise as the dessert of choice.

Directions: Nearest Tubes – Marble Arch, Hyde Park Corner

Halcyon Hotel ❀❀❀

81 Holland Park W11 3RZ
Map GtL: C3
Tel: 0171 2215411
Fax: 0171 2298516
Chef: Martin Hadden
Cost: *Alc* £39.50, fixed-price L £23 (2 courses)/D £29 (2 courses). H/wine £12
Times: Noon-last L 2.30pm/7pm-last D 10.30pm. Closed Sat L, between Xmas & New Year's Eve, Bhs.
Additional: Bar food; Sunday lunch; Children welcome; ❹ dishes
Seats: 55. Private dining room 12
Smoking: No pipes in dining room; Air conditioning
Accommodation: 43 en suite
Credit cards: 🔲 🔲 🔲 🔲 🔲 🔲

The setting is two imposing and smartly restored Belle Epoque town houses in a discreet location in the shade of leafy Holland Park – a cool retreat for those in the know and with money to spend. Dining takes place in The Room – a basement restaurant with a delightful ornamental garden and terrace for summer days. Chef Martin Hadden is a protégé of Nico Ladenis and he has learned his craft well; clarity, technical accomplishment and a dedication to top-drawer ingredients are his trademarks. Of course, luxuries turn up with relentless regularity in, say, a rosette of smoked salmon with caviar, calves' sweetbreads with morels and Parma ham, as well as foie gras in various guises (perhaps in a beautifully contrasting warm salad with caramelised oranges, or as a stuffing for breast of chicken). Half a dozen bread rolls and classy canapés are serious tone-setters, while the short concise menu could open with a rosette of scallops with fresh pasta or noisettes of pig's trotter with truffle oil, before moving on to braised shin of veal with Madeira sauce, noisettes of lamb with a herb crust or a 'busy but effective' dish comprising grilled sea bass with fennel cannelloni and a scarlet cherry tomato filled with basil purée. High levels of expertise are also evident in desserts such as a 'precise' chocolate tart with the finest of pastry served with pistachio ice cream. Espresso is excellent, petit fours are neatly done.

Directions: 200 metres up Holland Park Ave from Shepherds Bush roundabout. 2 mins walk from Holland Park Tube

The Halkin Hotel

Halkin Street Belgravia SW1X 7DJ
Map GtL: C2
Tel: 0171 3331000
Fax: 0171 3331100
Chef: Stefano Cavallini
Cost: Alc £50, fixed-price L £18 (2 courses). H/wine £16.50
Times: 12.30pm-last L 2.30pm/7.30pm-last D 11pm. Closed L Sat, L Sun, Bhs
Additional: Bar food; Sunday L; Children welcome; ❸ dishes
Seats: 45. Private dining room 30
Smoking: No pipes and cigars; air-conditioning
Accommodation: 41 en suite
Credit cards: ▬ ▦ ▭ ▼ ▣ ◖

The Halkin is sleek, chic and as cool as they come. A vase containing a single long-stemmed rose graces each table, waiters in dark navy Armani suits and buttoned-up tieless shirts parade around the stylishly modern Milanese dining room. Swags of pale green cloth are insouciantly draped over poles at the arched windows, semi-circular old paintings of formal gardens occupy one wall, a mosaic shows up on the floor. Stefano Cavallini produces what he calls 'essential Italian cuisine'. Interpretation is what counts here. Marinated red mullet is served with a salad of fennel and oranges, crab tortellini sits in a consommé with dried ceps and asparagus, while roast fillet of veal appears in straightforward guise with Parma ham, potatoes, tomatoes and olives. A light lunch on a sunny day began triumphantly with a memorable frothy chicken soup with truffles that had a real 'farmyard' aroma about them. High aspirations indeed. What followed was barely less impressive: rabbit ravioli with wild mushrooms and chunks of tender lobster was served in a pleasing mushroom jus, while a casserole of monkfish on a bed of young vegetables (asparagus, fresh peas, baby broad beans and slender carrots) came with soft poached quails' eggs in a delicate fishy broth. To finish, there was a prettily presented charlotte with thin slices of apple encasing a soft cinnamon-scented rice interior, accompanied by cinnamon ice cream. As a finale, a decent cup of espresso arrived with five different chocolates, three tuiles and candied orange peel. Sommelier Bruno Besa has selected an extensive range of Italian wines, listed regionally. Take advice and try something unusual but don't be mislead into thinking of them as a cheap option, there are some real classics included. A page of 'Halkin Selected' wines offers most by the glass. France gets a brief look, the rest of the world a token visit.

Signature dishes: Sliced veal fillet with tuna and mayonnaise sauce; monkfish casserole served with summer vegetables, poached quails' eggs and black truffle; scallop and chicken consommé; duck ravioli with Savoy cabbage and foie gras.

Directions: Between Belgrave Square & Grosvenor Place. Access via Chapel St into Headfort Place and L into Halkin St

The Hampshire ❀

See Where London Meets page 159

Hilaire ✿✿✿

68 Old Brompton Road SW7 3LQ
Map: A1
Tel: 0171 5848993
Fax: 0171 5812949
Chef: Bryan Webb
Owners: Bryan Webb, Dick Pyle
Cost: Fixed-price L £18.50-£23 (2-3 courses)/D £28.50-£34 (2-3 courses).
H/wine from £12.50
Times: 12.15pm-last L 2.30pm/6.30pm-last D 11.30pm.
Closed L Sat, Sun. Bhs
Additional: Children welcome
Seats: 60. Private dining room 50 + 25
Smoking: No pipes & cigars; air-conditioning
Credit cards: ▆ ▆ ▆ ▆ ▆

Directions: On N side of Old Brompton Rd about half way between South Kensington Tube and junction with Queensgate

Bryan Webb continues to provide a consistently high standard of robust, modern European cooking at this diminutive shop-front restaurant. Although the Mediterranean provides a rich and inventive seam in, for instance, minestrone of spring vegetables and pesto, roast sea bass with leek risotto and red wine sauce, and a braised shin of veal 'osso buco' with saffron risotto and gremolata, running through the repertoire is a more exotic vein, seen in the likes of rare-seared tuna with oriental salad and soya dressing, and braised Moroccan-style lamb with couscous. 'It is comforting to note that the operation barely misses a beat when Bryan Webb is not at the helm', commented one inspector on just such an occasion. That inspection lunch proved typical of the style so prevalent in the kitchen. Webb has little time for fancy excess, preferring to allow the quality of his ingredients to shine through. Perfectly cooked home-made tagliatelle, served in a plain white bowl, with rabbit, mustard sauce and wild mushrooms was a good balance of well-made sauce and morsels of rabbit. Oysters au gratin with Stilton and laverbread was another inspired combination with the sea-like taste of the oysters perfectly offset by the piquant creamy Stilton topping; a selection of bread from Sally Clarke was just what it needed to mop up excess juices. Braised hare with elderberry and juniper sauce, sampled as a main course, was as hearty as this kind of robust dish demanded – very rich indeed. Its counterpart was a dish of calves' liver, with 'a light as a feather' potato pancake, tiny onions and crisp strips of bacon and deep-fried sage. Desserts included a moreish and very creamy chilled rice pudding with prunes, and a sliver of chocolate tart served with a pot of alcoholic St Emilion mousse. Cheeses are provided by Neal's Yard. Wines are listed by style rather than origin, so if you fancy a 'fragrant, fruity and aromatic white' there's a whole page to choose from. Each section yields some stars with many in the mid-price range. Prime examples include Vernaccia from Teruzzi & Puthod at £19 and Cape Mentelle's understated Cabernet Merlot at £21. A decent collection of halves rises above the merely token.
Signature dishes: Oysters with laverbread and Stilton; scallops, vegetable relish and rocket.

Hogarth Hotel ✿

See Where London Meets page 159

Holiday Inn Crowne Plaza

See Where London Meets page 159

Holiday Inn Mayfair ✿

See Where London Meets page 159

Hotel Inter-Continental ✿✿✿

1 Hamilton Place Hyde Park Corner
W1V 0QY
Map: C2
Tel: 0171 3188577
Fax: 0171 4910926
Chef: Peter Kromberg
Owner: Inter-Continental Hotels
Cost: *Alc* £40, fixed-price L £28.50/D
£47 (7 courses). H/wine £15.
Times: 12.30pm-last L 3pm/7pm-last
D 10.30pm. Closed L Sat, D Sun,
Mon, 2 wks after Xmas
Additional: Bar food; Sunday L;
✿ dishes
Seats: 80. Jacket & tie preferred
Smoking: No-smoking area; no pipes
in dining room; air-conditioning
Accommodation: 460 en suite
Credit cards: all major cards accepted

The jewel in this modern hotel's crown is Le Soufflé, where
Peter Kromberg builds dishes based on simplicity and classic
skills. The signature soufflés, both savoury and sweet, are
perennial favourites, but what is outstanding is the finesse of
the repertoire in general, the light touch, and the sense of
balance. A tiny amuse-bouche of duck terrine and some
excellent breads from the trolley opened a well reported April
dinner. This took in a delicate salmon and avocado soufflé,
nicely set off by crème fraîche and chives. Next came a turbot
fillet with langoustine jus flavoured with a hint of cauliflower,
caviar and coriander, set on a smooth confit of creamed potato.
Truffled free-range chicken with basmati and morel mushroom
rice and goose liver scored equally well. Bread-and-butter
pudding was far from traditional, it was more of a spicy torte
with a rich and complementary fig syrup sauce. A good
number of wines are available by the glass, and the extensive
'Sommeliers Selection' offers 20 well-priced wines, over eight
below £20. A comprehensive run through Burgundy has
something to suit all pockets, and the Bordeaux section is
extensive with some interesting rare vintages; dust off your
octogenarian grandfather and spoil him with the Château
Latour 1918 at £680, or perhaps one of several more moderate
choices from this section for under £30. A tremendous half-
bottle section presents opportunity to be adventurous.
Signature dishes: Pot au feu of salmon with root vegetables;
charlotte of partridge with truffles and Savoy cabbage; Galette
of foie gras.

Directions: On Hyde Park Corner. Nearest Tube – Hyde Park
Corner

The Hothouse

An architecturally interesting brasserie located in a former spice warehouse majoring in wooden floors, exposed bricks, timbers and an eclectic decor. Informal atmosphere. Modish menu lists burgers, chargrills plus lobster and clam chowder, and confit of duck with ginger and pear compote.

Smoking: No-smoking area; air-conditioning
Credit cards: ▬ ▬ ▬ ▬ ⓒ

Directions: Nearest tube stations Tower Bridge and Wapping

78-80 Wapping Lane E1 9NF
Map GtL: D3
Tel: 0171 4884797
Fax: 0171 4889500
Chef: Marc Smith
Owner: Nigel Fenner-Fownes
Cost: Alc £20, fixed-price L & D £13.95. ☺ H/wine £10.50.
Times: Last L 3pm/D 11pm. Closed Sat L, Sun, Bhs
Additional: Bar meals; Children welcome; ◑ dishes

Hudson's Restaurant ✿

Victorian-style dining-room on the ground floor of the Sherlock Holmes Museum; evening diners can take advantage of free entry to the museum. Costumed staff serve salmagundi, Baskerville game pie, traditional mixed grill and Mrs Hudson's home-made bread-and-butter pudding. Mystery murders not included.

Credit cards: ▬ ▬ ▬ ▬ ▣ ⓒ

Directions: L towards Regents Park (Baker Street N side), next to Sherlock Holmes Museum

221B Baker Street NW1 6XE
Map: B4
Tel: 0171 9353130
Fax: 0171 2243005
Chefs: T Woneak, E Cole
Owner: Linda Riley
Cost: Alc £20-30, fixed-price L&D £16.95. ☺ H/wine £9.95.
Times: Last L 3pm/D 10.30pm (10pm Sun). Closed 25 Dec
Additional: Sunday L; Children welcome; ◑ dishes

Hyatt Carlton Tower Hotel, Grissini ✿✿   NEW

Cadogan Place SW1X 9PY
Map: B2
Tel: 0171 2351234
Telephone for details

Directions: Nearest Tube – Knightsbridge

Grissini has replaced the old Chelsea Room. Decorated in shades of lime and lilac (with staff uniforms to match), there's an airy, alfresco feel enhanced by the conservatory-style windows looking over Cadogan Square. Antipasti can start with pan-fried prawns wrapped in zucchini with crisp Parma ham and bisque vinaigrette, soups include a varied seafood and fish soup with toasted garlic croutons. Pasta and risotto can be taken either as first or main courses – the choice includes sautéed orrecchiette with broccoli and foie gras, and guinea-fowl tortelloni with wild mushrooms, asparagus and shaved Parmesan. Otherwise there could be pan-fried turbot with braised fennel, potato and Ligurian olives, and sautéed lamb cutlets encased in basil mousse with a balsamic reduction. Try the unusual pineapple carpaccio – thin slices of fruit spiced with saffron and ginger.

Hyde Park Hotel
Mandarin Oriental

Once used as residential chambers for gentlemen in Victorian times, this stately hotel with great views over Hyde Park has been brought smartly into the 90s through its new owners, the Mandarin Oriental Group. On the Park offers a menu with strong Italian influences, where a meal starts with a 'big choice of bread off the trolley' and a drizzle of olive oil. Roasted scallops on a broad bean purée and sweetcorn broth, roast breast of squab pigeon with hollowed out fondant potato (filled with bean purée), lentil and bean ragout and truffle sauce and hot chocolate soufflé with Grand Marnier ice cream, formed the components of one winter dinner. A well reported meal in summer included artichoke and roast garlic terrine, and tender best end of lamb with a fricassee of mixed beans and pulses, rosemary sauce and great spinach.

66 Knightsbridge SW1X 7LA
Map: B2
Tel: 0171 2352000
Fax: 0171 2354552
Chef: Ralph Porciani
Cost: Alc £43, fixed-price L £27. H/wine £19
Times: 12.30pm-last L 2.30pm/7.30pm-last D 11pm
Additional: Bar meals; Sunday L; Children welcome; ◑ dishes
Seats: 96. Private dining room 24
Smoking: Air-conditioning
Accommodation: 185 en suite
Credit cards: 🖬 🖼 🖃 🖬 💷 🖸

Directions: Nearest Tube – Knightsbridge

Ikkyu ✿   NEW

Scruffy basement but the Japanese food is excellent. A Japanese menu with basic English translations such as 'grilled sardines' and 'hot brown noodles', gives little indication of the quality of the dishes, or the authenticity. At a recent meal our inspector enjoyed a yakitori of grilled gizzards, hearts and livers.

67 Tottenham Court Road W1
Map: C3
Tel: 0171 6369280
Chef: Mr Kawaguchi
Owner: Mrs Komori
Cost: Alc £20. H/wine £9.50. ☺
Times: Last L 2.30pm/D 10.30pm. Closed L Sun, Sat

Additional: Children welcome; ◑ dishes
Smoking: No smoking; air-conditioning
Credit cards: 🖬 🖼 🖃 💷

Directions: Nearest Tube – Goodge Street

Imperial City ✿

Royal Exchange Cornhill EC3V 3LL
Map: G4
Tel: 0171 6263437
Fax: 0171 3380125
Chef: Chen Fatt Keong
Owner: Oriental Restaurants Group plc
Cost: Alc £30, fixed-price L&D £15.50-£24.95. ☺ H/wine £9.90.
Times: 11.30am–last D 8.30pm. Closed Sat, Sun, Xmas
Additional: Children welcome; ◑ dishes.
Smoking: Air-conditioning
Credit cards: 🖬 🖼 🖃 🖬 💷 🖸

Traditional favourites combine with Ken Lo-inspired innovative dishes at this popular Chinese in an old vault under the Royal Exchange – complete with bonsai bushes and ornamental rockery. Steamed salmon with black bean sauce and crackling Northern-style chicken with garlic have both been praised. Good quality ingredients and no MSG.

Directions: Royal Exchange, off Cornhill. Nearest Tube – Bank.

Indian Connoisseurs ❀

Tandoori lobster jalfrazi, khashi gazar (goat with baby carrots), and ashwi gosht (lamb with pumpkin) are just three of the novel dishes on the menu at this informal Bangladeshi restaurant. In more familiar territory, you can also get shish kebab, chicken tikka makhani and prawn bhuna. Freshly cooked breads, decent rice.

Smoking: No-smoking area. Air-conditioning
Credit cards:

Directions: Off Praed Street close to BR Paddington. Nearest Tubes: Paddington & Edgware Road. Opp St Mary's Hospital

8 Norfolk Place W2 1QL
Map: A4
Tel: 0171 402 3299
Chef: Kabir Miah
Owners: M Ahmed, A Rahman & K Rahman
Cost: *Alc* £15, fixed-price L £6.50/D £10.95. ☺ H/wine £6.95.
Times: Last L 2.20pm/D 11.45pm. Closed 25 Dec
Additional: Sunday L; No children under 11; ❹ dishes

Interlude ❀❀

The atmosphere is fussy and formal, service selective depending on the perceived status of the diner, and on our visit, a new chef had not really settled in. The ambitious menu reads well, and starts trendily with a cappuccino of lentil soup. A chicken liver parfait was of beautiful consistency but lacking in all flavour; the accompanying fig chutney, however, was crunchy and spicy. Equally, a potage of scallops and oysters was less than inspiring – a milky broth with only a distant flavour of fish, in which sat a small sad scallop and a tired grey oyster. Roasted guinea fowl with Sauternes jus, whilst tender and reasonably succulent, lacked a good, underlying gamey flavour but a sweetcorn risotto was firm and nicely crunchy. Seared grey mullet stuffed with a very pink sole mousse, served in a pool of pesto oil, came accompanied by some decent, light pasta. Chocolate marquise with coffee bean sabayon and praline ice cream, and mille-feuille of raspberry were both good.

Directions: Oxford Street end of Charlotte Street. Tubes – Tottenham Court Road, Goodge Street

5 Charlotte Street W1P 1HD
Map: C4
Tel: 0171 6370222
Fax: 0171 6370224
Chef: Anand Sastry
Owners: Charles Ullmann, Anand Sastry
Cost: *Alc* £45, fixed-price L £17.60/D £55 (7 courses). H/wine £14
Times: Noon-last L 2.30pm/7pm-last D 11pm. Closed L Sat, Sun, between Xmas/New Year, 2 wks Aug
Additional: No children under 12; ❹ dishes
Seats: 71. Private dining room 16
Smoking: No-smoking area; air-conditioning
Credit cards: ▬ ▦ ▦ 💳 🅒

I-Thai ❀❀

NEW

It is the ultimate in minimalist chic (wear black, anything else clashes with the decor), and chef Michael Hruschka probably has a quite a time with Lady Weinberg's tough presentation demands (all the food comes in black lacquer boxes), but he knows what he's doing in the kitchen. Skills honed at the Mandarin Peking, and at the Savoy, means that the complexities of East-meets-West cuisine are handled with a tremendous sense of balance. Honey-spiced duck with coriander raita, and sea bass, marinated overnight in oil with kaffir lime leaf, garlic, and ginger, cooked en papillotte, with pesto risotto, were both outstanding. And three different sorbets – apple and cardamom, passion fruit, and lemon grass and raisin – had the 'crusty business man at the next table, who had proclaimed it all girl's food, go into the kind of ecstasy that he had previously reserved for seeing the Princess of Wales three tables away.'

Hempel Hotel
31-5 Craven Hill Gardens W2
Tel: 0171 2989000
Chef: Michael Hruschka
Telephone for details

The Ivy ❀❀❀

'Arriving half-an-hour late due to heavy traffic, I wondered if they had re-let the table. I had booked three weeks in advance

1 West Street Covent Garden WC2H 9NE
Map: D3
Tel: 0171 8364751

and they could only fit us in at a table in the bar. Luckily there was the table and they hadn't doubted my word,' reported a relieved seasoned inspector who went on to enjoy the immaculate service, unpretentious atmosphere and the 'best meal of the week'. The Ivy is in an unassuming building, wedge shaped, with a real buzz to the atmosphere. The menu style reveals a French brasserie influence and global inspirations. English favourites take in the likes of salmon fish cakes, then there's curried chicken, bang-bang chicken and a selection of pasta dishes, plus some more trendy items such as seared yellow tuna. The directness of much of the cooking is welcome and dishes can have a spare luxury about them which works well. Leek and trompette tart, for example, was lifted by a drizzle of truffle oil. Calves' liver and bacon was everything it should be, with 'lovely' mash and crispy, streaky bacon. Desserts too, work well. Baked mascarpone custard with rhubarb was a close second to a sensational cappuccino brûlée. Espresso was good and strong, but it's a pity the Ivy truffles were an extra £2 for two. Both The Ivy and its sibling, Le Caprice, have certainly mastered the art of a concise wine list; there's something for everyone. Surprisingly reasonable (many are under £25) with a good number of halves all available by the glass.

Signature dishes: Champagne risotto with truffles; roast poulet des Laudes; iced Scandinavian berries with white chocolate sauce.

Fax: 0171 2409333
Chefs: Mark Hix, Des McDonald
Owners: Jeremy King, Christopher Corbin
Cost: *Alc* £35, fixed-price L £14.50 (Sat-Sun only). H/wine £9.50. ☺
Times: Noon-last L 3pm/5.30pm-last D midnight. Closed D 24 Dec, 25-26 Dec, 1 Jan,
Additional: Sunday L; Children welcome; ✪ dishes
Seats: 100. Private dining room 20-60
Smoking: Air-conditioning
Credit cards:

Directions: Nearest Tube: Leicester Square & Covent Garden

Jason's Restaurant ❀❀

Opposite 60 Blomfield Road W9 2PD
Map GtL: C3
Tel: 0171 2866752
Fax: 0171 2664332
Chef: Sylvain Howing Cheong
Owner: Anthony Hopkins
Cost: *Alc* £35, fixed-price L £14.95 (2 courses)/D £18.95 (2 courses). H/wine £9.95
Times: Noon-last L 3pm/6.30pm-last D 10.30pm. Closed D Sun, 25-26 Dec, 1 Jan
Additional: Bar food; Sunday lunch; Children welcome; ✪ dishes
Seats: 40.
Credit cards:

Mauritian cooking in Little Venice is the unlikely prospect in this cosmopolitan fish restaurant hard by the Grand Union Canal. Inside is a high-ceilinged modern room with brick walls and lots of tables; outside is a sun-trap terrace that draws the crowds when the weather obliges. Excellent service keeps the mood up-beat. The cooking has a colonial undercurrent but the flavours and spices are straight out of the Far East and the Pacific Rim. In practice this means strong creamy sauces as well as exotic ingredients which are used to telling effect with all kinds of piscine delights from near and far. Soupe de poissons, feuilleté de homard, grilled sea bass with fennel and salmon with champagne sauce highlight the French connection, but it's worth trying out crunchy soft-shell crab with Creole sauce, king prawns with white wine and wasabi, parrot fish with ginger and spring onions, or even grouper and vacqua.

Vegetarian alternatives are also available, while desserts tend towards pear tarte Tatin and crêpes suzettes.

Directions: Off Edgware Road. Nearest Tube – Warwick Avenue

Jimmy Beez ✿

Buzzy hang-out in cool Portobello Road. The joint jumps when live jazz is playing, but crowds pour in throughout the day for non-stop food that hits the 90s button head on. The menu globe trots for all that is currently in vogue: tempura artichokes with sweet and sour pak choy greens, pan-seared sea bass on black potatoes with 'fennel slaw' and red wine fish jus.

Smoking: No-smoking area; no pipes & cigars; air-conditioning
Credit cards: ▆ ▆ ▆ ▆

Directions: From Notting Hill Tube – 1.5 miles down Portobello Rd, from Ladbroke Grove – 2 min walk up Oxford or Cambridge Gardens.

303 Portobello Road W10
Map GtL: C3
Tel: 0171 9649100
Fax: 0171 9649200
Chefs: William Panton, Gary Lee
Owner: James Breslaw
Cost: Alc £25. H/wine £9
Times: Open 11am-last D 11pm. Closed 24-27 Dec, 31 Dec-2 Jan
Additional: Bar food; Sunday L; Children welcome; ◕ dishes

Kai Mayfair ✿✿

65 South Audley Street W1Y 5FD
Map: C3
Tel: 0171 4938988/8507
Fax: 0171 4931456
Chef: Vincent Looi
Owner: Bernard Yeoh
Cost: Alc £40. H/wine £15
Times: Noon-last L 2.15pm (Sat & Sun 12.30pm-3pm)/6.30pm-last D 10.45pm (Sun 10.30pm)
Additional: Children welcome. ◕ dishes.
Seats: 100. Private dining rooms 7 & 12
Smoking: Air-conditioning
Credit cards: ▆ ▆ ▆ ▆ ▆ ▆

In its new incarnation, this legendary Mayfair Chinese restaurant is one of the smartest and glitziest in town. The waitresses have swapped their traditional long dresses for ultra-smart beige trousers and black jackets, and the menu reads like a gastronome's tour of the regions – complete with historical notes and curious names: 'The Whims and Fancies of the Empress', 'Buddha Jumps Over the Wall', 'Mermaids in the Mist' and so on. 'Parcels of Prosperity' (miniature 'croissants' filled with king prawns) made a good impression on our inspector, as did bang-bang chicken with a nut sauce. More familiar-sounding dishes such as roast duck with pineapple are capably handled and the menu also deals in luxuries such as shark's fin, abalone, turbot and Dover sole without neglecting sweet and sour pork or sizzling fillet of beef. Service is efficient and well supervised. Jasmine tea is a fragrant brew, otherwise drink Chinese beer, sake or something from the weighty wine list.

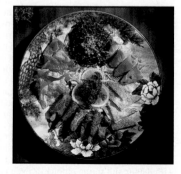

Directions: Marble Arch onto Park Lane, situated behind Dorchester, or Oxford St into N Audley St, pass American Embassy into S Audley St

Kalamara's Restaurant

A bustling, family-run restaurant, serving a wide range of highly-praised Greek dishes. Typical starters include 'varkoula' (baked courgettes topped with fresh salmon and béchamel sauce), and 'melitzanes me scordalia' (fried aubergines with a tangy garlic dip). The wine list includes several from Greece.

Additional: Children welcome; 🍃 dishes
Smoking: Air-conditioning
Credit cards: ▆ ▆ ▆ ▆

Directions: Nearest Tube Bayswater or Queensway

76-78 Inverness Mews W2 3JQ
Map GtL: C3
Tel: 0171 7279122
Fax: 0171 2219411
Chef: Antonio Jiminez
Owner: Mr F Ridha
Cost: *Alc* £22, fixed-price L/D £16. ☺
H/wine £9.50.
Times: Last L 2.30pm/D midnight.
Closed L Sat, L Sun

Kastoori

The Thanki family came to the UK from Uganda and the menu in their bright, spacious vegetarian restaurant includes many recipes from Kathia Wadi (a region of Gujerat where tomatoes grow in abundance) as well as several 'Indo-African' specialities. Typically enticing dishes might be green pepper curry given extra bite with peanuts and sesame seeds, chilli banana, and an assortment of green leaves in yogurt, onion and chilli sauce. Strangest of all, however, is the 'Thanki européene' (a 'Euroveg special' that includes leeks, rhubarb and much more). Recommended dishes from the main section of the menu are crisp sev puri, which are eaten whole and 'explode in the mouth with a range of textures and flavours', and tomato curry served with a thin paratha. Bhajias (including a version with cassava), samosas, various dosas and the like are also in evidence and the range of breads is worth exploring. Lassi, falooda and mango shakes are non-alcoholic alternatives to Kingfisher beer and wine.

Directions: Between Tooting Bec & Tooting Broadway tube stations

188 Upper Tooting Road
SW17 7EJ
Map GtL: C2
Tel: 0181 7677027
Chef: Manos Thanki
Owner: Dinesu Thanki
Cost: H/wine £7.25. ☺
Times: 12.30pm-last L 2.30pm/6pm-last D 10.30pm. Closed L Mon, L Tue, 1 wk mid Jan
Additional: Children welcome; 🍃 dishes
Seats: 82
Smoking: Air-conditioning
Credit cards: ▆ ▆ ▆

Ken Lo's Memories of China

A pleasant harbour-side restaurant with great views of the Thames and marina. Good Cantonese and Szechuan dishes feature on the menu. A typical meal might include vegetarian spring rolls, quick-fried beef in oyster sauce with mange-touts, and Szechuan hot-fried chilli chicken. Service is attentive and professional.

Additional: Sunday L; Bar meals L; Children welcome; 🍃 dishes
Smoking: Air-conditioning
Credit cards: ▆ ▆ ▆ ▆ ▆

Directions: King's Road, World's End. Turn L at Lots Road

Chelsea Harbour Yard
SW10 0XD
Map GtL: C2
Tel: 0171 3524953/4
Fax: 0171 3512096
Chef: Lam Tran
Owner: Michael Lo
Cost: *Alc* £28, fixed-price L £15. ☺
Times: Last L 2.15pm/D 11pm.
Closed L Sat, 25 Dec, 1 Jan

Ken Lo's Memories of China Restaurant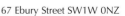

Ancient poems are inscribed on the walls of this simple, neat restaurant, with tables separated by wooden screens and a menu that includes some original ideas as well as an overview of Chinese regional cooking in dishes such as crispy soft-shell crab, iron-plate sizzled salmon, and Cantonese sweet and sour

67 Ebury Street SW1W 0NZ
Map: C2
Tel: 0171 7307734
Fax: 0171 7302992
Chef/Owner: K P But
Cost: *Alc* £25, fixed-price L £19.50/D £24.50. ☺ H/wine £13.50.

pork. One recommended starter is Peking kuo-tieh dumplings, steamed and sautéed and filled with finely minced meat and served with a vinegar/ginger dip. Other choices could include fragrant braised aubergine, fresh scallops steamed in the shell, served with hot, spicy black bean sauce, and bang-bang chicken, a cold Szechuan dish with a spicy, nutty sauce. Peking quick-fried diced chicken with cashew nuts had tender pieces of breast in a well-flavoured sweet sauce, served with lightly cooked mixed vegetables and moist, freshly cooked steamed rice, but a Mongolian barbecue of shredded lamb in lettuce puffs was disappointingly dry.

Directions: At the junction of Ebury Street and Eccleston Street. Nearest Tubes – Sloane Square & Victoria

Times: Noon-last L 2.30pm/7pm-last D 11pm. Closed L Sun, Bhs
Seats: 100. Private dining room 20
Smoking: Air-conditioning
Credit cards: 🟦 🟥 🟩 ✈ 💳 🟢

Kensington Park Thistle ❀

See Where London Meets page 160

Kensington Place ❀❀

Judging by the numbers of similar establishments that have appeared in the capital of late, it's clear that imitation really is the sincerest form of flattery. Kensington Place has style by the plateful. Through the glass frontage you can view the action in the buzzy, sprawling dining room that looks like a cross between Conran and Ikea. The pace is fast, the conversation loud and the food stays reliably on target. Breads deserve a special mention and the daily menu plunders the world larder in search of novelty, interest and good value. Grilled scallops with pea purée and mint vinaigrette is something of a classic, and rightly so. Otherwise the kitchen takes on board such things as chick pea and pancetta soup and steamed halibut with red chard and basil oil. Puddings are pretty offerings such as pear tarte Tatin or apple and sultana fritters.

201/205 Kensington Church Street
W8 7LX
Map GtL: C3
Tel: 0171 7273184
Fax: 0171 2292025
Chef: Rowley Leigh
Owners: Nick Smallwood, Simon Slater, Rowley Leigh
Cost: Alc £25, fixed-price L £14.50. ☺ H/wine £11.50.
Times: Noon-last L 3pm (3.30pm weekends)/6.30pm-last D 11.45pm (10.15pm Sun). Closed 3 days Xmas
Additional: Sunday L; Children welcome; ◑ dishes
Seats: 140
Smoking: No pipes; air-conditioning

Directions: 150 yds before junction of Kensington Church St & Notting Hill Gate

Laicram Thai ❀❀

Thai wooden carvings and colourful floating candles on each table add to the authentic atmosphere in this pleasantly appointed neighbourhood restaurant, and the mood is helped

1 Blackheath Grove
Blackheath SE3
Map GtL: E2
Tel: 0181 8524710
Chef/Owner: Mrs S Dhirabutra

along by waitresses in full costume. The menu covers the essential elements of Thai cuisine – from spicy salads to noodles – and there is a useful section for vegetarians. Good dishes from a recent meal included a plate of mixed starters (tender satays, fish cakes, steamed dumplings in garlic sauce), delicately spicy *tom kha gai* soup and a decent version of *gaeng phed ped yang* (roast duck curry). Our inspector also sampled a very pleasant mixed dessert (not normally on the menu) consisting of a wedge of Thai custard, a quenelle of sticky rice with yellow bean and coconut, and coconut pudding in a tiny bamboo basket. Jasmine tea and Thai beer suit the food, otherwise pick something from the short, mainly European wine list.

Directions: Off the main shopping street, in a side road near the Post Office. Opposite the station

Landmark Hotel

222 Marylebone Road NW1 6TQ
Map: E4
Tel: 0171 6318000
Fax: 0171 6318088
Chef: Georg Heise
Cost: Alc £35, fixed-price L £21.50/D £36.50. ☺ H/wine £17.50
Times: Noon-3pm/7pm-11pm. Closed L Sat, D Sun
Additional: Bar meals; Sunday L; Children welcome; ⍟ dishes
Seats: 80. Private dining 30
Smoking: No-smoking area; air-conditioning
Accommodation: 304 en suite
Credit cards: ▦ ▦ ▦ ▦ ▦

It is hard to imagine that this exciting-looking hotel was one a railway hotel, or indeed a block of offices, in previous incarnations. The centrepiece of this modern, top-class establishment is the atrium, discreetly lined with a range of shops and boutiques and often filled with live music; the place is busy and inviting by day, wonderfully atmospheric by night. The Dining Room offers an inventice, head-on mix of east and western influences. This translates as marinated quail's breast with warm potato salad and pepper-sherry vinegar sauce, baked halibut with pumpkin and ginger with stir-fry vegetables, and first-rate tiramisu (the output by the pâtissier is spot on). There's a short wine list with a few halves.

Directions: Directly opposite Marylebone BR & Tube stations

The Lanesborough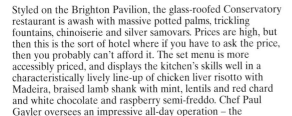

Hyde Park Corner SW1X 7TA
Map: C3
Tel: 0171 2595599
Fax: 0171 2595606
Chef: Paul Gayler
Cost: Alc £42, fixed-price L&D £23.50. H/wine £16.50
Times: Noon-last L 2.30pm/6.30pm-last D midnight.
Additional: Sunday L; Bar meals; Children welcome; ⍟ dishes
Seats: 106. Private dining rooms

Styled on the Brighton Pavilion, the glass-roofed Conservatory restaurant is awash with massive potted palms, trickling fountains, chinoiserie and silver samovars. Prices are high, but then this is the sort of hotel where if you have to ask the price, then you probably can't afford it. The set menu is more accessibly priced, and displays the kitchen's skills well in a characteristically lively line-up of chicken liver risotto with Madeira, braised lamb shank with mint, lentils and red chard and white chocolate and raspberry semi-freddo. Chef Paul Gayler oversees an impressive all-day operation – the

(The first review, top left, corresponds to:)
Cost: Alc £20
Times: Noon-last L 2.30pm/6pm-last D 11pm. Closed Mon, Bhs
Additional: Children welcome; ⍟ dishes
Seats: 50
Smoking: Air-conditioning
Credit cards: ▦ ▦ ▦ ▧ ▦

The Lanesborough

Smoking: Air-conditioning
Accommodation: 95 en suite
Credit cards: ▬ ▒ ▒ ▒

Directions: On Hyde Park Corner

breakfast selection alone is as long as many restaurant's entire menu, and includes kick-start dishes such as huevos rancheros with chorizo sausage and guacamole. Grilled chicken Caesar salad, grilled vegetable lasagne with coriander and roast garlic pesto, and Lanesborough fish and chips with saffron aïoli, bring some transatlantic flair to lunch-times; afternoon teas offer the works plus rare estate teas. Many dishes, such as goat's cheese feuilleté with roasted shallots, chargrilled Dover sole with scallion mash and caper oil, and spice roasted duckling with ginger and star anise cross-over between the lunch and dinner *cartes*. Throughout the year, there are a number of 'guest' menus, when Gayler works alongside visiting chefs. Our inspector chanced to arrive one night when the head chef from the Hassler Hotel in Rome was in situ, and enjoyed a highly accomplished meal of home-made fettucine with porcini mushrooms, fillet of sea bass in a potato crust scented with lemon and rosemary, with a light and creamy tea parfait for dessert. Special mention must also be made of the cocktail bar, under the impeccable supervision of Salvatore, where the list of vintage Cognac, whiskies and ports is unsurpassed.

Signature dishes: BBQ lamb rack with tabouleh, mint and chilli; crab spring roll with soy and ginger; steamed mussels with Asian pesto; corn-fed chicken with grilled asparagus, truffle and violette potatoes.

Langan's Brasserie ❀❀

The see-and-be-seen popularity of this bustling, legendary restaurant remains as high as ever – and the menu stays as impossibly long as ever too. Mainstays include Langan's bangers and mash and white onion sauce, roast duck with sage and onion stuffing and apple sauce, and their famous cod and chips. The cooking never reaches great heights, but is generally well-prepared, although it does tend to be speedily delivered. Our inspector enjoyed a meal of smoked duck with apple salad, followed by an excellent grilled fillet of sea bass served with a light and flavoursome garlic and butter sauce. Accompanying vegetables of broccoli, carrots and spinach were let down by some under-cooked boiled new potatoes. Poire Belle Hélène was the real thing, made with a whole poached pear, vanilla ice cream, fresh whipped cream and chocolate sauce.

Stratton Street W1X 5FD
Map: C3
Tel: 0171 4918822
Fax: 0171 4938309
Chefs: Dennis Mynott, Roy Smith
Owner: M. Caine
Cost: H/wine £9.50
Times: L 12.30-last L 3pm/D 6pm-
11.30pm Sun-Thurs (11.45pm
Fri,12.45am Sat). Closed Sun
Additional: Children welcome.
◑ dishes.
Seats: 200
Smoking: Air-conditioning
Credit cards: ▬ ▒ ▒ ▒

Directions: Stratton Street is about half-way along Piccadilly.
Nearest Tube – Green Park

The Langham Hilton ❀

See *Where London Meets* page 160

Launceston Place ❀❀

1A Launceston Place W8 5RL
Map: A2
Tel: 0171 9376912
Fax: 0171 9382412
Chef: Derek Francis
Owners: Nick Smallwood, Simon Slater
Cost: Fixed-price L/D (7pm-8pm Mon-Fri) £17.50. ☺ H/wine £10.50.
Times: 12.30pm-last L 2.30pm/7pm-last D 11.30pm. Closed L Sat, D Sun, Bhs
Additional: Sunday L (12.30pm-3pm); Children welcome; ✿ dishes
Seats: 85. Private dining room 12-22
Smoking: No pipes; air-conditioning
Credit cards: ▆ ▆ ▆ ▆ |C

'A smashing little haven away from the hustle and bustle of nearby Ken High', reports one inspector on this long-standing neighbourhood restaurant. Interesting art work on the walls, everything understated, and service quiet and professional, form a discreet backdrop to food that follows modern fashion, but from a kitchen that knows what it's about. Crab risotto comes with poached egg and hollandaise, grilled tuna with 'Sichuan' pepper and sweet and sour spring onions, for instance. The secret lies in top-notch ingredients, and good balance with no one flavour overpowering the others. Note an early summer lunch that took in home-made noodles tossed with wild asparagus, Parmesan and truffle oil, pan-fried salmon with blackened skin topmost 'cooked to a turn', with béarnaise sauce, a fine selection of cheeses in peak condition, and a strawberry and chocolate roulade.

Directions: Just south of Kensington Palace. Between Gloucester Road and High Street Kensington Tubes

Laurent ❀

Couscous holds centre stage in Laurent Farrugia's homely little front-room restaurant: the 'Royal version' is the full works and splendid with it. Brik a l'oeuf is the only starter, while desserts range from sorbets and ice creams to crêpes suzettes. Drink good strong coffee, mint tea or one of the beefy North African wines.

Smoking: No pipes and cigars
Credit cards: ▆ ▆ ▆ ▆

Directions: At junction of Finchley Rd with Cricklewood Lane. Nearest tube – Golders Green

428 Finchley Road NW2 2HY
Map GtL: C4
Tel: 0171 7943603
Chef/Owner: Laurent Farrugia
Cost: Alc £14. H/wine £9.20. ☺
Times: Last L 2pm/D 11pm. Closed Sun, 1st 3 wks Aug
Additional: Children welcome; ✿ dishes

Leith's Restaurant ❀ ❀ ❀

92 Kensington Park Road W11 2PN
Map GtL: C3
Tel: 0171 2294481
Fax: 0171 2211246
Chef: Alex Floyd
Owners: Leith's School of Food & Wine
Cost: Alc £42, fixed-price L £16.50/D £27.50. H/wine £15.50
Times: 12.15pm-last L 2.15pm/7pm-last D 11.30pm. Closed L Sat, Sun, L Mon, 2wks Xmas, 2 wks Aug
Additional: No children under 7; ❹ dishes
Seats: 75. Private dining room 36
Smoking: No pipes or cigars; air-conditioning
Credit cards: 💳 💳 💳 💳 💳

Leith's is nothing if not discreet. The Victorian town house with blue and gold railings out front and the entrance to one side belies the stylish interior. Lunch is popular, although the near-legendary assortment of hors d'oeuvre is not included. Our inspector began with a selection of classily made warm breads before sampling ravioli of braised salmon, which came topped with crisp tempura of oysters and surrounded by a sauce tinged with lemon grass. Following on was poached neck of lamb ('perfect for a spring lunch') on a tiny mound of leaf spinach and parsley pesto with a vegetable and white bean broth; in the same league you might also count roast ballotine of quail with black pudding, smooth lentil purée and mash. To finish, there was an accomplished rhubarb and vanilla sponge pudding accompanied by a slightly sharp rhubarb sorbet, and it's also worth mentioning a mango and raspberry tart served with roasted mangoes and a sweet passion fruit sauce. Dinner is a more elaborate *carte* offering the likes of salad of guinea fowl confit with crushed potatoes, beetroot and red onion relish, braised fillet of turbot with a soft basil crust, langoustines, tomato and caper butter sauce, and roast pear tart with five spice ice cream and honey custard. Mark-ups on an interesting wine list encourage good drinking – many bins of character are available for less than £30. A notable South African example is the mighty Meerlust Rubicon at £27.50, but both white and red Burgundy are worth consideration, as is a thoughtful selection from California.

Signature dishes: Roast scallops, spiced lemon couscous, artichokes and light curry butter; saddle of venison with celeriac and parsnip galette, foie gras and juniper 'jus'

Directions: 500 yds north of Notting Hill Gate

Lemonia ❀

89 Regent's Park Road NW1 8UY
Map GtL: C3
Tel: 0171 586 7454
Fax: 0171 483 2630
Chefs: Mr A Evangelou, Mr A Mittas
Owners: A & M Evangelou
Cost: Alc £17, fixed-price L £7.95/D £11.25. ☺ H/wine £10.25.
Times: Last L 3pm/D 11.30pm. Closed L Sat, D Sun, 25-26 Dec

A popular, stylish Greek Cypriot restaurant, with a large plant-filled conservatory. From the special week-day lunch menu, start with 'louvia' – a dish of black-eyed beans and spinach, followed, perhaps, by squid in white wine sauce and served with chargrilled vegetables and rice. To finish, Greek yogurt with honey and nuts.

Additional: Children welcome; ❹ dishes
Smoking: No cigars or pipes; air-conditioning
Credit cards: 💳 💳 💳 💳

Directions: Nearest Tube Chalk Farm. 200 metres from Primrose Hill Park

45 Lexington Street, W1R 3LG
Map: D3
Tel: 0171 4343401

Lexington

Splendid, laid-back hotel restaurant with plenty of modern art on the walls and live jazz Monday to Friday evenings. Recommended dishes include wild mushroom and truffle oil risotto, pan-fried chicken with noodles and Thai broth, and passionfruit and lemon tart.

Additional: ❹ dishes
Seats: 50. Private dining room 20
Smoking: No pipes or cigars; air-conditioning
Credit cards: ■ ▓ ▆ ▚ ▣ ▐

Directions: Nearest Tubes – Oxford Circus, Tottenham Court Road, Piccadilly Circus

Fax: 0171 2872997
Chef: Andy Farquharson
Owners: Simpsons of Cornhill
Cost: Alc £21, fixed-price L&D £10 (2 courses). H/wine £9.95
Times: Last L 2.45pm/D 10.45pm. Closed L Sat, Sun, Bhs

Livebait

Simple, lively seafood restaurant close to the Old Vic. Comfort may not be part of the equation – gleaming bottle green and white tiles, a black and white checkerboard floor, small close-packed tables, create a hard-edged spartan look – but Livebait aims high in the kitchen. The daily-changing menu features an eclectic range of dishes, drawing on influences from all parts of the globe: the Middle and Far-East, Mediterranean North Africa, South America, Japan and Northern Europe. The result is a vein of New World invention that produces such things as fajita of monkfish medallions and poulet de Bresse with roast tomato relish, guacamole and quince crème fraîche. Other global dishes might include teriyaki glazed halibut, served with an oriental-scented fish soup, palourde clams and noodles, and baked cod in a rosemary and garlic olive oil, served with couscous and a sausage Toulouse. The wine list is modern, imaginative and short, with a good range of white wines as well as some light, chilled reds, and a selection available by the glass.

43 The Cut SE1
Map: E3
Tel: 0171 9287211
Fax: 0171 9282279
Chef: Theodore Kyriakou
Cost: Alc £25. H/wine £9.95 ☺
Times: Noon-last L 3pm/5.30pm-last D 11.30pm. Closed Sun, Bhs
Additional: Children welcome
Seats: 76
Smoking: No cigars or pipes
Credit cards: ■ ▆ ▚ ▐

Directions: Near Old Vic theatre

Lola's ❀❀

Lola's sees the emergence of Alastair Little's former head chef, Juliet Peston, cooking under her own banner in an upstairs restaurant in Islington that has previously seen owners come and go. It is a difficult site to work, above an antiques arcade (formerly tram sheds), hard by Camden Passage, but several enthusiastic inspections indicate that Lola's should run and run. Peston stays true to the ingredients-based cuisine of Alastair Little, offering a daily changing short menu based on a totally simple approach. From Little comes a strong Ital/Med bias – roast pepper, bufala mozzarella and basil calzone with avocado salsa, and his basic you-get-what-you-see menu writing formula. She's not afraid to offer classic dishes such as steak and chips, Caesar salad, roast chicken breast with creamed leeks, asparagus, morels and mash, and do them very well.

359 Upper Street Islington N1
Map GtL: D3
Tel: 0171 3591932
Chef: Juliet Peston
Owners: Carol George, Morfudd Richards
Cost: Alc £30, fixed-price L £12. H/wine £9.50. ☺
Times: Noon-last L 2.30pm/6.30pm-last D 11pm. Closed D Sun
Additional: Sunday L; Children welcome; ❹ dishes
Seats: 80
Smoking: Air-conditioning
Credit cards: ■ ▓ ▆ ▚ ▣ ▐

Directions: Nearest Tube – Angel

London Hilton on
Park Lane ❀❀❀

22 Park Lane W1A 2HH
Map: C3
Tel: 0171 2084021
Fax: 0171 2084147
Chef: Jacques Rolancy
Cost: *Alc* £50; fixed-price L £33.95 (3
courses)/D £33.50/£44 (3/5 courses).
H/wine £15.50
Times: 12.30pm-last L 2.30pm/9pm-
11pm (Midnight Fri & Sat). Closed L
Sat, D Sun
Additional: Bar snacks; Sunday
brunch; Children welcome; ❹ dishes
Seats: 90.
Smoking: No pipes in dining room;
air-conditioning
Accommodation: 446 en suite
Credit cards: ▬ ▆ ▆ ▆ ▆ ▆

There is an exciting, international buzz about this well
established Park Lane hotel. The prize location, however, is
the Windows Bar and Restaurant located on the top floor,
where there are sweeping views over London, and Hyde Park
makes an attractive foreground. Although the great view and
soigné service make this quite a special place, these should not
detract from the cooking, which, under Lyon-born Jacques
Rolancy, produces precise dishes, described as *cuisine
bourgeoise légère*. There's a menu gastronomique which would
be fun in company, otherwise the menu tends towards the
creative and elaborate, with a slight leaning towards seafood.
Fulsome and winning explanations of the French menu (with
English subtitles), are provided by the friendly head waiters
and the wine waiter was full of the delights of Loire wines on
our March visit. An amuse-gueule of prawn terrine introduced
the seafood galette – a 'well-timed, true-tasting' crab claw,
fresh oysters and mussels bound with a subtle green mustard
sauce that was a 'picture on the plate'. Grilled sea bass with a
Szechuan pepper topping exuded all round excellence and
confidence; the pepper in particular, applied in moderation,
worked well with the fish and vegetable seasoning. Hot
chocolate soufflé tart with thyme ice cream was novel,
although chocolate and thyme might not be ideal companions.
Bread comes in the form of firm, continental-style rolls with
Isigny butter, and petits fours with coffee are professional
looking and tasting. Although leaning heavily towards France,
with a good covering of classic wines, this well balanced wine
list give more than a passing nod to the New World but plays it
safe with Lindemans, Penfolds, Wolf Blass and Gallo. Plenty of
top Châteaux, but smaller names offer good drinking: Haut-
Bages-Averous at £37, Chasse-Spleen at £40. The best bargains
are to be had on the Sommelier's Selection with some good
country wines at affordable prices. There are some top quality
wines in halves.
   Signature dishes: Goose in a spiced jelly, foie gras with fennel
confit; aspic of summer vegetables with a purée of vegetables
and tarragon; fricassée of chicken and lobster with baby onions
and cocotte potatoes; monk fish, pot-roasted with potatoes,
artichokes, baby onions and bacon.

Directions: Nearest Tube: Hyde Park Corner. Restaurant on
28th floor of hotel

London Marriott Hotel

See Where London Meets page 160

The Lowndes

21 Lowndes Street SW1X 9ES
Map: B2
Tel: 0171 8231234
Fax: 0171 2351154
Chef: Fred Smits
Owner: Hyatt Hotels
Cost: *Alc* £25-£30, fixed price L
£13.95 (2 courses)/D £17. ☺
H/wine £12.50.
Times: 11.00am-last D 11.15pm
Additional: Bar food; Children
welcome; ⊕ dishes
Seats: 36. Private dining room 22
Smoking: No-smoking area; no pipes
or cigars in dining room; air-
conditioning
Accommodation: 78 en suite
Credit cards: 🃏 🃏 🃏 🃏 🃏

Overlooking the gardens of Lowndes Square in Belgravia, this smart little hotel is just around the corner from its much larger stable-mate, the Hyatt Carlton Tower. Brasserie 21 serves food throughout the day and the menu is an undemanding, international mix of dishes that caters for all tastes and appetites. A number of dishes such as Caesar salad, crab cakes with lime mayonnaise, and deep-fried brie on green salad with crispy vegetables, can be ordered either as starters or main courses. Substantial sandwiches include the 'Knightsbridge Special' with smoked salmon, avocado, shrimps and quail eggs on toasted granary bread; alternatively the choice ranges from fish and chips with tartare sauce through osso buco with risotto Milanese to grilled corn-fed chicken suprême on mash with French beans. Freshly squeezed juices, such as melon or carrot, provide a vitamin booster.

Directions: Knightsbridge Tube, from Sloane Street take first L into Lowndes Square, located on the bottom right hand corner

Luna

The atmospheric interior is the colour of the night sky, with painted stars and planets on the ceiling. On summer nights, diners can watch the Milky Way for real, from the new open-air roof terrace, and almost convince themselves they are sitting under Mediterranean skies, especially after a few glasses of Valpolicella. The menu helps – lots of pasta, grilled meat and fish, home-made focaccia and antipasti of grilled vegetables, Parma ham and cheese. Main courses are fairly simple – baked cod with garlic mashed potatoes, parsley and garlic sauce, chicken grilled with sauté potatoes, red peppers and red pepper purée, and all the pasta dishes, such as farfalle with smoked salmon, cream and mixed herbs, or linguini with basil pesto, can be taken either as starters or main courses. Fresh fruit tart of the day or poached pears in red wine would make lighter desserts than rich chocolate cake with custard.

48 Chalk Farm Road NW1
Map GtL: C3
Tel: 0171 4824667
Fax: 0171 2840818
Chef: Emma Bruggen
Owner: Jessica Seal
Cost: *Alc* £16; Fixed-price L £6.95 (2
courses). ☺ H/wine £8.
Times: Noon – 11.30pm.
Closed 25, 26, 27 Dec
Additional: Sunday brunch;
Children welcome; ⊕ dishes.
Seats: 70. Private dining room 35
Smoking: No pipes and cigars;
air-conditioning
Credit cards: 🃏 🃏 🃏

Directions: Between Chalk Farm and Camden Town Tube stations, on the corner of Ferdinand Street

Maison Novelli ❀❀❀

29 Clerkenwell Green EC1R 0DU
Map GtL: D3
Tel: 0171 2516606
Fax: 0171 4901083
Chef: Richard Guest
Owner: Jean-Christophe Novelli
Cost: Alc £38. H/wine £12.50
Times: Noon-last L 2.30pm/6.30pm-last D 11.15 (midnight Fri, Sat).
Closed L Sat, Sun, Xmas, Bhs
Additional: No children under 4;
❀ dishes
Seats: 45. Private dining room 35
Credit cards: 💳 💳 💳 💳 💳

Although not actually the new kid anymore, Jean-Christophe Novelli is very much the new kid on the block in this up and coming area of London. Whilst it's still early days, Maison Novelli appears to be the flagship venture of a growing group that now takes in Novelli W8 as well as Novelli EC1, the brasserie next door to Maison Novelli. Ornate interior design, stunning personalised china and the Novelli Art Deco twirl logo on just about everything, edible or not, make this a particularly vibrant, if not totally comfortable restaurant. Things can get cramped and noisy, but all is forgiven when it comes to the stunning food. The actual cooking is in the hands of Richard Guest, with Jean-Christophe taking more of a Papal role, but the stimulating menu has all the Novelli hallmarks. His signature dish of cassoulet terrine is here, although it fights for recognition amidst the likes of scallop and baby squid 'nage', Chinese noodles and oyster froth. Grilled John Dory tasted as exquisite as it looked, tiny powerfully flavoured fillets with a bold-tasting sliver of foie gras and a wonderful green pea pod emulsion, and Garren rabbit 'Richard Guest' was equally immaculately prepared with succulent, clean flavour and texture. A vanilla seed pod risotto was smooth but not over creamy with a great bold flavour. Another speciality, stuffed pig's trotter, was exceptionally rich and served with an almond mash to die for. Service is prompt and professional, although there is a slight determination to explain every dish, whether or not you wish to know. There is a very sound wine list with some good classic claret and Burgundies, although prices are a little over-stretched.

Directions: Nearest Tube – Farringdon

Mamta ❀

'Eight Jewel Wonder' (eight fresh vegetables in a hot, spicy sauce), and saag paneer (spinach with home-made cheese lightly spiced with ginger and garlic), are amongst the chef's specials at this friendly vegetarian Indian restaurant. Excellent chutneys, paratha and basmati rice.

Smoking: No-smoking area
Credit cards: 💳 💳 💳 💳

Directions: Nearest Tube: Parsons Green

692 Fulham Road SW6 5SA
Map: A1
Tel: 0171 3715971
Fax: 0171 7365914
Chefs/Owners: D Kamdar,
M Daudbai
Cost: Fixed-price L £4.95/D from £7.25. ☺ H/wine £6.95.
Times: Last L-2.15pm/D 10.15pm.
Additional: Children welcome

Mandarin Kitchen

Spacious, bustling, cosmopolitan modern Chinese with all day opening. Kitchen specialises in fish, particularly lobster and crab, and the likes of fried king prawn in coconut sauce, monkfish fillet in garlic and black bean sauce. Meat dishes feature too, perhaps diced chicken with seasonal greens.

Additional: Sunday L; Children welcome; 🍴 dishes
Smoking: Air-conditioning. **Credit cards:** ▆ ▆ ▆ ▆ ▆ ◻

Directions: Opposite Queensway Tube; a few yards from Bayswater Tube

14 Queensway, W2 3RX
Map: C3
Tel: 0171 727 9012/9468
Chef: Mr Man
Owner: Mrs Helen Cheung
Cost: *Alc* £12, fixed-price L/D £9.90.
☺ H/wine £8.90.
Times: Noon – last D 11.20pm.
Closed 25-26 Dec

Market Restaurant NEW

Situated above a lively street-corner pub and decorated in bohemian-chic, this airy, relaxed hang-out offers sound modern cooking based on decent ingredients. The short evening carte may list pork and herb terrine with home-made brioche, blackened John Dory and baked cherry cheesecake. Excellent light lunch and Sunday brunch menus.

Smoking: Air-conditioning
Credit cards: ▆ ▆ ▆ ▆ ▆ ◻

Directions: Corner of Portobello Road and Lancaster Road. Nearest tube: Ladbroke Grove.

240A Portobello Road W11 1LL
Map GtL: C3
Tel: 0171 229 6472
Fax: 0171 229 2757
Chef: Greg Bleau
Proprietor: John Leyton
Cost: *Alc* £25. H/wine £9. ☺
Times: Last L 3pm/last D 11.30pm.
Closed D Sun, 25 Dec
Additional: Sunday L; Bar meals L;
Children welcome; 🍴 dishes

Mas Cafe

Popular neighbourhood hang-out with loud music and bottled beer. The cooking is inspired by the Med and North Africa, so expect wild mushroom ravioli with red pesto, and marinated chicken sandwich with chorizo. Salads are a strong point: try mozzarella, black grape and anchovy salad, with slices of wholesome brown bread.

Additional: Children welcome; 🍴 dishes
Smoking: Air-conditioning
Credit cards: ▆ ▆ ▆ ◻

Directions: Btw Ladbroke Grove & Westbourne Park Tube station. Parallel to Portobello Road

6-8 All Saints Road W11 1HA
Map GtL: C3
Tel/Fax: 0171 243 0969
Chef: Brian Scully
Owners: Snowhow Ltd
Cost: *Alc* £15-20. H/wine £9.50. ☺
Times: Last L 3.30pm/D 11.30pm.
Closed L Mon, 25 Dec, 1 Jan

Matsuri ❀❀

This is a classy operation in a glitzy part of town, right next to Quaglino's. Matsuri means 'festival' and the whole restaurant is decked out in appropriate style with photographs of celebrations, lanterns, fans and other colourful artefacts. The cooking centres on two great Japanese culinary traditions, old and new. On the one hand, there is the precision and ancient art of sushi, on the other, the modern theatricality of teppan-yaki. Lunch is a relatively affordable deal if you stay with the various set menus, which normally include miso soup, rice and pickles along with fillet steak, lobster, duck and pork grilled on iron plates by chefs wearing tall red toques. If you want a snack, there is also okonomi-yaki (Japan's answer to the pizza), or you can sample grilled rice balls. The full teppan-yaki experience generally begins with grilled yakitori, dobin

15 Bury Street SW1
Map: D3
Tel: 0171 8391101
Fax: 0171 9307010
Chef: Kanehiro Takase
Owner: JRK (UK) Ltd
Cost: *Alc* £40, fixed-price L £10 (2 courses)/D £35 (5 courses). H/wine £16.50
Times: Noon-last L 2.30pm/6pm-last D 10pm. Closed Sun, Bhs
Additional: Children welcome;
🍴 dishes
Seats: 133. Private dining room 16
Smoking: Air-conditioning
Credit cards: ▆ ▆ ▆ ▆ ▆

Matsuri

mushi clear soup served in a special pot, or chawan-mushi (a bizarre-looking steamed egg custard) and ends with lemon sorbet and green tea.

Directions: From Green Park Tube, walk towards Piccadilly Circus, turn right into St James', 1st left into Jermyn St. 1st right is Bury St

The Mayfair Inter-Continental, Opus 70 ❀❀

Stratton Street W1A 2AN
Map: C3
Tel: 0171 3447070
Fax: 0171 3447071
Chef: Michael Coaker
Cost: *Alc* £30, fixed-price L £16 (2 courses). ☺ H/wine £11.
Times: Noon-last L 2.30pm/6pm-last D 11pm. Closed L Sat
Additional: Sunday brunch (11.30-3pm); Children welcome
Seats: 85. Private dining room 12
Smoking: No pipes and cigars; air-conditioning
Accommodation: 287 en suite
Credit cards:

Famous as a haunt of showbiz stars and other celebs, the Mayfair is a fashionable as they come and the new Opus 70 restaurant strikes a typically up-beat note. As its name suggests, the dining room has a musical theme, contemporary artwork hangs on the taupe-coloured walls and the lighting is modern. Chef Michael Coaker has cooked for everyone from Princess Diana to Mel Gibson, and a recent inspection suggested that he is back on top creative form. Crispy duck is served with arugula and watercress, beetroot risotto is topped with scallops, while confit of rabbit is matched with excellent Thai pad (vermicelli pasta with spiced prawns), although the high point of a springtime meal was a first-rate dish of roast sea bass accompanied by aubergine purée, asparagus and turned vegetables. It's also possible to get grills and a few lighter offerings along the lines of pan-fried tuna on ciabatta with tomato relish. Desserts such as burnt orange iced soufflé, and blackberry tart with red wine granita bring up the rear.

Directions: From Hyde Park Corner, turn left off Piccadilly just below Green Park tube station.

McClements' Restaurant

John McClements' cooking has considerable flair and individuality, from the tiny croque monsieurs, smoked salmon and sour cream vol-au-vents, and mini-portion of lobster in a rich sauce that whet the appetite, to the excellent espresso with petits fours at the other end of the meal. In between, there may be Yorkshire pudding topped with pan-fried foie gras served with onion gravy, roast monkfish on a fine ratatouille sauce with crispy squid and butter beans, followed by a hot soufflé with Calvados anglaise.

2 Whitton Road Twickenham
Map GtL: B2
Tel: 0181 7449598
Chef/Owner: John McClements
Telephone for details

Directions: In a small parade of shops next to Twickenham station

Le Meridien

As we went to press it was confirmed, after months of rumour, that Marco Pierre White would be transfering The Restaurant from the Hyde Park Hotel to the refurbished Oak Room at Le Meridien in September 1997.

21 Piccadilly W1V 0BH
Tel: 0171 7348000 (Meridien Hotel)/
0171 2595380 (The Restaurant)
Telephone for details

Directions: On the N side of Piccadilly Circus

Mezzo

Still packing 'em in and the surprise, in what is reputedly the largest restaurant in Europe, is the high standard of cooking and service despite feeding in excess of 600 people a day. The Mezzanine is the spot for simpler meals with an Asian flavour; downstairs there is equally slick decor but more formal dining. There's certainly no lack of style in the *carte:* caviar, oysters, lobster and spit-roast guinea fowl with mash, roast salmon with Thai red curry and choy sum. Retro rules OK with beef Wellington, bouillabaisse, entrecôte béarnaise and veal kidneys with cavalo nero and black butter, and carrots Vichy on the side. You might not be able to linger too long, but after a glass or two of the excellent house bubbly, Mezzo will decant you into Wardour Street still buzzing.

100 Wardour Street W1
Map: D3
Tel: 0171 3144000
Fax: 0171 3144040
Chef: John Torode
Owner: Conran Restaurants
Cost: Alc £30/£35, fixed-price L £12.50/£15.50 (2-3 courses). Pre-theatre D £14. ☺H/wine £11.75.
Times: Noon-last L 3pm (Sun 12.30pm)/6pm-D 12.30am (2.30am Fri/Sat, 10.30pm Sun). Closed L Sat
Additional: Bar meals; Sunday L; Children welcome; ❸ dishes
Seats: 350
Smoking: Air-conditioning
Credit cards: ▓ ▓ ▓ ▓

Directions: Nearest Tube Piccadilly Circus

Mims

Individual cooking, with French-Mediterranean flair in a short, daily-changing menu, makes for distinctive eating at remarkably good prices. The menu descriptions give little away – langoustine salad or crab baklava, roast monkfish with herbed roast vegetables, or rabbit stew, green bean salad and new potatoes – but dishes are cooked to order and the results are well worth the wait. The emphasis is less on red meat, more on fish and poultry with dishes such as sauté of guinea fowl with shredded vegetable cake and foie gras sauce, pan-roast sea bass with roast fennel and potato soufflés, and pan-fried red mullet with tomato noodles and prawns. Desserts show equal flair – banana parfait with banana ice cream or an intriguing sweet soup of figs, port and cinnamon.

63 East Barnet Road EN4 8RN
Map GtL: C4
Tel/Fax: 0181 4492974
Chef: Mr A Al-Sersy
Owners: A Al-Sersy, P Azarfar
Cost: £26, fixed-price L £9.50 (2 courses)
Times: Noon-last L 2.30pm/6.30pm-last D 10.30pm. Closed L Sat, Mon, 1 wk Sept, 1 wk Xmas
Additional: Sunday L; No children under 7
Seats: 45
Smoking: No-smoking area
Credit cards: ▓ ▓

Directions: On East Barnet Road, opposite Sainsbury's

Ming ✿✿

35-36 Greek Street W1V 5LN
Map: D4
Tel: 0171 7342721
Fax: 0171 4370292
Chef: Mr Big & Mr Bun
Owner: Dennis Chung
Cost: Alc £8. Fixed-price L £8 (3 courses). ☺ H/wine £8.50.
Times: Noon-11.45pm, D from 5pm. Closed Sun
Additional: Children welcome; ❹ dishes.
Seats: 75. Private dining room 20
Smoking: No-smoking area; air-conditioning
Credit cards: ▩ ▨ ▨ ▨ ▨ ▨

A good story, apocryphal or not, always enhances a menu and draws interest to a particular dish. At Ming, a serene pink and green oriental haven in the midst of busy Soho, Ta T'sai Mi (lean pieces of tender lamb served with a slightly sweetened soy sauce), is reputed to be an eighteenth-century recipe from Emperor Qian Long's head chef. Curiously, some perfectly understandable dishes have cheery little descriptions – chicken with fresh coriander and lemon zest is "appetising and refreshing" – yet no further explanation is given for more inscrutable choices such as Chiu Yim slice eel and sea spice shredded pork. Cantonese and Pekinese specialities include mussels in black bean sauce, white fish rolls wrapped in bean skin and whole sea bass Siamese-style. Some inconsistencies in the cooking, however, have been noted – prawn delight, alas, failed to match its promise. Nonetheless, the menu assures us that Mr Edward's Pork, 'recommended by our gourmet client', is 'soft and melts in the mouth', so who are we to disagree?

Directions: Off Shaftesbury Ave, behind Palace Theatre

Mitsukoshi ✿✿

Dorland House
14-20 Lower Regent Street
SW1Y 4PH
Map: C3
Tel: 0171 9300317
Fax: 0171 8391167
Chef: Jiro Shimada
Owner: Mitsukoshi Restaurant
Cost: Fixed-price L £18.75 (4 courses)/D £36 (10 courses). H/wine £17.50
Times: 12.30-last L 2pm/6-last D 9.30pm. Closed Sat, 25-26 Dec, New Year, Easter
Additional: No children under 5; ❹ dishes
Seats: 91. Private dining rooms 4-30
Smoking: No pipes & cigars; air conditioning
Credit cards: ▩ ▨ ▨ ▨ ▨

The consistent number of Japanese diners is proof of Mitsukoshi's authenticity. In addition to the main dining-room, with its modern decor and lacquered black tables, there are a range of private salons, some with traditional low tables and cushions. The menu rotates around a good range of set meals, based on classic techniques such as sashimi, sushi, tempura and one-pot dishes cooked at the table. Staff are helpful in assisting the uninitiated to choose a balanced meal, and the service, if somewhat rigid, is very polite in true Japanese style. Fish is very good, and the sashimi dishes are bright and exquisitely fresh. The chef makes his own dashi stock from kelp and bonito tuna, and this is the base for many soups and sauces, such as the delicious miso soup flavoured with fermented soy beans, tofu and wakame seaweed. A particular speciality, which must be ordered a day in advance, is the Kaiseki menu, a multi-course banquet considered by many to be the pinnacle of Japanese cuisine. Very expensive.

Directions: One minute's walk from Piccadilly Circus

Miyama

Fashionably minimalist, Miyama serves mainstream Japanese food at reasonable prices. Set lunches are particularly good value, and could include soya bean soup, pasta with soy sauce, spring onion and horseradish paste, or beef teriyaki with bean sprouts. A good selection of well-prepared sushi is also offered.

Additional: Bar meals; Children welcome; ❹ dishes
Smoking: Air-conditioning
Credit cards: 📇 📇 📇 💳 💳 💳

Directions: Nearest tube station Green Park

38 Clarges Street W1Y 7PJ
Map: C3
Tel: 0171 4992443
Fax: 0171 4931573
Chef: Mr Miyama
Owners: Mr Miyama, Mr Miura
Cost: Fixed-price L £14/D £34 (6 courses). ☺ H/wine £10.
Times: Last L 2.30pm/D 10.30pm.
Closed L Sat, L Sun

Momo

NEW

Fashionable Moroccan restaurant down a discreet opening off Regent Street; the striking decor transports you at once to Casablanca. Young staff stride about like young revolutionaries in combat trousers, boots and tight T-shirts. Standard cooking of tagines and couscous.

Additional: No children under 8; ❹ dishes
Smoking: No pipes or cigars; air-conditioning
Credit cards: 📇 📇 📇 💳 💳 💳

Directions: Nearest tube Piccadilly. Heddon St is opposite Disney store on Regent St

15 Heddon Street WIR 7LG
Map: D3
Tel: 0171 4344040
Fax: 0171 2870404
Chef: Abudullah El Rgrachi
Owner: Momo Mazouz
Cost: Alc £30, fixed-price L £12.50.
☺ H/wine £12.50.
Times: Last L 1.45pm/last D 11pm.
Closed L Sat, Sun,

Momo

NEW

Tiny, unpretentious place, always full, always friendly. Well-known Japanese dishes such as tempura, teriyaki and sushi share the menu with more adventurous fare. Noodles are popular, or try a big bowlful of udon, with tempura, raw egg and seaweed in a piping hot broth.

Additional: Children welcome; ❹ dishes
Credit cards: 📇 📇 📇 💳 💳 💳

Directions: Opposite North Ealing underground station

14 Queens Parade W5 3HU
Map GtL: B3
Tel/Fax: 0181 9970206
Chef/Owner: Toyosaku Asari
Cost: Alc £25, fixed-price L £7.20/D £23.50-£30. ☺ H/wine £9.
Times: Last L 2.30pm/D 10pm.
Closed Sun, 1 wk Aug, 1 wk after Xmas

Monkey's ❀❀

Trend-setters may come and go, but Monkey's remains a bastion of the London restaurant scene. The intimate wood-panelled dining room is, not surprisingly, festooned with pictures and prints of anthropoid apes. Tom Benham delivers a version of classic French cuisine that is, in the words of one inspector, 'more reliable Volvo than flashy Lambourgini', but is none the worse for that. The cheaper of the two fixed-priced menus offers dishes such as sautéed calves' kidneys with grain mustard sauce and confit of duck with flageolet beans. For those wanting something more ambitious there is a velvety, unadorned foie gras terrine and fresh tasting turbot on a bundle of vegetable spaghetti with champagne sauce. Desserts take in hot treacle tart or mille-feuille of pancakes and Cointreau.

Directions: Corner of Cale St & Markhay St, 5 mins from Sloane Sq

1 Cale Street Chelsea Green SW3 3QT
Map: B1
Tel: 0171 3524711
Chef: Tom Benham
Owner: Mr. & Mrs. T. Benham
Times: 12.30pm-last L 2.30pm/7.30pm-last D 11pm. Closed D Sun, Xmas, Easter, 3 wks Aug
Additional: Sunday L; Children welcome.
Seats: 40
Smoking: No pipes in dining room; air-conditioning
Credit cards: 📇 📇 💳 💳

Mon Plaisir

*Close-set tables and picture-crammed walls characterise this bustling,
well-established French bistro set in the heart of Covent Garden. The
short selection of carefully prepared dishes, served by charming staff,
may feature Roquefort cheese soufflé, roast duck with honey, lemon
and ginger sauce and crème brûlée.*

Additional: Children welcome; 🍴 dishes
Smoking: Air-conditioning
Credit cards: 🟦 🟥 🟩 🟥 💳 🟥

Directions: Off Seven Dials. Nearest Tubes: Covent Garden,
Leicester Square

21 Monmouth Street, WC2
Map: D4
Tel: 0171 8367243
Fax: 0171 2474774
Chef: David Joly
Owner: Alain Lhermitte
Cost: *Alc* £23, fixed-price L £14.95/D
£19.95. ☺ H/wine £9.
Times: Last L 2.15pm/D 11.15pm.
Closed Sat L, Sun, 10 days Xmas,
Easter

Monsieur Max

It was still pretty new when our inspector called. No sign up,
but all the recent newspaper critiques were on display in the
window. Max Renzland's shop-fronted restaurant, his latest
venture, is simple in decor with closely packed cafeteria-style
tables and chairs. But it's very French with pictures and
memorabilia, and staff, led by head waiter François, all very
'French bistro professional' in long white aprons. Max has a
loyal following and it is not unusual for the place to do 150
covers on a Friday or Saturday night; there's generally a good
lively buzz. They crowd in for the dedicated French food that
hits the mark. Top quality, accurately cooked foie gras with
truffle dressing, brioche and mixed leaves, followed by pan-
fried pigeon with port sauce and mint risotto, and an excellent
prune and Armagnac tart with vanilla anglaise and vanilla
brûlée formed one well reported meal. The wine list is limited,
however, most people seem to bring their own – there is a £5
corkage and this is very popular.

Directions: On E side of Bushy Park

133 High Street
Hampton Hill TW12 1NJ
Map: C2
Chefs: Alan Bentley, Max Renzland
Owner: Max Renzland
Cost: Fixed-price L £14/D £23.
H/wine £8.50
Times: Noon-2.30pm (3pm Sun)/7pm-
10.30pm (11pm Fri, Sat). Closed L Sat
Additional: Sunday L; Children
welcome; 🍴 dishes
Seats: 40. Private dining room 30
Smoking: Air-conditioning
Credit cards: 🟦 🟥 🟩 🟥 🟥

The Montcalm-Hotel Nikko
London 🌸🌸

Great Cumberland Place
W1A 2LF
Map: B4
Tel: 0171 4024288
Fax: 0171 7249180
Chef: Jonathan Nicholson
Owners: Nikko Hotels (UK) Ltd

Old-fashioned courtesy and style are the hallmarks of this
dignified Georgian hotel. The kitchen presents a combination
of grand hotel fare mixed with modern imaginative dishes that
draw on eclectic sources; dishes such as a classic tournedos

Rossini are juxtaposed with the more modern, innovative roast scallop with boudin noir that our inspector chose to open a test meal, and found 'a well handled stab into difficult territory'. The main course, however, was a more traditional roast cannon of lamb with tomato concasse and a good tarragon scented jus, and pudding was a well conceived chocolate and lime parfait. For those staying the night, the Japanese breakfast menu is a must.

Credit cards: ▨ ▨ ▨ ▨ ▨

Directions: 2 blocks N of Marble Arch

Cost: A/c £30, fixed-price L/D £18. ☺ H/wine £16.
Times: 12.30pm-last L 2.30pm/6.30pm-last D 10.30pm. Closed L Sat, Sun
Additional: Bar meals; Children welcome; ✦ dishes
Seats: 60. Private dining room 16
Smoking: No-smoking area; air-conditioning
Accommodation: 120 en suite

Moshi Moshi Sushi

Sushi on the hoof, or Japanese fast food, at Liverpool Street Station. It's pretty much a case of help yourself from the conveyor belt, and payment is worked out according to how many colour coded little plastic plates you've accumulated. New this year is the range of vegetarian sushi, and packaged set Geta meals.

Additional: Bar meals; Children welcome; ✦ dishes
Smoking: No smoking; air-conditioning
Credit cards: ▨ ▨ ▨ ▨

Directions: Inside Liverpool St Station (upper walkway level)

Unit 24 Liverpool Street Station EC2M 7QH
Map: G4
Tel/Fax: 0171 2473227
Chef: Rollie Ongcoy
Owner: Ms Caroline Bennett
Cost: A/c £10. H/wine £8.60. ☺
Times: 11.30am-9pm. Closed Sat, Sun, Xmas & New Year

MPW ❀❀

Situated in one third of a rotunda, forming a crescent-shaped room, this newcomer to the Marco Pierre White stable was still finding its feet, and identity, when our inspector called. (No one seemed to know MPW existed, but then it had only been open a few days.) However, the place was busy and service brisk and efficient. Garry Hollihead runs the kitchen, offering a fairly lengthy menu of mainly classic dishes with a modern twist – soup of red mullet, rouille and Gruyère or wing of skate with winkles and beurre noir – alongside some real blasts from the past – cocktail of Dublin Bay prawns, sauce Marie Rose and chicken à la Kiev. Calves' liver proved to be excellent, finely sliced, slightly pink and tender, served on fluffy parsley pommes purée and topped by crispy Ventrenche bacon, and was followed by a good crème vanilla piled high with berries. Excellent coffee and petits fours.

Directions: Docklands Railway; main shopping mall of Canary Wharf

NEW

Second floor Cabot Place East Canary Wharf E14 4QT
Map GtL: E3
Tel: 0171 5130513
Fax: 0171 5130557
Chef: Garry Hollihead
Owners: Jimmy Lahoud; Marco Pierre White; Garry Hollihead
Cost: A/c £26. H/wine £10 ☺
Times: Noon-2.30pm/5.30pm-9pm. Closed Sat, Sun, 25-26 Dec
Additional: Children welcome; ✦ dishes
Seats: 200. Private dining room 30
Credit cards: ▨ ▨ ▨ ▨ ▨

Mulligan's of Mayfair ❀

Up-market Irish bar nestling in a quiet Mayfair street. The basement restaurant offers a short seasonal menu but retains the house specialities of oysters in a variety of guises, black and white pudding and Irish stew. Note herb crusted rack of Wicklow lamb, and baked fillet of Donegal salmon. Mashed potatoes came in a big bowl.

Seats: 50. **Credit cards:** ▨ ▨ ▨ ▨

Directions: Cork Street is between Burlington Gardens and Clifford Street.

13-14 Cork Street W1X 1PF
Map: C3
Tel: 0171 4091370
Fax: 0171 4092732
Chef: Sean Hanley
Owner: Mulligans Irish Whisky Emporiums Ltd
Cost: A/c £22. H/wine £8.50
Times: 12.30pm-last L 2pm/6.30pm-last D 10.45pm (Bar – pub hours)
Additional: Bar food; Sunday L

Museum Street Cafe

The location is on the tourist trail, a stone's throw from the British Museum, but this well supported little restaurant manages to feel almost domestic in scale. Chef/proprietors Mark Nathan and Gail Koerber have developed a fine tuned double act since 1989: he is responsible for main courses, she handles starters and desserts. In a clean-cut setting of close-packed unclothed tables they offer short, fixed-price lunch and dinner menus which change frequently. The choice may be limited – two starters, four mains, three sweets, plus Neals Yard cheeses – but the cooking is sharp and skilful to a fault. The chargrill is a favourite device, used for everything from corn-fed chicken (with pesto) and leg of lamb (with roasted aubergine purée) to salmon, which might come with a very 'moreish' red wine and shallot butter. Start with soup (such as spinach and Parmesan) or a modern salad, and finish with Valrhona chocolate cake or banana with Greek yogurt, honey and almonds. The wine list is pared down to two dozen bins, but each is a thoughtfully chosen cracker; five are offered by the glass.

Directions: Off Bloomsbury Way, near British Museum, between Tottenham Court Road

47 Museum Street WC1A 1LY
Map: D4
Tel/Fax: 0171 4053211
Chef/Owners: Gail Koerber, Mark Nathan
Cost: Fixed price L £16/D £22. ☺ H/wine £9.
Times: 12.30pm-last L 2.30pm/6.30pm-last D 9.30pm. Closed Sat, Sun. 1 wk Xmas,1 wk Easter, 1 wk Aug, Bhs.
Additional: Children welcome; ⬤ dishes.
Seats: 37
Smoking: No smoking establishment
Credit cards: ▬ ▬ ▬ ▬ ▣

Neal Street Restaurant 🌑🌑🌑

Antonio Carluccio's restaurant remains a little oasis of Italian culture and tradition in the heart of Covent Garden. Pink linen and cane chairs give a slightly old-fashioned look – the most striking decorative features are a rack of carved thumbsticks and an Eduardo Paolozzi wall relief on the theme of mushrooms, both suggestive of the ebullient owner's dual passion for the countryside and for fungi. The latter may be sampled in the guise of wild mushroom soup, warm mushroom and bacon salad, or roast skate with pickled wild mushrooms. Where there are fungi, truffles are never far behind – breast of truffled pigeon is served on salad, taglioni with truffle sauce. Classic regional Italian dishes include marinated eel Roman-style, hare and polenta and roast Tuscan squab with lentils and speck. Few starters are more minimalist, or more honest, than the house speciality – mixed sauté of wild mushrooms of the day, cooked in olive oil and the tiniest bit of garlic, with ciabatta. Head chef Nick Melmoth-Coombs cooks in suitable style – roast saddle of lamb was deliciously pink, studded with garlic and herbs, garnished with artichokes marinated in lemon and mint. A plate of accompanying vegetables included roast sweet red and yellow peppers, broccoli and finely sliced runner beans. Dessert was ginger pannacotta. A strong Italian influence in the wine list allows for some well priced selections – many interesting quality wines for under £25, as well as some rarer Italian classics: Tignanello '93 (£49.60), Solaia '93 (£90.60). A small representation from the New World and some classic favourites from France, although these carry a higher price tag.

Signature dishes: Lamb with artichokes; Grouse with chanterelles Venison with morel sauce; Bollito misto.

Directions: 2 minutes walk from Covent Garden Tube

26 Neal Street WC2H 9PS
Map: D4
Tel: 0171 8368368
Fax: 0171 2403964
Chef: Nick Melmoth-Coombs
Owner: Antonio Carluccio
Cost: Alc £50. H/wine £15
Times: 12.30pm-last L 2.30pm/6pm-last D 11pm. Closed Sun, 1 wk Xmas & New Year, Bhs
Additional: Children welcome; ⬤ dishes
Seats: 65. Private dining room 24
Smoking: Air-conditioning
Credit cards: ▬ ▬ ▬ ▬ ▣ ▣

Nico Central

Few changes, in terms of the menu, at least, but many would regard that as a positive point in these days of constant new sensation-seeking. Main courses revolve around dishes such as chargrilled rib-eye of beef with horseradish cream, roast breast of guinea fowl with honey roast parsnips and roast monkfish with herb risotto and basil oil. The modern French style is also evident in starters that include rillettes of fresh and smoked salmon with fresh tomato jelly, and boudin blanc served with an apple galette. Some of the shine, however, seems to have gone off the actual cooking: tartlette of mushroom duxelles with poached egg and béarnaise sauce, brill with butter noodles and fish cream sauce, and chocolate tart with coffee sauce anglaise have all been somewhat pedestrian, given the hitherto exceptionally high standard. We can happily report, though, the pommes purées are still as creamy and buttery as ever.

35 Great Portland Street W1N 5DD
Map: C4
Tel: 0171 4368846
Chef: André Garrett
Owner: Restaurant Partnership plc
Cost: Fixed-price D £27. H/wine £13
Times: Noon-last L 1.55pm/7pm-last D 10.55pm. Closed L Sat, Sun, 10 days Xmas, Bhs
Seats: 50. Private dining room 12
Smoking: No pipes or cigars; air-conditioning
Credit cards: ▊▊ ▊▊ ▊▊ ▊▊ ▊▊ ▊▊

Directions: Oxford St end of Portland St. 5 mins walk from Oxford Circus Tube

Nicole's

Watching the ladies-who-lunch is a popular pastime at this chic café in the Nicole Farhi fashion store. On the upper level it is all modern glass and stainless steel, below there is more comfort in the cool leather and classic English oak. Trendy it certainly is. Proceedings begin with breakfast at 10am, lunch moves along until 3.30pm, then it's time for tea. Dinner starts at 6.30pm, although the place seems to move seamlessly from one session to another. The food is tailor-made for svelte figures and fine-tuned appetites. Chargrilled Mediterranean vegetables come with salad leaves and soft goat's cheese, seared tuna is paired with lime and coriander relish. Among the main courses you might find grilled halibut with white beans, tapenade crostini and salsa verde, or calves' liver with roasted sweet potatoes and endives or, in more substantial vein, braised chicken breast with merguez sausages and winter vegetables. To finish, there might be beautifully light brioche tart with apricots and blackberries. The selection of breads should not be missed, and the wine list offers a great assortment by the glass.

158 New Bond Street, W1
Map: D4
Tel: 0171 4998408
Fax: 0171 4090381
Chef: Annie Wayte
Owner: Stephen Marks
Cost: Alc £30. H/wine £10.75 ☺
Times: 10am – last D 11pm. Closed Sat D, Sun
Additional: Bar food; Children welcome; ◑ dishes
Seats: 65
Smoking: No-smoking area; no cigars or pipes; air-conditioning
Credit cards: ▊▊ ▊▊ ▊▊ ▊▊ ▊▊ ▊▊

Directions: Nearest tube: Green Park or Bond St

Nipa Thai

The Royal Lancaster is an eighteen-storey monolith right by Hyde Park and the Nipa Thai Restaurant is its main venue for exciting dining. Not surprisingly the decor is all teak-wood panelling and ethnic artefacts, although there's no sense of themed overkill about the place. The chef earned her stripes at the hotel's sister establishment in Bangkok, so authenticity is assured. Many key ingredients are imported direct and the menu is of manageable proportions. Most of the benchmarks of the cuisine are on offer – soups, stir-fries, salads, curries, noodles and a healthy contingent of vegetarian dishes. Presentation is artistically inclined, flavours are clearly differentiated: the Nipa platter offers a varied selection of appetisers (satays, fish cakes and the like) with appropriate dips, chicken curry is mild, smooth and subtle; yam nuea (beef salad with cucumber and chillies) is correctly spicy. Service is from pleasant, traditionally dressed staff.

Lancaster Terrace W2 2TY
Map GtL: C3
Tel: 0171 2626737
Fax: 0171 7243191
Chef: Mrs Nongyao Thoopchoi
Owner: The Lancaster Landmark Hotel Co Ltd
Cost: Alc £26.Fixed-price L/D £23 (3 courses). ☺ H/wine £17
Times: Noon-2pm/6.30pm-10.30pm. Closed Sat L, Sun, Bhs
Additional: Bar meals; Children welcome; ◑ dishes.
Seats: 55
Smoking: No-smoking area in dining room; air-conditioning
Accommodation: 418 en suite
Credit cards: ▊▊ ▊▊ ▊▊ ▊▊ ▊▊ ▊▊

Directions: Next to Hyde Park on the Bayswater Road. Nearest Tube – Lancaster Gate

Nobu ❀❀

Part of the seriously trendy Metropolitan hotel, this is the place to close your Euro-business deal or plan next season's couture wardrobe over lunch. New York Japanese food has always been more innovative and experimental than that in London, and Nobu has transposed the whole roadshow from Manhattan to Mayfair, down to the American-style service. There's certainly a lot to learn about the menu – squid pasta, spicy sour shrimp, sea urchin tempura, black cod with miso and new-style sashimi, whilst touches of caviar and cream here and there reflect a forward-looking approach, as do westernised desserts such as rhubarb soup, ginger and peach tea sorbet and mitsuba cookies. More classic-style Japanese items, such as sushi, however, were less impressive. The omakase set menu stuck exclusively to fish when ordered by our inspector. It was of outstanding quality: salmon tartare with caviar made a brilliant appetiser, but a notably light and fresh oyster tempura was not best paired with a salad of bitter, spiky leaves. Fillet of sea bass came with incredible sour bean paste, followed by fillet of red mullet marinated in soy. Portions, however, tend to be minimalist, and it may be a better bet to order from the menu as you go along.

Metropolitan Hotel
19 Old Park Lane W1Y 4LB
Map: C3
Tel: 0171 4474747
Chefs: Nobu Matsuhisa, Mark Edwards
Owners: Robert de Niro, Nobu Matsuhisa, Drew Nieporent
Cost: Alc £50, fixed-price L £20/D £50. H/wine £13.50
Times: Noon-last L 2.15pm/6pm-last D 10.30pm. Closed L Sat, Sun
Additional: Sushi bar; Children welcome; 🍴 dishes
Seats: 140. Private dining room 50
Smoking: No-smoking area; air-conditioning
Credit cards: ▆ ▆ ▆ ▆ ▆ ▆

Directions: Nearest Tubes - Hyde Park/Green Park

Noughts 'n' Crosses ❀

Cosmopolitan flavours loom large in this bright lively restaurant. The kitchen dips into the global melting pot for such things as asparagus and Feta cheese filo tart with parsley, orange and fromage frais, or red snapper with spring onion and black bean sauce, or ostrich steak with mushroom and brandy sauce.

77 The Grove Ealing W5 5LL
Map GtL: B3
Tel: 0181 8407568
Fax: 0181 8401905
Chef: Anthony Ma
Owners: Jörgen Kunath & Anthony Ma
Cost: Alc £23.30, fixed-price D £21.50. ☺ H/wine £10.60.
Times: D only 7pm-last D10pm. Closed D Sun, Mon, Aug, 26 Dec-6 Jan
Additional: Sunday L (noon-2pm); Children welcome; 🍴 dishes
Smoking: No-smoking area
Credit cards: ▆ ▆ ▆ ▆ ▆

Directions: Nearest Tube – Ealing Broadway

Novelli W8 ❀❀

Part of Jean-Christophe Novelli's mini-empire, Novelli W8 proves to be a tiny place (formerly the Ark), just off the main drag and parallel to Kensington Church Street. Within, lots of mirrors create an illusion of space, and there are topical foody and French paintings and big flower arrangements. Since opening, the place has been bursting at the seams for both lunch and dinner, but there is a pocket handkerchief-sized patio for overspill; such is the popularity, this has been appropriated by customers, even in a drizzle. The food bears all the Novelli hallmarks. Note a meal that opened with home-smoked goose neck with gizzard and lightly dressed leaves, went on to home-fed Boulogne mussels papillotte with coconut, ginger juice and lemon balm (worth ordering for the

122 Terrace Gardens W8 4RT
Map GtL: C3
Tel: 0171 2294024
Owner: Jean-Christophe Novelli
Telephone for details

Directions: nearest Tube Notting Hill Gate

presentation alone), served with a side order of frites, and finished with banana Tatin and caramel ice cream. Staff are charming. The wine list is well priced and mostly French.

Oak Lodge Hotel ❀

See Where London Meets page 161

Oceana ❀❀

Jason Court 76 Wigmore Street
W1M 6BE
Map: C3
Tel: 0171 2242992
Fax: 0171 4861216

Chef: Andrew Thompson

Owner: Tony Kitous
Cost: *Alc* £20, fixed-price L&D £12 (2 courses). ☺ H/wine £9.70.
Times: Noon-last L 3pm/6pm-last D 11.15pm. Closed L Sat, Sun
Additional: Bar meals; ❹ dishes
Smoking: Air conditioning
Credit cards: ▬ ▦ ▥ ▧ ▨ ▢

Born again in Wigmore Street, this wildly refurbished basement restaurant and bar (formerly Baboon and later Holliheads) is still under the guidance of maverick entrepreneur Tony Kitous, so expect surprises. The decor is a riot of primary colours – especially oceanic blue – with lots of Japanese ikebana-style floral arrangements and polished marble floors. The food might be described as 'hard-core crossover', with influences from here, there and everywhere, but there is a noticeable transatlantic accent culled from the chef's trip to the States. Signature dishes set the tone: butternut squash soup with mascarpone dumplings, brilliant marinated shrimp spring rolls, braised ox-cheek 'bourguignon' with horseradish mash, chocolate and banana terrine with coconut crisps, for example. This is sexy food. Our inspector drooled over a plantain-crusted piece óf milky-fleshed halibut with a tangy black bean and clam relish, which was the star turn of a spring test meal. Light bar meals, weekly set lunches and a pre-theatre menu provide affordable back-up. The wine list hops around the world for inspiration.

Directions: Nearest Tube – Bond Street. Opposite St Christopher's Place

O'Conor Don-Ard-Ri Dining Room ❀

A little bit of the old country in the heart of the West End. A tremendously warm and lively atmosphere goes with soda bread and pints of Guinness, the Irish oysters, traditional Irish lamb stew with pearl barley, and apple and gooseberry crumble. More imaginative is roasted monkfish with deep-fried spinach and watercress sauce.

Additional: Bar food; Children welcome; ❹ dishes
Credit cards: ▬ ▦ ▥ ▧ ▢

Directions: Nearest Tube – Bond Street

88 Marylebone Lane W1
Map: C3
Tel: 0171 9359311
Fax: 0171 4866706
Chef: Conor Fitzpatrick
Owners: The O'Callaghan Family
Cost: *Alc* £18, fixed-price L&D £15. ☺ H/wine £8.95.
Times: Last L 2.30pm/D 10.30pm. Closed L Sat, Sun, Bhs, Xmas, Easter

L'Odéon ❀❀❀

It seems to go on for ever: 67 metres long, with nine large semi-circular windows directly overlooking Regent Street and Piccadilly Circus. The restaurant, on the first floor of an 1810 Nash terrace reached via a grand staircase sweeping up to the reception desk and cocktail area, is divided into sections, with seating either at banquettes or chairs, but even so some of the elegantly laid tables are rather close for comfort. Bruno Loubet is no longer connected with the business and the cooking has now passed into the hands of his former sous-chef Anthony Demetre. The menu remains rooted in French classical and provincial style, but with a twist – roast Hereford duck breast is served with a fruit-tea sauce, and tournedos of hake on squid casserole with mushroom ravioli, for example. On the whole there is nothing too dangerously different, and the full-blooded, guts-and-all-style, which was once Loubet's hallmark, seems to have mutated into a simpler, more accessible repertoire. One of the most expensive starters, roast scallops and black pudding on mashed potato with parsley and garlic coulis, worked well as an ensemble, although a goat's cheese risotto with plum tomatoes and marjoram suffered from sloppy rice and an overpowering cheese flavour. Main courses have been more consistent – roast sea bass with butter bean purée, and shrimp and caper sauce had fine fish with crisp skin and moist, succulent white flesh and a well-flavoured sauce, and sautéed calves' liver with pommes purée, crispy onions and veal jus was equally enjoyable. Those wishing to stay in traditional brasserie mode could start with Galway Bay rock oysters and continue with grilled rib eye of beef with shallot sauce. Desserts are worth saving space for, from a hot apple tart with smooth, alcoholic Calvados ice cream to a creamy rice pudding with morello cherries and kirsch anglaise. Cheeses each have their individual relish, so Montenebro is served with quince paste, Brie de Meaux with truffle oil, and mature Cheddar with home-made sweet pickle, and so on.
   Signature dishes: Fresh pea and foie gras soup; tournedos of monkfish on squid daube; hot chocolate tarte.

Directions: Piccadilly Circus, entrance in Air Street, opposite Café Royal

65 Regent Street W1R 7HH
Map: C3
Tel: 0171 2871400
Fax: 0171 2871300
Chef: Anthony Demetre
Owners: Pierre & Kathleen Condou
Cost: *Alc* £20.30, fixed-price L £17.50. ☺ H/wine £10.50.
Times: Noon-last L 2.45pm/5.30pm-last D 11.30pm. Closed L Sat, D Sun, Bhs
Additional: Sunday brunch; Bar meals; Children welcome; ❸ dishes
Seats: 220. Private dining room 20
Smoking: No-smoking area; no pipes & cigars; air-conditioning

Odettes ❀❀❀

130 Regents Park Road NW1 8XL
Map: C4
Tel: 0171 5865486/8786
Fax: 0171 5860508
Chef: David Kennedy
Owner: Simone Green
Cost: *Alc* £23, fixed-price L £10. ☺ H/wine £10.95.
Times: 12.30pm-last L 2.30pm/7pm-last D 11pm. Closed L Sat (rest), D Sun, 10 days Xmas, Bhs
Additional: Sunday L; Wine bar; Children welcome; ❸ dishes
Seats: 60. Private dining room 30
Smoking: No pipes & cigars; air-conditioning
Credit cards: ▬ ▬ ▬ ▧ 🄳 🄻

'Thoroughly charming and a touch romantic' neatly sums up the appeal of this thoroughbred among north London's neighbourhood restaurants. Inside the ground floor dining room are lots of little alcoves and 'boites': 'I counted 43 mirrors in our tiny area', observed a keen-eyed inspector. Chef David Kennedy is from the school of 'who-dares-wins' modern cooking and clearly isn't afraid to take risks. Bowls of glossy black marinated olives and three kinds of excellent peasant-style bread set the tone. After that, it's invention all the way. An innovative fresh crab salad with pear and coriander appears as a tower of flakes of crustacean with tiny dice of fruit layered between blinis, while saffron lobster and ginger risotto receives unexpected depth of flavour from cucumber stock, Parmesan and olive oil. In more substantial meaty territory, you might find anything from pan-fried calves' liver with creamed potatoes to chump of lamb layered with grilled red peppers, rosemary and chilli oil. To finish, chocolate espresso tart is definitely worth a wait, otherwise expect temptations like blood orange and Campari jelly or lemon and ginger candied sweet potatoes with vanilla ice cream. Considering what is offered, the price for all of this is exactly right. The no-choice set lunch remains one of the most irresistible bargains in the capital, and commendable brasserie-style dishes such as tempura of black pudding with salt cod mash are also available in the downstairs wine bar. The cosmopolitan wine list is simply and clearly presented, with the wines divided into styles rather than countries. Every month there are ten specially selected 'seasonal' wines offered from across the world and priced under £25. For those nervous about trying a whole bottle of something new, there are over twenty wines available by the glass, and the same number in halves, also six house wines at under £12. The classics have not been neglected however, with a Lynch-Bages 1978 (£86) and a Léoville-Las-Cases 1966 (£120) topping the bill.

Signature dishes: salad of smoked sea bass with braised plum tomatoes and basil dressing; tartare of scallops with coriander and lime, saffron oil and pepper dressing; honey-glazed fillet of hare with garlic potato pie and spiced beetroot sauce; roast cod fillet with truffle and baby leek lasagne, basil and red wine sauce.

Directions: By Primrose Hill. Nearest Tube – Chalk Farm

Odin's Restaurant ❀❀

Arguably the best of the Shepherd/Caine stable, the cooking here is totally focused on the goal of providing good English food matched with impeccable standards of service. This year, crab bisque received a rave as one of the best ever tasted, 'smooth in texture with white crab meat at the bottom of the bowl', and high quality ingredients made a roast duck with sage and onion stuffing and apple sauce equally memorable. This was served with shredded and crunchy white cabbage, creamy carrot and swede purée and 'earthy' new potatoes. Mrs Langan's chocolate pudding has stood the test of time, and if anything, was felt to be even more enjoyable than ever – light chocolate sponge slices filled with Jersey double cream, set on a superbly rich dark Bourneville chocolate sauce. Other great retro dishes that have come full circle include smoked eel mousse with horseradish and braised oxtail with celeriac purée.

27 Devonshire Street W1N 1RJ
Map: C4
Tel: 0171 9357296
Chef: Shaun Butcher
Owners: Richard Shepherd, Michael Caine
Cost: Fixed-price L &D £24.95. ☺ H/wine £9.50.
Times: 12.30pm-2.30pm/7pm-11.30pm. Closed Sat, Sun, Bhs
Additional: Children welcome; 🍴 dishes
Seats: 64
Smoking: Air-conditioning
Credit cards: ▬ ▨ ▨ ▨ ▨ ▨

Directions: At Marylebone High Street end of Devonshire Street. Nearest tubes – Baker Street, Regents Park, Great Portland Street

The Old Delhi ❀

48 Kendal Street W2
Map: B4
Tel: 0171 7249580
Chef: Ram
Owner: Nasser
Cost: *Alc*, fixed-price L £14.50
Times: Noon-last L 3pm/6pm-last D
11pm. Closed 1 wk Xmas
Additional: Children over 10 before
7pm; ❀ dishes
Smoking: Air-conditioning
Credit cards: ■ ▦ ▤ ▨

Discreetly smart, flower-filled and spotless Indian, with live harp music some nights. The menu extends to Persian specialities and the kitchen knows its spices. Plump prawns puree, gormeh sabsi (lamb with spinach and lime) and good old chicken Madras have all been endorsed. Try mint tea as an accompaniment.

Directions: Off Edgware Road. Nearest Tube – Marble Arch

Olivo ❀❀

21 Eccleston Street SW1W 9LX
Map: C3
Tel: 0171 7302505
Fax: 0171 8248190
Chefs: Marco Mellis, Giuseppe Sanna
Owners: M Sanna, JL Journade
Cost: *Alc* £35, fixed-price L £16.
H/wine £9.75
Times: Noon-last L 2.30pm/7pm-last
D 11pm. Closed L Sat, L Sun, Bhs
Additional: No children under 5;
❀ dishes
Seats: 42
Smoking: No pipes and cigars;
air-conditioning
Credit cards: ■ ▦ ▤ ▨ ▣

In a colourfully rustic setting of electric blue and bright yellow walls emblazoned with Aztec-style friezes, this ever-busy little place near Victoria station continues to deliver modern Mediterranean food with a strong accent and recent reports suggest that the cooking has lost none of its edge. What singles the place out is its tilt towards Sardinian cuisine, which shows up in dishes such as stuffed baby squid with plum tomatoes and basil, spaghetti with grated botarga (grey mullet roe) and *malloredus Sardi* (traditional pasta with sausages and tomato sauce). The chargrill is the focus of the action and centrepiece dishes tend to have just one flavouring – beef escalope with juniper berries, crisp-skinned monkfish with green olives, rolled pork fillet with deep-fried courgettes and so on. You could start with coppa with wild rocket, or marinated swordfish carpaccio, and finish with strawberries in balsamic vinegar. Fixed-price lunches are great value, and the regional Italian wine list includes a few from Sardinia.

Directions: From Buckingham Palace Road, opposite Victoria Station, turn into Eccleston Street. Olivo is on left

L'Oranger ❀❀❀

5 St James's Street SW1A 1EF
Map: C3
Tel: 0171 8393774
Fax: 0171 8394330
Chef: Marcus Wareing
Owner: Gordon Ramsay, Claudio
Pulze
Cost: *Alc* £50, fixed-price L £19.50/D
£27. H/wine £16
Times: Noon-last L 3pm/6pm-last D
11.15pm. Closed L Sun, 1 wk Xmas
Additional: Children welcome;
❀ dishes

First impressions are of an elegant French bistro-cum-brasserie from another era in a style 'that is slightly understated and perfectly suited to the restaurant's situation at the bottom of St James's Street, and the type of clientele, people who have made it', was one inspector's view. Marcus Wareing's short, seasonal menus offer well thought out dishes often using the unsung heroes of the food world – tongue, beef shank and mackerel – and a sure hand in the balancing act shows that he is performing well. Note a spring lunch that took in a near-perfect pressed terrine of ham and tongue with gherkins and parsley, barely held together, with the thinnest layers of

L'Oranger

Seats: 64. Private dining room 20
Smoking: No pipes & cigars; air-conditioning
Credit cards: ▨ ▨ ▨ ▨ ▨ ▨

spinach and set on a ribbon of choron sauce, and a superb shellfish ('a whole mound of mussels and clams') and hand-rolled pasta followed, its bouillon scented with olive oil and chilli, opened a spring lunch. Then came crispy fillet of cod with crushed new potatoes and bouillabaisse sauce, and a braised French rabbit leg in a glossy Madeira sauce ('all saucing here is noteworthy'), with whole cloves of 'squishy' yellow garlic confit and braised cabbage. Desserts 'exceeded expectations'. Both pecan pie with banana ice cream on a smattering of crème anglaise, and dark chocolate mousse with praline ice cream were stunning. Staff are smartly turned out, and although formal, are approachable. Both the set lunch and dinner menu are remarkable value. The wine list has a disappointing lack of wines by the glass, but a selection of well chosen bottles at reasonable prices offers some compensation.

Directions: Nearest Tube – Green Park. St James's Street is accessible by car via Pall Mall

Orsino ❀

Lively modern Italian where dishes from the daily-changing menu could include braised lamb fillet with tomatoes, black olives and mashed potatoes, roast hake fillet with spinach and artichoke, and smoked salmon, leek and ricotta ravioli with tomato and dill. There's also a small selection of traditional pizzas.

Additional: Children welcome; ❸ dishes
Smoking: No-smoking area; air-conditioning
Credit cards: ▨ ▨ ▨ ▨ ▨

Directions: Holland Park Tube

119 Portland Road W11 4LN
Map GtL: C3
Tel: 0171 2213299
Fax: 0171 2299414
Chef: Anne Kettle
Owners: Orsino Restaurants Ltd
Cost: Alc £35, fixed-price L £15.50. H/wine £10.50
Times: Noon – last D 11pm. Closed 24-25 Dec

Orso Restaurant ❀❀

When it opened more than a decade ago, Orso was in the vanguard of London restaurants serving Italian regional food. The setting is a crowded basement with pictures of famous Italians on the rustic-coloured walls and ceramic tiles from the old flower market in Covent Garden. Expect plenty of buzz, especially as the place tends to absorb overspill from its older brother Joe Allen's nearby. Pizzas and pastas show up favourably on the regularly changing menu, but there is much more besides. Grilled asparagus with blood orange and red onion salad or roast porcini with garlic and wilted spinach are

27 Wellington Street
WC2E 7DA
Map: D3
Tel: 0171 2405269
Fax: 0171 4972148
Chef: Martin Wilson
Owner: Richard Polo
Times: Noon – midnight. Closed 24-25 Dec
Additional: Sunday L; children welcome; ❸ dishes
Seats: 120

typical antipasti, while main courses could take in, say, grilled sea bass with Swiss chard and roasted peppers as well as venison steaks with pomegranate and roasted celeriac. A quartet of Italian cheeses form the alternative to desserts such as Amaretto slice or Vino Santo with cantucci. The regional Italian wine list is a joy to behold with gems scattered across the board and a loyalty to the cream of the country's producers.

Smoking: No-smoking area; air-conditioning
Credit cards: ▬ ▦ ▦ ▨ ▣

Directions: 1 block in from The Strand, 2 blocks down from Royal Opera House

Osteria Antica Bologna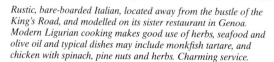

Inspired by dishes from all regions of Italy, this established trattoria specialises in simple Italian country cooking. Expect friendly and unpretentious surroundings and rustic dishes like bowls of pasta with salad, good antipasti – ricotta, spicy sausage and radicchio tart – and meaty main courses such as lamb cutlets with artichoke and lemon sauce.

Additional: Sunday L; Children welcome; ⓓ dishes
Smoking: Air-conditioning. **Credit cards:** ▬ ▦ ▦ ▨ ▣

Directions: Off Battersea Rise, between Wandsworth and Clapham Commons

23 Northcote Road SW11 1NG
Map Gtl: C2
Tel: 0171 9784771
Chef: Aurelio Spagnuolo
Owners: Aurelio Spagnuolo, Rochelle Porteous
Cost: *Alc* £18, fixed-price L £7.50. ☺ H/wine £7.50.
Times: Last L 3pm/D 11pm (11am-11.30 Fri & Sat, 10.30 Sun)
Closed 10 days Xmas, New Year

Osteria Le Fate ❀   NEW

Rustic, bare-boarded Italian, located away from the bustle of the King's Road, and modelled on its sister restaurant in Genoa. Modern Ligurian cooking makes good use of herbs, seafood and olive oil and typical dishes may include monkfish tartare, and chicken with spinach, pine nuts and herbs. Charming service.

Credit cards: ▬ ▦ ▦ ▨ ▣

Directions: On corner of Draycott Ave and Bray Place. Nearest Tube Sloane Square

Chelsea SW3
Map: A1
Tel: 0171 5910070
Fax: 0171 5813140
Chef/Owner: Sandro Caponnetto
Cost: Fixed-price L £13.50-£16.50/D £20.50. ☺ H/wine £11.50.
Times: Last L 2.30pm/D 11.30pm.
Closed Sun
Smoking: No smoking in dining room

Oxo Tower ❀❀

A much needed face lift has worked wonders for this faded Thames-side landmark. The cool, modern restaurant and adjacent bistro on the eighth-floor (fabulous elevated views across the Thames to St Pauls Cathedral), come courtesy of the team responsible for Fifth Floor at Harvey Nichols (see entry). The buzz is high decibel, although booking three weeks in advance was necessary before our inspectors could check it out. The cooking shows flair. A warm tart of lambs' sweetbreads, peas and morels with grain mustard hollandaise, and an open ravioli of chicken livers with bone marrow and Cabernet Sauvignon sauce kicked off that spring dinner. Then pan-fried fillet of halibut came with clam and mixed herb risotto, vermouth and tomato sauce, and scallops with chilli and crab salsa with avocado and crème fraîche. Dessert was nectarine tart with almond ice cream, and moelleux of chocolat (a chocolate brownie with a bitter chocolate filling). The wine list is not cheap but impressively extensive and well indexed, with a good choice from most of the wine producing countries.

8th Floor Oxo Tower Wharf
Barge House Street SE1
Map: E3
Tel: 0171 8033888
Fax: 0171 8033806
Chef: Simon Arkless
Owners: Harvey Nichols Restaurants Ltd
Cost: *Alc* £30, fixed-price L £24.50 ☺
Times: Last L 3pm/6pm-last D 11.30pm. Closed Sat L
Additional: ⓓ dishes
Seats: 135
Smoking: No pipes; air-conditioning
Credit cards: ▬ ▦ ▦ ▨ ▣ ▣

Directions: Nearest Tube – Blackfriars. In between Blackfriars Bridge and Waterloo Bridge

Le Palais du Jardin ❀

136 Long Acre WC2E 9AD
Map: D3
Tel: 0171 3795353
Fax: 0171 3795800
Chefs: Winston Matthews, Paul Morris
Owners: Le Palais du Jardin Ltd
Cost: Alc £25-£30. ☺
Times: Last L 3.30pm/5.30pm-last D midnight. Closed Sat, 25-26 Dec
Additional: Bar Food; Children welcome; dishes
Smoking: No pipes or cigars; air-conditioning
Credit cards: ■■ ■■ ■■ ■■ ■■ ■■

Oysters, lobster, mussels and langoustines are amongst the seafood specialities at this busy Covent Garden brasserie. Main courses include scallops, sole and salmon in a lemon and ginger sauce, Toulouse sausages, mashed potatoes with lentil and onion gravy, and daily dishes such as grilled corn-fed hen with a corn and Monterey Jack cheese galette, sugar-snap peas and confit of pine kernels.

Directions: Nearest Tubes Covent Garden and Leicester Square

Park Lane Hotel ❀❀

Under its new international owners (Sheraton), this landmark hotel is destined once more for great things. As well as the French-style Brasserie on the Park, and the Palm Court for afternoon teas (due to be redecorated in period style), Bracewells Restaurant offers formal, serious dining in a graceful setting of mirrored pillars and light wooden columns. Traditional dishes include Rossmore rock oysters, clear chicken soup with quail egg parcel, grilled or pan-fried Dover sole, roast best end of lamb with garlic and rosemary and classic grills. A separate menu features modern French cooking along the lines of wild rabbit, prune and bacon terrine with a warm baby leek salad, roast calves' sweetbreads on fennel and asparagus with lobster fritters and tarragon sauce, and Scottish scallops with artichoke mash and a black olive sauce. For dessert, try the wonderfully complex, but light, nougat glacé with a 'passion sauce'.

Directions: On Piccadilly, between Hyde Park Corner and Green Park Tube stations

Piccadilly W1X 8BX
Map: C3
Tel: 0171 4996321
Telephone for details

The People's Palace ❀❀

The cooking at this immense, riverside restaurant within the Royal Festival Hall is now back on form. Best tables are beside the large windows overlooking the Thames, but there is a relaxed and comfortable atmosphere throughout the lofty 50s room. Knuckle of ham, rabbit and foie gras had good, individual flavours and was carefully constructed and colourfully presented, although it would have been improved even further if it had been served a little less chilled. No problems, though, with a main course of grilled new season lamb steak, cooked pink to order, served on a bed of Puy lentils with a light red wine sauce. An extra dimension of

Royal Festival Hall
Belvedere Road SE1 8XX
Map: E3
Tel: 0171 9289999
Fax: 0171 9282355
Chef: Stephen Carter
Owner: David Levin
Cost: Alc £22, fixed-price L £10.50 (2 courses). ☺ H/wine £10.50.
Times: Noon-last L 3pm/5.30pm-last D 11pm. closed 25 Dec
Additional: Sunday L; Children welcome; dishes

flavour was provided by a slice of Roquefort butter melting over the lamb. This was accompanied by perfectly timed fresh spinach and mashed potatoes. The modern British menu now includes Pacific Rim numbers such as tamarind glazed goose confit with stir-fry pak choy and lime jus, and seared scallops with tempura vegetables, sweet chilli sauce and coriander chutney. Try the steamed chocolate pudding or mango tart with coconut sorbet for dessert.

Seats: 200
Smoking: No-smoking area; air conditioning
Credit cards: ■ ■ ■ ■ ■ ■

Directions: Level 3 of the Royal Festival Hall

Pied à Terre

34 Charlotte Street W1P 1HJ
Map: C4
Tel: 0171 6361178
Fax: 0171 9161171
Chef: Tom Aikens
Owner: David Moore
Cost: Alc £46, fixed-price L £22/D £52. H/wine £14
Times: 12.15pm-last L 2.15pm/7.15pm-last D 10.15pm. Closed L Sat, Sun, 2 wks Aug, Xmas
Additional: Children welcome; ⓓ dishes
Seats: 40. Private dining room 12
Smoking: No pipes & cigars; air conditioning
Credit cards: ■ ■ ■ ■ ■ ■

The small room is unassuming, decorated in shades of white, with some earthy floor tones and a few Andy Warhols, plus extremely comfortable modern leather chairs. But Tom Aikens has not got an easy job on his hands following in the footsteps of Richard Neat who turned this Charlotte Street address into a mecca for cosmopolitan diners. The menu reads well, there are exciting ideas and stimulating combinations of luxury ingredients with 'working-class' offal. Our overall impression is of a young chef with bags of talent who needs less attention and more space just to get on with perfecting the operation. Our inspection meal began on a high note with a stunning dish of quail consommé with confit quail, wild mushroom ravioli, quail breast and poached quail egg that displayed several levels of texture and flavour within the context of an oriental inspired broth. Offal cooking reached its apotheosis in an outstanding dish of braised pigs head and tongue with steamed trotter, celery purée, wild mushrooms, deep-fried brains and ears – in other words, everything but the squeal. Correction, there were squeals of pleasure despite this being brown food with a visual vengeance. Not many dishes perhaps, could stand comparison alongside, but our inspector nonetheless felt another main course of steamed pigeon breast, confit leg, Sardalaise potato and choucroute with foie gras, lacked the same degree of excitement and depth of flavour. Clumsy pastry work in a dessert of raspberry and pear mousse with raspberry mille-feuille, and in the balance of ingredients, was also disappointing after all that had gone before.

Directions: Nearest Tube – Goodge Street. S of BT Tower

Le Pont de la Tour

Well designed, well run and well patronised by the well-heeled (plus one of the most inviting riverside settings in London), no wonder this bit of the Conran Gastrodome is full to the gunnels most nights. The relaxing, minimalist decor with bare walls, marble shelving, and wire sculptures suspended in the foyer, makes for a great intimate atmosphere: it helps that tables are closely packed and customers are cosseted by swarms of well-trained staff. The menus major in fish and shellfish (something of a Conran trademark), breads from the in-house bakery and influences come from all over. The range might encompass anything from classic soupe de poisson and Chateaubriand to wackier exotica such as seared foie gras with sweetcorn rösti and candied orange. An inspection dinner suggested that the kitchen is capable of great things, as in brandade of cod with roast peppers, French beans and an intense tapenade, shellfish pot au feu zealously finished with Pastis, and roast squab pigeon with gratin dauphinoise and a morel and truffle jus. Desserts could include a neat caramelised apple tart. The wine list is a joy to behold, a weighty tome of the great and the godly, with excellent house wines by the glass, dazzling champagnes, superb dessert wines and much more.

Directions: SE side of Tower Bridge

The Butlers
Wharf Building
36d Shad Thames
SE1 2NQ

Map: G3
Tel: 0171 4038403
Fax: 0171 4030267
Chef: David Burke
Owner: Sir Terence Conran & Joel Kissin
Cost: Alc £52-£66, fixed-price L £27.50/pre/post theatre D £19.50. ☺ H/wine £11.95.
Times: Noon-3pm (12.30pm Sun)/6pm-11pm (11.30pm Sun). Closed L Sat
Additional: Sunday L; Bar meals; Children welcome; ● dishes
Seats: 105 (44 outside)/Bar & grill 70 (36 outside). Private dining room 10-20
Smoking: Air-conditioning
Credit cards: ■ ▨ ▨ ▨

Poons

The Soho branch of the family chain of restaurants rises up over three floors. Constant queues testify to the quality and value of the straightforward Cantonese cooking that features good dim sum, steamed, fried and deep-fried, and a wide choice of one-plate noodle, rice hot-pot and casserole dishes. Specialities include stewed lobster with ginger and spring onion, chicken baked in a salt crust, and steamed Chinese mushrooms stuffed with minced prawn, but Poons are most famous for their wind-dried meats and Peking duck. Vegetarian choices include mixed vegetables wrapped in bean sheets and mashed tofu and lotus seed mix. The set menus are particularly inexpensive, ranging from £7 to £17 per head for a seafood menu that includes fried scallops with asparagus and squid with chopped garlic.

Directions: Opposite Swiss Centre NCP car park, behind Empire Cinema. Nearest tube Leicester Square

4 Leicester Street WC2 7BL
Map: D4
Tel: 0171 4371528
Fax: 0181 4580968
Chef: Yuan Jin He
Owner: Wai Nam Poon
Cost: Alc £15, fixed-price L&D £14-£25. ☺ H/wine £7.30.
Times: Noon-last D 11.30pm. Closed 24-27 Dec.
Additional: Children welcome; ● dishes
Seats: 120. Private dining room 20-24
Smoking: Air-conditioning
Credit cards: ■ ▨ ▨ ▨

The Popeseye ✿

All you get is top quality Aberdeen Angus beef (popeseye, sirloin or fillet), in 6, 8,12 and 20 oz portions, served chargrilled with fries, salad, and cold sauces (horseradish, béarnaise and various mustards). Don't bother with anything less than 8oz – you'll regret not having had more. No starters, and forget puds. Extensive wine list given the limited menu, but moderately priced. A place for friends and fun.

Directions: Nearest Tube – Hammersmith. Restaurant located behind Olympia

108 Blyth Road W14
Map GtL: C3
Tel: 0171 6104578
Chef/Owner: Ian Hutchison
Cost: Alc £20. H/wine £9.50. ☺
Times: D only, 6.45pm-10.30pm. Closed Sun
Additional: Children welcome
Credit cards: None

La Porte des Indes

Stunning conversion of a former ballroom complete with sweeping staircase. The speciality is Indian/French colonial food, such as duck breasts cooked in an exotic blend of spices, but there is also a wide selection of other regional Indian dishes ranging from Hyderabadi lamb biryani to Parsee braised hot and sour beef and sun-dried apricots. Starters and puddings are the weakest links.

Smoking: No-smoking area; air conditioning
Credit cards: ▬ ▩ ▦ 🅿 ₵

Directions: Nearest Tube – Marble Arch. Behind Cumberland Hotel

32 Bryanston Street W1H 7AE
Map: D4
Tel: 0171 2240055
Chef: Mehernosh Mody
Owners: Blue Elephant International
Cost: *Alc* £35, fixed-price L £15/D £31. ☺ H/wine £9.50.
Times: Last L 2.30pm/last D midnight. Closed L Sat, 25-26 Dec
Additional: Sunday L; Children welcome; ✪ dishes

The Prince Bonaparte

Lively, converted Victorian pub with a cheap and cheerful bare boards look. The menu is as much a mix as the Notting Hillbilly clientele. Expect Thai baby corn, sugar snap and noodle salad with lime and sesame dressing and prawn crackers, as well as kingfish with chermoula, couscous, tomato and cucumber salad.

Additional: Bar food; Sun L; Children welcome; ✪ dishes
Seats: 85
Credit cards: None

Directions: Corner Chepstow and Talbot Roads. Nearest Tubes: Notting Hill Gate, Westbourne Park.

Map GtL: C3
Tel: 0171 2295912
Fax: 0171 7920911
Chef: Phillip Wright
Owners: Phillip Wright, Mark Harris
Cost: *Alc* £16. H/wine £8.50 ☺
Times: Last L 3pm/D 10.30pm. Closed Tue L, 25 Dec, 1 Jan

Putney Bridge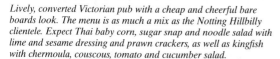

This strange, modern building sits like an alien space ship on the banks of the Thames, a slender bar-room base fanning out into a first floor restaurant of glass windows that catch the river views making the place spacious, light and airy. The cooking keeps it simple but imaginative, from seared tuna with soba noodle salad, to noisette of pork with spring onion and potato cake and black bean gravy, and the extraordinary sounding deep-fried salmon in blue corn seaweed batter, chips and tartare sauce. There are fresh-looking piles of langoustines with lemon and mayonnaise, rock oysters and pumpernickel bread, as well as duck neck terrine and 'babaganoush' with tomato and mint salad. A starter of risotto milanese came with a great bone marrow tapenade, followed by sea bass with courgette papardelle and piperade, full of vibrant and lively flavours. Desserts are not quite as on the ball as the other courses – sticky rice with coconut and mango with a layer of black wild rice was a brave but doomed idea; Bramley and Russet jelly with grilled Braeburns and green apple sorbet would have benefited from slightly more sweetness in the jelly, and more tartness in the sorbet. British cheeses are served with home-made pickle.

The Embankment SW15 1LB
Map GtL: C2
Tel: 0181 7801811
Fax: 0181 7801211
Chef: Paul Hughes
Owner: Trevor Gulliver
Cost: *Alc* £33, fixed-price L £17.50. ☺ H/wine £9.75.
Times: Noon-3pm (Sun 12.30pm)/6pm-11pm (Sun 7pm-10.30pm)
Additional: Bar meals L; Children welcome; ✪ dishes
Seats: 148
Smoking: No pipes; air-conditioning
Credit cards: ▬ ▦ ▨ ₵

Directions: Nearest tube – Putney Bridge. Walk out of station and across bridge. Restaurant is the first building on R, facing onto river

Quaglino's ✿✿

'Open five years and still a place to see, reservations are a must and there's a real buzz combined with a bit of Hollywood glitz', enthused one inspector on the Conran restaurant that seats hundreds and feeds thousands. It's a slick operation. The

16 Bury Street St James's SW1Y 6AL
Map: C3
Tel: 0171 9306767
Fax: 0171 9302732
Chef: Paul Wilson
Owner: Conran Restaurants

menu, changed seasonally, is brief, has a very French bistro/brasserie feel with a strong modern British bias, and features crustacea (heavily). Our inspection meal opened with crispy pork salad with ginger and coriander, and seared tuna with wasabi and soy, went on to calves' liver and bacon with real 'comfort food' mashed potatoes and lightly wilted spinach, and its counterpart, a good roasted sea trout with pea and sorrel beurre blanc. Dessert was a chocolate Pithiviers with Jersey cream 'worth ordering for the jug of cream alone'. The wine list is set out by grape variety, and over 100 wines are offered.

Cost: *Alc* £35, fixed-price L £14.50/D £19.50. ☺ H/wine £11.75.
Times: Noon-last L 3pm/5.30pm-11.30pm Mon-Thurs, 12.30am Fri-Sat, 10.30pm Sun
Additional: Bar food; Sunday L; Children welcome; ❹ dishes
Seats: 267. Private dining room 40
Smoking: No pipes & cigars; air-conditioning
Credit cards: ▇ ▨ ▨ ▨

Directions: Bury St runs parallel with St James's, and is adjacent to Jermyn St

Quality Chop House ❀❀

High-backed wooden booths, restored hand-made wallpaper, period lamps and old American wooden ceiling fans add to the nineteenth-century atmosphere at this ironically self-styled 'progressive working class caterer'. It has to be added, though, that the bench seating is very hard on the twentieth-century posterior. Still, the cooking is honest and uncomplicated, and the choice substantial. Our inspector enjoyed well-made and strongly flavoured gazpacho, followed by excellent grilled Dutch calves' liver and bacon with a 'very tasty' onion sauce and freshly prepared mashed potatoes, then a good raspberry tart. True to plebeian type, there's egg, bacon and chips on the menu, as well as pork chop with gherkin and mustard sauce, grilled spring chicken and salmon fishcake with sorrel sauce – sausage and mash, however, is made with Toulouse sausages. First courses are more chattering classes – artichoke vinaigrette, fish soup and rouille, Caesar salad, and we doubt any self-respecting British workman would be seen dead eating roast snails with garlic butter.

94 Farringdon Road EC1 3EA
Map: E4
Tel: 0171 8375093
Chef/Owner: Charles Fontaine
Cost: *Alc* £22. H/wine £10. ☺
Times: Noon-last L 3pm/6.30pm-last D 11.30pm. Closed L Sat, 10 days Xmas & New Year
Additional: Sunday brunch (noon-4pm); Children welcome; ❹ dishes
Seats: 40
Smoking: No pipes and cigars; air-conditioning
Credit cards: None

Directions: On the left-hand side of Farringdton Road, just before it meets Rosebery Avenue. Nearest Tube – Farringdon or King's Cross

Quincy's Restaurant ❀❀

Here is a neighbourhood restaurant par excellence. Its engaging appeal stems from the infectious charm of owner David Wardle, the informal relaxed mood of the place, and the great-value cooking that comes courtesy of David Philpott. No wonder most of the customers are regulars. The menu changes daily and the food is a couple of notches above bistro, both in terms of invention and execution: salmon is served in rice paper with chilli and courgette salad, ballotine of rabbit comes with crushed carrots and a light mustard butter sauce, while vegetarians might be treated to pumpkin ravioli with five-spiced greens and tomato oil. Fish specials vary with the market, and the choice of desserts might feature quince tarte Tatin with vanilla ice cream, or white chocolate parfait with prunes and Armagnac. The list of three dozen well chosen wines emphasises both quality and value.

675 Finchley Road NW2 2JP
Map GtL: C4
Tel: 0171 7948499
Chef: David Philpott
Owner: David Wardle
Cost: Fixed-price D £24. ☺ H/wine £9.
Times: D only, 7pm-11pm. Closed Sun, Mon, Xmas
Additional: Children welcome; ❹ dishes
Seats: 30
Smoking: Air-conditioning
Credit cards: ▇ ▨ ▨ ▨ ▨

Directions: Situated between Hendon Way & Cricklewood Lane on the Finchley Road

Quo Vadis ❀❀❀

NEW

26-29 Dean St W1V 6LL
Map: D4
Tel: 0171 4379585
Fax: 0171 4349972
Chef: Jeremy Hollingsworthy
Owner: Marco Pierre White
Cost: Fixed-price L £17.95.
H/wine £11

As a decorative experience, not everyone is able to come to terms with the flayed cows heads in formaldehyde installed by Damien Hirst in the upstairs bar. The ground floor dining room has a frontage of dramatic stained glass, stripped wood floors and Hirst's molecular model of DNA. Luckily, it's Marco Pierre White who oversees the cooking, and the menu features all his brasserie favourites such as foie gras and chicken liver parfait, and calves' liver with sage and pommes purées. Rotisserie favourites include a 'properly garnished' French spit-roast chicken which was 'just brilliant'. Other impressive dishes have been snails bourguignon with superb, benchmark béarnaise, and excellent, tender spit-roast suckling pig with superb apple sauce, fondant potato and a gentle, but well-defined marjoram jus. Puddings include Marco classics such as tarte Tatin of pears with spices, lemon tart, and caramelised apple tart with vanilla ice. In a commendable effort at accessibility, the wine list is prefaced by both a reasonably priced, imaginatively chosen 'sommeliers selection' and an excellent range of wines by the glass. There is quality across the globe – Australia displays a greater depth and choice of vintage (15 of Penfolds Grange) than is often the case. Masterly vintages are on offer from Bordeaux at suitably aristocratic prices, which for once correspond accurately to the strength of the particular year.
Signature dishes: Velouté of parsley and truffle, poached egg; steamed wing of skate, deep-fried capers and parsley, beurre rosette; spit-roasted Lancashire duck Marco Polo; roast rabbit, tomato confit, sage, celery heart, sauce chasseur.

Directions: Nearest Tube – Leicester Square

The Radisson Edwardian Hotel ❀

See *Where London Meets* page 161

The Radisson SAS Portman Hotel ❀❀

NEW

22 Portman Square W1H 9FL
Map: B3
Tel: 0171 2086000
Fax: 0171 2086001
Chef: Brian Kerr
Owners: Radisson SAS Portman Hotel London
Cost: Alc £35. H/wine £13
Times: D only 6.30pm-last D 10pm. Closed Sun, Bhs
Additional: Children welcome; ❹ dishes
Seats: 18
Smoking: No-smoking area; no pipes or cigars; air-conditioning
Accommodation: 279 en suite
Credit cards:

Seating only 18, the Library Restaurant claims to be the smallest hotel restaurant in London, which certainly makes it something of a talking point. The menu is as sophisticated as the decor, and home-made breads and rolls set the tone for a stylish, accurately cooked dinner of sautéed sweetbreads with mixed leaf salad, oranges and Grand Marnier flavoured dressing, followed by top quality turbot on a bed of wilted spinach with light grain mustard sauce and rösti potatoes. For dessert, our inspector chose a neat variation on a theme, with a crème caramel served with sultanas in rum syrup. Cafetière coffee comes with petits fours, truffles, fudge and florentines. The Portman Corner Restaurant has more informal, all-day dining with a modern menu that shows some spicy Asian influences.

Directions: Off Oxford St. Close to Marble Arch. Nearest Tube – Marble Arch

The Raj Vogue

One of the more traditional of traditional Indian restaurants, with a menu that is a cross-section of dishes from all over the sub-continent. Excellent ground lamb kebab with herbs, chicken saag with spinach and spices and subtly flavoured basmati rice. Rich, filling 'Pashwari' nan is stuffed with almonds and sultanas.

Smoking: No-smoking area; air-conditioning
Credit cards: ▆ ▆ ▆ ▆

Directions: Nearest tube – Archway. Opposite to The Whittington Hospital

34 Highgate Hill N19 5NL
Map GtL: C4
Tel: 0171 2729091
Fax: 0171 2811485
Chef: Mr Supail
Owners: Abed Choudhury, Syeda Rafiqua Choudhury
Cost: *Alc* £10. H/wine £7.70. ☺
Times: Last L 2.15pm/last D 11.30pm. Closed 25 Dec
Additional: Sunday L; Children welcome; ♨ dishes
Seats: 44

Rani ❀❀

There's a sort of Habitat goes colonial look to Rani, a vegetarian Gujerati restaurant just off Finchley Lane, where no meat, fish or eggs are allowed in the kitchen; the emphasis, instead, is on fresh vegetables, yogurt, rice, wheat and pulses, all enhanced by an intelligent use of spicing. Poppadums come with stunning home-made chutneys, perhaps fresh coriander or coconut, and first courses include various poori dishes and lentil soups, as well as hot starters such as bhajias, samosas and the less familiar *akhaa murcha*, cooked vegetables stuffed in large chillies coated with gram flour paste and deep-fried. Ripe bananas and fresh fenugreek leaves cooked in a richly spiced tomato gravy made a delicious, sweet curry main course; other choices include lots of exotic ingredients such as guvar, valour, pigeon peas, vall beans and dudhi, but it's worth being adventurous. Stuffed paratha is amongst an excellent range of breads. There is another branch of Rani at 3 Hill Street, Richmond, Surrey TW9 1SX. Tel: 0181 3322322.

7 Long Lane Finchley N3 2PR
Map GtL: C4
Tel/Fax: 0181 3494386
Chef: Mrs Sheila Pattni
Owner: Mr Jyotindra Pattni
Cost: *Alc* £13.50, fixed-price D £9.95 (2 courses). H/wine £8.50
Times: D only, 6pm-last D10pm. Closed 25 Dec
Additional: Sunday L (12.15pm-3.30pm); No children under 6; ♨ dishes
Seats: 90. Private dining room 23
Smoking: No-smoking area; no pipes and cigars
Credit cards: ▆ ▆ ▆ ▆ ▆

Directions: 5 min walk from Finchley Central Station

Ransome's Dock ❀❀

In a modern waterside complex where an ice factory used to be, this buzzy informal venue still makes productive use of its own artesian well. Martin and Vanessa Lam share the cooking, and their kitchen works to a zesty modern menu that moves from potted Morecambe Bay shrimps via Elizabeth David's spinach and Ricotta gnocchi with sage butter to Thai mussels with chilli, coconut and lemon grass. Ideas abound. An autumn inspection began confidently with seared Loch Fyne scallops with beetroot purée and walnut oil and continued in the same vein with thickly

Ransome's Dock
Battersea SW11 4NP
Map GtL: C2
Tel: 0171 2231611
Fax: 0171 9242614
Chef: Martin Lam
Owners: Martin & Vanessa Lam
Cost: *Alc* £25.Fixed-price L £11.50 (2 courses). ☺ H/wine £12.
Times: Noon-11pm (D from 6pm). Closed D Sun, Xmas

sliced Trelough duck breast with a shiny Pinot Noir sauce, two roasted figs and parsley mash. The devotion to impeccable ingredients also defines desserts such as pear and almond tart and hot prune and Armagnac soufflé, not to mention organic ice creams from Rocombe Farm. The wine list is a cracking assortment of exciting, high-quality bottles arranged by grape variety and style; don't miss the dessert wines and sherries.

Directions: Between Albert and Battersea Bridges. Nearest tube – Sloane Square

Additional: Sunday L; Children welcome; ❸ dishes.
Seats: 60.
Smoking: No pipes or cigars in dining room; air-conditioning
Credit cards: ▨ ▨ ▨ ▨ ▨

Rasa ❀❀

Since last year's guide, Rasa has had a completely new look. Pink predominates, the floor has terracotta tiles and there is wooden fretwork on the ceiling, but the food remains, thankfully, unchanged. Southern Indian vegetarian cooking has little in common with the ubiquitous tandoori house norm, and the flavourings depend on the well-balanced use of fresh herbs and spices. Interesting main courses include Mysore rave dosa, a large lacy crispy pancake made of semolina and rice batter with spices, and poori masala, fried puffed-up wheat bread served with turmeric-coloured potato curry. Curries, in fact, have their own section, and aubergines cooked with onions and spices and mixed with yogurt and white cashew nut sauce, and spinach and home-made curd cheese cooked in a mild creamy sauce are amongst the choices. Starters include plantain slices dipped in chickpea flour batter with black sesame seeds, a side order of cauliflower comes in a spicy tomato mixture, rice may be mixed with fresh coconut, black lentils and curry leaves, and there are light, crispy Keralan snacks to munch while ordering.

Directions: Bus no 73 from Oxford St, Angel, Kings Cross, Euston, BR from Liverpool St to Stoke Newington High St

55 Stoke Newington Church Street N16
Map GtL: D4
Tel: 0171 2490344
Fax: 0171 2498748
Chef/Owner: Sivadas Sreedharan
Cost: Alc £15, fixed-price D £15 (3 courses). ☺ H/wine £7.50.
Times: Noon–last L 2.30pm/6pm–last D 11pm. Closed L Mon, 25-26 Dec
Additional: Children welcome; ❸ dishes
Seats: 45
Smoking: No smoking in dining room; air-conditioning
Credit cards: ▨ ▨ ▨ ▨

Red ❀ NEW

A newcomer to the Soho scene, Red's minimalist touches and Russian-tinged dishes appeal to a cosmopolitan crowd. Food from the limited menu is adventurous, and includes the likes of 'Kievskie kotlety' – stuffed chicken breast in a walnut crust, served with crisp salad. For dessert vodka brûlée with raspberries is a must.

Smoking: Air-conditioning. **Credit cards:** ▨ ▨ ▨ ▨

Directions: Nearest tubes Tottenham Court Rd & Leicester Sq

4 Greek Street W1
Map: D4
Tel: 0171 2874448
Fax: 0171 2874452
Chef: Kevin Mcloud
Owners: Novoport Group Ltd
Cost: Alc £25, fixed-price L £15. ☺ H/wine £12.
Times: Noon – last D 11.15pm. Closed Sun, Xmas
Additional: ❸ dishes

Red Fort ❀❀

'Cane chairs, soft Indian music, green plants and rich wall hangings against a plain background; serious service – there's a splendidly uniformed doorman in national costume and staff are well turned out,' commented an inspector who had time to take note – service turned out to be 'slow and leisurely'. However, the concise menu is well researched, and although there is a range of familiar tandoori specialities, other dishes are not found elsewhere. Hara kebab is a delicate spinach and yam patty with melon seeds and cottage cheese for contrast, and dried fenugreek for flavour. Chota pasanda was mini

77 Dean Street W1V 5HA
Map: D4
Tel: 0171 4372115/2525
Fax: 0171 4340721
Chef: Sitangsu Chakravarty
Owner: Amin Ali
Cost: Alc £30, fixed price L buffet £12.50. ☺ H/wine £9.95.
Times: Noon-Last L 2.30pm/5.30pm-last D 11.30pm
Additional: Sunday L; Children welcome; ❸ dishes

Red Fort

Seats: 140. Private dining room 80
Smoking: No-smoking area; air-conditioning
Credit cards: ▨ ▨ ▨ ▨ ▨ ▨

escalopes of lamb marinated in malt vinegar and black pepper, then chargrilled, and josh-e-nawab had excellent marinated lamb served in a simple stock highlighted with cardamom and marrow. Murg bemisaal is apparently their most popular dish – a 'delicious moist' chicken arrives under a naan crust in a sauce of garlic, tomato, cinnamon and cloves.

Directions: In between Oxford St & Shaftesbury Ave. Nearest Tube: Piccadilly Circus or Tottenham Court Road

Redmond's

NEW

Followers of Redmond Hayward's progress will be pleased to see he has fetched up in this salubrious London suburb. His new abode has a stylish look, with bright sunny yellow walls hung with modern art, blonde floorboards and bucket chairs on spindly legs. Good ideas, up-to-date thinking and an innate sense of balance were typically demonstrated in a lunch of terrrine of duck confit with duck liver and fennel and a prune compote, followed by a superb combination of roast salmon fillet with wilted leaves and a mild curry dressing. The flavours of an excellent raspberry soufflé and a stunning lemon grass ice cream slightly fought each other, but our inspector decided it was more a niggle than a problem. Dinner allows Redmond's imagination more rein with spider crab broth with clams, mussels, limeleaf and coriander, and scallops and cod with lemon, garlic and parsley couscous and squid ink sauce amongst the hard-to-choose-from menu.

Directions: Located half way between Putney and Richmond on the South Circular Road at the Barnes end of Sheen

170 Upper Richmond Road West SW14
Map GtL: B2
Tel: 0181 8781922
Fax: 0181 8781133
Chef: Redmond Hayward
Owners: Redmond & Pippa Hayward
Cost: Fixed-price L £16.50/D £21. ☺
Times: Noon-last L 2.30pm/7pm-last D 10.30pm. Closed L Sat, D Sun, 3 days Xmas, Bhs
Additional: Sunday L; Children welcome; ◑ dishes
Seats: 50
Credit cards: ▨ ▨ ▨ ▨

Red Pepper

NEW

Bare boards, simple decor and an informal atmosphere characterise this bustling neighbourhood restaurant. Lively, modern Italian cooking specialises in 'designer' pizzas from a wood-fired oven. A short, imaginative menu may also list agnolotti filled with pumpkin and mint, cuttlefish, artichoke and saffron risotto, and tiramisu.

Additional: Children welcome; ◑ dishes
Smoking: No pipes or cigars; air-conditioning
Credit cards: ▨ ▨ ▨ ▨

Directions: Nearest tube Warwick Ave

8 Formosa Street W9
Map: C4
Tel: 0171 266 2708
Chefs: Paolo Zancca, Manni Pasquale, Salvatore Mante
Owners: Mr & Mrs Behzadi
Cost: Alc £22, fixed-price L £15/D £22. ☺ H/wine £9.
Times: Last L-2.30pm (Sun 3.30pm)/D 10.45pm (Sun 10.30pm). Closed L Mon-Fri, Xmas, New Year

The Restaurant ✿✿✿✿✿

'My greatest praise is that it was such an occasion that I was almost seduced into forgetting I was inspecting.' writes one seasoned inspector on an evening of awe-inspiring theatre at Marco Pierre White's flagship restaurant. As we went to press we were informed by Marco Pierre White that he had closed The Restaurant at the Hyde Park Hotel and would be transferring to the Oak Room at Le Meridien Hotel, Piccadilly. The following report details meals taken at The Restaurant, but gives an idea of what is likely to be experienced at Le Meridien:

There is not the hustle and bustle associated with other London restaurants, care and attention are second to none. The smart and courteous staff are plentiful and completely dedicated to customer welfare, and show no condescension or patronisation. The menu reads like a roll call of luxury ingredients, and dishes show a preciseness in presentation and execution with hidden depths of composition and flavour that can sometimes be almost too intense, but never quite. Perfection is almost an obsession. There have been many plaudits for the cooking this year. A delicate crab and tomato mille-feuille with tomato vinaigrette was so 'delightfully a hint of summer in spring', red mullet soup with saffron and rouille had all the aroma and flavours of the sea, as did a marinière of shellfish with basil and caramelised calamares. Main courses outdid the high standards set by the starters. A bressole of Bresse pigeon with foie gras, having gone through three cooking processes, was perfect in presentation, flavour and texture, a daube of Scottish beef was well hung, boosted by its port marinade, and gave off flavours the likes of which are almost unknown in these days of 'quick kill to table', rabbit croustillante was delicate, a succulent saddle with a herb risotto. Desserts were superbly crafted and visually stunning, pyramide, a passion fruit sorbet and vanilla ice cream encased in pyramid shape by thin sugar walls, being an example.

Signature dishes: Lamb's trotter farci with lamb's sweetbreads, sauce grebiche; confit of salmon 'Grossel'; pigeon en vessie; truffle en surprise.

Tel: 0171 2595380 (The Restaurant)
Fax: 0171 2354552
Tel: 0171 7348000 (Le Meridien Hotel)
Telephone for details

Restaurant 192 ✿

Honest cooking based on fresh ingredients at this friendly, restaurant. At inspection a full flavoured fish soup with Gruyère and rouille was followed by calves' kidneys on a spinach and celeriac gratin. Home-made vanilla cheesecake came with poached summer fruits on a fruit coulis.

Times: Last L 3pm/D 11.30pm. Closed Aug Bh, Xmas
Additional: Bar meals; Sunday L; Children welcome; ✿ dishes
Smoking: No-smoking area; air-conditioning
Credit cards: ▄ ▄ ▄ ▄ ⬚

Directions: 5 mins from Ladbroke Grove Tube station, 10 mins walk from Notting Hill Tube station.

192 Kensington Park Road
W11 2ES
Map GtL: C3
Tel: 0171 2290482
Fax: 0171 7277133
Chef: Albert Clark
Owners: A Mackintosh, J Armit, T Chassay
Cost: *Alc* £25, fixed-price L £9.50.H/wine £9.85.

Ristorante L'Incontro ❀❀

87 Pimlico Road SW1W 8PH
Map: C1
Tel: 0171 7303663/6327
Fax: 0171 7305062
Chefs: Danilo Minuzzo,
Henrique de Carvalho
Owner: Gino Santin
Cost: Alc £39.50, fixed-price L
£16.50-£20.50 (2-3 courses). ☺
H/wine £18.50
Times: 12.30pm-last L 2.30pm/7pm-
last D 11.30pm (Sun 10.30pm).
Closed L Sat & Sun, 25-26 Dec,
some Bhs
Additional: Children welcome;
❸ dishes
Seats: 65. Private dining room 35-40
Smoking: No pipes; air-conditioning
Credit cards: ▬ ▦ ▦ ▨ ▣ ⌂

Smart, chic and costed accordingly, L'Incontro is proud of its
Venetian roots; the food and the whole business are part of
that love-affair with this north-eastern region of Italy. Cooking
of consistent quality is evident in dishes such as potato gnocchi
with fresh tomato and basil, roast quail with polenta and wild
mushrooms, and grilled langoustines with lime. At lunch, two
set-price menus are offered, featuring a selection of pasta, fish
and meat dishes along the lines of tagliatelle with aubergines,
tomato and black olives, and grilled swordfish. A number of
'one-dish meals' are also available and there's a spare luxury
about them, warm lobster salad with rocket, tomato and onion,
for example, that goes with the price tag. Desserts range from
tiramisu soaked in rum with coffee and mascarpone, to ice
creams and sorbets. Heart stopping espresso with traditional
Venetian biscuits finish the meal. The Italian wine list features
wines from all the regions, but is aimed at the serious spender.

Directions: From Lower Sloane Street, left into Pimlico Road,
restaurant is on R. Nearest tube: Sloane Square

Ritz Hotel ❀❀❀❀

150 Piccadilly W1V 9DG
Map: C3
Tel: 0171 4938181
Fax: 0171 4932687

Chef: David Nicolls

Owners: Ellerman Investments

What can be said that hasn't been said before about one of the
most celebrated and romantic dining-rooms in the country?
True, there is a slight feel of faded elegance, but the fantasy on
a French theme still works its special magic. The murals are
glorious exercises in trompe l'oeil, swooning maidens abound,
and gilding is everywhere. The service is formal, charming and

impeccably correct. An entirely orchestrated evening is conducted to the soundtrack of the grand piano, and the waiters, too, seem to glide along in waltz time. Inevitably melba toast is a table fixture, but the bread trolley (and there are trolleys for almost every conceivable eventuality) is laden with rolls and whole loaves of various sorts. David Nicholls has worked hard over the years to raise the quality of the cooking. The setting might be as ornate, but a starter of thinly sliced scallop drizzled with olive oil and balsamic vinegar and flashed under a grill until the shellfish had just turned translucent, was an intelligent dish of the sort which should be fêted as a model of restraint. A slightly more elaborate main course, a pot au feu of sea bass and langoustines with fèves and fennel, was equally superb, deliciously fresh fish, sympathetically handled. Other dishes typical of Nicholl's style might include salad of smoked duck with pickled oyster mushrooms and fillet of venison with horseradish cream potatoes, caramelised pear and onion compote. There are also grills such as lamb cutlets or fillet of Aberdeen Angus beef. Scotch woodcock is an alternative to desserts such as hot mango and passion fruit soufflé or a rich chocolate dome with chocolate biscuit and wild strawberry sauce. Exemplary petits fours are served with a choice of tea or coffee.

Signature dishes: Crown of asparagus, lobster and rocket salad; fillet of wild salmon confit, butternut pumpkin and celery risotto; terrine of foie gras canard, celeriac and trumpet mushrooms with pan-fried foie d'oie; roast coriander scallops with truffle risotto.

Cost: *Alc* £55, fixed-price L £29. ☺ H/wine £17.50
Times: 12.30pm-last L 2.45pm/6pm-last D 11pm (10.30pm Sun)
Additional: Palm Court; Children welcome; ♨ dishes
Seats:120. Private dining room 50. Jacket & tie preferred
Smoking: Air conditioning
Accommodation: 130 en suite
Credit cards: ▬ ▬ ▬ ▬ 🖭 🄶

Directions: Nearest Tube – Green Park

Riva Restaurant ❀❀❀

'Spot-on rustic Italian' sums it up perfectly. Riva is a completely unassuming place that advertises itself as a 'cafe restaurant'. Inside is a long room with a mirror along one wall and architectural prints on the other. The floor is coir-matted, tables are on the small side, chairs are the schoolroom type. What is offered is a menu of classic regional dishes mainly from the north east of the country. There are few daring tricks or cunning surprises but the food is delivered with exemplary style and honesty. A recent inspection kicked off with frittelle, a glorious assortment consisting of fritto misto, salt cod cakes, deep-fried Mediterranean prawns and vegetable fritters, with an excellent balsamic vinegar dip. To follow, there was a perfectly executed, tender osso buco alla milanese in a gutsy vegetable-based sauce topped with gremolata and served with a near-perfect saffron risotto made with Carnaroli rice, while dessert was a zuppa inglese with wonderful Marsala-laced sponge. There is also a great deal more that is likely to please. Sapori is a fish feast for two, involving crab claws, salt cod with polenta, eel in herb sauce with lentils, mussels in tomato pesto and grilled oysters; otherwise look for penne with baby octopus and Swiss chard, duck breast with cinnamon and onion sauce, and agnello gratinato (roast best end of lamb, with mustard-mint sauce, pecorino and herbs accompanied by a spinach and barley pancake. The one page (30 bin) wine list is all Italian apart from two champagnes (but try the Prosecco di Valdobbiadene, £17, as an alternative), and most are under £20. Pinot Grigio is £16.50 and Le Volte from the Ornellaia stable £17.

Directions: Junction of Church Rd with Castelau Rd. Nearest Tube – Hammersmith

169 Church Road Barnes SW13 9HR
Map GtL: C3
Tel: 0181 7480434
Chef: Francesco Zanchetta
Owner: Andrea Riva
Cost: *Alc* £25
Times: Noon-last L 2.30pm/7pm-last D 11pm. Closed L Sat, 12-28 Aug, 25 Dec-4 Jan
Additional: Children welcome
Seats: 50
Smoking: No pipes and cigars
Credit cards: ▬ ▬ ▬ ▬ 🄶

River Café ❀❀❀

An inspector described a meal here as 'one of the most memorable of the year'. The setting helps – from the stunning kitchen behind the metal bar counter to the conservatory doors that extend dining out beside the river in summer. Rose Gray and Ruth Rogers inject a palpable air of enthusiasm that ignites the atmosphere. The wood oven and chargrill are the favoured cooking methods – wood-roasted whole baby organic pig is stuffed with celery, fennel and garlic and served with wood-roasted beetroots, celeriac and pumpkin, for example. The source of heat, however, almost takes second place to the very best ingredients from Italy and selected sources closer to home. The focus is in assembling plates of spot-on complimentary ingredients rather than in technical wizardry. A typical starter of 'great' bruschetta, crisped in the wood oven, topped with the best olive oil, sweet roasted red and yellow peppers and thick brined anchovies was flavoured with capers, marjoram and basil to create a real taste of the sun. Rosemary sprigs, stripped of their leaves, are used as skewers for some pieces of 'cracklingly fresh' scallops and monkfish; these 'kebabs' are then chargrilled and served with a simple anchovy and rosemary sauce, tiny haricots verts, anchovies and outstanding roasted-in-the-bunch vine tomatoes. A summery pudding was a textbook version of pannacotta full of vanilla seeds, with delicious, unadulterated fresh raspberries. The splendidly chauvinist wine list is (Champagne apart) entirely Italian and unfailingly well chosen. Tuscany takes the tapioca, with Chianti from Isole e Olena and Brunello di Montalcino from Argiano at moderate prices, although Allegrini's hedonistic 1990 Amarone Classico Della Valpolicella at £33 is a Veneto heavyweight of thumping good value.

Thames Wharf Studios
Rainville Road W6 9HA
Map GtL: C3
Tel: 0171 3818824
Fax: 0177 3816217
Chefs: Rose Gray, Ruth Rogers, Theo Randal
Owners: Rose Gray, Ruth Rogers, Richard Rogers
Cost: Alc £40. H/wine £9.50
Times: 12.30pm-last L 3pm/7.30pm-last D 9.45pm. Closed D Sun, Xmas, New Year, Bhs
Additional: Children welcome; ❁ dishes
Seats: 95
Smoking: No pipes & cigars
Credit cards: ▬ ▨ ▨ ▨ ▢

Directions: Off Fulham Palace Rd. Junction of Rainville Road and Bowfell Road. Nearest Tube – Hammersmith

Royal China ❀❀

Bustling, colourful, modern Chinese with a large Chinese clientele and prompt, efficient service. The lunch menu offers a large choice of one plate noodle dishes such as a good mixed seafood and shredded meat with a mix of soft and crisp noodles, and dim sum (amongst them some well reported prawn and chive dumplings and minced pork and roasted pork bun); dinner takes in a varied selection of familiar fare, mostly from the Cantonese region. Set menus for two or more people are worth considering as they are more imaginative than most. Jasmine tea is probably the best accompaniment.

13 Queensway W2 4QJ
Map GtL: C3
Tel/Fax: 0171 2212535
Chef: Simon Man
Owner: Pearl Investments Ltd
Cost: Alc £22, fixed-price D £22. ☺ H/wine £8.50.
Times: Noon-last D 11pm (11.30pm Fri, Sat, 10.30pm Sun)
Additional: Children welcome; ❁ dishes
Seats: 180. Private dining room 40

Smoking: Air-conditioning
Credit cards: ▬ ▨ ▨ ▨ ▨ ▢

Directions: Between Queensway & Bayswater Station.

Royal China ❀

Sister restaurant to the one of the same name in Queensway (see entry above)), this is a good place for lunchtime dim sums and noodles. Main courses include crab meat with soft noodles and spicy Singapore noodles with mixed meat and shredded vegetables. Service can be slow at busy times.

3 Chelverton Road Putney SW15
Map GtL: C2
Tel: 0181 788 0907
Telephone for details

Directions: N from traffic lights in Putney High Street, Chelverton Road is 2nd L. Nearest Tube – East Putney

Royal Garden Hotel ⊛⊛

2-24 Kensington High Street W8 4PT
Map GtL: C3
Tel: 0171 9378000/3611910
Fax: 0171 3611921
Chef: Paul Farr
Owner: The Goodwood Hotel Group
Cost: *Alc* £30. Fixed-price L £19.95 ☺
Times: Noon-last L 3pm/5.30pm-last
D 11.30pm. Closed L Sat, Sun, Bhs
Additional: Children welcome.
☙ dishes.
Seats: 86
Smoking: No-smoking area; no pipes
in dining room; air-conditioning
Accommodation: 402 en suite
Credit cards: ▬ ▬ ▬ ▬ ▣ ▢

As if AA endorsement were not sufficient enough, certain dishes on the *carte* of the lively Tenth restaurant appear with extra star billing. Crab and saffron pudding soufflé with watercress butter sauce, for example, comes recommended by Joan Plowright, and the rack of lamb with wild mushroom mash, fresh asparagus and tomato basil sauce by a whole trio of famous thesps. It's all in a good cause, though, and for each dish selected with the special logo, the hotel donates £1 to the National Youth Theatre of Great Britain. Another good idea is a range of set-price dinner menus alongside the main *carte*, especially when the £27.50 menu of chargrilled vegetables with red onion salad and oyster mushrooms, seared salmon with rocket and Parmesan risotto and fresh asparagus, and peach brûlée with a basil and peach compote sounds equally as tempting, if less up-beat, as the one for £40.25 of duck and apple cannelloni with fried cabbage and beetroot jus, roasted lobster and John Dory with a cardamom cream sauce and aromatic noodles and pavé of white and dark chocolate with an orange and Cointreau nage.

Directions: Next door to Kensington
Palace. Nearest Tube – Kensington
High Street

Royal Lancaster Hotel ⊛⊛

Lancaster Terrace W2 2TY
Map GtL: C3
Tel: 0171 2626737
Fax: 0171 7243191
Chef: Nigel Blatchford
Owners: The Lancaster Landmark
Hotel Co. Ltd
Cost: *Alc* £25, fixed-price L&D
£23.50. H/wine £17
Times: Noon-last L 2.30pm/6.30pm-
last D 10.30pm. Closed L Sat, D Sun
Seats: 70. Private dining room
Smoking: No-smoking area; no pipes
& cigars; air-conditioning
Accommodation: 418 en suite
Credit cards: ▬ ▬ ▬ ▬ ▣ ▢

Directions: Nearest Tube – Lancaster
Gate. Next to Hyde Park on the
Bayswater Road

There are fine views of Hyde Park from the windows of the first-floor Park Restaurant, and the dining room is suitably decorated with original paintings inspired by the outlook. Crystal chandeliers glitter above your head, elaborately draped and tasselled curtains hang at the windows; the mood is traditional and luxurious. The menu is fixed-price for two or three courses and it divides between mainstream French classics – asparagus with hollandaise, Dover sole meunière, fillet steak with béarnaise sauce – plus dishes with a more modern accent and some unexpected touches. Crab cake is served with sweetcorn risotto, duck confit comes with pickled beetroot salad, while, in more conventional vein, grilled sea bass arrives with saffron potatoes and red wine butter. The centrepiece of a recent inspection was roast breast of corn-fed chicken with soft garlic cloves, button onions, and a cream sauce suffused with morels, while proceedings concluded with cold caramelised orange tart with citrus compote. France dominates the lengthy hotel wine list.

Royal Westminster Thistle

See Where London Meets page 161

RSJ

Over the past 18 years, this likeable old-stager has expanded onto three levels, with pine-boarded floors and what might be described as 'subtle glimpses of Art Deco'. The kitchen follows an up-to-the-minute path picking up influences from France and the Med along the way. Fish is a strong suit: a starter of salmon cooked five ways with orange and walnut dressing impressed with its accuracy and exact presentation. Otherwise expect pan-fried sea bass on niçoise salad with basil oil, caramelised scallops with a tagliatelle of asparagus, baby fennel and a vanilla jus, or pan-fried calves' liver with Savoy cabbage and a sauce of Madeira and shallots. Vegetarians might go for a risotto of sun-dried tomatoes and pesto. As for desserts, there might be passionfruit tart with raspberry sauce or chocolate mille-feuille with coconut ice cream. The wine list is a pure joy; what it offers is a hand-picked collection that meanders tantalisingly and almost exclusively around the Loire, taking in great vineyards, little known treasures and even some biodynamic offerings along the way.

Directions: On the corner of Coin St and Stamford St; near National Theatre and LWT studios

13A Coin Street SE1 8YQ
Map: E3
Tel: 0171 9284554
Fax: 0171 6330489
Chef: Peter Lloyd
Owner: Nigel Wilkinson
Cost: *Alc* £25, fixed-price L&D £15.95. ☺ H/wine £9.95.
Times: Noon-2pm/6pm-11pm. Closed L Sat, Sun, Bhs
Additional: Children welcome; dishes
Seats: 90. Private dining room 20
Smoking: No pipes & cigars; air-conditioning
Credit cards: ▬ ▨ ▨ ▨ ▯

Rules

'This was one of my best meals at Rules', is an inspector's verdict on this appealing Covent Garden restaurant, reputedly the oldest in London. (Rules was established in 1798 and is celebrating its bicentenary this year.) Game remains a prominent feature and the rest of the menu is a celebration of the best of British produce and ideas: Aberdeen Angus beef makes various appearances in dishes such as steak, kidney and oyster pudding with creamed potatoes and root vegetable purée, and there are Morecombe Bay potted shrimps, an assortment of smoked fish with anchovy and horseradish, and Dover sole, or smoked haddock fish cakes. Spiced crab and avocado salad has been well reported, as has the generous steak and kidney pie. Raspberry syllabub trifle makes a fitting end to the meal although Welsh rarebit makes a savoury alternative. Wines come from the 'former colonies'.

Directions: Nearest Tube – Covent Garden

35 Maiden Lane Covent Garden WC2E 7LB
Map: D3
Tel: 0171 8365314
Fax: 0171 4971081
Chef: David Chambers
Owner: John P Mayhew
Cost: *Alc* £29, fixed-price L £15.95. ☺ H/wine £10.95.
Times: Noon-last D 11.30pm. Closed 3 days Xmas
Additional: Children welcome; dishes
Seats: 128
Smoking: No pipes in dining room; air-conditioning
Credit cards: ▬ ▨ ▨ ▨ ▨ ▯

Sabras ❀❀

Little wonder Sabras is not far off its quarter century. This clean and bright, simply decorated Indian vegetarian restaurant is, in its class, outstanding. The most striking feature is the pristine freshness of all the ingredients, with seasoning and balance of flavours that cannot be faulted. A seemingly pedestrian dish of *chevati-dal*, four varieties of split lentils cooked with garlic and spices, for example, was astonishingly good, as were masala dhosa, large, thin, crispy South Indian pancakes filled with potatoes, onions and spices, and the deluxe sev-puri, tiny deep-fried puffs filled with a savoury mixture which literally exploded in the mouth. Baby aubergines stuffed with gram flour and coconut and slowly cooked with aromatic spices were the perfect accompaniment to quick-fried rice with lemon, turmeric and mustard. Pistachio kulfi, a solid Indian ice cream made with thickened milk, sugar and cardamom makes a lovely ending to the meal.

Directions: Nearest tube – Willesden Green

Willesden High Road, NW10 2RX
Map Gtl: C3
Tel: 0181 4590340
Chefs/Owners: Hemant & Nalinee Desai
Cost: *Alc* £15. H/wine £9.95
Times: Telephone for lunch times. 6.30pm-10.30pm. Closed Mon
Additional: Children welcome; ❃ dishes
Seats: 32
Smoking: No-smoking area; no pipes & cigars
Credit cards: None

St George's ❀

In a building shared with the BBC, this unique hotel has a ground floor reception and no further public areas until the 15th floor. The views over London are stunning. A brasserie has taken over from the restaurant with an up-beat, modern menu along the lines of sirloin steak with crispy bacon and tarragon mash and red onion confit, and lemon tart with julienne of orange zest.

Directions: Langham Place is N end of Regent St

Langham Place W1N 8QS
Map: C4
Tel: 0171 6361939
Fax: 0171 4367997
Telephone for details

St John ❀❀

'Bring an appetite', advises an inspector. The setting is a former smokehouse on the edge of Smithfield Market – you can still see the racks above the bar in what was the smoke hole. This is a unique set-up devoted to the principle of 'nose to tail eating'; where else in London could you call in for a supper of duck hearts on toast, or bloodcake and fried egg? The cooking is unashamedly direct and generous, and it pulls no punches. Its roots may be 'down home' but the results are several notches above cloth-cap working class. Sausages are priced by the inch, pork rillettes come with a great pile of gherkins, proper brawn appears with chicory and sorrel, although the signature dish is roast bone marrow and parsley salad. Fish lovers could opt for native oysters or smoked haddock and potato soup and, in season, there are glorious game dishes such as perfectly roasted teal served on a purée of Jerusalem artichoke with a great bowl of buttered Brussels sprout tops. There's no obligation to have more than a snack and a pint of Youngs in the bar, but it would be sinful to miss out on school puddings such as plum crumble or stuffed baked apple. The well-chosen wine list provides plenty by the glass.

Directions: 3 mins walk from Farringdon Tube & BR stations. The restaurant is 100 metres from Smithfield Market on N side

26 St John Street EC1M 4AY
Map: F5
Tel: 0171 2514080/4998
Fax: 0171 2514998
Chef: Fergus Henderson
Owners: Trevor Gulliver
Ptrs: Fergus Henderson, Jon Spiteri
Times: Noon-last L 3pm/6pm-last D 11.30pm. Closed L Sat, Sun, Xmas/New Year
Additional: Bar meals; Children welcome; ❃ dishes
Seats: 100. Private dining room 22
Credit cards:

St Quentin Brasserie ☘☘

Just a hop and a skip from Harrods, and well worth the walk to sample the food at this quintessentially French brasserie. From the minute you enter this smart, traditional wood panelled room you are transported to Paris: the staff are French, the food simple but faultless. Here are the real brasserie staples of French onion soup, quenelles de brochette, confit, boudin blanc, pig's trotters stuffed with morels, tarte Tatin. An inspection lunch opened with the 'deepest, richest darkest green' nettle soup, served in a large, white individual tureen with excellent, crusty baguette ("no side plates, of course'). Leek and Gorgonzola risotto was properly soupy with a good balance of flavours, just a hint of cheese and a little leek in every mouthful, the rice slightly al dente. Prune and Armagnac mousse, recommended by the waiter, was 'amazing'. The extensive wine list is entirely French, with a super range offered by the glass.

Directions: Nearest Tube: South Kensington. Opposite The Brompton Oratory

243 Brompton Road SW3 2EP
Map: B2
Tel: 0171 5898005
Fax: 0171 5846064
Chef: Nigel Davis
Cost: Alc £27, fixed-price L £11 (2 courses). ☺ H/wine £9.90.
Times: Noon-last L 3pm/6.30pm-last D 11pm
Additional: Sunday L; Children welcome; ✿ dishes
Seats: 75-80. Private dining room 20
Smoking: No pipes & cigars; air-conditioning
Credit cards: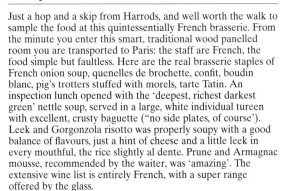

Salloos ☘☘

Mr Salahuddin (Salloos) set up his restaurant business in Pakistan in 1969 before moving to this Knightsbridge mews house ten years later. Remarkably, his head chef has stayed the course since the very beginning. The first-floor restaurant is a bright modern room with fretted windows, paintings secreted in little arches, brass fittings and warm colours. The cooking is a blend of Mughali and home cooking often inspired by family recipes. What sets the place apart from most of its rivals is the quality and freshness of the raw materials and the keenness of the spicing. Meat and fish are given exemplary treatment in the tandoori: marinated lamb chops are a speciality, but the range extends to flavoursome chicken shish kebab, quails and king prawns. Elsewhere, the kitchen delivers gosht khara masala scattered with pungent unground spices, murgh korma and haleem akbari (shredded lamb cooked with wheatgerm and lentils). Naan bread is good and fresh. Mr Salloos' daughters oversee the dining room with impeccable charm.

Directions: Nr. Hyde Park Corner – take 1st L into Wilton Place, 1st R opposite Berkeley Hotel. Nearest tube – Knightsbridge

62-64 Kinnerton Street, SW1X 8ER
Map: B2
Tel: 0171 2354444
Fax: 0171 2595703
Chef: Abdul Aziz
Owner: Mr Muhammad Salahuddin
Cost: Alc £30, fixed-price L £16/D £25 (4 courses). ☺ H/wine £12.50.
Times: Noon-last L 2.30pm/7pm-last D 11.15pm. Closed Sun, Dec 25-26
Additional: No children under 8, ✿ dishes
Seats: 65
Smoking: No pipes and cigars; air-conditioning
Credit cards: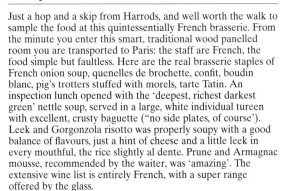

Entries in this Guide are based on reports filed by our team of professionally trained, full-time inspectors.

Samratt ⊛

Inexpensive, popular Indian restaurant just off Putney High Street. Starters include garlic chicken, vegetable samosas and mulligatawny soup. For a main course try the fiery chicken jalfrazee, or lamb sag with the onion, almond and spinach flavours shining through.

Additional: Children welcome; ⑤ dishes
Credit cards: ▆▆ ▨▨ ▀◥ ◪

Directions: 5 mins walk from Putney Bridge

18/20 Lacy Road SW15 1NL
Map GtL: C2
Tel: 0181 7889110
Chef: MD Lulu Miah
Owners: Mr SN Datta
Cost: Alc £17. ☺
Times: Last L 2.30pm/D 11.30pm.
Closed 25-26 Dec

San Lorenzo Fuoriporto ⊛

More than 25 years old and still capable of pulling in the crowds for rustic Italian food. Pappardelle with wild boar sauce, and braised lamb shank with polenta are typical dishes from the menu. Ciabatta is home-made, as are the ice creams. Smart decor, polite service, decent Italian wines.

Directions: Bottom of Wimbledon Hill Road, right into Worple Road, then first right into Worple Road Mews

Worple Road Mews SW19 7PA
Map GtL: C2
Tel: 0181 9468463
Fax: 0181 9479810
Telephone for details

Santini ⊛

29 Ebury Street SW1W 0NZ
Map: C1
Tel: 0171 7304094/8275
Fax: 0171 7300544
Chef: Giuseppe Rosselli
Owner: Gino Santin
Cost: Alc £37.50, fixed-price L £19.75. ☺ H/wine £15.
Times: Last L 2.30pm/D 11.30pm.
Closed L Sat, L Sun, Some Bhs, 25-26 Dec

Venetian cooking is the speciality of this smartly refurbished and very Italian restaurant. The expensive evening carte lists a wide choice of antipasti and pasta dishes, tagliatelle with fresh crab, for instance, alongside sea bass in herb sauce and braised knuckle of veal with saffron rice. Modestly priced lunch menu.

Additional: Children welcome; ⑤ dishes
Smoking: No pipes in dining room; air-conditioning
Credit cards: ▆▆ ▨▨ ▨▨ ▀◥ ◪ ⊂

Directions: On corner of Ebury Street and Lower Belgrave Street, 2 mins walk from Victoria station

Savoy Grill ⊛⊛

The great, the good, the famous, and the simply rich have gathered for lunch in the sophisticated surroundings of the Savoy Grill for decades. Today, the dining room continues to bustle with well-heeled guests, served by an army of waiters who provide appropriately polished service. The menu features

1 Savoy Hill, Strand, WC2R 0EU
Map: E3
Tel: 0171 8364343
Fax: 0171 2406040

Chef: David Sharland

Owner: The Savoy
Cost: Alc £45, fixed-price D £29.75.
H/wine £17.25
Times: 12.30pm-last L 2.30pm/6pm-
last D 11.15pm. Closed L Sat, Sun,
Aug, Bhs
Additional: Children welcome;
👶 dishes
Seats: 100
Smoking: No-smoking area;
air-conditioning
Accommodation: 202 en suite
Credit cards: ▬ ▬ ▬ ▬ ▬ ▬

dishes from the trolley at both lunch and dinner (for example beef Wellington on Tuesday evenings), plus a *carte* that mixes traditional favourites with more sophisticated offerings. These could include monk fish and lobster Thermidor with saffron noodles, wood pigeon with truffle sauce, salsify and French beans, and thinly sliced liver and bacon on creamed potato and cheddar. The choice of starters is eclectic, try clam chowder with garlic flutes or tortellini with scallops in vegetable broth. Sweets range from chocolate tart with white pastry, to lemon crème brûlée.

Directions: See following entry

The Savoy, River Restaurant

1 Savoy Hill Strand WC2
Map: E3
Tel: 0171 8364343
Fax: 0171 2406040
Chef: Anton Edelmann
Owner: The Savoy Group plc
Cost: Alc £45. Fixed-price D £42.50.
H.wine £17.25.
Times: 12.30pm-last L 2.30pm/7pm-
last D 11.30pm (10.30pm Sun).
Additional: Sunday L;
Children welcome; 👶 dishes.
Seats: 160. Jacket and tie preferred
Smoking: No-smoking area;
air-conditioning
Accommodation: 202 en suite.
Credit cards: ▬ ▬ ▬ ▬ ▬ ▬

Six nights out of seven, diners can dance the night away to a backdrop of the Embankment Gardens and the Thames. It's all very polished and consummately professional, with smart table settings, well-spaced tables, smoked salmon and dessert trolleys and dishes served under silver cloches. The *carte* highlights some of Anton Edelmann's signature dishes, such as roast sea bass on brandade with fennel and basil olive oil, exquisitely timed to give a fine balance of flavours. Our inspector chose to precede this with a Roquefort risotto with artichokes, equally exact, with a slight give to the rice and a distant hint of stock and wine. Sophisticated technique meets first-class ingredients in dishes such as courgette blossom filled with seafood on white crab meat, lobster and scallop fricassée in an orange

cream sauce, and sautéed breast of duck on couscous with
fantasy of vegetables. There are grand, wallet-stretching
ingredients such as lobster, gulls' eggs, goose liver and truffles,
but Edelmann also deals in a more bourgeois currency with
braised pig's trotters filled with smoked ham and sage and
traditional fish soup with rouille and garlic croûtons. A nod in
the direction of fashionable trends comes with grilled turbot in
a wasabi butter sauce with summer truffles, but for those times
when all one craves is a superb piece of beef, then
Chateaubriand with béarnaise sauce and soufflé potatoes will
hit the spot. A special seasonal menu has been devised with
the help of sommelier Werner Wissmann that expertly matches
food and wine; fillet of lamb on an aubergine purée with a
courgette tart, for example, is paired with Château
Monbousquet (St Emilion) 1990, and pine honey soufflé with
red wine ice cream (a test for any taste-buds), with Château
Loubens, grand cru (Ste Croix-du-Mont) 1989.

  Signature dishes: Twice-baked spinach and smoked haddock
soufflé with quail's eggs; fillet of lamb on aubergine caviar with
a courgette tart; mosaique of marinated tomatoes, aubergines
and goat's cheese; cappuccino soufflé with thyme ice cream.

Directions: From Embankment Tube, you can walk east through
the riverside gardens to the hotel

Scotts ❈

*Traditional old stager that's undergone a major facelift. Now light,
bright and airy, but still patronised by captains of industry tucking
into reconstructed English dishes and enjoying the old-school
service. Go for cock-a-leekie, deep-fried cod and chips, grilled Dover
sole, collop of veal and oyster with sautéed potatoes and wilted
spinach.*

Additional: Bar meals; Sunday brunch; Children welcome;
❈ dishes
Smoking: No-smoking area; no pipes; air conditioning
Credit cards: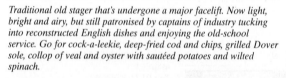

20 Mount Street W1 6HE
Map: C3
Tel: 0171 6295248
Fax: 0171 6298246
Chef: Nigel Davies
Owner: Groupe Chez Gerard plc
Cost: *Alc* £20, fixed-price L £22.75.
H/wine £13.
Times: Last L 3pm/last D 11.30pm.
Closed 25 Dec

Directions: Mount St runs between Park Lane and Berkeley Sq.
Nearest Tube – Green Park

Searcy's Brasserie ❈❈❈

Eschewing elaborate presentation, Richard Corrigan's cooking
concentrates on flavour and good ingredients that come from
all over the British isles, as well as Corrigan's native Ireland.
Wherever possible, he uses free-range and organic produce.
Classic country cooking is given an injection of cosmopolitan
flair in dishes such as herby smoked haddock croquettes served
on a bed of grated carrot flavoured with cardamom and curry
oil, and a lovely, fresh-tasting courgette and basil soup was
given added interest by basil, pepper and garlic croutons. Free-
range Welsh roast chicken breast was an imaginative variation
on a traditional theme, with a mousse of bread, bacon and
sage, garnished with salsify, wild mushrooms and various
greens. A refined interpretation of 'champ' was served
alongside. The chocolate tart, from Corrigan's French pastry
chef, was described as 'one of the best I've had' – thin pastry,
with rich, soft, yet light filling served with a little vanilla ice
cream and pool of raspberry coulis. Christophe Maison's

Library Floor
Barbican Centre
Silk Street EC2Y 8DS
Map: F4
Tel: 0171 5883008
Fax: 0171 3827247
Chefs: Richard Corrigan,
Tomaslav Ilic
Cost: £30, fixed-price L £20.50. ☺
Times: Noon-2.45pm/5pm-10.30pm.
Closed L Sat, 25-26 Dec
Additional: Bar meals; Sunday L;
Children welcome; ❈ dishes
Seats: 120
Smoking: No-smoking area;
air-conditioning
Credit cards: ▬▬ ▤ ▤ ➥ ⚉ ❴

chocolate truffles, with their crispy shell and almost runny filling are also unmissable. The restaurant itself has clean-cut and unobtrusive decor with large picture windows overlooking the complexities of the Barbican Centre. Service is watchful and un-intimidating. A concise list with something for everyone and champagne offered by the glass at £4.95 and £5.50. Some interesting Bordeaux include a Ch Maucaillou '89 at £30.50 and Ch Kirwan '88 at £59. From Corbières, the Ch Hélène, gris de gris, is good summer drinking at £13.50.

Signature dishes: Sauté of hare, chilli and chocolate pasta; fillet of red mullet, brandade of sardine and asparagus

Directions: Nearest Tubes – Barbican and Moorgate

The Selfridge Thistle ❀❀

Soft lighting and intimate booths muffle the swirl of traffic and shoppers all around this central hotel. The cooking is soundly based on classical principles, and the up-market dishes show considerable technical skills; artichoke bottoms, for example, wrapped in pasta, filled with creamed crab on a warm scallop and asparagus salad. Many dishes are layered – pan-fried monkfish on a 'mille-feuille' of creamed smoked haddock and celeriac, Scottish turbot topped with roasted skate with caper and watercress vinaigrette, but there are also traditional choices such as chargrilled spring chicken with a devil sauce. Some imaginative desserts include chocolate cannelloni filled with ricotta, pine kernels and orange, and honey-roasted pear with lemon grass ice cream.

Directions: Off Oxford Street behind Selfridge's department store. Equidistant from Bond Street or Marble Arch tubes

Orchard Street W1H 0JS
Map: B4
Tel: 0171 4082080
Fax: 0171 4937590
Chef: Mark Page
Owner: Thistle Hotels plc
Cost: Alc £25, fixed-price L&D £19.50. ☺ H/wine £13.50.
Times: 12.30pm-last L 2.30/6.30pm-last D 10.30pm.
Closed L Sat, Sun, mid Aug
Additional: Bar food; Children welcome; ♿ dishes
Seats: 60. Private dining room 14
Smoking: No-smoking area; no pipes or cigars; air-conditioning
Accommodation: 295 en suite
Credit cards: ■ ▦ ▦ ▦ ▣ ▯

755 Fulham Road ❀❀

755 Fulham Road SW6
Map: A1
Tel: 0171 3710755
Fax: 0171 3710095
Chef: Alan Thompson
Owners: Alan & Georgina Thompson
Cost: Fixed-price L £10 (2 courses)/D £18 (2 courses). H/wine £9.50
Times: 12.30pm-last L 2.30pm (Sun noon-4pm)/7pm-last D 11pm.
Closed D Sun, Mon, Bhs
Additional: Sunday L; children welcome
Seats: 60. Private dining room 30
Smoking: Air-conditioning
Credit cards: ■ ▦ ▦ ▦ ▯

The address may be easy to remember, but the choice once you get there is another matter. Alan and Georgina Thompson's modern blue and yellow restaurant is comfortable and relaxed, with seating either on banquettes or well-upholstered chairs. The orientation is New World, but that encompasses dishes as diverse as mille-feuille of sweetbreads and bacon, poached halibut with fennel and star aniseed and roast fillet of hare with truffled mushrooms and creamed Brussels sprouts. There is a lively air to the cooking, and a willingness to mix and match ideas without losing control –

griddled foie gras is wittily paired with Yorkshire pudding and Madeira, seared scallops with salt cod brandade and aubergine crisps. Otherwise, try sashimi of wild salmon with ginger, garlic and soy dressing or the breast of duck with sweetcorn purée and fondant potato. The set menu changes daily – a typical Saturday night's dinner might start with sautéed duck fillets with ceps and roquette, followed by roast hake with mussels and saffron jus and either a selection of cheese or pear sabayon with vanilla ice cream.

Directions: Nearest Tube – Parsons Green

Shaw's Restaurant ❀❀

119 Old Brompton Road SW7 3RN
Map: A1
Tel: 0171 3737774
Fax: 0171 3705102
Chef: Jean-Pierre Venuto
Owners: Sir Neil & Lady Shaw, David Bank, Torunn Fieldhouse
Cost: Alc £50, fixed price L £18.50/D £32.95. ☺ H/wine £14.50
Times: Noon-last L 2pm/7pm-last D 10pm. Closed L Sat, Sun, 1 wk Easter, 2 wks Aug, 1 wk Xmas
Additional: Children welcome; ⓪ dishes.
Seats: 45
Smoking: No pipes or cigars; air-conditioning
Credit cards: ▆ ▆ ▆ ▆ ▆ ▆

Directions: Nearest Tubes – Gloucester Road, South Kensington

There is an air of dependable solidity about this eighteenth-century coach house, with its rather gentrified atmosphere, gilt-framed mirrors and original paintings on the walls. Frances and Gerald Atkins have moved on, leaving Jean-Pierre Venuto in charge of the kitchen, but little else has changed. Lunch and theatre menus are short and to-the-point, dinner brings a more extensive choice although the style is similar. The cooking is sufficiently modern to challenge the palate, without setting any alarm bells ringing. Foie gras terrine with dandelion salad, aubergine flower with warm goat's cheese and red mustard leaves, and potato 'nets' garnished with quails' eggs, tofu and wild garlic suggest the kitchen has tapped into Britain's free larder for embellishment. Elsewhere there is plenty of sound technique and skill in, say, salt cod and sorrel soufflé with fennel salad, duo of rabbit with a spicy cumin jus, and peppered loin of lamb with polenta, green beans and ratatouille. Decent sweets might include glazed gâteau of young rhubarb with a 'superb' ginger sorbet. A clutch of quality wines by the glass and half bottles head the intelligently chosen list.

Shepherds ❀❀

Marsham Court Marsham Street SW1P 4LA
Map: D2
Tel: 0171 8349552
Fax: 0171 8280847
Chef: James Rice
Owners: Richard Shepherd, Michael Caine
Cost: Alc £39, fixed-price L&D £22.95. ☺ H/wine £10.95.

This smart, club-like restaurant co-owned by Michael Caine, is always a sound bet for English cooking along the endangered species lines of Stilton and onion tart, potted duck with cranberry compote, grilled calves' liver with bacon and onions, and Cumberland sausage and mash. Grilled tuna fish with rocket and horseradish sauce creeps in amongst the roast mallard with sage and onion stuffing and apple sauce, and the roast rib of beef and Yorkshire pud from the trolley, but thankfully that's about it. A little inconsistency in the execution, though, has been noted this year – black pudding with caramelised apples was a bit of a let-down and not helped by a rather heavy onion sauce. Desserts stick to the tried and tested – treacle tart and custard, apple and cinnamon crumble, and cabinet pudding, plus a few good cheeses.

Directions: Near Tate Gallery and Westminster Hospital. Nearest Tube – Pimlico

Times: 12.30pm-2.45pm/6.30pm-11.30pm. Closed Sat, Sun, Bhs.
Additional: Bar food; Children welcome; ❹ dishes.
Seats: 90. Private dining room 30
Smoking: Air-conditioning
Credit cards: ▃ ▃ ▃ ▃ ▣ ▢

Sheraton Park Tower ❀❀❀

As a Breton, Pascal Proyart can perhaps be forgiven a rather portentous menu quote about the 'magic and mysterious world of fish, shellfish and crustaceans', particularly in view of the fact that a meal in this classy, fish-orientated hotel restaurant displays his fine native understanding of the raw ingredients. The cooking shows considerable style and he shrewdly sticks with the deluxe repertoire he fully understands. Choosing the 'cuisine de la mer' *carte*, one might begin with tian of Cornish crab with provençale vegetables, or rock oysters served on ice or warm with champagne sabayon and caviar. Sea bass is a speciality, but other choices include roasted monkfish in peppercorns with a potato and morel dauphinoise, or St Pierre with ginger and coriander in a sauce of lobster with curry spices. There is a 'menu dégustation', as well as a 'menu de la mer,' which includes ballotine of salmon with truffade of cauliflower and keta caviar, as well as sole 'cuit au plat' with wild mushrooms and chive mousseline. Fish-eating, however, is not compulsory – the *carte* also includes meaty dishes such as traditional farmhouse stew of venison in a red wine sauce and sautéed spätzle, and roast lamb cutlet in a cage of puff pastry with a caviar of aubergine. Desserts are mainstream French – crème brûlée with vanilla bourbon and pancake of exotic fruits flambéed with Grand Marnier.
   Signature dishes: Scottish scallops glazed with a truffle sauce with copeaux of smoked foie gras; whole cooked sea bass in a crust of Guérande sea salt, with a blend of virgin olive oil and flat parsley (for two); sea bass roasted on its skin with crushed potato and a light jus of girolles; wild feuilleté of Dublin Bay prawns with celeriac and chervil.

Directions: Nearest Tube – Knightsbridge

101 Knightsbridge SW1X 7RN
Map: B2
Tel: 0171 2356067
Fax: 0171 2358231
Chef: Pascal Proyart
Owner: Sheraton Park Tower Hotel
Cost: *Alc* £45, fixed-price L £19.50-£22.50/D £34-£48. ☺ H/wine £15.50
Times: Noon-last L 3pm/6pm-last D 11pm
Additional: Sunday L; Children welcome; ❹ dishes
Seats: 80
Smoking: No-smoking area; air-conditioning
Accommodation: 289 en suite
Credit cards: ▃ ▃ ▃ ▣

Simply Nico ❀❀❀

In July 1996, Simply Nico (like its sibling Nico Central) transferred to The Restaurant Partnership and Richard Hugill took on the lead role as chef. Little else has changed. The ground floor dining room is long, narrow and bare-boarded, with clean colours and a general air of discreet bonhomie. MPs tend to use the place as a bolt-hole from the House, while other customers are drawn from Westminster and beyond. Menus are fixed-price for two or three courses and the kitchen's heart is in the world of the brasserie. It trots out such things as confit of guinea fowl terrine with shallot and orange dressing, boudin blanc with apples, spinach and Madeira sauce, and grilled leg of lamb steak with ratatouille and a rosemary beurre noisette. A recent inspection lunch began in fine style with a neatly presented tartlet of artichokes and mushrooms with a poached egg, followed by spanking-fresh fillet of cod,

48a Rochester Row SW1P 1JU
Map: D2
Tel: 0171 6308061
Fax: 0171 8288541
Chef: Richard Hugill
Owner: The Restaurant Partnership
Cost: H/wine £13
Times: Noon-last L 2pm/7pm-last D 11pm. Closed L Sat, Sun, 1 wk Xmas, Bhs
Additional: No children under 12; ❹ dishes
Seats: 45
Smoking: No pipes & cigars; air-conditioning
Credit cards: ▃ ▃ ▃ ▃ ▣ ▢

roasted and served on a compote of tomatoes with basil oil that perfectly complemented the fish. As an accompaniment, great chips and silky pommes purée are worth every penny of the extra cost. There's a simplicity and honesty about the cooking here that belies the skill that defines matters behind the scenes. Desserts are winners all the way: sharply flavoured roast rhubarb crumble with soothing clotted cream, glazed pear with liquorice ice cream, or crème brûlée with soft Italian cheese and red fruits, for example. Service by smartly turned out staff is attentive and professional, although smiles may be in short supply. An easy to read concise wine list comprising 50 bins from around the world. Some interesting selections mostly under £25. Good value are Viognier at £19, St-Joseph Deschant from Chapoutier at £24.50. La Volte Ornellaia from the Antinori stable is worth a try at £20.

Signature dishes: Chilled asparagus flan with pea sauce; terrine of smoked, marinated and fresh salmon; roast duck breast with ceps and Sicilian olives; pear tarte Tatin with vanilla ice cream.

Directions: Corner of Emery Hill Street. Nearest Tube: Victoria

Simpsons in the Strand ❀❀

Simpson's is considered by many as a great British institution. Founded in 1828 as a place where gentlemen could drink coffee, play chess and read the latest journals, the century-long stream of literary and political stars has put the place on every tourist's hit list. Although the ambience remains the same, recent reports indicate a slight slip in quality; indifferent service has altered the whole atmosphere, and one inspector laments the loss of the 'efficient professional approach of days gone by'. But the food remains a mix of well-known traditional dishes such as Simpson's potted shrimps, joints of beef or lamb from the famous wagon, treacle roll and custard and Welsh rarebit, and more up-to-date offerings of chicken and leek terrine, marinated fillet of beef with mashed parsnips, cranberries and walnuts, and iced orange mousse with a raspberry sauce.

Directions: Nearest Tube: Charing Cross. In the middle of the Strand between Charing Cross & Waterloo Bridge. Next to the Savoy Hotel.

100 Strand WC2R 0EW
Map: D3
Tel: 0171 8369112
Fax: 0171 8361381
Chef: Nigel Boschetti
Owner: Savoy Group
Cost: *Alc* £30, fixed-price L & D £10 (2 courses). ☺ H/wine £13.50.
Times: Noon-last L 2.30pm/5.30pm-last D 11pm (Sun 9pm).
Closed 25-26 Dec, 1 Jan, Good Friday
Additional: Sunday L; Children welcome (no babies); ❹ dishes
Seats: 350.
Private dining room 20-150
Smoking: No pipes; air-conditioning
Credit cards: 🟦 🟦 🟦 🟦 🟦

Singapore Garden ❀❀

An attractive modern restaurant with a pleasing decor of pastel green. The menu offers an extensive choice of standard Singapore, Malaysian and Chinese influenced dishes, plus a few chef's specials. Prices, however, are reasonable. A dinner in late spring took in crispy aromatic duck, wafer thin pancakes and good plum sauce, beef rendang in a highly spiced sauce, oyster chicken served with lots of baby sweetcorn, peppers and carrots, and some 'san choy pau' – finely minced pork with mixed vegetables and served with iceberg lettuce. Drink jasmine tea.

Smoking: No pipes or cigars; air-conditioning
Credit cards:

Directions: Off Finchley Road, on R before Belsize roundabout. Nearest Tube: Swiss Cottage or Finchley Road. No parking restrictions

83/83a Fairfax Road NW6 4DY
Map GtL: C4
Tel: 0171 3285314
Fax: 0171 6240656
Chef: Mrs Siam Kiang Lim
Owners: Lim family
Cost: *Alc* £17.50, fixed-price L £5.95/D £17.50 (5 courses). ☺ H/wine £10.25.
Times: Noon-last L 2.45/6pm-last D 10.45pm (11.15pm Fri & Sat).
Closed 1 wk Xmas
Additional: Sunday L; Children welcome; ❹ dishes
Seats: 100. Private dining room 50

Snows-on-the-Green

Bunches of lavender, sunflowers and tiled tables conjure up a provençale look in this lively neighbourhood restaurant. The kitchen does dip its toes into the Med but keeps faith with true Brit flavours. Dishes are gutsy, combinations bold. The fixed-price lunch is reckoned to be 'wonderful' value for money for two or three courses, according to an inspector who found plenty to enjoy in the shape of heartwarming split pea, ham and mint soup, braised lamb shank with herb gnocchi and olive gravy, followed by a delightful pumpkin frangipane tart with clotted cream. Other options might include squid-ink risotto, seared sea bream with flageolets and rosemary oil, chargrilled calves' liver with chestnuts, Brussels sprouts and beetroot relish, and tarte Tatin. Sebastian Snow now has an extra pair of hands in the kitchen and is as likely be seen out front as behind the stove. The short wine list complements the food both in depth and quality.

Directions: Nearest Tube: Hammersmith & Shepherd's Bush Green. Opposite Brook Green, half way up Shepherd's Bush Rd

166 Shepherd's Bush Road
Hammersmith W6 7PB
Map GtL: C3
Tel: 0171 6032142
Fax: 0171 6027553
Chef/Owner: Sebastian Snow
Cost: Alc £20, fixed-price L £15.50.
☺ H/wine £9.95.
Times: Noon-last L 3pm/6pm-D 11pm. Closed Sat L, Sun D, 3 days Xmas
Additional: Sunday L; Children welcome; ◑ dishes
Seats: 70. Private dining room 24
Smoking: Air-conditioning
Credit cards: ▨ ▨ ▨ ▨ ▨ ▨

Soho Soho

Cosmopolitan and fun, with an eclectic bilingual menu that mixes classic French numbers (Marseilles fish soup), with pretty wild Mediterranean influences (wild mushroom and wild rice risotto, and wild boar stewed in red wine with sautéed chestnuts and fresh pasta). The rotisserie menu includes specialities such as spit-roast chicken with saffron rice and chorizo sausage.

Cost: Alc £35. H/wine £9.95. ☺
Times: Noon-last L 2.45pm/6pm-last D 11.30pm. Closed L Sun
Smoking: No-smoking area; no pipes & cigars; air-conditioning
Credit cards: ▨ ▨ ▨ ▨ ▨ ▨

Directions: Nearest Tube – Tottenham Court Road, Leicester Square

11 Frith Street W1V 5TS
Map: D4
Tel: 0171 4943491
Chef: Laurent Lebeau
Owner: Group Chez Gerard

Sonny's

A long serving neighbourhood favourite with bags of atmosphere, modern art and photographs on the off-white walls, chrome and leather chairs and a fire at the end of the long split-level dining room. Changes in the kitchen but the style seems unlikely to move far from its current blend of modern British and Mediterranean with a few forays into the Far East. The menu promises such things as black pudding and potato cake with pear and Calvados vinaigrette, roast rump of lamb with aubergine and basil purée, and grilled tuna with oriental vegetables, sweet soy and ginger. To finish, pear tarte Tatin comes with crème anglaise while mango and champagne jelly is served with a fromage blanc sorbet. A café menu is served from 10.30pm to 4pm at the zinc bar counter, where you can expect dishes such as spinach and goat's cheese tart, and steak sandwich with tarragon butter and frites; there's also a food shop next door. The lively young wine list offers a healthy clutch by the glass.

Directions: From Castlenau end of Church Road, on left by shops. Nearest Tube - Hammersmith

94 Church Road Barnes
SW13 0DQ
Map: C3
Tel: 0181 7480393
Fax: 0181 7482698
Chef: Leigh Diggins
Owners: Rebecca Mascarenhas, James Harris
Cost: Alc £22.50, fixed-price L £12 (2 courses)/D £22.50. ☺ H/wine £9.50
Times: 12.30pm-last L 2.30pm/7.30pm-last D 11pm. Closed D Sun, Easter Mon, May Day, 24-27 Dec
Seats: 90
Smoking: No pipes & cigars; air-conditioning
Credit cards: ▨ ▨ ▨ ▨ ▨

Sotheby's, The Café ❀❀

Run with tremendous style, this tiny café spills out into the entrance hall of the famous auction house, a place so busy that the atmosphere can't fail to be lively. The clientele is notable for its sheer variety, from ladies-who-lunch, business suits and elegantly draped 10-foot-tall models. The menu changes daily, offering morning coffee, afternoon tea, and lunch with a choice of three or four dishes at each course, allowing for a light snack or a three-course blow out. Lunch in autumn took in a velvety rich parsnip soup, and an excellent salad of marinated duck, with figs and cherry tomatoes on lightly dressed mixed leaves. Alternatives might be penne with field mushrooms, spinach and Parmesan cream, or cod and chervil fishcakes with tartare sauce. To finish, try a satisfying treacle tart with clotted cream. Service is spot on. The short but global wine list offers a good choice by the glass.

Directions: Nearest tube – Bond Street

34 Bond Street W1
Map: D4
Tel: 0171 4085077
Fax: 0171 4085920
Chef: Caroline Cromby
Owner: Alfred Taubman
Cost: Alc £25. H/wine £9.75. ☺
Times: Noon-last L 2.30pm.
Closed D Sun, L Sat, last 2 wks Aug
Additional: Sunday L; ❹ dishes
Smoking: No-smoking area; no pipes or cigars; air-conditioning
Credit cards: ■ ■ ▦ ▤ ➳ ▣

The Square ❀❀❀

New location, new look. But the same exciting cooking from Philip Howard who seems to have been further inspired by the move. The setting is a high-ceilinged ground floor space with a big window frontage; plain walls are lifted by contemporary paintings, the floor is parquet and the tables well-spaced. Most of the smartly attired staff are cheerful and well-informed. The modern French menu is short but well-balanced. A cracking pace was set by a signature dish of terrine of foie gras, guinea fowl and artichokes, larded with full-flavoured cured ham. Equal pleasure was gained from a parfait, ballotine and rillettes of duck, accompanied by a light, brioche-like toasted raisin bread. Seared tuna with sauce vierge and olive noodles was beautifully cooked, pink in the middle and delicately seasoned, served with a chutney of spiced pickles, tomato, shallots and lime juice. Another fine main course was rump of lamb with aubergine caviar and artichokes – roundels of sliced pink lamb on a bed of aubergine, rosemary, sun-dried tomato and artichoke, each flavour distinct, each enhancing the taste of the tender, perfectly timed lamb. Although there is much use of luxury ingredients – steamed cod with leeks, oyster and caviar, roast Bresse pigeon with a ravioli of foie gras – all the produce is of exceptional quality; note the prime condition of accompanying vegetables such as roasted savoury potato on a bed of young spinach. A near perfect crème brûlée was much appreciated, as was an assiette of chocolate that consisted of chocolate tart (almost soufflé-like in its filling), a smooth, wicked dark chocolate ice cream, a white chocolate cream and a filo chocolate roll accompanied by a fresh, sweet apple purée.
Signature dishes: Roast halibut with pea purée, button onions and lardons; crisp red mullet with olive broth, basil oil and tomato; loin of venison with caramelised vegetables and port; Roast British pigeon with a ravioli of foie gras.

32 King Street St James's SW1Y 6RJ
Map: C3
Tel: 0171 4957100
Fax: 0171 4957150
Chef: Philip Howard
Owners: Nigel Platts-Martin, Philip Howard
Cost: Alc L £40, fixed-price D £39.50. H/wine £13.50
Times: Noon-3pm/7pm-11pm (10pm Sun). Closed L Sat, L Sun, Xmas
Additional: Children welcome; ❹ dishes
Seats: 85. Private dining room 18
Smoking: No pipes & cigars; air-conditioning
Credit cards: ■ ■ ▦ ▤ ➳ ▣ ▣

Directions: Nearest Tube: Green Park

The Stafford ❀❀

After the completion of a massive programme of building and refurbishment, The Stafford is rediscovering the heights of luxury that were its trademark for decades. The restaurant, for example, is very elegant, with large, well-spaced tables on two

16-18 St James's Place SW1A 1NJ
Map: D4
Tel: 0171 4930111
Fax: 0171 4937121
Chef: Chris Oakes
Owners: Stafford Hotel

levels. In the kitchen, Chris Oakes has taken time to settle in but is beginning to win friends for his cooking. The menu successfully combines the traditional with the innovative, which means the *carte* is split in two, with straightforward 'classic' grills to one side, and the more interesting creative dishes, changed every two months, on the other. A spring dinner produced a very well made shellfish risotto, creamy and intense, followed by a tender, full-flavoured sliced French duck breast, just pink, with a cream and wild mushroom sauce of considerable technical competence. Choosing from the traditional part of the menu, a good treacle tart with clotted cream came with lots of fruit berry garnish. Do ask the sommelier for a tour of the 350-year-old wine cellars. The American Bar is a popular destination in its own right.

Cost: *Alc* £40, fixed-price L £20/D £26. H/wine £15
Times: 12.30pm-last L 2.15pm/6pm-last D 10.30pm. Closed L Sat
Additional: Bar meals; Sunday L; Children welcome; ❸ dishes
Seats: 50. Jacket & tie preferred
Smoking: No pipes; air-conditioning
Accommodation: 80 en suite

Directions: Nearest Tubes St James & Green Park. 5 mins St James's Palace

Star of India

The decor resembles 'a Roman bath' and the menu is equally unpredictable in this long-serving, popular Indian restaurant. Baby lamb chops cooked in milk then deep-fried in rice batter is finger food for the 90s, while pudina machli is marinated diced grouper cooked in a pot sealed with puff pastry. Finish with tandoori pineapple.

154 Old Brompton Road SW5 0BE
Map: A1
Tel: 0171 3732901
Telephone for details

Directions: Nearest Tube – Gloucester Road

Stephen Bull Restaurant

Stephen Bull is in expansionist mood, having opened a new restaurant in St Martin's Lane (see entry). But this, the first restaurant in his mini-empire, is still popular and buzzing. Staff are slick, smart and friendly, decor is white with vibrant pastels, clever lighting, wood floor, and the hand-written menu reassuring yet imaginative. Changes have also taken place here. John Hardwick (ex sous chef, The Square) had only just taken over in the kitchen when we visited but his cooking showed promise. Good terrine of foie gras, chicken, artichoke and baby leek with onion compote, was followed by a busy dish of roast rabbit, onion tart, and white bean cassoulet, plus spinach, cabbage, a 'duxelle-like mix of the liver' and glazed by a rich reduction. Hot rhubarb fondant with well made mascarpone sorbet to finish. A decent fistful of house wines head the wide-ranging list.

5-7 Blandford Street W1H 3AA
Map: B4
Tel: 0171 4869696
Fax: 0171 4903128
Chef: John Hardwick
Owner: Stephen Bull
Cost: *Alc* £24. H/wine £14 ☺
Times: Noon-last L 2.15pm/6.30pm-midnight. Closed L Sat, Sun, 1 wk Xmas
Additional: Children welcome; ❸ dishes
Seats: 53
Smoking: No pipes and cigars; air-conditioning
Credit cards: 🔲 🔲 🔲 🔲

Directions: Off Marylebone High St, 75 yards down on the left, Nearest Tube – Bond Street

Stephen Bull Smithfield 🏵🏵

Wacky papier-mâché sculptures add a sense of fun to the colourful post-modern interior, which is always busy and bustling. Service, however, can suffer as a result and at times is rushed. Best dish we've sampled this year has been a tender, well marinated, pan-fried fillet of lamb served on a bed of couscous and spinach with a nicely flavoured harissa jus with roasted garlic. Mushroom, leek and Parmesan tart was tasty, and a well-made custard helped set to rights a dryish warm

71 St John Street EC1 4AN
Map: E5
Tel: 0171 4901750
Fax: 0171 4903128
Chef: Danny Lewis
Owner: Stephen Bull
Cost: *Alc* £20 ☺
Times: 12.15pm-last L 2.30pm/6.30pm-last D 10.30pm. Closed L Sat, Sun, 10 days Xmas, Bhs

Stephen Bull Smithfield

Additional: Children welcome;
 dishes
Seats: 120
Smoking: No-smoking area; no pipes
and cigars in dining room;
air-conditioning
Credit cards:

Directions: Halfway between
Clerkenwell Rd & Smithfield Market

lemon pudding. Interesting dishes include crepinette of braised oxtails with red wine jus and crispy salmon parcel with lemon grass butter. An unusual selection of Spanish delicacies or rock oysters, carpaccio of tuna with shaved fennel, and swordfish tartare with avocado salsa from the seafood bar add an extra dimension to the menu. Note this restaurant used to be called Stephen Bull Bistro; the name has changed as the style has become less bistro.

Stephen Bull
St Martin's Lane ❀❀ NEW

The third of Stephen Bull's restaurants is in the heart of Theatreland – diners may return after the curtain falls for dessert and coffee. The menu shows flair, the cooking stretches rather than breaks the rules and owes more to new wave European finesse than Pacific Rim gutsiness. Once through the glass frontage and small winebar, the interior is stark yet welcoming with modern banquettes on one side; the most colourful object is the menu cover. A starter of boudin of lamb's sweetbreads with field mushrooms and buttered celery had good offal flavour, and was followed by a ballotine of chicken and foie gras with vegetable fondant and bacon. A well conceived and successfully executed dessert, chocolate and hazelnut tart with raspberry ice cream, was a felicitous combination of contrasting flavours and textures.

Directions: Nearest Tube – Leicester Square

12 Upper St Martin's Lane
WC2H 9DL
Map: D3
Tel: 0171 3797811
Fax: 0171 4903128
Chef: Jon Bentham
Owner: Stephen Bull
Cost: H/wine £12
Times: Noon-2.30pm/5.45pm-
11.30pm. Closed L Sat, Sun,
1 wk Xmas, Bhs
Additional: Children welcome;
❀ dishes
Seats: 68
Smoking: No pipes & cigars;
air-conditioning
Credit cards: ▬ ▨ ▧ ▣

The Stepping Stone ❀❀

Only organic, free-range meat is used at this modern, double-fronted restaurant in a Victorian terrace on a broad tree-lined road, fondly referred to by locals as 'the Champs-Elysée of South London'. The short, succinct menu offers excellent value for money, as well as lively, well-focused combinations. Griddled diver caught scallops are served with Jerusalem artichoke fritters and couscous, best-end rack of lamb with pumpkin mash and sautéed courgettes. More good ingredients include roast mallard braised with red cabbage, chestnuts and herb dumplings, and fillet of trout grilled with samphire and beurre blanc, and an old-fashioned dish, given a makeover, is steamed wild rabbit pudding with beetroot relish and winter

123 Queenstown Road SW8 3RH
Map GtL: C2
Tel: 0171 6220555
Fax: 0171 6224230
Chef: Peter Harrison
Owners: Gary & Emer Levy
Cost: *Alc* £23, fixed-price L £10.50 (2
courses). ☺ H/wine £8.95.
Times: Noon-last L 2.30pm /7pm-last
D 11pm. Closed L Sat, D Sun,
Xmas wk, Bhs
Additional: Sunday L;
Children welcome; ❀ dishes
Seats: 55

greens. The hard-working kitchen makes its own bread, pickles (to go with chicken liver parfait), as well as black pudding (bravely served "pizza" style with Manchego cheese).

Directions: Nearest Tube: Clapham Common. From Lavender Hill/Wandsworth Road cross-roads, head up Queenstown Road towards Chelsea Bridge. Restaurant on L after 0.50 mile

Stratfords

A smart, airy modern French restaurant specialising in fish. Uncomplicated dishes include grilled lemon sole with rice, fillet of sea bass roasted with garlic, and monkfish served with tomatoes and basil. Typical starters include warm goat's cheese salad, moules marinière, and roulade of smoked salmon.

Additional: Sunday L; Bar meals; Children welcome; ꙮ dishes
Smoking: No cigars or pipes
Credit cards: ▀▀ ▒▒ ═══ ▜▛ ▣ Ⅽ

Directions: Nearest tube: High Street Kensington

7 Stratford Road W8
Map GtL: C3
Tel: 0171 9376388
Fax: 0171 9383435
Chef: Alain Patrat
Owner: Edna Martin
Cost: Alc £30, fixed-price L/D £12
Times: Last L 3pm/D 10.45pm

The Sugar Club ꙮꙮ

No membership needed at this bright, modern restaurant, just a taste for Pacific Rim cooking and minimalist decor. The *carte* at lunch and dinner may be short, but that doesn't necessarily make the choice any the easier. Our inspector finally decided upon grilled whole scallops as a first course, precisely cooked and served with a flavoursome sweet chilli sauce and crème fraîche. Alongside were warm wholemeal rolls and salted butter. Corn-fed chicken breast was given some oomph with an effective combination of wild mushrooms, lentils and tapenade. Freshly cooked, well seasoned vegetables included new potatoes, swede and green beans. Upside down pear, banana and polenta cake with crème fraîche made a light and quite delicious dessert, followed by a good blend of filtered coffee with cream. The restaurant occupies two floors, with the lower ground floor reserved for non-smokers. Staff are attentive, but some need a charm school refresher course.

Directions: Parallel with Portobello Road, nearest tube is Westbourne Park

33 All Saints Road W11
Map GtL: C3
Tel: 0171 2213844
Fax: 0171 2292759
Chef: Peter Gordon
Owners: Vivienne Hayman, Ashley Sumner
Cost: Alc £35.Fixed-price L £15.50. H/wine £10.50.
Times: 12.30pm-last L 2.30pm/6.30pm-last D 11pm. Closed Notting Hill Carnival.
Additional: Sunday L; ꙮ dishes.
Seats: 75
Smoking: No-smoking area; no pipes and cigars; air-conditioning
Credit cards: ▀▀ ▒▒ ═══ ▜▛ Ⅽ

Suntory ꙮꙮ

Established in London for more than 20 years and now with 16 branches world-wide, Suntory portrays the moneyed, international face of Japanese haute cuisine. At lunchtime it is possible to eat affordably if you sit in the ground floor shabu-shabu room and order conservatively from one of the daily specials (tempura on rice with grated yam, and ohitashi plus miso soup and pickles on Tuesday, for example); there are also lacquered bento boxes – including one for ladies only. Otherwise the *carte* has a range of sushi, sashimi, sunomono salads and various dishes focusing on different cooking techniques. The remainder of the action takes place downstairs in the teppan-yaki room, where tables are partitioned off by wooden screens and chefs go about their work, grilling luxuries like foie gras, scallops, lobster and fillet steak on hot plates in

72 St James's Street
SW1A 1PH
Map: C3
Tel: 0171 4090201
Fax: 0171 4990208
Chef: Mr N Hoshino
Owner: Suntory Ltd
Cost: Alc £50, fixed-price L £15 (2 courses)/D £49.80 (5 courses). H/wine £17
Times: Noon-last L 2pm/6pm-last D 10pm. Closed Sun, Easter, Xmas, New Year
Additional: No children under 6; ꙮ dishes
Seats: 120. Private dining room 6-7

front of you. The selection of sakés is one of the best in the capital and – if cost is no problem – there are some fine vintage clarets on the wine list.

Directions: At the bottom of St James's Street, opposite St James's Palace. Nearest Tube – Green Park

Smoking: Air-conditioning
Credit cards: ▮▮ ▥ ▤ ▨ ▣ ▢

Supan Thai Restaurant ✿

Locally popular Thai restaurant with quite smart decor, helpful staff and a straightforward, good-value menu. Chicken satay, tom yum soup and green chicken curry have been enjoyed of late, but also look for steamed dumplings, som tum salad and assorted noodle dishes. Vegetarians are well catered for.

Smoking: No pipes or cigars. **Credit cards:** ▮▮ ▥ ▨ ▢

Directions: At Harrow Road end of Fernhead Road, at its junction with Elgin Avenue

4 Fernhead Road W9 3ET
Map: B3
Tel: 0181 9699387
Chef/Owner: Mr A Piempreecha
Cost: *Alc* £15. H/wine £7.50. ☺
Times: D only, 6.30pm–last D 10.45pm. Closed Xmas/New Year
Addditional: Children welcome; ◑ dishes

Swallow International Hotel ✿

See Where London Meets page 162

Tabaq ✿

Taking its name from a special serving dish used in Pakistan and India, Tabaq specialises in Lahori cooking, using recipes and techniques that have been passed down through generations. Dishes to look out for include lamb's kidneys cooked with onion, tomatoes and mild spices, and karahi fish, marinated and sautéed with spices from Lahore.

Smoking: No-smoking area; air-conditioning
Credit cards: ▮▮ ▥ ▤ ▨ ▢

Directions: Just off the South Circular, close to Clapham South tube station

47 Balham Hill SW12 9DR
Map GtL: C2
Tel: 0181 6737820
Fax: 0181 6732701
Chef: Manzoor Ahmed
Owner: M M Ahmed
Cost: *Alc* £18.50, fixed-price L £5.95. ☺ H/wine £8.50.
Times: Last L 2.45pm/D midnight. Closed Sun, 25 Dec
Additional: Children welcome; ◑ dishes

Tamarind ✿✿

20 Queen Street W1X 7PJ
Map: C3
Tel: 0171 6293561
Fax: 0171 4995034
Chef: Atul Kochhar
Cost: *Alc* £35, fixed-price L £16.50. ☺ H/wine £13.50.
Times: Noon–last L 3pm/6pm–last D 11.30pm. Closed Sat L, Xmas
Additional: Sunday L; Children welcome; ◑ dishes
Seats: 95
Smoking: Air-conditioning
Credit cards: ▮▮ ▥ ▤ ▨ ▣ ▢

Expert spicing, distinctive flavours and exciting, contemporary interior design, make this stylish place a benchmark for modern

Indian restaurants. Central focal points are two gigantic beehive-shaped tandoor ovens, source of a range of interesting breads and kebabs such as unleavened minted paratha, monkfish marinated in saffron and yogurt, and supreme of chicken marinated in green chilli and mustard. Carefully cooked curries include prawns in a light tomato and coriander sauce, lamb in a delicate creamy sauce, and the classic rogan josh. Spicy kidney bean cakes with a coconut coating, tandoori capsicum stuffed with potatoes, nuts and paneer, and cheese and vegetable koftas are amongst an above-average vegetarian choice. Kulfi comes in three flavours, pistachio, mango, or almond and saffron, but there is also carrot halva and gulab jamun for the sweet-toothed. This is a considered, serious exploration of a cuisine that is a far cry from the standard curry house fare; nor does it charge curry house prices.

Directions: From Green Park Tube head for Hyde Park, and turn 4th R into Half Moon St and walk to end (Curzon St). Turn L, and Queen St is 1st R

La Tante Claire ❀❀❀❀❀❀

68 Royal Hospital Road SW3 4HP
Map: B1
Tel: 0171 3526045
Fax: 0171 3523257
Chef/Owner: Pierre Koffmann
Cost: Alc £60, fixed-price L £27. H/wine £14
Times: 12.30pm-last L 2pm/7pm-last D 11pm. Closed Sat, Sun, Xmas, Easter, Aug
Additional: Children welcome
Seats: 48. Jacket & tie preferred at D
Smoking: No pipes
Credit cards: ▨ ▨ ▨ ▨ ▨

Directions: Between Embankment and Sloane Sq, near Army Museum

'Even when the heat is on, Pierre Koffmann's eyes still manage to smile. He's serious, dedicated and modest', observed an inspector. Craftsmanship is Pierre Koffmann's business, and the kitchen is his workshop. He is, probably, the archetypal chef/proprietor. At a time when many of his peers have found it convenient to delegate and leave the creative donkey work to others, he is at the stove, using his hands. While others flirt with novelty and fashionable trifles, his devotion and energy are focused on the time-consuming business of cooking. All this, of course, does not come cheap. The *carte* carries a minimum charge of £50 (which barely pays for two courses), but there is a set lunch that brings delights a-plenty for around half that price. Whichever you choose, the cooking is of a consistency and unassuming style that sets it apart. Koffmann is true to his roots: memories of Gascony (to borrow the title from his first book) provide the spark, the broader canvas of French regional cuisine is what he explores. The menu is short and written entirely in French without translation or compromise – although relaxed but formal waiters will decode and explain when needed. Great bread rolls, a choice of six or seven, begin proceedings in true Gallic style – 'close your eyes and you could be in France'. From then on it is precision, disciplined but spirited stuff all the way. Sometimes the simplicity can deceive, as in a starter of warm langoustines with a gentle shallot dressing and impeccably prepared large white beans from Tabe that is a Koffmann favourite. All a dish like this requires is some crispy bacon for 'oomph' and a classical dressed salad. Equally classical might be daube of ceps and pigeon, moist gamey meat atop a little mound of spinach surrounded by a ring of purée and the simplest and most exquisite of sauces. The garnish was a single, perfect snail beignet. The repertoire oozes real gems, whether it be a galette of foie gras with Sauternes and roasted shallots, a 'frivolité' of seafood, or 'pied de cochon aux morilles et pommes mousseline', a signature dish that is often emulated, seldom equalled. Desserts prove that great meals should end on a high. An inspection concluded with 'pain d'epice au chocolat, sauce vin rouge': fabulous pastry consisting of deep, rich chocolate with spiced ginger sponge brilliantly matched by a thick, sweet red wine sauce and some vanilla ice cream for good measure. The final flourish comes in the shape of deep, rich espresso served from fine bone china.

Tatsuso ❁❁❁

The prices may be high but this is nonetheless one of the best Japanese restaurants in London. Even in the less expensive Teppan-yaki room, lunch prices start at £23 for a set menu and climb in leaps and bounds to £78, and that's before you add on the drinks. The whole operation is very smart and slickly run, and although staff are not always too fluent in English, they're generally gracious and helpful. Serious Japanese classic cooking can be sampled in the basement restaurant, but lone diners are best off in the Sushi bar, or at one of the aforementioned Teppan-yaki tables, clad in a white pinny, watching a chef periodically come along and throw a few tasty morsels onto a hot plate. It's great fun to watch, but the real secret is in the skill of the chef and the pristine nature of all the ingredients. There are a few nibbles to whet the appetite – pâté, omelette and crisp broccoli – then exceptionally good dobin mushi soup, intense and full of flavour, drunk out of tiny cups, with fish, prawns and mushrooms to be fished out with chopsticks at the end. Choose from raw prawns, salmon, chicken or beef fillet and eat with steamed rice, plus onions, mushrooms, courgette and beansprouts all cooked on the hotplate with the meat. There are desserts of ice cream and fresh fruit. Order wine to impress, but otherwise stick to the kirin, saké or tea.

32 Broadgate Circle EC1M 6BT
Map: G4
Tel: 0171 6385863
Fax: 0171 6385864
Chef: N Yamanaka
Owner: Terutoshi Fujii
Cost: *Alc* £40, fixed-price L £35/D £58 (7 courses). H/wine £14
Times: 11.30am-last L 2.30pm/6pm-last D 9.45pm. Closed Sat, Sun
Additional: Children welcome; ❹ dishes
Seats: 125. Private dining room 10. Jacket & tie preferred
Smoking: Air-conditioning
Credit cards: ▰ ▰ ▰ ▰ ▱ ▱

Directions: Ground floor of Broadgate Circle. Nearest Tube: Liverpool St Station

The Thai Garden ❁

Modest little vegetarian (plus fish) Thai restaurant. Food is simple with flavours clear rather than complex. Cauliflower in coconut soup with galanga; yum ta-ley – mixed seafood in a slightly spicy sauce with lime juice and lemon grass very evident; broth-like gaeng ped – Thai aubergines and mixed vegetable curry with coconut cream, have all been well reported.

Smoking: No-smoking area; no pipes & cigars
Credit cards: ▰ ▰ ▰

Directions: 2nd left off Roman Road (1-way street); nearest Tube: Bethnal Green

249 Globe Road E2 0JD
Map Gtl: D3
Tel: 0181 9815748
Chef: Mrs Napathorn Duff
Owners: Suthinee and Jack Hufton
Cost: *Alc* £20, fixed-price L/D £7.50. ☺ H/wine £7.50
Times: Last L 2.45pm/last D 10.45pm. Closed Sat L, Sun L, Bhs
Additional: Children welcome; ❹ dishes
Seats: 32; private room 12-14

Thailand ⊛

The cheerful, friendly atmosphere generated by Mrs Herman, who generally does the cooking, is part of the charm of a place that though small and modest, does boast a good range of dishes. Expect fishcakes with green bean and chilli paste, hot and sour chicken soup, fish curry cooked in coconut cream, plus some Laotian-style dishes.

Smoking: Air-conditioning
Credit cards: ▬ ▦ ▆

Directions: Opposite Goldsmiths' College. Nearest Tubes: New Cross, New Cross Gate

15 Lewisham Way SE14 6PP
Map GtL: D3
Tel: 0181 6914040
Chef/Owner: Mrs Kong Herman
Cost: Alc £20. Fixed-price D £18-£20. ☺ H/wine £8.50.
Times: D only, Last D 10.30pm. Closed Sun, Mon
Additional: No children under 12; ⏃ dishes

33 St James Restaurant ⊛⊛

'It felt very New York chic in here, classy without being stuffy', observes an inspector. The decor is refined, with an eye for impact, tables are well spaced and at lunch, as one would expect in this part of Mayfair, the clientele is mostly males 'of a certain age', and well-heeled American tourists. The menu is thoroughly modern, although a short grill section of lobster, Dover sole and fillet of Scotch beef, covers more traditional tastes. Otherwise, there's seared scallops glazed under a light curry Sauternes sauce, braised pig cheek with buttered mash potato and parsley sauce, or fillet of British farmed ostrich on wilted rocket with a chervil vinaigrette. However, maize-fed chicken salad with corn pancakes opened our early summer lunch. Then came monkfish with home-made noodles in a lime and ginger broth, simply served but with stunning flavours, and an extravagant cherry and chocolate clafoutis with crème fraîche sorbet and hot chocolate sauce as a finale. There's a good choice of wines by the glass.

Directions: Nearest Tube: Green Park

33 St James Street SW1 1HD
Map: C3
Tel: 0171 9304272
Fax: 0171 9307618
Chef: Kristian Smith-Wallace
Owner: Vincenzo Defeo
Cost: Alc £31, fixed-price L £16.95 (2 courses)/D £22.95 (2 courses). H/wine £16
Times: Noon-last L 2.30pm/6pm-last D 11.30pm. Closed L Sat, Sun, Xmas, Bhs
Additional: Children welcome; ⏃ dishes
Seats: 75. Private dining room 35
Smoking: No-smoking area; no pipes; air-conditioning
Credit cards: ▬ ▦ ▆ ▆ ▦ ▆

Thistells ⊛

Unpretentious and honest neighbourhood restaurant with a mix of European and Egyptian cooking – in other words, lamb couscous followed by crème brûlée. A former butcher's shop still with the original tiling, and a bright continental feel.

Directions: Nearest BR Station – East Dulwich

65 Lordship Lane SE22
Map GtL: D2
Tel: 0181 2991921
Telephone for details

The Tower Thistle

See Where London Meets page 162

Tui Restaurant

Tom yum soup served in a fire pot is a guaranteed best-seller in this simply appointed Thai restaurant on two floors. Other dishes from the accessible 50-dish menu include satays, curries, tord mun (fish rissoles with peanut vinaigrette) and gaisub pudprig (stir-fried minced chicken with chilli and basil).

Additional: Children welcome; dishes
Smoking: No pipes & cigars; air-conditioning
Credit cards: ▄▄ ▄▄ ▄▄ ▄▄ ▄▄ ▄▄

Directions: Nearest Tube – South Kensington. On corner of Thurloe Place & Exhibition Road

19 Exhibition Road SW7 2HE
Map: A2
Tel: 0171 5848359
Fax: 0181 7410393
Chefs: Mr & Mrs Kongsrivilai
Owners: Ekachai Tui Thapthimthong
Cost: *Alc* £22, fixed-price L £10. ☺
H/wine £9.50.
Times: Last L 2.15pm (3pm Sun)/last D 10.45pm (10.30pm Sun). Closed Xmas, Bhs

Turners Restaurant

Brian Turner's gregarious Yorkshire personality does much to drive this stylish and elegant fixture of the Chelsea restaurant scene. He is less often in the kitchen these days, more likely to be out front greeting and seating. His amiable presence is easily felt when he's around, easily missed when he's not. His cooking is defined by the rules of technique and the classic schooling of French cuisine before the flashy new boys came along. The fixed-price daily menu (two or three courses) must remain one of the lunchtime bargains in this upper-crust neighbourhood. You might pick, for example, confit of duck with mustard oil and balsamic dressing, move on to steamed fillet of salmon on a bed of spinach and a white wine and butter sauce, then finish off with cheese or blackcurrant parfait. The *carte*, by contrast, puts on a French accent. To start there might be salade niçoise with fresh tuna and green beans, a fine puff pastry tart piled with tomatoes, sweet peppers and basil or, our inspector's choice, a delicate crab sausage seasoned with Thai spices and coriander and set on a sauce of green peas. Main courses call into play such entrenched ideas as grilled rib of beef with bone marrow and garlic sauce, a stew of monkfish, mussels and salmon with saffron, and lightly sautéed calves' kidneys with rösti, shallots and a red wine jus. To finish there are exemplary desserts such as a warm chocolate and coconut fondant cake served with home-made coconut ice cream; otherwise choose a savoury along the lines of toasted goat's cheese in a bacon and potato cream sauce. Service throughout is well practised, competent and relaxed. The wine list concentrates on France but does briefly touch other major wine producing countries. Something to suit all pockets from a short but impressive Director's Choice with some expensive classics to a Bin End list that's more reasonably priced. The main body presents a good number of wines for under £25.

Signature dishes: fine chicken liver pâté with foie gras; roast rack of English lamb with a herb crust; banana and toffee Tatin.

Directions: South Kensington or Knightsbridge tube stations; behind Harrods

87-89 Walton Street SW3 2HP
Map: A1
Tel: 0171 5846711
Fax: 0171 5844441
Chef: C Curran
Owner: BJ Turner
Cost: *Alc* £42.70, fixed-price L £12.50-£15/D £29.50. ☺
H/wine £13.50.
Times: 12.30pm-last L 2.15pm/7.30pm-last D 11pm (6pm-8.30pm Sun). Closed L Sat, Bhs
Additional: Sunday L; Children welcome L & early evening;
Seats: 56. Private dining room 6-8
Smoking: Air-conditioning
Credit cards: ▄▄ ▄▄ ▄▄ ▄▄ ▄▄ ▄▄

Union Cafe

It is the simple honesty and commitment to first-rate raw materials that impresses at this light, airy café tucked away behind Oxford Street. There's also an infectious enthusiasm for food which customers find irresistible. Eggs are free-range from Martin Pitt, bacon and sausages from Heal Farm in Devon, juices and many other ingredients are organic, cheeses are from Neal's Yard. This translates into a short daily menu with a forthright Mediterranean accent – although other influences show up in, say, mixed meze with home-baked honey pitta bread, and carrot, parsley and Gruyère tart. You might begin with roast red pepper and chilli soup with basil oil or a plate of charcuterie with pickles, before moving on to chargrilled royal bream with rocket, herb potatoes and new season's extra virgin olive oil or roast corn-fed chicken breast with wild mushrooms, Swiss chard and rosemary. Also open for breakfast, from 9.30am, when the menu promises waffles with bananas, huevos rancheros and more. Drinks encompass home-made lemonade and herb teas while the jazzy wine list favours daring modern stuff from the New World.

Directions: Nearest Tube – Bond Street

96 Marylebone Lane W1M 5FP
Map: C3
Tel: 0171 4864860
Chef: Caroline Brett
Owners: Caroline Brett, Sam Russell
Cost: Alc £30. H/wine £10.50 ☺
Times: 12.30pm-3.30pm/6.30pm-10.30pm. Closed Sun
Additional: Breakfast (9.30am-noon Mon-Fri); Children welcome; ♨ dishes
Seats: 70
Credit cards: ▬ ▬ ▬ ▣

Vasco & Piero's Pavilion

Long-established and very popular Italian that combines both traditional trat dishes with more interesting, robust regional specialities. Highly recommended from our last inspection meal are grilled polenta, asparagus and Parmesan, home-made spinach and ricotta tortelloni, and to finish, torta di Riso with orange sauce.

Additional: Children welcome (no babies); ♨ dishes
Smoking: No pipes; air-conditioning
Credit cards: ▬ ▬ ▬ ▣

Directions: On corner of Great Marlborough Street & Noel Street. Nearest tube: Oxford Circus

15 Poland Street W1V 3DE
Map GtL: D4
Tel: 0171 4378774
Chef: Vasco Matteucci
Owners: Vasco Matteucci, Tony Lopez
Cost: Alc £30, fixed-price D £14.95. ☺ H/wine £8.95.
Times: Last L 3pm/D 11pm. Closed Sat, Sun, Bhs

The Veeraswamy

As we went to press we learnt that The Veeraswamy had been sold to the owners of Chutney Mary (see entry, London). A major refurbishment is planned, after which the restaurant will re-open with a completely new set up.

Directions: Entrance near junction of Swallow St & Regent St, located in Victory House. Entrance in Swallow Street.

99-101 Regent Street W1R 8RS
Map: C3
Tel: 0171 7341401
Fax: 0171 4398434
Telephone for further details

Veronica's

'This is certainly not your usual run-of-the-mill British food', observes an inspector of this unimposing shop-front restaurant that's boldly decorated within. Veronica Shaw goes to great pains to ensure authenticity, and this place is great for those wishing to try out such medieval treats as 'frytours of pasternakes' – deep-fried veg in a sweet and sour sauce. Our inspector settled for an Elizabethan roast beet and cheese tart, the beets and currants (used a lot in ancient savoury foods) diced and held together by the melted cheese and served with

3 Hereford Road
Bayswater W2 4AB
Map GtL: C3
Tel: 0171 2295079
Fax: 0171 2291210
Chefs: Antonio Feliccio, Veronica Shaw
Owners: Veronica & Philip Shaw
Cost: Alc £25, fixed-price L&D £16. ☺ H/wine £9.50.

Veronica's

Times: Noon-last L 2.30pm/7pm-last
D midnight. Closed L Sat, Sun, Bhs,
2 days Xmas
Additional: Children welcome;
🍴 dishes
Seats: 60. Private dining room 30
Credit cards: ▆ ▆ ▆ ▆ ▆ ▆

a sour cream and chive sauce. Then the organic dish of the day ('for they attempt to steer you towards a healthier style of eating here, with little symbols showing low fat or high fibre choices'), which was couscous with vegetables and a very fresh tasting tomato and basil sauce. Parson's hat was also sampled, a fish version of Cornish pasty made with John Dory, smoked haddock and salmon. Pudding was a nineteenth-century Scottish chocolate treat served with cinnamon ice cream and brown sugar meringue.

Directions: Nearest Tube: Bayswater, Queensway & Notting Hill Gate. Hereford Rd runs parallel to Queensway in between Bayswater Rd and Westbourne Grove.

Vong 🏵🏵🏵

Vong continues to be packed night after night, and has not lost its way after last year's opening hype. It's a hugely enjoyable place helped by staff who are able to make recommendations enthusiastically and confidently. The restaurant is on three levels, the decor strikingly modern: curved surfaces, polished floors, great colours, with a window giving a glimpse of what is going on in the kitchen. Daniel del Vecchio shows deft skills with spicing and he has established good discipline in the kitchen, exemplified by the accuracy of the cooking and provision of dishes such as 27 vegetables simmered in their own juices and spices. An inspection meal confirmed the quality. Raw tuna and vegetables wrapped in rice paper, quail rubbed with Thai spices, crab spring roll with tamarind dipping sauce, prawn satay with oyster sauce and chicken and foie gras dumplings with a truffle dipping sauce showed accuracy and balance. There were main courses of a signature dish rabbit curry and braised carrot, the breast meat deep-fried, joint meat off the bone, a little skewer of the liver, surrounded by a dash of coconut milk, and roast halibut, with good seared skin, shellfish jus and fruit chutney. Desserts are distinguished – crisp rice crêpes with raspberries with a coconut ice cream is an example. The bright, breezy wine list is arranged by style and grape type with a plethora of stylish wines for less than £20. A laudable selection of wines by the glass includes an ebullient Touraine Sauvignon from Chapelle de Cray (£13.50 by the bottle).

Signature dishes: Mussels, Thai basil and glass noodles; lobster and daikon roll, rosemary and ginger vinaigrette.

Directions: 600yds from Harrods, nearest Tube – Knightsbridge

The Berkeley Hotel
Wilton Place SW1X 7RL
Map: B2
Tel: 0171 2351010
Fax: 0171 2351011
Chefs: Jean-Georges Vongerichten,
Daniel del Vecchio
Owners: Jean-Georges Vongerichten,
Savoy Group plc
Cost: *Alc* £35, fixed-price L £20. ☺
H/wine £14.50
Times: Noon-last L 2.30pm/6pm-last
D 11.30pm. Closed L Sun
Additional: Bar food; no babies;
🍴 dishes
Seats: 140
Smoking: No pipes and cigars;
air-conditioning
Credit cards: ▆ ▆ ▆ ▆ ▆ ▆

Wagamama ❀

Great fun, good-value noodle bar in a simple basement near British Museum. No booking, some queuing, and eat at shared tables. Cooking goes on behind a long counter running the length of the room, Go for chicken ramen with side dishes of gyoza (dumplings with interesting fillings), and edamame (salted green soya beans in the pod).

Credit cards: ▬ ▨ 🗪 🄲

Directions: Nearest Tube – Tottenham Court Road

4A Streatham Street WC1A 1JB
Map: D4
Tel: 0171 3239223
Fax: 0171 3239224
Owner: Alan Yau
Cost: Alc £8, fixed-price L £8 (2 courses). ☺
Times: Noon-last D 11pm
Additional: Children welcome;
🅭 dishes
Smoking: No smoking restaurant; air-conditioning

Wagamama ❀

A 'new-style' Japanese noodle bar dedicated to 'positive eating'. You know you've arrived in the 21st century when you eat here- waiters tap your orders into hand-held computers which relay the info to the kitchen. New dishes include zaru soba – blanched green tea soba noodles with shiitake mushroom.

Smoking: No smoking restaurant; air-conditioning
Credit cards: ▬ ▨ 🗪 🄲

Directions: Nearest tube – Piccadilly Circus

10a Lexington Street WC1A 1JB
Map GtL: D4
Tel: 0171 2920990
Fax: 0171 7341815
Owner: Alan Yau
Cost: 2 courses £8-£9. ☺
H/wine £8.50.
Times: Noon-last D 11pm (10.30pm Sun). Closed Xmas
Additional: Children welcome;
🅭 dishes

The Waldorf Meridien ❀❀

Dinner is now served amidst the Edwardian splendour of the Palm Court, famous for its afternoon and weekend tea dances. As well as the *carte*, there are pre and post theatre menus and also Sunday jazz brunches. Service is still on formal lines, but less grandiose than formerly and altogether less stuffy. The cooking, too, has become lighter and brighter to match. Tiny fritters of crispy quail were tasty and dressed with a superb mâche salad with roasted pine nuts. Pan-fried sea bass was full of freshness and flavour, with a superb, slightly scrunchy exterior, served with a purée of potato and a drizzle of truffle oil. Other dishes worth trying include oyster champagne soup, roasted rack of lamb with black olive polenta and Greek figs and caramelised apple brûlée with rhubarb sorbet. And for all chocoholics – a speciality chocolate menu featuring dishes such as crème brûlée with guanaja, chocolate surprise pancakes, and Valrhona chocolate tart with orange mousse.

Directions: Nearest tube, Covent Garden

Aldwych WC2B 4DD
Map: E4
Tel: 0171 8362400
Fax: 0171 8367244
Chef: Andrew Demetriou
Cost: Alc £30, fixed-price L&D £21.95. ☺ H/wine £15.
Times: Noon-last L 2.30pm/6pm-last D 11.15pm
Additional: Bar food; Sunday brunch; Children welcome; 🅭 dishes
Seats: 120. Private dining up to 420. (Jacket & tie preferred for tea dance)
Smoking: No-smoking area
Accommodation: 292 en suite
Credit cards: ▬ ▨ ▨ 🗪 🄰 🄲

The Washington ❀

See Where London Meets page 162

The Westbury ❀

See Where London Meets page 163

The White House Hotel ❀

See Where London Meets page 163

White Tower ❀❀

'I don't think anything has changed here for twenty years or so; it's terribly old fashioned in the nicest sense', reports our inspector on this 100-year-old London institution. The interior still sports the same green gloss paint decor and 'in spite of hundreds of pictures of famous old Greeks, it somehow has the feel of an English country house'. Nowadays, the menu is not all Greek; they have taken 'the best bits' and added modern European dishes, but the sound cooking skills remain. White onion soup glazed with an apple and cheese crust, or terrine of chanterelles and ceps with a tomato and basil dressing, followed by roast rump of lamb with grilled asparagus and a tomato and basil butter, or roast brill with steamed leeks and a light horseradish sauce, show the range. The famous duck menu remains with pre-booking required for pressed duck 'Rudolf Stulik', made famous by the Bloomsbury Set.

Directions: Off Oxford Street/Tottenham Court Road, nearest tubes Tottenham Court Road & Goodge Street

1 Percy Street W1
Map: D4
Tel: 0171 6368141
Fax: 0171 4368658
Chef: Ken Whitehead
Owner: The Restaurant Partnership plc
Cost: Fixed-price L&D £19.50-£22.50. ☺ H/wine £10.95.
Times: 12.30pm-last L 2.30pm/6pm-last D 11pm. Closed L Sat, Sun
Additional: Children welcome; ❹ dishes
Seats: 40. Private dining rooms
Smoking: Air-conditioning
Credit cards: ▨ ▨ ▨ ▨ ▨ ▨

Wilson's ❀❀

If you hear the sound of bagpipes in Shepherd's Bush, the chances are that it is emanating from Wilson's. Be-kilted Bob Wilson looks after the front of house, whilst Robert Hilton holds sway in the kitchen. Scotland influences some dishes, although France also has its say. On the one hand you might find Finnan haddock pudding with a spinach and bacon salad, and haggis with mashed potato and swede; on the other are baked goat's cheese with walnut and orange salad, confit of duckling with apple and Calvados sauce, and roast cod fillet on a bed of spiced lentils with tomato and chive vinaigrette. Desserts naturally include Atholl brose with strawberries and Framboise, alongside steamed syrup pudding and lemon and lime posset from the other side of the border.

Directions: Nearest Tube - Hammersmith

236 Blythe Road W14 0HJ
Map GtL: C3
Tel: 0171 6037267
Fax: 0171 6029018
Chef: Robert Hilton
Owners: Bob Wilson, Robert Hilton
Cost: Alc £18
Times: 12.30pm-last L 2.30pm/7.30pm-last D 10pm. Closed L Sat, D Sun
Additional: Sunday L; Children welcome; ❹ dishes
Seats: 44
Smoking: No pipes and cigars; air-conditioning
Credit cards: ▨ ▨ ▨ ▨ ▨

Wiltons ❀❀

Wiltons' many regulars clearly enjoy the clubby atmosphere, discreet banquette seating and professional attentive staff, as well as a classic English fish and game menu, although there are meat dishes as well. Our inspector was well satisfied with a meal of crab salad – fresh white meat in a generous portion, topped with a good dressing – and poached halibut, correctly cooked and served on the bone with hollandaise sauce. Vegetables were surprisingly poor – although fresh enough, the small new potatoes lacked flavour and the spinach was overcooked. No complaints, however, with an excellent bread-and-butter pudding, moist in the centre, with a crisp topping and fine flavour. A weak note was struck at the end with a poor blend of coffee, not helped by the fact it had been standing around a while.

Directions: Opposite Turnbull & Asser (shirtmakers), and near Piccadilly Circus & Ritz Hotel. Nearest Tube – Green Park

55 Jermyn Street SW1Y 6LX
Map: C3
Tel: 0171 6299955
Fax: 0171 4956233
Chef: Ross Hayden
Owners: Rupert, Richard & James Hambro
Cost: Alc £50. H/wine £16.50
Times: Noon-2.30pm/6pm-10.30pm. Closed Sat
Additional: Bar meals; Sunday L; No children under 12; ❹ dishes
Seats: 100. Private dining room 18. Jacket & tie preferred
Smoking: No pipes; air-conditioning
Credit cards: ▨ ▨ ▨ ▨ ▨ ▨

The Windmill on The Common

Southside Clapham Common
SW4 9DE
Map GtL: C2
Tel: 0181 6734578
Fax: 0181 6751486
Chef: Louise Griffiths
Owners: Youngs Brewery
Cost: Alc £20, fixed-price D £14.95.
☺ H/wine £9.95.
Times: D only, 7pm-last D 9.45pm.
Closed D Sun
Additional: Bar Food; Sunday L
(noon-2pm); Children welcome;
🎍 dishes
Smoking: No pipes or cigars;
air-conditioning
Accommodation: 29 en suite
Credit cards: 💳 💳 💳 💳 💳 💳

A neighbourhood watering hole since 1729, now a popular hotel with three traditional bars and an intimate panelled restaurant. Typical dishes from the fixed-price menu might be sautéed chicken livers on dressed leaves, braised steak in Madeira with wild mushrooms, and summer pudding. Interesting youthful wines, Young's real ales.

Directions: Nearest Tubes – Clapham Common or Clapham South

Woodlands Restaurant

A smart place serving a good range of vegetarian dishes from South India. Our inspector enjoyed 'medu vada' – fried lentil doughnuts with a light crisp coating and served with sambar and coconut chutney, followed by 'rava masala dosa' – cream of wheat pancake filled with potatoes and nuts.

Additional: Children welcome; 🎍 dishes
Seats: 70
Smoking: Air-conditioning
Credit cards: 💳 💳 💳 💳 💳

77 Marylebone Road W1M 5GA
Map: C3
Tel: 0181 4863862
Fax: 0171 4874009
Chef: Mr Krishna
Owner: Mr Sood
Cost: Alc £14. H/wine £9. ☺
Times: Last L 2.45pm/D 10.45pm.
Closed 25 Dec

Directions: Nearest Tube – Bond Street

Yo! Sushi ⊕

The 60 metre conveyor belt (on which the staple sushi dishes revolve) is Britain's longest. Some of the sushi is made by robot, there are three robotic drinks trolleys, the music is banging techno and dancey beats and the clientele is typical Soho nouveaux bohemian. Good quality, if perhaps rough and ready, but immense fun.

Additional: Children welcome; 🎍 dishes
Smoking: No-smoking establishment; air-conditioning
Credit cards: 💳 💳 💳 💳 💳 💳

52-53 Poland Street W1 3DF
Map: C3
Tel: 0171 2870443
Fax: 0171 2872324
Chef: Nacer
Owner: Simon Woodroffe
Cost: Alc £10, fixed-price D £10. ☺
H/wine £3.50
Times: Noon-midnight.
Closed 25 Dec

Directions: Nearest Tubes – Oxford Circus, Tottenham Court Road, Piccadilly Circus

Yumi

As Japanese restaurants go, this is a rather 'low-key' establishment, much favoured by the expense-account crowd. On the ground floor is a modest sushi bar and several low tatami tables with bright cushions dotted around for those who want to sit shoeless and cross-legged; downstairs is a more conventional dining area with private rooms partitioned off for ceremonial *kaiseki* banquets. The main menu offers some intriguing interlopers in the shape of minced tuna burgers, grilled mango topped with rice cake and miso paste, and Camembert and smoked salmon tempura, alongside *oshitashi* (spinach salad with soy dressing), *chawan mushi* (a bizarre-looking egg custard), chicken yakitori and salmon teriyaki. Sushi set dinners provide good value: pickled vegetables dotted with sesame seeds serve to whet the appetite, two kinds of clear soup are offered and the quality of the morsels of vinegared rice topped with glistening fresh fish and a dab of nose-clearing wasabi is high. Service is some of the most courteous and gentle that the Japanese can offer.

Directions: A few yards east of the junction of George Street with Gloucester Place. Nearest Tube – Marble Arch

110 George Street W1H 5RL
Map: B4
Tel: 0171 9358320
Fax: 0171 2240917
Chef: M Sato
Owners: Miss Y Fujii, T Osumi
Cost: Fixed-price D £38 (7 courses). H/wine £7.20
Times: D only, 5.30pm-last D 10.30pm. Closed Sun, 1 wk Aug, 2 wks Xmas
Additional: No children under 10; ⓓ dishes
Seats: 74. Private dining room 16
Smoking: No pipes or cigars; air-conditioning
Credit cards: ▆ ▆ ⓐ ⓒ

Zafferano

15 Lowndes Street SW1X 9EY
Map: B2
Tel: 0171 2355800
Fax: 0171 2351971
Chef/Owner: Giorgio Locatelli
Cost: *Alc* £28, fixed-price L £19.50/D £25.50. H/wine £10.70
Times: Noon-last L 2.30pm/7pm-last D 11pm. Closed Sun, 2 wks Aug, 2 wks Dec
Additional: Children welcome; ⓓ dishes
Seats: 53
Smoking: Air-conditioning
Credit cards: ▆ ▆ ▆ ▆ ⓒ

Georgio Locatelli's true passion is for cooking. The rather uninspired decor and dark blue oval-backed chairs that look like Grand Hotel rejects, reflect his lack of concern with inessentials. The crowds come for the wonderful Italian food, not the fripperies. All produce is purchased fresh each day, so some dishes on the menu may not always be available. Dishes are described sparely, but still sing of pleasures to come – octopus salad with new potatoes and celery, fresh nettle risotto, lamb sweetbreads in sweet and sour sauce. The chargrill is used for spring lamb, tuna with rocket and tomato, and for a stunning starter of squid with intensely roasted plum tomatoes, in which the body is stuffed with the minced tentacles, breadcrumbs and herbs. Our inspector followed this with classic linguine alla vongole with 'fantastic' clams, wee strands of very mild chilli, lots of parsley and more wonderful Tuscan olive oil. One of Locatelli's own favourites is veal kidneys with artichoke, cooked pink and with the whole leaves and the hearts half-coated in a buttery, meaty lentil sauce. Chocolate and almond tart was really good chocolate but a rather heavy slab overall, although it was redeemed by a fabulous pistachio ice-cream chockfull of nuts.

Champagne apart, the wine list is as chauvinist as one would hope. Many great names, Antinori, Allegrini, Aldo Conterno, are there in the company of hefty price tags. But joys are to be had for considerably less – Lira with the deliciously fruity Salice Salentino Riserva from Candido at £14.50, a notable example.

Signature dishes: Papardelle, broad beans and rucola; sea bream with spinach and balsamic vinegar; roasted rabbit, polenta, Parma ham.

Directions: Behind Sloane St – around corner from Carlton Tower Hotel. Nearest Tube – Knightsbridge

Zen Central

Seriously considered designer chic is the hallmark of the Zen chain of Chinese restaurants and the Mayfair branch is typical of the overall style and philosophy of the group. The decor is rarefied and cool, with minimalist black and white colour schemes, a domed atrium and mirrors covering much of the wallspace. The menu is equally distinctive; it steers a course that Westerners can follow with ease, isn't afraid to borrow or adapt from other cultures and delivers the goods. Coriander and crab meat croquettes, Szechuan crispy shredded beef, and roast duck fillets with pineapple and ginger pleased our inspector, but the choice also extends to crispy seaweed with pine kernels, veal cutlets in black pepper sauce and pork chops with lemon grass, plus deluxe specials such as braised abalone with oyster sauce or baked lobster with tangerine peel and crushed garlic. First rate jasmine tea is the ideal accompaniment, otherwise dip into the upper-crust wine list.

Directions: Off Curzon Street, near Curzon Cinema, and behind London Hilton/Dorchester hotels. Nearest tube Green Park

20-22 Queen Street W1X 7PJ
Map: C3
Tel: 0171 6298103/8089
Fax: 0171 4936181
Chef: Mr Ming Kong Kwan
Owners: Tealeaf Ltd
Cost: *Alc* £28, fixed-price L £28 (3 courses)/D £38 (4 courses).
H/wine £16.
Times: 12.15pm-last L 2.30pm/6.30pm-last D 11.15pm.
Closed 24-25 Dec
Additional: Sunday L; Children welcome; dishes
Seats: 90.
Smoking: No pipes or cigars; air-conditioning
Credit cards:

Zen Garden

15-16 Berkeley Street W1X 5AE
Map: C3
Tel: 0171 4931381
Fax: 0171 4912655
Telephone for details

A smart, expensive West End Chinese restaurant with very attentive and helpful staff. Real Peking duck, which needs to be ordered with advance notice, is amongst a number of interesting specials that also include an unusual dish made with crisp dough and topped with a thin cover of rice paste. A more familiar steamed prawn dumpling was succulent and light, and crispy beef with sweet chilli was tender and well-flavoured, garnished with shredded carrots and spring onions. Braised scallops with bamboo shoots, Chinese leaves, beans and spring onions on the other hand, lacked flavour despite being served with a good white wine sauce. Freshly cooked steamed rice was moist, if a little lumpy, and jasmine tea came fresh and hot.

Directions: Off Berkley Square, opp Mayfair Hotel. Nearest Tube – Green Park

ZenW3 ⚜⚜

Typically 'Zen' in style, this Hampstead outpost of the up-market Chinese chain looks as high-tech as its relatives. A conservatory glass front extends upwards to include a galleried second-floor dining area; waterfalls cascade down one side of the stairs, light streams in from the glass roof. The kitchen claims to be an MSG-free zone and the neatly presented 112-dish menu goes for healthy creativity in a big way, with the emphasis on spicy salads, steamed fish, 'lightning-fried' meat and so forth. One feature is the section of Vietnamese-style 'wraps' – cuttlefish cakes in green lettuce, spiced mixed vegetables in radichio, for example. 'Saint Jacks' are plump steamed scallops in black bean sauce, grilled Peking dumplings come with a red vinegar and ginger dip and there's also a promising selection for vegetarians. Other items worth noting are the satays, giant prawns steamed with fennel seeds and chicken fillet with spring onions cooked in a paper bag.

Directions: 2 mins down hill from Hampstead Tube next to P.O.

83 Hampstead High Street NW3 1RE
Map GtL: C4
Tel: 0171 794 7863
Fax: 0171 794 6956
Chef: K L Tang
Owner: Tealeaf Ltd
Cost: *Alc* £25, fixed-price L £16.50/D £26.50. ☺ H/wine £10
Times: Open L – last D 11.15pm. Closed Xmas
Additional: Children welcome; ⓓ dishes
Seats: 130. Private dining room 24
Smoking: Air-conditioning
Credit cards: ▆ ▆ ▆ ▆ ▆ ▆

Zoe ⚜⚜

Technicolor greens, reds, blues and orange are splattered on the walls and the menu aims for vibrancy. The ground floor cafe-cum-cocktail bar offers up-beat dishes like chilli-spiked mussel cakes on baby spinach. Downstairs the menu is trendy Med-inspired with coriander-crusted rump of lamb, risotto of couscous, wild rice and sun-dried tomato plus roasted red onions.

Smoking: No-smoking area; air-conditioning
Credit cards: ▆ ▆ ▆ ▆ ▆ ▆

Directions: Nearest Tube: Bond Street. Entrance at junction of Barrett St & St James St

3-5 Barrett Street W1M 5HH
Map: C4
Tel: 0171 2241122
Fax: 0171 9355444
Chef: Troy Reid
Owner: Simpsons of Cornhill
Cost: *Alc* £20, fixed-price L&D £12.50. H/wine £8.95
Times: Last L 2.30pm/last D 11.30pm. Closed Sun, Xmas, Bhs
Additional: Café (11.30am-11.30pm); Children welcome; ⓓ dishes

Zujuma's ⚜

A modern Indian restaurant decorated in rust reds and oranges, with bare pale wood tables. Through a window into the kitchen Zuju Shareef can be seen coolly preparing dishes such as 'shami' – finely ground lamb baked with garam masala , and 'murgh methi' – chicken in a thick spinach, coriander and fenugreek sauce.

Smoking: No-smoking area; air-conditioning
Credit cards: ▆ ▆ ▆ ▆ ▆

Directions: From A3 take Tibbetts Corner exit, follow signs for Wimbledon; through Wimbledon village, at 2nd mini-r/bout take 2nd exit. Located on R, 0.5 mile down road. Train station 200 yds, on R

58a Wimbledon Hill Road SW19
Map GtL: C2
Tel: 0181 879 0916
Fax: 0181 944 0861
Chef/Owner: Zuju Shareef
Cost: *Alc* £17, fixed-price L £9.95. ☺ H/wine £9.75.
Times: Noon – last D 11pm
Additional: Children welcome; ⓓ dishes
Seats: 60

Where London meets

The hotels listed below are dedicated to building their reputations on what happens in their restaurants and all hold our coveted one rosette award for food. Although not the most obvious choice as a meeting place for a working lunch, or to wind down and relax over dinner, we think these hotels are amongst London's best kept secrets.

Baileys Hotel

A late nineteenth-century hotel complete with high ceilings, plush drapes and parquet flooring. The informal Baileys Bistro serves mod Med dishes with the occasional oriental twist. Try baked tart of tomato and mozzarella with pesto dressing, or seared tuna steak with couscous, pine nuts and black bean sauce.

Smoking: No-smoking area; no cigars or pipes; air-conditioning
Accommodation: 213 en suite. **Credit cards:** ▬ ▦ ▦ ▦ ▣ ▢

Directions: Opposite Gloucester Road tube station

Baileys Hotel
140 Gloucester Road SW7 4QH
Map: A2
Tel: 0171 331 6308
Fax: 0171 370 3760
Chef: Carl Dovey
Owners: Baileys Hotel
Cost: *Alc* £18, fixed-price D £9.95.
☺ H/wine £9.90.
Times: D only, 6pm – last D 10.30pm
Additional: Bar meals;
Children welcome; ❹ dishes

Bardon Lodge Hotel

Small hotel on the edge of the village of Blackheath. The Lamplight restaurant offers a good standard of cooking from an imaginative menu. Warm seafood salad and a comforting Lancashire hot-pot have been well reported; finish with gooseberry and lime tart.

Smoking: No smoking in dining room
Accommodation: 30 en suite. **Credit cards:** ▬ ▦ ▦ ▢

Directions: Blackheath/Greenwich exit from A2. Left at 1st r/about, last exit from 2nd r/about

Stratheden Road SE3 7TH
Map GtL: C2
Tel: 0181 853 4051
Fax: 0181 858 7387
Chef: David Stewart
Owner: David Williams
Cost: Fixed-price D £15. ☺
H/wine £8.95.
Times: D only, 7pm-9.30pm.
Closed D Sun
Additional: Children welcome;
❹ dishes

Basil Street Hotel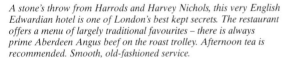

A stone's throw from Harrods and Harvey Nichols, this very English Edwardian hotel is one of London's best kept secrets. The restaurant offers a menu of largely traditional favourites – there is always prime Aberdeen Angus beef on the roast trolley. Afternoon tea is recommended. Smooth, old-fashioned service.

Additional: Sunday L; Bar meals; Children welcome; ❹ dishes
Accommodation: 93 en suite. **Credit cards:** ▬ ▦ ▦ ▦ ▣ ▢

Directions: Nearest Tube – Knightsbridge

Basil Street Knightsbridge SW3 1AH
Map: C3
Tel: 0171 5813311
Fax: 0171 5813693
Chef: James Peake
Owners: Mrs M Beeching,
Mrs S Crofton-Atkins
Cost: *Alc* £24.50, fixed-price L £9. ☺
H/wine £13.95
Times: Last L 2.30pm/D 10pm

The Berkshire

The first floor restaurant of this Oxford Street hotel is both cosy and plush. Service is friendly and the atmosphere less formal than one might imagine. The cooking is modern and a spring meal included salmon roulade, lamb fillet with chickpea couscous, and lemon tart with raspberry sauce.

Directions: Opposite Bond Street tube station

Oxford Street W1N 0BY
Map: C3
Tel: 0171 629 7474
Fax: 0171 629 8156
Telephone for details

Conrad International

Chelsea Harbour
SW10 0XG
Map GtL: C2
Tel: 0171 8233000
Fax: 0171 3516525
Chef: Peter Brennan
Owner: Eurospa (Chelsea) Ltd
Cost: Alc £14. Fixed-price D £22.50
(3 courses). ☺ H/wine £18.50.
Times: Last L 2.30pm/last D 10.30pm

*The restaurant of this modern, luxury hotel looks out over yachts
and cruisers moored in the marina at Chelsea Harbour. Fish comes
in a variety of guises, from tandoori marinated monkfish with
coconut and lemon scented rice and onion bhaji to cod 'n chips in
Guinness batter with mushy peas and tartare sauce. Meat dishes are
equally global in concept.*

Additional: Bar food; Sunday L; No children under 4; ♦ dishes
Smoking: No pipes; air-conditioning
Accommodation: 160 en suite
Credit cards: ▬ ▬ ▬ 🅐

Directions: Nearest Tube – Fulham Broadway or Earls Court

Copthorne Tara ❀

Scarsdale Place
off Wrights Lane W8 5SR
Map GtL: C3
Tel: 0171 9377211
Fax: 0171 9377100
Chef: Klaus Hohenauer
Cost: Alc £30. H/wine £13. ☺
Times: D only, 7pm-last D 11pm.
Closed D Sun

*Classic British dishes such as roast rack of lamb and jugged hare in
port wine sauce feature on the menu at the wood-panelled Jerome K
Jerome restaurant. More contemporary dishes include grilled duck
breast with honey and thyme and seared fillet of monkfish with
wholegrain mustard and tarragon sauce.*

Additional: ♦ dishes
Smoking: No-smoking area; no pipes & cigars; air-conditioning
Accommodation: 825 en suite
Credit cards: ▬ ▬ ▬ 🅐

Directions: Nearest Tube – High Street Kensington

Gloucester Hotel ❀

4-18 Harrington Gardens
SW7 4LH
Tel: 0171 4114212/3736030
Fax: 0171 3730409
Chef: Graham Riley
Owners: Millennium Hotels & Resorts
Cost: Alc £25, fixed-price L/D £25. ☺
H/wine £9.90.

*Modern hotel in South Kensington which features the stylish South
West 7, where imaginative up-to-date British cooking comes with a
strong Mediterranean accent. Try terrine of sea bass, salmon and
roasted red peppers, followed by monkfish wrapped in Parma ham
with nori seaweed.*

Times: Last L 3pm/D 10.45pm
Additional: Sunday L; Bar meals; Children welcome; ♦ dishes
Smoking: No-smoking area; air-conditioning
Accommodation: 548 en suite
Credit cards: ▬ ▬ ▬ ▚ 🅐 ℂ

Directions: 1 minute from Gloucester Road tube station

The Hampshire 🏵

A stylish period hotel in the heart of London's West End. Meals are taken in the plush, intimate surroundings of Celebrities Restaurant – expect dishes such as fillet of red mullet with vegetable and shellfish ratatouille, breast of duck with Sauternes sauce, and roast rump of lamb with new potato and mint salad.

Smoking: No-smoking area; air-conditioning
Accommodation: 124 en suite. **Credit cards:** 🟦 📇 🖃 💱 💷 Ⓒ

Directions: S side of Leicester Square on corner with St Martin's Street

Leicester Square WC2H 7LH
Map: C3
Tel: 0171 8399399
Fax: 0171 9308122
Chef: Colin Button
Owners: Radisson Edwardian Hotels
Cost: Alc £25, fixed-price L/D £18. ☺ H/wine £14.25.
Times: Last L 2.30pm/last D 11pm
Additional: Sunday L; Bar meals; Children welcome; 🍴 dishes;

Hogarth Hotel 🏵

Friendly modern hotel, convenient for Earls Court, with a good choice of dishes at Trumps restaurant, such as cappuccino of roasted langoustine and lentils, pan-fried magret of duck with sweet potato rösti and rich fig sauce, and grilled tuna set on Mediterranean vegetables with garlic mash quenelles.

Smoking: No smoking in dining room
Accommodation: 85 en suite. **Credit cards:** 🟦 📇 🖃 💱 💷 Ⓒ

Directions: 150 yds from Earl's Court tube station

33 Hogarth Road Kensington SW5 0QQ
Map GtL: C3
Tel: 0171 3706831
Fax: 0171 3736179
Owners: Marston Hotels
Cost: Alc £20, fixed-price L £15/D £17. ☺ H/wine £11.95.
Times: Last L 2pm/last D 9.30pm
Additional: Bar food; Sunday L; Children welcome; 🍴 dishes

Holiday Inn Crowne Plaza 🏵

Mock Tudor-style restaurant within a busy Airport hotel. Smartly dressed staff take pride in serving dishes such as gravad lax of salmon with smoked halibut and smoked salmon, three collops of wild boar, venison and beef with Madeira sauce and desserts from the trolley.

Smoking: No-smoking area; no cigars or pipes; air-conditioning
Accommodation: 375 en suite. **Credit cards:** 🟦 📇 🖃 💱 💷

Directions: 2 miles N of junction 4 M4/A408

Stockley Road UB7 9NA
Map GtL: A2
Tel: 01895 445555
Fax: 01895 445122
Chef: John Witherley
Owner: Bass – Holiday Inns.
Cost: Alc £35, fixed-price L £15.95. H/wine £12.50
Times: Last D 10.15pm Closed L Sat, Sun, Bhs
Additional: 🍴 dishes
Seats: 46. Jacket & tie preferred

Holiday Inn Mayfair 🏵

3 Berkeley Street W1X 6NE
Map: C2
Tel: 0171 4938282
Fax: 0171 6292827
Chef: Barry Brewington
Cost: Alc £20, fixed-price D £18.95. ☺ H/wine £12.50.
Times: Last L-2.30pm/last D 10.30pm. Closed Sat
Additional: Sunday L; Bar meals L; Children welcome; 🍴 dishes
Smoking: No-smoking area; air-conditioning
Accommodation: 185 en suite
Credit cards: 🟦 📇 🖃 💱 💷

Directions: Nearest Tube: Green Park

Enjoying a splendid central location just a few steps from Piccadilly and Bond Street, this modern hotel offers an international menu. Fresh ingredients are used to create dishes with bold flavours. Expect roast cod on cheesy mash and chicken in white wine and herbs.

Kensington Park Thistle ❀

16-32 De Vere Gardens W8 5AG
Map GtL: C3
Tel: 0171 9378080
Fax: 0171 9377616
Chef: Patrick Riddwer
Owners: Thistle Hotels
Cost: Alc £22, fixed-price D £21.50.
☺ H/wine £13.50
Times: D only, 6pm-10.30pm.
Closed Sun, Mon, Aug
Additional: No children under 7;
❸ dishes
Smoking: Air-conditioning
Accommodation: 352 en suite
Credit cards: 💳 💳 💳 💳 💳 💳

There is an intimate atmosphere to the Cairngorm Grill, with its dark wood panelling and chandeliers (a view of the kitchen is allowed through frosted glass). Dishes include roulade of sea salmon and Japanese seaweed, chargrilled lamb cutlet, and Dover sole.

Directions: Nearest Tubes: High Street Kensington, Gloucester Road

The Langham Hilton ❀

The first 'grand' hotel in the capital, dating from 1865, offers a modern menu in Memories restaurant, where meals are often accompanied by a harpist. At a test meal fresh asparagus with a rich caviar beurre blanc, was followed by breast of duck, pink and tender, with an orange and honey sauce.

Directions: N end of Regent Street, opp BBC. Nearest Tube – Oxford Circus

1 Portland Place W1N 4JA
Map: C4
Tel: 0171 6361000
Fax: 0171 3232340
Chef: George Fuchs
Cost: Alc £40. Fixed-price L £24/ D£30.75. H/wine £16
Times: Noon-3pm. 6pm-10.45pm
Telephone for further details

London Marriott Hotel ❀

Grosvenor Square W1A 4AW
Map: C3
Tel: 0171 4931232
Fax: 0171 4913201
Chef: Nick Hawkes
Owner: Marriott Hotels
Cost: Alc £25.75, fixed-price L £19.50. ☺ H/wine £15.75.
Times: 11am-last L 4pm/4pm-last D 10.30pm. Closed L Sat, 24 Dec, 1 Jan
Additional: Sunday L; Bar meals; Children welcome; ❸ dishes
Smoking: No-smoking area; air-conditioning
Accommodation: 221 en suite
Credit cards: 💳 💳 💳 💳 💳 💳

Rillettes of Cornish mackerel with hot-smoked eel, breast of Gressingham duck roasted with London gin, cannon of English lamb with black pudding and parsley, and traditional cod in beer batter and chips, are amongst the modish specialities at this smart, multi-national hotel dining room, elegantly fitted with cherry-wood panelling.

Directions: Nearest Tube – Bond Street

Oak Lodge Hotel ⊛

NEW

Converted family home in Enfield's leafy suburbs offering a friendly welcome and good home-cooking. Choose from a seasonal carte providing a varied range of dishes. At inspection tender calves' sweetbreads with well-cooked vegetables followed mushroom soup, with lemon brûlée for pudding.

80 Village Road Bush Hill Park
Enfield EN1 2EU
Map GtL: D5
Tel: 0181 3607082
Chef: Mark Lees
Owners: John and Yvonne Brown
Cost: Alc £22.50
Times: D only, 7.30pm-10pm.
Closed D Sun
Additional: Sunday L (1.30pm-4pm);
Children welcome; ❺ dishes
Smoking: No smoking in dining room
Accommodation: 5 en suite
Credit cards: ▬ ▦ ▨ ⚏ ⚏ ⚏

Directions: Exit 25 M25, turn 2nd
right signed Enfield; hotel 1m from
railway station and A10

The Radisson Edwardian Hotel ⊛

A stylish, period hotel hard by Heathrow Airport, offering a choice of eating options for the international traveller. An enjoyable test meal in the elegant Henley's Restaurant yielded leeks wrapped in Black Forest ham with mustard sauce, followed by fresh lemon sole filled with spring vegetables with a beurre blanc sauce.

Smoking: No-smoking area; air-conditioning
Accommodation: 459 en suite
Credit cards: ▬ ▦ ▨ ⚏ ⚏

Directions: On the A4, eastbound side

Bath Road Hayes UB3 5AW
Map GtL: C2
Tel: 0181 7596311
Fax: 0181 7594559
Chef: Jean Claude Sandillon
Owner: Radisson Edwardian Hotel
Cost: Alc £19.90, fixed-price D
£29.50. H/wine £13.50
Times: Last L 2.30pm/D 10.30pm.
Closed L Sat, L Sun
Additional: Bar meals;
Children welcome; ❺ dishes

Royal Westminster Thistle ⊛

Discreetly located hotel with smart, stylish restaurant offering an imaginative choice of modern English dishes. A typical meal could include smoked tomato ravioli with pancetta, morels and broad beans, and sautéed noisettes of lamb on a port sauce. Fish is a strength.

Directions: From Victoria station walk to Buckingham Palace along Buckingham Palace Road. Hotel opposite Royal Mews

49 Buckingham Palace Road
SW1W 0QT
Map: D2
Tel: 0171 8341821
Fax: 0171 9317542
Chef: Bruce Smith
Owners: Thistle Hotels
Cost: Alc £23, fixed-price D £21.95.
☺ H/wine £13.80.
Times: D only, 6pm-10.30pm.
Closed Sun, 2 wks after Xmas
Additional: Sunday L; Bar meals;
Children welcome; ❺ dishes
Smoking: No-smoking area; air-
conditioning
Accommodation: 134 en suite
Credit cards: ▬ ▦ ▨ ⚏ ⚏ ⚏

Swallow International Hotel ❀

An eclectic menu of modern British dishes is served in Blayneys Restaurant at this busy Swallow hotel. Expect main courses such as fillet of Atlantic cod with minted broad beans and asparagus; Barbary duck breast with parsnip mash and caramelised apple; and roast confit of guinea fowl with sauce lyonnaise.

Additional: Sunday L; Bar meals; Children welcome; ◑ dishes
Smoking: No-smoking area; air-conditioning
Accommodation: 422 en suite
Credit cards: 💳 💳 💳 💳 💳 💳

Cromwell Road SW5 0TH
Map: A2
Tel: 0171 9731000
Fax: 0171 2448194
Chef: Bernhard Engelhardt
Owners: Swallow International Hotels
Cost: Alc £27.25, fixed-price D £21.50. ☺ H/wine £15.
Times: 6pm – last D 11pm.
Closed Dec 23-27

Directions: Nearest tube stations: Gloucester Road & Earls Court

The Tower Thistle ❀

St Katherine's Way
E1 9LD
Map: G3
Tel: 0171 4812575
Fax: 0171 4884106
Chef: Russell Allen
Cost: £45, fixed-price L £25.50/D £28.50. H/wine £15.50
Times: 12.30pm-last L 2pm/7pm-last D 10.15pm. Closed Sun, Bhs
Additional: No children under 14; ◑ dishes
Seats: 80. Jacket & tie preferred
Smoking: No-smoking area
Accommodation: 802 en suite
Credit cards: 💳 💳 💳 💳 💳

With wonderful views over the Thames and Tower Bridge, the Princes Room offers a wide selection of dishes such as roast leg of rabbit with coleslaw and crispy pancetta, and grilled red mullet with artichoke and sauce vierge. Carefully crafted cooking.

Directions: Adjacent to Tower of London and Tower Bridge on North shore of River Thames

The Washington ❀

This smart, modern, air-conditioned hotel offers an informal brasserie-style menu. Dishes range from fish 'n' chips, and Caesar salad with chargrilled chicken breast, to roasted monkfish tail with garlic, smoked bacon and a light saffron jus.

Smoking: No smoking in dining room; air-conditioning
Accommodation: 173 en suite
Credit cards: 💳 💳 💳 💳 💳 💳

5-7 Curzon Street W1Y 8DT
Map: C3
Tel: 0171 4997000
Fax: 0171 4956172
Chef: Simon Sylvester
Cost: Alc £23, fixed-price D £10. ☺ H/wine £13.
Times: Last L 3pm-last D 11pm
Additional: Bar meals; Sunday L; Children welcome; ◑ dishes

Directions: Nearest Tube – Green Park

The Westbury

Bond Street W1A 4UH
Map: C3
Tel: 0171 6297755
Fax: 0171 6294496
Chef: John McCann
Owners: The Westbury Hotel
Cost: Alc £21, fixed-price L/D £15. ☺
H/wine £21.50.
Times: Last L 2.30pm/D 10pm.
Closed Sat/Sun L
Additional: Sunday L; Bar meals D;
Children welcome; ☻ dishes
Smoking: No-smoking area; no cigars
or pipes
Accommodation: 244 en suite
Credit cards:

Although set in the heart of London's classiest shopping district, this distinctive hotel is named after Long Island's famous polo ground. Lively modern dishes are served in La Méditerannée: typical main courses include grilled swordfish with sauce vierge, and roast rump of lamb with a sun-dried tomato and rosemary crust.

Directions: Nearest Tubes: Oxford Circus, Piccadilly Circus, Bond Street

The White House Hotel

Albany Street NW1 3UP
Map: D4
Tel: 0171 3871200
Fax: 0171 3880091
Chef: Clinton Lovell
Owner: Lomondo Limited
Cost: Alc £35, fixed-price L £18.75/D
£22.75. ☺ H/wine £12.
Times: Last L 2.30pm/D 11pm.
Closed L Sat, Sun
Additional: Bar meals L;
Children welcome; ☻ dishes
Smoking: No-smoking area;
air-conditioning
Accommodation: 584 en suite
Credit cards:

Classic French cuisine at expense-account prices includes seared fillet of red mullet with fennel nage, deep-fried basil and garlic potato fritters, roasted best end of lamb with Sarladaise potatoes and truffle, as well as Chateaubriand for two with soufflé potatoes and béarnaise sauce.

Directions: Nearest Tube – Great Portland Street

ENGLAND
BEDFORDSHIRE

ASPLEY GUISE,
Moore Place Hotel

The Square MK17 8DW
Map 4: SP93
Tel: 01908 282000
Fax: 01908 281888
Chef: Clive Southgate
Owner: Vickers family
Cost: *Alc* £25, fixed-price L&D
£20.95. H/wine £10.95
Times: 12.30pm-last L
1.45pm/7.30pm-last D 9.45pm.
Closed L Sat
Additional: Bar meals L; Sunday L;
Children welcome; ✪ dishes
Seats: 50. Private dining room 40

An attractive, red-brick Georgian mansion set in the centre of a quiet village, yet conveniently located for the M1. Meals are served in The Greenhouse, an airy, Victorian-style conservatory restaurant, where an interesting selection of modern British dishes is offered on a weekly-changing set menus and carte. High points of our last test meal included an excellent roasted panaché of seafood (featuring a good selection of fresh fish), and a delicious hot chocolate tart with a dark, rich combination of flavours and textures. The main course was duck accompanied by a subtle thyme jus and a sweet asparagus marmalade. Attention to small details, such as crisp and colourful fresh vegetables and good strong coffee with home-made petits fours, show care. Friendly and attentive service.

Smoking: No pipes & cigars
Accommodation: 54 en suite
Credit cards: ▇▇ ▇▇ ▇▇ ▇▇ ▇ ▇

Directions: In centre of village

BEDFORD, **Knife & Cleaver**

Houghton Conquest MK45 3LA
Map 5: TL14
Tel: 01234 740387
Fax: 01234 740900
Chefs: Chris Bishop, Kirk Gillingham, Anne Huckle
Owners: David & Pauline Loom
Cost: *Alc* £22, fixed-price L £13.50/D
£18.50 (Mon-Fri). ☺ H/wine £9.95.
Times: Last L 2.30pm/D 9.30pm.
Closed Sun D, 27-30 Dec
Additional: Sunday L; Bar meals;
Children welcome; ✪ dishes

A popular country inn with a serious approach to food. The blackboard menu of daily fish specials might include dishes such as braised fillet of salmon with chestnut mushrooms, and pan-fried monkfish with a Cajun spiced sauce. Meals can be enjoyed in the Victorian-style conservatory or al fresco on the flower-filled terrace.

Smoking: No cigars or pipes
Accommodation: 9 en suite
Credit cards: ▇▇ ▇▇ ▇▇ ▇▇ ▇ ▇

Directions: M1/J12/13, between A6 & B530. 2m N of Ampthill, 5m S of Bedford

BEDFORD,
Woodlands Manor Hotel

Green Lane,
Clapham MK41 6EP
Map 5: TL04
Tel: 01234 363281
Fax: 01234 272390
Chef: Rae Johnson
Owners: Pageant Hotels
Cost: *Alc* £30, fixed-price L £15.95/D
£22.50. ☺ H/wine £11.
Times: Last L 2pm/last D 9.30pm
Additional: Sun L; Bar meals;
Children welcome; ✪ dishes

The character of the manor house has been retained with sympathetic furnishings, and the restaurant is an elegant room with high ceilings and large windows. From an imaginative menu, ham and watercress sausage on ratatouille proved a good choice, followed by roast saddle of lamb with a caper-spiked sauce.

Smoking: No-smoking area; no pipes or cigars
Accommodation: 36 en suite
Credit cards: ▇▇ ▇▇ ▇▇ ▇▇ ▇

Directions: A6 Bedford-Kettering, follow sign to Clapham, then first R in to Green Lane. Hotel 200m on R

DUNSTABLE,
Old Palace Lodge Hotel ❀

Ivy-clad hotel conveniently close to the town centre. The carte and daily menu offer international favourites such as mushroom chow mein, sirloin steak pizziola, beef Stroganoff and chicken Kiev. Britain is represented by home-made game terrine and locally made Toddington sausage with creamed potatoes and onion gravy.

Accommodation: 68 en suite
Credit cards: ▬ ▬ ▬ ▬ ▣ ℂ

Directions: From M1/J11 take Dunstable exit at r/about. At 2 miles road passes under bridge. Hotel on R hand side opposite church.

Church Street LU5 4RT
Map 4: TL02
Tel: 01582 662201
Fax: 01582 696422
Chef: Arif Huseyin
Owner: Andrew Weir Hotels
Cost: *Alc* £30, fixed-price D £19.50.
☺ H/wine £10.50.
Times: Last L 1.45pm/D 9.45pm.
Closed Bhs
Additional: Sunday L; Bar meals;
Children welcome; ❹ dishes
Smoking: No-smoking area; air conditioning

FLITWICK, Flitwick Manor Hotel ❀❀❀

Church Road MK45 1AE
Map 4: TL03
Tel: 01525 712242
Fax: 01525 718753
Chef: Richard Salt
Cost: *Alc* £40.45, fixed-price L £20.95. H/wine £14.50
Times: Noon-last L 1.30pm/7pm-last D 9.30pm
Additional: Sunday L; No children under 12 at D; ❹ dishes
Seats: 50. Private dining rooms 20-10. Jacket and tie preferred
Smoking: No smoking in dining room
Accommodation: 15 en suite
Credit cards: ▬ ▬ ▬ ▬ ▣ ℂ

Flitwick lives in a cossetted world of its own, even though it is a mere 10 minutes drive from the M1. This stylish Queen Anne mansion is set in 50 acres of grounds that were once a deer park: the gardens are impeccably manicured and there is even a croquet lawn as well as a sun-soaked terrace for fine days. New owners and a new chef in the shape of Richard Salt seem set to enhance the hotel's already enviable reputation. The interior is elegantly done out in gracious, classical style and meals are served in the formal elegance of the Brooks Room with windows overlooking the grounds. Fixed-price menus are complex and modern in style: monkfish is roast, chilled and spiced and served with a salad of baby spinach and rocket with a foie gras wun-tun, apricot coulis and balsamic jus, while pan-fried escalope of salmon is given an oriental twist when it is served in a hot-pot of mussels infused with coconut, lemon grass and coriander. Meat and game receive similar treatment: pot-roast duck sampled one lunchtime was moist and thinly sliced over a cream, coriander and chilli sauce, while rump of local lamb might be set on a gâteau of spinach and braised Puy lentils with a basil cream sauce. As a finale, espresso coffee soufflé sent one inspector into raptures with its perfect richness, and the icing on the cake comes in the shape of seductive petits fours, including a banana ice-cream lollipop on a cocktail stick coated in Belgian chocolate. Staff know what pampering is all about. A good wine list features some quite impressive older vintages and a well-represented European selection.
Signature dishes: Braised lamb's sweetbreads and truffled

cream potatoes enhanced with Madeira sauce; pan-fried scallops, gâteau of aubergine, courgette and tomato with piquant red pepper cream; hot-smoked haunch of venison set in a juniper and orange sauce; roast best end of local lamb in a delicate warm vinaigrette of rosemary and black olives.

Directions: On A5120, two miles from M1 junction 12

WOBURN,

Paris House Restaurant ❀❀

Woburn Park MK17 9PQ
Map 4: SP93
Tel: 01525 290692
Fax: 01525 290471
Chef/Owner: Peter Chandler
Cost: Alc £42, fixed-price L £25 (3 courses)/D £45 (5 courses). H/wine £12
Times: Noon-last L 2pm/7pm-last D 9.30pm. Closed D Sun, Mon, Feb
Additional: Sunday L; Children welcome, ❀ dishes
Seats: 45. Private dining room 14
Smoking: No pipes and cigars
Credit cards: ▆ ▆ ▆ ▆ ▆ ▆

Directions: On A4012, 1.5 miles out of Woburn towards Hockcliffe, through huge archway

Barra Singha deer graze gracefully in the grounds of Woburn Park as you meander along the drive towards this extraordinary black-and-white timbered house. Its name derives from the fact that it was erected for the Paris Exhibition in 1878, then dismantled, brought over to England and reconstructed on the Duke of Bedford's estate. Chef/proprietor Peter Chandler has been in residence since 1983 and there is, appropriately, a Gallic thrust to his cooking. Typically, a recent inspection began with fisherman's soup (a version of bouillabaisse) and continued with a rich sauté of hare braised in local beer with a touch of dark chocolate. Here and there a more exotic idea surfaces, as in spicy chicken and coriander sticks in peanut sauce. It's back to the classics, however, for desserts such as tarte Tatin or an unctuous chocolate soufflé with a cube of rum-drenched sponge hidden at the bottom. A few New World wines add depth to the mainly French list.

BERKSHIRE

ASCOT, The Berystede ❀

Timber-framed Victorian residence with turrets and expansive wooded grounds. Promising cooking offers the likes of chicken liver parfait with Bramley apple chutney, breast of chicken served on a seared escalope of salmon with a buttery flavoured chive sauce, and bitter chocolate marquise with a coffee sauce anglaise.

Smoking: No smoking in dining room.
Accommodation: 91 en suite. **Credit cards:** ▆ ▆ ▆ ▆

Directions: M3/J3, follow signs for Ascot.

Bagshot Road
Sunninghill SL5 9JH
Map 4: SU96
Tel: 01344 23311
Fax: 01344 872301
Chef: Jon Powell
Cost: Alc £32, fixed-price L £15.95/D £24.95. ☺ H/wine £14.75.
Times: Last L 1.45pm/last D 9.45pm. Closed L Sat
Additional: Sunday L; Bar meals; Children welcome; ❀ dishes

ASCOT, Jade Fountain ❀

Formal atmosphere for a smart Chinese in a village outside Ascot.
While the menu varies little from many other similar establishments,
the quality of the cooking is sound. Szechuan prawns and crispy
duck are recommended. Drink jasmine tea.

Additional: Sunday L; Children welcome; ❹ dishes
Smoking: No cigars or pipes. **Credit cards:** ▨▨ ▨▨ ▨▨ ▨▨ ▨▨ ▨

Directions: 1.5 miles from Ascot

38 High Street Sunninghill
Ascot SL5 9NE
Map 4: SU96
Tel: 01344 27070
Chef: Chee Kin Lee
Owners: Che Kin Lee, Ka Fai Lee,
Steven Chu, Robert Man
Cost: Alc £22.50, fixed-price L
£21.50/D £22.50. ☺ H/wine £10.25
Times: Last L 1.50pm/D 10.30pm.
Closed 24-27 Dec

ASCOT, Royal Berkshire Hotel ❀

London Road Sunninghill SL5 0PP
Map 4: SU96
Tel: 01344 23322
Fax: 01344 27100
Chef: Paul Sutcliffe
Cost: Alc £24.50, fixed-price L
£24.50/D £35.50. H/wine £14.95
Times: Noon-last L 2.15pm/7pm-last
D 9.15pm. Closed L Sat
Additional: Bar food; Sunday L;
Children welcome; ❹ dishes
Smoking: No pipes and cigars

Imposing, conference-orientated Queen Anne mansion with an
attractive, if rather formal, restaurant. Bouillabaisse, medley of
seafood with basil sauce, and beef fillet with foie gras and port wine
were amongst a top-of-the-range choice. Flambéed winter fruits
made a clever dessert.

Accommodation: 63 en suite
Credit cards: ▨▨ ▨▨ ▨▨ ▨ ▨

Directions: M4/J10, or A30, follow A329 through Ascot. Hotel
is on L after 1.5 miles. From M3/J3 take A322

BRACKNELL,
Coppid Beech Hotel ❀❀

John Nike Way RG12 8TF
Map 4: SU86
Tel: 01344 303333
Fax: 01344 301200
Chef: Neil Thrift
Cost: Alc £29.50, fixed-price D
£20.95. ☺ H/wine £12.50
Times: Noon-last L 2.30pm/7pm-last
D 10.30pm. Closed Sat L
Additional: Bar food; Sunday L;
Children welcome; ❹ dishes
Seats: 100.
Smoking: No-smoking area; air-
conditioning
Accommodation: 205 en suite
Credit cards: ▨▨ ▨▨ ▨▨ ▨▨ ▨ ▨

The cooking might be modern British, but the decor is disconcertingly Alpine, complete with peaks, wooden shutters and balconies. Perhaps the adjacent bierkeller, ski-slope and ice-rink help explain the theme. The carte includes straightforward grills, steak, Dover sole and suprême of chicken with mustard sauce, as well as more complex dishes such as pan-fried veal sweetbreads layered between buttered chervil and filo pastry biscuits, served with a rich Madeira gravy, and roasted steak of sea bass with a tomato and courgette tart, baby spinach and Pernod butter. A well constructed, marinated gâteau of tomato with warm shellfish on salad leaves with balsamic vinegar, and plump, seared scallops with braised endives, smoked bacon and tarragon opened one test meal. Then came pan-fried breast of duck on a bed of buttered spinach with morel sauce, and chargrilled tuna with fennel confit, plum tomatoes and red pepper juice. Desserts took in apple and raspberry compote with cider sorbet and baked Alaska. The wine list covers all countries and has a good selection by the glass.

Directions: From M4/J10, follow A329 (M) to 1st exit. At roundabout take 1st exit to Binfield; hotel 300 metres on R

BRAY, The Fat Duck

'It is pure joy to eat in a restaurant like this', enthuses our inspector, reprising the encomiums of last year's *Guide*. This high praise is attributed to several factors – a self-taught chef with a small brigade of others of similar ilk, a questioning mind and unbridled enthusiasm. Heston Blumenthal displays a controlled passion about his ingredients and combinations; as such, the menu is constantly evolving as dishes are re-worked and refined. One recent inspiration – *Kouign-amann* tarte Tatin – comes from an old Breton cookbook. Marinated green olives sharpen the appetite for high-wire starters such as crab feuillantine (made with a reduction of crab shell) with marinated salmon, crystallised seaweed, foie gras and oyster vinaigrette – in the event, easier on the palate than the thought processes. Côtes de porc, hinting of salt, sage and garlic, with braised lettuce and Parmentier of andouillette were all carried along by the decidedly unsentimental roasted pig's ear jus. Other thrilling ideas might include velouté of celeriac with cabbage stuffed with frogs' legs and choucroute, roast chicken with maize and vanilla farce, chervil, crépinette of macaroni and roasting juices, and salted butter caramel with cacao sorbet. At times, the franglais menu descriptions almost smack of deliberate obscurantism – one can make a fair guess at deconstructing 'risotto of crab with roquette, a cassonade of red pepper and its chlorophyll' but you still need an explanation. Happily, Blumenthal also has the sense and confidence to serve much more straightforward dishes (such as fabulous steak and chips with sauce moelle) and get them spot on, harder than it sounds. An old listed building with beamed interior is the setting for these culinary explorations – there may be no tablecloths, but Reidel glasses show where priorities lie.

Signature dishes: Petit-salé of duck, pommes purées; Chicken stuffed with sweetcorn and vanilla, crépinette of macaroni and roasting juices; roast red mullet, gâteau of celeriac, spinach and beef marrow, a reduction of red wine and carrot; roast venison, gratin of époisse, confit of chestnuts and shallots, sauce poivrade.

High Street Maidenhead SL6 2AQ
Map 4: SU97
Tel: 01628 580333
Fax: 01628 776188
Chef: Heston Blumenthal
Owners: Heston Blumenthal, Susanna Blumenthal
Cost: *Alc* £36, fixed-price £16.50. H/wine £14
Times: Last L 2pm (3pm Sun)/7pm-9.30pm (10pm weekends). Closed D Sun, Mon, 2 wks Xmas
Additional: Sunday L; Children welcome; ✪ dishes
Seats: 50
Smoking: No pipes
Credit cards: ▬ ▬ ▬ ▬ ▬

Directions: In centre of Bray

BRAY, **Monkey Island Hotel** ❀

Bray-on-Thames SL6 2EE
Map 4: SU97
Tel: 01628 23400
Fax: 01628 784732
Chef: Ian Butcher
Cost: Alc £45, fixed price L £20/D
£28. H/wine £13.75.
Times: Last L 2.30pm/D 9.30pm
Closed L Sat, 26 Dec-15 Jan
Additional: Bar Food; Sunday L;
Children welcome; ◑ dishes
Smoking: No-smoking area
Accommodation: 25 en suite
Credit cards: ▆ ▆ ▆ ▆ ▆ ▆

*Privately owned hotel with an idyllic location – on an island a mile
downstream from Maidenhead with access by footbridge or boat.
Here it is possible to achieve a real feeling of exclusivity and peace.
Ambitious menu offers the likes of roasted breast of duck on a
blueberry sauce with roasted shallots and asparagus mille-feuille.*

Directions: M4/J8/9, A308 (M) (Windsor) 1st L to Bray, 1st R
into Old Mill Lane, hotel at end

BRAY, **Waterside Inn** ❀❀❀❀

The Waterside Inn still modestly styles itself a restaurant with
rooms, albeit one to which guests can arrive by private boat as
well as Rolls-Royce. The long windows of the dining-room,
decorated in warm yellows and greens, overlook the Thames
and it is the perfect setting for dinner on a summer evening.
The cosy, bright bar is a pleasure to drink in, and is amusingly
decorated with life-sized papier-mâché figures, as well as
Michel Roux's books, pictures and awards. The whole place
oozes quality, but in the most relaxed kind of way. Staff are
highly polished, discreet and unfailingly helpful. The cooking
is French to the core. A first course lobster consommé, full of
deep flavour, was served with a ravioli of lobster, lamb with
leek mousse and tarragon jus was sweet, pink and accurately
cooked, accompanied by mushrooms and nutty tasting
spinach. Pasta with smoked chicken and sorrel with tiny
artichoke hearts and shavings of a superb Parmesan was a
wonderful balance of sweet and sharp flavours, and monkfish
stuffed with fish mousse, served with a beurre noisette and
fresh truffle was also spot on. The ultimate accolade in
luxurious simplicity, though, must go to a dish of warm oysters
with truffle and caviar. Applause for the perfect timing of an
impeccable raspberry soufflé, as well as a soft, yet fleshy peach
roasted with honey and lavender and served with an intense,
clean-flavoured redcurrant sorbet. Exclusively French and
impeccably sourced, the depth of quality in the wine list is
undeniable. Chave, Guigal, Jaboulet, Lafite, Latour, d'Yquem,
Jadot, the roll-call of greats seems never ending. For those
with an unlimited budget, Bordeaux is the place to splash out
with better vintages and greater maturity on offer than in
Burgundy or Rhône. Bargain hunters will return empty
handed, but there are outstanding producers available at £30
or less – crus Beaujolais from Duboeuf, notably Morgon
Domaine Jean Descombes at £22, and Bourgeois or Crochet
in Sancerre.

Ferry Road SL6 2AT
Map 4: SU97
Tel: 01628 620691
Fax: 01628 784710
Chefs: Michel Roux, Mark Dodson
Owner: Michel Roux
Cost: Alc £75, fixed-price L £30.50
(weekdays) £45.50 (Sat,Sun)/D £69.50
(5 courses). H/wine £20
Times: Noon-last L 2pm (2.30pm
Sat/Sun)/ 7pm-last D 10pm. Closed
Mon, L Tues, D Sun (3rd wk Oct-2nd
wk April), 26 Dec for 5 weeks
Additional: No children under 12;
◑ dishes
Seats: 75. Private dining room 8
Accommodation: 9 en suite
Credit cards: ▆ ▆ ▆ ▆ ▆ ▆

Signature dishes: Fricassée de Saint-Pierre, nage fine au citron vert; l'assiette de grenadins, rouelle de rognon et pithiviers de ris de veau et son jus; Filets de lapereau grillés aux marrons glacés; pêchéz gourmand selon 'Michel'.

Directions: On A3089 towards Windsor, turn L before M/way overpass for Bray. Restaurant clearly signposted.

MAIDENHEAD,

Fredrick's Hotel ❀❀❀

Shoppenhangers Road SL6 2PZ
Map 4: SU88
Tel: 01628 635934
Fax: 01628 771054
Chef: Brian Cutler
Owner: Fredrick W Lösel
Cost: Fixed-price L £21/D £31.50. H/wine £14
Times: Noon-last L 2pm/7pm-last D 9.45pm. Closed L Sat, Xmas & New Year
Additional: Lounge meals, Sunday lunch; Children welcome; ❸ dishes
Seats: 60. Private dining rooms 130
Smoking: No cigars and pipes in dining room; air conditioning
Accommodation: 37 en suite
Credit cards: ▬ ▨ ▨ ▧

In a sense, there is something other worldly about Fredrick's – the style of decor is bourgeois European deluxe, and the cooking would not be out of place in Brussels or Strasbourg. For over twenty years, the eponymous Fredrick Lösel has run this special, individual hotel along with a loyal team of well-drilled and willing staff. Brian Cutler has been chef for the last ten years, and continues to prove that classical cuisine, quality ingredients and precision of execution can still produce memorable dishes. Some may sound a little old fashioned, but that's not necessarily a bad thing – a hot cream cheese and orange soufflé had real flavour and depth, and roast squid with crab filling on linguine was spot-on, with delicious ink sauce. Evergreens include smoked wild Scotch salmon, fresh asparagus with sauce hollandaise, grilled calves' liver and bacon, roast duckling with Bramley apples (for two), Dover sole and Scottish lobster cooked to choice. The latter also appears in dishes such as lobster, potato gnocchi and macaroni gratin, and in lobster bisque. An excellent Sunday luncheon menu includes leek, potato and mussel soup, goujons of sole frites and sauce rémoulade, roast rib of Aberdeen Angus from the trolley, and fillet sole Véronique. The *carte* is not completely retro, but chicken fillets in tempura, and five-spice tiger prawn and asparagus salad is about as trendy as it gets. A predominantly French wine list with some top quality wines on offer. A good range of clarets with some reasonably priced Cru Bourgeois. Not much available for under £25. Perhaps better to splash out on something really special, quite a few good wines are available in halves.

Directions: From A404M exit Cox Green, turn L at roundabout; from A308 take next turning to station bridge.

Signature dishes: Roast best-end of new-season's lamb with couscous and grilled vegetables; Langoustine and squid on potato salad with truffle dressing; Partridge and pig's cheek en cocotte with champagne sauerkraut; Braised oxtail bourguignonne.

MAIDENHEAD, Ye Olde Bell

Imaginative cooking is served in this traditionally panelled restaurant, which overlooks the hotel's patio and ornamental gardens. A chicken liver terrine was particularly enjoyed at a recent meal, followed by medallions of monkfish with a creamy crayfish sauce. A good choice of vegetarian dishes is also offered.

Times: Last L 2pm/Last D 9.30pm.
Additional: Sunday L; Bar meals; Children welcome; ⍟ dishes
Accommodation: 41 en suite
Credit cards: ▉ ▉ ▉ ▉

Directions: Take A4130 to Henley, at East Arms pub turn R into Hurley village. Hotel 800 yds down road

Hurley Maidenhead SL6 5LX
Map 4: SU88
Tel: 01628 825811
Fax: 01628 825939
Chef: Adrian Offley
Owners: Jarvis Hotels
Cost: *Alc* £30, fixed-price L £17.95/D £23.95.

NEWBURY,
Donnington Valley Hotel

Set in a 1,000 acre estate complete with an 18-hole golf course and facilities for shooting and fly fishing, this modern red brick hotel has acquired an enviable reputation for outstanding hospitality and excellent facilities. Food remains a strength and a recent meal taken in the aptly named Gallery Restaurant was well up-to-the-mark. Highlights included a skilfully executed Roquefort cheese soufflé tempered with sweet onion, raisin and apple chutney, and accurately timed roast loin of lamb served with rosemary dumplings, a swede rösti and superb dauphinoise potatoes. Other choices might include a salad of sautéed scallops with deep-fried basil, pan-fried calves' liver with a Jerusalem artichoke purée, and grilled fillet of beef with roasted cherry tomatoes. Desserts range from a platter of exotic fruits with a 'citrus nectar' to iced chocolate and fig terrine. The wine list is a massive tome running to 300 bins, some from the proprietor's award-winning Californian winery.

Old Oxford Road
Donnington RG14 3AG
Map 4: SU46
Tel: 01635 551199
Fax: 01635 551123
Chef: Kelvin Johnson
Cost: Alc £29.50, fixed-price L £17.50 (3 courses)/D £19.50 (3 courses). ☺ H /wine £10.45.
Times: Noon-last L 2pm/7pm-last D 10pm
Additional: Bar Food; Sunday lunch; Children welcome; ⍟ dishes
Seats: 120. Private dining rooms 140. Jacket & tie preferred
Smoking: No smoking in dining room; air-conditioning
Accommodation: 58 en suite
Credit cards: ▉ ▉ ▉ ▉

Directions: Exit M4/J13, take A34 S/bound and exit Donnington Castle. Turn R over bridge then L

NEWBURY, Foley Lodge Hotel

Set in landscaped gardens, this former Victorian hunting lodge is now an established conference and function hotel. A typical meal served in the Wellingtonia Restaurant might start with a light smoked

Stockcross RG20 8JU
Map 4: SU46
Tel: 01635 528770
Fax: 01635 528398
Chef: Ian Webb

chicken consommé with mushroom ravioli and continue with honey roast duckling with a champagne sauce.

Smoking: No smoking in dining room
Accommodation: 68 en suite
Credit cards:

Directions: On B4000, 500 yds from junction with A4

Owner: Sir Peter Michael
Cost: Alc £30. H/wine £9.95
Times: Last D 9.30pm.
Closed L Mon-Sat, D Sun & Mon
Additional: Sunday L only; Bar meals;
❸ dishes

NEWBURY,
Hollington Country House ❀❀

See *Highclere, Hampshire page 382*

NEWBURY,
Regency Park Hotel ❀❀

The Regency Park is a popular, well equipped conference hotel with the added attraction of being set in five acres of lovely grounds. The main action takes place in the Terraces Restaurant, a light, airy room with lots of pastel shades and light oak. The kitchen delivers creditable modern English cooking from a *carte* or daily fixed-price menu. Starters might include cappuccino of wild mushroom soup, or a terrine of pork and bacon with a peppered Cumberland sauce. Principal dishes encompass a duet of salmon and turbot on a champagne sauce, pan-fried medallions of pork fillet with apple and shallot confit, and a couple of vegetarian options such as filo pastry layered with avocado, asparagus and cashew nuts. Some speciality flambé dishes are also offered. Desserts could be a hot chocolate fudge cake with two chocolate sauces, or iced kiwi parfait on a fruit coulis.

Directions: From Thatcham A4 turn R into Worthfield Road, then L. Hotel is on R

Bowling Green Road RG18 3RP
Map 4: SU46
Tel: 01635 871555
Fax: 01635 871571
Chef: Jeff Cadden
Owner: Regency Park Hotel
Cost: Alc £33, fixed-price L £16.95/D £22 (3 courses). ☺ H/wine £11.95.
Times: 12.30pm-last L 2.30pm/6.30pm-last D 10.15pm
Additional: Bar food; Sunday lunch; Children welcome; ❸ dishes
Seats: 65. Private dining room 100
Smoking: No pipes and cigars; air-conditioning
Accommodation: 46 en suite
Credit cards:

PANGBOURNE, **Copper Inn** ❀❀

Church Road RG8 7AR
Map 4: SU78
Tel: 0118 9842244
Fax: 0118 9845542
Chef: Darren Snell
Owners: Michel Rosso, Roy Tudor Hughes

What was originally an early Victorian coaching inn has been transformed over the years into a stylish hotel with conference facilities and a swish interior created by the Designers Guild of Chelsea. Bouillabaisse and paella are the specialities of the

house and the menu has distinct provençale overtones. Typical starters might be sauté of scallops and langoustines in garlic butter with pancetta and sugar snap peas, or terrine of duck foie gras with apple and Calvados jelly and toasted brioche. Main courses run from breast of duckling and its confit with citrus and rosemary sauce, and baked rack of lamb with a basket of sautéed beans to a gâteau of corn fritters, aubergines and roasted peppers. Bringing up the rear there might be glazed lemon tart, caramelised pears with pear ice cream and ginger biscuits or a trio of sorbets. The wine list is a personal selection from owner Michel Rosso.

Cost: Alc £25, fixed-price L £9.50 (2 courses). ☺ H/wine £11.95.
Times: Noon-last L 2.30pm/7pm-last D 9.30pm
Additional: Bar food; Sunday L; Children welcome; ♨ dishes
Seats: 70. Private dining room 8/10
Smoking: No-smoking area
Accommodation: 22 en suite
Credit cards: 🔲 🔳 🔳 🔳 🔳 🔳

Directions: At junction of A329 Reading/Oxford and A340, next to parish church.

SHINFIELD, **L'Ortolan** 🏵🏵🏵🏵🏵

A lot has happened at this solid Georgian brick house over the years. Nico Ladenis came and went, John Burton-Race settled in. Ten years on, his ornithologically named restaurant is right at the top of the gastronomic tree. The interior is refreshingly relaxed, neither reverential, nor rustically twee. Apricot walls are hung with botanical prints, and two plant-filled conservatories look out onto mature quince and apple trees in the garden. A choice of fixed-price menus and a *carte* culminates in the hedonistic delights of the five-course 'menu gourmand' that inhabits a realm where price seems irrelevant. Deluxe ingredients are brought into play, although they are used with purpose rather than for showy effect. Descriptions are as restrained, true and balanced as the cooking itself: slices of fresh foie gras are pan-fried, wrapped in baby spinach and garnished with sea salt; a skate wing is poached then set on an onion cream masked with a lentil-spiked vinaigrette, while breast of guinea fowl is served with ceps. Burton-Race is a chef of relentless energy who succeeds in producing food of unerring accuracy. Even at lunchtime, when the dining room may be quiet, there's no lack of urgency or adrenalin in the kitchen. A near-faultless inspection meal began in impeccable style with perfect canapés each zinging with its own distinctive taste. After that, came precisely timed langoustine tails, wrapped in a coil of potato, then roasted and served with finely cut root vegetables and a green vegetable purée of great depth. The main course was a stunner: wild duck breast with 'an almost live, savage flavour of the marshes', cooked dark brown outside, daringly pink within. Puréed quinces (probably the only fruit that could hold its own against such potent gaminess) provided the foil and the whole dish was rounded off with a reduced Armagnac sauce and glazed vegetables. Desserts ooze finesse and understated brilliance: our inspector's hot chocolate tart was, in reality, a dark chocolate soufflé hiding a molten ganache baked inside a biscuit crust and presented with delicate white chocolate ice cream and a vanilla-laden sauce anglaise. Supporting such virtuoso displays is a brigade of staff who show consummate restraint and consideration without 'fawning or fussing'.

Signature dishes: noix de coquilles St Jacques en robe de saumon et crème de celeri rave; lasagne de homard a l'huile de truffe; pigeon sauvage au foie gras, garniture hivernale sauce vin rouge; queue de boeuf en crépinette et sa sauce au vin rouge.

Church Lane RG2 9BY
Map 4: SU76
Tel: 0118 9783883
Fax: 0118 9885391
Chef/Owner: John Burton-Race
Cost: Alc £70, fixed-price L £29.50/£39.50 (3 courses)/D £39.50 (3 courses). H/wine £20
Times: Noon-last L 2.30pm/7pm-last D 9.30pm. Closed D Sun, all Mon
Additional: Sunday lunch; Children welcome; ♨ dishes
Seats: 55. Private dining room 30
Credit cards: 🔲 🔳 🔳 🔳 🔳 🔳

Directions: From M4/J 11, take A33 (Basingstoke). At roundabout L to Three Mile Cross, L towards Shinfield, R opposite The Hungry Horse pub. Restaurant on L, 1 mile.

SONNING, The French Horn ❀❀

RG4 6TN
Map 4: SU77
Tel: 0118 9692204
Fax: 0118 9442210
Chef: Gille Company
Owner: The Emmanuel Family
Cost: Alc £45, fixed-price L £18/D £30. H/wine £11.50
Times: Noon-last L 2pm/7pm-last D 9.30pm. Closed Good Fri.
Additional: Sunday lunch; Children welcome; ❹ dishes
Seats: 70. Private dining room 24
Accommodation: 20 en suite
Smoking: No pipes
Credit cards: ▄▄ ▄▄ ▄▄ ▄▄ ▫ ▫

The Thames laps the garden of this up-market restaurant-with-rooms. Once inside, the dining room's picture windows make the best of the river views. The feel of the decoration and an abundance of smartly uniformed staff, 'possibly too many at times,' contribute to a certain refined richness that is reflected in the cooking. The signature duck dish, spit-roasted in front of the fire in the bar, and served with apple sauce and sage stuffing, is well worth ordering for the sense of theatre alone; it is carved at the table with great aplomb. But bold simplicity is perhaps not the style – spanking fresh pan-fried scallops and Dublin bay prawns came with a citrus sauce and spinach mousseline, fillets of roasted lamb with a potato gratin, a confit of red peppers and extra vegetables on the side. Lemon tart for dessert was tangy with a firm brittle topping. The wine list is praiseworthy for its content and interest.

Directions: M4 exit 8/9 & A4, village centre, on the river

STREATLEY,
Swan Diplomat Hotel ❀❀

High Street RG8 9HR
Map 4: SU58
Tel: 01491 873737
Fax: 01491 872554
Cost: Alc £35, fixed-price D £29.50. H/wine £12
Times: D only, 7.30pm-last D 9.30pm. Closed 25 Dec
Additional: Brasserie; Sunday L; Children welcome; ❹ dishes
Seats: 50. Private dining room 18 & 32. Jacket and tie preferred
Smoking: No pipes and cigars in dining room
Accommodation: 46 en suite
Credit cards: ▄▄ ▄▄ ▄▄ ▄▄ ▫ ▫

An enviable riverside setting by the banks of the Thames offers the prospect of glorious views of the water from the terrace and the 'period boat' moored alongside. Formal dinners (and Sunday lunch) are served to an international clientele in the aptly named Riverside Restaurant with its pastel colour schemes and cane furniture. The kitchen works to a classic French repertoire with Mediterranean overtones. Typical examples from the current menu might include, say, ravioli of woodland mushrooms and apple with red pepper dressing, medallion of beef topped with foie gras and Savoy cabbage, and chocolate and raspberry tart with a duo of sauces. Light meals are also available throughout the week in the Duck Room Brasserie.

Directions: Follow A329 from Pangbourne, on entering Streatley turn R at traffic lights. The hotel is on L before bridge

WINDSOR, Aurora Garden Hotel

A conservatory-style restaurant, decorated with hand-stencilled clematis flowers, overlooking the hotel's floodlit water garden and terrace. An enjoyable meal comprised spinach and ricotta cheese cannelloni, roast pork fillet with a mild mustard cream sauce, and apple pie with ice cream.

Accommodation: 19 en suite
Credit cards: 🔲 🔲 🔲 🔲 🔲 🔲

Directions: From M4 take A308 (Staines); at 3rd roundabout take 3rd exit (Bolton Ave). Hotel is 500yds on R

14 Bolton Avenue SL4 3JF
Map 4: SU97
Tel: 01753 868686
Fax: 01753 831394
Chef: Denton Robinson
Cost: Alc £25, fixed-price L&D £15.95. H/wine £8.95. ☺
Times: Last L 2pm/last D 9pm
Additional: Bar meals; Sunday L; Children welcome; ❹ dishes
Smoking: No pipes & cigars

WINDSOR, The Castle Hotel ⚙⚙

High Street SL4 1LJ
Map 4: SU97
Tel: 01753 851011
Fax: 01753 830244
Cost: Alc £26.50, fixed-price L £14.50/D £26.50. H/wine £14
Times: 12.30pm-last L 2.30pm/7pm-last D 9.45pm
Additional: Bar food; Sunday L; Children welcome; ❹ dishes
Smoking: No smoking in dining room
Accommodation: 104 en suite
Credit cards: 🔲 🔲 🔲 🔲

Anton Mosimann once famously said there was nothing new in the best cooking, but you would never know it from the ever intensifying search for new flavours and combinations. The keen young chef at this popular tourist and business hotel, in the royal shadow of Windsor Castle, is taking no chances, claiming to have a patent on a starter of 'compression' of salmon (lightly poached and seasoned) and Savoy cabbage with a cumin cream. Duck with a truffle infusion served with a rich thyme-flavoured jus accompanied by traditional creamed potato, caramelised shallots and simply prepared discs of carrots and courgettes on a parsnip purée, would have been just the job on a cold winter's day if the flavourings had been more evident. The balance of contrasting flavours was more effective in a dessert of warm, slightly sharp, apple charlotte and a sweet, delicate sauce Anglaise heightened by a dash of Calvados.

Directions: In town centre, opposite Guildhall

WINDSOR, Oakley Court Hotel ❀❀

Windsor Road
Water Oakley SL4 5UR
Map 4: SU97

Tel: 01753 609988
Fax: 01628 37011
Chef: Murdo MacSween
Owners: Oakley Court Hotel
Cost: *Alc* £40, fixed-price L £24/D
£34. H/wine £14.95. ☺
Times: 12.30pm-2pm/7pm-10pm
Additional: Bar meals L; Sunday L;
Children welcome; ❸ dishes
Seats: 70. Private dining room 25;
Jacket and tie preferred
Smoking: No pipes and cigars
Accommodation: 113 en suite
Credit cards: 🖪 🖭 🖭 🗺 🖭 🖾

The Court itself is a grandiose Victorian Gothic edifice built in
the style of a French château; add to that an incomparable
riverside setting with grounds sweeping down to the banks of
the Thames and you have the ingredients for a rather special
experience. The hotel will even arrange boating on the water if
you fancy a little 'messing about'. Formal meals are served in
the Boulestin restaurant. Our inspector opted for the
'Gourmand Menu' and sampled bold, rich duck liver parfait
with onion marmalade and good toasted brioche before moving
on to pan-fried scallops with a vivid saffron sauce and vermicelli.
He also praised first-class fillet of beef served with a bright,
simple reduction, tiny slivers of foie gras and vegetables in the
shape of braised fennel and baby carrots. A powerful Cheddar
and Parmesan soufflé also scored well, and the meal ended
fulsomely with a selection of 'taster' puddings including a dainty
little crème brûlée, raspberry mille-feuille, and quenelles of rich
chocolate truffles. More informal dishes with an international
flavour are served in Boaters' Brasserie overlooking the river.

Directions: Beside the Thames, off the A308 between Windsor
and Maidenhead.

YATTENDON,
Royal Oak Hotel ❀❀❀

The Square RG18 0UF
Map 4: SU57
Tel: 01635 201325
Fax: 01635 201926
Chef: Robbie Macrae

This quintessential English country inn, with its wisteria-clad
walls and attractive garden, has been welcoming guests for 300

years. Here, Robbie Macrae cooks with great style and punchy self-confidence; the value-for-money food in the bar is as carefully prepared as that in the pretty dining-room. The bold yellow decor, floral drapes and abundance of flowers makes for a highly congenial atmosphere, helped along by a charming waiting team, under the guidance of Corinne Macrae, who ensures everyone is well looked after. Good breads, olives and appetisers set the tone, followed by, on our visit, chargrilled scallops, bright with freshness, set off by a light cinnamon velouté and dressed leaves. A roast spiked breast of duck was exceptionally succulent, cooked pink, with a robust flavour – masterful saucing, with a fairly strong hint of honey to the demi-glace, gave classical consistency and sheen. The addition of a confit of colourful spinach and a good, crispy rösti potato cake, together with 'divine', sweet parsnips resulted in a combination of memorable dimensions. A delicious hot soufflé of Mirabelle plums, properly risen and with a smooth texture, served with a complementary and not oversweet plum sauce, made an equally impressive dessert. Alternatively, choose from a very good cheeseboard, followed by coffee and petits fours.
  Signature dishes: Pavé of halibut en papillotte with lemon grass, lemon thyme and coriander; assiette of duck-leg confit, pan-fried liver, breast of magret with lentils.

Directions: M4/J12 follow signs towards Pangbourne turn L for Yattendon; in centre of the village

Owner: Regal Hotel Group
Cost: Alc £35. H/wine £9.50
Times: Noon-last L 2pm/7.30pm-last D 9.30pm
Additional: Bar food; Sunday L; Children welcome; 🍴 dishes
Seats: 30. Private dining room 10
Smoking: No smoking in dining room
Accommodation: 5 en suite
Credit cards: 🔳 🔳 🔳 🔳 🔳 🔳

BRISTOL

BRISTOL, Bell's Diner ❀

Off-beat converted grocer's shop bedecked with all manner of old bottles, jars, and school-room chairs. Rustic cooking is the order of the day and the menu overflows with eclectic ideas. Mussels are steamed with ginger and black beans, braised lamb is served with baby turnips, rosemary and balsamic vinegar, roast cod comes with lentils, parsley and walnut salsa.

Additional: Sunday L; Children welcome; 🍴 dishes
Smoking: No smoking in dining room
Credit cards: 🔳 🔳 🔳

Directions: Corner premises in York Road, Montpelier

1 York Road BS6 5QB
Map 3: ST57
Tel: 0117 9240357
Chef: Peter Taylor
Owners: Peter Taylor, Shirley-Ann Bell, Mark Hall
Cost: Alc £16.25, fixed-price L £7.50/D £15. ☺ H/wine £8.50.
Times: Last L 2.30pm/D 10.30pm. Closed L Sat, D Sun, 1 wk Xmas, Easter & Aug

BRISTOL, Berkeley Square Hotel ❀❀

A hop and a skip from the university, art gallery and Clifton village, this Georgian hotel has the added bonus of being located in a peaceful square with its own secure parking. Since our last recommendation, Nightingales Restaurant has ceased offering Cajun-style cooking, with the kitchen going all out for modern British cooking. Seven or eight choices are offered at the first two courses, with a strong emphasis on fish, and an additional vegetarian selection. Starters of chilli-marinated

15 Berkeley Square
BS8 1HB
Map 3: ST57
Tel: 0117 9254000
Fax: 0117 9252970
Chef: Tim Shaw
Cost: Alc £30, fixed-price D £17. ☺ H/wine £8.95.
Times: 7pm-last D 9.45pm. Closed Sun, New Year's Eve

tiger prawns, sautéed and served on a julienne of vegetables, thinly sliced fresh salmon with wasabi (Japanese horseradish), lemon and straws of leek, carrot and daikon, and pan-fried lamb's kidneys flamed in brandy and finished with cream and Dijon mustard show a kitchen plucking ideas from a global hat. Main courses are equally eclectic. Grilled Gressingham duckling, for example, comes with a drunken pear, balsamic and port sauce, and cep 'raviolini' and root vegetable straws has a white wine and herb cream.

Directions: Top of Park Street turn L at traffic lights into Berkeley Square, hotel on R

Additional: Bar food; Children welcome; ④ dishes
Seats: 45. Private dining room 12
Smoking: No pipes or cigars
Accommodation: 42 en suite
Credit cards: ▬ ▦ ▦ ▦ ▣ ▢

BRISTOL, **Blue Goose** ❀

A casual restaurant, with electric blue walls, climbing plants and contemporary jazz playing in the background. Expect unpretentious Euro dishes such as roast duck with gin and grapefruit sauce, and spinach and goats cheese in filo pastry. For dessert try home-made lemon ice cream with glazed kumquats.

Additional: Children welcome; ④ dishes
Smoking: Air-conditioning
Credit cards: ▬ ▦ ▦ ▢

Directions: From city centre, A38 N (Stokes Croft) approx 2 miles to Horefield. On L, corner of Ash & Gloucester Rds

Gloucester Road
Map 3: ST57
Tel: 0117 9420940
Fax: 0117 9444033
Chef: Ian Leitch
Owner: Arne Ringner
Cost: Fixed-price D £14.50. ☺ H/wine £9.25
Times: D only, 7pm – last D 10pm. Closed Sun, Bhs

BRISTOL, **Bristol Marriott Hotel** ❀

The 70s façade may fail to inspire, but the refurbished restaurant provides a pleasant, intimate setting for some innovative cooking. Expect fresh asparagus in puff pastry with raspberry hollandaise, lamb with port sauce, and orange and lemon tart. The wine list is comprehensive.

Additional: Bar food; Children welcome; ④ dishes
Smoking: No-smoking area; air-conditioning
Accommodation: 289 en suite
Credit cards: ▬ ▦ ▦ ▦ ▣ ▢

Directions: Close to Bristol city centre, at the Old Market, opposite castle ruins

Lower Castle Street, Bristol, BS1 3AD
Map 3: ST57
Tel: 0117 9294281
Fax: 0117 9276377
Chef: Joe Beaver
Cost: Fixed-price D £19.50. ☺ H/wine £11.45.
Times: D only, 7.30pm-last D 10.30pm. Closed Sun, Bhs

BRISTOL,
Glass Boat Restaurant ❀❀

Moored alongside Bristol Bridge, the converted vessel has a glass panelled dining room, with comfortable pale blue seating, which affords maximum light even on the greyest of days. The modern Anglo-French carte changes every two months, supplemented by a daily set lunch and dinner menu. The cooking has its peaks and troughs – our inspector was captivated by a wonderful iced passion fruit soufflé, but found a venison, wild rabbit and foie gras terrine less than memorable. Nonetheless, the kitchen generally works to a consistently high standard. There is a good choice of dishes, perhaps a duck, ham and herb salad with griddled baby sweetcorn and tomato concasse with hazelnut oil dressing, or

Welsh Back BS1 4SB
Map 3: ST57
Tel: 0117 9290704
Fax: 0117 9297338
Chef: Michel Lemoine
Owner: Arnie Ringner
Cost: Alc £25, fixed-price L £10.95 (2 courses)/D £17.50 (3 courses). ☺ H/wine £9.75.
Times: Noon-last L 2.15pm/6pm-last D 10.45pm. Closed L Sat, Sun, 24 Dec-8 Jan
Additional: Children welcome; ④ dishes

Glass Boat Restaurant

Seats: 90. Private dining room 40
Smoking: No-smoking area; air-conditioning
Credit cards:

steamed breast of chicken with lemon tagliatelle and a chicken jus and virgin olive oil emulsion. A touch of orientalism creeps in with main courses such as mixed seafood tempura served with a spiced miso and mirin dip. The restaurant is also open for breakfasts of eggs Benedict and scrambled egg with smoked salmon. The eclectic wine list includes a large selection under £20.

Directions: By Bristol Bridge in the old centre of Bristol

BRISTOL, Harveys ❀❀❀

12 Denmark Street BS1 5DQ
Map 3: ST57
Tel: 0117 9275034
Fax: 0117 9275003
Chef: Daniel Galmiche
Owner: John Harvey & Sons
Cost: *Alc* £33.80, fixed-price L £15.95/D £39.95 (6 courses). H/wine £12
Times: Noon-last L 1.45pm/7pm-last D 10.45pm. Closed L Sat, Sun, Bhs
Additional: No children under 8; ❹ dishes
Seats: 70-80. Private dining room 40
Smoking: No-smoking area; air-conditioning
Credit cards:

Harveys is synonymous with the wine trade. Visitors are welcome to explore the labyrinthine thirteenth-century cellars, which are full of memorabilia, vintage sherry casks and racks of bottles of every description, which make up what is now a Wine Museum. Next stop the restaurant, a vaulted, high-ceilinged room decorated with contemporary works of art, where smartly dressed waiters know their job, and the atmosphere is smart and snappy. New chef Daniel Galmiche's cooking is full of energy and enthusiasm and he knows how to deliver dishes that convince with their clear, uncluttered flavours and presentation. Two starters sampled during an inspection sum up the style perfectly: carpaccio of beef tenderloin was served with basil oil and a green bean and mushroom salad, while red tuna given similar treatment came with a tiny dice of provençale vegetables. Both were conceived with vibrant panache. Among main courses, pan-fried fillet of turbot, crispy on top and with milky white flesh was laid on a celeriac purée with a perfectly balanced jus of veal, mushrooms and grain mustard. Almost as impressive was grilled, marinated chicken breast served on spinach and accompanied by juices infused with olive oil and lemon zest. Spiced crème brûlée accompanied by a caramelised pear cake was a novel idea. Cheeses are a star turn, notably a crustless Roquefort-type from Robin Condon in Totnes.

The wine list is well set out, easy to use, with an impressive array of clarets and Burgundies, however, they do carry hefty price tags. For more reasonably priced drinking Southern Rhône and Loire wines are a good bet – Gigondas, Ch de Raspail and Paul Prieur Sancerre are £19. A New Zealand Chardonnay from Nobilo in Poverty Bay is £16.

Signature dishes: Roast farm pigeon served with sautéed new potatoes, sea salt and jus infused with herbs and sherry vinegar; roast sea bass with candied tomatoes and olive juice complemented by balsasmic vinegar and fried basil leaves.

Directions: City centre off Unity Street at bottom of Park Street, opposite City Hall and Cathedral; follow signs for Harveys Wine Museum

BRISTOL, **Howards Restaurant**

1A-2A Avon Crescent
Hotwells BS1 6XQ
Map 3: ST57
Tel: 0117 9262921
Fax: 0117 9255585
Chef: David Short
Owner: Christopher Howard
Cost: Alc £20.25, fixed-price L £13/D £15. ☺ H/wine £7.95.
Times: Noon-last L 2.30pm/7pm-last D 11pm. Closed Sun, Sat L, Xmas, Bhs
Additional: Children welcome; ⑨ dishes
Seats: 65. Private dining room 26
Smoking: No-smoking area
Credit cards: 🔳 📷 📷 🔳

Two interconnecting shop-fronted rooms face the river, which is less of an attraction when the tide is out. Howards, however, is a congenial and friendly place, with Anglo-French food that is liked for its pleasing lack of fussiness. As well as the hand-written *carte*, specials and fixed-priced three-course menus are chalked on a blackboard. Fresh fish comes from Cornwall, and the locally bought meat is of impressively high quality. A starter of brioche filled with wild mushrooms and served with a rich mushroom sauce was simple but effective, and our inspector followed this with breast of duck 'cooked beautifully pink, retaining succulence, tenderness and superb flavour', perfectly paired with a smooth but delicate honey, orange and rosemary sauce. Fresh vegetables in abundance – red cabbage, carrots, fennel in provençal sauce, new and dauphinoise potatoes – were full of honest, down-to-earth flavour. Poached pears with home-made vanilla ice cream and warm dark chocolate sauce is one of the rather tempting desserts.

Directions: 5 mins. from city centre following signs for M5/Avonmouth, On the dockside over a small bridge, close to SS Great Britain.

BRISTOL, **Hunt's Restaurant**

Housed in a Grade II listed building in the oldest part of
Bristol city centre, Hunt's pleases with its blend of simplicity
and elegance. Fresh flowers adorn the neat dining room, staff
are smart and relaxed. Andrew Hunt's cooking is 'on-the-up',
according to an inspector who visited in April. Freshly baked
breads are a speciality, and very good they are, too. Lunch is
an affordable fixed-price affair, seasonal evening menus move
up a gear. Spanking fresh scallops direct from Brixham might
be served tantalisingly with tomato, basil and coriander while
fricassée of monkfish and crab is scented with saffron. Away
from the sea you might find maize-fed guinea fowl delicately
flavoured with apples, Calvados and sweet marjoram, or veal
cutlet with sweet and sour peppers. Crème brûlée is an
exemplary version served with a compote of spring rhubarb
and elderflowers, otherwise finish with iced lemon parfait with
oatmeal meringue and cranberry coulis. France gets top billing
on the carefully chosen wine list.

Directions: City centre, 25 yds from St John's Arch

26 Broad Street BS1 2HG
Map 3: ST57
Tel/Fax: 0117 9265580
Chef: Andrew Hunt
Owner: Andrew & Anne Hunt
Cost: Alc £30, fixed-price L £13.95.
☺ H/wine £9.50.
Times: Noon-last L 2pm/7pm-last D
10pm. Closed L Sat, Sun, Mon, 1 wk
Easter, 1 wk Aug Bhs, 10 days Xmas
Additional: Children welcome;
🄪 dishes
Seats: 40; Jacket and tie preferred
Credit cards: 🔲 🔲 🔲 🔲 🔲

BRISTOL, **Markwicks**

'Provence meets modern England in Art Deco setting' could
be the headline for this coolly elegant restaurant located in the
vaults of a former bank. The *carte* is short and pacy, and
delivers well. Rack of lamb with roasted ratatouille, garlic and
rosemary sauce ably demonstrated the skill of the kitchen, as
did a perfectly executed apricot and mascarpone tart. There is
a strong emphasis on vegetables – an exciting selection
included a medley of minted peas, beans and smoked bacon.
Vegetarians do unusually well with dishes such as wild
mushroom tart with Parmesan and truffle oil. The menu also
includes bourgeois classics such as provençale fish soup with
aïoli and sauce rouille, and fillet steak au poivre. At times,
however, individual flavours can get lost in a crowd – our
inspector's starter of pan-fried scallops with sun-dried tomato
risotto, pesto and Parmesan suffered as a result.

Directions: Top end of Corn Street beneath Commercial Rooms

43 Corn Street BS1 1HT
Map 3: ST57
Tel/Fax: 0117 9262658
Chef: Stephen Markwick
Owners: Stephen & Judy Markwick
Cost: Alc £30, fixed-price L £15/D
£21.50 (3 courses). ☺ H/wine
£10.50.
Times: Noon-last L 2pm/7pm-last D
10pm. Closed D Sat, Sun, Mon,1 wk
Xmas, 1 wk Easter, 2 wks August
Additional: 🄪 dishes
Seats: 40. Private dining room: 6 &
8-19
Credit cards: 🔲 🔲 🔲 🔲 🔲

BRISTOL, Red Snapper ✿

1 Chandos Road Redland BS6 6PG
Map 3: ST57
Tel: 0117 9737999
Chef: John Raines
Owner: John & Joanna Raines
Cost: Fixed-price L £12. ☺
H/wine £9.
Times: Last L 1.45pm/Last D 10pm.
Closed D Sun, Mon, 1 wk Xmas, 2
wks Aug
Additional: Sunday L; Children
welcome; 🍴 dishes

Tucked away in a residential area, this neighbourhood hang-out has an informal look of bare boards, Formica-topped refectory tables, aluminium-framed chairs. Modern British cooking takes in wild mushrooms and chargrilled polenta, marinated pork with a plum/ginger sauce, and apricot and Muscat crème brûlée.

Smoking: No pipes and cigars
Credit cards:

Directions: Telephone for directions

BRISTOL, Restaurant Lettonie ✿✿✿✿

9 Druid Hill Stoke Bishop BS9 1EW
Map 3: ST57
Tel: 0117 9686456
Fax: 0117 9686943
Chef: Martin Blunos
Owner: Siân & Martin Blunos
Times: 12.30pm-last L 2pm/7pm-last
D 9pm. Closed Sun, Mon, 2 wks
Xmas, 2 wks Aug
Additional: Children welcome;
🍴 dishes
Seats: 24
Credit cards: ▆ ▆ ▆ ▆ ▆ ▆

It may come as a surprise to discover truly top-class cooking lurking behind the door of these unassuming premises in a parade of shops, but Lettonie is something special. Martin and Siân Blunos run the place as a family affair and have imbued it with a genuine sense of domestic intimacy. Tables are uncluttered, cheerful impressionist prints line the walls, the wallpaper is bright and striped. The overall effect is unexpectedly European. Honesty – and passion – plus a staggering degree of technical accomplishment sum up Blunos' approach to the kitchen. His roots may be in Eastern Europe, but his cooking is locked into France at its most contemporary. Some influences come from the annals of classical cuisine but the man himself revels in creativity: he tries out an idea, tweaks it, refines it and tries again. The results of his endeavours are, quite simply, stunning. Right from the start, he lays his cards on the table. When it comes to baking, for example, he has no truck with fancy additions of the sun-dried kind: his white rolls are what bread is all about – moist, crisp, yeasty and perfectly seasoned. After that, there might be a dainty, square-shaped cheese soufflé offset by a slighly more powerful tomato relish. The menu itself is fixed-price for three courses (set lunches and suppers are also available on various days). It would be hard to better a borsch terrine of faultless clarity and texture, layered with beetroot, carrot and onion. Main courses dazzle with their sheer fine-tuned brilliance. Incomparable roast cod fillet comes with purées of swede and celeriac arranged around a clam sauce with accompanying nettle fritters, while pig's trotter (boned, braised and stuffed with a combination of chicken mousse, belly pork and sweetbreads) is paired with a Madeira sauce. And it's not difficult to imagine the serious-minded complexity behind pan-fried turbot with kipper ravioli on creamed parsley and a

spiced sauce or rump of lamb with crisp garlic fritters and a
thyme leaf sauce. Desserts are ravishing, impeccable creations:
banana ice cream scooped into a perfectly shaped biscuit basket
with rich caramel sauce or a clean tasting apple and vanilla
parfait accompanied by an apple sorbet.

Six house wines under £16.00 provide the best value with
some good easy drinking – Aotea Sauvignon Blanc (£13.65);
Quina de la Rosa from Portugal (£13.85) – and a good range of
halves. The Pelorus methode champenoise from the makers of
Cloudy Bay deserves a try at £26.40. Ch Senejac provides an
excellent mid-priced choice at £27.55.

Signature dishes: Scrambled duck egg with Sevruga caviar,
with blinis and a glass of iced vodka; braised haunch of
venison, Madeira sauce.

Directions: Across Clifton Downs (away from the City) in a small
row of shops at bottom of hill

BRISTOL, Swallow Royal Hotel

College Green BS1 5TA
Map 3: ST57
Tel: 0117 9255100
Fax: 0117 9251515
Chef: Giles Stonehouse
Owner: Swallow Hotels
Cost: *Alc* £29, fixed-price D £24. ☺
H/wine £12.
Times: D only, 7.30pm-last D
10.30pm. Closed Bhs
Additional: Bar food
Smoking: No-smoking area; air-
conditioning
Accommodation: 242 en suite
Credit cards: 🔳 🔳 🔳 🔳 🔳 🔳

Live harp music plays most evenings in this impressively
restored 1886 building right next to the cathedral. The
restaurant is in the original Palm Court – a stunning room on
four floors that reminded one inspector of a Greek temple,
with its statues, columns of Bath stone and stained glass
ceiling. Excellent breads and appetisers such as chicken liver
parfait form the prelude to an ambitious-sounding menu of
complex modern dishes. The high point of a recent meal was
crisp-crusted chicken breast served with a wild mushroom
risotto, chicken livers piled to one side and a rosemary cream
sauce. Other options from the *carte* might include lobster
consommé with mango, cannon of Welsh lamb with a potato
galette and a tian of vegetables, and a 'spiral' of Scottish
salmon with shredded mange-touts and a saffron sauce. To
finish, there might be a trio of lemon desserts – a tart, a custard
and a tangy citrus ice cream, or hot pecan soufflé with red fruit
coulis.

Directions: City centre, next to cathedral

BUCKINGHAMSHIRE

ASTON CLINTON, The Bell Inn

Aylesbury HP22 5HP
Map 4: SP81
Tel: 01296 630252
Fax: 01296 631250
Chef: D Campbell
Owner: Mr Michael DG Harris
Cost: *Alc* £29, fixed-price L £12-£15
(2-3 courses)/D £21 (2 courses). ☺
H/wine £12.95.
Times: 12.30pm-last L
1.45pm/7.30pm-last D 9.30pm
Additional: Sunday L; Children
welcome; ⑤ dishes
Seats: 80. Private dining room 20 &
12
Smoking: No smoking in dining room
Accommodation: 20 en suite
Credit cards: ▬ ▬ ▬ ▬

Renovation and reinvestment are conjuring up some of that old Bell magic. Owned by the Harris family for more than half a century, this pedigree Home Counties address seems set for a new lease of life. Manager George Bottley helps to maintain an enduring sense of tradition, but the cooking has received a vigorous injection of life. The modern world has finally burst through the door in the shape of seared scallops with Thai spices, crisp shredded vegetables and a ginger, coriander and soy dressing, for example. But the technically assured kitchen can also deliver such things as fresh turbot cooked on olive-oil scented potatoes served with chanterelles and a light herby stock. Desserts usher in coffee and Tia Maria soufflé and sablé of pear with cinnamon sauce, and so on. Of course, there is still room for the old guard: Aylesbury ducks have their own menu, and Sunday roasts are still carved from trolleys. The wine list is nothing if not weighty, with the emphasis firmly on the output of established French châteaux.

Directions: In the centre of the village on the A41, 4 miles from Aylesbury. 10 mins M25/J20

ASTON CLINTON,
West Lodge Hotel

Named after the French hot air balloonists, the Montgolfier restaurant in this small nineteenth-century hotel, not surprisingly, has a charming hot air ballooning theme; adventurous guests can even take rides in the real thing. The French cuisine has equally lofty ambitions, and although the weekly-changing menu is short, it is lucid and admirably constructed. Home-made ravioli with chicken in a grain mustard sauce, grilled slice of salmon with a Noilly Prat sauce and vegetables, and cream of carrot soup with watercress and chopped chives, are typical first courses. Confit of duck is a staple in the repertoire, either served with bacon, shallot and red wine sauce, or roast with salad leaves and tarragon potato rösti.

NEW
Aylesbury HP22 5HL
Map 4: SP81
Tel: 01296 630362
Fax: 01296 630151
Chef: Philippe Brillant
Owners: Irene & Jeff Burlinson
Cost: Fixed-price D £30 (3 courses).
H/wine £15
Times: D only Thurs/Fri/Sat, 7pm-9pm
Additional: Bar meals; No children
under 12; ⑤ dishes
Seats: 25
Smoking: No smoking in dining room;
air-conditioning
Accommodation: 7 en suite
Credit cards: ▬ ▬ ▬ ▬ ▣ ▢

Directions: On A41 between Aylesbury and Hemel Hempstead.

AYLESBURY, Hartwell House

Oxford Road HP17 8NL
Map 4: SP81
Tel: 01296 747444
Fax: 01296 747450
Chef: Roger Barstow
Owner: Historic House Hotels
Cost: Fixed-price L £26.50/D £42 (3 courses). H/wine £12.90
Times: 12.30pm-last L 1.50pm/7.30pm-last D 9.45pm.
Additional: Buttery (7.30am-3pm); Sunday L; No children under 8; ✿ dishes
Seats: 80. Private dining rooms
Smoking: No smoking in dining room
Accommodation: 46 en suite
Credit cards:

Country houses don't come much grander than this most majestic of stately homes. Built at the turn of the seventeenth century, later modified, and once used as an upper-crust bolt hole by Louis XVIII of France, it is now one of the jewels in the crown of the Historic House Hotels group. Outside is 90 acres of landscaped parkland complete with a trout lake, inside there's much to delight the eye in the magnificent Jacobean staircase, the extraordinarily delicate ceiling plasterwork, and deep sofas spread around three breathtaking lounges. The whole place seems to ooze star quality. There's also class and confidence a-plenty in the kitchen, where new chef Roger Barstow heads a disciplined and expert brigade. Here is a chef firing on all cylinders. A perfectly light and airy boudin of Cornish crab in a natural skin served on a tomato confit with a shellfish dressing showed real precision, accuracy and cleverly orchestrated simple flavours. An inspection dinner continued with a brilliantly cohesive dish of five components each with a role to play: fillet of venison with leeks, chestnuts, a little rösti and a light sage jus. The peak of it all was a trio of chocolate puddings on a lime and vanilla syrup – each contributing its flavours, contrasts and textures. The quality of the yeasty warm bread rolls, canapés and exquisite petits fours reinforce the impression that this is a really serious set-up. Service is courteous and old-school professional to a T. Lighter meals can also be eaten in The Buttery.

Directions: 2 miles from Aylesbury on A418 (Oxford)

BUCKINGHAM, Villiers Hotel   NEW

3 Castle Street MK18 1BS
Map 4: SP63

Former 400-year-old coaching inn, superbly renovated and set around a cobbled courtyard. A meal in the elegant Henry's Restaurant produced well executed dishes, including stuffed roast quail on rösti with plum sauce, and pheasant wrapped in bacon with partridge salmis tartlet and port sauce.

Smoking: Air-conditioning
Accommodation: 38 en suite
Credit cards: 🔲 🔲 🔲 🔲

Directions: Town centre – Castle Street is to R of Town Hall near main square.

Tel: 01280 822444
Fax: 01280 822113
Chef: Paul Stopps
Owners: Dawn Park Ltd
Cost: Alc £21.25, set L Sun £14.75/D £17.75. ☺ H/wine £10.95.
Times: Last D 10pm
Additional: Bar meals; Children welcome; ⓓ dishes

BURNHAM,
Burnham Beeches Hotel ❀

Set in ten acres of lawns and gardens, this elegant Georgian manor house continues to offer consistent cooking. Attention to detail produces honest flavours in such dishes as pan-fried duck breast with truffle jus and roasted garlic, and venison braised with port wine and shallots.

Smoking: No-smoking area
Accommodation: 75 en suite
Credit cards: 🔲 🔲 🔲 🔲 🔲

Directions: Off A355 via Farnham Royal roundabout

Grove Road SL1 8DP
Map 4: SU98
Tel: 01628 429955
Fax: 01628 603994
Chef: Lawrence Bryant
Owners: County Hotels Ltd (QMH)
Cost: Alc £22.50, fixed-price L £18.50/D £22.50. ☺ H/wine £12.
Times: Last L 1.30pm/D 9.45pm.
Additional: Bar Food; Sunday L; No children under 12; ⓓ dishes

CHENIES, Bedford Arms Thistle ❀

A charming, homely nineteenth-century inn complete with a traditional-style bar and a richly furnished restaurant. Smoked salmon roulade and maize-fed chicken with mushroom farce are typical of the mainly French-inspired carte.

Directions: M25, J18/A404 towards Amersham, turn R to Latimer/Chenies, hotel is visible 200yds

Chenies WD3 6EQ
Map 4: TQ09
Tel: 01923 283301
Fax: 01923 284825
Chef: Peter O'Connel
Owner: Thistle Hotels
Cost: Alc £30, fixed-price L £30 (3 courses)/ D £21 (3 courses). H/wine £11.50
Times: Last L 2.30pm/D 10pm Closed Sat L
Additional: Bar Food; Sunday L; Children welcome; ⓓ dishes
Smoking: No pipes
Accommodation: 10 en suite
Credit cards: 🔲 🔲 🔲 🔲 🔲 🔲

DINTON, La Chouette ❀❀

Ebullient Frederic Desmette is an avid ornithologist, so he named his cottagey little restaurant after a bird (an owl to be precise), and lined the walls of his pretty blue dining room with personal photographs of rare species. He also likes jazz,

Westlington Green
Nr Aylesbury
HP17 8UW
Map 4: SP71
Tel/Fax: 01296 747422
Chef/Owner: Frederic Desmette

and groovy sounds play in the background. Frederic's roots are in Belgium and there are echoes of the home country in some of the dishes on his sensibly short menu. Meals always begin with a whole peasant-style loaf served up with board and bread knife. Starters might feature salad of scallops with fine beans and salade de mâche, terrine of three fishes with sour sauce or fricassée of lobster with leeks. There's also plenty of fish among main dishes such as fillet of cod with chive cream sauce or monkfish with vodka sauce, although gigot of lamb and rib of beef with béarnaise sauce also get a look in. Main dishes come with a barrow-load of simple but skilfully prepared vegetables. At lunchtime there's the option of a fixed-price, three-course menu which can be served in less than one hour if required. What is remarkable is that this is virtually a one-man show. Alsace and the French regions dictate the tone of the wine list.

Cost: Alc £35, fixed-price L £10 (3 courses). H/wine £10. ☺
Times: Noon-last L 2pm/7pm-last D 9pm. Closed Sun
Additional: Children welcome; ◑ dishes
Seats: 30
Smoking: No pipes or cigars in dining room
Credit cards: ▆ ▆ ▆ ▆

Directions: On the A418 at Dinton

IVINGHOE, The King's Head

Creeper-clad, seventeenth-century former posting house that retains much of its original character in its low beamed bars and candle-lit dining room. Traditional dishes dominate the varied menus. Expect salmon soufflé with horseradish sauce, lamb noisettes with Madeira sauce, and freshly baked profiteroles to finish.

Smoking: No smoking in dining room; air-conditioning
Credit cards: ▆ ▆ ▆ ▆ ▆ ▆

Directions: From M25/J20. Take the A41(M) towards Tring. Turn R, B488 (Ivinghoe). Hotel on R at the junction with B489

Ivinghoe LU7 9EB
Map 4: SP92
Tel: 01296 668388/668264
Fax: 01296 668107
Chef: Patrick O'Keefe
Owner: Forte plc (Granada)
Cost: Alc £24.25, fixed-price L £13.50/D £24.25. H/wine £15.95. ☺
Times: Last L 1.45pm/D 9.30pm. Closed D Sun
Additional: Sunday L; Children welcome; ◑ dishes

MARLOW, The Compleat Angler

Famous Thames-side hotel where the restaurant, directly beside the fast-flowing river, offers both traditional and contemporary food. Unfussy stalwarts such as grilled Dover sole and roasted fillet of beef with béarnaise sauce, or the more modern pan-fried red mullet with spiced aubergine and tapenade, and Gressingham duck, confit, braised with tarragon jus and noodles.

Directions: From junction 8/9 of M4 or junction 4 of M40 take A404; hotel is on south bank of river by bridge

Marlow Bridge SL7 1RG
Map 4: SU88
Tel: 01628 484444
Fax: 01628 486388
Chef: Fred Testka, Michael MacDonald
Owner: Forte UK Hotels
Cost: Alc £45, fixed-price L £18.95 (2 courses) £24.50 (3 courses)/D £34.50 (3 courses). H/wine £15
Times: 12.30pm-last L 2pm/7.30pm-last D 10pm
Additional: Sunday L; Children welcome; ◑ dishes
Seats: 95. Private dining room 120
Smoking: No smoking in dining room
Accommodation: 62 en suite
Credit cards: ▆ ▆ ▆ ▆ ▆ ▆

MARLOW, Danesfield House

Henley Road SL7 2EY
Map 4: SU88
Tel: 01628 891010
Fax: 01628 890408
Chef: Giles Thompson
Owner: Danesfield House Hotel Ltd
Cost: *Alc* £40, fixed-price L £24.50/D
£34.50. H/wine £16.50
Times: Noon-last L 2.30pm/7pm-last
D 10pm
Additional: Bar food (brasserie);
Sunday L; Children welcome;
🌏 dishes
Seats: 45. Private dining room up to
110. Jacket and tie preferred
Smoking: No smoking in dining room;
air-conditioning
Accommodation: 87 en suite
Credit cards: 💳 💳 💳 💳 💳 💳

Built in castellated Gothic style in 1899, Danesfield House is
now 'a very impressive hotel' set in 65 acres of formal gardens
and lakes overlooking the River Thames and the Chilterns.
Formal dining takes place in the grand Oak Room with its
ornate plaster ceiling and fine oak panelling. Menus follow the
seasons and the chef's training at The Connaught shows in the
blend of classical French and traditional English dishes. Typical
starters might include seared Devon scallops in saffron and
citrus chowder or terrine of foie gras with grape chutney and
toasted brioche, while main courses extend to roast rack of
Kent lamb with garlic confit, and medallions of Suffolk venison
with redcurrant and juniper sauce. Desserts are textbook
favourites like crème brûlée or chocolate pithiviers with
apricot sauce. Lighter meals such as moules marinière with
fries or smoked chicken and bacon Caesar salad are served in
The Orangery. The wine list is an excellent selection of quality
bins from reputable sources.

Directions: M40/J4, A404 to Marlow, then A4155 to Henley.
Hotel 2 miles on L

TAPLOW, Cliveden Hotel

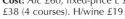

Maidenhead
SL6 0JF
Map 4: SU98
Tel: 01628 668561
Fax: 01628 661837
Chef: Ron Maxfield
Cost: *Alc* £60, fixed-price L £28/D
£38 (4 courses). H/wine £19

From The Terrace dining room six enormous windows
overlook the formal Italianate parterre of this grandest of
grand country house hotels. Hung with portraits from the
Cliveden Collection, this is *the* authentic stately home
experience, where visitors are treated as 'house guests' and

dinners are as luxurious as they were in the heyday of Nancy Astor. Chef Ron Maxfield is in charge of both The Terrace and Waldo's restaurant, named after an American who sculpted the colossal Fountain of Love. Waldo's is for serious gourmet eating at serious prices – crisp mille-feuille of scallops with young asparagus and trompette mushrooms on a tomato and Reisling sauce might precede nage of Scottish lobster or fillet of lamb niçoise with a tian of aubergine on a light anchovy sauce, and hot mirabelle soufflé with liquorice ice cream. In season there may be game such as roast woodcock with a mousse of livers, Savoy cabbage and walnut sauce or roast snipe with caramelised apples and blackberries. A special £75 'Truffle Menu' includes truffles at almost every course; the centrepiece is 'pot au feu' of free-range guinea fowl cooked with Périgord truffles, baby vegetables and cream with a light sauce made from the cooking juices. A stately wine list, pages toned red and white as appropriate, is consistently well chosen and shows some imagination in the New World selection. Claret has plenty of maturity and there is an exemplary range of white Burgundy with a terrific selection of half-bottles. Italy is certainly worth a look with many good names including Chianti Classico from Isole e Olena at £23.

Directions: On the B476, 2 miles north of Taplow

Times: 12.30pm-last L 2.30pm/7.30pm-last D 10.30pm.
Additional: Sunday L; Children welcome; 🙂 dishes
Seats: Waldos 28, Terrace 65. Private dining room
Smoking: No smoking in dining room
Accommodation: 38 en suite
Credit cards: ▮ ▮ ▮ ▮

CAMBRIDGESHIRE

BYTHORN, **Bennett's Restaurant**

Part of a nineteenth-century village pub, the separate restaurant sports a pitched-pine ceiling, polished tables and red-tiled floor. Bold flavours and generous portions are the hall mark of Bill Bennett's cooking. Starters include pan-fried pigeon breast with wild mushroom sauce, and Roquefort quiche topped with crispy bacon.

Smoking: No cigars or pipes
Credit cards: ▮ ▮ ▮ ▮ ▮

Directions: Btw Kettering & Huntingdon on A14/A1-M1 link road

The White Hart, Bythorn, Huntingdon, PE18 0QM
Map 4: TL07
Tel/Fax: 01832 710226
Chef/Owner: Bill Bennett
Cost: *Alc* £28.50. H/wine £9.50. 🙂
Times: Last L 2pm/D 10pm. Closed Sun D, Mon, 26 Dec, 1 Jan
Additional: Bar food; Sunday L; Children welcome; 🙂 dishes

CAMBRIDGE, Arundel House

Chesterton Road CB4 3AN
Map 5: TL45
Tel: 01223 367701
Fax: 01223 367721
Chefs: Mark Searle, Simon Patten
Owner: Arundel House Hotel
Cost: Alc £21, fixed-price L £10.95/D
£15.95. ☺ H/wine £8.95.
Times: Last L 1.45pm/D 9.30pm.
Closed 25-26 Dec
Additional: Bar food; Sunday L;
Children welcome; ◑ dishes
Smoking: No smoking in dining room;
air-conditioning
Accommodation: 105 (99 en suite)
Credit cards: 💳 🖻 🖾 🐾 💷 C

*Looking out over Jesus Green, the well-refurbished Arundel House
serves sensibly priced meals in its Victorian Conservatory. The
extensive carte ranges from fillet of pork Louisiana to roast duck
with Grand Marnier, blackberry and kiwi sauce, plus lots of
vegetarian choice.*

Directions: On A1303, overlooking River Cam

CAMBRIDGE,
Cambridge Garden House

*A riverside location, second to none in Cambridge, is the scoring
point here. Otherwise, a new chef and a recently decorated dining
room suggest the hotel is aiming high on other fronts too. Chicken
terrine with sweet pepper coulis, saddle of lamb with celeriac and
grain mustard sauce and exotic fruit savarin are typical dishes.*

Times: Last L 1.45pm/D 9.45pm
Additional: Bar meals; Sunday L; children welcome; ◑ dishes
Smoking: No smoking in dining room; air-conditioning
Accommodation: 117 en suite
Credit cards: 💳 🖻 🖾 🐾 💷 C

Granta Place
Mill Lane CB2 1RT
Map 5: TL45
Tel: 01223 259988
Fax: 01223 316605
Chef: John Gardiner
Owner: Queens Moat House Hotels
Cost: Alc £28, fixed-price L £10.95/D
£16.95. ☺ H/wine £12.95.

Directions: City centre, from Trumpington Street past
Fitzwilliam Museum, L into Mill Lane

CAMBRIDGE, Cambridge Lodge

*Comfortable hotel on the outskirts of Cambridge. Popular restaurant
with menus covering everything from moules marinière, and
suprême of chicken with red wine and mushroom sauce to ostrich
steak with pâté in a sage and red wine sauce.*

Cost: Alc £25, fixed-price L £ 15.95/D £19.95. ☺
H/wine £9.50.
Times: Last L 1.45pm/D 9.15pm Closed D Sun, L Sat, 26-31
Dec
Additional: Bar food; Sunday L; Children welcome; ◑ dishes
Smoking: No pipes and cigars in dining room
Accommodation: 13 rooms
Credit cards: 💳 🖻 🖾 🐾 💷 C

139 Huntingdon Road CB3 0DQ
Map 5: TL45
Tel: 01223 352833
Fax: 01223 355166
Chef: Peter Reynolds
Owners: Mrs S Hipwell,
Mr D Chamberlain

Directions: One mile N of city on A1307

CAMBRIDGE,
Midsummer House

Midsummer Common
CB4 1HA
Map 5: TL45
Tel: 01223 369299
Fax: 01223 302672
Chef: Anton Escalera
Owners: Russell Morgan, Anton Escalera
Cost: *Alc* £36, fixed-price L £23/D £45 (9 courses). H/wine £11.95
Times: 12.30pm-last L 1.45pm/7.30pm-last D 10pm. Closed L Sat, Mon, D Sun, Mon, 1 wk Jan
Additional: Sunday L; Children welcome; ❸ dishes
Seats: 35. Private dining room 15
Smoking: No-smoking area
Credit cards: ▆ ▆ ▆ ▆ ▆ ▆

Anton Escalera is a Streatham boy (of Dutch and Spanish origin) with many talents. He is responsible for both the cooking and the interior design of this updated Victorian villa by the banks of the River Cam. His clever use of colour and style is reflected in the seasonal *carte*: tartare of veal and roasted pumpkin, roast suckling pig with lemon scented juices, minestrone of red fruit compote and red wine sorbet. Earthy, robust ingredients are refined to great effect – rabbit stuffed with confit of garlic, served with a pearl barley risotto of snails, braised rump of lamb gilded with sweetbreads, cabbage, foie gras and scallops, and a duck cassoulet with a sauce richly enhanced by dried figs. Poached langoustine and crab ravioli in a saffron cream was impressively well-constructed, as was another starter of game terrine served with cubes of port jelly. A main course of sirloin of beef, roasted whole, was served with a Savoy cabbage parcel of meltingly tender oxtail and a side plate of an individual crispy Yorkshire pudding filled with excellent fried onions. However, just when you think you've got Escalera summed up, he ploughs a surprisingly straight furrow with clean, classic dishes such as steamed Dover sole with hollandaise and celeriac purée, or prune and almond tart with Armagnac ice cream. Details reflect his passion about his food and restaurant – a selection of marinated olives to nibble at on arrival, then a huge basket of home-made rolls and bread, Parmesan and garlic, walnut, sun-dried tomato, basil, white and granary. To make the permutations even harder, there is also a choice of butters – unsalted, anchovy, garlic, herb and paprika. Canapés include salmon confit croûte, celeriac and beetroot crisps, although our inspector groaned inwardly at the sight of this year's culinary cliché, a cappuccino of white beans with truffle oil. At the other end of the meal, good cafetière coffee is served with a generous tray of goodies including macaroons, brandy snaps, tuilles, truffles, tartlets and mini-clafoutis.

Directions: Park (if possible) in Pretoria Road, off Chesterton Road, then walk across the footbridge to Midsummer House

DUXFORD, **Duxford Lodge**

Ickleton Road CB2 4RU
Map 5: TL44
Tel: 01223 836444
Fax: 01223 832271
Chef: Kevin Bingham

Paradise is a red-brick house set in enclosed gardens in the centre of the village. Named after the oil paintings and water-colours of birds of paradise that decorate the intimate, fin de

Duxford Lodge

Owners: Ronald & Suzanne Craddock
Cost: Alc £25, fixed-price L & D
£18.50 (3 courses). ☺ H/wine £9.85.
Times: Noon-last L 2pm/7pm-last D
9.30pm. Closed L Sat, 25-30 Dec
Additional: Bar food L; Sunday L;
Children welcome; ✿ dishes
Seats: 46. Private dining rooms 26/10.
Smoking: No smoking in dining room;
air-conditioning
Accommodation: 15 en suite
Credit cards: ▆ ▆ ▆ ▆ ▆ ▆

siècle restaurant, 'Le Paradis' aspires to be worthy of the name.
Our inspector might not have been able to make a divine
judgement but he was inspired enough to sing the praises of a
beautifully timed dish of roasted John Dory and scallops set on
a bed of buttered spinach accompanied by a balsamic vinegar
and herb dressing. A first course of chargrilled breast of pigeon
had plump, tender, full-flavoured meat, and was served on a
lightly cooked bed of couscous with a hot vinaigrette sauce.
Honey and lemon soufflé was more lemon than honey, but
enjoyable nonetheless, as was some freshly made Colombian
coffee and mints. Only rather plain, overcooked vegetables
proved a disappointment. The *carte* and fixed-price menus are
supplemented by daily vegetarian and fish dishes.

Directions: M11/J10, take A505 eastbound then 1st turning R to
Duxford; take R fork at T-junction, entrance 70 yards on L

ELY, Lamb Hotel NEW

*Predominantly modern British cooking contrasts with the historic
setting at this hotel, parts of which date from the thirteenth century.
Quality fresh ingredients make for well presented dishes with good
clear flavours. Lamb has been well reported, served on a parsnip
and potato rösti with a rich port wine jus.*

Smoking: No-smoking area; no pipes or cigars; air-conditioning
Accommodation: 32 en suite. **Credit cards:** ▆ ▆ ▆ ▆

Directions: Follow A10 to Ely, then city centre signs. Hotel on
corner of High St adjacent cathedral

2 Lynn Road CB7 4EJ
Map 5: TL58
Tel: 01353 663574
Fax: 01353 662023
Chefs: S Mather, I Hudson
Owner: Mr R Lilley
Cost: Alc £18, fixed-price L £9.25/D
£15.95. ☺ H/wine £8.50.
Times: Last L 2.15pm/last D 9.30pm
Additional: Bar meals; Sunday L;
Children welcome; ✿ dishes

ELY, Old Fire Engine House Restaurant

*Charming brick farmhouse dating from the eighteenth century. Pine
tables, polished floors and antique pieces create a warm atmosphere,
and there is a lovely mature garden. Country cooking is based on
local produce. Seasonal offerings of lovage soup, local asparagus,
Norfolk marsh samphire, and jugged hare, as well as steak and
kidney, pork chops in Suffolk cider, and fresh plaice with dill sauce.*

Smoking: No smoking in dining room. **Credit cards:** ▆ ▆ ▆ ▆

Directions: Facing St Mary's Church in town centre

25 St Mary's Street CB7 4ER
Map 5: TL58
Tel: 01353 662582
Fax: 01353 666966
Chef: Terri Kindred
Owners: Ann Ford, Michael Jarman
Cost: Alc £21. ☺
Times: Last L 2pm/D 9pm. Closed D
Sun, Bhs, Dec 24-Jan 6
Additional: Sunday L; Children
welcome; ✿ dishes

FOWLMERE,
The Chequers Inn Restaurant

Fowlmere, SG8 7SR
Map 5: TL44
Tel: 01763 208369
Fax: 01763 208944
Chef: Louis Gambie
Owners: N.S. & P. Rushton
Cost: *Alc* £15.10. H/wine £9.25. ☺
Times: Noon-last L 2pm/7pm-last D
10pm. Closed 25 Dec

Samuel Pepys once stayed the night at this fine sixteenth-century inn and period charm still survives, especially in the galleried restaurant. Today, visitors can sample good modern cooking in such dishes as lamb noisettes on herb polenta with ratatouille and black olives, and lemon tart with lime sauce.

Additional: Bar food; Children welcome; ◑ dishes
Credit cards: 🔳 🔳 🔳 🔳 🔳 🔳

Directions: Btw Royston & Cambridge, B1368 turn off the A10

HUNTINGDON,
Old Bridge Hotel

PE18 6TQ
Map 4: TL27
Tel: 01480 452681
Fax: 01480 411017
Chef: Nick Steiger, David Bevan
Owner: John Hoskins (Huntsbridge Ltd)
Cost: *Alc* £22. H/wine £8.45. ☺

A handsome ivy-clad hotel set on the banks of the River Ouse. The same menu is offered throughout, from the panelled restaurant to the informal Terrace. A spring meal included a colourful pasta dish with tangy goat's cheese, and chicken and tarragon boudin on a creamy mash.

Additional: Sunday L; Children welcome; ◑ dishes
Accommodation: 24 rooms
Credit cards: 🔳 🔳 🔳 🔳 🔳 🔳

Directions: Off A1 near junction with A1-M1 link and A604/M11

KEYSTON, **Pheasant Inn** ✿✿

Huntingdon PE18 0RE
Map 4: TL07
Tel: 01832 710241
Fax: 01832 710340
Chef: Martin Lee
Owner: John Hoskins
(Huntsbridge Ltd)
Cost: *Alc* £20. H/wine £9.45 ☺
Times: Noon-last L 2pm/6pm-last D
10pm (7pm-10pm Sun). Closed Xmas
Day D
Additional: Children welcome;
◑ dishes
Seats: 94.
Smoking: No-smoking area
Credit cards: 🔳 🔳 🔳 🔳 🔳 🔳

This thatched inn started life as a village watering hole and locals can still be found drinking pints at the bar, but these days the place is almost entirely given over to food. You can sit at rustic tables in the bar area or head for the Red Room where linen cloths are laid up and waitresses serve. One menu is offered throughout the pub. The monthly menu strikes all the right mod Med notes with plenty of sun-dried tomatoes, balsamic vinegar and rocket. The kitchen does dip its toes into other waters; note warm chicken liver mousse with tomato and port sauce and shiitake mushrooms, or wild boar sausages, Dijon mustard and onion sauce. Elsewhere, contemporary ideas abound: chargrilled scallops come with courgette chutney and a thyme and orange sauce, best end of lamb with basil pasta and fricassée of wild mushrooms. Part of the Huntsbridge Group, owner/Master of Wine John Hoskins has put together a dazzling modern wine list with a dozen by the glass and quality across the board.

Directions: In the village centre, clearly signposted off A14

MELBOURN, Pink Geranium

'Pink, pink, pink!' exclaimed an inspector, having walked through the pretty garden to reach this equally charming fifteenth-century thatched cottage. Business is apparently booming, now that Steven Saunders has joined the ever-growing legions of TV chefs and his young attentive staff provide good service in the dining room and conservatory. The seasonal *carte* is supplemented by a fixed-price daily menu of so-called 'contemporary' dishes. A typical meal from the former might commence with mille-feuille of chargrilled tuna with crispy aubergine, sweet pimentos and basil oil before, say, cannon of wild venison with lentil mousseline, porcini risotto, Chianti jus and Parmesan croustade, or breast of duckling with its own confit, griottine cherries and roasted vegetables. To finish, you might choose a plate of English and French cheeses with home-made sultana soda bread or a dessert such as caramelised orange tart with bitter chocolate sorbet. The strong wine list begins with a first-rate collection of bottles for £15 and under, otherwise there is some particularly interesting stuff from France.

Station Road Royston SG8 6DX
Map 5: TL34
Tel: 01763 260215
Fax: 01763 262110
Chefs: Steven Saunders, Mark Jordan
Owners: Sally & Steven Saunders
Cost: *Alc* £38; fixed-price L £10/D £20. H/wine £10.
Times: Noon-last L 2pm/7pm-last D 10pm. Closed L Sat, D Sun, Mon
Additional: Sunday L; Children welcome; 🍴 dishes
Seats: 65. Private dining room 18
Smoking: No smoking in dining room
Credit cards: 🔲 🔲 🔲 🔲 🔲

Directions: On A10 between Royston and Cambridge. In centre of the village, opposite the church

MELBOURN, Sheen Mill

Station Road SG8 6DX
Map 5: TL34
Tel: 01763 261393
Fax: 01763 261376
Chef: Ian Wilson
Owners: Carlo & Jenny Cescutti
Cost: *Alc* £23.50; fixed-price L £15.95/D £22.50. ☺ H/wine £8.95.
Times: 12.30pm-last L 1.55pm/7.30pm-last D 9.55pm. Closed D Sun, Bhs
Additional: Bar food L; Sunday L; Children welcome; 🍴 dishes
Seats: 100; Jacket and tie preferred
Smoking: No pipes or cigars in dining room
Accommodation: 8 en suite
Credit cards: 🔲 🔲 🔲

As the name suggests this beguiling restaurant is in a lovingly restored seventeenth-century watermill straddling the River Mel, and you can still see the water flowing beneath the building. The gardens and conservatory are a dream in summer and there are wondrous views of the river from the elegantly furnished restaurant. The kitchen works to a repertoire of modern British dishes, with a few French and Mediterranean influences for good measure. Typical starters might range from duck and green peppercorn sausage on tarragon and grain mustard jus to polenta topped with mozzarella accompanied by anchovy and black olive salad and sun-dried tomato relish. Main courses include, say, noisettes of venison with a cranberry tartlet and port jus, or sea bream with capers and beurre blanc plus a handful of flambéed dishes, Bringing up the rear are desserts such as hot apple and pear tarte Tatin or cinnamon wafers with honey ice and a compote of black plums. France is the main contributor to the serviceable wine list.

Directions: Take 2nd exit from A10 Melbourn by-pass signed Melbourn. Sheen Mill is 300yds down Station Road on R

SIX MILE BOTTOM,
Swynford Paddocks Hotel

A fine English country house with a dusky pink dining room sporting large windows overlooking the grounds. Traditional Anglo dishes with an Irish lilt are offered from an extensive menu. Specialities include Beartan parcel of roast fillet steak with bacon and stuffing in a pickled walnut sauce.

Times: Last L 2pm/D 9.30pm. 4 days Xmas/New Year
Additional: Bar food; Sunday L; Children welcome: ❸ dishes
Smoking: No smoking in dining room
Accommodation: 15 en suite
Credit cards: ▆ ▆ ▆ ▆ ▆ ▆

Newmarket CB8 0UE
Map5: TL55
Tel: 01638 570234
Fax: 01638 570283
Chef: Patrick Collins
Owner: Peter Bottomley
Cost: *Alc* £25, fixed-price D £25 (4 courses). ☺ H/wine £11.75.

Directions: On A1304 6 miles S-W of Newmarket

WANSFORD, **The Haycock Hotel**

Celebrated seventeenth-century coaching inn set in delightful grounds beside the River Nene. There's a wide choice of eating options – the formal dining room has a reputation for good traditional English cooking. Typical dishes may include rack of lamb with redcurrant jelly, whole Dover sole and roast sirloin of beef.

Additional: Bar Food; Sunday L; Children welcome; ❸ dishes
Smoking: No-smoking area
Accommodation: 50 en suite
Credit cards: ▆ ▆ ▆ ▆ ▆ ▆

Wansford PE8 6JA
Map 4: TL09
Tel: 01780 782223
Fax: 01780 783508
Chefs: Adrian Doughty
Owners: Arcadian Hotels
Cost: *Alc* £28, fixed-price L £18.95. ☺ H/wine £9.95.
Times: Last L 2pm/D 9.45pm. Closed L Sat

Directions: In village centre between A1 & A47

WISBECH,
Crown Lodge Hotel

A hotel with many commendable attributes, including good food and willing, friendly service. There is a weekly set-price meal and a carte strong on grills. Recommended dishes include French onion soup, and poached breast of Norfolk chicken filled with crab meat and served with a brandied shellfish sauce.

Downham Road, Outwell PE14 8SE
Map 5: TF40
Tel: 01945 773391
Fax: 01945 772668
Owners: Mr & Mrs Moore
Telephone for details

Directions: Five miles S-E of Wisbech on A1122 close to junction with A1101

CHESHIRE

ALDERLEY EDGE,

Alderley Edge Hotel ⊛⊛

Macclesfield Road SK9 7BJ
Map 7: SJ87
Tel: 01625 583033
Fax: 01625 586343
Chef: Steven Kitchen
Owner: JW Lees (Brewers) & Co
Cost: *Alc* £34, fixed-price L £15.50/D £22.95. ☺ H/wine £12.95.
Times: Noon-last L 2pm/7pm-last D 10pm
Additional: Bar food L; Sunday L; Children welcome; ✿ dishes
Seats: 80. Private dining rooms 20-26. Jacket & tie preferred
Smoking: No pipes in dining room; air-conditioning
Accommodation: 32 en suite
Credit cards: ▆ ▩ ▤ ▨ ₵

Built in 1850 as the residence for one of Manchester's cotton kings, this extended sandstone mansion overlooking the Cheshire plain is still in fine fettle. Formal meals are eaten in the split-level conservatory – which takes full advantage of the views – and the whole place is clearly popular with locals and visitors alike. The ambitious tone of the menus suggests that the kitchen is not one to hide its light under a bushel: a terrine of goose and chicken livers is served with sun-dried tomatoes, leeks and fig jam; collops of monkfish come with vegetable couscous and curry broth; while peppered medallions of venison are presented on a balsamic vinegar sauce. Desserts are equally showy with a duo of chocolate mousses (one dark, one white) appearing on the plate as cleverly wrought 'teardrops', and gingerbread pudding gets a kick from some mulled wine sauce.

Directions: A538 to Alderley Edge, then B5087 Macclesfield road

BOLLINGTON,

Mauro's Restaurant ⊛⊛

Enzo Mauro's cheerful restaurant lies on the main road through the old village of Bollington. Crisp white linen contrasts with deep yellow walls, fresh flowers are on every table, and the cooking is spot on. A trolley laden with antipasti 'alla caprese' is offered in the bar – luscious fresh sardines, marinated red peppers, anchovies, big fat asparagus, for example. To the table comes 'pizzetta' – lightly fried dough topped with tomato purée and mozzarella. Then perhaps, a large bowl of plump mussels, followed by 'excellent' sea bass (fish is a speciality), simply chargrilled with lemon juice and mint, and served with crisp, sweet sugar snap peas, wilted spinach and sauté potatoes. Or there could be fettucine with oil, garlic and chilli, home-made gnocchi with a mixed vegetable sauce and basil, a classic veal escalope with Marsala wine sauce and, to finish, a very good courgette and walnut

88 Palmerston Street SK10 5PW
Map 7: SJ97
Tel: 01625 573898
Chef/Owner: Vincenzo Mauro
Cost: *Alc* £21. H/wine £9. ☺
Times: 12.15pm-last L 2pm/7pm-last D 10pm. Closed Sun (except L 1st Sun of month), 25-26 Dec
Additional: Children welcome; ✿ dishes
Seats: 48. Jacket and tie preferred
Smoking: No pipes and cigars in dining room
Credit cards: ▆ ▩ ▤ ▜ ₵

cake soaked in whisky with cream cheese mixed with shredded orange peel to add a refreshing sharpness. Excellent Italian wine list.

Directions: Situated on the main street of the village, at the Pott Shrigley end

BROXTON, **Broxton Hall Hotel** ✼

Antique-furnished Tudor hall with magnificent period features set in five stunning acres south of Chester. A good selection of soundly cooked dishes is served in an elegant restaurant overlooking the garden. Typical choices may include fish soup and beef Stroganoff, with apricot and almond tart to finish.

Additional: Bar Food L; Sunday L; Children welcome; ❸ dishes
Smoking: No cigars or pipes
Accommodation: 10 en suite
Credit cards: ▆ ▆ ▆ ▆ ▆ ▆

Whitchurch Road CH3 9JS
Map 7: SJ45
Tel: 01829 782321
Fax: 01829 782330
Chef: James Makin
Owners: Rosemary & George Hadley
Cost: *Alc* £20, fixed-price L £15.90/ D £23.90. ☺ H/wine £10.75.
Times: Last L 1.45pm/D 9.30pm
Closed 25 Dec, 1 Jan

Directions: On A41 halfway between Whitchurch and Chester, at Broxton roundabout

CHESTER, **Chester Grosvenor** ✼✼✼

Eastgate CH1 1LT
Map 7: SJ46
Tel: 01244 324024
Fax: 01244 313246
Chef: Paul Reed
Cost: *Alc* £49.50, fixed-price L £22.50/D £40 (5 courses). H/wine £11.50
Times: Noon-2.30pm/7pm-9.30pm. Closed D Sun, L Mon, 25-26 Dec
Additional: Sunday L; Children welcome; ❸ dishes
Smoking: No smoking in dining room; air-conditioning
Seats: 40. Private dining room 18. Jacket and tie preferred
Accommodation: 86 en suite
Credit cards: ▆ ▆ ▆ ▆

You don't have to own a race-horse to dine here, but it's no surprise that quite a few followers of the turf, plus the *crème de la crème* of Cheshire society, come here to celebrate/commiserate after a day at the nearby races. Horsy pictures, signature sous-plates and lots of polished wood, silver and over-sized glasses give a formal air to the Arkle restaurant, part of the glossy city-centre hotel owned by the Duke of Westminster. Tail-coated staff are experienced and discreetly professional. Good ingredients tend to be given a rather convoluted treatment, a high-risk strategy that usually pays dividends in the hands of chef Paul Reed. Our inspector opened with a cannelloni of calves' sweetbread with Dublin Bay prawns and a Mediterranean fish sauce, which also included mousseline, sun-dried tomatoes and chive butter sauce. Welsh lamb cutlets followed, with pesto tortellini, fennel gnocchi, whole roast garlic cloves, and yet more oven-dried tomatoes. Other dishes in the repertoire, a mix of modern English and French, might include parfait of wild duck with hot smoked breast of wild duck and a salad of chestnuts, casserole of seafood and shellfish with ginger, star anise,

seaweed and seasonal vegetables, and carved loin of venison with egg pasta, caramelised turnips, red wine celery and a juniper scented sauce. Desserts tend to the excessively fancy – a good lime tart with citrus syrup, pistachio topped *îsles flottantes*, raspberries, orange and lime came dressed for Ladies Day in a spun sugar hat. As might be expected from such a swanky set-up, there are lots of extras – canapés (really good tartare of salmon, and onion bhaji), an excellent range of breads carved from a trolley, an amuse-bouche of good duck parfait with smoked breast, sorbet, and even a pre-dessert dessert (orange flummery with citrus syrup). A tremendous wine list, well set out with some of the lesser known wines explained in depth. A page of reserve vintage Burgundies has vintages going back to the 50s and prices up to £500. The Sommelier's selection offers a clutch of interesting wines with a broad price span to suit all pockets – Cuvée Signée St Chinian (£19.50), Viognier, Dom St Hilaire (£19). France is covered in great depth.

Signature dishes: Poached breast of guinea fowl with a pressing of leeks, wild mushrooms, and a truffled infused stock; cutlets of Welsh lamb with fennel gnocchi, oven-dried tomatoes, pesto tortellinis and sweet garlics; fillet of beef topped with a crust of horseradish and parsley, crushed parsnips and oxtail; carved loin of venison with egg pasta, caramelised turnips, red wine, celery and juniper scented sauce.

Directions: City centre adjacent to the Eastgate Clock and Roman Walls

CHESTER,
Crabwall Manor Hotel

Parkgate Road Mollington CH1 6NE
Map 7: SJ46
Tel: 01244 851666
Fax: 01244 851400
Chefs: Michael Truelove, Kevin Woods
Owner: Carl Lewis
Cost: *Alc* £35. H/wine £13.50
Times: Noon-last L 2pm/7pm-last D 9.30pm
Additional: Sunday L; Children welcome; dishes
Seats: 80. Private dining room 100. Jacket and tie preferred
Smoking: No-smoking area; no pipes and cigars; air-conditioning

Accomplished cooking, polished service and a fine view of Chester city skyline make a meal at Crabwall Manor something of a special occasion. The dining-room is built conservatory-style out into the garden of the extended, red-brick seventeenth-century manor house, with its distinctive clock tower and turrets. Kevin Woods cooks with care, accuracy and imaginative attention to detail, under the watchful eye of executive chef Michael Truelove, now general manager. Good canapés, served in the bar or lounge, might include cod and potato beignet and Stilton and pear tartlets. At the table, there are honest-to-goodness home-made brown and white rolls. A fashionable frothy white bean soup with girolles combined robust flavour with a light, airy texture; a

main course of sea bass with ginger and chilli and wafer-thin sesame crisps showed surprising delicacy of flavour. Only a rather one-dimensional bitter chocolate tart lacked the lightness of touch that otherwise distinguished the rest of our inspector's meal. The same *carte*, a mixture of French and English, modern and classical influences, is offered both at lunch and dinner, and all dishes are cooked in a simpler way on request. Meals for children under 12 are half price. The wine list has been distilled into a well-annotated selection of just under 50 wines, with champagne, country wines and prestigious single French vineyards standing out as highlights. Although there are no half-bottles, there is a fair choice under £20, including a few good-value gems.

Signature dishes: Tagliatelle of oysters with red wine and shallots; Cannelloni of scallops; Risotto of lobster with wild mushrooms; Braised partridge paupiette.

Accommodation: 48 en suite
Credit cards: ▬ ▤ ▤ ▼ 🐷 ℭ

Directions: From A56 take A5117 then A540. Set back from the A540 north of Chester

CHESTER, **Curzon Hotel**

Small, privately-owned Victorian hotel, a mile from the city centre and racecourse and noted for warm hospitality and quality Swiss-influenced cooking. At inspection excellent rösti potatoes accompanied a traditional dish of pork with mushrooms, white wine and cream, and home-made apple strudel came with delicious hot vanilla sauce

Smoking: No smoking in dining room
Accommodation: 16 en suite
Credit cards: ▬ ▤ ▼ ℭ

Directions: From M53 take A483 Wrexham/Chester, turning R towards Chester. At 3rd roundabout take 2nd L onto A5104 (Saltney). Hotel 500yds on R.

52-54 Hough Green CH4 8JQ
Map 7: SJ46
Tel: 01244 678581
Fax: 01244 680866
Chefs: Markus Imfeld, Rob John
Owners: Yvonne & Markus Imfeld
Cost: *Alc* £16.50, fixed-price D £15 (3 courses). ☺ H/wine £8.75.
Times: D only, 7pm-9pm.
Closed 23-30 Dec
Additional: Children welcome;
🍴 dishes
Seats: 40. Jacket & tie preferred

CHESTER,
Gateway To Wales Hotel ❀❀

Welsh Road Deeside CH5 2HX
Map 7: SJ46
Tel: 01244 830332
Fax: 01244 836190
Chef: Nicholas Walton
Owners: Mr WG Corbett,
Mrs DK Harford-Corbett

An eighteenth-century theme runs through the decor in the modern purpose-built hotel, especially in the Louis XVI lounge bar and the Regency restaurant. The kitchen performs best in the evening when a five-course seasonal *carte* is

supplemented by a four-course fixed-price menu. Layered vegetable terrine set in fennel jelly with aïoli, cannelloni of crab and ginger poached in bouillabaisse sauce, and braised rump of lamb on a bed of roast parsnips and baby leeks with a tapenade jus and mint salsa, are typical dishes from the repertoire. The cheese course always highlights unusual British farmhouse varieties, Celtic Promise served with drop scones or Perroche goats' cheese with Orkney Isle biscuits, for example. Lunch tends to be a simpler affair. A fair number of half-bottles back up the international wine list.

Directions: From Chester follow signs for Deeside/Queensferry taking A548. Turn R at roundabout, to 2nd roundabout, where hotel can be seen. Near RAF Sealand

Cost: Alc £25.75, fixed-price L/D £17.50. ☺ H/wine £8.50.
Times: Noon-last L 2.30pm/7pm-last D 9.30pm.
Additional: Bar food; Sunday L; Children welcome; ❹ dishes
Seats: 40. Private dining rooms 8 & 110
Smoking: No smoking in dining room
Accommodation: 39 en suite
Credit cards: ▅ ▆ ▆ ▆ 🄟 🄛

CHESTER,
Mollington Banastre Hotel ☗

Bacchanalian, hand-painted fruit and vines decorate the walls of the stylishly refurbished Garden Room restaurant. Mille-feuille of avocado and Cornish crab glazed with cheese, and maize-fed chicken stuffed with a Lancashire mousse (aka black pudding), are amongst a good selection of accurately cooked dishes on the modern English carte.

Additional: Bar Food L; Sunday L; Children welcome; ❹ menu
Smoking: No smoking in dining room.
Air-conditioning
Accommodation: 63 en suite
Credit cards: ▅ ▆ ▆ ▆ 🄟 🄛

Directions: Bear L at end of M56 onto A5117, L at roundabout onto A540, the hotel is 2 miles on R

Parkgate Road CH1 6NN
Map 7: SJ46
Tel: 01244 851471
Fax: 01244 851165
Chef: Ron Knox
Owner: Arcadian Hotels.
Cost: Alc £30, fixed price L £16 (3 courses)/D £ 20 (3 courses). H/wine £10.75
Times: Last L 2pm/D 9.45pm Closed L Sat, D Sun

HANDFORTH, Belfry Hotel ☗

Stanley Road SK9 3LD
Map 7: SJ76
Tel: 0161 437 0511
Fax: 0161 499 0597
Chef: Martin Thompson
Owner: Mr Andrew Beech
Cost: Alc £32, fixed-price L £16.50/ D £19.50. ☺ H/wine £12.
Times: Last L 2pm/D 10pm. Closed 25-26 Dec, 1 Jan
Additional: Bar Food; Sunday L; Children welcome; ❹ dishes
Accommodation: 80 en suite
Credit cards: ▅ ▆ ▆ ▆ 🄟 🄛

A modern hotel, convenient for Manchester and the motorway network, which has been owned by the Beech family for 30 years. Good choice of tried and trusted dishes along the lines of quenelles of duck and chicken liver parfait with Oxford sauce, rack of spring lamb basted in heather honey with Madeira sauce and onion and grain mustard tartlets, and fresh raspberry brûlée. Good wine list.

Directions: A34 to Handforth, at end of village

HOLMES CHAPEL,

The Old Vicarage Hotel ❀

Part seventeenth-century, this Grade 11 listed building on the northern edge of the village offers a sound standard of cooking. The carte is supplemented by daily blackboard specials and could take in wild mushroom terrine, roast breast of duck on a soy and plum sauce, or baked fillet of halibut with red pesto on a spinach sauce.

Smoking: No smoking in dining room
Accommodation: 25 en suite
Credit cards: ▬ ▦ ▤ 𝒞

Directions: 500 yds from Holmes Chapel centre on A50 Knutsford road

Knutsford Road
CW4 8EF
Map 7: SJ46
Tel: 01477 532041
Fax: 01477 535728
Chef: Kenneth Howard
Owner: Luis Barbera
Cost: *Alc* £14.50, fixed-price L £14
Times: Last L 1.45pm/D 9.45pm
Additional: Bar Food; Sunday L; Children welcome; ❹ dishes

KNUTSFORD, **Belle Epoque** ❀

Statues, rich fabrics, enormous flower vases on each table, add to the stunning Art Nouveau influenced decor. Brasserie-style menu draws on French and Italian influences, and makes good use of local produce. Tomato and fennel tart on marjoram gravy, cod fillet with mustard cheese sauce, and crème brûlée, made up one inspection meal.

Smoking: No-smoking area. **Accommodation:** 7 en suite
Credit cards: ▬ ▦ ▤ ▦ 𝔻 𝒞

Directions: Two miles off A50/2 miles from M6/J19

60 King Street WA16 6DT
Map 7: SJ77
Tel: 01565 633060
Fax: 01565 634150
Chef: David Mooney
Owners: Nerys & Keith Mooney
Cost: *Alc* £17.95, fixed-price L £9.50 (3 courses), D £17.95 (3 courses). ☺ H/wine £9.50.
Times: Last L 1.45pm/D 10pm.
Closed L Sat, Sun, Bhs
Additional: No children under 12; ❹ dishes

KNUTSFORD, **Cottage Restaurant** ❀

Although open-plan in design, the restaurant and bar of this smart, modern hotel still have a few private corners. Ingredients are carefully chosen – locally grown asparagus served with a lemon and butter sauce, for example. Sea bass could come with Chinese five-spice and tomato sauce, and baked Alaska is a blast-from-the-past.

Additional: Bar food L; Sunday L; Children welcome; ❹ dishes
Accommodation: 12 en suite
Credit cards: ▬ ▦ ▤ ▦ 𝒞

Directions: On A50 halfway between Knutsford and Holmes Chapel

London Road, Allostock WA16 9LU
Map 7: SJ77
Tel: 01565 722470
Fax: 01565 722749
Chef: Steve Burrell
Owners: WF Fletcher, C Lowe
Cost: *Alc* £19.50, fixed-price L&D £10.95 ☺ H/wine £8.95.
Times: Last L 2pm/last D 9.30pm.
Closed D Sun

KNUTSFORD, **Cottons Hotel** ❀

Convenient for the M6 and Manchester Airport, Cottons was designed with a New Orleans theme. This extends into the Magnolia Restaurant where menus have a noticeable Cajun influence. Crab cakes with pepper sauce, fish and prawn casserole Cajun-style, and roast lamb with lentils, show the range.

Smoking: No-smoking area; air-conditioning
Accommodation: 99 en suite
Credit cards: ▬ ▦ ▤ ▦ 𝔻 𝒞

Directions: From M6 exit 19/A556 (Stockport). Turn R at lights (A50 to Knutsford). Hotel 1.5 miles on R

Manchester Road WA16 0SU
Map 7: SJ57
Tel: 01565 650333
Fax: 01565 755351
Chef: Gary Jenkins
Owner: Shire Inns
Cost: *Alc* £22, fixed-price L £12/D £20. ☺ H/wine £7.
Times: Last L 2pm/last D 9.45pm.
Closed L Sat
Additional: Bar food; Sunday L; Children welcome; ❹ dishes

KNUTSFORD, Dick Willett's

A sixteenth-century barn has been converted into a farmhouse-style vegetarian restaurant for the Toft Hotel. Dick Willett's is the name, and TV chef Jean Davies creates favourite dishes such as buckwheat crêpes with mushrooms, creamy corn and tomato risotto, and perhaps, spicy Thai vegetables with lemon grass, taken from an authentic Bangkok recipe.

Accommodation: 11 en suite. **Credit cards:** ▬ ▒ ▨ ▧ ▢

Directions: One mile S of Knutsford on A50

Toft Road WA16 9EH
Map 7: SJ77
Tel: 01565 634443
Fax: 01565 632603
Chef: Jean Davies
Owners: Jean & Tony Davies
Cost: Fixed-price D £19.75. ☺ H/wine £9.50.
Additional: ⚘ menu only
Smoking: No-smoking premises

KNUTSFORD, Longview Hotel

55 Manchester Road WA16 0LX
Map 7: SJ77
Tel: 01565 632119
Fax: 01565 652402
Chef: James Falconer Flint
Owners: Pauline & Stephen West
Cost: Alc £16. H/wine £9.25
Times: D only, 6.30pm-last D 9pm. Closed Sun, Mon, Bhs
Additional: Bar food (D only); Children welcome; ⚘ dishes
Smoking: No smoking in dining room
Accommodation: 23 en suite
Credit cards: ▬ ▒ ▨ ▧ ▢

Welcoming hotel with a decidedly Victorian feel to the restaurant. The kitchen offers a good selection of dishes, perhaps venison steak in buttered oats, herbs and nuts, steamed John Dory on a bed of saffron noodles, or a vegetarian choice of pine nut and carrot roast.

Directions: From M6 junc 19, A556 (Chester, Northwich). Turn L at lights (Knutsford), L again at roundabout, A50. Hotel 200yds on R

LYMM, Lymm Hotel

The Bridgewater is a comfortable hotel restaurant with polished service and imaginative modern British cooking. Menus include a daily fixed-price, supplemented by short list of steak choices. Expect salmon with deep-fried leeks and lobster sauce, and mandarin cheesecake with fruit coulis.

Directions: Near the village centre

Whitbarrow Road WA13 9AQ
Map 7: SJ68
Tel: 01925 752233
Fax: 01925 756035
Chef: Duncan Mackintosh
Telephone for details

NANTWICH, Churche's Mansion

An atmospheric sixteenth-century half-timbered merchant's house, with gabling and overhanging upper storeys. Within, clues to the building's mediaeval past lie in a large inglenook fireplace in the bar and carved panelling in the main dining room. Opened as a restaurant in 1992, Churche's Mansion is noted for quality modern British cooking built around the best local produce. A recent meal started with a warm smoked duck breast salad, with toasted pine kernels, wild rice and a blueberry dressing. This was followed by tender best end of lamb with minted leeks and provençale couscous. For dessert, a

Hospital Street CW5 5RY
Map 7: SJ65
Tel: 01270 625933
Fax: 01270 627831
Chef: Graham Tucker
Owners: Amanda Simpson, Robin Latham
Cost: Alc £28.70, fixed-price L £17.25/D £26.75. H/wine £10.25
Times: Noon-last L 2.30pm/7pm-last D 9.30pm. Closed D Sun, Mon, 2 wks Jan

smooth white chocolate mousse wrapped in tangy dark chocolate and glazed with fresh raspberries. During the summer months lunch can be taken in the walled garden, while on warm evenings guests can sit outside on the patio and enjoy drinks before dinner.

Directions: M6/J16, follow A500 towards Nantwich. At T junction turn R. Car park is on L immediately before next r/bout

Additional: Sunday L; No children under 10 at D; 🌢 dishes
Seats: 55. Private dining room 24 or 48
Smoking: No smoking in dining room
Credit cards: ▆ 🖼 🖼 🔌 🖾 🄲

NANTWICH, **Rookery Hall** 🏵🏵

Worleston CW5 6DQ
Map 7: SJ65
Tel: 01270 610016
Fax: 01270 626027
Chef: David Alton
Owners: Arcadian Hotels
Cost: Fixed-price L £17.50
(4 courses)/D £37.50 (5 courses).
H/wine £12.50
Times: 12.30pm-last L 2pm/7pm-last D 9.45pm
Additional: Bar food; Sunday L; Children welcome; 🌢 dishes
Seats: 30. Private dining rooms 60-20-12
Smoking: No smoking in dining room
Accommodation: 45 en suite
Credit cards: ▆ 🖼 🖼 🔌 🖾 🄲

When it was acquired by an Austrian banking baron in 1867, Rookery Hall was transformed from Georgian mansion into mini-château, complete with a schloss tower at the back. Today it stands in 38 acres of its own gardens and wooded parkland fringing the banks of the River Weaver. An impressive fountain adds interest, while inside guests are cossetted in the grand mahogany-panelled dining room. The menu runs to four courses – including British and Irish cheeses with home-baked hazelnut and date bread. Highpoints of the test meal were accurately roasted loin of lamb with wild mushrooms, herb dumplings and creamed spinach with a 'robust' sauce, followed by a faultless cinnamon and apple soufflé with Calvados sauce – a real classic example of the genre, timed to a T and bursting with flavour. The wine list is a praiseworthy selection with a laudable number by the glass and informative notes on suppliers that make for fascinating reading.

Directions: On the B5074 north of Nantwich; situated 1.5 miles on right towards Worleston village

PRESTBURY,
White House Restaurant 🏵🏵

Displays of antique Macclesfield silk and lace set the tone at this converted farmhouse on the edge of Manchester's commuter belt. The restaurant divides into three, culminating in a semi-private section with murals depicting Greek urns overflowing with fruit. A lunchtime visit in October yielded crab croquettes with a sweetcorn relish spiked with fresh green chillies before baked fillets of brill on a colourful assemblage of baby vegetables with a nage butter sauce, then raspberry tiramisu with twirled raspberry coulis and vanilla. The full *carte* zooms rapidly into the contemporary world of oak-smoked

Map 7: SJ97
Tel: 01625 829376
Fax: 01625 828627
Chef: Ryland Wakeham, Mark Cunniffe
Owners: Ryland & Judith Wakeham
Cost: *Alc* £26.50, fixed-price L £12.95/D £16.95. ☺ H/wine £11.50.
Times: Noon-last L 2pm/7pm-last D 10pm. Closed D Sun, L Mon, 25 Dec
Additional: Bar food L; Sunday L; Children welcome; 🌢 dishes

salmon with roast beetroot terrine, griddled scallops with sweet and sour gingered melon salsa and pak choi greens. Influences and ideas leap off the page. Some dishes are designated 'Spa Cuisine' because of their reduced oil, butter and cream and the menu also promises 'blue plate specials' (re-styled old favourites). A strong contingent of New World wines steals the limelight on the carefully assembled list. Accommodation is in White House Manor just down the road.

Directions: Village centre on A538 N of Macclesfield

Seats: 75. Private dining room 40
Smoking: No pipes and cigars in dining room
Accommodation: 11 en suite
Credit cards:

PUDDINGTON, **Craxton Wood** ❀❀

Parkgate Road L66 9PB
Map 7: SJ37
Tel: 0151 3394717
Fax: 0151 3391740
Chef: M Beaumont
Owner: Médard-Antony Jean Petranca
Cost: Alc £26, fixed-price L & D £19.85 (4 courses). ☺
H/wine £12.85.
Times: 12.30pm-last L 2pm/7.30pm-last D 10pm. Closed Sun, last 2 weeks Aug, 1st week Jan
Additional: Children welcome; ❧ dishes
Seats: 85. Private dining rooms 12/50. Jacket and tie preferred
Smoking: No pipes in dining room
Accommodation: 14 en suite
Credit cards:

A friendly welcome and good service are part of the appeal of this large, peaceful house, run by the Petranca family since 1967. The menus are seasonal but the overall choice is a fair one, with a balanced selection across the board. Colour and freshness were the keys to an autumnal meal that kicked off with a moist potato cake, full of chives and haddock, surrounded by smoked haddock in a mustard cream sauce. This was followed by noisettes d'agneau à la niçoise, 'succulent lamb, delicious at this time of year', served just pink on ratatouille with a 'luscious' port sauce, and the meal finished with crème brûlée, which came with a side dish of fresh blackberries, strawberries, raspberries and redcurrants. There's an extensive range of wines, some of them displayed in the illuminated wine cellars.

Directions: From end of M56 (direction N Wales) take A5117 (Queensferry). R at 1st roundabout onto A540 (Hoylake). Hotel 200 yds after next traffic lights.

SANDBACH,
Chimney House Hotel ❀   NEW

Half-timbered, mock-Tudor building in eight acres of grounds handily placed for the Peak District and Manchester Airport. Meals in the Patio restaurant run along the lines of gravlax with potato 'biscuits', and venison with chestnuts, crispy noodles and five-spice sauce, and chocolate mousse with burnt orange and Grand Marnier sauce.

Smoking: No smoking in dining room; air-conditioning
Accommodation: 48 en suite. **Credit cards:**

Directions: M6/J17 follow A534 to Congleton. Hotel 0.5 mile on R

Congleton Road CW11 0ST
Map 7: SJ76
Tel: 01270 764141
Fax: 01270 768916
Chef: Thomas Burns
Owners: Regal Hotels
Cost: Alc £25. Fixed-price L £12/D £18. ☺ H/wine £10.45.
Times: Last L 2pm/last D 10pm
Additional: Bar meals; Sunday L; Children welcome; ❧ dishes
Seats: 60. Private dining room 80.

SANDIWAY,

Nunsmere Hall Hotel ❀❀❀

Tarporley Road Oakmere
Northwich CW8 2ES
Map 7: SJ67
Tel: 01606 889100
Fax: 01606 889055
Chef: Simon Radley
Owner: Julie & Malcolm McHardy
Cost: Fixed-price L £16.95 (2
courses), D (Sun only) £30 (3
courses). H/wine £13.50
Times: Noon-last L 1.45pm/7pm-last
D 9.45pm (9.15pm Sun).
Additional: Bar food L; Sunday L;
No children under 10; ❀ dishes
Seats: 60. Private dining rooms 42.
Jacket and tie preferred
Smoking: No smoking in dining room
Accommodation: 32 en suite
Credit cards: ▆ ▆ ▆ ▆ ▆ ▆

Malcolm and Julie McHardy took over this magnificent turn-
of-the-century mansion in 1987 and have worked
enthusiastically to provide an immaculate country house hotel
that includes some impressive public rooms, and good
bedrooms. New in the kitchen this year is Simon Radley, and
his cooking deliberately aspires to the setting; he offers a
careful and attentive version of modern country house
cooking. A parcel of poached salmon studded with crab, sweet
carrot sauce and griddled scallops, potted spiced duck with foie
gras, duck ham and sultana brioche and a mosaic of globe
artichoke and potatoes with hens egg and crispy Alsace bacon
are three first courses. These may be matched at main course
by roast best-end of lamb with aubergine moussaka and a
casserole of kidneys, or steamed fillet of brill with braised
fennel and shellfish bouillabaisse, or tortellini of goat's cheese
with sweet pepper and basil. Of a dinner taken in March, our
inspector reported warmly on canapés 'which were really very
good', a Finnan haddock tartlet with smoked salmon and
poached egg 'the mix of flavour quite special', and osso buco
with a lovely sticky texture, served with baby vegetables and
spinach that was 'deep green and looked full of iron.' Only the
dessert, deep-fried coconut ice cream fritters sounded an off-
note – the batter was too thick and the ice cream had melted.
However, crushed raspberries and the pineapple candy served
with the dish were lovely. Excellent coffee and freshly made
petits fours restored the balance. Staff are superb, managing
that fine balance between being friendly and giving
professional service with effortless ease. A generally youthful
wine list covers most bases and offers plenty of choice for
under £20. Bordeaux has a range of good petits châteaux from
the recent early drinking vintages and there are some reliable
rather than exciting names from the New World.

Signature dishes: Osso buco with langoustine tails, garden
herb risotto and light pan juices; steamed brill with Thai spice,
wilted greens and crispy fried oysters; roast pheasant with
raspberries and iced lemon verbena; Scotch fillet of beef with
vegetable fondants and oxtail dumpling.

Directions: From Sandiway take the A49, one mile on left.

TARPORLEY, The Wild Boar

Distinctive black and white timbered hotel, formerly a seventeenth-century hunting lodge. The varied carte and fixed-price menu may offer game terrine with cranberry and juniper chutney, followed by rack of lamb or whole Dover sole.

Additional: Bar Food; Children welcome; ⑤ dishes
Smoking: No smoking in dining room; air conditioning
Accommodation: 37 en suite
Credit cards: ▆ ▆ ▆ ▆ ⊆

Directions: Two miles from Tarporley on A49 towards Whitchurch

Whitchurch Road Beeston CW6 9NW
Map 7: SJ56
Tel: 01829 260309
Fax: 01829 261081
Chef: Andrew Griffiths
Owner: Pageant Hotels
Cost: Alc £25, fixed-price L £14.50/D £22. ☺
Times: Last L 2pm/D 9.45pm

WARRINGTON,
Daresbury Park Hotel 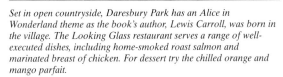 NEW

Set in open countryside, Daresbury Park has an Alice in Wonderland theme as the book's author, Lewis Carroll, was born in the village. The Looking Glass restaurant serves a range of well-executed dishes, including home-smoked roast salmon and marinated breast of chicken. For dessert try the chilled orange and mango parfait.

Times: Last L 2pm/D 10pm
Additional: Sunday L; Bar meals; Children welcome; ⑤ dishes
Accommodation: 140 en suite
Credit cards: ▆ ▆ ▆ ⊆

Directions: M56/J11 onto A56 to Warrington. Just on L off roundabout

Daresbury WA4 4BB
Map 7: SJ68
Tel: 01925 267331
Fax: 01925 265615
Chef: David Chapman
Owners: De Vere Hotels Ltd/Greenalls
Cost: Alc £23, fixed-price L £14/D £25. ☺ H/wine £11.50.

WARRINGTON,
Park Royal International

Spacious, modern hotel, well placed for the M56 and Manchester Airport. Consistent modern cooking takes in hot seafood pancake and duck liver terrine with port, and redcurrant sauce, to freshly caught turbot, and pheasant with Madeira sauce. Extensive wine list.

Directions: M56/J10, follow A49 signed Warrington, R towards Appleton Thorn at 1st lights; hotel 200 yds on R

Stretton Road Stretton WA4 4NS
Map 7: SJ68
Tel: 01925 730706
Fax: 01925 730740
Chef: Tom Rogers
Owners: Park Royal International Hotel
Cost: Alc £21, fixed-price L £13.95/D £16.95. ☺ H/wine £9.45.
Times: Last L 2.30pm/D 10pm
Additional: Bar meals; Sunday L; Children welcome; ⑤ dishes
Smoking: No-smoking area; air-conditioning
Accommodation: 125 en suite
Credit cards: ▆ ▆ ▆ ▆ ▆ ⊆

WARRINGTON,
Rockfield Hotel

Delightful family-run hotel set in attractive grounds. Swiss dishes reflect Thomas Züger's origins; look out for onion soup from Basle, Zurich geschnetzeltes, and the fondues on the extensive carte. Otherwise there are steaks, fish and vegetarian dishes.

Additional: Sunday lunch; Children welcome; ❸ dishes
Smoking: No-smoking area
Accommodation: 12 en suite
Credit cards: ▆ ▆ ▆ ▆

Directions: From M6/J20 take A50 (Warrington) to fork with A56 (1.50 miles). Turn L into Victoria Rd. Alexandra Rd is 60 yds on R.

Alexandra Road
Grappenhall WA4 2EL
Map 7: SJ68
Tel: 01925 262898
Fax: 01925 263343
Chef: Thomas Züger
Owners: Thomas & Esther Züger
Cost: Alc £16, fixed-price D £16. ☺
H/wine £8.95.
Times: 7pm-last D 9pm. Closed L Mon-Sat

WILMSLOW, **Bank Square** ❀❀

As the name suggests, previously a bank, one of many still in existence in this area of upmarket Wilmslow. A bustling bar on the ground floor, operates as a café bar during the day (popular with shoppers), with the informally smart restaurant upstairs- parquet floor, plain white walls. There's good sourcing of ingredients with fish delivered daily by Neave of Fleetwood and meat from Donald Russell. Distinct and clear flavours appeared to be the hallmark of the kitchen at inspection. Note a meal that took in coarse duck liver pâté with a spicy chutney, a sauté of fresh ceps mixed into home-made spaghetti with poached Pacific oysters, roasted rump of lamb sliced onto crispy shredded cabbage and topped with diced tomato and marjoram, roasted halibut on a 'delicious' creamy risotto generously packed with large pieces of lobster and surrounded by a red wine vanilla jus, and apple Tatin and prune and Armagnac parfait.

4-6 Bank Square SK9 1AN
Map 7: SJ88
Tel: 01625 539754
Telephone for details

WILMSLOW, **Stanneylands** ❀❀

Stanneylands Road SK9 4EY
Map 7: SJ88
Tel: 01625 525225
Fax: 01625 537282
Chef: James Lally
Owner: Gordon Beech
Cost: Alc £29.50, fixed-price L £13.50/D £35 (7 courses). H/wine £12
Times: 12.30pm-last L 2pm/7pm-last D 9.45pm. Closed D Sun
Additional: Sunday L; Children welcome; ❸ dishes
Seats: 80. Private dining room 100. Jacket and tie preferred
Accommodation: 32 en suite
Credit cards: ▆ ▆ ▆ ▆ ▆ ▆

A privately-owned hotel with polished, professional service. Oak panelling and classical decor may typify the restaurant decor, but the kitchen concentrates on contemporary dishes; indeed, food is taken very seriously. Expect main courses such as roasted breast of corn-fed chicken with pea risotto and crisp pancetta bacon, seared calves' liver with creamed pulses and fried sage beignets, and steamed sea bass with fennel and a sweet onion relish. Starters are equally impressive. Try rillettes of red mullet with basil on black olive tapenade, or smoked and roasted loin of rabbit with a ginger and apple salad. A separate menu of British cheeses is available as an alternative to desserts. The long wine list displays an impressive depth and variety, and offers plenty of half-bottles as well as quality vintages from around the world.

Directions: M56/J5, straight on at roundabout. Follow signs for Wilmslow & Moss Nook. At traffic lights R, through Styal, L at sign for Handford onto Station Rd. Follow into Stanneylands Rd, hotel on R

WILMSLOW,

Pinewood Thistle

A modern, well appointed hotel set in spacious grounds a short distance from Manchester Airport. An inspection meal in the Terrace restaurant included pheasant and apricot galantine, and rosettes of lamb baked in poppy seed pastry crusts with a sweet redcurrant sauce.

Accommodation: 58 en suite
Credit cards: ▆▆ ▆▆ ▆▆ ▆▆ ▆ ▆

Directions: 3 miles from M56/J5 turn off A34 onto B5358 towards Wilmslow. Hotel on L before Handforth Station

180 Wilmslow Road SK9 3LG
Map 7: SJ88
Tel: 01625 529211
Fax: 01625 536812
Chef: Ian Mitchell
Cost: Alc £23, fixed-price D £17.50.
☺ H/wine £9.90.
Times: Last L 2pm/last D 9.45pm
Additional: Sunday L; Children welcome; ❹ dishes
Smoking: No smoking in dining room; air-conditioning

CORNWALL & ISLES OF SCILLY

ALTARNUN, Penhallow Manor

A small Georgian-style house dating back to 1842. The restaurant's well-balanced menu features local fish, meat and game, and is complemented by a carefully selected wine list. Expect dishes such as smoked mackerel pâté with gooseberry conserve, and baked fillet of turbot with lemon and parsley.

Directions: From Launceston A30 8 miles; 1 mile after B3257 take slip road to Altarnun, hotel near church

Penhallow PL15 7SJ
Map 2: SX28
Tel: 01566 86206
Fax: 01566 86179
Telephone for details

BRYHER, Hell Bay Hotel

Part of an old farmhouse, the original cosy beamed restaurant opens into a spacious room with dramatic views of the Atlantic Ocean and headlands. Local produce features, including plenty of fish and seafood. Fillets of sole make a fine main course with lobster sauce, crab feuilleté and fresh vegetables.

Additional: Bar L; No children under 5; ❹ dishes
Smoking: No smoking in dining room
Accommodation: 11 en suite.
Credit cards: ▆▆ ▆▆ ▆▆

Directions: By boat from main island of St Mary's

Isles of Scilly TR23 0PR
Map 2: SW17
Tel: 01720 422947
Fax: 01720 423004
Chef: David Edge
Owner: Mrs Atkinson
Cost: Fixed-price D £21 (4 courses).
☺ H/wine £10.
Times: 7.15pm-last D 8.45pm.
Closed end Oct-Mar

CALSTOCK,

Danescombe Valley ❀❀

Set alongside a beautiful bend in the River Tamar, near the great viaduct, the nineteenth-century villa has been a hotel ever since it was built. Reminiscent of a plantation home, with verandas and balconies, guests can relax with a pre-dinner drink in either the slate-floored bar, by the wood-burning stove, or on one of the comfy sofas in the sitting room. Anna Smith takes back-seat in the kitchen nowadays, but three talented chefs have taken over. The no-choice, four-course menu has developed a more Cal-Ital note with dishes such as warm duck breast with cranberry salad, and marinaded chicken with a lime and honey mint sauce with mixed wild and basmati rice, oven-roasted ratatouille and fine beans, or the menu might be built around saddle of roe deer with port sauce, or lamb with a mustard and herb crust. West Country unpasteurised farmhouse cheeses are outstanding. The wine list is notable for its selection of Italian wines.

Lower Kelly
PL18 9RY
Map 2: SX46
Tel: 01822 832414
Fax: 01822 832446
Chefs: Chris Drew, Melissa Haywood, Jill Urwin
Owners: Martin & Anna Smith
Cost: Fixed-price D £30 (4 courses). H/wine £9.60
Times: D only, 7.30pm-last D 8pm. Closed Nov-Mar
Additional: No children under 12
Seats: 12
Smoking: No smoking in dining room
Accommodation: 5 en suite
Credit cards: ▆ ▆ ▆ ▆ ▆ ▆

Directions: 0.5 mile west of Calstock village along lane next to river

CONSTANTINE,

Trengilly Wartha Inn ❀❀

TR11 5RP
Map 2: SW
Tel: 01326 340332
Fax: 01326 340332
Chef: Mike Maguire
Owners: Mike & Helen Maguire, Nigel & Isabel Logan
Cost: Fixed-price D £21.50. ☺
Times: Last L 2.15pm/D 9.30pm. Closed 25 Dec
Additional: Bar meals; Sunday L; Children welcome; ❹ dishes
Seats: 28
Accommodation: 6 (5 en suite)
Credit cards: ▆ ▆ ▆ ▆ ▆ ▆

A bustling country inn set in the seclusion of a deep wooded valley, with views down towards Polpenwith Creek on the Helford river. There is an atmospheric, dark wooded bar that offers an extensive fish-centred menu, and a smart pastel green restaurant where more serious cooking is served. The kitchen delivers punchy, modern English dishes such as roast saddle of wild rabbit stuffed with home-dried tomatoes and green peppercorns, grilled fillet of sea bass, served on a soft saffron risotto with braised broad beans, and rosette of Scottish salmon with a light shellfish cream sauce. Wine is a passion here, to the extent that the owners have set up a small merchant operation as a sideline. The wine list boasts depth and character, with many good bottles from Europe (in particular the Spanish selection) and a number of wines available by the half-bottle.

Directions: In Constantine village turn L at top of hill, follow signs for Gweek, one mile out of village turn L, follow signposts to hotel.

CONSTANTINE BAY, Treglos Hotel ❀

Friendly, family-run hotel overlooking the spectacular North Cornwall coastline. The restaurant specialises in local produce, notably fresh fish. A recent test meal highlighted a robust fish bisque and a delicious roast leg of lamb with cranberry and orange preserve.

Smoking: No smoking in dining room; air conditioning
Accommodation: 44 en suite. **Credit cards:** ▆ ▆

Directions: Take B3276 (Constantine Bay). At village stores turn right, hotel is 50 yards on left

Padstow PL28 8JH
Map 2: SW87
Tel: 01841 520727
Fax: 01841 521163
Chef: Paul Becker
Owners: Mr J Barlow
Cost: *Alc* £30, fixed-price L £11.50/D £22. ☺ H/wine £9.
Times: Last L 1.30pm/D 9.15pm.
Additional: Bar meals; Sunday L; No children under 7 at D; ❹ dishes

FALMOUTH,
Falmouth Beach Resort

From its unrivalled beach-side position this popular hotel has a spectacular view of Falmouth Bay. Crab bisque, escalopes of lamb with Madeira sauce and crème brûlée could be a typical meal in Ospreys. There is also a popular carvery.

Smoking: No smoking in dining room
Accommodation: 125 en suite. **Credit cards:** ■■ ■■ ■■ ■■ 🄟 £

Directions: From A39 to Falmouth follow signs to seafront and Gyllyngvase Beach. Hotel opposite Gyllyngvase Beach

Gyllyngvase Beach TR11 4NA
Map 2: SW83
Tel: 01326 318084
Fax: 01326 319147
Chef: Nick Preston
Owner: David Evans
Cost: Alc £22.90. H/wine £7.60. ☺
Times: Last L 2pm/last D 11pm
Additional: Sunday L; Bar meals; No children under 6; 🍴 dishes

FALMOUTH, **Greenbank Hotel**

There are unrivalled views of Falmouth Harbour from this spacious hotel restaurant. The interior achieves a colonial effect with cane furniture and lush greenery. Seafood figures prominently, and dishes include Helford mussels, with saffron and West Country cider, and monkfish provençale with a white wine, tomato and tarragon sauce.

Smoking: No cigars or pipes
Accommodation: 61 en suite. **Credit cards:** ■■ ■■ ■■ 🄟 £

Directions: 500yds past Falmouth Marina overlooking the water

Harbourside TR11 2SR
Map 2: SW83
Tel: 01326 312440
Fax: 01326 211362
Chef: Richard Kevern
Owner: Nigel Gebhard
Cost: Alc £22.45, fixed-price L £9/ D £18.95. ☺ H/wine £7.95.
Times: Last L 2pm/D 9.45pm Closed 23 Dec-10 Jan
Additional: Bar Food; Sunday L; Children welcome; 🍴 dishes

FALMOUTH, **Penmere Manor**

A listed building of historic importance set in five acres of sub-tropical gardens and woodlands. The restaurant is romantically set amid huge indoor plants and paintings of famous Cornish gardens. There is a good choice of modern English dishes, including plenty of seafood, and an extensive list of wines.

Mongleath Road TR11 4PN
Map 2: SW83
Tel: 01326 211411
Fax: 01326 317588
Chef: Stephen Mather
Owners: Andrew Pope, Elizabeth Rose
Cost: Alc £21, fixed-price L £10.75/D £19. ☺ H/wine £7.25.
Times: Last L 2pm/D 9pm. Closed 23-27 December
Additional: Bar food; Sunday L; Children welcome; 🍴 dishes
Smoking: No smoking in dining room
Accommodation: 38 en suite
Credit cards: ■■ ■■ ■■ ■■ 🄟 £

Directions: Turn L into Mongleath Road off A39 1 mile after Hill Head roundabout

FALMOUTH,
Pennypots Restaurant ⊛⊛⊛

After their move from Blackwater, Kevin and Jane Viner are now firmly ensconced in Maenporth. The light airy restaurant is just across the road from the beach and there are glorious views of Falmouth Bay from the large patio windows fronting the dining room. White oak wood, blue and ivory colour schemes

Maenporth Beach TR11 5HN
Map 2: SW83
Tel/Fax: 01326 250251
Chef: Kevin Viner
Owners: Kevin & Jane Viner
Cost: Fixed-price D £26.50. H/wine £8.50

and comfortable rattan-backed chairs unpholstered in classy velvet signal that this is a serious venue, although the inanimate bears perched on top of the loo doors and gazing down from every corner add a touch of whimsy. The formula of a short repertoire, fixed-price for two or three courses is unchanged from the Blackwater days, and Kevin's cooking is based resolutely on top-notch raw materials from local sources. Fish is a strong suit, whether it be a single scallop, roasted and sliced into the thinnest of rings with an oriental sauce tweaked with herbs and garlic, or an inspired creation involving a little tower of smoked salmon and crab topped with a dot or two of mock caviar and set on a melon vinaigrette, or even something as simple as a lobster (pincer-clawed fresh from the boats), grilled with garlic and herb butter. Other dishes show that Kevin knows how to make sauces: grilled duck breast with confit of the leg and big plump blueberries on a rich red wine jus, or grilled loin of lamb with 'heavenly' sweetbreads on a delicate thyme and tomato reduction, for example. As for dessert, crème brûlée laced with cognac comes highly recommended, although the real star is a signature dish, bread-and-butter pudding with a dollop of clotted cream. Jane Viner tends front of house and keeps an eagle eye on proceedings. House wines are worth ordering and the extensive list provides plenty of half-bottles.

Signature dishes: Steamed sea bass with a saffron and vermouth sauce; fillet of venison, roasted and served on a cognac and prune sauce with spiced pears.

Directions: 3 miles S of Falmouth, follow signs for Maenporth

Times: D only, 7pm-last D 9.30pm.
Closed Sun, Mon, 4 wks winter
Additional: Children welcome;
🍴 dishes
Seats: 40
Smoking: Air-conditioning
Credit cards: ▀ ▀ ▀ ▀ ▀ ▀

FALMOUTH,

Royal Duchy Hotel 🏵🏵

Cliff Road TR11 4NX
Map 2: SW83
Tel/Fax: 01326 319420
Chef: Des Turland
Owner: Mr P Brend
Cost: *Alc* £20, fixed-price L £9.75/D £20. ☺ H/wine £8.25.
Times: Last L 2pm/D 9pm
Additional: Bar food L; Sunday lunch; Children welcome; 🍴 dishes
Seats: 90. Jacket and tie preferred
Smoking: No pipes & cigars
Accommodation: 44 en suite
Credit cards: ▀ ▀ ▀ ▀ ▀ ▀

A fine period hotel commanding spectacular sea views from its cliff top position close to the town. Interesting menus show a serious approach to cooking. From a menu that takes in seafood ravioli, wild mushroom soup, and pork with a smooth, well balanced cider and chive butter sauce, our inspector chose creamed smoked chicken and watercress soup, steamed fillets of Cornish lemon sole with a delicate lemon, chervil and vermouth sauce, and a superb warm caramelised pear tart served piping hot with a bitter chocolate sauce and 'a dollop' of Poire William ice cream. Polished service.

Directions: Hotel is at Castle end of Promenade

FOWEY, **Food for Thought**

The quayside setting, and the views over the estuary are a major draw, but the cooking at Martin and Caroline Billingsley's delightful little restaurant continues to impress inspectors. Inside, the stone walls, wooden beams and open fire create just the right, warm atmosphere. Unsurprisingly, fresh seafood features prominently, with crab and langoustine, moules marinière and fish soup leading the starters, with perhaps goat's cheese and red pepper salad as an alternative. Main courses are dependent on the day's catch and could take in sea bass with shell fish and saffron cream sauce, or monkfish with olive oil, garlic, tomato and basil. Rack of lamb and crispy duck are favourite meat options. Desserts include bread-and-butter pudding and clotted cream and sticky toffee pudding.

Directions: Walk down to the quay from the town centre car park

The Quay PL23 1AT
Map 2: SX15
Tel: 01726 832221
Fax: 01726 832060
Chef: Martin Billingsley
Owner: Martin & Caroline Billingsley
Cost: *Alc* £30, fixed-price D £16.95. H/wine £7.50
Times: 7pm-last D 9pm. Closed Sun, 23 Dec-mid March
Seats: 38
Smoking: Air-conditioning
Credit cards:

FOWEY, **Fowey Hotel** 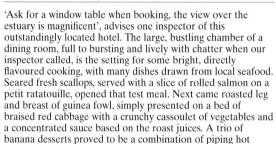 **NEW**

'Ask for a window table when booking, the view over the estuary is magnificent', advises one inspector of this outstandingly located hotel. The large, bustling chamber of a dining room, full to bursting and lively with chatter when our inspector called, is the setting for some bright, directly flavoured cooking, with many dishes drawn from local seafood. Seared fresh scallops, served with a slice of rolled salmon on a petit ratatouille, opened that test meal. Next came roasted leg and breast of guinea fowl, simply presented on a bed of braised red cabbage with a crunchy cassoulet of vegetables and a concentrated sauce based on the roast juices. A trio of banana desserts proved to be a combination of piping hot banana fritter, a warm banana profiterole, and an intense banana ice cream.

The Esplanade PL23 1HX
Tel: 01726 832551
Fax: 01726 832125
Telephone for details

FOWEY, **Marina Hotel**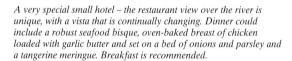

A very special small hotel – the restaurant view over the river is unique, with a vista that is continually changing. Dinner could include a robust seafood bisque, oven-baked breast of chicken loaded with garlic butter and set on a bed of onions and parsley and a tangerine meringue. Breakfast is recommended.

Seats: 32
Smoking: No smoking in dining room
Accommodation: 11 en suite
Credit cards:

Directions: From A38 Dobwalls take A390 to St Austell. At Lostwithiel take B3269 to Fowey

Esplanade, Fowey, PL23 1HY
Map 2: SX15
Tel: 01726 833315
Fax: 01726 832779
Chef: Steven Vincent
Owners: John & Carol Roberts
Cost: *Alc* £20, fixed-price D £16 (3 courses). ☺ H/wine £8.95.
Times: 7pm- 8.30pm. Closed L, Jan/Feb
Additional: No children under 10; 🍴 dishes

GILLAN, **Tregildry Hotel**

From its elevated position, Tregildry takes in spectacular sea views, and there is direct access from the hotel grounds to the beach and coastal footpaths. Modern ideas abound in the kitchen, which builds menus around local produce. Fresh Cornish fish appears with caramelised red cabbage, for example, or local mushrooms are marinated in lemon juice

Gillan TR12 6HG
Map 2: SW52
Tel: 01326 231378
Fax: 01326 231561
Chef: Huw Phillips
Owners: Huw & Lynne Phillips
Cost: Fixed-price D £19.50 (4 courses). ☺ H/wine £9.75.

and garlic and cooked in butter and cream, and there are Cornish ice creams or West Country cheeses. The short choice, fixed-price dinner menu tries to take in all tastes. The adventurous will note spiced chicken and coconut soup, and pan-fried magret of duck breast glazed with honey and served with a fresh mango, ginger and soy sauce, whilst the traditionalists will opt for home-made country pâté with spiced chutney, and chargrilled ribeye steak with French fries and mixed salad.

Directions: A3083 from Helston (Lizard Road), take 1st L for St Keverne. Follow signs for Manaccan and Gillan

Times: D only, 7pm-last D 8.45pm.
Closed Nov-Feb
Additional: No children under 8;
🍷 dishes
Seats: 30
Smoking: No smoking in dining room
Accommodation: 10 en suite
Credit cards: 🔳 🔳 🔳 🔳

GOLANT, Cormorant Hotel ❀❀

This must be one of the loveliest spots in Britain. The hotel lies above the unspoilt fishing village of Golant and makes the most of the stunning views over the Fowey Estuary; every bedroom has a full length picture window. This is a relaxed, delightful place. The kitchen builds its menus around the best of Cornwall's fresh produce with the emphasis on fish, and has built up a sound reputation. Local crab and moules marinière, fillet of sea bass on a Pernod, cream and pink peppercorn sauce, whole bass with fennel and provençale herbs, and Fowey salmon, are typical offerings, whilst chargrilled fillet steak comes from a Cornish protected herd, or there's rack of Cornish lamb roasted with rosemary and black pepper crust for meat eaters.

Directions: Turn from A390 St Austell Rd onto B3269 to Fowey. Turn L to Golant. Go to end (almost to water's edge), entrance on R

Fowey PL23 1LL
Map 2: SX15
Tel/Fax: 01726 833426
Chef: John Keen, George Elworthy
Owners: Mr & Mrs G Elworthy
Cost: Fixed-price D £16.50. ☺
H/wine £9.50.
Times: Last L 2pm/D 9pm
Additional: Bar food L; Sunday L;
Children welcome; 🍷 dishes
Seats: 25
Smoking: No smoking in dining room
Accommodation: 11 en suite
Credit cards: 🔳 🔳 🔳 🔳 🔳

HELSTON, Nansloe Manor ❀❀

Charming, small eighteenth-century manor standing in four acres of well-tended gardens and wooded grounds. There is a highly professional stamp to the whole family-run organisation. Inspection included accurately cooked salmon with butter sauce and a decent fish soup with rouille and croûtons. A particularly wide choice of desserts might include potted Kirsch and cherry scented mousse with a zingy orange sauce, and iced rum and raisin parfait set in a dark chocolate cup served on a sweet blackcurrant compote – and if you wish, you can have a dollop of clotted cream on them all.

Directions: 300yds from junction of A394 and A3083 down a well-signed drive

Meneage Road, Helston, Cornwall, TR13 0SB
Map 2: SW62
Tel: 01326 574691
Fax: 01326 564680
Chef: Howard Ridden
Owners: The Ridden family
Cost: *Alc* £25, fixed-price L £12. ☺
H/wine £10.40.
Times: Noon-last L 1.30pm/ 7pm-last
D 8.30pm
Additional: Bar meals L; Sunday L;
No children under 12; 🍷 dishes.
Seats: 40
Smoking: No smoking in dining room
Accommodation: 7 (6 en suite)
Credit cards: 🔳 🔳 🔳 🔳

LISKEARD, Pencubitt Country House Hotel ❀❀

A Victorian country house in an elevated position, with magnificent views of the East Looe valley, yet secluded in two acres of mature landscaped gardens. The restaurant is gaining a reputation locally for imaginative five-course dinners that are built around quality local ingredients where possible. Dinner in May produced a smooth chicken liver parfait, then a light broth with finely diced vegetables and infused with fresh herbs,

Station Road PL14 4EB
Map 2: SX26
Tel: 01579 342694
Chef: Michael Kent
Owners: M & C Kent
Cost: Fixed-price D £18.50. ☺
H/wine £10.
Times: D only, 7pm-8.30pm.
Closed Xmas

Pencubitt Country House Hotel

Additional: No children under 12
Seats: 30
Smoking: No smoking in dining room
Accommodation: 8 en suite
Credit cards: ▨ ▨

a centrepiece of pan-fried breast of duck, cooked pink but with a crisp skin, and served with spinach, fresh pineapple, a red wine sauce, and dusted with five-spice and, from puddings displayed on a table in the dining room, a strawberry Pavlova, with West Country cheeses to follow. There's a shortish wine list with a few half bottles and a pleasant 'very drinkable' French house wine.

Directions: Follow BR Park & Ride signs. Hotel signs visible 250 yds from rail station on B3254

LISKEARD,
Well House Hotel ✿✿✿

St Keyne PL14 4RN
Map 2: SX26
Tel: 01579 342001
Fax: 01579 343891
Chef: Cameron Brown
Owner: Nick Wainford, Ione Nurdin
Cost: Fixed-price L&D £21.95 (2 courses) £26.95 (3 courses). H/wine £8.50
Times: 12.30pm-last L 1.45pm/7pm-last D 8.45pm
Additional: No children under 8 at D; ◐ dishes
Seats: 32
Smoking: No-smoking area
Accommodation: 9 en suite
Credit cards: ▨ ▨ ▨ ▨ ▨ ▨

Nicholas Wainford's personable presence and hospitality count for a great deal in this turn-of-the-century house built on the site of St Keyne's legendary well. Tranquillity prevails and the views out towards the Looe valley are a dream. A number of personnel changes have bedevilled the kitchen of late, but proceedings seem to be back on an even keel with the arrival of Cameron Brown. The formula is simple: menus are priced according to the number of courses taken. Events kick off with cracking little canapés – perhaps a beef kebab served hot with green peppers cooked in soy, a tiny tartlet of salmon and avocado in heavenly light pastry, and a crispy croûton with apple in a mayonnaise – not to mention great breads professionally shaped into knots. A test meal proved a duck and pork terrine served on onion marmalade to be a successful starter, but the main course was clearly in a different league – collops of monkfish had been topped with a brioche crust, roasted to perfection and appeared on the plate with squid ink tagliatelle, tiny concasse of tomato and an uncloying lobster sauce. 'A sensation'. West Country cheeses from Tavistock are alternatives to desserts such as peach brûlée laced with peach brandy and topped with ultra-thin caramel. Good cafetière coffee comes with classy petits fours, clearly based on really high quality chocolate. The wine list has a noticeable French bias, with clarets showing the owner's personal preference. Yet a good few wines from the rest of Europe and the New World, a fair number are priced at under £20, and over a dozen halves are listed. House wines are from France, Australia and Chile.

Directions: At St Keyne Church follow signs to St Keyne Well, the restaurant is 0.5 miles further

MARAZION, **Mount Haven Hotel**

Turnpike Road TR17 0DQ
Map 2: SW53
Tel: 01736 710249
Fax: 01736 711658
Chef: Simon Morley-Smith
Owners: John & Delyth James
Cost: Alc £20.25, fixed-price L £8.50/D £18.50. ☺ H/wine £8.50.
Times: Last L 1.45pm/D 9pm (8.30pm Oct-March). Closed L Oct – Mar
Additional: Bar food; Sunday L; Children welcome; ❹ dishes
Smoking: No smoking in dining room
Accommodation: 17 en suite
Credit cards: ▆ ▆ ▆ ▆ ▆

Part of this building dates back 200 years and used to be coaching house stables. The split-level restaurant, completely refurbished this year, offers an extensive choice, with an emphasis on seafood from nearby Newlyn. Dishes include fish soup, and rounds of monkfish tail poached in white wine.

Directions: Through village to end of built-up area

MAWNAN SMITH,
Budock Vean Hotel

The prospect of walks down to the Helford River – not to mention a nine-hole golf course – bring the crowds to this appealing hotel. Local produce and home-grown herbs are used effectively in generous dishes such as chicken and hazelnut terrine, fillet of beef with Madeira sauce and raspberry Romanoff. Excellent staff.

Additional: Sunday L only; Bar meals: Children welcome: ❹ dishes
Smoking: No smoking in dining room
Accommodation: 58 en suite
Credit cards: ▆ ▆ ▆ ▆ ▆

Mawnan Smith
TR11 5LG
Map 2: SW72
Tel: 01326 250288
Fax: 01326 250892
Chef: Darren Kelly
Owners: Messrs. K, C & M Barlow
Cost: Alc £29.50, fixed-price D £19.50 (4 courses). ☺ H/wine £9.
Times: Last L 2.15pm (bar)/9pm. Closed 3-31 Jan

Directions: Three miles S of Falmouth. Straight on at Mawnan Smith for 1.5 miles. Hotel on L

MAWNAN SMITH,

Meudon Hotel

Late-Victorian mansion set in sub-tropical gardens leading down to Bream Cove and the sea. Local fish is the star of the show in the elegant conservatory restaurant, otherwise expect duck liver pâté, cauliflower and Shropshire Blue soup, roast fillet of pork with onion confit and desserts such as chocolate mousse.

Additional: Bar food only L Mon-Sat; Sunday L; Children welcome; ✿ dishes
Smoking: No-smoking area
Accommodation: 29 en suite
Credit cards: ▬ ▒ ▒ ▒ ▒ ▒

Directions: Take A39 towards Falmouth. At Hillhead roundabout turn L; Meudon is 4 miles on L

Mawnan Smith
TR11 5HT
Map 2: SW72
Tel: 01326 250541
Fax: 01326 250543
Chef: Alan Webb
Owner: Mr Harry Pilgrim
Cost: Fixed-price L £15 /D £25. H/wine £10
Times: Last L 2pm/last D 9pm. Closed Dec-Feb

MAWNAN SMITH,

Trelawne Hotel

Mawnan Smith TR11 5HS
Map 2: SW72
Tel: 01326 250226
Fax: 01326 250909
Chef: Nigel Woodland
Owners: Mr & Mrs Gibbons, Mr & Mrs Bond
Cost: Fixed-price D £18.50. H/wine £8.50
Times: 12.30pm-last L 1.30pm/7pm-last D 8.30pm. Closed 23 Dec-12 Feb
Additional: Bar food L; Children welcome; ✿ dishes
Seats: 36
Smoking: No smoking in dining room
Accommodation: 14 en suite
Credit cards: ▬ ▒ ▒ ▒ ▒ ▒

In an enviable position between the Fal and the Helford River, with superb views over the coastline to the Lizard, this friendly hotel has been in the Gibbons family for almost a quarter of a century. The kitchen team hasn't been in residence quite as long, but the cooking remains on course. A new restaurant called The Hutches (after a group of rocks lying off the coast close to the hotel) is the setting for meals that highlight local produce. 'A daily harvest from land or sea' might feature, say, roast fillet of salmon with white wine and dill cream or sauté of calves' liver with lamb's sweetbreads and bordelaise jus. Otherwise, the repertoire extends to ravioli of seafood finished in a cappuccino of crab and chervil, breast of chicken with chargrilled vegetables and a coriander pesto, and magret of duckling with port and lime sauce and roasted plums. Rounding things off are desserts such as hot banana mille-feuille with coconut ice cream and chilled lemon soufflé with fresh strawberries in Kirsch syrup. More than 100 wines provide sound drinking across the range.

Directions: Three miles S of Falmouth on coast road to Mawnan Smith

MOUNT HAWKE, Tregarthen
Country Cottage Hotel

A cottage-style hotel in pleasant rural surroundings, serving traditionally cooked food from a set menu. A summer meal began with broccoli and Stilton soup with a freshly baked roll, followed by roast pork with apple sauce, and a home-made apple and almond tart with whipped cream.

Accommodation: 6 en suite
Credit cards: None

Directions: From the A30 turn off at Three Burrows roundabout onto the B3277 St Agnes road, take first left and follow signs to Mount Hawke, approx 2m

Map 2: SW56
Tel: 01209 890399
Fax: 01209 891041
Chef: Mrs Hutton
Owners: Mr & Mrs C Hutton
Cost: Fixed-price D £12. ☺
Times: D only, 7pm-last D 9pm. Closed Xmas week
Additional: Children welcome; ● dishes
Smoking: No smoking in dining room

MOUSEHOLE, Cornish Range

Charming, seaside village setting for former pilchard press specialising in fish and seafood. The cooking is constant and the apparent simplicity of dishes such as moules marinière, smoked salmon parcels with crab and prawns, fish pie and crab Florentine belies the quality of ingredients and the serious intent of the kitchen.

Additional: Sunday L (winter only); Children welcome; . ● dishes
Smoking: No-smoking area
Credit cards: ▬ ▭ ▬ ▢

Directions: Mousehole is 3 miles from Penzance, via Newlyn

6 Chapel Street TR19 6SB
Map 2: SW42
Tel: 01736 731488
Fax: 01736 732255
Chef: David Rashleigh
Owner: Sue Perry
Cost: £20. H/wine £9.25. ☺
Times: D only, 6.30pm-9.30pm (summer)/7pm-9pm (Thu-Sat only, winter)

MOUSEHOLE,
Old Coastguard Inn

The Parade TR19 6PR
Map 2: SW42
Tel: 01736 731222
Fax: 01736 731720
Chef: Mrs A Wood
Owners: PS Wood, AW Treloar
Cost: Fixed-price L&D £16.50. ☺ H/wine £7.95.
Times: Last L 2.30pm/D 9.30pm. Closed Jan to end Feb for L
Additional: Bar meals; Children welcome; ● dishes
Smoking: No smoking in dining room
Accommodation: 23 en suite
Credit cards: ▬ ▬ ▬ ▢

Fish is the order of the day at this relaxing old inn whose gardens run down to the sea. Crab and fish soup, grilled scallops and salmon with a warm lemon dressing, and monkfish baked with olive oil and chopped fennel show a lively approach. Duck breast with port wine sauce, and fillet steak with herb butter for meat eaters.

Directions: From Penzance take coast road through Newlyn. Inn 1st large building on L as you enter the village, just after public carpark

NEWQUAY,
Corisande Manor

A Victorian manor house built for an Austrian count. Ships' timbers were used as roof beams in the restaurant, which overlooks the Gannel estuary and the sea. The best fresh ingredients give the food real flavour and the short menu offers an imaginative choice of dishes. There is also a remarkable range of wines.

Times: D only at 8pm
Additional: Children welcome
Smoking: No smoking in dining room
Accommodation: 12 en suite
Credit cards: ▪️ ▪️ ▪️ ▫️

Riverside Avenue,
Pentire TR7 1PL
Map 2: SW86
Tel: 01637 872042
Fax: 01637 874557
Chef: Chris Grant
Owners: David & Chris Grant
Cost: Fixed-price D £18. ☺ H/wine £9.50.

Directions: Off the main road down the Pentire headland, left at Newquay Nursing Home into Pentire Crescent, then R into Riverside Avenue

NEWQUAY, **Hotel Bristol**

Narrowcliff TR7 2PQ
Map 2: SW86
Tel: 01637 875181
Fax: 01637 879347
Chef: Malcolm Jackson
Owners: The Young family
Cost: *Alc* £18.50, fixed-price L £11/D £18.50. ☺ H/wine £8.50.
Times: Last L 1.45pm/D 8.45pm
Additional: Bar food L; Sunday L; No children under 4; ☺ dishes
Accommodation: 74 en suite
Credit cards: ▪️ ▪️ ▪️ ▪️ ▫️ ▫️

For 75 years the Young family have run this traditional seaside hotel, popular for summer holidays and conferences in quieter months. The daily changing menu offers the likes of fresh asparagus mayonnaise, cream of parsnip and fennel soup, fried North Coast seafood platter with sauce rémoulade, jam roly poly, and cheese to finish.

Directions: From A30 take A39 then A392. Turn R onto A3058 and follow signs for seafront hotels for 2.5 miles along Henver Road and Narrowcliff

NEWQUAY, **Whipsiderry Hotel**

A short fixed-price menu is served each evening at this comfortable hotel, noted for home-cooked dishes such as individual lamb lasagne, and brill and mushrooms served in a puff pastry case with a crab sauce. To finish, there is a selection of gâteaux and patisseries, or the cheeseboard.

Trevelgue Road TR7 3LY
Map 2: SW86
Tel: 01637 874777
Chefs: Lisa Burbidge, David Evens
Owners: R E and A H Drackford
Credit cards: ▪️ ▪️ ▪️ ▫️
Telephone for further details

Directions: Take B3267 (Padstow) and turn R 0.5 mile out of Newquay

PADSTOW,

Old Custom House Inn

A fine quayside hotel, which boasts a popular restaurant and a lively bar. The menu features a mix of English and classical French dishes, with an emphasis on fresh fish. Expect grilled fillet of turbot with mango and garlic beurre blanc, baked monkfish in filo pastry, and medallion of pork with cider and basil.

Smoking: No smoking in dining room; air conditioning
Accommodation: 26 en suite
Credit cards: ▆ ▆ ▆ ▆ ▆ ▆

Directions: From Wadebridge take A389 (Padstow). Second turning on R after Padstow school, go round sharp bend at bottom of hill. Restaurant is opposite entrance to harbour car park

South Quay
PL28 8ED
Map 2: SW97
Tel: 01841 532359
Fax: 01841 533372
Chef: Neil Markram
Owners: St Austell Brewery
Cost: Alc £18. ☺ H/wine £6.25.
Times: Last L 2pm/D 9.30pm.
Closed 1 May
Additional: Sunday L; Bar meals;
Children welcome; ◑ dishes

PADSTOW, St Petroc's House

Part of Rick Stein's growing local empire, with The Seafood Restaurant (see entry) as its flagship, this casual bistro is in what is one of the oldest buildings in town. Informality rules, with paper napkins on the tables, staff dressed in polo-type shirts and modern art on the walls. The short menu changes regularly and you can order three courses or a single dish. Fish looms large in the shape of, say, deep-fried squid with aïoli, grey mullet with garlic, chilli and virgin olive oil or grilled fillet of hake on a mound of buttered cabbage and bacon. Away from the sea, there might also be tomato and basil soup – 'a sensation', commented one inspector – confit of duck with caramelised red cabbage, and steak with frites. Desserts are simple things like sticky toffee pudding or lemon tart. Coffee is reckoned to be a 'fabulous' brew. Around 30 wines are lively, modern and eminently affordable.

Directions: Follow one-way around harbour, take 1st L, situated on the R

4 New Street PL28 8EA
Map 2: SW97
Tel: 01841 532700
Fax: 01841 532942
Chef: Jason Fretwell
Owner: Rick & Jill Stein
Cost: Fixed-price L&D £17.95 (3 courses). ☺ H/wine £10.50.
Times: 12.30pm-last L 1.30pm/7pm-last D 9.30pm. Closed Mon, Xmas
Additional: Sunday lunch; Children welcome
Seats: 38. Private dining room 10
Smoking: No smoking in restaurant
Accommodation: 26 en suite
Credit cards: ▆ ▆ ▆ ▆

PADSTOW,

The Seafood Restaurant

Rick Stein's TV fame has put the fishing village of Padstow on the map, and brought people from far and wide to visit his celebrated seafood restaurant. Menus change twice daily, geared around what fish is available, with the more imaginative dishes available at dinner. The hallmark of the cooking is tiptop freshness plus simplicity of technique; the unfussy style was displayed in a first course of steamed, sweet and succulent scallops served in their shells à la chinoise with a very lightly flavoured jus of ginger, soya, sesame and spring onions. One of the most popular choices is the dramatic-looking platter of fruits de mer, a stunning selection of shellfish served with mayonnaise and shallot vinegar. Puddings are a particular delight with a light, smooth, vanilla-flavoured pana cotta served balanced by tart stewed rhubarb, and a 'yummy' bacardi and white chocolate torte being particularly enjoyed. The restaurant itself has a bright summery feel created by the clever use of mirrors,

Riverside PL28 8BY
Map 2: SW97
Tel: 01841 532485
Chef: Rick Stein
Owners: R & J Stein
Cost: Alc £40, fixed-price L £26.50/D £32.50. H/wine £10.95
Times: Noon-last L 2pm/7pm-last D 10pm. Closed Sun, 14 Dec-7 Feb
Additional: No children under 5
Seats: 75
Accommodation: 10 en suite
Credit cards: ▆ ▆ ▆ ▆

colourful prints, crisp linen and wicker chairs. The buzz goes on from midday to midnight – this is still a great experience. Not surprisingly white wines feature strongly on the wine list and an opening page lists a dozen wines 'of the moment' – half of them well priced at under £16. Try the much fêted Ch de Sours rosé from Esme Johnstone at £13.50. A strong white Burgundy section contains big names and reputable growers, notably Olivier Leflaive and Drouhin; naturally these command considerably higher prices. The New World section is worth a look, several wines are not usual restaurant listings.

Directions: Situated on South Quay

PENZANCE, Tarbert Hotel

A good choice of food is offered at this attractive hotel, including extensive fish and vegetarian menus. Dishes range from a 16oz Dover sole baked with fresh herb butter, spinach and lentil bake, to a hunk of Cornish lamb with garlic and rosemary jus.

Additional: No children under 6; ⬥ dishes
Seats: 30. **Smoking:** No smoking in dining room
Accommodation: 12 en suite
Credit cards: ▬ ▥ ▥ 🐾

11-12 Clarence Street TR18 2NU
Map 2: SW43
Tel: 01736 363758
Fax: 01736 331336
Chef: Philip Thomas
Owners: Patti & Julian Evans
Cost: Alc £18, fixed-price D £15. ☺
H/wine £8.50.
Times: D only 7pm-last 8.30pm.
Closed Jan

Directions: At top of Market Jew St continue into Alverton St. At traffic lights turn R into Clarence St

PENZANCE,
Ward's Brasserie   NEW

Useful town centre location for this relaxed, informal brasserie. Chef/proprietor Alan Ward cooks lively food from a repertoire that is robustly modern in style but backed up by some old traditional favourites. Typical starters, for example, include Stilton and almond soufflé, terrine of local fish wrapped in toasted seaweed, and a plate of mussels in white wine and herbs. A meal in March began with a smooth chicken liver pâté, garnished with mixed leaves and served with a fruity home-made peach chutney. Catch of the day was fillet of cod, cooked with lemon grass, honey and chilli, served with mange-touts and new potatoes. For dessert, a light redcurrant posset was served with copious amounts of double Cornish cream. Other desserts include white and dark chocolate cheesecake, raspberry meringue, and West Country cheeses with apple and celery. The wine list is short and simple, featuring a small selection of bottles from both the New and Old Worlds.

12-13 Chapel Street TR18 4AW
Map 2: SW53
Tel: 01736 363540
Chef: Alan Ward
Owners: Alan & Sue Ward
Cost: Alc £17, fixed-price L £8.95. ☺
H/wine £6.50.
Times: Noon-last L 2pm/7pm-last D 10pm. Closed 2 wks Jan/Feb, D Sun-Tues (Oct-May)
Additional: Sunday L;
No children under 12; ⬥ dishes
Seats: 43
Smoking: No-smoking area
Credit cards: ▬ ▥ 🐾 ▢

Directions: In town centre

POLPERRO, The Kitchen

Sensible customers let chef-patron Ian Bateson choose for them – after all, he knows what he cooks best, and the eclectic menu is fairly extensive. The pretty pink and pine cottage restaurant, on a steep street down from the village car park, sets the tone with both fishy and foody pictures on the walls. Indeed, ingredients couldn't be fresher and everything is

The Coombes PL13 2RQ
Map 2: SX25
Tel: 01503 272780
Chefs/Owners: Ian & Vanessa Bateson
Cost: Alc £19. H/wine £9
Times: D only, 7pm-9.30pm.
Closed Sun & Mon, Nov – Easter

cooked to order, with the *carte* revolving mainly around the daily fish and seafood specials, perhaps chargrilled scallops with garlic butter, monkfish prawn and scallop Thermidor or whole lemon sole chargrilled over rosemary with lemon and herb butter. In addition there are dishes from around the world (Moroccan lamb and Thai chicken), traditional dishes (chicken suprême and roast leg of pork with scrumpy cider, apple and mustard sauce), and lots of choice for veggies. Everything is served with freshly baked bread. A summer pudding, served with a big dollop of clotted cream, arrived as a burgundy tower simply begging to be eaten and exploding with fresh fruit flavours. It's not easy to please everyone all the time, but The Kitchen pulls it off with impressive dexterity.

Additional: No children under 10; 🌢 dishes
Seats: 24
Smoking: No smoking in dining room
Credit cards: 🔳 🔤

Directions: Between the harbour and the car park

POLZEATH,
Cornish Cottage Hotel 🏵🏵

You can be sure of a warm welcome at this charming small hotel, within a short walk of spectacular cliff paths and the beach; you can also be sure of a meal of considerable sophistication. The Gourmet Restaurant lives up to its name – ravioli of langoustine is served with a saffron nage infused with chervil and presented on a bed of wild mushrooms with a medley of green vegetables, and medallions of beef fillet are laid onto a bed of pulse vegetables surrounded by a horseradish jus enhanced with brandy and served with boiled potatoes and baby turned vegetables, topped with julienne of leek. The set-price menu might include roast loin of Cornish lamb on a red onion compote with roast potatoes and tomato and basil jus, and baked escalope of cod with saffron potatoes, orange butter and coriander sauce. The effort in the kitchen is unflagging and continues apace with elaborate desserts such as 'Melody of Chocolate' – orange chocolate ganache, plain chocolate parfait and white chocolate ice-cream set on a pool of milk chocolate anglaise.

Rock Wadebridge PL27 6UF
Map 2: SW97
Tel: 01208 862213
Fax: 01208 862259

Change of CHEF

Chef: Tim Rogers

Owners: Clive & Christine Mason
Cost: *Alc* £33, fixed-price D £27.50 (5 courses). 🙂 H/wine £10.
Times: D only, 7pm-9pm. Closed Nov 15-30
Additional: Sunday L; No children under 12; 🌢 dishes
Seats: 32
Smoking: No smoking in dining room
Accommodation: 12 en suite
Credit cards: 🔳 🔤 🔤 🔳 🔳 🔳

Directions: From Wadebridge/Camelford pass the 'Bee Centre' and take the R fork. The hotel is 300 yds on R.

PORT GAVERNE,
Port Gaverne Hotel 🏵

Near Port Isaac PL29 3SQ
Map 2: SX08
Tel: 01208 880244
Fax: 01208 880151
Chef: Ian Brodey
Owner: Mrs Midge Ross
Cost: *Alc* £19.95. H/wine £6.75 🙂
Times: Last L 2pm/D 9pm. Closed early Jan-14 Feb
Additional: Bar food; Sunday L; No children under 7 in dining room; 🌢 dishes
Smoking: No smoking in dining room
Accommodation: 17 en suite
Credit cards: 🔳 🔤 🔤 🔳 🔳 🔳

Local seafood is the star turn at this 300-year-old inn nestling in a Cornish cove. Crab soup is a speciality, but try sautéed scallops with citrus juices or chargrilled monkfish. Carnivorous alternatives might be honey-roast duck breast with cherry sauce or rack of Cornish lamb. Great atmosphere – especially on busy nights.

Directions: Signposted from B3314 2 miles from Delabole

PORTHLEVEN, Critchards Seafood Restaurant

It's a lovely spot right on the harbour, and a stone floor, dark floral oilcloths and some nautical touches add to the atmosphere of this restaurant that specialises in seafood. Expect a good lobster Thermidor, and sea bass with cucumber and yogurt sauce. There are also a number of Thai influenced dishes.

Additional: No children under 6 in main restaurant; dishes
Smoking: No smoking establishment
Accommodation: 2 en suite
Credit cards:

The Harbour Head
TR13 9JA
Map 2: SW62
Tel: 01326 562407
Fax: 01326 564444
Chef: Jo Critchard
Owners: Steve & Jo Critchard
Cost: Alc £27. H/wine £9.95. ☺
Times: D only, 6.30pm-9.30pm. Closed Sun, Jan

Directions: Overlooking the harbour

PORTREATH, Tabb's Restaurant

Competent modern cooking in a well-converted former forge close to the harbour. A seasonally-changing carte and fixed-price menu, served in the high-ceilinged, stone-walled dining room, may list smooth chicken liver pâté with home-baked bread, braised wild rabbit with woodland mushrooms, brandy and cream, and kiwi pavlova

Additional: Sunday L only (noon-1.45pm); Children welcome; dishes
Smoking: No pipes or cigars
Credit cards:

Tregea Terrace
Map 2: SW54
Tel: 01209 842488
Chef: Nigel Tabb
Owners: Nigel & Melanie Tabb
Cost: Alc £20, fixed-price D £12.95. ☺ H/wine £7.95.
Times: D only, 7pm- 9pm. Closed Tue, 2 wks Nov, Jan

Directions: At the centre of the village, under the viaduct

PORTSCATHO, Gerrans Bay Hotel

An attractive and comfortable hotel in the heart of the Roseland peninsula, within walking distance of Portscatho beach. The kitchen uses the best of local produce as well as home-grown herbs in traditional English dishes such as roast rack of lamb with apricot and mint stuffing, and tomato and red pepper soup.

Gerrans TR2 5ED
Map 2: SW83
Tel: 01872 580338
Fax: 01872 580250
Telephone for details

Directions: Off A3078 to St Gerrans, 100 yds past church on St Anthony Rd

PORTSCATHO,
Roseland House Hotel

Rosevine TR2 5EW
Map 2: SW83
Tel: 01872 580644/320
Fax: 01872 580801
Telephone for details

An attractive cliff-top hotel, with superb sea views and a secluded beach at the end of a wooded path. Chef-owner Carolyn Hindley prepares a five-course set meal of traditional English cooking: typical dishes include roast beef and Yorkshire pudding, and tender roast Cornish spring lamb with fresh local vegetables.

Directions: Off A3078, hotel signed on R, 2 miles after Ruan High Lanes

REDRUTH, **Penventon Hotel**

Redruth TR15 1TE
Map 2: SW64
Tel: 01209 214141
Fax: 01209 219164
Chef: Paul Naylor
Owners: Paula & David Pascoe
Cost: *Alc* £15, fixed-price L £ 10.75/D £14. ☺ H/wine £8.45.
Times: Last L 2pm/last D 9.30pm
Additional: Bar food (L only); Sunday L; Children welcome; ● dishes
Accommodation: 60 en suite
Credit cards: ▆ ▆ ▆ ▆

An extensive range of French, Italian and English inspired dishes are offered in the Dining Galleries at this fine, family-run Georgian manor house set in ten acres of grounds. Typical choices may include Cornish fish soup, spaghetti carbonara, beef fillet en croûte with Madeira sauce, and lobster thermidor.

Directions: On Redruth intersection of A30, 1 mile S of town centre

RUAN HIGH LANES,
The Hundred House Hotel ✸

Truro TR2 5JR
Map 2: SW93
Tel: 01872 501336
Fax: 01872 501151
Chef: Kitty Eccles

Real country-house party atmosphere, with the elegant dining room opened to non-residents only when space permits. Soup, in the guise of Cornish crab laced with whisky, could be followed by

The Hundred House Hotel

Owners: Mike & Kitty Eccles
Cost: Fixed price D £22.50 (5 courses) ☺ H/wine £8.
Times: D 7.30pm. Closed Nov – Feb
Additional: ☺ dishes
Smoking: No smoking in dining room
Accommodation: 10 en suite
Credit cards: ▆ ▆ ▆

roast loin of pork with red cabbage and duchess potatoes. Intriguing desserts along the lines of baked Kea plums (tiny local ones, like damsons), or gooseberry and elderflower meringue. Fine local cheeses.

Directions: On A3078 4 miles after Tregony on right-hand side

SENNEN, The Land's End Hotel

The hotel may be beside the seaside, but access to the latter, via steep cliffs, is not easy without crampons. Still, the compensation is splendid sea views from the conservatory style dining room towards the Longships lighthouse and Isles of Scilly. The fixed-price 'Taste of Olde England' menu is largely based on traditional nineteenth-century recipes, such as rillettes of pheasant with wow-wow sauce, Hindle chicken (cornfed chicken with prune and almond stuffing), hotchpotch of game braised with port and juniper and served with parsley dumplings, and escalopes of Lundy rabbit pan-fried with Reform sauce. Highlights of our inspector's meal were crisply-fried salmon and parsley fishcakes with anchovy butter sauce, and an individual raspberry pavlova. Although a parsnip, pear and ginger soup proved a touch over-complicated, the repertoire is a refreshing change from the salsa and shiitake school of modern British cooking

Sennen Penzance TR19 7AA
Map 2: SW32
Tel: 01736 871844
Fax: 01736 871599
Chef: Lawrence Botcher
Owners: Land's End Hotel
Cost: Fixed-price D £25.95. ☺ H/wine £9.40.
Times: 11am-last L 2.30pm/7pm-last D 9.30pm.
Additional: Sunday L; Bar meals; Children welcome; ☺ dishes
Seats: 70. Private dining room 200. Jacket and tie preferred
Smoking: No smoking in dining room
Accommodation: 33 en suite
Credit cards: ▆ ▆ ▆ ▆ ▆

Directions: A30 from Penzance; in Land's End complex

ST AUSTELL,
Boscundle Manor Hotel ✿

A listed eighteenth-century building with a comfortable dining room full of antique tables, fresh flowers and candles. Chef-proprietor, Mary Flint, offers a daily menu of mainly traditional dishes based on seasonal produce. Expect the likes of pâté maison, and fried turbot with a mushroom and sour cream sauce.

Additional: Children welcome
Smoking: No smoking in dining room
Accommodation: 10 en suite
Credit cards: ▆ ▆ ▆ ▆ ▆

Tregrehan PL25 3RL
Map 2: SX05
Tel: 01726 813557
Fax: 01726 814997
Chef: Mary Flint
Owners: Andrew & Mary Flint
Cost: Fixed-price D £25. ☺ H/wine £9.50
Times: D only 7.30pm-8.30pm Closed Sun to non-residents

Directions: 2 miles E of St Austell, off A390 on road signposted Tregrehan

ST AUSTELL,
Carlyon Bay Hotel

Top-class leisure hotel with stunning sea views from its unique cliff-top location. The aptly named Bay View restaurant offers a carte designed to suit every taste, with a wide choice of dishes featuring local fish, meat and game. Try roast Cornish monkfish with basil and garlic on a bed of spiced cucumber.

Sea Road PL25 3RD
Map 2: SX05
Tel: 01726 812304
Fax: 01726 814938
Chef: Paul Leakey
Owners: Brend Hotels
Cost: *Alc* £25, fixed-price L £10.50/D £24 (5 courses). ☺ H/wine £8.50.
Times: Last L 2pm/D 9pm
Additional: Bar food L; Sunday L; Children welcome; ❹ dishes
Smoking: No-smoking area
Accommodation: 72 en suite
Credit cards: ▬ ▬ ▬ ▬ ▬ ▬

Directions: A390 towards St Austell; from town follow Charlestown then Carlyon Bay/Crinnis. Hotel at end of Sea Road near Cornwall Coliseum

ST IVES, Chy-an-Dour Hotel

There are wonderful views from this old sea captain's house as it overlooks the harbour and St Ives Bay. The short set-price dinner menu might offer prawn cocktail Marie Rose, a soup or sorbet, suprême of chicken with grain mustard and brandy sauce, and fresh pineapple and mango in Pineau des Charentes.

Additional: No children under 5; ❹ dishes
Smoking: No smoking in dining room
Credit cards: ▬ ▬ ▬ ▬

Directions: Hotel on main road into St Ives, A3074

Trelyon Avenue,
St Ives, TR26 2AD
Map 2: SW54
Tel: 01736 796436
Fax: 01736 795772
Chef: David Watson
Owners: David and Renée Watson
Cost: Fixed-price D £17.50. H/wine £5.60. ☺
Times: D only, 7.30pm – 8pm

ST IVES, Garrack Hotel

Locally caught seafood and home-grown produce highlight the various menus at this established, family-run hotel that enjoys fine views over Porthmeor Beach. Well prepared dishes may include crab and brandy bisque, followed by seafood medley with gingered couscous and pimento coulis, with crème brûlée to finish.

Higher Ayr TR26 3AA
Map 2: SW54
Tel: 01736 796199
Fax: 01736 798955
Chef: Benjamin Reeve
Owners: Kilby family
Cost: *Alc* £25, fixed-price D £18.50. ☺ H/wine £8.25.
Times: D only, 7pm-8.30pm
Additional: Bar Food; Sunday L only; Children welcome; ❹ dishes
Smoking: No smoking in dining room
Accommodation: 18 en suite
Credit cards: ▬ ▬ ▬ ▬ ▬ ▬

Directions: Follow signs for 'Portmeor Beach and Car Parks'

ST IVES, Mermaid Seafood Restaurant

The emphasis is on fresh fish at this lively restaurant carved out of a former sail loft and awash with old Chianti bottles, local memorabilia and bric-à-brac. Crates of live lobsters were being delivered by local fishermen as our inspector tucked into a well made coquilles St Jacques (with Newlyn scallops), spanking fresh sea bass with a lightly spiced sauce, and crème brûlée.

Smoking: No-smoking area; no pipes & cigars
Credit cards: ▄ ▨ ▨ ▣

Directions: Along Harbour Street towards the Sloop Inn, turn L. Restaurant is at top of street on R.

21 Fish Street TR26 1LT
Map 2: SW54
Tel: 01736 796816
Fax: 01736 798727
Chef: Helen Scott-Smith
Owners: Trevor & Helen Scott-Smith
Cost: Alc £21. H/wine £7.50. ☺
Times: D only, 6.30pm-9.30pm. Closed Sun, Feb
Additional: Children welcome; 🍴 dishes

ST IVES, Pig 'n' Fish

'No changes to this popular, mainly fish restaurant,' reports this year's inspector on Paul and Debby Sellars' relaxed, unpretentious place. Up stairs with views over the famous Sloop Inn to the sea beyond, wooden floors, part stone wall and beamed ceiling form a backdrop to Paul's inspired, clean-flavoured cooking. An early summer inspection opened with a 'delightful' smoked haddock on a light risotto cake with an equally light curry sauce, the whole topped with a poached egg. Next came spicy cod in a shallot and red wine sauce and Puy lentils – flavours were distinct, accompanying vegetables excellent. For pudding, a superb chocolate soufflé cake with a slightly warm chocolate sauce. Although fish is the thing here, a meat dish does appear on the menu, perhaps Gressingham duck breast with chicory and balsamic vinegar, for example.

Directions: 300 yards from St Ives Tate Gallery

Norway Lane TR26 1LZ
Map 2: SW54
Tel: 01736 794204
Chef: Paul Sellars
Owners: Debby & Paul Sellars
Cost: Alc £26, fixed-price D £19.50. ☺ H/wine £9.50.
Times: D only, 6.45pm-last D 9.30pm. Closed Sun, Mon, mid Dec-Mar
Additional: No children under 2
Seats: 30
Smoking: No pipes or cigars
Credit cards: ▄ ▨ ▣

ST IVES, Skidden House

Said to be the oldest hotel in St Ives, Skidden House has welcomed visitors for nearly 500 years. The restaurant 'Le Fouquet' uses the best of local produce in its French-style dishes. Try escalopes of Cornish veal with a mushroom and cream sauce, or grilled lemon sole with toasted almonds.

Directions: A30 to St Erth r/bout then A3074 to St Ives; follow to railway/coach station, then first R. Hotel is 30 metres on R

Skidden Hill TR26 2DU
Map 2: SW54
Tel: 01736 796899
Fax: 01736 798619
Chef: Dennis Stoakes
Owners: Skidden House Hotel
Cost: Alc £26, fixed-price D £22.50. ☺ H/wine £10.
Times: D only, 7pm – 8.30pm
Additional: 🍴 dishes
Smoking: No smoking in dining room
Accommodation: 7 en suite
Credit cards: ▄ ▨ ▨ ▨ ▣ ▣

ST KEYNE,
Old Rectory House Hotel ✿

Liskeard PL14 4RL
Map 2: SX26
Tel: 01579 342617
Chef: Mrs Pat Minifie
Owners: Mr & Mrs Minifie
Cost: *Alc* £17.50, fixed-price D
£17.50. ☺ H/wine £7.90.
Times: D only, 7pm- 8.30pm.
Closed Xmas
Additional: Sunday L (noon-2pm);
No children under 12; ✿ dishes
Smoking: No smoking in dining room
Accommodation: 8 en suite
Credit cards: ▬ ▦

Total peace and quiet is assured in this personally run Victorian
country house set in three acres of grounds. The daily fixed-price
menus offer sound cooking based around local produce. Expect
cream of carrot and cardamom soup, roast rack of lamb with a pea
purée in a light pastry case, and a tangy caramelised lemon tart.

Directions: 3 miles from Liskeard on B3254

ST MARTIN'S,
St Martin's on the Isle ✿✿✿

Isles of Scilly
TR25 0QW
Map 2: SW28
Tel: 01720 422092
Fax: 01720 422298
Chef: Patrick Pierre Tweedie
Owner: Peter Sykes
Cost: *Alc* £35, fixed-price D £35 (4
courses). H/wine £14.
Times: D only, 7pm-last D 10pm.
Closed Nov-Feb
Additional: Bar food; No children
under 12; ✿ dishes
Seats: 60
Smoking: No smoking in dining room
Accommodation: 30 en suite
Credit cards: ▬ ▦ ▦ ▦ ▦ ▦

The sunsets can be spectacular, the views stunning. Designed in
the 1980s from a cluster of cottages nestling on the hillside
overlooking the sea, this hotel also boasts its own beach, jetty
and yacht. As if that wasn't enough, the cooking here is of a
very high order indeed. The appropriately named Tean
Restaurant, done out in blue and gold, is hung with pictures by
local artists. Patrick Pierre Tweedie won his spurs in England
with the Roux Brothers and in France with legendary names
like Bocuse and Robuchon; no wonder his food draws heaps of
plaudits from inspectors. Fish naturally looms large on the daily,
no-choice set menu and on the seasonal *carte*: artichoke and
scallop fricassée is served with langoustine and saffron infusion,
a sauté of brill and lobster receives a champagne and Keta
caviar beurre blanc, while silver sea bream is filled with tomato

confit and accompanied by a ground black olive vinaigrette. Away from fish, the menus promise, say, pot-roast guinea fowl breast with Parma ham, sage sauce and a port jus, or roast rack of Cornish lamb with garlic crust, spring vegetables and lamb jus. A recent inspection began impressively with an ultra-modern amuse bouche of salmon and cod tartare with seared scallops before a near-perfect Stilton soufflé with plenty of depth and lightness. The main course moved even higher: a superb piece of pan-fried halibut was served impeccably with asparagus, truffled new potatoes and a creamy sauce of morilles on a bed of spinach. To finish, a selection of raspberry desserts featuring a delice, hot soufflé, sablé, and brandy snap basket filled with sorbet. The wine list is 'user friendly', but there's not much in the way of inspiring choice.

Signature dishes: Mille-feuille of Tean Sound grey mullet and smoked pork loin with thyme and poultry jus; chilled Carnwethers crab soufflé with walnut and grain mustard vinaigrette.

Directions: 28 miles from Penzance via helicopter, steamship or aircraft, then 20-minute launch boat ride

ST MARYS, Star Castle Hotel

The castle, dating from 1593, forms an eight pointed star, and stands on the fortified Garrison Hill commanding impressive views of the island and the sea. The fixed-price dinner menu offers a good choice of dishes such as baked Scillonian brill with prawn and crab crumble on lime butter.

Additional: Bar meals L; No children under 8; ❹ dishes
Smoking: No smoking in dining room
Accommodation: 33 en suite
Credit cards: ▬ ▭ 🄿 ℂ

The Garrison TR21 0JA
Map 2: SW28
Tel: 01720 422317
Chef: Christopher Evans
Owners: John & Mary Nicholls
Cost: Fixed-price D £21.50. ☺
H/wine £8.50.
Times: Last L 1.30pm/last D 8.30pm.
Closed mid Oct–mid Mar

Directions: Flights available from Lands End, Plymouth, Exeter, Bristol & Southampton. Helicopter or ferry from Penzance. Hotel taxi meets all guests from airport or quay

ST MAWES, Idle Rocks Hotel

Harbour Side
TR2 5AN
Map 2: SW83
Tel: 01326 270771
Fax: 01326 270062
Chef: Alan Vickops
Owner: Mr & Mrs EK Richardson

The Waters' Edge restaurant makes the most of the hotel's location with picture windows looking out across the harbour to the St Anthony headland. The nautical theme continues with brass ship lamps, cosy *alc*oves and wooden panelling, which all add to the relaxed atmosphere. One *carte* and one set-price dinner menu are available, each offering a good range of modern British cooking with a French accent. Fresh, locally-landed fish is a speciality – dishes might include grilled fillet of John Dory with creamed basil and leek purée, and pan-fried scallops with a warm potato and olive dressing. Meat is equally well handled. An inspection meal in August took in a savoury pancake filled with smoked chicken and avocado purée and rack of West Country lamb with wild mushrooms and a port sauce. Desserts include hot raspberry and pistachio soufflé and dark chocolate mousse with hazelnuts and honeycomb ice cream. Lunch sees a less formal but equally appealing menu, served in the bar and on the terrace.

Cost: *Alc* £30, Fixed-price D £23.50 (3 courses). ☺ H/wine £9.55.
Times: Noon-last L 3pm/7pm-last D 9.15pm
Additional: Bar food L; No children under 7; ✪ dishes
Seats: 60
Smoking: No smoking in dining room
Accommodation: 24 en suite
Credit cards: ■ ■ ■ ■ ▣

Directions: Take the A3078 to St Mawes. Hotel is on L as you enter the village, at water's edge

ST MAWES, Rising Sun Hotel

Delightful fishing village with the Rising Sun occupying an enviable harbourside location. The bar retains the character of a village inn, whilst the Brasserie offers sound modern cooking with an emphasis on fresh fish and shell fish, some of it landed on the quay in front of the inn.

Truro TR2 5DJ
Map 2: SW83
Tel: 01326 270233
Fax: 01326 270198
Owner: St Austell Brewery
Cost: *Alc* £20, fixed-price D from £15.95. ☺ H/wine £9.50.
Times: Last L 2pm/last D 9pm

Additional: Bar meals; Sunday L; Children welcome; ✪ dishes
Smoking: No-smoking area
Accommodation: 8 en suite
Credit cards: ■ ■ ■ ■ ▣

Directions: On harbour front

ST MELLION, St Mellion Hotel

It's straight down the fairway and into the restaurant of the St Mellion Golf and Country Club, sited bang in the middle of two 18- hole golf courses, including the championship one designed by Jack Nicklaus. Menus change daily, and there are some particularly good fish and seafood dishes such as Cornish mussels with smoked bacon, venison and white wine cream sauce, and suprême of salmon with wild mushrooms and Noilly Prat. Creamy sauces are clearly popular with the golfing fraternity – mignons of beef fillet are served with a paprika, cream and brandy sauce and medallions of monkfish with watercress sauce and tagliatelle of vegetables. No-nonsense options include Cornish smoked salmon with onion and capers, grilled sirloin steak with game chips and home-made treacle sponge pudding. Service is attentive and friendly, and guests are left feeling neither rushed nor overpowered.

Saltash PL12 6SD
Map 2: SX36
Tel: 01579 351351
Fax: 01579 350537
Chef: Ian Crook
Owners: Messrs M & H Bond
Cost: *Alc* £20, fixed-price D £19.50 (3 courses). ☺ H/wine £9.95
Times: D only (restaurant), 7.30pm-9.30pm
Additional: Sunday L only (12.30pm-2pm); Brasserie (7am-9pm); Children welcome; ✪ dishes
Seats: 70. Private dining room 30-90
Smoking: Air-conditioning
Accommodation: 56 en suite
Credit cards: ■ ■ ■ ■ ▣ ▣

Directions: On the A388 about 4 miles N of Saltash

ST WENN, Wenn Manor

Notable features of this former vicarage are the 45ft well in the bar, the garden grotto and the candlelit dining room. Locally caught fish figures prominently, and other options might be roast rack of lamb or baked chicken breast with pistachios. Meals can also be taken in the bright new conservatory.

Accommodation: 3 en suite
Credit cards: ▬ ▦ ☲ ⊠ ⎙ ⌐

Directions: Halfway between A30/A39, next to church in village

St Wenn Bodmin PL30 5PS
Map 2: SX16
Tel: 01726 890240
Fax: 01726 890680
Chef: Jo Stretton-Downes
Owner: P & J Stretton-Downes
Cost: Alc £20, fixed-price L £20. ☺ H/wine £10.
Times: Last L 1.45pm/D 9.30pm. Closed Sun, 7 days Xmas
Additional: Bar food L; No children under 10; ◑ dishes
Smoking: No cigars or pipes

TALLAND BAY, Allhays Country House ✤

Attractive country house hotel surrounded by beautiful scenery. Carefully constructed set dinner (served at 7pm) draws on local produce, some from the hotel's own garden. Care is evident. Everything is home-made, down to the breads, there's a meat/fish alternative for main course, a choice of dessert, and an excellent cheeseboard.

Accommodation: 7 (5 en suite)
Credit cards: ▬ ▦ ☲ ⊠ ⎙ ⌐

Directions: From Looe A387 (Polperro), after 2.5 miles L at hotel sign. 1st large house on R

Near Looe PL13 2JB
Map 2: SX25
Tel: 01503 272434
Fax: 01503 272929
Chef: Lynda Spring
Owners: Brian & Lynda Spring
Cost: Alc £16.80, fixed-price D £16.80 (3 courses). ☺ H/wine £7.95.
Times: D at 7pm. Closed L, Xmas-New Year
Additional: No children under 10; ◑ dishes
Smoking: No smoking in dining room

TALLAND BAY, Talland Bay Hotel ✤

Visitors are likely to be charmed by this beautiful Cornish house that stands in an elevated position overlooking Talland Bay. Daily menus offer rillettes of pork with a warm cucumber pickle, and fillets of locally caught monkfish roasted with a fresh herb crust and a sweet vinaigrette. Bread and butter pudding makes a traditional finish.

Smoking: No smoking in dining room
Accommodation: 19 en suite
Credit cards: ▬ ▦ ☲ ⊠ ⎙ ⌐

Directions: Follow A387 Polperro road from Looe, hotel signed from crossroads

Near Looe PL13 2JB
Map 2: SX25
Tel: 01503 272667
Fax: 01503 272940
Chef: Paul Kingswood
Owners: Barry & Annie Rosier
Cost: Alc £29.50, D £21 (3 courses). ☺ H/wine £8.75.
Times: Last L 2pm/D 9pm. Closed Jan
Additional: Bar food L; Sunday lunch; No children under 5; ◑ dishes

TINTAGEL, Trebrea Lodge Hotel ✤

Set in four acres of beautiful wooded hillside, this imposing Cornish manor house is a perfect, tranquil retreat. Dinner is served at 8pm in the oak-panelled dining room, and might include smoked trout mousse, pork tenderloin in a honey and ginger sauce, and Cornish yarg with water biscuits and oat cakes.

Smoking: No smoking in dining room
Accommodation: 7 en suite
Credit cards: ▬ ▦ ☲ ⊠ ⌐

Directions: From Camelford (A39) follow signs to Tintagel. 1 mile before village turn R for Trenale

Trenale PL34 0HR
Map 2: SX08
Tel: 01840 770410
Fax: 01840 770092
Chef: Sean Devlin
Owners: John Charlick & Sean Devlin
Cost: Fixed-price D £21. ☺ H/wine £9.
Times: D only, 7pm for 8pm. Closed 4 Jan – 13 Feb
Additional: No children under 12; ◑ dishes

TRESCO, The Island Hotel

A magnificent island that takes in stunning gardens, idyllic beaches and no cars are visitors first impressions of Tresco as they are whisked from the heliport or pier (by tractor and trailer), to receive the warmest of welcomes at this splendid hotel. Meals are served in the big, airy dining room whose immense windows give panoramic views of the other islands. Local fish features on a menu that looks to the Mediterranean for inspiration; haddock with brioche crust, sautéed leaf spinach and coriander and Chardonnay cream sauce, baked fillet of cod with olive tapenade, pan-fried aubergine, beefsteak tomato and balsamic dressing, for example. Inspection produced good home-made bread, a vibrant chargrilled swordfish with olives, capers, anchovies, rosemary with a chilli and ginger salsa, then chilled summer berry and yoghurt soup, steamed fillet of turbot with saffron creamed potato and fresh beetroot sauce, and orange, rum and raisin iced parfait for dessert.

Directions: Situated on north-eastern tip of island

Isles of Scilly
TR24 0PU
Map 2: SW17
Tel: 01720 422883
Fax: 01720 423008
Chef: Christopher Wyburn Risdale
Owner: Robert Dorrien-Smith
Cost: Alc £35, fixed-price D £30 (5 courses). ☺ H/wine £10.25
Times: Noon-last L 2.15pm/6.45pm-last D 9.30pm. Closed Nov-Feb
Additional: Bar food L; Sunday L; Children welcome; ᴓ dishes
Seats: 110. Jacket and tie preferred
Smoking: No pipes and cigars in dining room
Accommodation: 40 en suite
Credit cards: ▆ ▆ ▆ ▆ ▆

TRESCO, New Inn

Established as the social centre of Tresco, this well run hostelry, formerly a row of fishermen's cottages, has a 'smugglers' inn' feel. Owner/chef Graham Shone's imaginative cooking makes good use of local produce, especially fish. Expect cauliflower and bacon soup, gigot of monkfish with saffron niçoise, and lemon tart.

Smoking: No smoking in dining room
Accommodation: 14 en suite. **Credit cards:** ▆ ▆ ▆ ▆

Directions: 250 yds from the harbour (private island, contact hotel for details)

Isles of Scilly TR24 0QQ
Map 2: SW17
Tel: 01720 422844
Fax: 01720 423200
Chef: Graham Shone
Owners: Graham & Sue Shone (Tresco Estate)
Cost: ☺
Times: D 7.30pm-8.30pm (High season 7-9)
Additional: Bar food L (noon-2pm) & D; Children welcome; ᴓ dishes

TREYARNON BAY,
Waterbeach Hotel

Vicky Everington's wholesome six-course dinners are a prime attraction at this personally run hotel. Genuine soups and desserts such as raspberry cheesecake flank generous centrepieces like roast loin of pork, salmon steak with almond sauce or savoury lentil crumble. Quiet and peaceful, great views.

Smoking: No smoking in dining room
Accommodation: 21 en suite. **Credit cards:** ▆ ▆ ▆ ▆

Directions: 4 miles from Padstow on coastal road to Newquay

Treyarnon Bay, PL28 8JW
Map 2: SW87
Tel: 01841 520292
Fax: 01841 521102
Chef: Mrs V Etherington
Owners: Mr & Mrs A Etherington
Cost: Fixed-price D £15 (6 courses). H/wine £6.50
Times: 7.30pm-D 8.15pm. Closed L, Nov-Mar
Additional: No children under 5; ᴓ dishes

TRURO, Alverton Manor

A former convent, in six acres of picturesque landscaped grounds, this impressive sandstone house is now the scene of more worldly pleasures. The short, well-structured menu includes a good choice of local fish and seafood – Cornish seafood and mussel soup, queen scallops grilled with lime, coriander, chilli and linguini, and lemon sole grilled on the bone, filled with prawns and served with a pink grapefruit and dill butter sauce. Dishes are adventurous without being too bold –

Tregolls Road
TR1 1XQ
Map 2: SW84
Tel: 01872 276633
Fax: 01872 222989
Chef: Colin Gilbert
Owner: Mr Sagim
Cost: Alc £29.50, fixed-price L from £6.75 (1 course)/D £19.50. ☺ H/wine £9.95.

Alverton Manor

Times: 11.45am-last L 1.45pm/7pm-last D 9.30pm
Additional: Bar Food L; Sunday L; Children welcome; ❹ dishes
Seats: 40. Private dining rooms. Jacket and tie preferred
Smoking: No smoking in dining room
Accommodation: 34 en suite
Credit cards: ▬ ▦ ▦ ☶ 🄮 🄲

noisettes of venison on a potato and celeriac rösti with a port wine, redcurrant and bitter chocolate sauce and chargrilled fresh tuna loin marinated with ginger, garlic, chilli and lime leaves are as exotic as it gets. Desserts stay in the reassuringly familiar territory of crème brûlée and pecan pie with honey sauce.

Directions: from the Truro by-pass, take A39 to St Austell. Just past the church on L.

TRURO, Oliver's Restaurant ❀❀

Below the Wig & Pen pub, but run as a separate entity, this popular restaurant is bedecked with caricatures of the legal profession (the Law Courts are nearby) on its yellow emulsioned walls. The menu is fixed-price for two or three courses and it offers plenty of choice across the board. Our inspector opted to begin with a robust cassoulette of shellfish and local market fish in a smooth winey liquor, before sampling well-timed medallions of chargrilled calves' liver neatly stacked on a bed of sweet potato and onion mix with some finely chopped red cabbage accompanied by a light cider jus. Other choices might include poached fillet of salmon with raspberry vinaigrette on a bed of leaves, and suprême of chicken stuffed with crab on a lemon and mint butter. Desserts are stylishly presented offerings such as an iced duo of chocolate parfaits with 'dew drops' of orange sauce and brandy snap basket filled with poached fruit on a fruit coulis. The soundly chosen wine list includes several by the glass.

Castle Street TR1 3DP
Map 2: SW84
Tel/Fax: 01872 273028
Chef: Colin Hankins
Owners: David & Serena London
Cost: Alc £20, fixed-price L&D £19. ☺ H/wine £8.75.
Times: Noon-last L 2.30pm/6.30pm-last D 10pm. Closed D Sun, D Mon
Additional: Bar meals; Sunday L; Children welcome; ❹ dishes
Seats: 30
Smoking: No pipes & cigars
Credit cards: ▬ ▬ ☶ 🄲

Directions: Below Law Courts in the city centre

VERYAN-IN-ROSELAND,
The Nare Hotel ❀

Set in sub-tropical gardens adjoining the coastal path, this hotel offers stunning views over Gerrans Bay and Carne Beach. The restaurant takes full advantage of the location, in both visual and culinary terms. Local seafood is a feature, including crab and lobster, and prime Cornish steak is another favourite.

Accommodation: 36 en suite. **Credit cards:** ▬ ▦

Directions: Through village passing New Inn on L, continue 1 mile to sea

Carne Beach TR2 5PF
Map 2: SW93
Tel: 01872 501279
Fax: 01872 501856
Chef: Malcolm Sparks
Owner: Mrs T N Gray
Cost: Alc £31. Fixed price L £12.50/D £28. H/wine £9.75
Times: Last L 2pm/D 9.30pm Closed 3 Jan-3 Feb
Additional: Bar meals L; Sunday L; Children welcome; ❹ dishes
Smoking: No pipes & cigars

CUMBRIA

ALSTON,
Lovelady Shield Hotel

CA9 3LF
Map 12: NY74
Tel: 01434 381203
Fax: 01434 381515
Chef: Barrie Garton
Owners: Mr & Mrs K Lyons
Cost: Fixed-price L £14.95/D £26. ☺
H/wine £8.95.
Times: 12.30pm-last L 1.30pm/7pm-last D 8.30pm. Closed 3 Jan-3 Feb
Additional: Bar food L; Sunday L by arrangement; No children under 5
Seats: 30
Smoking: No smoking in dining room
Accommodation: 12 en suite
Credit cards:

There is a quiet, unspoilt air to this peacefully located hotel that stands in two acres of carefully tended grounds. Orders are taken in the drawing-room (in cold weather warmed by a roaring fire), and the service is friendly and attentive. First courses might include grilled Cumberland black pudding on a bed of apple and red onion, braised with dry cider and scented with juniper and rosemary, or a soft mousse of Orkney crab served with a cucumber and chive salad and crunchy oat biscuits. Grilled fillets of grey mullet with fresh asparagus and melting anchovy and walnut butter, and loin of local lamb cooked 'rosy pink' with a sauce made from the pan juices, whole redcurrants and a hint of mint, are amongst the choice of main courses on the nightly changing menu. A small pot of warm rice pudding was well-flavoured with vanilla and topped with glazed, crispy Kiwi fruit – a nice idea that worked well.

Directions: Off the A689, 2.5 miles from East Alston; signposted at top of drive

AMBLESIDE, Borrans Park Hotel

A stylish Georgian restaurant with a relaxed and cheery atmosphere. The set four-course menu offers simple but consistent cooking like roast ham with Cumberland sauce. Desserts such as summer fruit tart and bilberry fool are served from a sweet trolley that goes round the tables twice to allow for extra helpings.

Times: D only, 7pm-last D 8pm. Closed Xmas
Additional: No children under 7; ❹ dishes
Smoking: No smoking in dining room
Accommodation: 12 en suite
Credit cards:

Borrans Road LA22 0EN
Map 7: NY30
Tel: 015394 33454
Fax: 015394 33003
Chef: Kate Lewis
Owner: Andrew Whitehead
Cost: Fixed-price D £17.50. ☺
H/wine £8.95.

Directions: Turn L off A591 at Waterhead traffic lights to Ambleside, hotel 0.5 miles, opposite rugby field

AMBLESIDE,
Nanny Brow Hotel

Mature grounds surround this charming country house while the restaurant makes the most of the beautiful views over Langdale Valley. An added bonus is the keen imagination at work in the kitchen, producing fine regional dishes that take in the likes of fennel and tomato soup, and roast duck on garlic and potato rösti with red wine sauce. An early summer dinner showed the kitchen on top form, with a refined terrine of rabbit with leeks, home-made piccalilli and onion salsa, fresh lavender sorbet, then pavé of salmon in a feuilletage lattice with fresh ochra, duchess potatoes and a light vin blanc nage lifted gently with chopped shallots, and for dessert, deep-fried chocolate ravioli, filled with mascarpone, and served with crème anglaise. Endorsements too for small details such as bread – granary, white and sun-dried – canapés and petits fours.

Clappersgate LA22 9NF
Map 7: NY30
Tel: 015394 32036
Fax: 015394 32450
Chef: Joe Hargraves
Owners: Michael & Carol Fletcher
Cost: *Alc* £22.50, fixed-price D £18.50. ☺ H/wine £11.99.
Times: D only, 7.30-last D 8.45pm
Additional: No children under 9 at D; ⓖ dishes
Seats: 42. Private dining room 12.
Jacket and tie preferred
Smoking: No smoking in dining room
Accommodation: 18 en suite
Credit cards: 💳 💳 💳 💳 💳 💳

Directions: One mile from Ambleside on the A593 to Coniston

AMBLESIDE, **Rothay Manor**

Set in landscaped gardens, this Regency-styled hotel enjoys a warm and relaxing atmosphere. Visitors choose from a short menu, perhaps poached fillet of salmon topped with avocado, coriander and tomato salsa or casseroled breast of chicken with chopped smoked bacon in white wine.

Smoking: No smoking in dining room; air-conditioning
Accommodation: 18 en suite. **Credit cards:** 💳 💳 💳 💳 💳

Directions: Quarter of a mile out of Ambleside on the Coniston road

Rothay Bridge LA22 0EH
Map 7: NY30
Tel: 015394 33605
Fax: 015394 33607
Chefs: Jane Binns, Colette Nixon
Owners: Nigel & Stephen Nixon
Cost: Fixed-price L £13/D £23, £26, £29. H/wine £12.
Times: Last L 2pm (1.30pm Sun)/last D 9pm. Closed 3 Jan-10 Feb
Additional: Bar food; Sunday L; Children welcome; ⓖ menu
Seats: 70. Private dining room 32

AMBLESIDE, **Wateredge Hotel**

Borrans Road,
Waterhead LA22 0EP
Map 7: NY30
Tel: 015394 32332
Fax: 015394 31878
Chefs: Mark Cowap, Stephen Marsden
Owners: Mr & Mrs Derek Cowap
Cost: Fixed-price D £26.90. H/wine £12.50
Times: Last L 2pm/D 7pm-8.30pm. Closed mid Dec-mid Jan
Additional: Bar food L; No children under 7; ⓖ dishes
Smoking: No smoking in dining room
Accommodation: 22 en suite
Credit cards: 💳 💳 💳 💳 💳

A pair of sympathetically extended seventeenth-century fisherman's cottages set in secluded gardens on the shores of Lake Windermere. Besides period charm and tasteful accommodation, this delightful hotel offers traditional six-course dinners based on fresh produce. Expect carrot and orange soup, baked chicken breast with tarragon and mustard sauce, and apple pie.

Directions: From A591 N to Ambleside, fork L at traffic lights after Ambleside sign. Skirt lake for few hundred yards, hotel is on L

APPLEBY-IN-WESTMORLAND,
Royal Oak Inn

CA16 6UN
Map 7: NY30
Tel: 017683 51463
Fax: 017683 52300
Chefs: Stuart Good, Hilary Cheyne
Owners: Colin & Hilary Cheyne
Cost: *Alc* £15. H/wine £8.40. ☺
Times: Last L 2pm/last D 9pm.
Closed 25 Dec
Additional: Sunday L; Bar meals;
Children welcome; ❹ dishes
Smoking: No-smoking area; no pipes
or cigars
Accommodation: 9 en suite
Credit cards: 💳 💳 💳 💳 💳 💳

A traditional inn, complete with open fires and beams, offering two dining rooms, one no smoking, and a diners' lounge. There is a good choice of dishes, including fresh fish, Malayan chicken curry, Bongate lamb pudding and steaks. Leeky links – leek and cheese sausages – are among the interesting vegetarian options.

Directions: On A66 13 miles from M6 junction 40 (Penrith) and 38 miles from Scotch Corner. Appleby rail station on Leeds-Settle-Carlisle line

APPLEBY-IN-WESTMORLAND,
Tufton Arms Hotel

Market Square CA16 6XA
Map 12: NY62
Tel: 017683 51593
Fax: 017683 52761
Chef: David Milsom
Owners: Mr & Mrs W D Milsom
Cost: *Alc* £13, fixed-price D £20.50.
☺ H/wine £8.50.
Times: Last L 2pm/last D 9.15pm
Additional: Bar food; Sunday L;
Children welcome; ❹ dishes
Accommodation: 21 en suite
Credit cards: 💳 💳 💳 💳 💳 💳

An attractive market town setting for this stylishly restored Victorian coaching inn. In the elegant Conservatory Restaurant a good choice of dishes range from steak and kidney pie and pasta carbonara, to pigeon in red wine and rack of lamb with redcurrant sauce. Good wine list.

Directions: In centre of Appleby on B6260, 12 miles from M6/J38

BASSENTHWAITE,
Armathwaite Hall

Stately seventeenth-century mansion set in 400 acres of magnificent parkland beside Bassenthwaite Lake. Impressive panelled dining room offering lake views, a six-course dinner menu and an interesting

Keswick CA12 4RE
Map 11: NY23
Tel: 017687 76551
Fax: 017687 76220
Chef: Kevin Dowling

carte. Typical dishes may include red lentil and clam soup, steamed turbot with champagne and oyster sauce and apple strudel.

Accommodation: 43 en suite. **Credit cards:** ▆ ▆ ▆ ▆

Directions: From M6/J40 take A66 to Keswick then A591 towards Carlisle. Turn L by Castle Inn, 8m to hotel.

Owners: Graves family
Cost: Alc £35, set L £14.95/D £32 (6 courses). H/wine £10.95
Times: Last L 1.45pm/D 9.30pm
Additional: Sunday L; Bar meals L; Children welcome; ⓓ dishes
Smoking: No smoking in dining room

BASSENTHWAITE,

Castle Inn Hotel ❀

The Thomas de Quincy is a modern hotel restaurant with rich Victorian-style decor, large candlelit tables and comfortable seating. At a test meal a starter of corn-fed chicken terrine was beautifully presented, followed by an accurately cooked ragoût of salmon in a vegetable and white wine sauce with lobster ravioli.

Directions: On the A591 6 miles north of Keswick

Keswick CA12 4RG
Map 11: NY23
Tel: 017687 76401
Fax: 017687 76604
Telephone for details

BASSENTHWAITE,

Overwater Hall Hotel ❀

Set in 18 acres of grounds and woodland within hiking distance over fields to Overwater Tarn, this Grade II listed Victorian mansion puts on a grand face. A typical meal might be a salad of mixed smoked fish with quail's eggs and cherry tomatoes, a soup (say, cream of carrot and orange), then fillet of lamb flamed in cognac with a mint cream sauce, and Cumberland rum nicky and a British cheeseboard.

Accommodation: 13 en suite. **Credit cards:** ▆ ▆ ▆ ▆

Directions: Take A591 from Keswick to Carlisle, after 6 miles, turn R at the Castle Inn. Hotel is signposted after 2 miles.

Ireby CA5 1HH
Map 11: NY23
Tel/Fax: 017687 76566
Chef: Adrian Hyde
Owners: Adrian & Angela Hyde, Stephen Bore
Cost: Fixed-price D £23.50(5 courses). ☺ H/wine £8.95.
Times: D only, 7pm-9pm
Additional: Sunday L (12.30pm-2pm); No children under 4; ⓓ dishes
Smoking: No smoking in dining room

BORROWDALE,

Borrowdale Gates Hotel ❀

Grange, Keswick CA12 5UQ
Map 11: NY21
Tel: 017687 77204
Fax: 017687 77254
Chefs: Michael Heathcote
Owners: Terry & Christine Parkinson
Cost: Fixed-price D £25.50 (4 courses). H/wine £12
Times: Last L 1.30pm/last D 8.45pm. Closed Jan
Additional: Bar food (L only); Sunday L; Children welcome; ⓓ dishes
Smoking: No smoking in dining room
Accommodation: 28 en suite
Credit cards: ▆ ▆ ▆ ▆ ▆

Surrounded by the rugged fells of the beautiful Borrowdale valley, this family-run Victorian hotel offers an imaginative, daily changing dinner menu in its attractive dining room. Enjoyed at inspection were leek and tarragon soup, seared tuna with roasted peppers, and apple tart with cinnamon flavoured crème anglaise

Directions: B5289 from Keswick. After 4 miles turn R over double humpback bridge to Grange village. Hotel 400yds through village on R

BRAMPTON, **Farlam Hall** ❀❀

Hallbankgate CA8 2NG
Map 12: NY56
Tel: 016977 46234
Fax: 016977 46683
Chef: Barry Quinion
Owners: Quinion & Stevenson families
Cost: Fixed-price D £30 (4 courses). H/wine £12.95
Times: D only, 8pm for 8.30pm. Closed 24-30 Dec
Additional: No children under 5; ◑ dishes on request
Seats: 40. Private dining room 20. Jacket & tie preferred
Smoking: No pipes or cigars in dining room
Accommodation: 12 en suite
Credit cards: ▬ ▦ ▦ ▦ ◉

Set in the relatively undiscovered northern reaches of the Lake District, this historic country house remains a popular retreat with tourists and travellers. Parts of the Hall date from the sixteenth century although it was substantially improved in Victorian times to include landscaped gardens with a stream and ornamental lake. Long serving incumbents, the Quinions and the Stevensons, run the place in personal relaxed style, and Barry Quinion's daily four-course dinner menus are carefully structured. Begin with, say, cream of carrot and lettuce soup or salmon and parsley fish cake with saffron and red pepper sauce, before moving on to breast of Gressingham duckling with Calvados sauce, roulade of sole with basil and cream sauce, or grilled noisettes of local lamb with rosemary and white wine sauce. Lemon tart with raspberry coulis is a creditable dessert, and the selection of English farmhouse cheeses has drawn effusive praise. Around forty affordable wines include a fair sprinkling of halves.

Directions: 2.5 miles SE of Brampton on the A689

CARLISLE, **Crosby Lodge Hotel** ❀

High Crosby CA6 4QZ
Map 12: NY45
Tel: 01228 573618
Fax: 01228 573428
Chefs: Michael & James Sedgwick
Owners: Michael & Patricia Sedgwick
Cost: Fixed-price L £16/D £28. ☺ H/wine £12.50.
Times: Last L 1.30pm/last D 8.45pm. Closed D Sun (non residents), Xmas, New Year
Additional: Bar Food L; Sunday L; No children under 5; ◑ dishes
Smoking: No pipes or cigars
Accommodation: 11 en suite
Credit cards: ▬ ▦ ▦ ▦ ◉

Crenellated Georgian country house overlooking mature parkland and the River Eden. Noted for hospitality and food, especially some delicious home-baking. Interesting menus may feature wild boar and venison terrine with Cumberland sauce, duck with orange sauce, and banana and toffee roulade. Impressive wine list.

Directions: 3 miles from M6/J44 on A689 towards Carlisle Airport/Brampton. R at Low/High Crosby sign, 1 mile on R

CARLISLE, Crown Hotel

Mainly traditional dishes are offered at this hotel restaurant. A salmon combination of called 'Conservatory' made an excellent starter: Loch Fyne smoked salmon, home-cured gravad lax and a Thai fishcake with a cucumber and lime pickle, each item beautifully presented in a scallop dish.

Wetheral CA4 8ES
Map 11: NY45
Tel: 01228 561888
Fax: 01228 561637
Chef: Martin Strand
Owners: Shire Inns Limited
Cost: Alc £18. H/wine £10.
Telephone for further details

CARTMEL, Aynsome Manor Hotel

Grand manor house built in 1512 for the Earl of Pembroke, now an enchanting family-run hotel. Five-course dinners are served in the stately dining room. Trout roulade with horseradish and yoghurt sauce, tomato and celery soup, and breast of guinea fowl with redcurrant sauce are typical options. Desserts are from the trolley.

Smoking: No smoking in dining room
Accommodation: 12 en suite. Credit cards: ■ ▦ ▨ ⚲ ▯

Directions: Leave A590 signed Cartmel. Hotel is 0.5 mile N of Cartmel village on R

Grange over Sands LA11 6HH
Map 7: SD37
Tel: 015395 36653
Fax: 015395 36016
Chef: Victor Sharratt
Owners: P Anthony & Margaret Varley
Cost: Fixed-price D from £16. ☺ H/wine £8.
Times: D only, 7pm-8.30pm. Closed D Sun
Additional: Sunday L for 1pm; No children under 5

CARTMEL, Uplands Hotel

Dinner (7.30 for 8pm) follows the same set pattern as ever at this delightful Lakeland country hotel, which boasts splendid views over to the Morecambe Estuary. There is a choice at three of the four courses – soup comes in the form of a tureen with warm wholemeal bread. A typical spring dinner might start with a feta and Emmental cheese and onion tart served on dressed leaves with home-made date chutney, or fresh langoustines served with vegetable strips and tarragon sauce, followed by courgette and rosemary soup. Main courses present a difficult choice between grilled whole Dover sole with chive and lemon sauce, roast loin of spring lamb with mint sauce and redcurrant and caper sauce, and roast local guinea fowl with bread sauce and port wine sauce. Vegetables are as strong a feature here as in co-owner John Tovey's Miller Howe restaurant – an imaginative selection might include carrots with mint, purée of celeriac with almonds, spring cabbage with juniper, broccoli cooked in sesame oil, and potatoes with bacon and onion. Desserts include raspberry and apple pie with cream and strawberry shortcake.

Directions: 1 mile up road signed Grange opposite the Pig & Whistle pub in Cartmel

Haggs Lane
Grange over Sands LA11 6HD
Map 7: SD37
Tel: 015395 36248
Fax: 015395 36848
Chef: Tom Peter
Owners: Tom & Diana Peter, John Tovey
Cost: Fixed-price L £15/D £27 (4 courses). H/wine £9.
Times: 12.30pm for 1pm/7.30pm for 8pm. Closed Mon, L Tue & Wed
Additional: Sunday L; No children under 8; ⚬ dishes
Smoking: No smoking in dining room
Seats: 28
Accommodation: 5 en suite
Credit cards: ■ ▦ ▨

CONISTON, The Old Rectory Hotel

Relaxing Victorian hotel where four-course dinners are served at 7.30pm. There's a choice of desserts such as raspberry vacherin or home-made ice creams, otherwise expect the likes of haddock smokies, followed by fillet of pork Normandy with interesting vegetables, and a well-selected trio of cheeses.

Credit cards: ■ ▨ ⚲ ▯

Directions: 2.5 miles south of Coniston on the A593, just before Torver

Torver LA21 8AX
Map 7: SD39
Tel: 015394 41353
Fax: 015394 41156
Chef: Carolyn Fletcher
Owners: Paul & Carolyn Fletcher
Cost: Fixed-price D £14. ☺ H/wine £8.95.
Times: D only at 7.30pm
Smoking: No smoking in dining room; air conditioning

CROOKLANDS, Crooklands Hotel

Minutes from the M6, yet in a peaceful rural location, this extended former farmhouse provides an ideal stop-over. Visitors can dine in the slate-floored bar, or in the beamed Hayloft Restaurant where a brasserie-style menu offers smoked haddock and potato soup, and rack of lamb with red wine jus.

Smoking: No-smoking area, air-conditioning
Accommodation: 30 en suite. **Credit cards:** 🟦 ▤ ▤ 🅿️

Directions: 1.5 miles from M6/J36; 4 miles from Kendal A65

Milnthorpe Near Kendal LA7 7NW
Map 7: SD58
Tel: 015395 67432
Fax: 015395 67525
Chef: Colin Scott
Owners: Neil & Hedda Connor
Cost: Alc £18.95. H/wine £7.95. ☺
Times: Last L 2pm/D 9pm.
Closed 26 Dec
Additional: Bar Food; Sunday L;
🍴 dishes

CROSTHWAITE, The Punchbowl

What more could anyone want? A rural pub in an idyllic location with log fires, old beams, a friendly welcome and good food at honest prices is a package that's hard to beat. Especially when the cooking has an urban polish rarely found outside the metropolis. Duck leg confit is authentically slow cooked, served on a bed of braised cabbage with damson juice and red wine, tuna is roasted in sesame oil with a soy ginger sauce and served with wholewheat noodles and vegetables. There is the confidence to do classic, rarely seen dishes, such as fillet of cod bonne femme, chicken schnitzel and floating islands – and do them correctly, and there's no apology or irony implied for serving jumbo prawns deep-fried in crispy batter with tartare sauce. Local air-dried ham is served with grated celeriac, mayonnaise grain mustard, shaved Parmesan and white truffle oil; both game terrine and gravad lax with blinis are home-produced. There is a first-class selection of local and British farmhouse cheeses, including some unpasteurised ones, but also tarte Tatin, and white chocolate truffle cake.

Directions: M6/J36 (Kendal). L onto A540 (Barrow). R at Jaguar dealership and follow A5074 until Crosthwaite sign. Top of lane on L next to church

Kendal LA8 8HQ
Map 11: NY30
Tel: 015395 68237
Fax: 015395 68875
Chefs: Steven Doherty, Duncan Collinge
Owners: Steven & Marjorie Doherty
Cost: Alc £25. H/wine £12. ☺
Times: Noon-last L 2pm/6pm-last D 9pm. Closed 25 Dec
Additional: Sunday L; Children welcome; 🍴 dishes
Seats: 80
Smoking: No-smoking area
Accommodation: 3 en suite
Credit cards: 🟦 ▤ ▩ 🅲

ESKDALE, Bower House Inn

An eighteenth-century farmhouse combining the character of a country inn with an attractive restaurant. Game is a regular feature of the Anglo/French menus – wild pheasant with cranberries and fresh vegetables, for example. Desserts such as rum and raisin cheesecake will satisfy the sweet tooth.

Holmbrook CA19 1TD
Map 6: NY10
Tel: 01946 723244
Fax: 01946 723308
Chef: Margaret Johnson
Owners: Mr & Mrs DJ Connor
Cost: Fixed price D £19.50. ☺
H/wine £7.95.
Times: Last L 2pm (bar)/D 8.30pm
Additional: Bar meals; No children under 8; 🍴 dishes
Smoking: No smoking in dining room
Accommodation: 24 en suite
Credit cards: 🟦 ▤ ▩ ▩ 🅲

Directions: 4 miles from A595 coast at route at Holmbrook.

GLENRIDDING,
Glenridding Hotel

Friendly, village-centre hotel with fine views of Ullswater. Series of public rooms take in a lively bar and informal restaurant, as well as the main dining room looking onto the lake. Good honest cooking in dishes such as Cumberland pork pâté with apricot sauce, country vegetable soup, rack of lamb with sauce Robert, and lemon soufflé.

Additional: Bar food; Sunday L; Children welcome; ✪ dishes
Smoking: No smoking in dining room
Accommodation: 40 en suite
Credit cards: 🟦 🟦 🟦 🟦 🟦 🟦

Directions: In the centre of the village

Penrith CA11 0PB
Map 12: NY53
Tel: 017684 82228
Fax: 017684 82555
Chefs: Paul Lloyd, Jared Steiner
Owner: John Melling
Cost: Alc £15, fixed-price D £26.50.
☺ H/wine £10.95.
Times: Open all day from noon-last D 9.45pm

GRASMERE, # Gold Rill Hotel

Quietly situated country house hotel enjoying uninterrupted lake and fell views. Fair cooking of a daily changing four-course dinner menu along the line of deep-fried ham and sweetcorn beignets with a sweet and sour sauce, tomato and tarragon soup, roasted haunch of venison with a smoked bacon and red wine sauce, and sticky toffee pudding.

Additional: Bar snacks L (12.15pm-1.45pm);
No children under 5; ✪ dishes
Smoking: No smoking in dining room
Accommodation: 25 en suite
Credit cards: 🟦 🟦 🟦

Directions: M6/J36 then A590/591: Red Bank Road in centre of village opposite St Oswalds Church. Hotel 200yds on L

Red Bank Road LA22 9PU
Map 11: NY30
Tel/Fax: 015394 35486
Chef: Ian Thompson
Owners: Paul & Cathy Jewsbury
Cost: Fixed-price D £18.50. ☺
H/wine £9.80.
Times: D only, 7.30pm-8.30pm

GRASMERE, # Grasmere Hotel

Broadgate LA22 9TA
Map 11: NY30
Tel/Fax: 015394 35277
Chef: Gretchen Riley
Owners: Paul & Gretchen Riley
Cost: Fixed-price D £15 (5 courses).
☺ H/wine £9.50.
Times: D only, 6.45pm-last D 7.30pm. Closed Jan
Additional: Bar meals D. No children under 16; ✪ dishes
Smoking: No smoking in dining room
Accommodation: 12 en suite
Credit cards: 🟦 🟦 🟦

Sheltered in grounds that stretch down to the River Rothay, this hotel serves good value traditional English dishes. Main courses might include poached fillet of plaice and sautéed breast of turkey. At a recent meal locally smoked Cumberland and venison sausages were served with wholegrain mustard.

Directions: A short distance from the village centre, by the river

GRASMERE,

Michael's Nook Hotel ❀❀❀❀

Ambleside LA22 9RP
Map 11: NY30
Tel: 015394 35496
Fax: 015394 35645

Chef: Mark Treasure

Owner: Mr R S E Gifford
Cost: Fixed-price L £31.50 (4 courses)/D £41.50 (5 courses) £48.50 (6 courses). H/wine £10.50
Times: 12.30pm-1pm/7.30pm- last D 8pm
Additional: No children under 7
Seats: 50. Private dining room 35. Jacket & tie preferred
Smoking: No smoking in dining room
Accommodation: 14 en suite
Credit cards: 📷 📷 📷 📷 📷 📷

Good food has long been one of the great strengths of this stunning hotel overlooking Grasmere. However, the arrival of chef Mark Treasure has moved the set-up into top gear. Since our last inspection he has really found his feet and consolidated his brigade; the result is formidable. Here is up-to-the-minute, ambitious cooking brimming with confidence, in a style that Treasure himself describes as European, but pulls influences from all over the Mediterranean, and incorporates his own interpretations of many benchmark French classics. Canapés, for instance, are terrific, dainty little examples of the dishes featured on the menu: a tartlet of braised ham hock with garlic and thyme; a small monkfish beignet with hollandaise; a tiny piece of seared salmon with pesto; a piece of hot foie gras on a crisp crouton. Breads too, are truly exceptional, just a notch below those offered by Pierre Koffmann at Tante Claire, and Michael Caines at Gidleigh Park. A dinner in February produced some top-drawer dishes: excellent Parma ham risotto, the rice flavoured by some pied de mouton mushrooms, and the ham crisped up on top of the rice, and outstanding texture – just a bit of bite and a good amount of liquid without being sloppy; duck confit with a claret glaze, the rich purpley reduction just enough to cut the fatty meat, and served with a tower of fondant potato, some caramelised shallots and a base of excellent spinach; spot-on chocolate marquise with an exceptional bitter chocolate flavour. The six-course gourmet dinner is a balance between unashamed luxury ingredients – foie gras, lobster, truffles – and Mark Treasure's straightforward approach which works on the exact yet rounded flavours that are brought out. Lunches also keep pace, with a typical meal including boned quail, leek and truffle tortellini, then chicken and tarragon bouillon, followed by braised ham hock, cassoulet of garlic, foie gras and thyme, with coconut soufflé to finish. Service is led by the proprietor, Reg Gifford, who is very much at ease as a host.

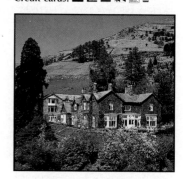

Directions: On N side of Grasmere. From A591, turn uphill at The Swan, bear L for 400yds.

The wine list deserves applause for some very fair mark ups particularly in respect of mature Bordeaux and Burgundy. Elsewhere, there is abundant choice under £20 with some creditable New World examples, including the spirited Meerlust Rubicon at £19.75. Half-bottles abound.

Signature dishes: Smoked best-end of lamb, shallot mousseline; deep-fried langoustine, hollandaise; red mullet potage; braised ham hock, cassoulet of garlic, thyme and tomato.

GRASMERE, **Oak Bank Hotel**

Traditional Lakeland house by the River Rothay where obvious effort goes into house-party style dinners in which Windermere char with grapes or pork with stage and onion stuffing might be preceded by Thai crab cakes or fennel and pear soup. Popular slow-cooked Aga dishes include spring lamb moutard.

Additional: Bar food L; Children welcome; ❸ dishes
Smoking: No smoking in dining room
Accommodation: 15 en suite.
Credit cards: 💳 💳 ▯

Directions: 4 miles Ambleside, 8 miles Windermere, 12 miles Keswick

Broadgate LA22 9TA
Map 7: NY30
Tel: 015394 35217
Chefs: Paul Barber,
Sharon Savasi
Owners: Mr & Mrs AL Savasi
Cost: Fixed-price D £16.75 (5 courses). ☺
Times: Last L 2pm/last D 8pm.
Closed Jan

GRASMERE,
Rothay Garden Hotel

Set in the beautiful vale of Grasmere, this traditional Lakeland building has a conservatory restaurant overlooking two acres of illuminated gardens. The ambitious menu might include delicately poached salmon with basil fondue, or game terrine with mulberry coulis. Home-made desserts, such as sticky toffee pudding, are also popular.

Directions: From the south take junction 36 from M6 and follow the A590/A591 to Grasmere. From the north take junction 40 from M6 and follow A66 to Keswick, then A591 to Grasmere

Broadgate LA22 9RJ
Map 11: NY30
Tel: 015394 35334
Fax: 015394 35723
Chef: Andrew Burton
Owner: Christopher Carss
Cost: Fixed-price L £9.50/D £19 (5 courses). ☺ H/wine £10.50.
Times: Last L 1.45pm/last D 9pm
Additional: Sunday L; Bar meals L; No children under 5; ❸ dishes
Smoking: No smoking in dining room
Accommodation: 26 en suite
Credit cards: 💳 💳 💳 ▯

GRASMERE, **The Swan**

Famous old inn, over 300-years-old. Meals at this sophisticated village hostelry might start with sauté chicken livers with bacon and garlic, or rollmop herrings with dill mayonnaise, followed by Scottish sirloin of beef with red wine jus, or roast loin of pork with orange and brandy sauce.

Smoking: No smoking in dining room
Accommodation: 38 en suite. **Credit cards:** 💳 💳 💳 💳 💳 ▯

Directions: On the A591

Ambleside LA22 9RF
Map 7: NY30
Tel: 015394 3555
Fax: 015394 3547
Chef: Beverley Holmes
Cost: Alc £18.95, fixed-price L £10
Additional: Bar food, Sunday L; No children under 5; ❸ dishes

GRASMERE, White Moss House

This gem of a Lakeland house gained fame because it was bought by William Wordworth for his son, and the poet himself was often to be seen on walkabout in the area. Since 1980, however, it has been the domain of Sue and Peter Dixon who have nurtured it into one of the most captivating of country house hotels. Guests sit down to dinner at 8pm in the cottagey dining room in the oldest part of the building. What they are offered is a five-course menu (with no choice until desserts) that is firmly in keeping with the atmosphere of the place. Ingredients are chosen with loyalty to the region and the seasons, and they are proudly publicised. An inspection taken in April showed exactly what the kitchen is about. Proceedings began with baby fennel, apple and asparagus soup before peat-smoked Whitby haddock 'married' with Westmorland smoked cheese, chives and chervil. The centrepiece was crispy roast Lakeland mallard (cooked in the Aga) with a sauce of local damsons, port and Pinot Noir accompanied by splendid vegetables including tiny glazed turnips and a purée of salsify, celeriac and parsnip with heather honey. To finish there was sticky toffee pudding with pecan and toffee sauce followed by some rare British cheeses. The cumulative effect was one of unaffected Englishness.

Rydal Water Ambleside LA22 9SE
Map 11: NY30
Tel: 015394 35295
Fax: 015394 34612
Chefs: Peter Dixon, Colin Percival
Owners: Mr & Mrs P Dixon
Cost: Fixed-price D £27.50 (5 courses). H/wine £9.50
Times: D only 8pm. Closed Sun, Dec-Feb
Additional: No Children under 8
Seats: 18
Smoking: No smoking in dining room
Accommodation: 8 (7 en suite)
Credit cards: ▬ ▬ ▬ ▬

Directions: On A591 between Grasmere and Ambleside opposite Rydal Water

GRASMERE, Wordsworth Hotel

Ambleside LA22 9SW
Map 11: NY30
Tel: 015394 35592
Fax: 015394 35765
Chef: Bernard Warne
Owner: R Gifford
Cost: Fixed-price L £18/D £31 (4 courses). H/wine £13
Times: 12.30pm-2pm/7pm-9pm (9.30pm Fri, Sat)
Additional: Bar food L; Sunday L; Children welcome; ❸ dishes
Seats: 65. Private dining room 16 & 80. Jacket & tie preferred
Smoking: No smoking in dining room; air-conditioning
Accommodation: 37 en suite
Credit cards: ▬ ▬ ▬ ▬ ▬

Although bang in the centre of the village, there is a peaceful atmosphere to this grand tourist bolt hole, helped, no doubt, by the fact that it lies close to the churchyard where William Wordsworth is buried. In the restaurant, fittingly decorated throughout in daffodil yellow, the setting is civilised and gracious with table appointments in Wedgwood and silver, lots of fresh flowers and a conservatory. The kitchen shows a determined willingness to please, cooking with enthusiasm a blend of contemporary and traditional dishes in a modern style. Results on the plate are enjoyable, as could be seen in a spring dinner that took in leek and ham hock terrine with a beetroot chutney, chicken soup, then fillet steak with black pudding, foie gras, creamed potato and a Madeira jus, and a white chocolate box with bitter chocolate and orange mousse to finish. Excellent small details too, from bread that included a wedge of shallot and Cheddar cottage loaf, a slice from a fruit bloomer, a delicately baked petit pain, an amuse-bouche of barquette filled with roasted sesame and onion cream quiche base, to the florentines of the petits fours.

Directions: In the village centre next to the church

HOWTOWN, Sharrow Bay

Sharrow Bay
Penrith CA10 2LZ
Map 12: NY41
Tel/Fax: 017684 86301
Chefs: Johnnie Martin, Colin Akrigg
Owners: Francis Coulson, Brian Sack
Cost: Fixed-price L £32.25 (4 courses)/D £42.75 (5 courses). H/wine £13.95
Times: 1pm-last L 1.30pm/8pm-last D 8.30pm. Closed end Dec-end Feb
Additional: Sunday L; No children under 13; ❸ dishes
Seats: 65. Jacket and tie preferred
Smoking: No smoking in dining room; air conditioning
Accommodation: 28 en suite
Credit cards: 🃏

The year 1998 will be a landmark, marking the fiftieth season of Sharrow Bay. When Francis Coulson bought the place, he had in mind a new kind of retreat, 'the country house hotel'. The house itself, built in 1840, is still a gem with its low angled roof and wide eaves reminiscent of a villa on the Italian lakes. In fact the setting is Ullswater, with 12 acres of grounds and gardens and the Hellvelyn mountains in the distance. The views continue to enchant visitors from all corners of the globe. Inside, much pleasure hinges around the food served in the two dining rooms. Lunch is four courses, dinner runs to six (including British cheeses). In the evening, guests assemble and sit down at 8pm for a measured bonanza of Anglo/French dishes with assured flavours, based around an abundance of Lakeland produce ranging from Mr Woodall's Waberthwaite ham to saddle of local venison. An inspection meal ran as follows: duck foie gras with Stilton, bacon and onion rösti in Madeira sauce; fillet of halibut with sweet and sour sauce and a suissesse cheese soufflé; tender pink noisette of lamb with a dariole of leeks and courgettes in white wine, tomato and thyme sauce and, to crown it all, a delectable sticky toffee sponge in a class of its own. The kitchen also shows its prowess and confidence with smoked chicken consommé with a herb dumpling, fried scallops with provençale vegetables, smoked salmon and pesto, and fried calves' liver with a red onion marmalade and a Dubonnet and orange sauce, not to mention Old English syllabub. Wonderful afternoon teas and breakfasts simply add to the delights of a stay at this most remarkable of country hotels.

Signature dishes: roast leg of Lakeland spring lamb served with onion sauce, mint sauce and gravy made with the goodness of the lamb; escalope of local Eden salmon served on a bed of buttered spinach, with a champagne and salmon caviar sauce; Scottish grouse roasted on a bed of celery, apple and onions, served with bread sauce, bacon, allumette potatoes, redcurrant jelly and port wine gravy made from juices; roast saddle of local venison served with celeriac purée, glazed apple, roasted chestnuts and juniper berry and dill sauce.

Directions: Turn off A592 through Pooley Bridge, turn R (signed to Howtown), hotel 2 miles

KESWICK, Dale Head Hall ✾

Splendid, family-run country house set in secluded grounds overlooking Thirlmere. Noted for its warm hospitality and modern British cooking, the short, imaginative five-course dinner menu may feature apple and celery soup, baked brill with watercress sauce, and treacle tart. Good wines.

Smoking: No smoking in dining room
Accommodation: 9 en suite
Credit cards: ▣ ▦ ▦ ▧ ▣

Directions: 12 miles M6/J40, half way between Keswick and Grasmere.

Lake Thirlmere
CA12 4TN
Map 11: NY22
Tel: 0800 454166
Fax: 017687 71070
Chefs: Malcolm Mavin, Caroline Bonhenburg
Owners: Mr & Mrs A Lowe & family
Cost: Fixed-price D £25 (6 courses).
Times: D only, 7.30pm-8.30pm
Additional: No children under 12; 🍴 dishes

KESWICK, Grange Hotel ✾

Daily changing five-course dinners, featuring honest cooking, are an attraction at this elegant Lakeland house, set above the town with superb views of the surrounding fells. Expect carrot and coriander soup, guinea fowl with cranberry and tarragon sauce, and chocolate and brandy terrine to finish.

Smoking: No smoking in dining room
Accommodation: 10 en suite
Credit cards: ▣ ▦

Directions: A591 (Windermere) for 1 mile. 1st R, hotel 200yds on R

Manor Brow
Ambleside Road CA12 4BA
Map 11: NY22
Tel: 017687 72500
Chef: Colin Brown
Owners: Mr & Mrs D Miller
Cost: Fixed-price D £19.75 (5 courses). ☺ H/wine £9.25.
Times: D only, 7pm-last D 8pm.
Closed mid Nov-mid March
Additional: No children under 7; 🍴 dishes

KESWICK, Swinside Lodge ✾✾

Newlands CA12 5UE
Map 11: NY22
Tel/Fax: 017687 72948
Chef: Christopher Astley
Owner: Graham Taylor
Cost: Fixed-price dinner £24 (4 courses). ☺
Times: D only, 7.30pm-8pm.
Closed Dec-mid Feb
Additional: No children under 12
Seats: 18
Smoking: No smoking throughout
Accommodation: 7 en suite
Credit cards: None

This little gem of a Victorian lakeland hotel is set in its own gardens, surrounded by pasture and with Derwentwater only a five-minute stroll away. Although the five-course dinners offer no choice until dessert, they are carefully constructed and, in fact, many guests do not look at the menu beforehand, preferring to be surprised. A late spring visit produced some lovely new season lamb with cep flavoured couscous and rosemary sauce, a pan-fried fillet of cod on a bed of endive and potato salad with dill and lemon vinaigrette, plus some well-made leek and watercress soup. Star of the meal was a 'melt-in-the-mouth' blackcurrant delice on a thin sponge base with a matching sorbet. Other nights there may be home-made pasta with oyster mushrooms, white wine and parsley sauce, cream of fennel soup, baked fillets of Borrowdale trout with watercress stuffing and dill butter sauce, and either glazed lemon tart, or warm apple and almond pudding with Greek yoghurt. The house is unlicensed but guests are welcome to bring their own wine and a complimentary sherry is served prior to dinner.

Directions: 3 miles SW of Keswick. Take the A66 for Cockermouth, L at Portinscale, follow road to Grange

KESWICK,

Thwaite Howe Hotel

Relaxed, personally run hotel surrounded by magnificent views. A five-course dinner is served at 7pm. Although no choice, good country-house cooking takes in citrus prawns with grapefruit and orange slices and zesty mayonnaise, silky textured vegetable soup, stuffed breast of chicken with wild mushrooms and bacon, and a delicious lemon posset.

Smoking: No smoking in dining room
Accommodation: 8 en suite
Credit cards: ■ ▬ ▰ □

Thornthwaite CA12 5SA
Map 11: NY22
Tel: 017687 78281
Fax: 017687 78529
Chef: Mary Kay
Owners: Harry & Mary Kay
Cost: Fixed-price D £16.50. ☺
H/wine £7.95.
Times: D only at 7pm, booking essential. Closed Nov-Feb
Additional: No children under 12

Directions: From A66 W of Keswick, follow signs to Thornthwaite Gallery. Hotel signed from there.

KIRKBY LONSDALE,

Cobwebs Restaurant

A Victorian country house set in four acres of grounds in the quiet Roman town of Kirkby Lonsdale. There's a daily changing, fixed four-course menu, presented before dinner, but booking in advance is a necessity. Home-made starters might include butter bean and lemon soup, and cornet of lemon sole filled with wild salmon mousse.

Smoking: No smoking in dining room
Accommodation: 5 en suite
Credit cards: ■ ▬

Leck Cowan Bridge LA6 2HZ
Map 7: SD67
Tel/Fax: 015242 72141
Chef: Yvonne Thompson
Owners: Yvonne Thompson & Paul Kelly
Cost: Fixed price D £25. ☺
H/wine £8
Times: D only, 7.30pm-8pm.
Closed Sun, Mon, Jan- Feb
Additional: No children under 12; ◖ dishes

Directions: From M6/J36 take A65 (Skipton), 8 miles to Cowan Bridge, L to Leck, hotel on L 200 yds

KIRKBY LONSDALE, Hipping Hall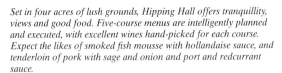

Set in four acres of lush grounds, Hipping Hall offers tranquillity, views and good food. Five-course menus are intelligently planned and executed, with excellent wines hand-picked for each course. Expect the likes of smoked fish mousse with hollandaise sauce, and tenderloin of pork with sage and onion and port and redcurrant sauce.

Smoking: No smoking in dining room
Accommodation: 7 en suite
Credit cards: ■ ▬ ▬ ▰ □

Cowan Bridge LA6 2JJ
Map 7: SD67
Tel: 015242 71187
Fax: 015242 72452
Chef: Jocelyn Bryant
Owners: Ian & Jocelyn Bryant
Cost: Fixed-price D £24 (5 courses).
☺ H/wine £16.
Times: D at 8pm. Closed Nov-Feb
Additional: No children under 12; ◖ dishes

Directions: On A65, 2.5 miles E of Kirkby Lonsdale

MUNGRISDALE, **The Mill Hotel** ✿

Pentrith CA11 0XR
Map 11: NY33
Tel: 017687 79659
Fax: 017687 79155
Chef: Eleanor Quinlan
Owners: Richard & Eleanor Quinlan
Cost: Fixed-price D £23 (5 courses).
☺ H/wine £9.75.
Times: D only, 7pm-8pm.
Closed Nov-Feb
Additional: Children welcome;
❹ dishes
Smoking: No smoking in dining room
Accommodation: 7 en suite
Credit cards: None

Memorable desserts highlight the well balanced five-course dinners,
served at this peaceful former seventeenth-century mill cottage.
Beetroot and parsnip soup, and herbed loin of lamb with caper sauce,
followed by lemon and ginger pudding and good cheeses should
satisfy the heartiest of Lakeland appetites. Well-chosen list of wines.

Directions: Mungrisdale is signed on A66 midway between
Penrith & Keswick. Hotel 2 miles N of A66

NEWBY BRIDGE, **Lakeside Hotel** ✿✿

Ulverston LA12 8AT
Map 7: SD38
Tel: 015395 31207
Fax: 015395 31699
Chef: Didier Bievaime
Owner: Neville Talbot
Cost: Fixed-price D £27.50.
H/wine £12
Times: D only, 7pm-9.30pm
Additional: Bar meals L; Sunday L
only; Children welcome; ❹ dishes
Seats: 65. Private dining room 26;
air-conditioning
Smoking: No smoking in dining room
Accommodation: 72 en suite
Credit cards: ▬ ▦ ▨ ▧ ▣ ▨

Peacefully set on the southern shore of Lake Windermere, next
to the steamer and steam railway terminus, this is a spacious,
comfortable hotel. Good views from the large conservatory
adjoining the stately restaurant where sound cooking is a
major plus to a stay here. Typical dishes may include French
onion soup, herb-crusted rack of lamb with Dijon mustard, and
hot walnut and apricot pudding. Our inspector opted for
raviolo of goat's cheese with artichoke, then a coconut and
pineapple sorbet, followed by duckling with a confit of the leg
bound by a chiffonade of cabbage; accompanying vegetables
were simple but well cooked. Dessert was a chocolate parfait
with a coffee bean sauce, smooth, light, but rich with it. Service
is attentive, courteous, and thorough with good detail and skill.
The wine list reflects a high calibre cellar, and you pay for the
privilege.

Directions: M6/J36 follow A590 to Newby Bridge, R over
bridge, follow Hawkeshead Road for 1 mile

RAVENSTONEDALE,

Black Swan Hotel

Near Kirkby Stephen CA17 4NG
Map 12: NY62

Only ten minutes drive from the M6, this popular hotel is the focal point of a picturesque village. Antique furniture, a log fire in the bar, real ales, and well cooked traditional food that steers away from modern concepts, are all major pluses. Expect celery and apple soup, Gressingham duck with brandy sauce, and trifle.

Tel: 015396 23204
Fax: 015396 23604
Chef: Mrs NW Stuart
Owners: GB & NW Stuart
Cost: *Alc* £15, fixed-price L £9.75/D £23 (5 courses). ☺ H/wine £6.
Times: Last L 2pm/D 9pm

Additional: Bar food; Sunday L; Children welcome; ◑ dishes
Seats: 40. Private dining room 16
Smoking: No smoking in dining room
Accommodation: 16 en suite.
Credit cards: ▬ ▦ ▦ 🔖

Directions: M6/J38/A685 (Brough). Through Kirkby Stephen, then to Ravenstonedale

TEMPLE SOWERBY,

Temple Sowerby House Hotel

Near Penrith, CA10 1RZ
Map 12: NY62

Elegantly furnished former farmhouse with Georgian additions, set in extensive grounds in the village centre. Honest English fare, competently prepared from quality raw ingredients, is served in the attractive dining areas. Expect mushroom soup, sautéed venison with caramelised apples, port and redcurrants, and prune and Armagnac tart.

Tel: 017683 61578/0800 146147
Fax: 017683 61958
Chef: Andrew Walker
Owners: Cécile & Geoffrey Temple
Cost: *Alc* £25. H/wine £9.75 ☺
Times: 11am-6pm/D 7pm-8.45pm

Additional: Bar food L; Sunday L; Children welcome; ◑ dishes
Smoking: No smoking in dining room
Accommodation: 12 en suite.
Credit cards: ▬ ▦ ▦ ▰ ▢

Directions: On A66 5 miles E of Penrith in village centre

TROUTBECK,

Queen's Head Hotel ✿ NEW

Town Head LA23 1PW
Map 7: SD40

A popular seventeenth-century coaching inn with beamed ceilings, log fires and an Elizabethan four-poster bed built into the bar. Eat in the relaxing bar, or the more formal restaurant; soundly cooked food is served in both. Expect steak, ale and mushroom cobbler, and pot roast venison studded with apricots.

Tel: 015394 32174
Fax: 015394 31938
Chef: Sean Morrell
Owners: Mark Stewardson, Joanne Sherratt
Cost: *Alc* £16.75. H/wine £8.75 ☺
Times: Last L 2pm/D 9pm.
Closed 25 Dec

Additional: Children welcome; ◑ dishes
Accommodation: 9 en suite.
Credit cards: ▬ ▦ ▰ ▢

Directions: On the A592, approx 2 miles from Windermere

ULVERSTON, Bay Horse Inn

LA12 9EL
Map 7: SD27
Tel: 01229 583972
Fax: 01229 580502
Chef/Owner: Robert Lyons
Cost: *Alc* £25, fixed-price L £15.75.
☺ H/wine £13.95
Times: Noon-last L 1.30pm/7.30pm-
last D 8pm. Closed L Sun, L Mon
Additional: Bar food L; No children
under 12; ♨ dishes
Seats: 50. Private dining room 30 &
20
Smoking: No smoking in dining room
Accommodation: 7 en suite
Credit cards: ▬ ▦ ▧ ▨

Despite the drab approach route, through bland industrial
estates and past a vast factory, the Bay Horse enjoys a
picturesque setting with stunning views across the Levens
Estuary. Essentially an old-style inn, the inn is home to an
excellent restaurant, where a short but well-balanced menu is
served. Created with flair by the skilled hand of Bobby Lyons,
dishes to look out for include tender roast grouse with game
chips and gaufrette potatoes; Aberdeen Angus steak with crisp
green beans and shredded spring cabbage, and chilled
gazpacho – a tangy, smooth blend of tomatoes, peppers, onion
and bread crumbs. Desserts are along the lines of fresh
raspberry and frangelico mousse, served with hot, freshly
baked buttery shortbread. The small loyal team of staff
provide friendly but professional service, ensuring that a visit
to the Bay Horse is always pleasurable.

Directions: From A590 entering Ulverston follow signs for
Canal Foot

WATERMILLOCK, Leeming House

Penrith CA11 0JJ
Map 12: NY42
Tel: 017684 86622
Fax: 017684 86443
Chef: Adam Marks
Owners: Forte UK Ltd
Cost: *Alc* £18.50 (ex Sun), fixed-price
D £31.50 (4 courses) £37.95 (6
courses). H/wine £13.45

An elegant Regency hotel overlooking Ullswater and the
rugged fells beyond. It was not far from here that Wordsworth
wrote his famous poem; it is still possible, despite the ever-
increasing numbers of visitors to the area, to "wander lonely as
a cloud". If striding up some of the region's more challenging
hills doesn't grab you, then perhaps a relaxing stroll in the
hotel's 20 acres of terraced lawns and woodland (where red

squirrels are often sighted) is more for you. Either way be sure to experience the modern British cooking of Adam Marks, served in the delightful mirrored dining room. Main courses might include grilled fillet of Cornish sole with lemon oil, cinnamon rice and wood-roasted peppers, grilled breast of Lunesdale duckling with creamy onion sauce and a cranberry and port coulis, and roast loin of pork with shallot gravy and traditional stuffing. The wine list features some interesting bottles from the New and Old Worlds.

Directions: From M6/J40 A592 (Ullswater) then signs for Patterdale. Hotel is 2.5 miles along W shore of lake in Watermillock

Times: 12.30pm-last L 1.45pm/7.30pm-last D 8.45pm
Additional: Sunday L; Bar meals; Children welcome; 🍴 dishes
Seats: 60. Private dining room 33. Jacket and tie preferred
Smoking: No smoking in dining room
Accommodation: 40 en suite
Credit cards: ▆ ▆ ▆ ▆ ▆ ▆

WATERMILLOCK,
Old Church Hotel ❁

Penrith CA11 OJN
Map 12: NY42
Tel: 017684 86204
Fax: 017684 86368
Chef: Kevin Whitemore
Owner: Kevin & Maureen Whitemore
Cost: Alc £25. H/wine £12.50. ☺
Times: D only, 7.30pm-8.15pm. Closed Sun, Nov-March
Additional: No children under 8
Smoking: No smoking in dining room
Accommodation: 10 en suite
Credit cards: ▆ ▆ ▆

Beautifully maintained eighteenth-century house on the shores of Ullswater with views of the surrounding fells. Quality ingredients highlight such dishes as penne with prosciutto and sun-dried tomatoes, pork fillet with horseradish cream sauce, and honey and walnut tart.

Directions: On A592 2 miles S of Poole Bridge, 15 minutes' drive from M6/J40

WATERMILLOCK, Rampsbeck
Country House Hotel ❁❁❁

Penrith CA11 0LP
Map 12: NY42
Tel: 017684 86442
Fax: 017684 86688
Chef: Andrew McGeorge
Owners: TI & MM Gibb
Cost: Fixed-price L £22/D £26-£38.50 (4 courses). H/wine £10.25
Times: L by prior arrangement (except Sun L)/7pm-last D 8pm.
Additional: Bar food L; Sunday L; No children under 7; 🍴 dishes
Seats: 40. Jacket and tie preferred
Smoking: No smoking in dining room
Accommodation: 21 en suite
Credit cards: ▆ ▆

Rampsbeck has much to commend it: a wonderful lakeside setting, 18 acres of grounds, warm hospitality, and the skilful cooking of Andrew McGeorge. They do things in style here. Dinner is a grand affair, with a choice of three menus – a vegetarian, table d'hôte and a *carte* – plus a host of extras: delicious canapés, an appetiser, sorbet course, and petits fours with coffee. That creativity and flair is at work in the kitchen is in no doubt, and ingredients are treated with respect, allowing authentic flavours to shine through. A spring dinner opened with an amuse-gueule of lobster tortellini with lobster sauce and julienne of spring vegetables, before going on to lovely, big juicy pan-fried scallops, served with a herb risotto presented in a tower containing a leaf of leek – 'just perfect'. Vegetable soup was based on a pronounced chicken stock base and was lightly spiced with ginger, with finely sliced vegetables just gently cooked. Roast suprême of corn-fed guinea fowl proved to be plump and tender and came with a 'lip smacking' jus garnished with ceps, which would have been quite enough, but in addition were some some fondant potato, a strongly flavoured boudin of leg meat, and a small piece of foie gras, which 'whilst enjoyable, did little to enhance the main ingredient'. Dessert was a warm, dense chocolate tart, with pistachio ice cream and an exceptionally light chocolate and pistachio mousse. Creative in presentation, rich in flavour, pastry work is an obvious strength of the brigade. Home-made bread is excellent too; six different rolls including olive and an unusual Cumberland sausage flavour, were offered at dinner. Wines are listed by style rather than geography, an approach that some will find user friendly, others frustrating. The contents however are unquestionably accessible, with a global range of imaginative bins displaying impressive value for money. Notable examples include the 1989 vintage of the superlative Château Musar from Lebanon at £18.50 and the elegant Château Léoville Barton from the same vintage at £22.50. A respectable number of bins are also available in half bottles.

Signature dishes: Steamed sea bass with langoustine noodles and a tomato and basil dressing; poached white peach with pan-fried foie gras and a passion fruit dressing; roasted grouse with damsons; Cumbrian venison with creamed celeriac and Parmentier potatoes.

Directions: M6/J4, follow signs to Ullswater, turn R at water's edge. hotel 1.25 miles on R

Rampsbeck Country House Hotel

WINDERMERE,
Beech Hill Hotel ❀❀

Terraced extensions stretching down to the jetty on Lake Windermere are a magnet for guests visiting this ever-improving hotel. Dinner is served in the plush surroundings of the elevated Gallery Restaurant which provides stupendous views of the lake and Langdale Fells. A new chef is at the helm and he is already proving his worth, judging by recent reports. The daily changing fixed-price menu is backed up by a *carte* of accomplished modern dishes with cream and richness in abundance. Interesting home-baked breads (smoked salmon with ginger, for example) and good amuse-bouche set the tone, before starters such as 'melt-in-the-mouth' confit of Cartmel duck on a bed of couscous with blueberry sauce, or cold salad of marinated ostrich. Next comes a soup or sorbet before main

Newby Bridge Road
Cartmel Fell
LA23 3LR
Map 7: SD49
Tel: 015394 42137
Fax: 015394 43745
Chef: Nick Stopford
Owner: Keith & Ann Richardson
Cost: Fixed-price D £27.50 (3 courses).
Times: D only, 7pm-last D 9.30pm
Additional: Bar food; Sunday L; Children welcome; ❸ dishes
Seats: 80. Private dining room 20
Smoking: No smoking in dining room

Beech Hill Hotel

Accommodation: 53 en suite
Credit cards:

courses along the lines of grilled fillet of sea bass on pommes Anna with a vegetable basket and rich herb butter sauce, or mille-feuille of local smoked chicken accompanied by leek fricassée. To finish, a trio of chocolate truffe with its trio of liqueur laced sauces founded on 'a pint of clotted cream' proved to be a calorifically risky extravaganza. The wine list is sound and includes representatives from many lands.

Directions: On A592, Newby Bridge 4 miles from Windermere

WINDERMERE,
Fayrer Garden House

Lyth Valley Road
Windermere LA23 3JP
Map 7: SD49
Tel: 015394 88195
Fax: 015394 45986
Chefs: Edward Wilkinson
Owner: Iain & Jackie Garside
Cost: Fixed-price D £19.50. ☺
H/wine £8.95.
Times: Last L 1.45pm/last D 8.15pm
Additional: Bar meals L;
No children under 5; ♦ dishes
Smoking: No smoking in dining room;
air-conditioning
Accommodation: 18 rooms
Credit cards:

A Victorian country house standing in five acres of grounds, with a beautiful conservatory restaurant overlooking Lake Windermere. The fixed-price menu changes daily to reflect market availability of seasonal produce. Popular dishes include potted Morecambe Bay shrimps, roast breast of Barbary duck and tangy lemon tart.

Directions: On A5074 1 mile from town centre

WINDERMERE,
Gilpin Lodge Hotel ❀❀❀

Over the years, Christine and John Cunliffe have transformed this turn-of-the-century Lake residence into 'an exceptionally nice hotel' with an endearing mood of honest homeliness. 'Food is our pleasant obsession' proclaims their brochure and

Crook Road LA23 3NE
Map 7: SD49
Tel: 015394 88818
Fax: 015394 88058
Chef: Christopher Davies
Owners: John & Christine Cunliffe

Gilpin Lodge Hotel

Cost: *Alc* (L only) £16, fixed-price D
£27.50 (4 courses). H/wine £11.75.
Times: Noon-last L 2.30pm/7pm-last
D 8.45pm
Additional: Bar food L; Sunday L;
No children under 7; ⚫ dishes
Seats: 65. Private dining rooms 14-28
Smoking: No smoking in dining room
Accommodation: 14 en suite
Credit cards: 🔲 🔲 🔲 🔲 🔲

that is easy to believe. Light meals and lunches are served in
the lounge or dining room and the menu aims for flexibility –
have just a roast beef sandwich or a bowl of mussels or pick
something more substantial such as grilled salmon with
mustard and dill butter. The four-course dinner menu is an
ambitious affair providing plenty of choice across the board.
Suprême of wood pigeon and home-made sausage is served on
a bed of celeriac and spring cabbage with a thyme jus, while
roast red snapper arrives on a julienne of peppers and fennel
with sherry vinaigrette. At inspection, chargrilled scallops
appeared with sweet potato, bacon and parsnip lyonnaise
tinged with an orange, mussel and coriander jus. Next was an
intense lobster bisque laced with cognac and finished with
whipped crème fraîche. After a palate-cleansing apple and
Calvados sorbet, came roast breast of Goosnargh duckling,
with pink flesh and skin just crisp, served with a confit of leg,
candied parsnip and a spicy sauce of honey, thyme and grain
mustard. A fair selection of farmhouse cheeses can be ordered
instead of desserts such as baked vanilla cream and sugar-
crusted strawberries with a glazed Champagne sabayon. The
carefully assembled wine list offers plenty of fine drinking
from around the world, with half bottles providing strong
back-up.

Directions: M6/J36 & A590/(Kendal), then B5284 for 5 miles

WINDERMERE,
Hillthwaite House Hotel ✿

Thornbarrow Road LA23 2DF
Map 7: SD49
Tel: 015394 43636
Fax: 015394 88660
Telephone for details

*The restaurant at this long established hotel has lovely views over the
lake and surrounding area. The restaurant is an attractive room, in
three parts, with a conservatory extension. Expect duck with bean
sprouts in an orange sauce, excellent potato soup, lamb's liver with
red onions and Madeira sauce, and crème brûlée.*

WINDERMERE, # Holbeck Ghyll ✿✿

Holbeck Lane
LA23 1LU
Map 7: SD49
Tel: 015394 32375
Fax: 015394 34743
Chef: Jake Watkins
Owners: David & Patricia Nicholson
Cost: Fixed-price D £25-£29 (3-4
courses).

Once used as a hunting lodge by Lord Lonsdale (of 'boxing
belt' fame), this charming Victorian mansion has breathtaking
views of Lake Windermere and Langdale Fells. A recently
completed terrace restaurant now provides an alternative
setting to the magnificent oak-panelled dining room, and both
have a great outlook onto the countryside. New chef Jake
Watkins (ex-Hunters, Alresford) is a passionate cook who is

Holbeck Ghyll Hotel

Times: Noon-last L 2.30pm/7pm-last D 8.45pm
Additional: Sunday L; No children under 8; 🍴 dishes
Seats: 45. Private dining room 20
Smoking: No smoking in dining room
Accommodation: 14 en suite
Credit cards: ▨ ▨ ▨ 🄯 🄳

aiming high. Four-course dinners begin in style with imaginative canapés (deep-fried crisp beetroot and cabbage, for example) plus excellent mini-rolls. As a starter our inspector opted for chargrilled tuna with sauce vierge and a decoration of mixed herbs and diced pepper. The main course was a mille-feuille of potato, braised white cabbage and guinea fowl enriched with a slice of pâté de foie gras. To finish, there was a full flavoured ginger parfait served with an assortment of diced dried fruits. Over 100 wines provide reliable drinking from around the world.

Directions: 3 miles N of Windermere on A591. Turn R into Holbeck Lane. Hotel is 0.5 miles on L

WINDERMERE,
Langdale Chase Hotel

Windermere LA23 1LW
Map 7: SD49
Tel: 015394 32201
Fax: 015394 32604
Chef: Wendy Linders
Owner: Thomas G Noblett
Cost: Alc £20, fixed-price L £15 (4 courses)/D £26 (5 courses). ☺ H/wine £11.
Times: Last L 2pm/D 8.45pm
Additional: Bar food; Sunday L; Children welcome; 🍴 dishes
Smoking: No smoking in dining room; air-conditioning
Accommodation: 30 en suite
Credit cards: ▨ ▨ ▨ ▨ 🄳 🄯

Stately late-Victorian mansion set within terraced gardens and grounds on the shores of Lake Windermere. Panoramic lake views from the restaurant. A well structured dinner menu lists imaginatively cooked dishes. Expect pork terrine with grape chutney, seared red mullet with tapenade, or guinea fowl with braised Puy lentil sauce.

Directions: On the A591 3 miles N of Windermere, 2 miles S of Ambleside

WINDERMERE, **Lindeth Fell Hotel** ✤

Lyth Valley Road Bowness LA23 3JP
Map 7: SD49
Tel: 015394 43286
Fax: 015394 47455
Chef: Diana Kennedy
Owners: Patrick & Diana Kennedy
Cost: Fixed-price D £19. ☺ H/wine
£7.50.
Times: Last L 1.30pm/last D 8.30pm
Additional: Bar Food L; Sunday L;
No children under 7 at D; ◑ dishes
Smoking: No smoking in dining room
Accommodation: 15 en suite
Credit cards: ▬ ▬

*Charming hotel with two dining rooms – one in traditional
Edwardian style, the other a conservatory with views of Lake
Windermere and mountains. Expect pancakes with oriental duck
filling, garden-herb soup, monkfish medallions, chargrilled Scotch
fillet of beef with mushroom and thyme sauce, brown sugar
meringues with butterscotch sauce, and queen of puddings.*

Directions: 1 mile S of Bowness on A5074 Lyth Valley Road

WINDERMERE,
Lindeth Howe Country House ✤

*From its elevated position amid secluded gardens, this Edwardian
residence enjoys magnificent views across Lake Windermere. Sound
cooking highlights the daily-changing dinner menus. Our inspector
sampled excellent home-made bread, accurately cooked salmon and
dill fishcakes, and a rich banana parfait with strawberry coulis.*

Longtail Hill Storrs Park LA23 3JF
Map 7: SD49
Tel: 015394 45759
Fax: 015394 46368
Chef: Paul White
Owners: C & ME Baxter
Cost: Fixed-price D £21 (5 courses).
☺ H/wine £8.95.
Times: D only, 7pm-8.30pm

Additional: Sunday L (noon-1.30pm); Children welcome;
◑ dishes
Smoking: No smoking in dining room
Accommodation: 15 en suite
Credit cards: ▬ ▬ ▬ ▬

WINDERMERE,
Linthwaite House Hotel ✤✤

Crook Road Bowness
LA23 3JA
Map 7: SD49
Tel: 015394 88600
Fax: 015394 88601
Chef: Ian M Bravey
Owner: Handmade Hotels Ltd
Times: 12.30pm-last L
1.30pm/7.15pm-last D 8.45pm
Additional: Bar food L; Sunday L; No
children under 7; ◑ dishes
Seats: 45. Private dining room 20
Smoking: No smoking in dining room
Accommodation: 18 en suite
Credit cards: ▬ ▬ ▬ ▬ ▬

Formerly an Edwardian gentleman's residence, Linthwaite House is set in 14 acres of enchanting gardens with spectacular views across to Lake Windermere. Lunch is served in the conservatory, more ambitious evening meals in the opulent dining room with its polished antique tables and fine paintings on the walls. An inspection began promisingly with grilled scallops served on deep-fried leeks with a delicate chervil sauce before grilled trout fillet with a honey and whisky dressing. The main course was tian of local lamb layered with whole sun-dried tomatoes, fried filo pastry and home-made pesto, accompanied by redcurrant and mint sauce. Desserts range from sticky toffee pudding with fudge sauce to crème brûlée with oat crunchies, while the dazzling selection of British cheeses must rank as one of the most impressive in the north. Wines by the glass and plenty of 'easy drinking' ensure that the list is approachable.

Directions: Take 1st L off A591 at roundabout NW of Kendal (B5284). Follow for 6 miles, hotel is 1 mile after Windermere Golf Club on L

WINDERMERE,
Miller Howe Hotel ֍֍

The years roll by, but Miller Howe continues to rank as one of the all-time classic Lakeland hotels, and it's easy to see why. The views from the wooded hillside are breathtaking, while the decor is a sumptuous extravaganza of collectables, gilt cherubs and much more. This is John Tovey's home and it is lovingly tended. Dinner remains a theatrically orchestrated showpiece: the curtain goes up at eight o'clock on the dot and the show begins with distinctive canapés followed by a speciality bread. A starter such as crispy black pudding and mustard salad with innumerable additions gets the act going before, say, leek and garden pea risotto and a typically flamboyant main course – seared fillet of salmon on roasted tomato purée with glazed baby fennel and a sauce of white wine, chives and basil, for example. Vegetables remain abundant and colourful, desserts could range from lavender crème brûlée to steamed chocolate pudding. Impressively chosen New World wines from top producers steal the limelight on the classy list.

Rayrigg Road LA23 1EY
Map 7: SD49
Tel/Fax: 015394 45664
Chef: Chris Blaydes
Owner: John Tovey
Cost: Fixed-price L £15(3 courses)/D £32 (4 courses). H/wine £16.50
Times: 12.30pm-last L 1.30pm/7.30pm for 8pm. Closed early Dec-mid Feb
Additional: Sunday lunch; No children under 8. ♨ dishes
Seats: 64. Private dining room 30
Smoking: No pipes and cigars; air-conditioning
Accommodation: 12 en suite
Credit cards: ▆▆ ▆▆ ▆▆ ▆

Directions: On A592 between Windermere and Bowness

WINDERMERE,
Old England Hotel ֍

Views across Lake Windermere add to the enjoyment of a meal at the relaxed Old England. Contemporary British cooking features in typical main courses such as pan-roasted fillet of pork with black cherries, Marsala and wine, and collops of monkfish flamed with brandy.

Smoking: No smoking in dining room
Accommodation: 76 en suite
Credit cards: ▆▆ ▆▆ ▆▆ ▆ ▆

Directions: M6/J36, W on A592, hotel is behind St Martins Church at Bowness Bay

Church Street
Bowness LA23 3DF
Map 7: SD49
Tel: 015394 42444
Fax: 015394 43432
Chef: Andrew Hipwell
Owners: Forte Heritage
Cost: Alc £23, fixed-price L £11.95/D £20.95. ☺ H/wine £11.50.
Times: Last L 2pm/D 9.15pm
Additional: Sunday L; Bar meals L; Children welcome; ♨ dishes

WINDERMERE,
Roger's Restaurant ✤

Sound Anglo/French dishes at this intimate restaurant, where a meal in March featured pan-fried pigeon with smoked bacon and a subtle walnut dressing, and fresh grilled sea bass with tomato and basil. The iced chocolate parfait with bitter chocolate sorbet is recommended.

Smoking: No-smoking area; no cigars or pipes
Credit cards: ▬ ▬ ▬ ▬ ▣ ▢

Directions: Close to Windermere railway station, opposite Tourist Information Centre

4 High Street LA23 1AF
Map 7: SD49
Tel: 015394 44954
Chef: Roger Pergl-Wilson
Owners: R & AA Pergl-Wilson
Cost: *Alc* £20, fixed-price D £16.50.
☺ H/wine £9.80.
Times: D only, 7pm-9.30pm.
Closed Sun
Additional: Children welcome;
❹ dishes

WITHERSLACK, Old Vicarage Country House Hotel ✤✤

Grange over Sands LA11 6RS
Map 7: SD48
Tel: 015395 52381
Fax: 015395 52373
Chef: Stanley Reeve
Owner: Reeve & Brown families
Cost: Fixed-price L £13.50 (3 courses)/D £27.50 (4 courses).
H/wine £10.50
Times: 12.30-last L 2pm/7.30-last D 9pm
Additional: Sunday lunch; Bar meals L; Children welcome; ❹ dishes
Seats: 35. Private dining room 10
Smoking: No smoking in dining room
Accommodation: 14 en suite
Credit cards: ▬ ▬ ▬ ▬ ▢

Built in 1803 and personally maintained for more than two decades, this Georgian country house has an air of away-from-it-all comfort and gentility. The house is surrounded by enchanting mature gardens and grounds (complete with a damson orchard) in the Winster Valley not far from Lake Windermere. Booking is essential for dinner in the Victorian-style restaurant, which features a collection of antique pots and bottles unearthed from the grounds. Home-made breads (including a version laced with Cumberland molasses) set the tone and the kitchen puts great store by British regional ingredients – whether it be Orkney beef, Lakeland lamb or farmhouse cheeses. A capably executed inspection showed the style: marinated beef with garlic, olives and lightly dressed salad leaves was followed by baked fillet of smoked haddock on thinly sliced new potatoes with a mustard beurre blanc, and rounded off with rhubarb and orange pudding with orange sauce and a jug of cream.

Directions: Off A590. Take turning in village signposted to church

DERBYSHIRE

ASHBOURNE, Callow Hall

Mappleton Road
DE6 2AA
Map 7: SK14
Tel: 01335 343403
Fax: 01335 343624
Chefs: David & Anthony Spencer
Owners: David, Dorothy & Anthony Spencer
Cost: *Alc* £34.50, fixed-price D £35 (4 courses). ☺ H/wine £10.25.
Times: 7.30pm-last D 9.30pm. Residents only D Sun. Closed 25-26 Dec, 1 wk Feb
Additional: Bar food; Sunday L (12.30pm-1.30pm); Children welcome; ◑ dishes
Seats: 60. Private dining room 30
Smoking: No smoking in dining room
Accommodation: 16 en suite
Credit cards: ▨ ▨ ▨ ▨ ▨ ▨

Along a tree-lined drive overlooking the valleys of Bentley Brook and the River Dove is this creeper-clad Victorian residence, home of the Spencer family for the last 15 years. Their ancestors began baking in Ashbourne in 1724 and the tradition continues: the kitchen is nothing if not industrious, producing not only breads but preserves, sausages and home-cured bacon as well. Guests can choose between the light, airy daytime restaurant done out in lemons and creams or the more intimate dining room decorated entirely in red. Fresh fish from the market shows up well in the guise of roast monkfish with fennel and anise sauce, or king scallops with braised red cabbage, coriander seeds and lemon dressing, while meat-lovers might opt for loin of lamb with roasted garlic and mint stuffing or boned guinea fowl wrapped in smoked bacon with morels and Madeira sauce. To finish, expect desserts such as prune and lemon bavarois, or rice and cinnamon pudding glazed with caramel, in addition to all kinds of home-made ice creams. The 100-strong wine list is a world-wide collection at realistic prices.

Directions: 0.75 mile from Ashbourne; A515 (Buxton), sharp L by Bowling Green Pub, 1st R Mappleton Road

ASHFORD-IN-THE-WATER,
Riverside House Hotel

Fennel Street
Bakewell DE45 1QF
Map 7: SK17
Tel: 01629 814275
Fax: 01629 812873
Owners: Roger & Sue Taylor
Cost: *Alc* £28.75, fixed-price L £14.55/D £33 (5 courses). H/wine £13.75
Times: Noon-last L 2pm/7pm-last D 9.30pm
Additional: Bar food; Sunday L; No children under 5; ◑ dishes
Seats: 50. Private dining room 12. Jacket & tie preferred

Mature gardens leading to the River Wye surround this restful, home-from-home hotel in the village centre. Dinner is served in the two dining-rooms at highly polished antique tables set with sparkling silver and crystal. After an appetiser, the aspirational 'menu gourmand' may start with boudin blanc, sautéed spinach and haricot beans on a tomato sauce, or roast cod on a bed of celeriac chips with tarragon sabayon and deep-fried capers. Then, perhaps, seared rosette of salmon with a ragout of mussels, leeks and artichokes in a red wine fumet, or loin of venison on a risotto of Savoy cabbage and smoked bacon in a juniper, port and celery sauce. There is often venison from the nearby Chatsworth Estate. Desserts are along more traditional lines, but pecan nut and maple syrup pudding

Riverside House Hotel

with custard sauce will tempt fogies and non-fogies alike. If it all sounds too formal, there's grilled Cumberland sausages and mash in the Terrace Buttery instead.

Directions: 2 miles from centre of Bakewell on A6 (Buxton). In Ashford village next to Sheepwash Bridge

Smoking: No smoking in dining room
Accommodation: 15 en suite
Credit cards:

BAKEWELL, Croft Hotel ❀

Fine Victorian hotel with an impressive galleried hall and period-style restaurant. Dinner is a set four-course meal with a choice at starters and puddings only. Expect the likes of smoked trout pâté, a soup or sorbet, braised steak au poivre in red wine, and apricot fudge pudding.

Accommodation: 9 en suite
Credit cards:

Directions: A6 from Bakewell towards Buxton, 1.7 miles turn R (A6020). After 0.75 miles turn L signed Great Longstone. Hotel on R in village.

Great Longstone DE45 1TF
Map 8: SK26
Tel: 01629 640278
Chef: Lynne Macaskill
Owners: RA & L Macaskill
Cost: Fixed-price D £22.50. ☺
H/wine £8.75
Times: Last D 7.30pm.
Additional: No children under 12;
❸ dishes
Smoking: No smoking in dining room

BAKEWELL,
Renaissance Restaurant ❀

Converted barn, now a comfortably appointed restaurant that overlooks a small walled garden. Home-grown herbs and fresh produce are used to create some imaginative dishes. Typical choices may include mushroom terrine with butter cream dill sauce, and rack of lamb on a minted potato galette with lemon thyme sauce.

Additional: Bar meals; Sunday L; Children welcome; ❸ dishes.
Smoking: No smoking in dining room
Credit cards:

Directions: From Bakewell roundabout in town centre take A6 Buxton exit. 1st R into Bath Street (one-way).

Bath Street, Bakewell, Derbyshire,
DE45 1BX
Map 8: SK26
Tel: 01629 812687
Chef: Eric Piedaniel
Owners: Mr & Mrs Piedaniel, Mrs Beraud
Cost: *Alc* £19.50. Fixed-price D £17.95. ☺ H/wine £9.80.
Times: Last L 2pm/D 10pm Closed D Sun, Mon, 2 wks Jan, 2 wks Aug

BASLOW, Cavendish Hotel ❀❀

Acquired by the Duke of Devonshire around 1830 and boasting an enviable location on the edge of Chatsworth Estate, the Cavendish is a real thoroughbred among country

Bakewell DE45 1SP
Map 8: SK27
Tel: 01246 582311
Fax: 01246 582312
Chef: Nick Buckingham

Cavendish Hotel

Owner: Eric Marsh
Cost: *Alc* £32.25, fixed-price L/D £32.25 (3 courses). H/wine £17.50
Times: 12.30pm-last L 2pm/7pm-last D 10pm.
Additional: Bar meals; Sunday L; Children welcome; ✿ dishes
Seats: 45. Private dining room 18
Smoking: No smoking in dining room
Accommodation: 23 en suite
Credit cards: ■ ■ ■ ■ ▣ ▢

hotels. Over 300 fine works of art line the walls (some collected by redoubtable proprietor Eric Marsh). History may be part of its enduring appeal, but the kitchen takes a more modern view of things. Tuna steak is presented on a colourful niçoise salad, wild mushroom terrine is served warm to bring out its inherent earthy flavours, while breast of chicken might be wrapped in Japanese nori seaweed and served with a spicy dressing, wasabi and noodles. Flavours are vivid, presentation impressive. To finish, there are desserts such as apple strudel with vanilla and cinnamon custard or hot chocolate soufflé with hot vanilla sauce. The wine list is comprehensive, but don't miss the range of vintage ports, some of which are now quite rare. Lighter meals are served all day in the Garden Room conservatory.

Directions: On the A619 in the village of Baslow

BASLOW,

Fischer's, Baslow Hall ❀❀❀

Calver Road DE45 1RR
Map 8: SK27
Tel: 01246 583259
Fax: 01246 583818
Chef: Max Fischer
Owners: Max & Susan Fischer
Cost: Fixed-price L £18/£22 (2-3 courses)/D £42 (4 courses). H/wine £9.50
Times: Noon-last L 1.30pm/7pm-last D 9.30pm. Closed D Sun (except residents), 25-26 Dec

Max and Susan Fischer's Derbyshire manor house exudes warmth and comfort. Charming public rooms centre around the restaurant and the slightly more casual Café Max, and there is also an attractive lounge with a log fire and drinks trolley. Max Fischer's cooking is worth travelling for, but his individualistic style does not fall into the mould of country restaurants. It is innovative without being outlandish and the repertoire of dishes includes such modern conceptions as calves' liver with ginger and lime, and breast of duckling with sesame cabbage and oriental sauce, although traditionalists will be equally delighted with terrine of foie gras with duck confit, and naturally reared beef fillet with béarnaise sauce. A late winter dinner started with good, seared scallops, Szechuan vegetables and a spicy sauce vierge that had emphatic Chinese flavours. The main course was a Pierre Koffmann-style pig's trotter with morels, sweetbreads and chicken mousse, and a mound of potato purée. Pudding was an assembly of rhubarb puddings – some crème brûlée with rhubarb base, a fabulous rhubarb and ginger strudel, some strips of dried rhubarb à la Gordon Ramsay's strawberries, and a very good sorbet.

A fairly concise list that still manages to cover many of the important wines in key areas. Short snappy descriptions make good reading and provide guidance. Some decent drinking under £25 – Fleurie La Madonne from Duboeuf (£18); Poggio alle Gazze 95, Tenuta dell'Ornellaia, a Sauvignon Blanc in the New World style (£21). Good halves – Ch de Monthelie 90 is a lone diners' treat at £22.50.

Signature dishes: Croustillante of sea bass with a chervil velouté; turbot, roasted in potato with tomato oil and herb pesto; whole roast partridge, off the bone, on choucroute; roast sea scallops on gazpacho vegetables.

Additional: Café Max L & D; Sunday L; No children under 12 at D
Seats: 40. Private dining rooms 12-24. Jacket & tie preferred
Smoking: No smoking in dining room
Accommodation: 6 en suite
Credit cards: 🌑 📇 📇 📇 📇 📇

Directions: On right of A623 Stockport Road as you leave Baslow towards Calver.

BELPER, Makeney Hall Hotel ❀❀

Milford DE56 0RS
Map 8: SK34
Tel: 01332 842999
Fax: 01332 842777
Chef: Kevin Woodyet
Owners: Mr & Mrs A Holmes
Cost: Alc £33, fixed-price L £13.50 (4 courses)/£19.50 (5 courses). ☺
H/wine £9.65.
Times: Noon-last L 1.45pm/7pm-last D 9.45pm. Closed L Sat
Additional: Bar food; Sunday L; Children welcome; 🍴 dishes
Seats: 64. Private dining rooms 170
Smoking: No pipes and cigars; air conditioning
Accommodation: 45 en suite
Credit cards: 🌑 📇 📇 📇 📇 📇

We're not sure just who Lavinia is or was, but the oak-panelled restaurant that bears her name does her proud. The *carte* is fairly concise and ambitions are realistically kept in check – better a perfectly cooked Dover sole or steak, than an over-complicated disaster on the plate. Not that the cooking lacks interest or skill – baked sea-bass is served with a celery, fennel and tomato compote finished with a Pernod sauce, braised lamb shanks with tomato, garlic and rosemary in a port sauce. Some dishes take their cue from good home-cooking ideas – fillet of rainbow trout is baked in a parchment parcel and served with buttered almonds and capers, and roast baby chicken comes with caramelised root vegetables and piquant sauce. There may be home-made treacle sponge pudding with custard sauce for afters, although a pineapple and almond tart with brown bread ice-cream sounds pretty good as well. Meals are also served in the Garden Room, half-built of glass, jutting out into the beautifully landscaped gardens that surround the hotel.

Directions: Join A6 N of Derby & turn R into Milford. Hotel is 0.25 miles, just past Garden Centre

BUXTON, Lee Wood Hotel

13 Manchester Road SK17 6TQ
Map 7: SK07
Tel: 01298 23002
Fax: 01298 23228
Chef: Sean Ballington
Owner: Mr J C Millican
Cost: Alc £25, fixed-price D £22. ☺
H/wine £10.95.
Times: 12.15pm-last L 2pm/7.15pm-
last D 9.30pm
Additional: Bar food; Sunday L;
Children welcome; ◑ dishes
Seats: 80. Private dining room 10-150
Smoking: No-smoking area, no pipes
and cigars
Accommodation: 37 en suite
Credit cards: ▬ ▦ ▨ ▣ [

Real foliage and plants fill the conservatory restaurant at this
friendly, family-run hotel. The green theme is also reflected in
a particularly wide choice of vegetarian dishes, such as risotto
of wild and long-grain rice blended with wild woodland
mushrooms, pistachio nuts, pine kernels and asparagus tips.
The rest of the *carte* is equally extensive, with main courses
ranging from collops of local moorland venison, pan-fried and
served on rösti potato with a rich bilberry and Burgundy wine
sauce, to noisettes of English lamb scented with fresh tarragon
and topped with toasted goat's cheese and served on a piquant
Reform sauce. Most dishes, including starters such as hard
boiled quails' eggs served in savoury pastry barquettes napped
with lemon mayonnaise and topped with an anchovy fillet, are
fairly complicated in concept, but the kitchen is flexible
enough to provide an omelette or cold meats and seasonal
salads for those wanting something a little simpler.

Directions: Follow A5004 Long Hill to Whaley Bridge. Hotel
300 metres beyond the Devonshire Royal Hospital

BUXTON, Portland Hotel

32 St John's Road SK17 6XQ
Map 7: SK07
Tel: 01298 22462
Fax: 01298 27464
Chef: Dermat Schultz
Owners: Brian & Linda Millner
Cost: Fixed-price L £7.50/D £19.95.
☺ H/wine £11.
Times: Last L 2pm/D 9.15pm. Closed
L Sat
Additional: Bar food; Sunday L;
Children welcome; ◑ dishes
Smoking: No pipes and cigars
Accommodation: 25 en suite
Credit cards: ▬ ▦ ▨ ▚ ▣ [

*A popular hotel close to Buxton's opera house. A good selection of
competently cooked food is offered in the shaded conservatory of
the Park Restaurant. Main courses include pan-fried pork tenderloin
topped with Stilton, sautéed beef steak with spring onions, and
grilled halibut steak with lemon juice.*

Directions: On A53 opposite Pavilion Gardens and Opera House

DERBY, Mickleover Court Hotel

Etwall Road Mickleover DE3 5XX
Map 8: SK33
Tel: 01332 521234
Fax: 01332 521238
Chef: Martin Clayton
Owners: Mickleover Court Hotel Ltd
Cost: *Alc* £20. H/wine £11. ☺
Times: Last L 2.30pm/D 10pm
Additional: Bar Food; Sunday L;
Children welcome; ☺ dishes
Smoking: No-smoking area; no pipes
& cigars; air-conditioning
Accommodation: 80 en suite
Credit cards: ■■ ■■ ■■ ■■ ■■ ℂ

Traditional and classical dishes cooked in modern style highlight the extensive carte at this impressive modern hotel on the edge of Derby. Typical dishes include roasted red peppers with basil and garlic, quail and venison casserole, with chocolate mousse for pudding.

Directions: From Mickleover take A516 (Uttoxeter) hotel is L of 1st roundabout

DOVERIDGE, The Beeches Farmhouse Hotel ❀❀

Doveridge DE6 5LR
Map 7: SK13
Tel: 01889 590288
Fax: 01889 590559
Chef: Barbara Tunnicliffe
Owners: Barbara & Paul Tunnicliffe
Cost: *Alc* £18.50, fixed-price L £8.95-
£10.95. ☺ H/wine £7.95.
Times: Last L 2pm/D 9pm. Closed D
Sun, 25 Dec
Additional: Bar Food L; Sunday L;
Children welcome; ☺ dishes
Accommodation: 10 en suite
Credit cards: ■■ ■■ ■■ ■■ ℂ

Still very much a working farm, with the restaurant situated in a series of rooms belonging to the original eighteenth-century farmhouse. Low beams, quarry tiles and polished floorboards abound. The kitchen makes good use of fresh seasonal ingredients for hand-written menus that show a degree of skill as well as country robustness. An inspection meal taken in November began with lightly cooked Scottish scallops wrapped in sage leaves and bacon and served on a bed of leaves with finely diced tomato. Next came an appropriate autumnal dish of roast guinea fowl with chestnut butter with a crab apple and chestnut sauce, accompanied by some vibrant green leeks and an unusual piece of red cabbage pie. To finish, a berry brûlée had a decent consistency. Service is willing and friendly.

Directions: Turn off A50 (Uttoxeter-Derby) at Doveridge, down Marston Lane, (signed Waldley). At Waldley take 1st R then 1st L

HATHERSAGE, George Hotel

A stone-built, village-centre hotel dating from the sixteenth-century, set amidst stunning Peak District scenery. The elegant restaurant offers sound cooking. At an early summer meal roasted pepper soup, pot-roasted lamb, and a generous portion of pear and almond tart, were well reported.

Additional: Sunday L; Children welcome; dishes
Smoking: No smoking in dining room
Accommodation: 19 en suite
Credit cards: ▆▆ ▆▆ ▆▆ ▆▆ ▆▆ ▆

Main Road S30 1BB
Map 8: SK83
Tel: 01433 650436
Fax: 01433 650099
Chef: Ben Handley
Owner: Eric Marsh
Cost: Alc £15.20, fixed-price D £16.95. ☺ H/wine £13.50.
Times: Noon-10pm

Directions: In village centre on A625

MATLOCK, Riber Hall

Tansley DE4 5JU
Map 8: SK35
Tel: 01629 582795
Fax: 01629 580475
Chef: Patrick Salvadori
Owner: Alex Biggin
Cost: Fixed-price L £16/D £32. H/wine £12.75
Times: Last L 1.30pm/D 9.30pm
Additional: Sunday L; Children welcome; dishes
Smoking: No smoking in one dining room
Accommodation: 14 en suite
Credit cards: ▆▆ ▆▆ ▆▆ ▆▆ ▆▆ ▆

Splendid Elizabethan manor house, strong on atmosphere, and surrounded by stunning gardens and countryside. Modern cooking takes in the likes of terrine of pork fillet with spicy mushroom and coriander chutney, chicken boudin, lightly curried with a Calvados and apple sauce, or medallions of roasted monkfish with samphire and a trio of pepper coulis.

Directions: One mile up Alders Lane and Carr Lane off A615 at Tansley

MELBOURNE,
The Bay Tree Restaurant

A cosy beamed restaurant, built in 1790 as a coaching inn, where everything is cooked to order from good fresh produce. An imaginative choice of dishes includes 'bolognaise' pancake, fresh fish of the day, Lunesdale duckling with a pear and ginger sauce, and raspberry Drambuie oaty crumble.

Additional: Sunday L; children welcome
Smoking: No pipes & cigars; air-conditioning
Credit cards: ▆▆ ▆▆ ▆▆ ▆▆ ▆▆ ▆

4 Potter Street DE73 1DW
Map 8: SK32
Tel: 01332 863358
Fax: 01332 865545
Chef: Rex Howell
Owners: Victoria Talbott, Rex Howell
Cost: Alc £35. H/wine £11.95.
Times: Last L 2pm/last D 9.45pm.
Closed L Sat, D Sun, Mon

Directions: Town centre

RIDGEWAY, The Old Vicarage Restaurant ✿✿✿

The setting is very English: a Victorian stone-built vicarage surrounded by lovely gardens. Within, the lounge is a stylish mix-and-match of sunny yellows and golds and shades of midnight blue, the restaurant, in Wedgwood blue, has lots of polished touches - fresh flowers, starched white damask napkins, elegant white Wedgwood china. The formula is simple with the menu, fixed-price at lunch and dinner, offering a choice of five at each course. Tessa Bramley and her team offer cooking that has many fine qualities of accuracy and balance, dishes as varied as red snapper with a crispy skin in a lime and chilli marinade, and an English classic, roast loin of pork with mushroom stuffing, crackling, wild mushroom sauce and roasted parsnips. A winter lunch from that same menu showed ambition. The appetiser, a Thai fishcake with a vanilla bisque given distinctive flavour from a garnish of crisp ginger strips, augured well. What followed next came as no surprise: fillet of brill served on accurately cooked saffron noodles with a good, well-balanced pesto, pot-roasted pheasant with tangerine and mace set on a bed of shredded celeriac cooked in garlic and juniper, the darker flesh presented on truffled mashed potato with a small portion of liver 'farce' alongside, and to finish, a trio of desserts that comprised a sharp, tangy lemon tart, a warm passion fruit soufflé with passion fruit coulis, and a sweet lime sorbet served in a crisp tuille basket. Small details are just as memorable. Home-made breads include delicious Italian (ciabatta-like texture), spring onion and rosemary rolls and delicate, lovingly made petits fours. Service is friendly but unobtrusive.

Directions: S/E of Sheffield off the A616 on B6054; follow signs for Ridgeway Cottage Industries. Restaurant is 300yds on L

Ridgeway Moor S12 3XW
Map 8: SK48
Tel: 0114 2475814
Fax: 0114 2477079
Chefs: Tessa Bramley, Nathan Smith, Andrew Gilbert
Owners: Tessa & Andrew Bramley
Cost: Fixed-price L £28/D £38 (4 courses). H/wine £15
Times: 12.30pm-last L 2pm/7pm-last D 10.30pm. Closed L Sat, D Sun, Mon, 10 days from 1 Jan
Additional: Sunday L; Children welcome; ✿ dishes
Seats: 50. Private dining room 12
Smoking: No smoking in dining room
Credit cards: 💳 💳 💳 💳 💳 💳

ROWSLEY, East Lodge ✿

Dating back three centuries, East Lodge is an elegant house set in ten acres of Derbyshire countryside. A recent meal featured chicken liver parfait with Yorkshire sauce, cocotte of potted rabbit and bacon, and pan-fried duck breast with Chinese spices. For dessert look out for the dark chocolate and brandy terrine.

Accommodation: 15 en suite
Credit cards: 💳 💳 💳

Directions: Hotel drive access on A6, 5 miles from Matlock and 3 miles from Bakewell

Matlock DE4 2EF
Map 8: SK26
Tel: 01629 734474
Fax: 01629 733949
Chef: Simon Hollings
Owners: Mr & Mrs P Mills
Cost: Fixed-price D £19.95. ☺ H/wine £8.95
Times: Last L 2pm/D 9.30pm
Additional: Sunday L; .Bar meals L; Children welcome; ✿ dishes
Smoking: No smoking in dining room

SOUTH NORMANTON, Swallow Hotel ✿

Close to the M1/J28, this relaxed modern hotel offers good modern cooking in the elegant and formal Pavilion Restaurant. The comprehensive carte may list duck liver parfait with onion and apricot marmalade, and calves' liver with caramelised onion and oranges and red wine gravy.

Credit cards: 💳 💳 💳 💳 💳

Directions: From M1/J28 – A38 (signed Mansfield). At 100 yards 1st L into car park

Carter Lane East DE55 2EH
Map 8: SK56
Tel: 01773 812000
Fax: 01773 580032
Chef: Alan McGilveray
Cost: Alc £25, fixed-price L £13.50/D £21. ☺ H/wine £12.
Times: Last L 2pm/D 9.45pm.
Additional: Bar food L; Sunday L; Children welcome; ✿ dishes
Accommodation: 161 en suite

THORPE, **Izaak Walton**

Named after the renowned fisherman and author, the hotel is located in the Peaks overlooking Thorpe Cloud. A summer meal in the Haddon Restaurant included a smooth chicken liver parfait, roast saddle of veal with sautéed mushrooms finished with Marsala and crème fraîche, and tangy lemon tart.

Directions: One mile W of Thorpe on the Ilam road

DE6 2AY
Map 7: SK15
Tel: 01335 350555
Fax: 01335 350539
Chef: Don Harding
Cost: Fixed-price L £14.50/D £22.75
(4 courses). ☺ H/wine £9.95
Times: Noon-last L 2.15pm (Sun only)/7.30pm-last D 9.15pm
Telephone for further details

DEVON

ASHBURTON,

Holne Chase Hotel

Newton Abbot
TQ13 7NS
Map 3: SX77
Tel: 01364 631471
Fax: 01364 631453
Chef: Wayne Pearson
Owner: Sebastian & Philippa Hughes
Cost: *Alc* £29.50, fixed-price L £20/D £25 (3 courses). H/wine £10.25
Times: Noon-last L-2pm/7.15pm-last D-9pm
Additional: Bar food L; Sunday L; No children under 10 at D; ♨ dishes
Seats: 45. Private dining room 12
Smoking: No smoking in dining room
Accommodation: 18 en suite
Credit cards:

Once the hunting lodge to Buckfast Abbey, this family-run country hotel is noted for its unpretentiousness and breathes tranquillity. It stands in 270 acres of parkland with easy access to some of the most ancient oak woods in the country, as well as boasting enchanting walks along the banks of the River Dart. The views – and the sunsets – are stunning. Many herbs and vegetables come from the hotel's Victorian walled garden, bread is baked on the premises. The dining room is comfortable with lots of space between good-sized tables, pretty fresh flowers, friendly service. There's a good choice between the daily changing menu and the *carte*, and there are always two simple dishes, such as a plain beef fillet or fresh fish. Wayne Pearson's strength lies in his honest approach to good quality ingredients, which means a pleasing simplicity shines through. This was noted in a spring inspection dinner that opened with canapés of smoked chicken pancake, went on to mousseline of scallop surrounded by succulent, lightly poached scallops and a pesto cream, a chicken liver parfait, then spring lamb with an imaginative spinach mousse filled with mint jelly, and finished with bread and butter pudding with a pleasant, crisp, buttery top and crème anglaise, and a lemon tart. The wine list is extensive, reads well, and offers some interesting bins with a good range of prices.

Directions: Travelling from N & E, take 2nd Ashburton turning off A38. 2 miles to Holne Bridge, hotel is 0.25 miles on R. From Plymouth take 1st Ashburton turn

ASHWATER, **Blagdon Manor** ✿✿

Ashwater EX21 5DF
Map 2: SX39
Tel: 01409 211224
Fax: 01409 211634
Chef: Gill Casey
Owners: Tim & Gill Casey
Cost: Fixed price D £18.50. ☺
H/wine£8.50.
Times: D at 8pm for residents only
Additional: Sunday L; Bar food;
Children welcome;
Seats: 14. Jacket & tie preferred
Smoking: No smoking in dining room
Accommodation: 7 en suite
Credit cards:

'A quite delightful little place which oozes charm and good taste' enthused one inspector of Gill and Tim Casey's seventeenth-century manor house. The formula is designed for resident guests: set meal of three courses, likes and dislikes checked, menu left in bedroom, then all gather together 'dinner party-style' at 8pm around a magnificent rosewood table. An autumn dinner commenced with well flavoured, slightly crumbly toasted goat's cheese served with salad, lamb cutlets with rösti potato, all served with a mint and redcurrant jus. Accompanying vegetables were simple in concept but had 'lovely flavours'. For dessert, pineapple, apricots, grapes and melon lightly poached in honey and served with a superb zabaglione ice cream. Breakfast brings some excellent home-made preserves.

Directions: Take A388 Holsworthy Road from Launceston. Turn R at 2nd Ashwater sign, then 1st R. Hotel few hundred metres on R.

AXMINSTER,
Fairwater Head Hotel ✿

An extended Edwardian country house set in lovely gardens surrounded by rolling countryside. The restaurant, with its Axminster carpets, fine china and linen, has garden views from most tables. The set-price dinner menu might offer smoked mackerel pâté, watercress soup, beef Stroganoff, and dessert from the sweet trolley.

Smoking: No smoking in dining room
Accommodation: 20 en suite
Credit cards:

Near Axminster EX13 5TX
Map 3: ST30
Tel/Fax: 01297 678349
Chef: Ian Cartar
Owner: Judith Lowe
Cost: Alc £12. Fixed-price D £20. ☺
H/wine £8.50.
Times: Last L 1.30pm/D 8.30pm.
Closed Jan & Feb
Additional: Bar Food ; Sunday L;
Children welcome; ⬤ dishes

Directions: From Axminster or Lyme Regis take B3165 to Crewkerne. Hawkchurch village is signposted and hotel signs on approach to village

BAMPTON,
Bark House Hotel ✿✿

The house is so-named because, until the last war, it was used to store the bark from Exmoor Forest that found its way to the local tanning industry. A new regime has settled in well and the kitchen is starting to produce some well thought out dishes

Oakford Bridge EX16 9HZ
Map 3: SS92
Tel: 01398 351236
Chef/Owner: Alastair Kameen
Cost: Fixed-price D £17.50. ☺
H/wine £7.50.

with a degree of flair and imagination. A test meal in the cottagey, beamed dining room began with a buttery mushroom tartlet topped with hollandaise before fillet of salmon served with a tangy orange jus. Other choices from the short fixed-price menu might include an unusual starter consisting of a crisp whole apple filled with garlicky cream cheese, coated in mayonnaise and served on a purée of walnuts and dates, while main courses might feature venison pudding or pan-fried medallions of lamb with onion marmalade and rosemary jus. Desserts such as strawberry tart with fresh damson coulis and cherry and cinnamon crumble with smooth egg custard sauce make an appealing finish. The wine list provides affordable drinking from sound sources.

Directions: M5/J27 (Tiverton). Take A396 N of Tiverton signposted Minehead. Oakford Bridge is about 9 miles N of Tiverton

Times: 12.15pm-last L 1.30pm/7.15pm-last D 8pm. Closed 4-31 Jan
Additional: Bar meals L; Sunday L (Oct-April); Children welcome; ❸ dishes
Seats: 14
Smoking: No smoking in dining room
Accommodation: 6 en suite
Credit cards: None

BARNSTAPLE,

Halmpstone Manor ❀❀

Fish, fresh from Bideford Quay, features regularly on the hand-written, five-course dinner menu at this charming, family-run, small manor house. Typically, Mediterranean crab soup might be followed by monkfish and bacon kebab, then roasted local farm duckling with sherry and orange sauce. Alternatively, there might be an equally well thought-out meal of warm salad of green leaves with avocado, quails eggs and Roquefort, smoked trout with horseradish sauce and escalope of veal with a white wine and crème fraîche sauce, or vichyssoise followed by baked sea bass with sauce vierge and fillet of Devonshire steak with black pepper, mushroom and cream sauce. The only choice comes with cheese and dessert when it may be difficult to decide between a roll-call of old favourites such as tiramisu, banoffee pie and sticky toffee pudding. Guests are taken care of extremely well, and the candlelit, panelled dining room has an air of friendly informality.

Directions: From Barnstaple take A377 to Bishop's Tawton. At end of village turn L for Cobbaton; sign on R

Bishop's Tawton EX32 0EA
Map 2: SS53
Tel: 01271 830321
Fax: 01271 830826
Chef: Mrs Jane Stanbury
Owners: Mr & Mrs C W Stanbury
Cost: Fixed price D £35 (5 courses). H/wine £10
Times: L by arrangement/7pm-last D 9pm. Closed Nov-Jan
Additional: ❸ dishes
Seats: 24
Smoking: No smoking in dining room
Accommodation: 5 en suite
Credit cards: 💳 💳 💳 💳

BARNSTAPLE, **Royal & Fortescue,
The Bank** ❀ **NEW**

The Bank, a stylish café-bistro-bar is, as the name suggests, converted from a former bank next door to the hotel. Dishes range through Caesar salad, 'Texas Toothpicks' and burgers, to Thai chicken, steaks, and fajitas. Popular desserts include tiramisu and pecan pie.

Additional: Sunday L; Bar meals; Children welcome; ❸ dishes
Accommodation: 47 en suite
Credit cards: 💳 💳 💳 💳

Directions: A361 into Barnstaple, along Barbican Rd signposted town centre; turn R into Queen St & L (one way) Boutport St. Hotel on L

Boutport Street
EX31 1HG
Map 2: SS53
Tel/Fax: 01271 42289
Chef: Mr R Loman
Owners: Brend Hotels
Cost: Alc £17. Fixed-price L £11, D £15. ☺ H/wine £7.95.
Times: Noon-2pm/7pm-last D 9.15pm

BOVEY TRACEY,
Edgemoor Hotel ✿✿

Haytor Road TQ13 9LE
Map 3: SX87
Tel: 01626 832466
Fax: 01626 834760
Chef: Edward Elliot
Owners: Pat & Rod Day
Cost: Fixed-price D £19.50 – £22.50
(2-3 courses). ☺ H/wine £7.50.
Times: 12.15pm-last L 1.30pm/7pm-
last D 9pm. Closed 6 days over New
Year
Additional: Bar food; Sunday L;
No children under 8 at D; ✤ dishes
Seats: 40
Smoking: No smoking in dining room
Accommodation: 17 en suite
Credit cards: ▬ ▨ ▨ ▨ ▨ ▨

Built in 1870, and originally the home of Bovey Tracey Grammar
School, this peaceful country house was converted into a hotel in
1920. Today it looks the part, with stylish wallpaper, pink curtains
and tables with lacy cloths in the subtly elegant restaurant.
Dinner is served by candlelight and the monthly-changing fixed-
price menu offers good value and plenty of variety. First courses
might feature duck and pistachio nut terrine, grilled Camembert
with plum sauce or Edgemoor smokies (smoked haddock in
white wine sauce with savoury éclairs). Main courses could range
from medallions of pork with orange and rosemary in apricot
sauce and lambs' liver with Dubonnet and redcurrant to fish
specials. Vegetables are simply prepared and spot-on, while
desserts could feature oranges in Grand Marnier or French
chocolate flan. Bar food is also available lunchtimes and
evenings. Forty wines are affordably priced.

Directions: From A38 take A382 (Drumbridges). Cross first mini
roundabout & turn L at 2nd roundabout. Bear L towards Haytor.
Hotel 0.25 mile on R

BRANSCOMBE, **The Masons Arms** ✿

*Once the watering hole of smugglers, The Masons Arms is a civilised
fourteenth-century inn, a pleasant half-mile walk to the coast. Local
fish, meat and game are used in dishes such as steak and oyster pie
with puff pastry, slow roasted rack of lamb with rosemary and
redcurrants, and grilled lemon sole with herb butter.*

Branscombe EX12 3DJ
Map 3: SY18
Tel: 01297 680300
Fax: 01297 680500
Chef: Saul Vickery
Owner: Murray Inglis
Cost: Alc £19, fixed-price L £9.95/D
£19. ☺ H/wine £12.
Times: Last L 2.30pm/D 9.30pm
Additional: Sunday L; Bar meals;
Children welcome; ✤ dishes
Smoking: No-smoking area
Accommodation: 21 rooms (most en
suite)
Credit cards: ▬ ▨ ▨

Directions: Turn off A3052 (Exeter to
Lyme Regis) and follow road through
Branscombe

BROADHEMBURY, Drewe Arms

A traditional English inn, nestling in a peaceful village of thatched houses. Kerstin Burge cooks while husband Nigel welcomes guests and takes orders. The set menu is flexible, and could include dishes such as crab Thermidor, fillet of turbot, and hot chicken and bacon salad.

Directions: From M5/J28, 5 miles on A373 Cullompton to Honiton. Pub 1 mile NE of Broadhembury turning

Broadhembury EX14 0NF
Map 3: ST10
Tel/Fax: 01404 841267
Chef/Owners: Kerstin & Nigel Burge
Telephone for details

BURRINGTON, Northcote Manor

Secluded seventeenth-century stone manor house surrounded by 20 acres of landscaped gardens and woodland. A peaceful and relaxed atmosphere pervades the baronial lounge and comfortable restaurant. The daily changing five-course menu may include scallops in dill cream with wild rice, and paillard of beef with pink peppercorn sauce

Smoking: No smoking in dining room
Accommodation: 12 en suite
Credit cards: 🔲 🔲 🔲 🔲 🔲

Directions: A377 Exeter to Barnstaple. Turn into private drive opposite Portsmouth Arms railway station (Don't enter Burrington)

Nr Portsmouth Arms Station
EX37 9LZ
Map 3: SS61
Tel: 01769 560501
Fax: 01769 560770
Chef: Andreas Berrhuber
Owner: David Boddy
Cost: Fixed-price D £24.50 (5 courses). ☺
Times: D only, 7.30pm-8.30pm.
Closed Jan-Feb
Additional: 🌢 dishes

CHAGFORD, Easton Court Hotel

Look out for home-made terrines, hearty soups and scrumptious puddings at this lovely old, thatched Tudor house. Soundly cooked main courses too. Look out for roast loin of pork carved onto a cider and apple glaze, and grilled fillets of mackerel with a sharp gooseberry purée.

Additional: No children under 12
Smoking: No smoking in dining room
Accommodation: 8 en suite
Credit cards: 🔲 🔲 🔲 🔲 🔲

Directions: On the A382 by turning to Chagford

Easton Cross TQ13 8JL
Map 3: SX78
Tel: 01647 433469
Fax: 01647 433654
Chef: Ian Wanstall
Owners: Gordon & Judy Parker
Cost: Fixed-price D £22 (5 courses). ☺ H/wine £7.95.
Times: D only, 7.30pm-last D 8.15pm

CHAGFORD, Gidleigh Park

Newton Abbot
TQ13 8HH
Map 3: SX78
Tel: 01647 432367
Fax: 01647 432574
Chef: Michael Caines
Owners: Paul & Kay Henderson
Cost: Fixed-price D £52.50 (4 courses). H/wine £17.50
Times: 12.30pm-last L 2pm/7pm-last D 9pm
Additional: Bar food L; Sunday L
Seats: 35
Smoking: No smoking in dining room
Accommodation: 15 en suite
Credit cards: 🔲 🔲 🔲 🔲 🔲 🔲

Gidleigh Park is an experience. The quest for perfection starts amongst the seemingly endless, narrow winding lanes that finally lead to this wonderfully secluded, mock-Tudor house, set within Dartmoor National Park. On entry, you are welcomed into a very sophisticated but mellow country house; an open log fire burns cheerily, every ornament and every picture is in just the right place and the dining-room, simply, almost plainly decorated in soft peachy colours, has glorious views over the gardens and hills beyond. As well as a four-course fixed price menu, there is a daily changing speciality menu and a short lunch menu. Canapés, such as tiny melt-in-the-mouth goujons, are a foretaste of Michael Caines's great talents. The small but exemplary selection of freshly baked bread is another indicator of the overall quality. Then an appetiser, perhaps a beautifully presented little bowl of various mushrooms in a light summery jus. A June meal then began in earnest with a terrine of duck confit that managed to be simultaneously firm yet soft and smooth, accompanied by foie gras, shallots and a salad dressed with walnut vinaigrette. Another first course, warm chicken mousse with morel mushrooms, asparagus and a Gewürztraminer sauce was full of subtle tastes, and exquisitely accesorized with tiny sprigs of asparagus. These were followed by two main courses of memorable dimensions; roast best end and saddle of local lamb was sweet and tender, astutely offset by the gamier taste of lamb's sweetbreads, tian of spinach and ratatouille with roast garlic, whilst a John Dory was impeccably cooked and served with a galette of aubergine, tomato and courgette and a lemon thyme sauce. Caines is dedicated to producing the best food possible, using only the best produce available and concepts can be as simple as they are elegant – organically reared local sirloin steak is served with truffled potato purée, roast Trelough duckling with honey and spices. A dessert of apple mousse with cider ice cream had clear, true flavours, as did a spot-on pistachio soufflé served with pistachio ice. The wine list is extensive. Quality wines of Bordeaux and Burgundy are covered in depth with some classic vintages. However, take this ideal opportunity to sample some of the stunning Italians. Alsace is also extensive, Clos Ste Hune Rieslings from Trimbach, although not cheap due to their rarity, are quite remarkable. French regional wines offer value for money; several are under £30. Eight quality wines by the glass.

Gidleigh Park

Directions: Chagford Square turn R at Lloyds Bank into Mill Street, after 150 yd R fork, straight across crossroads into Holy Street. Restaurant is 1.5 miles.

CHAGFORD, **Mill End Hotel** ❀

The former flour mill has six miles of private fishing, plus the welcoming atmosphere of a private country house. The pretty restaurant serves dishes such as scallops with bacon and mushroom in brandy cream sauce and medallions of venison in marjoram butter with brown sugar, sultana and chestnut purée. Don't miss the award-winning cheese selection.

Smoking: No smoking in dining room
Accommodation: 17 en suite. **Credit cards:** ▬ ▬ ▬ ▩ ▢

Sandy Park TQ13 8JN
Map 3: SX78
Tel: 01647 432282
Fax: 01647 433106
Chef: Alan Lane
Owners: Julian Peck, Jill Day
Cost: Fixed-price L £14.50/ D £25. ☺
H/wine £10.95.
Times: Last L 1.45pm/D 8.45pm
Additional: Bar meals L; Sunday L;
Children welcome; ❹ dishes

Directions: From Exeter take A30 to Whiddon Down, turn S on A382 (Moretonhampstead) – don't turn into Chagford at Sandy Park; hotel is at Dogmarsh Bridge

CHARDSTOCK,
Tytherleigh Cot Hotel

A thatched fourteenth-century ciderhouse, carefully converted into an attractive village hotel. The conservatory restaurant overlooks a fountain and waterfall, and offers a daily menu as well as specials such as smoked salmon and seaweed roulade, and Membury trout stuffed with mackerel and lemon.

Accommodation: 18 en suite. **Credit cards:** ▆▆ ▆▆▆

Directions: From M5/J25 take A358 to Axminster via Ilminster. 4 miles from Chard at Tytherleigh village turn R – Chardstock 1 mile

Axminster EX13 7BN
Map 3: ST30
Tel: 01460 221170
Fax: 01460 221291
Chef: Andrew Witheridge
Cost: Alc £23, fixed-price D £15.95. ☺ H/wine £11.95.
Times: D only, 7pm – last D 9.30pm.
Additional: No children under 12; ♨ dishes
Smoking: No smoking in dining room; air-conditioning

CHILLINGTON,
White House Hotel

The pavilion-style restaurant was added to this listed building in 1995; it takes full advantage of garden views. At our most recent inspection warming watercress and sweet potato soup was followed by rack of lamb with shallots, then delicious chocolate roulade. Good selection of local cheeses.

Smoking: No smoking in dining room
Accommodation: 8 en suite. **Credit cards:** ▆▆ ▆▆▆ ▆▆

Directions: On the A379 towards Dartmouth, 4.5 miles E of Kingsbridge

Kingsbridge TQ7 2JX
Map 3: SY85
Tel: 01548 580580
Fax: 01548 581124
Chef: David Alford
Owners: Michael Roberts & David Alford
Cost: Fixed-price D £11.45. ☺ H/wine £7.85.
Times: D only, 7pm-last D 8.30pm. Closed Jan-Mar, 10 days Nov
Additional: No children under 5; ♨ dishes

CHITTLEHAMHOLT,
Highbullen Hotel

With spectacular views across the Mole and Taw valleys, this splendid Victorian mansion is a popular retreat. Honest home-cooked food, listed on a daily-changing set menu, is a bonus. Well-reported dishes have included first-class celery soup and a shoulder of lamb with spicy rice stuffing. Impressive wines.

Smoking: No smoking in dining room; air-conditioning
Accommodation: 35 en suite. **Credit cards:** ▆▆ ▆▆ ▆▆ ▆

Directions: At Chittlehamholt, 1 mile through village

Chittlehamholt, Umberleigh, EX37 9HD
Map 3: SS62
Tel: 01769 540561
Fax: 01769 540492
Chef: Colette Potter
Owners: Hugh & Pam Neil
Cost: Fixed-price D £18.50. ☺ H/wine £9.50.
Times: Last L 2pm/D 9pm
Additional: Bar food; No children under 8

COLYFORD, **Swallows Eaves Hotel** ✿

Dating from the 1920s, this attractive wisteria-clad hotel has a pleasant restaurant decked out with fresh flowers and crisp linen. The fixed-price dinner offers a choice of starters and puddings with a set main course along the lines of medallions of pork tenderloin with prunes, white wine and cream.

Smoking: No smoking in dining room
Accommodation: 8 en suite
Credit cards: ▆▆ ▆▆ ▆▆ ▆

Directions: In the centre of the village on the A3082

Swan Hill Road Colyton EX13 6QJ
Map 3: SY29
Tel: 01297 553184
Fax: 01297 553574
Chef: Jane Beck
Owners: Jane & Jon Beck
Cost: Fixed-price D £19. ☺ H/wine £8.95.
Times: D only, 7pm-last D 9pm. Closed Jan
Additional: No children under 14; ♨ dishes

CROYDE, Kittiwell House Hotel ❀

It dates from the sixteenth century, and this thatched hotel comes complete with beams, panelled walls and log fires. The kitchen provides a good choice of soundly cooked food along the lines of chicken and Stilton soup, lobster filo parcels with basil cream sauce, and fresh raspberries with honeycomb ice cream.

Smoking: No smoking in dining room
Accommodation: 12 en suite
Credit cards: ■■ ■■ ■■ ■■ ▣

Directions: At top end of Croyde village

St Mary's Road EX33 1PG
Map 2: SS43
Tel: 01271 890247
Fax: 01271 890469
Chefs: David Raynor
Owners: Yvonne & James Lang
Cost: *Alc* £25, fixed-price D £17.50.
☺ H/wine £9.80.
Times: D only, 7pm-9pm Closed Jan-Feb
Additional: Sunday L (noon-2pm).
Children welcome; ♨ dishes

DARTMOUTH,
The Carved Angel ❀❀❀

Many youthful shooting stars and comets have blazed through the culinary firmament since this particular Angel first took flight in the 1970s, but its consistency and philosophy remain untarnished. The strength of place lies partly in the setting: the glass-fronted building is hard by the River Dart and, if you are sitting upstairs, the waterscapes are magnificent. Inside there are no barriers between kitchen and dining room; work is done in full view, there's no mystique, no suspicion that sleight of hand is going on behind closed doors. Redoubtable Joyce Molyneux still holds sway – semi-retired, she still puts in a few sessions a week and her ideology defines what happens here – although Nick Coiley is given free rein to guide the ship. Freshness of supplies, and an approach that puts its faith in natural simplicity rather than high art are what single out the food. The river yields a plentiful crop, the sea and the local countryside provide their own contribution: scallop and artichoke chowder, pan-fried sea bass with fennel and a curry sauce, steamed brill steak with clams, cockles and chervil – the kitchen relishes avidly what is seasonal. Balancing this might be meatier offerings in the shape of warm salad of goose confit, roast best end of lamb with ratatouille and deep-fried garlic, or calves' liver and sweetbreads with spinach and a Madeira sauce. The option of cut-price lunch deals means that the food is becoming ever more accessible. An inspection lunch taken on a winter's day was everything one might expect from a set-up that understands its materials, but is prepared occasionally to venture away from its home base. Borsch with mushroom turnovers was perfectly appropriate for the weather, while the main dish – braised duck with soy sauce and lemon grass served with cornbread and a startling pineapple pickle – saw the kitchen in an even more eclectic mood. Blood orange tart remains a favourite dessert, otherwise there might be coconut and lemon soufflé or rhubarb and Pernod jelly.

Signature dishes: scallop and artichoke chowder; grilled Dart salmon with sorrel mayonnaise; Dittisham plum parfait; braised venison with bacon, red wine and pig's trotters.

Directions: Dartmouth centre, on the water's edge

2 South Embankment TQ6 9BH
Map 3: SX85
Tel: 01803 832465
Fax: 01803 835141
Chefs: Nick Coiley, Joyce Molyneux
Owners: Joyce Molyneux, Meriel Matthews, Nick Coiley, Zoë Wynne
Cost: *Alc* £37.50, fixed-price lunch £24-£29/D £40-£45 (2-3 courses). H/wine £15
Times: 12.30pm-2.30pm/7.30-last D 9.30pm. Closed D Sun, Mon, 6 wks from 1 Jan
Additional: Sunday L; Children welcome; ♨ dishes
Seats: 50. Private dining room 18
Smoking: No smoking in dining room
Credit cards: ■■ ■■ ■■ ▣

DARTMOUTH, **Dart Marina**

Sandquay TQ6 9PH
Map 3: SX85
Tel: 01803 832580
Fax: 01803 835040

Beautiful river views and imaginative meals combine to make a visit to Dart Marina an enjoyable one. Typical starters include green-lip giant mussels cooked in white wine, smoked salmon with lemon and cracked pepper, and king prawns grilled on a skewer with garlic butter and lemon.

Chef: Malcolm Whybrow
Owners: Forte Heritage
Cost: Fixed-price L £12.50/D £24.95.
☺ H/wine £10.70.
Times: Last L 2.30pm/D 9pm
Additional: Sunday L; Bar meals;
Children welcome; ❹ dishes

Smoking: No smoking in dining room; air-conditioning
Accommodation: 50 en suite
Credit cards: 💳 💳 💳 💳 💳 💳

Directions: A379 from Torbay via Philip car ferry, or A381 from Totnes. By the marina

DARTMOUTH,
The Exchange ✿✿

5 Higher Street TQ6 9RB
Map 3: SX85
Tel/Fax: 01803 832022

The building, a wealthy merchant's house dating from the sixteenth century, has converted well to a restaurant on two floors, as well as providing a comfortable lounge. The formula is straightforward: a short, simple menu, backed up by weekly blackboard specials, with the kitchen delivering tried and tested dishes with an international flavour rather than setting the world on fire with all the right modern noises; look, instead, for Greek lamb shank or Swiss cheese fondue. The cooking, however, shows skill. Crab cake with tomato and chilli sauce opened a test meal, followed by a New Orleans-style Jambalaya, a mixture of rice, chicken, prawns, smoked ham and sausage, seasoned with cayenne. Crème brûlée was a good example of the dish, and came with a separate selection of fresh fruit. The wine list has as global a range as the food.

Chef/Owner: David C Hawke
Cost: Alc £20-£22. H/wine £8.50. ☺
Times: Noon-last L 2pm/7pm-last D 10pm. Closed Tue, Xmas, Feb
Additional: Sunday lunch; ❹ dishes
Seats: 50
Credit cards: 💳 💳 💳 💳

Directions: In town centre near parish church

EAST BUCKLAND,
Lower Pitt Restaurant ✿

Barnstaple EX32 0TD
Map 2: SS53
Tel/Fax: 01598 760243

Log fires, low beams and lintels characterise this sixteenth-century former farmhouse. One dining room is in the old dairy, the other one in the conservatory. Fresh local and home-grown produce is used to good effect in dishes such as game bourguignon, and a seafood selection in tarragon and parsley sauce.

Chef: Suzanne Lyons
Owners: Suzanne & Jerome Lyons
Cost: Alc £25. H/wine £8.90. ☺
Times: D only, 7pm-last D 9pm.
Closed Sun, Mon, Xmas, 1 Jan
Additional: No children under 8;
❹ dishes

Smoking: No smoking in dining room
Accommodation: 3 en suite
Credit cards: 💳 💳 💳 💳 💳

Directions: Two miles N of the A361 (N Devon Link Road), near East Buckland village church

EXETER, **Barton Cross** ✿✿

Huxham EX5 4EJ
Map 3: SX99
Tel: 01392 841245
Fax: 01392 841942

'Smashing little hotel, well maintained and with high levels of hospitality and service,' comments an inspector of this seventeenth-century thatched house. A bonus is the lovely setting in glorious Devon countryside, just five miles from

Chef: Paul George Bending
Owners: Mr & Mrs B Hamilton

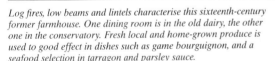

Barton Cross

Cost: Alc £22.50, fixed-price L
£18.50/D £22.50. ☺ H/wine £9.25.
Times: L by prior arrangement/
6.45pm-last D 9pm
Additional: Children welcome;
☺ dishes
Seats: 45. Private dining room 12
Smoking: No smoking in dining room
Accommodation: 7 en suite
Credit cards: ■■■■ ⚫

Exeter. Our inspector also sung the kitchen's praises. The
breads are all home-made, as are the simple petits fours and
canapés, and the set menus draw on local produce for
inspiration. At a December lunch, this translated as wild
mushroom tart with tarragon cream, 'Huxham winter platter'
(bresaola with duck confit and brioche), guinea fowl breast
spiced with coriander and served with warm winter fruit
compote, roast loin of venison with a root vegetable casserole,
and fresh damsons brûléed in a saffron custard, and a warm
tarte Tatin of apples and pears. The wine list offers an
extensive selection to suit all palates and pockets.

Directions: 4 miles N of Exeter on A396. At Stoke Canon, turn
R at church

EXETER, **Buckerell Lodge** ✿✿

Topsham Road
EX2 4SQ
Map 3: SX99
Tel: 01392 221111
Fax: 01392 491111
Chef: David Grindrod
Owners: Bruce & Pat Jefford
Cost: Alc £17, fixed-price L £12.50/D
£18.50. ☺ H/wine £9.95.
Times: Noon-last L 2pm/7pm-last D
10pm
Additional: Bar food; Sunday L;
Children welcome; ☺ dishes
Seats: 60. Private dining rooms 10-130
Smoking: No smoking in dining room;
air-conditioning
Accommodation: 54 en suite
Credit cards: ■■■■ ⚫

Conveniently placed for the city centre and its amenities, yet
set in acres of parkland, this privately run hotel caters for
everyone from up-market coach parties to business people and
holiday makers. Snacks are served in the Lodge bar, fine dining
takes place in the light, airy Raffles Restaurant. The kitchen is
capable of producing cleverly wrought, intricate dishes with
saucing as a notable strength; our inspector was also impressed
by the quality of the home-baked breads. A test dinner kicked
off with crab and salmon terrine prettily offset by a pleasing
pesto sauce, while main courses included lamb served on a bed
of leeks with a thyme and port reduction, as well as tenderloin
of pork with a compote of apple and Parma ham and another
excellent reduction – this time flavoured with apple and sage.
To finish, mille-feuille of white and dark chocolate proved

more successful than plum tarte Tatin. The well-spread, detailed wine list features some interesting bins from around the world.

Directions: 5 minutes from M5J30, follow signs for Exeter city centre. Aiport 5 miles, station 2 miles

EXETER,

Ebford House Hotel ❀❀

Ebmouth Road Ebford EX3 0QH
Map 3: SX99
Tel: 01392 877658
Fax: 01392 874424
Chef: Paul Bazell
Owners: Mr & Mrs DT Horton
Cost: Fixed-price L £15.95/D £22.50.
☺ H/wine £8.65
Times: Noon-last L 1.30pm/7pm-last D 9.30pm. Closed L Sat, Sun, Xmas
Additional: Bar food; Children welcome; ❹ dishes
Seats: 50. Private dining room 12
Smoking: No smoking in dining room
Accommodation: 16 en suite
Credit cards: ▬ ▤ ▨ ➷ ▢

Set in its own landscaped grounds a couple of miles from Exeter, this classic Georgian country house owes much to the care and attention of its owners, the Hortons. Informal meals are served in Frisco's bistro where home-baked breads, local seafood and splendid puddings are particularly noteworthy. Otherwise dine in Horton's – a fine Georgian room where guests are offered a choice of fixed-price menus. Starters such as smoked chicken and pesto tortellini with mushroom sauce or pigeon terrine with foie gras could be followed by, say, pan-fried venison with port and juniper berries topped with aubergine crisps, mint-crusted loin of lamb with Madeira and redcurrant sauce, or the catch of the day. Around 80 wines have been well chosen for quality and value.

Directions: On A376 Exmouth road near Topsham

EXETER,

Lord Haldon Hotel ❀

Dunchideock EX6 7YF
Map 3: SY19
Tel: 01392 832483
Chef: Robin Webber
Owners: S & M Preece
Cost: *Alc* £25, fixed-price L £11.50/D £18.50. ☺ H/wine £8.95
Times: Last L 1.30pm/last D 8.30pm

The Chandelier Restaurant is the former coach house of this Georgian stately home-turned-hotel. There is quite a following from locals and visitors alike for the carefully prepared food. A spring meal comprised chicken liver pâté, breast of duck with cranberry marmalade, and a good banoffee pie.

Additional: Sunday L; Bar meals; Children welcome; ❹ dishes
Smoking: No smoking in dining room
Accommodation: 23 en suite
Credit cards: ▬ ▤ ➷ ▢

Directions: Leave M5/J31, take A30 (Okehampton); follow signs to Ide. Through village for 2.5 mile, L after phone box, follow for 0.5 mile; hotel L after low stone bridge

EXETER, St Olaves Court ✸✸

Mary Arches Street EX4 3AZ
Map 3: SY19
Tel: 01392 217736
Fax: 01392 413054
Chefs: John Winstanley, Robert Dracket, Jos Davey
Owners: Raymond & Ute Wyatt
Cost: *Alc* £29, fixed-price L&D £11.50-£14.50 (2-3 courses). ☺
H/wine £10.50.
Times: Noon-last L 2pm/6.30-last D 9.30pm. Closed L Sat, L Sun
Additional: Bar food L; Children welcome; ✿ dishes
Seats: 45. Private dining room 14 & 8
Smoking: No smoking in dining room
Accommodation: 15 en suite
Credit cards: ▉ ▉ ▉ ▉ ▣ ▯

Fine Georgian building, now a personally run hotel, standing in its own walled garden in the centre of the city, only 400 yards from the cathedral. The public rooms revolve around Golsworthy's, the hotel's intimate, candlelit restaurant. The hand-written menus offer a pleasing balance between fish, meat, game and vegetarian dishes and the cooking shows both flair and imagination with pistou salad, grilled saddle of wild boar with soured cabbage and apple, prune and black pudding compote, and glazed lemon tart with home-made sorbet and raspberry coulis, showing the range. A spring dinner opened well with an appetiser of smoked chicken and tarragon boudin served with a basil vinaigrette. This was followed by chicken liver parfait, fillet of brill with spinach cream, and to finish, vanilla panna cotta with baked rhubarb and biscotti. Good coffee and excellent petits fours too.

Directions: Follow signs to city centre, then 'Mary Arches P'; hotel is opposite car park entrance

GITTISHAM,
Combe House Hotel ✸

Personally run Elizabethan manor house offering everything from light lunches to fixed-price dinners. Baking is a strength, and the menus are in the country-house style of rillettes of wild boar with mixed leaves, an excellent version of seafood risotto with a fine balance of different fish, and noisettes of Welsh lamb with roasted vegetables, gratin dauphinoise and rosemary jus.

Honiton EX14 0AD
Map 3: SY19
Tel: 01404 42756
Fax: 01404 46004
Chef: Thérèse Boswell
Owners: John & Thérèse Boswell
Cost: *Alc* £24, fixed-price L £14.50. ☺ H/wine £11.50.
Times: Last L 1.45pm/last D 9.30pm. Closed 2 wks end Jan- beginning Feb

Additional: Bar food L; Sunday L; No children under 10; ✿ dishes
Smoking: No smoking in dining room
Accommodation: 15 en suite
Credit cards: ▉ ▉ ▉ ▉ ▣ ▯

Directions: In Gittisham village off A30 & A303 south of Honiton

GULWORTHY,
The Horn of Plenty ❀❀❀

Gulworthy
PL19 8JD
Map 2: SX47
Tel/Fax: 01822 832528
Chef: Peter Gorton
Owners: Ian & Elaine Gatehouse
Cost: Fixed-price L £17.50/D £29.50
(3 courses). H/wine £11.50
Times: Noon-last L 2pm/7pm-last D
9pm. Closed Mon L, 25-26 Dec
Additional: Sunday L; No children
under 13; ❀ dishes
Seats: 50. Private dining room 12
Smoking: No smoking in dining room
Accommodation: 7 en suite
Credit cards: ▮ ▮ ▮ ▮

The Horn of Plenty is a place of fond memories, old and new –
and the view from the dining-room over the Tamar Valley
remains as lovely as ever. The famous name carries a set of
expectations, but ones which are well fulfilled by the present
owners, Elaine and Ian Gatehouse. A set price, three-course
dinner offers six choices per course, preceded by excellent
canapés such as chicken tikka kebabs, puffy cheese fritters and
little mushroom tarts – all to be wolfed down in front of the
lovely open fire in the lounge. Kitchen ambitions are evident in
dishes which demand tight timing, such as tempura-fried lemon
sole topped with prawns and scallops, served with spicy Thai
dressing, and a warm chocolate cake with melted chocolate
centre garnished with three ice-creams. Our inspector's first
course of goat's cheese parcel with hazelnuts, sage and
beetroot was both beautifully presented and light as a feather,
and a fine mushroom sauce accompanied a main course of
chicken on creamed potatoes with parsley purée. Lemon tart,
temptingly decorated with swirls of blackcurrant sauce, had a
good, crunchy glaze although the crust was perhaps not quite
as crisp as it might have been. Irresistible home-made petit
fours, however, ensured a full-to-bursting-point departure for
one satisfied diner.

Nine house wines under £12.25, and by the glass. The
popular Salice Salentino Riserva is deliciously fruity (£11.75),
Gerard Mouton's Givry from the Côtes Chalonnaise is soft and
elegant (£19.50). Plenty to choose from the higher end of the
Burgundy scale with Drouhin, Ampeau and Jadot featuring
highly. A good result from two Bordeaux producers in Chile –
Dom Paul Bruno, Cabernet Sauvignon (£20.00).
Signature dishes: Sauté of foie gras on a potato and parsnip
pancake with fresh figs; Roast lamb with wild mushrooms,
garlic and rosemary polenta; Grilled sea bass with asparagus,
tomato confit and prawn sauce; Horn of Plenty tuille, crème
fraîche ice-cream and fruit compote.

Directions: 3 miles from Tavistock on A390. Turn R at
Gulworthy Cross, then signed

HAYTOR, **Bel Alp House**

Splendid six-course set dinners are served at this elegant Edwardian mansion, and there are superb views from the dining room over Dartmoor. Options are available at most courses and our inspector particularly enjoyed duck breast with juniper sauce, and a dessert of three home-made ice creams.

Accommodation: 8 en suite
Credit cards: ▨ ▨ ▨ ▨ ▨ ▨

Directions: 1.5 miles W of BoveyTracey off B3387 to Haytor

Bovey Tracey TQ13 9XX
Map 3: SX77
Tel: 01364 661217
Fax: 01364 661292
Chef: Ian Davidson
Owners: Jack & Mary Twist
Cost: Fixed-price D £30 (six courses) ☺
Times: 7.30pm-last D 9pm.
Additional: Children welcome;
🍴 dishes
Smoking: No smoking in dining room

HAYTOR, **Rock Inn**

A delightful sixteenth-century village inn, perfectly placed for checking out Dartmoor. After a day exploring, return for supper by candlelight, taking in, perhaps, grilled goat's cheese with leek and peppercorn sauce, and freshly caught fillet of salmon, with roasted garlic and hazelnut butter sauce. Local produce is used wherever possible.

Accommodation: 9 en suite
Credit cards: ▨ ▨ ▨ ▨ ▨

Directions: In Haytor village on A3387, 3 miles from A382

Haytor Vale Newton Abbot
TQ13 9XP
Map 3: SX77
Tel: 01364 661305
Fax: 01364 661242
Chef: Philip Hurrell
Owner: Christopher Graves
Cost: Alc £20. H/wine £7.95. ☺
Times: Last L 2.15pm/D-9.30pm
Additional: Bar food; Sunday L;
Children welcome; 🍴 dishes
Smoking: No smoking in dining room

HOLSWORTHY,
Court Barn Hotel NEW

Clawton EX22 6PS
Map 2: SS30
Tel: 01409 271219
Fax: 01409 271309
Chef: Sue Wood
Owners: Robert & Sue Wood
Cost: Fixed-price L £12.50/D £21. ☺
H/wine £8.25.
Times: Last L 2pm/D 9pm. Closed L Sat, early Jan
Additional: Sunday L; Bar food L;
No children under 8; 🍴 dishes
Smoking: No smoking in dining room
Accommodation: 8 en suite
Credit cards: ▨ ▨ ▨ ▨ ▨ ▨

A building of historical and architectural interest, dating from the seventeenth century, set amid rolling countryside. Well-reported cooking is complemented by an award-winning wine list. Dishes include prawn and almond quiche, rack of lamb with raspberry sauce, and summer pudding.

Directions: 2.5 miles S of Holsworthy on A388, next to Clawton church

HONITON, **Home Farm Hotel** NEW

Former farmhouse with all the works: thatch, a small beamed restaurant, wide range of dishes based on local produce, and an interesting wine list. Rack of lamb (which was cooked to perfection),

Wilmington E14 9JR
Map 3: ST10
Tel: 01404 831278
Fax: 01404 831411
Chef: Barry Bingham

and chocolate rum torte from the 'irresistible' dessert trolley, were highlights of an inspection meal.

Smoking: No smoking in dining room
Accommodation: 13 en suite
Credit cards: ▆▆ ▆▆ ▆▆ ▆▆ ▆▆ ▆

Directions: Three miles E of Honiton in village of Wilmington

Owners: AJ & EL Cressy
Cost: Alc £21, fixed-price L&D £14.50. ☺ H/wine £8.95.
Times: Last L 2.15pm/last D 9.15pm. Closed Xmas wk
Additional: Bar meals; Sunday L; Children welcome; ❸ dishes
Seats: 32

HORRABRIDGE,
Overcombe Hotel ❀

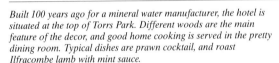

Small, Edwardian hotel on the edge of the village only yards from the open sweep of Dartmoor. This is a welcoming, friendly place – the owners treat all guests as personal friends. Food is imaginative. A typical meal could be nectarines stuffed with salmon, breast of duck with sloe gin sauce, spiced apple and blackberry meringue pie, with local cheeses to follow.

Smoking: No smoking in dining room
Accommodation: 11 en suite
Credit cards: ▆▆ ▆▆ ▆▆ ▆

Directions: Off A386 past Yelverton r/bout, direction Tavistock. 1st L after Horrabridge sign

Near Yelverton PL20 7RN
Map 2: SX56
Tel/Fax: 01822 853501
Chef: Brenda Durnell
Owners: Maurice & Brenda Durnell
Cost: Fixed-price D £13. ☺ H/wine £6.50.
Times: D only, 7.30pm-8.15pm
Additional: Children welcome; ❸ dishes

ILFRACOMBE, Elmfield Hotel ❀

Built 100 years ago for a mineral water manufacturer, the hotel is situated at the top of Torrs Park. Different woods are the main feature of the decor, and good home cooking is served in the pretty dining room. Typical dishes are prawn cocktail, and roast Ilfracombe lamb with mint sauce.

Smoking: No smoking in dining room
Accommodation: 14 en suite
Credit cards: ▆▆ ▆▆

Directions: From Barnstaple on A361, at 1st lights L (Wilder Road), L next lights, L into Torrs Park. At top of hill on the L

Torrs Park EX34 8AZ
Map 2: SS54
Tel: 01271 863377
Fax: 01271 866828
Chef: Ann Doody
Owners: Ann & Derek Doody
Cost: Alc £25, fixed-price D £15. ☺ H/wine £7.50.
Times: Last L 1.45pm/D 7.30pm. Closed Nov-Apr
Additional: Bar Food L; No children under 8; ❸ dishes

IVYBRIDGE,
Glazebrook House Hotel ❀

South Brent TQ10 9JE
Map 3: SX65
Tel: 01364 73322
Fax: 01364 72350
Chef: David Merryman
Owners: Fred & Chris Heard
Cost: Alc £25.50, fixed-price L £14.50/D £19.50. ☺ H/wine £9.95.
Times: Last L 2.15pm/last D 9pm
Additional: Sunday L; Children welcome; ❸ dishes
Accommodation: 10 en suite
Credit cards: ▆▆ ▆▆ ▆▆ ▆▆ ▆

Stylish cooking in pleasant, intimate surroundings at this charming family-run hotel on the edge of Dartmoor. Pan-fried scallops in a pastry crust with chive butter sauce, crabmeat wrapped in smoked salmon with a tomato and basil vinaigrette, lamb with a rosemary and almond mousse and red wine sauce, and banana soufflé with rum sauce are all highly recommended.

Directions: Follow B&B signs from A38 South Brent to Glazebrook

KINGSBRIDGE,

Buckland-Tout-Saints Hotel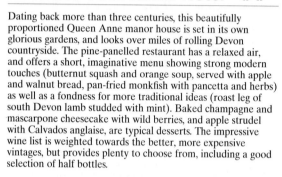

Dating back more than three centuries, this beautifully proportioned Queen Anne manor house is set in its own glorious gardens, and looks over miles of rolling Devon countryside. The pine-panelled restaurant has a relaxed air, and offers a short, imaginative menu showing strong modern touches (butternut squash and orange soup, served with apple and walnut bread, pan-fried monkfish with pancetta and herbs) as well as a fondness for more traditional ideas (roast leg of south Devon lamb studded with mint). Baked champagne and mascarpone cheesecake with wild berries, and apple strudel with Calvados anglaise, are typical desserts. The impressive wine list is weighted towards the better, more expensive vintages, but provides plenty to choose from, including a good selection of half bottles.

Directions: 2 miles N of Kingsbridge on A381. Through village of Goveton, 500 yds past church

Goveton TQ7 2DS
Map 3: SX74
Tel: 01548 853055
Fax: 01548 856261
Chef: Tom Woods
Owner: Mr AP Hardstaff
Cost: *Alc* £30, fixed-price L £16.50/D £30 (4 courses). H/wine £9.75
Times: 12.30pm-last L 1.45pm/7.30pm-last D 9.30pm
Additional: Sunday L; Bar meals L; No children under 6; ✿ dishes
Seats: 45. Private dining room 15-20. Jacket & tie preferred
Smoking: No smoking in dining room
Accommodation: 13 en suite
Credit cards: ▬ ▬ ▬ ▢

KINGSKERSWELL,

Pitt House Restaurant

Picture postcard pretty, this fifteenth-century thatched cottage seats just 30 lucky diners. Polished antique tables, beamed ceilings, log fires, lace-edged table linen and sparkling crystal set the scene for the carefully cooked meals and friendly service. Enjoyable dishes include pork with apples and cider, and iced honey parfait.

Additional: Sunday L; No children under 10 at D; ✿ dishes
Smoking: No smoking in dining room
Credit cards: ▬ ▬ ▬ ▢

Directions: Torquay road from Newton Abbot, 1st R, follow road to junction & turn L, parish church on R. Take 1st R, restaurant 50yds on L

2 Church End Road TQ12 5DS
Map 3: SX86
Tel: 01803 873374
Chef: Stephen Sanders
Owners: Mr & Mrs Rogers
Cost: *Alc* £24, fixed-price L £12.95. H/wine £9.50. ☺
Times: Last L 1pm/last D 9pm. Closed D Sun, Mon, last 2 wks Jan/Aug

LEWDOWN,

Lewtrenchard Manor

Built around 1600, on the site of a dwelling recorded in the Doomsday Book, this is a gloriously atmospheric Jacobean House. It stands on high ground with views over the Lewtrenchard Estate and Dartmoor and close by is the River Lew. Inside there are stunning ornate ceilings and granite window frames, superb carvings and oak panelling. The whole

Okehampton
EX20 4PN
Map 2: SX48
Tel: 01566 783256
Fax: 01566 783332

Chef: Jason Buck

place is etched with architectural embellishment. The kitchen delivers a menu of skilfully wrought modern dishes along the lines of seared black pudding and scallops with a salad of frisée and truffle, roast rabbit with a smoked bacon and spring onion pudding served with a grain mustard bouillon, and pan-fried duck breast with lemon spätzle and five-spice sauce. A favourable inspection began with good home-baked breads and a terrine of corn-fed chicken and tarragon wrapped in Parma ham, and ended on a high note with a subtly flavoured caramel and date soufflé served with date ice cream. The heavyweight wine list is worth serious consideration.

Directions: Take A30 for Lewdown, after 6 miles turn L at signpost for Lewtrenchard. Follow signs for 0.75 mile

Owners: James & Susan Murray
Cost: Fixed-price D £28. H/wine £9
Times: D only, 7.15pm-last D 9.30pm
Additional: Bar snacks L; Sunday L (12.15pm-1.45pm); No children under 8
Seats: 45. Private dining room 18. Jacket & tie preferred
Smoking: No smoking in dining room
Accommodation: 9 en suite
Credit cards:

LIFTON, Arundell Arms ❀❀❀

PL16 0AA
Map 2: SX38
Tel: 01566 784666
Fax: 01566 784494
Chef: Philip Burgess, Nick Shopland
Owner: Mrs Anne Voss-Bark
Cost: Fixed-price L £15.50/D £27.50. H/wine £10
Times: 12.30pm-last L 2pm/7.30pm-last D 9.30pm. Closed 3 evenings Xmas
Additional: Bar food; Sunday L; Children welcome; ❹ dishes
Seats: 70. Private dining room 30
Smoking: No smoking in dining room
Accommodation: 28 en suite
Credit cards:

In 1996 the redoubtable Anne Voss-Bark was awarded the MBE for 'an outstanding contribution to tourism'. For some 36 years, her presence has contributed hugely to the success of this much loved 200-year-old coaching inn. This is a sporting hotel 'par excellence', with 20 miles of salmon and trout fishing rights on the River Tamar and its tributaries, not to mention the prospect of hunting and shooting on the moors. High quality meals are served in the flagstoned bar, but even more impressive is the full repertoire devised for the spacious dining room, which is dominated by a huge chandelier and a dramatic flower arrangement. Philip Burgess is a creative chef, capable of producing vibrant dishes with clear, natural flavours. There's a deceptive simplicity about some of his ideas, but none the worse for that. Raw materials are chosen with an eye for the season and the locality. A meal taken in springtime began assertively with superbly fresh fritters of sole coated in featherlight saffron batter, accompanied by a green mayonnaise and some lightly dressed leaves livened up with chervil, tarragon, hard-boiled egg, anchovies and some secret ingredients. To follow there was a mixed grill of duck, chicken and guinea fowl, each one acutely timed and served with apricot and ginger chutney. Again, the simplicity struck home. To finish, steamed chocolate sponge exploded in the mouth with sheer intensity of flavour and the accompanying plain chocolate sauce and a blob of clotted cream worked like a dream. The wine list is a well-balanced slate of around 80 bins with prices kept well in check.
   Signature dishes: Casserole of monkfish, sole, scallops and Tamar salmon with saffron and St.Enodoc asparagus;

marinated fillet of English lamb, roasted with rosemary and honey, served with a warm salad of baby summer vegetables and a piquant sauce; fillet of wild venison with herb crust, parsley tartlet and rich shallot and red wine sauce; braised oxtails with prunes, roasted root vegetables and Madeira sauce.

Directions: Just off A30 in village of Lifton

LIFTON, Lifton Hall 🏵🏵

A small, luxury hotel in traditional English style. In Herbs Restaurant you can choose from an extraordinarily long *carte*, or make life easier for yourself and take the set two- or three-course menu. Either way, the cooking is careful, accurate and full of flavour without being over-complicated. Dinner starts with an amuse-bouche – on our visit a demi-tasse of fresh green pea soup with a just-out-of-the-pod flavour. Roast spiced duck breast with a punchy honey and soya sauce was remarkable for the crispy noodle nest that accompanied it, strands of noodles shooting skyward as if electrocuted. Fillet of beef was fulsomely praised, and came with gently grilled wild mushrooms. Crunchy and rich fudge brownies, aimed at chocoholics, were unashamedly combined with intense chocolate, vanilla and Mars bar ice creams. The wine list is good value and has some exciting bins from lesser known regions.

PL16 0DR
Map 2: SX38
Tel: 01566 784263/863
Fax: 01566 784770
Chef: Mary Dodds
Owner: RG & ME Dodds
Cost: *Alc* £23, fixed-price D £19.50.
☺ H/wine £7.50.
Times: D only, 7.30pm-last D 9.30.
Closed Sun, Mon
Additional: Bar food; Children welcome; 🌢 dishes
Seats: 35
Smoking: No smoking in dining room
Accommodation: 11 en suite
Credit cards: 💳 ▩ ▩ ▩ ▩ ▢

Directions: Leave A30 signposted Lifton Down/Tavistock. Hotel is 300yds from village on L

LIFTON,
Thatched Cottage Hotel 🏵

Sprytown PL16 0AY
Map 3: SS74
Tel: 01566 784224
Fax: 01566 784334
Chef: Rita Willing, Victoria Bryant
Owners: G & R Willing, V Bryant, J Purr
Cost: Fixed price D £21.50.
Times: Last L 2pm/D 9.30pm
Additional: Sunday L;
no children under 12; 🌢 dishes
Smoking: No-smoking area; no cigars & pipes
Accommodation: 5 en suite
Credit cards: 💳 ▩ ▩ ▩ ▩ ▢

Thatched by name and thatched by nature, this 400-year-old cottage sits comfortably in more than two acres of prettily landscaped gardens complete with a pond. The hotel boasts two dining rooms, where menus promise the likes of cucumber soup, duck breast with gooseberry sauce, and spotted dick with clotted cream.

Directions: From A30 at Stowford turn S on C 493 2 miles to Sprytown Cross – straight ahead 100yds on R

LYDFORD,

Castle Inn Restaurant

Lydford EX20 4BH
Map 2: SX58
Tel: 01822 820242
Fax: 01822 820454
Chef: Mo Walker
Owners: Clive & Mo Walker
Cost: *Alc* £19, fixed-price L from
£5.50/D £15.95. ☺ H/wine £9.95.
Times: Last L 2.20pm/D 9.30pm
Additional: Sunday L; Bar meals L;
No children under 5; ✿ dishes

A traditional West Country inn to the west of Dartmoor. In the restaurant, bowed ceilings and crackling fires create an intimate, romantic atmosphere. Good country cooking along the lines of pheasant and chestnut casserole, and braised woodpigeon with meadow mushrooms, are served. Steak and kidney pie is a speciality.

Accommodation: 10 en suite
Credit cards: ▬ ▬ ▬ 🥘 🄟 £

Directions: From A30 take A386 towards Tavistock. Lyford signposted to right after 5 miles

LYMPSTONE,

River House Restaurant 🏵🏵

The Strand EX8 5EY
Map 3: SX98
Tel: 01395 265147
Chef: Shirley Wilkes
Owner: Michael Wilkes
Cost: Fixed-price L & D £28.95 (2 courses). H/wine £9.95
Times: Noon-last L 1.30pm/7pm-last D 9.30pm (10.30pm Sat). Closed Sun, Mon (except residents)
Additional: No children under 6; ✿ dishes
Seats: 34. Private dining room 14
Smoking: No smoking in dining room
Accommodation: 3 en suite
Credit cards: ▬ ▬ ▬ 🥘

Glorious riverside views are one of the great attractions at this agreeable restaurant-with-rooms on the Exe estuary. One of the best vistas is from the first-floor dining room, although guests may also be distracted by the art collection – most of which is for sale. Fresh fish shows up strongly on the fixed-price menus: whole lemon sole is stuffed with lemon and herbs and served with lemon sauce, turbot is poached in stock and served with a sauce made from the cooking juices. Elsewhere expect dishes such as warm salad of Lunesdale duck with leek and pepper dressing, Catalan chicken, and rack of lamb with Madeira sauce. Vegetables (often harvested from the garden) are regularly endorsed by inspectors. Desserts generally include such things as lemon roulade, sticky toffee pudding and iced chocolate and apricot brandy terrine. The varied wine list has a decent selection of half-bottles.

Directions: In Lower Lympstone, approx 2 miles off A376 Exeter-Exmouth road

LYNMOUTH, ## Rising Sun Hotel

Harbourside EX35 6EQ
Map 3: SS74
Tel: 01598 753223
Fax: 01598 753480
Chef: David Lamprell
Owners: Hugo & Pamela Jeune

A fourteenth-century thatched inn overlooking a tiny harbour that is crammed full of boats bobbing about on the swell. Once the haunt of smugglers, the hotel is etched with history – crooked ceilings, thick walls and uneven oak floors add to its

Rising Sun Hotel

Cost: Alc £25; fixed-price L £17.50.
H/wine £9.75
Times: Noon-last L 1.30pm/7pm-last
D 8.45pm
Additional: Bar food L;
No children under 8
Seats: 38.
Smoking: No smoking in dining room
Accommodation: 16 en suite
Credit cards:

time-worn character. The intimate restaurant specialises in local Exmoor game and freshly-caught seafood. Main courses from the *carte* might include grilled fillet of turbot with shredded apple and a light rhubarb butter sauce, medallions of venison with a pear and blackberry compote, and pan-fried suprême of chicken with oyster mushrooms and a tarragon sauce. Or note the components of one well-reported meal that took in salad of duck breast, with nicely complementing prune and apple flavours, roast rack of lamb with Savoy cabbage and a red pepper sauce, and a dessert of summer fruits with a rum-flavoured cream and pistachio nut sauce. Lunch time snacks and light meals are served in the bar. The wine list offers reliable and affordable drinking, with a selection of fine wines from around the world.

Directions: M5/J23 (Minehead). take A39 to Lynmouth, opposite the harbour

LYNTON, Chough's Nest Hotel ✿

Originally built by a Dutch millionaire, this beautiful stone hotel enjoys spectacular views towards Countisbury headland. Thoroughly cosmopolitan cooking is the mainstay of the innovative dinner menus, served in the bright airy dining room. Expect steamed sea bass with ginger or red snapper fillet with pesto.

Smoking: No-smoking establishment
Accommodation: 12 en suite. **Credit cards:** ▆ ▆ ▆ ▆ ▆

Directions: From Lynton Parish Church in centre, turn onto North Walk. Last hotel on L.

North Walk EX35 6HJ
Map 3: SS74
Tel: 01598 753315
Chef: Andrew Collier
Owners: Joanna & Andrew Collier
Cost: Fixed-price D £18 (4 courses).
☺ H/wine £6.10.
Times: Last L 2pm/D 8pm. Closed Nov-March
Additional: No children under 5;
❹ dishes

LYNTON, Combe Park Hotel ✿

Seventeenth-century former hunting lodge in a lovely spot leading down to Hoar Oak Water. There's a daily changing, set five-course dinner menu with puddings a highlight; blackberry and apple flapjack, crème brûlée, and chocolate roulade make seconds hard to resist.

Additional: No children under 12; ❹ dishes
Smoking: No smoking in dining room
Accommodation: 9 en suite. **Credit cards:** None taken

Directions: At Hillsford Bridge, junction of A39/B3223

Hillsford Bridge
EX35 6LE
Map 3: SS74
Tel: 01598 752356
Fax: 01598 753484
Chef: Mrs S Barnes
Owners: Mr & Mrs Barnes, Mr Walley
Cost: Fixed-price D £19 (5 courses).
☺ H/wine £9.
Times: D only, 7pm-last orders 7.15pm

LYNTON, Highcliffe House

John Bishop and Steven Phillips have worked tirelessly to restore this Victorian 'gentleman's summer residence' situated 800 feet above the bay overlooking the two Lyn rivers and the Exmoor coastline. Hospitality is their forte. Dinner is served in the intimate atmosphere of the candlelit restaurant and the four-course menu varies nightly. Our inspector began with soft goat's cheese on rounds of roasted aubergine, before a palate cleansing lemon and rosemary sorbet. The main course was brill with a red wine sauce and a garnish of bacon and mushrooms, although the choice might extend to pot-roast Exmoor venison with poached pear and a redcurrant sauce, or grilled chicken with lemon, garlic and rosemary on a bed of braised Puy lentils. Dessert on this occasion was a fairly judged iced lemon brûlée. Two dozen wines provide plenty of eminently affordable drinking.

Directions: Turn off the A39 at Lynton; hotel is up Sinai Hill on L

Sinai Hill EX35 6AR
Map 3: SS74
Tel/Fax: 01598 752235
Chef: Steven Phillips
Owners: Steven Phillips, John Bishop
Cost: Fixed-price D £25 (4 courses)
Times: D only, 7pm-8.30pm
Additional: Bar meals L; ◑ dishes
Seats: 12. Jacket and tie preferred
Smoking: No smoking in dining room
Accommodation: 6 en suite
Credit cards: ■ ■ ■ ■

LYNTON, Lynton Cottage Hotel

An absolutely stunning location overlooking the Lyn Valley and Lynmouth Bay brings the crowds to this charming 300-year-old hotel. Fixed-price menus feature capably prepared dishes based on good quality raw materials and puddings are particularly noteworthy: hot ones come straight from the oven, cold ones are fresh and enjoyable.

Directions: In North Walk off main road through town

North Walk EX35 6ED
Map 3: SS74
Tel: 01598 752342
Fax: 01598 752597
Telephone for details

MARTINHOE,
Old Rectory Hotel

The restaurant at this former Victorian rectory is a spacious, uncluttered room with beautiful antique furniture. The kitchen demonstrates a flair for unusual combinations of ingredients, belying the simple menu descriptions. A typical dinner might include potted prawns in smoked salmon, and caramelised pork fillets.

Additional: No children under 15; ◑ dishes
Smoking: No smoking establishment
Accommodation: 8 en suite
Credit cards: None taken

Directions: R at Blackmore gate onto A39 (Parracombe). Use Parracombe by-pass, take 3rd L at Martinhoe Cross

Parracombe EX31 4QT
Map 3: SS64
Tel: 01598 763368
Fax: 01598 763567
Chef: Suzanne Bradbury
Owners: John & Suzanne Bradbury
Cost: Fixed-price D £24.
H/wine £10.
Times: D served at 7.30pm, last orders-6.30pm

MORETONHAMPSTED,
Blackaller Hotel ❀

North Bovey,
TQ13 8QY
Map 3: SX78
Tel/Fax: 01647 440322
Chef: Mrs H Phillips
Owners: Mrs H Phillips, Mr P Hunt
Cost: Fixed-price D £21. ☺ H/wine
£7.90.
Times: D only, 7.30pm-8.30pm.
Closed Mon, Jan, Feb
Additional: No children under 12;
◑ dishes
Smoking: No smoking in dining room
Accommodation: 5 en suite
Credit cards: None taken

A seventeenth-century woollen mill on the river bank, surrounded by woods and moor. The farmhouse restaurant features the simple cooking of Hazel Phillips, whose well-judged dishes might include intense chicken and brandy pâté with a fruity Cumberland sauce, and seared fillet of salmon with roast red pepper dressing.

Directions: From M5 – A30 Okehampton Road. Then Marsh Barton sign onto B3212 (Moretonhampstead). Take North Bovey road from there

PARKHAM,
Penhaven Country House ❀

Bideford EX39 5PL
Map 2: SS32
Tel: 01237 451711
Fax: 01237 451878
Chef: Richard Copp
Owners: Maxine & Alan Wade
Cost: *Alc* £25, fixed-price L £9.95/D
£13.95. ☺ H/wine £10.95.
Times: D only 7.15pm-8.45pm.
Additional: Sunday L (12.15pm-1.30pm); No children under 10;
◑ dishes
Smoking: No smoking in dining room
Accommodation: 12 en suite
Credit cards:

A resident colony of badgers is one novel attraction at this converted seventeenth-century rectory set in 11 acres of gardens and woodland. Another bonus is the food served in the Orangery restaurant, where menus are built around supplies of local fish, meat and home-grown vegetables. Bread is home-baked and vegetarians are well catered for.

Directions: From A39 at Horns Cross, follow signs to Parkham and turn L after church

PLYMOUTH,
Chez Nous Restaurant ❀❀❀

Gallic reds, whites and blues define the decor in Jacques and Suzanne Marchal's long-serving restaurant. Between them, this friendly duo have managed to create a mood of genuine

13 Frankfort Gate PL1 1QA
Map 2: SX45
Tel/Fax: 01752 266793
Chef: Jacques Marchal
Owners: Jacques & Suzanne Marchal

Chez Nous Restaurant

Cost: Fixed-price L&D £29.50 (3 courses). H/wine £10.50
Times: 12.30pm-last L 2pm/7pm-last D 10.30pm. Closed Sun, Mon, 3 weeks Feb, 3 weeks Sept
Additional: Children welcome
Seats: 28
Credit cards:

intimacy and warmth which has proved captivating over the years. Shutters exclude the world outside, French posters and menus from exalted establishments across the Channel adorn the walls of the dining room. The daily hand-written menu follows the market, with fish from Plymouth showing up strongly. An inspection lunch in February yielded pan-fried red mullet on a bed of fennel with tomato concasse, and also roasted cod with a pesto crust, both proving that top notch raw materials work best when they are allowed to speak for themselves. What impresses is the clarity and deceptive simplicity of each dish; Marchal is not a chef who needs to gild the lily to get good notices. There's also much to enjoy if meat and game are the order of the day: a version of bresaola prepared with venison is served with chives, chicken breast is paired with ginger sauce, Devon lamb is enlivened with fresh herbs. Crème brûlée and steamed sponge puddings tempt those with a longing for nursery desserts, but alternatives appear in the shape of, say, chocolate and almond torte served with a raspberry sauce and rose petal ice cream, or grilled pineapple spiced with pepper. The wine list is as patriotically Gallic as the food, although a few New World vintages put in an appearance, along with a selection from Banyuls (grown near the Spanish border).

Signature dishes: Asperges a l'essence de truffes; coquilles St Jacques au gingembre; confit de canard au choux vert; filet de boeuf aux champignons sauvage.

Directions: Frankfort Gate is a pedestrianised street between Western Approach & Market Avenue

PLYMOUTH, **Duke of Cornwall** ✿

Victorian Gothic hotel whose domed dining room, complete with marble pillars and magnificent chandelier, makes an impressive backdrop for some up-to-date cooking. Dishes range from poppy seed salmon on a lemon grass skewer with lemon and lime beurre blanc, to baked ostrich fillet with caramelised fruit and Madeira sauce.

Millbay Road PL1 3LG
Map 2: SX45
Tel: 01752 266256
Fax: 01752 600062
Chef: Tim Baily
Cost: Fixed-price L £12.50.
Times: Last L 2pm/D 10pm. Closed L Sat

Additional: Bar Food L; Sunday L; Children welcome; ❹ dishes
Smoking: No smoking in dining room
Accommodation: 70 en suite
Credit cards: ▆▆ ▆▆ ▆▆ ▆ ⌐

Directions: City centre, follow signs " Pavilions", hotel road is opposite

PLYMOUTH, **Kitley** ❀❀

A long tree-lined drive leads up to this fine Tudor revival house, built from Devonshire 'marble' and decorated with considerable flair. Set in 300 acres of rolling fields along the Yealm estuary, the Kitley Estate provides a peaceful retreat from the stresses of modern life. The kitchen produces up-to-date dishes. At a meal in May – taken in the striking book-lined dining room – our inspector enjoyed a starter of seared scallops, topped with a crispy frisson of finely shredded vegetables, and served with a beurre blanc sauce. This was followed by freshly caught sea bass (from the hotel's own lake), served with a herb mash and light jus with a touch of tomato concasse. The wine list is a proper match for the high standard of cooking here; a serious selection with a several vintages by the half-bottle.

Directions: From Plymouth take A379 (Kingsbridge). Entrance btw villages of Brixton & Yealmpton on R (10 mins)

The Kitley Estate
Yealmpton PL8 2NW
Map 2: SX56
Tel: 01752 881555
Fax: 01752 881667
Chef: Christopher Tanner
Owners: Traditional Hotels Ltd
Cost: *Alc* £30, fixed-price L £13.50/D £27.50. ☺ H/wine £10.
Times: Noon-last L 1.45pm/7pm-last D 9.15pm
Additional: Bar meals; Sunday L; Children welcome; ❹ dishes
Seats: 40. Private dining room 16
Smoking: No smoking in dining room
Accommodation: 12 en suite
Credit cards: ▆▆ ▆▆ ▆▆ ▆▆ ⓒ

ROCKBEARE, **The Jack In The Green Inn** ❀❀

The exterior of this roadside pub may look unassuming, but travellers wanting a pit-stop on the A30 are in for a treat once they get inside. An easy-chair reception area, beams and photographs of the early days of the inn set the tone, but the real attraction is the food. The young chef learned his trade at Gidleigh Park, Chagford (see entry) and it shows. One blackboard menu is served throughout and the style is innovative. Our inspector opted for grilled goat's cheese with beetroot fritters, warm confit of duck with shallots, and 'super quality' sausage and mash, but the repertoire extends to fillet of sea bream with sweet pepper sauce, grilled pigeon breasts with bacon, cabbage and parsnip shavings, and wild mushroom risotto. Desserts are equally lively: fresh figs baked with honey, and apricot bread and butter pudding, for example. A dozen wines are served by the glass from a neat modern list.

Directions: 5 miles E of Exeter on the A30

Rockbeare EX5 2EE
Map 3: SY09
Tel: 01404 822240
Chef: Matthew Mason
Owner: Charles Manktelow
Cost: *Alc* £16, fixed-price L/D £14.95 (3 courses). ☺ H/wine £7.75.
Times: Noon-last L 1.45pm/6.30pm-last D 9.45pm. Closed 25 Dec
Additional: Bar food; Sunday L; No children under 10; ❹ dishes
Seats: 60. Private dining room 30
Smoking: No-smoking area
Credit cards: ▆▆ ▆▆ ▆▆ ⓒ

SALCOMBE, **Bolt Head Hotel** ❀

There are panoramic views of Salcombe estuary from this comfortably furnished hotel dining room. Freshly caught fish,

South Sands TQ8 8LL
Map 3: SX73
Tel: 01548 843751
Fax: 01548 843060
Chef: John Gallagher
Owner: Colin Smith
Cost: Fixed-price D £24. ☺ H/wine £8.75.
Times: Last L 2pm/D 9pm. Closed Nov-Mar
Additional: Bar food L; Sunday L; Children welcome; ❹ dishes
Smoking: No smoking in dining room
Accommodation: 28 en suite
Credit cards: ▆▆ ▆▆ ▆▆ ▆▆ ② ⓒ

lobster and crab are delivered daily, and the four-course dinner menu might offer gâteau of Salcombe crab, poached fillet of John Dory, a traditional roast and a choice of sweets from the trolley.

SALCOMBE,
Soar Mill Cove Hotel

Overlooking one of the most stunningly beautiful stretches of Devon coastline, Soar Mill naturally attracts holidaymakers by the score. Wide patio windows open to face Eddystone lighthouse on the horizon, and diners often stretch their legs between courses to stroll in the garden or on the beach. Fresh local seafood is naturally a star turn: crab cakes are a speciality, but the kitchen can also produce red mullet baked *en papillote* with leek mousse on a Sauvignon sauce, steamed turbot with ginger and lime hollandaise, sautéed monkfish and Salcombe scallops with chive and cinnamon butter, and so on. For meat eaters, there might be fillet of ruby beef with cream and brandy sauce or mignons of local lamb pan-fried with leeks and bulb fennel. West Country cheeses come with walnut bread, while desserts range from Devonshire junket with pear and plum compote to hot soufflé oranges.

Directions: A381 to Salcombe, through village follow signs to sea.

Soar Mill Cove
Malborough TQ7 3DS
Map 3: SX73
Tel: 01548 561566
Fax: 01548 561223
Chef: Keith S Makepeace, Andrew Cannon
Owner: The Makepeace family
Cost: *Alc* £23, fixed-price D £34 (4 courses). H/wine £11
Times: Noon-last L 2pm/7.30pm-last D 9pm. Closed 2 Nov-23 Dec, 3 Jan-7 Feb
Additional: Bar food L; No children under 6 at D; ✪ dishes
Seats: 48
Smoking: No smoking in dining room
Accommodation: 20
Credit cards:

SALCOMBE, Tides Reach Hotel

Loyal guests return year after year to this delightfully unfussy, family-run hotel facing South Sands beach. Staff go out of their way to make everyone feel relaxed, and nothing is too much trouble. The dinner menu mixes interesting modern combinations with traditional favourites, albeit with a new twist – grilled whole Dover sole, for example, is presented on a roasted sweet pepper sauce, roast rib of Devon beef served with a three-colour peppercorn sauce. Risotto of red rice with Dublin Bay prawns had a good nutty texture and was well-flavoured, topped with three plump specimens, and a warming main course of oxtail with grapes and walnuts was not only enormous, but rich and unctuous, even if it did not quite fall off the bone in the expected way. Note, however that quite a lot of dishes on the fixed-price menu carry extra supplements. Creamy desserts include nectarine mousse with lemon and lime sauce and coffee cream profiteroles with chocolate sauce.

Directions: Take cliff road towards sea and Bolt Head

South Sands TQ8 8LJ
Map 3: SX73
Tel: 01548 843466
Fax: 01548 843954
Chef: Finn Ibsen
Owners: Edwards family
Cost: *Alc* £30.50, fixed-price D £24.75. ☺ H/wine £9.95.
Times: D only, 7pm-9pm. Closed Dec, Jan
Additional: Bar meals L; No children under 8; ✪ dishes
Seats: 90. Jacket & tie preferred
Smoking: No smoking in dining room
Accommodation: 38 en suite
Credit cards:

SIDMOUTH, Brownlands Hotel ❀

Set on the peaceful wooded slopes of Salcombe Hill, this fine Victorian country hotel looks out across the valley to the town and sea below. The five-course set price menu includes international favourites such as escalope of turkey Marsala, pork with prunes in Armagnac, and fillets of lemon sole véronique.

Smoking: No smoking in dining room
Accommodation: 14 en suite

Directions: Take A3052 (Exeter – Sidford), turn R at crossroads past Blue Bull Inn onto Fortescue Rd. Hotel in 1 mile

Sid Road EX10 9AG
Map 3: SY18
Tel/Fax: 01395 513053
Chefs: Laurence Barber, Janice May
Owners: Peter, Diane & Steven Kendall-Torry
Cost: Fixed-price D £18.95. ☺ H/wine £8.40.
Times: 7pm – last D 8pm. Closed Nov – Mar
Credit cards: None taken
Additional: Sunday L; Bar meals L

SIDMOUTH, Riviera Hotel ⊛

Esplanade EX10 8AY
Map 3: SS72
Tel: 01395 515201
Fax: 01395 577775
Chefs: Mark Leavers, Christian Miguel
Owner: Peter Wharton
Cost: A/c £23.50, fixed-price L
£13.50/D £23. ☺ H/wine £9.50.
Times: Last L 2pm/D 9pm
Additional: Bar Food L only; Sunday
L; Children welcome; ⦿ dishes
Smoking: No cigars or pipes;
air-conditioning
Accommodation: 27 en suite
Credit cards: ▬ ▦ ▭ ▣

*An elegant, impeccably maintained Regency property on the
seafront overlooking Lyme Bay. The carte and daily set-price menu
offer a good choice of familiar grills and traditional favourites.
Specialities of the house are Chateaubriand béarnaise (for two),
lobster Thermidor and a number of flambé dishes.*

Directions: In the centre of the Esplanade overlooking Lyme
Bay

SIDMOUTH, Victoria Hotel ⊛

Esplanade EX10 8RY
Map 3: SS64
Tel: 01395 512651
Fax: 01395 579154
Telephone for details

*An imposing Victorian building overlooking the sea. The restaurant
menus demonstrate flair and imagination: typical dishes include
smoked salmon and horseradish mousse, and medallions of lamb
with mushroom and whisky sauce. The wine list boasts a wide
choice of fine wines from around the world.*

Directions: At the western end of the esplanade

SOUTH MOLTON, Marsh Hall Country House Hotel ⊛

South Molton EX36 3HQ
Map 3: SS72
Tel: 01769 572666
Fax: 01769 574230
Chef: Judy Griffiths
Owners: Tony & Judy Griffiths
Cost: Fixed price D £18.50 (4
courses). ☺ H/wine £9.
Times: D only, 7pm-9pm
Additional: Bar food;
No children under 12
Smoking: No smoking in dining room

*The Victorian frontage hides the seventeenth-century origins of this
charming, personally run hotel. Good home-cooking is based on
fresh ingredients, with herbs, vegetables and fruit all home-grown.
A spring inspection meal produced hearty tomato and basil soup,
succulent sirloin steak with brandy and peppercorn sauce, and light
fruit terrine from a trolley that also offered tiramisu and lemon
meringue pie.*

Accommodation: 7 en suite
Credit cards: ▬ ▦ ▭ ▣ ▣

Directions: Off A361 signed North Molton; first R, then R again

SOUTH MOLTON, Whitechapel Manor ⊛⊛⊛

South Molton EX36 3EG
Map 3: SS72
Tel: 01769 573377
Fax: 01769 573797
Chef: Mathew Corner

Hungry hunters can be severe critics, but roast partridge with
rösti potatoes and wild mushrooms is a firm favourite with
the autumnal shooting parties who regularly come to this

idyllically located Grade 1 listed manor house. Our inspector's meal also started with a bang, with a rich, moist salmon and crab fishcake served with lime and chervil butter sauce. This was followed by roasted rump of English lamb, served pink, on puréed celeriac with rosemary jus and Puy lentils. Good vegetables included mange-tout, carrots, baby corn, broccoli and new potatoes. Mathew Corner's fixed price *carte* also ended with a flourish – a chocoholic's dream pudding in the form of warm chocolate tart, attractively presented with a zig zag of crème anglaise, and served with pistachio ice cream. The cheese course, which commands a £6 supplement, features interesting local choices. There are some very decent Bordeaux, Burgundy and New World wines; it's worth finishing a bottle off by the log fire as night peacefully envelops the old stone house and wilds of Exmoor beyond.

Signature dishes: Pan-fried calves' liver with caramelised baby vegetables and balsamic jus on creamed potatoes; Seared red mullet with provençale dressing; Seared scallops on risotto nero; Duck confit on crushed potato with sesame and soy dressing.

Directions: From Tiverton take A361, Whitechapel signed at roundabout. Right after 0.75 mile

Owners: Mrs M Aris, Mr C Brown
Cost: Fixed-price D £35. H/wine £12
Times: Noon-last L 1.45pm/7pm-last D 8.45pm
Additional: Sunday L; Children welcome
Seats: 24. Private dining room 8
Smoking: No smoking in dining room
Accommodation: 11 en suite
Credit cards: ▓ ▓ ▓ ▓ ▓

STAVERTON, Sea Trout Inn ❀❀

Staverton, TQ9 6PA
Map 3: SX76
Tel: 01803 762274
Fax: 01803 762506
Chef: John Hughes
Owners: Andrew & Pym Mogford
Cost: Fixed-price D £18.50. ☺ H/wine £6.95.
Times: Noon-last L 2pm/7pm-last D 9.30pm. Closed D Sun
Additional: Bar food; Sunday L; No children under 6; ◑ dishes
Seats: 35.
Accommodation: 10 en suite
Credit cards: ▓ ▓ ▓ ▓ ▓

The origins of this fifteenth-century building were obscured by a previous landlord, who changed the name from Church House Inn in order to commemorate catching a large sea trout in the nearby River Dart. Nowadays, the fishing theme is evident throughout, whether in the extensive bar areas, the conservatory restaurant, or the cottage-style bedrooms. Praise for this very busy restaurant and bar came in the form of a summer meal whose highlight was a wild mushroom soup with sherry. This was closely supported by a good Caesar salad and smoked chicken, then oriental duck and black bean sauce and breast of chicken with gambazola ('marvellous aromas when the chicken was cut into') with a port wine jus and scattered with whole baked garlic cloves. Cherry crème brûlée brought up the rear. The comprehensive wine list includes a notable choice of wines served by the glass or carafe.

Directions: In village centre, from A38 turn onto A384 to Staverton

TAVISTOCK, **Bistro 19**

Smart and laid-back, with an ash-panelled bar at the front leading down into the main dining area, and offering good food at reasonable prices. A plant-filled courtyard at the back provides further seating. Dishes range from pan-fried prawns in garlic butter to sirloin steak with pepper sauce.

Smoking: No pipes or cigars in dining room
Credit cards: ▆ ▆ ▆

19 Plymouth Road PL19 8AU
Map 2: SX47
Tel: 01822 617581
Chef: Julie R Gibb
Owners: Julie R Gibb & Mr L P Gibb
Cost: *Alc* £9.50, fixed-price L £9.50/D £16. ☺
Times: Last L 2pm/last D 9pm.
Closed D Sun, Mon, 24 Dec-1 Jan
Additional: Sunday L; Bar meals L; Children welcome; ● dishes

TAVISTOCK, **Moorland Hall**

Small, personally run country house hotel set in its own lovely gardens, right on the edge of Dartmoor. Simple home-cooking offers particularly good baking and lavish puddings. Expect warm salad of chicken livers with sherry and cream and creamy fish pie. Short wine list with some good value items.

Smoking: No-smoking area in dining room; no pipes or cigars
Accommodation: 7 en suite. **Credit cards:** ▆ ▆ ▆

Directions: Signposted from centre of Mary Tavy, on A386, 4 miles N of Tavistock

Brentnor Road PL19 9PY
Map 2: SX47
Tel: 01822 810466
Chef: Gill Farr
Owners: Gill & Andrew Farr
Cost: Fixed-price D £15 (5 courses). H/wine £7.50
Times: 6.30pm-last D 8.30pm
Additional: Children welcome; ● dishes
Seats: 18

THURLESTONE,
Heron House Hotel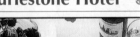

A sea-side hotel with views across to Plymouth Sound and Cornwall. The restaurant serves modern English dishes such as roast fillet of red bream served with Puy lentils, and pan-fried guinea fowl with roasted shallots. To satisfy that sweet tooth, try marinated fresh fruits with Devonshire clotted cream for dessert.

Accommodation: 17 en suite. **Credit cards:** ▆ ▆ ▆ ▆

Directions: From Kingsbridge take Salcombe road (A381) ignoring all signs for Thurlestone; R for Hope Cove, straight on at crossroads, fork R at Galmpton for Thurlestone Sands

Thurlestone Sands TQ7 3JY
Map 3: SX76
Tel: 01548 561308/561600
Fax: 01548 560180
Chef: David Newland
Owner: Pearl Rowland
Cost: Fixed-price D £19.95. ☺ H/wine £9.50.
Times: Last L 2.30pm/7pm-8.30pm
Additional: Bar food L; Children welcome; ● dishes
Smoking: No smoking in dining room

THURLESTONE,
Thurlestone Hotel

Kingsbridge
TQ7 3NN
Map 3: SX76
Tel: 01548 560382
Fax: 01548 561069
Chef: Hugh Miller
Owners: The Grose Family
Cost: *Alc* £24, fixed-price L £12/D £24. ☺
Times: Last L 2pm/D 9pm.
Additional: Bar food L; Sunday L; Children welcome; ● dishes
Smoking: No smoking in dining room
Accommodation: 65 en suite
Credit cards: ▆ ▆ ▆ ▆ ▆

The superb location, overlooking the South Devon coast, is part of this hotel's attraction. In its elegant restaurant, enjoyable dishes include wild mushroom and rosemary soup, salmon with leeks, and a wickedly delicious treacle tart. The wine list offers an interesting selection, including some by the glass.

Directions: A381 (Kingsbridge), then A379 (Churchstow), turn onto B3197, then turn into lane signposted Thurlestone

TORQUAY, Corbyn Head Hotel

Panoramic views over Torbay are a big plus at this popular seafront hotel. Breads and ice creams are made in-house and the kitchen draws heavily on fish from Brixham. Ambitious sounding dishes range from California Caesar salad and game terrine with yellow pepper marmalade to scallop and lobster soufflé and monkfish with coriander pesto.

Accommodation: 51 en suite. **Credit cards:**

Directions: On seafront at Livermead

Torquay Road Seafront Livermead TQ2 6RH
Map 3: SX96
Tel: 01803 213611
Fax: 01803 296152
Chef: David Berry
Owners: Julian & Anne Cook
Cost: Alc £21.50, fixed-price D £21.50. H/wine £10.50
Times: Last L 2.30pm/last D 9pm
Additional: Sunday L
Smoking: No smoking in dining room

TORQUAY, The Grand NEW

Edwardian hotel with fine views over the bay. Imagination is evident in dishes offered from the short set-price menu in the Gainsborough Restaurant. Couscous with prawns and coriander, guinea fowl with red cabbage and juniper glaze, and apple tartlet with thyme and Armagnac cream, show the range.

Directions: From M5 take A380 to Torquay. At seafront turn 1st right. Hotel on corner 1st on left

Sea Front TQ2 6NT
Map 3: SX96
Tel: 01803 296677
Fax: 01803 231462
Chef: Michel Nijsten
Cost: Fixed-price L £14.85 (Sun only)/ D £24.75. H/wine £9.90
Telephone for further details

TORQUAY, Imperial Hotel

Park Hill Road
TQ1 1DG
Map 3: SX96
Tel: 01803 294301
Fax: 01803 298293
Chef: Jonathan Binns
Cost: Fixed-price D £27.50. H/wine £16
Times: Last L 2.30pm/D 9.15pm. Closed Mon-Sat L
Additional: Sunday L; Bar meals L; Children welcome; 🌢 dishes
Smoking: No-smoking area; air-conditioning
Accommodation: 167 en suite
Credit cards:

Fresh-tasting meals with Mediterranean and classic French influences are offered in The Regatta restaurant, which enjoys sweeping views across the harbour. Typical dishes include chargrilled fillet of lamb with basil polenta, roasted sweet sea scallops with fennel salad, and pan-fried Dover sole with nut-brown butter.

Directions: M5 to Exeter, A380 then A3022 to Torquay. Park Hill Road is off Torwood Street/Babbacombe Road, just N of new harbour

TORQUAY, Mulberry House

Chef/proprietor Lesley Cooper continues with her winning formula of sound cooking and fresh ingredients. Her informal restaurant offers traditional dishes such as baked fillet of salmon with a plum lemon sauce, and smoked ham rissoles with spiced cranberries. A great place for Sunday lunch.

Smoking: No smoking throughout
Accommodation: 3 en suite
Credit cards: None taken

Directions: From the seafront turn up Belgrave Road, then 1st L into Scarborough Road.

1 Scarborough Road TQ2 5UJ
Map 3: SX96
Tel: 01803 213639
Chef/Owner: Lesley Cooper
Cost: *Alc* £12.50, fixed-price L £7.95.
☺ H/wine £8.50.
Times: Last L 1.30pm/D 9pm. Closed D Sun, Mon & Tue, 1st 2 wks Jan
Additional: Sunday L; Children welcome; ❹ dishes

TORQUAY, Orestone Manor ❀❀

Rockhouse Lane Maidencombe
TQ1 4SX
Map 3: SX96
Tel: 01803 328098
Fax: 01803 328336
Chef: Neale O'Brien
Owner: Bill & Gill Dagworthy
Cost: *Alc* £25, fixed-price D £25.50
(4 courses). ☺ H/wine £9.75.
Times: D only, 6.30pm-9pm.
Closed 1st 2 wks Jan
Additional: Sunday L (Noon-1.15pm);
No children under 10; ❹ dishes
Seats: 40. Private dining room 12
Smoking: No smoking in dining room
Accommodation: 18 en suite
Credit cards: ▨ ▧ ▤ ▨ ▢

The Georgian country lodge, on the edge of Torquay, is perched high above the cliffs overlooking the Channel; the restaurant benefits from the resultant views. Against this magnificent backdrop, the kitchen sensibly does not overreach itself in terms of ambition, concentrating instead on bringing out inherent flavours in such dishes as a well judged provençale vegetable tart with Parmesan crust, excellent fillets of lamb with red wine, mint sauce and onion chutney, and a good strawberry sablé. Local produce comes through in Pithiviers of local venison with bacon lardons and red wine jus, for example, and the proximity to the sea is celebrated by tournedos of home-smoked salmon wrapped in seaweed and served with a lime, ginger and coriander sauce. Service is relaxed and unstuffy, but slick. The wine list is of reasonable depth with an emphasis on the New World.

Directions: Off B3199 Torquay/Teignmouth coastal road, turn R on Watcombe Hill opposite Brunel Manor.

TORQUAY,
The Osborne Hotel ❀❀ NEW

Forming the centrepiece of an elegant Regency terrace, with uninterrupted views over the bay, The Osborne has often been described as 'Bath by the sea'. After a game of tennis or a swim in the pool, or maybe just a stroll in the lovely gardens, appetites will be whetted enough to sample a range of

Hesketh Crescent Meadfoot TQ1 2LL
Map 3: SX96
Tel: 01803 213311
Fax: 01803 296788
Chef: Wayne Maddern
Cost: *Alc* £27, fixed-price D £17.95.
☺ H/wine £9.45.

The Osborne Hotel

Times: D only, 7pm-9.30pm
Additional: Brasserie; Sunday L
(brasserie); Children welcome;
❸ dishes
Seats: 60. Private dining room 70
Smoking: No smoking in dining room
Accommodation: 29 en suite
Credit cards: ▆ ▆ ▆ ▆ ▆

interesting dishes at the elegant, peach and dark green
Langtry's restaurant. The cooking has an assured sense of
direction and keenness shines through. Our inspector started
with a moist, poached fillet of plaice with a lemon and chive
butter sauce, and went on to enjoy a main course of guinea
fowl with caramelised apples and a curry sauce. Dessert was a
vanilla and chocolate roulade, beautifully presented.
Vegetarian dishes include sauté of gnocchi with fresh basil
served on a red pepper coulis.

Directions: Follow A3022 to seafront and turn L towards
Harbour. At Clock Tower turn L; at next junction/traffic lights
turn R. Follow rd over brow of hill and down other side. The
gates of Hesketh Crescent and hotel are opposite.

TORQUAY,
The Table Restaurant

Blink and you could miss the white painted, end-of-terrace
Victorian house in Babbacombe's main street. Keep your eyes
peeled, for the property contains a 20-seat restaurant, home to
Julie Tuckett's promising cooking. Good value fixed-price
menus are offered – two courses at lunch, three at dinner.
Highlights of our test meal was a starter of filo pastry filled with
locally caught crab and avocado, which came with a delightfully
dressed, crisp salad garnish, and a fine main course of roast
fillet of salmon on a creamed haddock with a Pernod sauce that
provided a good balance of flavours, despite the accompanying
local vegetables requiring a little more love and attention. A
larger than average selection of wines by the half-bottle or glass
supplements a comprehensive wine list.

135 Babbacombe Road TQ1 3SR
Map 3: SX96
Tel/Fax: 01803 324292
Chef/Owner: Mrs Julie T Tuckett
Cost: Fixed-price L £11.85/D £26.50.
H/wine £11.50
Times: 12.15pm-last L
1.45pm/7.15pm-last D 9.45pm.
Closed L Sat, Mon, 4 wks Feb-March
Additional: No children under 11
Seats: 16. Private dining up to 20
Credit cards: ▆ ▆ ▆ ▆ ▆

Directions: From Torquay follow signs to Babbacombe.
Restaurant on L hand side when approached from harbour

TUCKENHAY,
The Maltsters Arms

*A busy country inn, particularly popular in the summer months. We
inspected in the winter, and found smooth chicken liver parfait, beef
and ale casserole with herb dumplings and new potatoes. Dessert
could be a tangy lemon tart, or perhaps chocolate parfait. Lovely
riverside setting.*

Bow Creek Tuckenhay
TQ9 7EQ
Map 3: SX85
Tel: 01804 23350
Telephone for details

TWO BRIDGES,
Prince Hall Hotel ✿

Local ingredients such as Devon crab, Brixham lemon sole and Dartmoor venison feature regularly on the short, nightly changing menu at this comfortable country house hotel set amidst spectacular moorland scenery. One novel idea is lamb bourguignon served with a savoury scone and clotted cream.

Smoking: No smoking in dining room
Accommodation: 9 en suite. **Credit cards:** 🔲 🔳 🔳 🔳 🔳 🔳

Directions: From Two Bridges take B3357 Dartmeet Road; hotel is hidden 1 mile on R

Near Two Bridges
PL20 6SA
Map 2: SX96
Tel: 01822 890403
Fax: 01822 890676
Chefs: Adam Southwell, Les Pratt
Owners: Adam & Carrie Southwell
Cost: Fixed-price D £22. ☺ H/wine £8.75.
Times: D only, 7pm-8.30pm Closed Jan
Additional: No children under 8; 🍴 dishes

TWO BRIDGES,
Two Bridges Hotel ✿✿

The Two Bridges are in fact adjacent to this rural hotel beside the West Dart River. The open, log-burning fires provide a suitably warm welcome, and the congenial bar offers the opportunity to sample the local Jail Ale from a brewery in the same ownership as the hotel. By comparison, the no smoking, candlelit restaurant, with its stained glass windows, is relatively formal. The cooking is hearty and big with flavour; pan-fried Brixham squid with bitter leaves had resonances of a Basque dish, with its tangy chilli, garlic and peppercorn aromatics. Roast baby quail, plump and bursting with forcemeat and wild rice, together with fresh wild mushrooms, confidently showcased the kitchen's undoubted technical skills, and the accompanying lyonnaise potatoes could hardly have been bettered. Clotted cream bread-and-butter pudding with English custard was excellent. After dinner, enjoy coffee in the magnificent Music Room where the baby grand is played most weekends.

Directions: From Tavistock take B3357, hotel at junction with B3312

Dartmoor PL20 6SW
Map 2: SX96
Tel: 01822 890581
Fax: 01822 890575
Chef: Peter Woods
Owner: Warm Welcome Hotels
Cost: *Alc* £22.50, fixed-price L £9.95 (3 courses)/D £17.95 (4 courses). ☺ H/wine £9.95.
Times: Noon-last L 2.30pm/6.30pm-last D 9.30pm
Additional: Bar food; Sunday L; Children welcome; 🍴 dishes
Seats: 80
Smoking: No smoking in dining room
Accommodation: 25 en suite
Credit cards: 🔲 🔳 🔳 🔳 🔳 🔳

VIRGINSTOWE, Percy's ✿✿

Coombeshead, Beaworthy EX21 5EA
Map 2: SX39
Tel: 01409 211236
Fax: 01409 211275
Chef: Tina Bricknell-Webb
Owners: Tony & Tina Bricknell-Webb

Tina and Tony Bricknell-Webb have long been crusading for home-grown and local produce and the gardens of their 40-acre estate provide a healthy supply of vegetables, salad leaves

and herbs, most of which are grown organically. Meals are served in a 400-year-old Devon longhouse with polished wood floors and tall, straight-backed ash chairs. Breads (such as warm carrot) are baked on the premises and, needless to say, the quality and freshness of the kitchen garden is peerless. Strips of cuttlefish come with an acutely spiked chilli dressing and a selection of seven or eight 'gorgeous still living leaves', while breast of Barbary duck is served with rosemary jus and brilliant vegetables. As a finale, our inspector revelled in the harvest delights of blueberry and red fruit baba with an alcohol-soaked cakelet and rosemary ice cream. The wine list has a broad sweep of bins with plenty by the glass.

Cost: *Alc* £21.25, fixed-price D £19.50. ☺ H/wine £8.95.
Times: Noon-last L 2pm/6.30pm-last D 9pm
Additional: Sunday L; No children under 8; 🍴 dishes
Seats: 40. Private dining room 18
Smoking: No smoking establishment
Accommodation: 8 en suite
Credit cards: 🔲 🔲 🔲 🔲 🔲 🔲

Directions: Follow signs to restaurant from Gridley Corner A388 (St Giles on the Heath) or at Metherell Cross, B3218 (Okehampton-Bude)

WHIMPLE, Woodhayes Hotel ֎֎

EX5 2TD
Map 3: SY09
Tel: 01404 822237
Fax: 01404 822337
Chef/Owners: Michael & Katherine Rendle
Cost: Fixed-price D £27.50 (6 courses). H/wine £11.50
Times: D only, 7.30pm for 8pm. Closed 4 days Xmas
Additional: No children under 12; 🍴 dishes
Seats: 18
Smoking: No smoking in dining room
Accommodation: 6 en suite
Credit cards: 🔲 🔲 🔲 🔲 🔲

Seven courses may sound at least one too many for most feeble modern appetites, but dinners are intelligently constructed, with portions in keeping with the length of the meal. And there are few more agreeable spots in which to while away the time over a well-paced, civilised meal than this thoroughly charming little hotel. Typically, dinner might start with smoked salmon mousse, followed by carrot and orange soup with coriander (plus lovely home-made bread), then a simple but superbly good fillet of brill with cheese tartar crust. A short pause comes with a sorbet, pink grapefruit perhaps, served in a tiny crystal glass, then it's on to the roast rack of lamb with creamed garlic and thyme, almond cake with orange and blackcurrants and a selection of local cheeses. Then, just when you think it is all over, coffee comes with little home-made biscuits. Reservations are essential as the restaurant only seats 18, and residents take precedence.

Directions: On A30 midway Honiton/Exeter. Straight down Whimple Road, first building on R

WINKLEIGH, **Pophams** ⬤⬤⬤

Pophams does not really fit into any category – except one shaped by individuality, enthusiasm and utter charm. There are no menus in this tiny three-table restaurant, in a sleepy village on the edge of Dartmoor, only a blackboard on which the dishes of the day are written (note – they are open for lunch only, which runs from 11.30am till a civilised 'whenever'). The walls are hung with black and white photos of old movie stars, and mirrors which fail to make the place seem larger. Dennis Hawkes engagingly explains all the daily changing dishes, whilst co-owner and chef Melvyn Popham beavers away behind the glass refrigerated cabinet, which is still in situ from the days when the property was a deli. The cooking is relatively simple in construction, but depends on top quality produce, accurate cooking and strength of flavour. Freshly baked granary bread comes straight from the oven, served with unsalted Devon butter, to be followed by, perhaps warm onion tart with crème fraîche and duck terrine with Calvados apple purée. Our inspector sampled 'some of the best flavoured prawns ever', served with strips of smoked salmon, spears of English asparagus and a light lemon dressing, as well as a crisp wholemeal tartlet with a rich, fresh crab filling. Roast breast of chicken then arrived, the skin rubbed with garden herbs and sea salt, enhanced by a light, fresh tomato and herb sauce, its counterpart, a fillet of salmon, was simply and perfectly cooked, served on wilted spinach and creamed potato, with a light red pepper sauce. Boned best end of local lamb with mushroom pâté in puff pastry and roast fillet of beef with port and red wine sauce were both on the menu on a day picked at random in March. Desserts are delicious – from shortcake biscuits, layered with crème pâtissière and fresh strawberries, to Bacardi and lime jelly and chocolate marquise with coffee Tia Maria sauce, depending on the season. Pophams is unlicensed – but guests are welcome to bring their own and there is no corkage charge. There is, however, freshly squeezed fruit juice, coffee and iced tea.

Castle Street EX19 8HQ
Map 3: SX60
Tel: 01837 83767
Chef: Melvyn Popham
Owners: Melvyn Popham, Dennis Hawkes
Cost: Alc £22
Times: L only 11.30am-3.30pm. Closed Sun, Mon, Feb
Additional: No children under 14; ⬤ dishes
Seats: 10
Smoking: Totally no smoking establishment; air-conditioning
Credit cards: ▬ ▭

Directions: In village centre, about 9 miles from Okehampton

WOOLACOMBE, **Little Beach Hotel** ⬤

A welcoming family-run hotel in a superb position overlooking Morte Bay. The well-appointed dining room – only open to hotel guests – is the setting for sound cooking. Typical starters could include tomato stuffed with tuna, capers and cheese, and mushroom and barley soup.

Additional: No children under 6; ⬤ dishes
Telephone for further details

The Esplanade EX34 7DJ
Map 2: SS44
Tel: 01271 870398
Fax: 01271 870051
Chef: Lorraine Woollard
Owners: Howard & Christie Braydon
Cost: Fixed-price D £25. H/wine £7.25
Times: D only, 7.30pm-last D 8.15pm. Closed Nov-Mar

Directions: Take A361 through Barnstable towards Ilfracombe. Woolacombe signposted at Mullacot roundabout. In Woolacombe turn R onto Esplanade.

WOOLACOMBE,
Watersmeet Hotel ⬤⬤

Watersmeet is aptly named. It's perched on a rocky inlet with a private path down to the beach and spectacular views out to sea. The setting is well matched by sound modern ideas from

Mortehoe EX34 7EB
Map 2: SS44
Tel: 01271 870333
Fax: 01271 870890
Chef: JB Wheeldon & J Prince

Watersmeet Hotel

Owners: Mr & Mrs JB Wheeldon
Cost: Alc £20, set D £26.50. ☺
H/wine £9.85.
Times: 12.30pm-last L 2pm/7pm-last
D 8.30pm. Closed Dec & Jan
Additional: Sunday L; Bar meals L;
No children under 8; ♨ dishes
Seats: 60. Private dining room 30.
Jacket & tie preferred
Smoking: No smoking in dining room
Accommodation: 25 en suite
Credit cards: ▆ ▆ ▆ ▆ ▆ ▆

the kitchen. A meal in August started with spinach and cottage cheese crêpes, followed by a well-flavoured fish soup. Then honey roasted breast of duck, served finely sliced on a kumquat. Other main courses include sautéed calves' liver with bacon and caramelised onions, roulade of lemon sole with a smoked salmon mousse and Noilly Prat sauce, and lightly cooked breast of Exmoor pheasant served with mulled fruits and game sauce. For dessert, a warm treacle tart served with a scoop of clotted cream. Staff are noted for their friendly and natural approach.

Directions: M5/J27. Follow A361 to Woolacombe, R at beach car park, 300 yds on R

YARCOMBE,
Belfry Country Hotel ❀

A tastefully converted Victorian village school with great countryside views. The pine-panelled dining room features a log fire and a 'schoolroom' theme. The fixed-price menu and small carte might include Yarcombe pheasant braised in red wine, and pan-fried sirloin steak with tomatoes and mushrooms.

Smoking: No smoking in dining room
Accommodation: 6 en suite
Credit cards: ▆ ▆ ▆ ▆ ▆

Directions: On A30 7 miles E of Honiton in village centre

Devon EX14 9BD
Map 3: ST20
Tel: 01404 861234
Fax: 01404 861579
Chef: Jackie Rees
Owners: Jackie & Tony Rees
Cost: Alc £21.15. Fixed-price D
£13.95 (2 courses). ☺ H/wine £9.50.
Times: D only, 7pm-8.45pm. Closed
last 2 wks Feb, 1st 2 wks Nov
Additional: No children under 12;
♨ dishes

YELVERTON, Moorland Links ❀

Modern hotel situated within Dartmoor National Park with splendid country views and a generally peaceful air. Simple flavours and sound, uncomplicated cooking came through in a meal of home-made vegetable soup, fillet of trout on a bed of lasagne with a frothy herb sauce, and lemon parfait with a home-made shortbread base.

Smoking: No smoking in dining room
Accommodation: 44 en suite
Credit cards: ▆ ▆ ▆

Directions: On A386, within Dartmoor National Park

Yelverton PL20 6DA
Map 2: SX96
Tel: 01822 852245
Fax: 01822 855004
Chef: Stephen Holmes
Owner: Forestdale Hotels Ltd
Cost: Fixed-price £17.95. ☺
H/wine £8.95.
Times: Last L 2pm/D 10pm.
Closed L Sat, 23 Dec-2 Jan
Additional: Bar food; Sunday L;
Children welcome; ♨ dishes

DORSET

BEAMINSTER,
Bridge House Hotel ⊛⊛

Built as a church dwelling in the thirteenth century, Bridge House is now a charming little hotel catering for all-comers. Meals are eaten in the pleasing setting of the Georgian dining room with its oak beams, panelling and views of the walled garden. The kitchen works to fixed-price menus based around supplies of local produce: the results are generous and skilfully executed. The Bridge House starter of smoked meats and fish with marinated mushrooms is a fixture, but you might also begin with prawns in whisky cream sauce. Main dishes take in pan-fried pigeon breasts with a robust Madeira sauce, as well as tenderloin of pork with apricots and cashew nuts, and grilled lemon sole with herb butter. Prune and brandy parfait is a typical sweet. Meals kick off with home-made cheese straws and finish with coffee and truffles in the lounge. The wine list is well balanced and surprisingly extensive.

3 Prout Bridge DT8 3AY
Map 3: ST40
Tel: 01308 862200
Fax: 01308 863700
Chef: Jacky Rae
Owner: Peter Pinkster
Cost: Fixed-price L £13.50/D £20.50.
☺ H/wine £9.95.
Times: Last L 2pm/D 9pm
Additional: Sunday L;
No children under 5; ❹ dishes
Seats: 36. Private dining room 16
Smoking: No smoking in dining room
Accommodation: 14 en suite
Credit cards: ▰ ▰ ▰ ▰ ▰ ▰

Directions: On A3066, 200m down hill from town centre

BLANDFORD FORUM,
Castleman Hotel ⊛⊛

Formerly the Dower House in the estate village of Chettle, this is now a rather elegant hotel which still retains many of its impressive original features. The building boasts a galleried hall, a Jacobean fireplace graces the drawing room, and the garden is bordered by a ha-ha, while the restaurant is noted for its fine plasterwork ceilings. Barbara Garnsworthy made her name at the Moonacre in Alderholt and she continues to build her menus around supplies of local produce. Dishes change daily, but you can expect things like duck, pork and pheasant terrine with spiced kumquats, guinea fowl with onion sauce and red cabbage, and fillet of turbot with leeks and herb sauce. An inspection meal yielded other pleasures in the shape of light Stilton and walnut soufflé, followed by sautéed scallops with coriander, garlic and ginger served with garlic-perfumed rice. The finale was a rich chocolate cake with a chocolate fudge topping served with decent home-made chocolate ice cream.

Chettle DT11 8DB
Map 3: ST80
Tel: 01258 830096
Fax: 01258 830051
Chef: Barbara Garnsworthy
Owners: Barbara Garnsworthy,
Edward Bourke
Cost: Alc £20. H/wine £8. ☺
Times: D only, 7pm-10pm.
Closed Feb
Additional: Sunday L (Noon-2pm);
Children welcome; ❹ dishes
Seats: 40
Smoking: No smoking in dining room
Accommodation: 8 en suite
Credit cards: ▰ ▰ ▰ ▰ ▰

Directions: One mile from the A354. Hotel is signposted within village

BOURNEMOUTH,
Carlton Hotel ⊛⊛

Award-winning gardens and leisure facilities add to the allure of this stately hotel in a quiet location overlooking Poole harbour and Hengistbury Head. The views can be enjoyed from the grand dining room, where smartly turned out, professional staff provide service of the old school. A recent visit confirmed that the place is back on form. To start, a terrine of duck layered with onion marmalade was beautifully presented with mixed leaves and dollops of cranberry dressing.

East Overcliff BH1 3DN
Map 4: SZ09
Tel: 01202 552011
Fax: 01202 299573
Chef: Neil Wiggins
Owner: Menzies Hotels & Leisure Ltd
Cost: Alc £26, fixed-price L £15.50/D £21.50. ☺ H/wine £12.50.
Times: Noon-last L 1.45pm/7pm-last D 9.45pm

Next came roast monkfish sandwiched with buttered spinach and served with a chunky tomato salsa and a platter of 'pleasant' vegetables, while proceedings concluded with a chocolate mousse enriched with brandy and garnished with red berries. The comprehensive wine list has a decent selection of half-bottles.

Directions: M3/M27, follow A338 (Bournemouth). Follow signs to town centre and East Overcliff. Hotel is on seafront

Additional: Bar meals; Sunday L; Children welcome; dishes
Seats: 120. Private dining room 200
Smoking: No smoking in dining room
Accommodation: 71 en suite
Credit cards: ■■■ ▓▓▓ ▥▥ ▚▚ ▣▣ ▢

BOURNEMOUTH, Chine Hotel ❀

Boscombe Spa Road BH5 1AX
Map 4: SZ09
Tel: 01202 396234
Fax: 01202 391737
Chef: Paul Bingham
Owners: FJB Hotels.
Cost: Fixed-price L £14.50/ D £17.50. ☺ H/wine £9.50.
Times: Last L 2pm/D 8.30pm Closed L Sat
Additional: Bar Food; Sunday L; Children welcome; menu
Smoking: No smoking in dining room
Accommodation: 91 en suite
Credit cards: ■■■ ▓▓▓ ▥▥ ▚▚ ▣▣ ▢

From the restaurant there are spectacular views across the hotel gardens to the sea beyond. An up-to-date menu takes in crab and chicken terrine on a mange-tout, sun-dried tomato vinaigrette, pan-fried guinea fowl with apple black pudding and a mustard fondue, and sticky toffee pudding. Also imaginative vegetarian choices and excellent British farmhouse cheeses.

Directions: From M27, A31 and A338 follow signs to Boscombe Pier, Boscombe Spa Road is off Christchurch Road near Boscombe Gardens

BOURNEMOUTH, Farthings ❀❀

Originally a Victorian coach house, but now a country-house restaurant-with-rooms with a large conservatory extension overlooking landscaped gardens. Bar snacks are available at lunchtime, but most attention focuses on the choice of menus available in the restaurant. To start there might be halibut marinated in cider and sage on a mango coulis or warm salad of pigeon with a cabbage and smoked ham parcel edged with redcurrant jus. Main courses divide between meat and fish, and there are also a few options for vegetarians. Expect dishes such as grilled red mullet on rosemary butter sauce with candied onions and spinach, and roast duck with crushed peppercorns, poached pear and a honey and blueberry sauce. For dessert there might be a dark chocolate box filled with orange mousse or iced mixed parfait with Italian meringue and winter berry coulis. The informative, well annotated wine list has plenty of good drinking from around the world.

5/7 Grove Road BH1 3AS
Map 4: SZ09
Tel: 01202 558660
Fax: 01202 293766
Chef: Wayne Asson
Owners: Tom & Sheila Porteous
Cost: Alc £25, fixed-price L £13.95/ D £24.75 (4 course). ☺ H/wine £9.75.
Times: Noon-last L 2pm/7pm-last D 10pm
Additional: Bar Food L; Sunday L; Children welcome; dishes
Seats: 45. Jacket & tie preferred
Smoking: No-smoking area
Accommodation: 5 rooms
Credit cards: ■■■ ▓▓▓ ▥▥ ▚▚ ▣▣ ▢

Directions: On roundabout, top of hill on Bath Road going from Pier to Lansdowne

BOURNEMOUTH,

Langtry Manor Hotel ❀

It's romance all the way in this Victorian edifice, built by King Edward VII for his mistress Lillie Langtry. The dining room occupies a resplendent, chandeliered baronial hall complete with Tudor tapestries. Game soup makes a typically lavish starter and the daily menu also features a rendezvous of scampi and scallops and cinnamon beignets with chocolate sauce.

Smoking: No smoking in dining room
Accommodation: 28 en suite
Credit cards: ▄▄ ▒▒ ▒▒ ▐▌ ▣ ⓒ

Directions: On the East Cliff, at corner of Darby and Knyveton roads

26 Derby Road BH1 3QB
Map 4: SZ09
Tel: 01202 553887
Fax: 01202 290115
Chef: Stuart Glanville
Owner: Mrs P Hamilton-Howard
Cost: *Alc* £21.25, fixed-price D £19.75. ☺ H/wine £8.95.
Times: D only 7pm-9pm
Additional: Children welcome;
❸ dishes

BOURNEMOUTH, **Queens Hotel** ❀

Family-run, seaside hotel with splendid views over the bay. Lifts (and a zig-zag path) lead down to the beach. A typical dinner could be baked eggs en cocotte, lobster bisque, grilled halibut with a white wine butter sauce, or marinated strips of pork fillet, stir-fried with vegetables and ginger and served with rice noodles, and cherry meringue pie.

Smoking: No smoking in dining room; air-conditioning
Accommodation: 112 en suite
Credit cards: ▄▄ ▒▒ ▒▒ ▐▌ ▣ ⓒ

Directions: Follow signs to East Cliff, hotel is one road back from seafront

Meyrick Road East Cliff BH1 3DL
Map 4: SZ09
Tel: 01202 554415
Fax: 01202 294810
Chef: William Summerell
Owners: Mr & Mrs A Young
Cost: Fixed-price L £8.95/ D £16.95.
☺ H/wine £9.95.
Times: Last L 1.30pm/D 8.30pm
Additional: Bar Food; Sunday L;
Children welcome; ❸ dishes

BOURNEMOUTH,

Royal Bath Hotel ❀❀

The choice on the set dinner menu at Oscars Restaurant is sensibly short, with the result the kitchen is able to concentrate on the quality and flavour of each dish. Melon has become a cliché starter, but it is re-invigorated here as a gâteau of melon pearls topped with foie gras and served with a split balsamic coulis. Most dishes have a friendly familiarity, but when accurately cooked there is nothing wrong with a good smoked mackerel pâté, cream of leek and potato soup, pan-fried skate wing with herb butter and lemon, or calves' liver with garlic potato purée and onion gravy. The dessert list is equally concise – as well as ice creams and sorbets, there may be American baked cheesecake with chocolate sauce, tangerine mousse with fresh fruit coulis or lemon tart served with 'plouche' of fruits.

Directions: Follow signs for Bournemouth Pier and beaches

Bath Road BH1 2EW
Map 4: SZ09
Tel: 01202 555555
Fax: 01202 554158
Chef: Gary Paine
Owners: De Vere Hotels
Cost: *Alc* £35, fixed-price L £16.50/D £23.50. H/wine £11.60
Times: 12.30pm-last L 2.15pm/6.30pm-last D 10.15pm.
Additional: Sunday L; Children welcome; ❸ dishes
Seats: 200. Private dining 60
Smoking: No-smoking area; no pipes or cigars in dining room
Accommodation: 131 en suite
Credit cards: ▄▄ ▒▒ ▒▒ ▣

BOURNEMOUTH, **Sophisticats** ❀

Feline paraphernalia sets the tone in this long-established restaurant on the outskirts of town. The kitchen pleases the old guard with smoked salmon mousse and fillet steak, but shows a touch more

43 Charminster Road, BH8 8UE
Map 4: SZ09
Tel: 01202 291019
Chef: Bernard Calligan
Owners: John Knight, Bernard Calligan

invention with terrine of marinated chicken breasts or monkfish with Phillipino sweet and sour sauce and sautéed almonds. Black Forest pancakes and Pavlova are typical desserts.

Smoking: No pipes and cigars
Credit cards: None taken

Directions: 1 mile from town centre

Cost: *Alc* £25. H/wine £8.95. ☺
Times: D only, 7pm-9.30pm.
Closed Sun, Mon, 2 wks Jan & July
Additional: Children welcome;
❸ dishes

BOURNEMOUTH, Wessex Hotel

The Wessex has a great West Cliff location close to the sea, a superb leisure club, and is popular with families in the summer. The kitchen makes good use of fresh produce with dishes such as potato seafood cake, New Forest cassoulet, and an appetising dessert trolley sporting the likes of chocolate truffle cake and fresh fruit salad.

Accommodation: 84 en suite
Credit cards:

Directions: Follow signs to West Cliff

West Cliff Road, BH2 5EU
Map 4: SZ09
Tel: 01202 551911
Fax: 01202 297354
Chef: John Wilson
Owner: Forestdale Hotels
Times: D only, 7pm-9.30pm (7-9pm Sun)
Additional: Bar meals L; Children welcome; ❸ dishes
Smoking: No smoking in dining room

BRIDPORT, Bridge House Hotel

Meals are served in the cellar of this eighteenth-century house on the eastern edge of town. The kitchen shows its worth with warm home-baked rolls, wholesome carrot soup, and generous helpings of seafood fricassée with delicate Noilly Prat sauce on Basmati rice. Steaks are a meaty alternative.

Accommodation: 10 en suite
Credit cards:

Directions: Into Bridport (East Street). Hotel is 1st Georgian building on R

115 East Street
DT6 3LB
Map 3: SY49

Tel/Fax: 01308 423371
Chef: Simon Badger
Owner: Simon & Trish Badger
Cost: *Alc* £20, Fixed price D £15. ☺ H/wine £7.
Times: D only 7.30pm-9pm.
Closed Sun
Additional: Children welcome;
❸ dishes
Smoking: No smoking throughout

BRIDPORT, Horseshoes

In a pretty village setting, this stone-built inn has original pine panelling, two cosy dining rooms and a large restaurant with wonderful country views. The menu offers a good choice of fresh local fish, a range of pasta dishes, and meat and game including home-made burgers and mustard rabbit.

Accommodation: 4 (2 en suite)
Credit cards:

Directions: In the village of Powerstock, 5 miles NE of Bridport, signposted off A3066 Beaminster Road.

Powerstock DT6 3TF
Map 3: SY49
Tel: 01308 485328
Fax: 01308 485577
Chef: Patrick Ferguson
Owners: Diana & Patrick Ferguson
Cost: *Alc* £20, fixed-price L £7.50. ☺ H/wine £8.75.
Times: Last L 2pm/D 9.30pm
Additional: Bar Food; Sunday L; Children welcome; ❸ dishes
Smoking: No smoking in dining room

BRIDPORT,
Riverside Restaurant

There are views of the River Brid – paddle, rowing boats and all – from the windows of this lively restaurant, with its wooden floors and walls adorned with paintings by local artists. For more than 35 years, Arthur and Janet Watson have been specialising in fresh local seafood in all its forms. The kitchen relies on the day's

West Bay
DT6 4EZ
Map 3: SY49
Tel: 01308 422011
Chef: Mike Mills,
Nic Larcombe
Owner: Janet & Arthur Watson

catch for its repertoire, but on a typical day you might find dishes such as grilled fillet of brill with crispy spinach and sorrel sauce, roast turbot with assorted mushrooms and sea bass with minted leeks and hollandaise, as well as deep-fried cod in Guinness batter with home-made mushy peas. Steaks and hams please the carnivores, and vegetarians also get a look in. Puddings tend to be nursery favourites such as banana split, fresh fruit salad, and toffee and fudge ice cream with hot chocolate sauce. Plenty of affordable whites show up on the wine list.

Directions: In the centre of West Bay by the river

Times: Noon-last L 2.30pm/6.30pm-last D 8.45pm. Closed D Sun, Mon, 1 Dec-1 March (approx)
Additional: Sunday L; Children welcome; ✦ dishes
Seats: 80
Smoking: No pipes and cigars
Credit cards: ■ ▦ ▨ ◎

BRIDPORT,
Roundham House Hotel

Built as a gentleman's residence at the turn of the century, the elevated position gives stunning views over Dorset countryside and Lyme Bay; magnificent sunsets are a feature. Typical dishes are smoked salmon, rack of lamb with rosemary, and French pear tart.

Smoking: No smoking in dining room
Accommodation: 8 en suite. **Credit cards:** ▦ ▨

Directions: From roundabout on A35 S of Bridport take road to West Bay, then 2nd L into Roundham Gardens

Roundham Gardens, West Bay Road, DT6 4BD
Map 3: SY49
Tel: 01308 422753
Chef: Jeremy Thomas
Owners: Daphne & Jeremy Thomas
Cost: *Alc* £20, fixed-price D £16.50. ☺ H/wine £8.95
Times: D only, 7pm-9pm. Closed Jan-Feb
Additional: Sunday L (12.30pm-2pm); Children welcome; ✦ dishes

CHARMOUTH,
Thatch Lodge Hotel   NEW

A fourteenth-century building with thatched roof, cobb walls and oak beams, yet the kitchen focuses on modern British cooking. Drinks are served at 7.30pm in the lounge or the conservatory under a 200-year-old vine, and dinner in the Inglenook Restaurant at 8pm. Only 14 diners can be seated so priority is given to hotel residents.

Accommodation: 7 en suite. **Credit cards:** ■ ▦ ▨ ▩ ◎

Directions: Charmouth is clearly signposted off the A35 2 miles east of Lyme Regis. Hotel on The Street

The Street DT6 6PQ
Map 3: SY39
Tel/Fax: 01297 560407
Chef: Andrea Ashton-Worsfold
Owners: Christopher Worsfold, Mrs A Ashton-Worsfold
Cost: Fixed-price D £18.50. ☺ H/wine £8.50.
Times: D only at 7.30pm. Closed Feb
Smoking: No-smoking hotel

CHIDEOCK,
Chideock House Hotel NEW

Main Street DT6 6JN
Map 3: SY49
Tel: 01297 489242
Fax: 01297 489184
Chef: Anna Dunn
Owners: Anna & George Dunn
Cost: *Alc* £20. H/wine £9.50. ☺
Times: D only, 7pm-9pm.
Closed Jan 2-31
Additional: Sunday L (Noon-2pm); No children under 12; ✦ dishes
Accommodation: 9 (not all en suite)
Credit cards: ■ ▦ ▨ ▩ ◎

Bags of appeal at this delightful part-thatched house that dates from the fifteenth century. Anna Dunn's cooking relies on fresh ingredients and a simple approach to produce the likes of twice-baked spinach soufflé, succulent breast of duck with onion marmalade given zest by cumin and oranges, and crème brûlée.

Directions: 3 miles W of Bridport, fronting onto A35 in centre of village.

CHRISTCHURCH,

Avonmouth Hotel NEW

The hotel is situated alongside Mudeford Quay, right at the water's edge, the restaurant providing panoramic views over both the quay and Christchurch Harbour. Local fish figures prominently, including lobster and king crab, and specialities such as oven roasted sea bass with a pine kernel crust.

Accommodation: 42 en suite. **Credit cards:** 🔳 🔳 🔳 🔳 🔳

Directions: Close to the bridge over the Avon on A35 (Bournemouth-Lyndhurst). Mudeford is on the edge of Christchurch Harbour, and the hotel is on the approach to Mudeford Quay

95 Mudeford
BH23 3NT
Map 4: SZ19
Tel: 01202 483434
Fax: 01202 479004
Chef: Ian Morton
Owners: Forte Granada
Cost: *Alc* £19.95, fixed-price D £19.95. ☺ H/wine £10.95.
Times: Last L 2pm/last D 8.45pm
Additional: Sunday L; Bar meals L; Children welcome; 🔳 dishes
Smoking: No smoking in dining room

CHRISTCHURCH,

Splinters Restaurant

12 Church Street BH23 1BW
Map 4: SZ19
Tel/Fax: 01202 483454
Chef: Eamonn Redden
Owners: Timothy Lloyd, Robert Wilson
Cost: *Alc* £27.45, fixed-price L £13.95 (2 courses)/D £24.95 (3 courses). H/wine £10.80
Times: Noon-last L 2.30pm/7pm-last D 10.30pm
Additional: Bar food L; Sunday lunch; Children welcome; 🔳 dishes
Seats: 40. Private dining room 22
Smoking: No smoking in dining room
Credit cards: 🔳 🔳 🔳 🔳 🔳

Housed in a pair of historic buildings – one Georgian, the other Victorian – Splinters is divided up into three intimate dining areas: the cellar room is lined with classic vintages, the ground floor is a lunchtime bar/brasserie, the upstairs drawing room is used for post-prandial coffee and drinks. The atmosphere is relaxed, staff are attentive. Dinner is fixed-price for two or three courses and the kitchen is in a cosmopolitan mood. A recent inspection meal yielded chicken and leek dumplings with foie gras sauce followed by succulent pan-fried sea bass with wine, cream and tomato sauce. Otherwise, the choice extends to bubble and squeak with black pudding, warm crab rösti with avocado and salsa, and Kashmir chicken. The restaurant has links with the Chocolate Society, so you can expect desserts along the lines of iced saffron parfait with Manjari chocolate and tea sauce. Affordable wines are drawn from most of the popular regions.

Directions: Splinters is on L side of cobbled street directly in front of Priory Gates

CHRISTCHURCH,

Waterford Lodge Hotel ❀❀

Matching food and wine is one of the hardest things to get right, and mistakes can sometimes be costly, so one welcomes a menu that includes suggested wines alongside each main course, especially when the cooking goes in for pretty unusual combinations. Suprême of chicken filled with crab and coriander on an almond cream, for example, is matched with a Beaune *premier cru*, and a roulade of pork tenderloin filled with apricots and spinach on a coarse grain mustard sauce is paired with a Barolo Reserva. Whether or not these are suitable for first courses such as duck breast stir-fried with courgettes, lemon grass oil and green onions, or feuilleté of escargots in gorgonzola sauce is left open for the customer to decide. Puddings offer a difficult choice, with or without wine, although our inspector found a cream cheese mousse with lemon sauce and candied lemons was a creamy but not cloying end to a meal which also included cream of carrot and orange soup, and beef Stroganoff with shiitake mushrooms and herb scented basmati rice.

87 Bure Lane Friars Cliff Mudeford BH23 4DN
Map 4: SZ19
Tel: 01425 272948
Fax: 01425 279130
Chef: Stephen Lavender
Owners: NG & MJ Badley
Cost: Fixed-price L £15/D £23. ☺ H/wine £11.
Times: Noon-last L 1.30pm/7pm-last D 9pm
Additional: Bar food; Sunday L; No children under 5; ❹ dishes
Seats: 35. Private dining room 10-100
Smoking: No pipes and cigars
Accommodation: 20 en suite
Credit cards:

Directions: From A35 Somerford roundabout take A337 towards Highcliffe, at next roundabout turn R to Mudeford, hotel on L

CORFE CASTLE,

Mortons House Hotel ❀

Sympathetically extended, personally-run Elizabethan manor with charming views over the historic village. The stylish restaurant serves an interesting selection of carefully prepared dishes. Follow crab and tomato bisque with guinea fowl braised in sherry with bacon and mushrooms and round off an enjoyable meal with orange and almond torte.

East Street BH20 5EE
Map 3: SY98
Tel: 01929 480988
Fax: 01929 480820
Chef: Christopher Button
Owners: Mr & Mrs David Langford
Cost: Fixed-price L £15 (4 courses)/D £20 (5 courses). ☺ H/wine £10.
Times: Last L 2pm/D 8.30pm

Additional: Bar Food L ; Sunday L; Children welcome; ❹ dishes
Smoking: No smoking in dining rooms
Accommodation: 17 en suite
Credit cards:

Directions: In centre of village on A351

CRANBORNE,

La Fosse at Cranborne ❀

An unpretentious restaurant in a sleepy little Dorset village. The short lunch menu is exceptional value for money, and could include dishes such as thick fillet of cod with a champagne sauce, and tandoori chicken with minty yoghurt. Summer lunches can be taken al fresco in the walled garden.

London House The Square BH21 5PR
Map 4: SU01
Tel: 01725 517604
Fax: 01725 517778
Chef: MJ LaFosse
Owners: MJ LaFosse, BV LaFosse
Cost: *Alc* £20, fixed-price L £6/D £10.50. ☺ H/wine £8.95
Times: Last L 1.45pm/D 9.30pm. Closed Mon, L Sat, D Sun

Additional: Sunday L; Children welcome; ❹ dishes
Smoking: No smoking in restaurant
Accommodation: 3 en suite
Credit cards:

Directions: M27 – W on to A31 to Ringwood, then to Verwood, then Cranborne

DORCHESTER, **The Mock Turtle**

'What a haven on a cold and rainy February day', exclaimed our inspector. The Hodder family have been running this bow-fronted former rectory since 1989 and have turned it into an admirable venue for townspeople and holidaymakers alike. The restaurant is intriguingly made up of eating areas on three levels, with lots of nooks and crannies dotted around. The handwritten lunch menu is outstanding value for dishes such as velvety Jerusalem artichoke soup, a duo of pâtés, and duck breast studded with sesame seeds and served with blackcurrant sauce. Fish also shows up in the shape of, say, a delice of halibut with beurre blanc on a bed of risotto or a ragout of brill, squid, salmon and sole. Desserts are equally inviting; Benedictine mousse with Tia Maria sauce, and malted bread and butter pudding have both passed muster. The evening repertoire is fleshed out with more fruits of the sea and vegetarian dishes. Wines are as keenly priced as the food.

34 High West Street DT1 1UP
Map 3: SY69
Tel: 01305 264011
Chef: Raymond Hodder
Owners: Raymond, Alan & Vivien Hodder
Cost: Fixed-price L £14.50 (3 courses)/D £22 (3 courses). ☺ H/wine £8.95.
Times: Noon-last L 2pm/7pm-last D 9.30pm. Closed Sun; Mon & Sat L, 25-26 Dec & 1 Jan
Additional: Children welcome; ⏺ dishes
Seats: 50
Smoking: No-smoking area; No pipes & cigars in dining room; air-conditioning
Credit cards: ▬ ▬ ▬ ▣

Directions: Town centre, top of High West Street

DORCHESTER, **Yalbury Cottage**

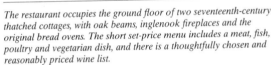

The restaurant occupies the ground floor of two seventeenth-century thatched cottages, with oak beams, inglenook fireplaces and the original bread ovens. The short set-price menu includes a meat, fish, poultry and vegetarian dish, and there is a thoughtfully chosen and reasonably priced wine list.

Lower Bockhampton DT2 8PZ
Map 3: SY69
Tel: 01305 262382
Fax: 01305 266412
Chef: Nick Larby
Owners: Heather & Derek Furminger
Cost: Fixed-price D £19. ☺ H/wine £9.
Times: D only, 7pm-9pm. Closed 29 Dec-22 Jan

Additional: Children welcome; ⏺ dishes
Smoking: No smoking in dining room
Accommodation: 8 en suite
Credit cards: ▬ ▬ ▬ ▣

Directions: Two miles east of Dorchester, off A35

EVERSHOT, **Summer Lodge** ✿✿✿

'The epitome of the English country house' was how one inspector summed up this delightful place, formerly the dower house of the Earls of Ilchester. It would be hard not be enchanted when the weather is perfect, flowers are in bloom and the walled gardens look their best. But even in winter (when log fires blaze), the place loses none of its magic charge. Nigel and Margaret Corbett have been here for almost two decades and the set-up owes much to their diligence. Tim Ford offers a daily 'Country Cooking' menu running to four courses as well as a seasonal *carte* and he knows his way around the modern repertoire. Here is a kitchen that is perfectly at home with boudin of Dover sole marbled with truffles served on a bed of creamed leeks, as well as something more robust like roast breast of Melbury pheasant with braised chestnuts. Meals begin with splendid canapés, a bowl of herby black and green olives, and expertly fashioned home-baked rolls. A test dinner kicked off in assured style with a tomato and rosemary tartlet served straight from the oven with a simple basil dressing to set it off, before a generous tureen of creamy fennel soup which was left on the table. Then came pan-fried fillet of salmon, crispy on the outside, timed to perfection, and served with dill and cardamom sauce that was just right in flavour and texture. As a sprightly finish there was a light duo of chocolate

DT2 0JR
Map 3: ST50
Tel: 01935 83424
Fax: 01935 83005
Chef: Tim Ford
Owners: Nigel & Margaret Corbett
Cost: *Alc* £35, fixed-price L £11.75/D £32.50 (4 courses). H/wine £11.50
Times: 12.30pm-last L 2pm/7.30pm-last D 9pm
Additional: Bar food L; Sunday L; Children welcome; ⏺ dishes
Seats: 50. Private dining room 20
Smoking: No smoking in dining room
Accommodation: 17 en suite
Credit cards: ▬ ▬ ▬ ▬ ▣ ▣

mousses served in a thin pastry case and flavoured with cinnamon, although there are also local farmhouse cheeses with home-made raisin bread on show. Staff go about their work with smiling faces.

Directions: 1 mile W off A37, between Dorchester and Yeovil. Entrance in Summer Lane

GILLINGHAM, Stock Hill Country House Hotel ✿✿✿

Stock Hill SP8 5NR
Map 3: ST82
Tel: 01747 823626
Fax: 01747 825628
Chefs: Peter Hauser, Lorna Connor
Owner: Peter & Nita Hauser
Cost: Fixed-price L £20/D £30 (4 courses). H/wine £13.50
Times: 12.30pm-last L 1.30pm/ 7.30pm-last D 8.30pm.
Closed L Mon, L Sat
Additional: Sunday L;
No children under 6; ✿ dishes
Seats: 24. Private dining room 12
Smoking: No smoking in dining room
Accommodation: 10 en suite
Credit cards: 🟥 📇 📇 💳 💳

There are lovely views from the restaurant of this luxurious Victorian country house hotel over landscaped, formal gardens. Peter Hauser works practically single-handed in the kitchen, his style combines modern ideas with a traditional Austrian slant and many of the ingredients are grown in his extensive kitchen garden. Canapés are served in the ornate, antique-filled lounge, before an amuse-bouche at the table, perhaps a demi-tasse of lightly curried parsnip soup. Breads are particularly impressive, especially the lemon brioche. A main course of breast of Aga roasted duck came with a great, intense jus lightly flavoured with berries – an excellent dish that updated well with a light stir-fry of mangetout, courgettes and carrots. Mashed potatoes with nutmeg were especially delicious. Our inspector chose as dessert a well done construction of swan-shaped meringue, vanilla ice cream, whipped cream and an intense chocolate sauce. One enduring speciality is wickedly tempting Salzburger Knockerlin. Staff are friendly and welcoming and cosset guests throughout their stay, from afternoon tea with delicious Austrian pastries, to coffee with home-made petits fours served in front of a roaring fire. The wine list is nicely done, not long, but with some good wines including, of course, several from Peter Hauser's homeland, Austria. Try them, for they are rare on lists here, and these are all priced at under £25. Otherwise there are four very good house wines at £13.50, and some 20 halves, good Bordeaux but nothing prohibitively expensive. Or try the Pinot Noir from Enrique Mendoza in Alicante at £18.20.

Directions: 3 miles off A303 on B3081

HIGHCLIFFE,
The Lord Bute Restaurant

Lymington Road BH23 4JS
Map 4: SZ29
Tel: 01425 278884
Fax: 01425 279258
Chefs: Christopher Denley
Owners: Simon & Christopher Denley, Stephen Caunter
Cost: *Alc* £20, fixed-price L £9.50 (2 courses)/D £17.95 (3 courses). ☺
H/wine £10.50.
Times: Noon-last L 2pm/7pm-last D 10pm. Closed D Sun & Mon, L Sat
Additional: Sunday L; No children under 8; ✪ dishes
Seats: 80
Smoking: No-smoking area
Credit cards: ■ ■ ■ ■ ▧

Discreetly tucked away behind one of the original lodges to Highcliffe Castle – formerly owned by Lord Bute's family – this pleasing little restaurant draws a loyal following with its sedate classical style and creditable classical cooking. A test lunch of cream of broccoli and potato soup, followed by Hinton Chicken (coated in herbs and served on a grainy mustard jus) and ginger and walnut tart with apricot coulis displayed all the right ingredients and flavours. The kitchen is also capable of delivering, say, lobster bisque, beef Wellington and grilled salmon with lemon in an oyster and sherry cream sauce. More up-beat dishes are also available on the popular brasserie menu, which deals in such things as grilled sardines with tomato and basil sauce, bangers and mash with white onion sauce and pan-fried minute steak on a rösti.

Directions: Follow the A337 to Lymington, situated opposite St Mark's churchyard in Highcliffe

LYME REGIS, **Kersbrook Hotel**

Charming thatched hotel dating from the eighteenth century. Steak and kidney pudding, chicken, leek and parsley pie, Irish stew with crusted dumplings, and Lyme Bay fish pie reveals a kitchen that relishes the traditional elements of British cooking, whilst tournedos Rossini and sole véronique explore a rich classic seam.

Smoking: No smoking in one dining room; no pipes or cigars
Accommodation: 10 en suite
Credit cards: ■ ■ ■ ■ ▧

Pound Road DT7 3HX
Map 3: SY39
Tel: 01297 442596
Chef: Norman Arnold
Owners: Mr & Mrs EH Stephenson
Cost: *Alc* £16.50 (5 courses), fixed-price L £8.50/D £16.50. ☺
H/wine £8.
Times: Last L 2pm/D 9pm.
Closed D Sun
Additional: Bar food L; Sunday L; Children welcome; ✪ dishes

Directions: Town centre – go along main street (Pound Street), turn R at car park into Pound Road, hotel on L

MAIDEN NEWTON,
Le Petit Canard

Dorchester Road DT2 0BE
Map 3: SY59
Tel: 01300 320536
Chef: Geoff Chapman
Owners: Lin & Geoff Chapman

The decor is as simple and uncluttered as the menu, but the cooking includes some eye-catching ideas. Rabbit, mushroom and bacon mille-feuille with caramelised onion wafers, and roast chicken breast on garlicky greens and roasted tomato butter both lift standard ingredients into a new league. Duck may be imaginatively served two ways – either shredded with spicy hash browns salad with roasted pepper dressing as a starter, or slow-roasted on a bean sprout nest and black pepper sauce. The latter ingredient is startlingly reprised in a dessert of passionfruit tartlet with black pepper ice cream, although there are less exotic choices such as white chocolate rum and raisin cheesecake as well. There are daily soup and fish dishes, plus a selection of English farm cheeses. The wine list is a good match for the food.

Cost: Fixed-price D £22.50. ☺
H/wine £11.95.
Times: D only, 7pm-last D 8.45pm.
Closed Sun, Mon
Seats: 30
Smoking: No smoking in dining room
Credit cards: ▬ ▬ ▬

Directions: In the centre of Maiden Newton 8 miles from Dorchester

POOLE,
Harbour Heights Hotel

A pleasant seaside hotel with impressive views of Poole Harbour, Brownsea Island and the Purbeck Hills. The restaurant offers a contemporary menu with Mediterranean and oriental overtones. A winter meal might start with chicken parfait served with apple marmalade, and be followed by pan-fried steak with a green peppercorn sauce.

73 Haven Road
Sandbanks BH13 7LW
Map 4: SZ09
Tel: 01202 707272
Fax: 01202 708594
Chef: Carmine Santorello
Owners: A G Burden, P H Shee
Cost: *Alc* £20.50, fixed-price L £5/D
£16.50. ☺ H/wine £9.50.
Times: Last L 2pm/D 9.30pm

Additional: Sunday L; Bar meals; Children welcome; 🌢 dishes
Smoking: No cigars or pipes
Accommodation: 48 en suite
Credit cards: ▬ ▬ ▬ ▬ ▣ ⬚

Directions: Midway between Poole and Bournemouth

POOLE, Haven Hotel ⚜⚜

Banks Road
BH13 7QL
Map 4: SZ09
Tel: 01202 707333
Fax: 01202 708796
Chef: Karl Nagler
Owner: FJB Hotels
Cost: *Alc* £35, fixed-price L £15/D
£22.50 (4 courses). H/wine £9.75
Times: Last D 10pm Closed 23 Dec-2
Jan
Additional: Sunday L; Children welcome; 🌢 dishes

There is a choice of dining-rooms, large and small, at this attractive hotel overlooking Poole Bay. Local produce is given a continental touch in raviolis of scallops and artichoke purée, jellied fish terrine and fricassée of veal kidneys with roasted apples and cider scented mustard sauce. There are some stimulating ideas on the *carte*, such as pan-fried loin of wild boar with celeriac purée, pickled mushrooms and red wine sauce enriched with bitter chocolate, and a dessert soup of chocolate and rich home-made vanilla ice cream. The set menu plays it safe with liver pâté, grilled fillet of halibut with creamy leeks, crispy bacon and red wine sauce, and gratinated strawberries set on a rice pudding glazed with Kirsch sabayon.

Directions: Follow signs to Sandbanks Peninsula; hotel next to Swanage ferry departure point

Seats: 160. Private dining room 36
Smoking: No smoking in dining room
Accommodation: 94 en suite
Credit cards: ■ ▨ ▨ ▧ ▣ ◖

POOLE,
Mansion House Hotel ❀❀

Thames Street
BH15 1JN
Map 4: SZ09
Tel: 01202 685666
Fax: 01202 665709
Chef: Gerry Godden
Owner: Robert Leonard
Cost: Fixed-price L £13.50/D £24.50
(3 courses). ☺ H/wine £12.50.
Times: Noon-last L 2pm/7pm-last D
9.30pm. Closed L Sat, D Sun, L
May/Aug Bhs
Additional: Bar food; Sunday L;
Children welcome; ❹ dishes
Seats: 85. Private dining room 40
Smoking: No smoking in dining room;
air-conditioning
Accommodation: 28 en suite
Credit cards: ■ ▨ ▨ ▧ ▣ ◖

This listed Georgian building, just off the quay, was built by founders of the Newfoundland cod trade; the original fireplace features marble cod. The cherry-wood panelled dining room is the setting for some sound cooking with a lively Mediterranean edge and some oriental trimmings. The fixed-price menu is especially good-value at lunch, while members of the Mansion House's dining club and hotel guests get a 15% discount on all normal prices. An inspection meal commenced with a choice of breads, herb and olive oil, walnut, and sultana, before going on to smoked haddock soufflé with tomato and chive salad. Monkfish came wrapped in local Dorset air-dried ham, and iced lemon parfait with a good tuille of raspberries with sabayon and raspberry coulis. Very popular locally.

Directions: Follow signs to Channel Ferry/Poole Quay, L at bridge, 1st L is Thames Street

POOLE, Salterns Hotel ❀❀

38 Salterns Way
Lilliput BH14 8JR
Map 4: SZ09
Tel: 01202 707321
Fax: 01202 707488
Chef: Nigel Popperwell
Owner: John & Beverley Smith
Cost: Alc £25, fixed-price L £15/D
£19 (4 courses). ☺ H/wine £10.
Times: Noon-last L 1.45pm/7pm-last
D 9.30pm
Additional: Bar food; Sunday L;
Children welcome; ❹ dishes
Seats: 50. Private dining rooms 120
Smoking: No-smoking area; no pipes
and cigars; air-conditioning
Credit cards: ■ ▨ ▨ ▧ ▣

In a south facing position, set right beside Poole marina, with glorious views across the harbour to Brownsea Island, this modern hotel has got a lot going for it. The kitchen is noted for its use of local fish in cooking that is familiar with modern trends. Dishes such as lobster and scallop terrine with a champagne and dill vinaigrette, fillet of sea bass with langoustine butter, and Poole Bay Dover sole with a lemon and lime butter, show the range. Pairings of meat and fruit are evident in pan-roasted guinea fowl set on cabbage and bacon and served with a raspberry fondue, or roasted duck breast with a compote of apricots and figs and garnished with a plum spring roll. The lengthy wine list offers a good range and fair prices.

Directions: From Poole take B3369 for Sandbanks; after 1.5 miles in Lilliput turn R (Salterns Way). Restaurant on R at end

POOLE, Sandbanks Hotel ❀

15 Banks Road
BH13 7PS
Map 4: SZ09
Tel: 01202 707377
Fax: 01202 708885
Chef: Robert Jones
Owner: FJB Hotels
Cost: *Alc* £29, fixed-price L £14.50/D £18.50. ☺ H/wine £11.95.
Times: Last L 2pm/D 9pm
Additional: Bar food; Sunday L; Children welcome; ❸ dishes
Smoking: No smoking in dining room
Accommodation: 105 en suite
Credit cards: 💳 💳 💳 💳 💳 💳

Panoramic views over Poole Bay and the Purbeck Hills, with direct access to the beach, are part of the attraction of this well equipped large hotel. Quenelles of pike with lobster sauce, brandy and queen scallops, steamed monkfish with banana on a mild curry sauce, or various steaks, and petit pot au chocolat, could be a typical meal in the restaurant.

Directions: From Poole or Bournemouth, follow signs to Sandbanks Peninsula

POOLE,
The Warehouse Brasserie ❀

An informal atmosphere for this large first-floor room of a converted warehouse. Fish is a speciality. A winter lunch produced good fishcakes, venison sausages with a sauce of red wine, juniper berries, mustard and redcurrant jelly, served on a bed of fresh spinach and potato fried in mace butter. Treacle tart for dessert.

The Quay
BH15 1HJ
Map 4: SZ09
Tel/Fax: 01202 677238
Chefs: David Ricketts, Richard Smith
Owners: David & Anne Ricketts
Cost: *Alc* £17. H/wine £7.25. ☺
Times: Last L 2.15pm/D 10pm.
Closed Sun, 26 Dec-12 Jan

Additional: Bar Food L; Children welcome; ❸ dishes
Smoking: No pipes & cigars
Credit cards: 💳 💳 💳 💳 💳 💳

Directions: End of High Street, 1st floor Newfoundland House, on the Quay

PORTESHAM,
Millmead Country Hotel ❀

Welcoming privately run hotel whose kitchen shows a commitment to fresh ingredients. Carrot and orange soup, pork fillet with rosemary, garlic and black peppercorns, or poached salmon steak with white wine and dill sauce, with a classic crème caramel to finish, shows the range. Simple cooking but well executed.

Accommodation: 6 en suite. **Credit cards:** ▬ ▬

Directions: In the village

Goose Hill DT3 4HE
Map 3: SY68
Tel: 01305 871432
Fax: 01305 871884
Chef/Owner: Graham Williams
Cost: Fixed-price D £17.50. ☺
H/wine £8.50.
Times: D only, 7.30pm-9pm
Additional: 🔿 dishes
Smoking: No smoking in dining room

SHAFTESBURY, La Fleur de Lys ❀❀

25 Salisbury Street SP7 8EL
Map 3: ST82
Tel: 01747 853717
Chefs: D Shepherd, M Preston
Owners: D Shepherd, M Preston, DM Griffin
Cost: Alc £30, fixed-price D £23.50. ☺ H/wine £11.
Times: Noon-last L 2.30pm/7pm-last D 10pm. Closed D Sun, L Mon
Additional: Sunday L; Children welcome; 🔿 dishes
Smoking: Strictly no smoking before 10pm
Seats: 40. Private dining room 12
Credit cards: ▬ ▬ ▬ ▬

Nouvelle Cuisine might have come and gone, but this first floor restaurant, overlooking the Blackmoor Vale, is happily immune to such trends. The Anglo-French cooking charts its own steady course and emphasises quality ingredients and precise, sophisticated technique over passing fads and fancies; seared and roasted fillet of turbot is served with fennel, Cornish crab and a Pernod sauce, whilst pan-fried noisettes of English lamb comes on a potato rösti with baked garlic and baby onions in a smoky bacon sauce. First courses might be something as simple as a plate of Scotch smoked salmon with lemon and olive oil and dill dressing, or a more complex ballotine of chicken stuffed with pistachio nuts, sweetbreads and wild mushrooms served with a grain mustard dressing. Passionfruit beignets soufflés with raspberry ice cream and a warm passionfruit custard is typical of a fine choice of desserts.

Directions: Town centre, near the Post Office, on the main road

SHAFTESBURY,
Royal Chase Hotel ❀❀

Originally built as a monastery, this personally run country-town hotel still retains some echoes of the past while catering for the needs of today's customers. The restaurant is named the Byzant (after the ancient water ceremony enacted in the town), and here there is a serious attempt to produce modern dishes with a degree of imagination. Pan-fried pigeon breast

Royal Chase Roundabout SP7 8DB
Map 3: ST82
Tel: 01747 853355
Fax: 01747 851969
Chef: Anthony Sayers
Owners: Royal Chase Hotel
Cost: Alc £25, fixed-price L&D £17. ☺ H/wine £9.50.

Royal Chase Hotel

Times: Noon-last L 2pm/7pm-last D 9.30pm. Closed L Sat
Additional: Bar food; Sunday L; Children welcome; 🌢 dishes
Seats: 65. Private dining room 10-100
Smoking: No smoking in dining room
Accommodation: 35 en suite
Credit cards: ▊▊ ▊▊ ▊▊ ▊▊ ▊▊ ▊▊

comes with Puy lentils in a rich Cognac sauce, while home-smoked medallions of beef fillet – heavily redolent of oak – are accurately timed and accompanied by Madeira sauce. Baked apple is a typical dessert, although at inspection it lacked the promised 'pastry prison' and apple pearls. The extensive wine list includes several noteworthy, quality bins.

Directions: On roundabout where A350 crosses A30 (avoid town centre)

SHAFTESBURY,
Wayfarers Restaurant   NEW

Sherborne Causeway SP7 9PX
Map 3: ST82
Tel: 01747 852821
Chef: Mark Newton
Owners: Mark & Clare Newton
Cost: Alc £25.65, fixed-price L&D £12.95. ☺ H/wine £8.
Times: Noon-last L 1.30pm (bookings only)/7pm-last D 9.15pm. Closed D Sun, Mon, L Sat, 2 wks after 25 Dec
Additional: Sunday L; 🌢 dishes
Seats: 35. Private dining room 20
Credit cards: ▊▊ ▊▊ ▊▊ ▊▊

The seasonally changing menu is short but the descriptions of each dish at this eighteenth-century cottage restaurant are fulsome: griddle-seared fillet of beef wrapped in bacon, lightly home-smoked over oak, bay and juniper, served with little braised beef and kidney quenelles in a port wine sauce; crèpinettes of crab and langoustine, sub-titled as three demi-pancakes filled with white crab meat, split langoustine tails and Japanese seaweed, drizzled with anchovy butter on lemon-scented celeriac. Luckily, the dashing verbosity does not undermine the kitchen's undoubted ability, evident in an inspection meal of roasted scallops wrapped in bacon with sesame blinis and cucumber and caper mayonnaise, followed by fillet of lamb with aubergine, courgette and roasted garlic, and a white and plain chocolate parfait.

Directions: 2 miles W of Shaftesbury on main A30 heading towards Sherborne and Yeovil

SHERBORNE, Eastbury Hotel NEW

Long Street DT9 3BY
Map 3: ST61
Tel: 01935 813131
Fax: 01935 817296
Chefs: Andrew Wheatcroft, Mark Vaughan
Owners: Mr & Mrs TPR Pickford
Cost: Alc £21, fixed-price L £12.95
Times: Last L 2pm/last D 9.30pm
Additional: Sunday L; Bar meals; Children welcome; 🌢 dishes

Charming Georgian townhouse located in a quiet road in the centre of town. The conservatory restaurant looks out over a pretty walled garden and offers sound cooking. Expect fresh tagliatelle of scallops and crabmeat, loin of English lamb roasted in mustard seeds with a rosemary, mint and thyme jus, and steamed chocolate pudding.

Smoking: No-smoking area
Accommodation: 15 en suite
Credit cards: ▊▊ ▊▊ ▊▊ ▊▊

Directions: 800 metres from Abbey

SHERBORNE,

Pheasants Restaurant

Andrew Overhill has turned his imposing hamstone Georgian residence into a highly sought after restaurant-with-rooms, equally popular with tourists and visitors to the prestigious local schools. His kitchen draws its inspiration from far and wide, although a seasonal undercurrent runs through the regularly changing menus. A starter of superb fresh asparagus with poached scampi and chive butter sauce provided our inspector with his first taste of summer, while lightly cooked fillet of brill with cream and dill sauce plus a garnish of mussels was accompanied by gloriously minty new potatoes. In addition, the repertoire embraces everything from Scotch broth and Finnan haddock with prawn sauce, to roast loin of lamb with pancetta and aubergines, and roast goose with black truffles. Desserts such as a delice de Cassis look exceedingly pretty on the plate. The wine list is a well-spread selection from around the world.

24 Greenhill DT9 4EW
Map 3: ST61
Tel/Fax: 01935 815252
Chefs: Neil Cadle, Darren Lawrence
Owner: Andrew Overhill
Cost: Alc £23, fixed-price L £13.50/D£23. ☺ H/wine £9.
Times: Noon-last L 2pm/6.30pm-last D 9.45pm. Closed D Sun & Mon, 2 weeks mid-Jan
Additional: Sunday L; Children welcome; ✿ dishes
Seats: 40-45. Private dining room 10. Jacket & tie preferred
Smoking: No pipes and cigars
Accommodation: 6 en suite
Credit cards: ▬ ▭ ▨ 🄲

Directions: At the top of the High Street, A30 (Salisbury/Yeovil)

STURMINSTER NEWTON,

Plumber Manor

Hazelbury Bryan Road DT10 2AF
Map 3: ST71
Tel: 01258 472507
Fax: 01258 473370
Chef: Brian Prideaux-Brune
Owner: Richard Prideaux-Brune
Cost: Fixed-price D £20 (3 courses). ☺ H/wine £10.
Times: D only 7.30pm-last D 9.30pm. Closed Feb
Additional: Sunday L only (12.30pm-1.30pm); Children welcome; ✿ dishes
Seats: 44. Private dining rooms 22. Jacket & tie preferred
Accommodation: 16 en suite
Credit cards: ▬ ▦ ▨ 🄳 🄲

Home to the Prideaux-Brunes since its inception in the 1700s, this striking Jacobean manor scores heavily with its beguiling rural setting deep in the heart of Thomas Hardy's Wessex. All around are extensive lawns, and the Divelish stream (a tributary of the Stour) meanders through the grounds. The restaurant occupies three elegant rooms and the kitchen puts its faith in local ingredients. Bold combinations, particularly involving liqueurs and fruit, appear in, say, duck with Cassis and black cherries or venison with Grand Marnier and apples. As a starter, boned quail stuffed with wild rice in filo pastry has been expertly and accurately cooked, likewise sole with ginger and soy and brill with creamy mustard sauce. A 'surprising' range of home-made desserts includes crème brûlée and a distinctly flavoured almond Pavlova. The wine list majors in Bordeaux and Burgundies, although a few New World wines also receive an airing.

Directions: At Sturminster Newton cross the packhorse bridge, R to Stalbridge (A537). 1st L to Hazelbury Bryan. Two miles on L opposite Red Lion

SWANAGE, The Cauldron Bistro

There is a refreshing spirit of adventure to the menu at this friendly, small bistro. Ostrich, bison and Eldon wild blue pork feature amongst some unusual meats; fish dishes are equally intrepid with loin of blue marlin chargrilled with lemon, thyme and garlic, and a shrimp and huss stir-fry with fresh coriander and rice served in the wok. More familiar items include chicken liver pâté with pine nuts and berry coulis, a bowl of local mussels steamed in white wine, garlic, onion and cream, and honey roast confit of duck with sauté potatoes, sweet peppers, bacon and herbs. Vegetarians are equally well treated with main courses such as wild wood mushrooms with tagliatelle, Parmesan and white truffle oil. Desserts play it safe with wholemeal treacle tart and chocolate truffle cake, although honey and saffron custard gives a pleasing regional twist to bread and butter pudding.

Directions: At lower end of the High Street, opposite The Old Quay.

5 High Street BH19 2LN
Map 4: SZ07
Tel: 01929 422671
Chef: Terry Flenley
Owners: Terry & Margaret Flenley
Times: Noon-last L 1.30pm/6.30pm-last D 9.15pm. Closed L Mon, L Tue summer (L&D in winter), Jan
Additional: Sunday L; Children welcome; ◑ dishes
Seats: 36
Smoking: No pipes and cigars
Credit cards: ■ ▥ ▨ ▩ ▣

SWANAGE, Grand Hotel

Burlington Road BH19 1LU
Map 4: SZ07
Tel: 01929 423353
Fax: 01929 427068
Chef: Simon Hallam
Owner: Grand Hotel
Cost: Fixed price D £16.95. ☺ H/wine £8.25.
Times: D only, 7pm- 9.30pm
Additional: Bar meals L; Sunday L only (Noon-1.30pm); Children welcome; ◑ dishes
Smoking: No-smoking area in dining room
Accommodation: 30 en suite
Credit cards: ■ ▥ ▨ ▩ ▣ ▯

Appealing cliff-top hotel commanding sweeping vistas across Swanage Bay. The Renaissance Restaurant combines an imaginative daily changing dinner menu with the best of the sea views. Carefully prepared dishes may include chicken and apricot terrine with herb mayonnaise, seafood ragout, and banana and toffee mousse. Cheerful service.

Directions: From North Beach end of town into Ulwell Road, 2nd on R

WAREHAM, Kemps Hotel

Former Victorian rectory set in open Dorset countryside where the ambitious cooking shows good imagination and sound technique. Good tartare of local crab, correctly made French onion soup, honey roasted duckling with apples and an orange sauce, and a chocolate and rum flan are typical examples of the style.

Smoking: No smoking in dining room
Credit cards: 💳💳💳💳💳

Directions: On A352 midway between Wareham and Wool

East Stoke BH20 6AL
Map 3: SY98
Tel: 01929 462563
Fax: 01929 405287
Chef: Philip Simpkiss
Owners: Paul & Jill Warren
Cost: Alc £22, fixed-price L £9.95/D £19.95. ☺ H/wine £8.95.
Times: Last L 1.30pm/D 9.30pm Closed Sat L
Additional: Bar food L; Sunday L; Children welcome; 🌢 dishes

WAREHAM, Priory Hotel

The sixteenth-century Priory of Lady St Mary clings to its history, while offering all the delights of an English country manor house. It stands in four acres of enchanting gardens running down to the banks of the River Frome, and inside there are sumptuous echoes of the past – especially in the atmospheric vaulted stone cellars. The kitchen is nothing if not industrious, producing first-rate breads, canapés and petits fours in addition to a repertoire of classy modern dishes. A superior duck confit and foie gras terrine with brioche impressed at inspection, as did a deceptively simple asparagus soup. Elsewhere you might find baked monkfish on basil mash with pancetta and sweet pepper sauce, or roast calves' kidney on creamed Savoy cabbage with morel and port cream sauce, while desserts such as intensely flavoured passion fruit mousse and summer pudding are served from the trolley. Also note the dazzlingly good selection of English cheeses, not to mention the magnificent wine list – a serious tome bulging with great vintages.

Directions: Town centre between the church and the River Frome

BH20 4ND
Map 3: SY98
Tel: 01929 551666
Fax: 01929 554519
Chef: Stephen Astley
Owners: Stuart & John Turner
Cost: ☺
Times: 12.30pm-2pm/7.30pm-last D 10pm
Additional: Bar food L; Sunday L; No children under 8; 🌢 dishes
Seats: Garden 24, Cellar 48
Smoking: No smoking in dining room
Accommodation: 19 en suite
Credit cards: 💳💳💳💳💳💳

WEST BEXINGTON,
The Manor Hotel

Just five hundred yards from Chesil Beach, the sixteenth-century building enjoys dramatic views of the south Dorset coast. Flagstone floors, Jacobean-panelled walls and beamed ceilings create atmosphere. Fish is a speciality. Try fillet of Dover sole with mustard and bacon.

Directions: Off B3157 Bridport to Weymouth road, turning seawards at The Bull, Swyre

Beach Road,
West Bexington,
Dorchester DT2 9DF

Map 3: SY58
Tel: 01308 897616
Fax: 01308 897035
Chef: Clive Jobson
Owners: Richard & Jayne Childs
Cost: Fixed-price L £ 16.95/D £20.95. ☺ H/wine £8.35.
Times: Last L 1.30pm/D 9.30pm
Additional: Bar food; Sunday L; Children welcome; 🌢 dishes
Accommodation: 13 en suite
Credit cards: 💳💳💳💳💳

WEYMOUTH, Perry's Restaurant

The Victorian merchant's house across the road from the old harbour is now a congenial restaurant specialising in fresh fish, but with plenty more besides. Dining areas with half-panelled walls and black-topped marble tables are on two levels and there's a patio for al fresco repasts. Printed lunch and dinner menus are supplemented by blackboards where seafood from Newlyn market provides the focus. If fish is your bag, you might go for Helford oysters, Cornish mussels or something more elaborate like a gratin of crab with Chablis and cheese sauce. Alternatives appear in the shape of smooth terrine of chicken livers with apple chutney, couscous, or roast fillet of Dorset lamb coated in brioche crumbs and served with red wine sauce. 'Sharrow Bay' toffee pudding made the perfect finish to an inspection meal. Espresso coffee is a strong, dark cupful. Locally brewed 'Old Rot' and some bottled beers supplement the serviceable wine list.

Directions: On western side of old harbour – follow signs for Brewers Quay

4 Trinity Road, The Old Harbour DT4 8TJ
Map 3: SY67
Tel: 01305 785799
Chef: Andy Pike
Owners: Raymond, Alan & Vivien Hodder
Cost: *Alc* £22, fixed-price L £15 (3 courses). ☺ H/wine £8.95.
Times: Noon-last L 2pm/7pm-last D 9.30pm. Closed D Sun winter, L Mon & Sat, 25-26 Dec, 1 Jan
Additional: Sunday L; Children welcome; ♨ dishes
Seats: 60. (summer garden 16). Private dining room 30. Jacket & tie preferred
Smoking: No cigars or pipes.
Credit cards: ▆ ▨ ▨ ▨

WEYMOUTH, The Sea Cow

A popular harbour-side restaurant with white walls, beamed ceilings and plenty of windows overlooking the water. The style is modern English with an emphasis on fresh fish and seafood. Expect dishes such as grilled lemon sole with garlic butter, and pan-fried wing of skate with capers and lemon butter.

Smoking: No-smoking area; No cigars or pipes
Credit cards: ▆ ▨ ▨ ▨

Directions: On the quay – park in large car parks near town bridge, 5 mins walk to restaurant

7 Custom House Quay DT4 8BE
Map 3: SY67
Tel: 01305 783524
Chef: Terence Michael Woolcock
Owners: Terence & Susan Woolcock
Cost: *Alc* £21. ☺
Times: Last L 2pm/D 10.15pm. Closed 25-6 Dec, 1 Jan
Additional: Sunday L; Children welcome; ♨ dishes

WIMBORNE, Les Bouviers

Oakley Hill Merley BH21 1RJ
Map 4: SZ09
Tel/Fax: 01202 889555
Chef/Owner: James Coward
Cost: Fixed-price L £8.75 (2 courses)/D £23.95 (5 courses). ☺ H/wine £8.95.
Times: Noon-last L 2.15pm/7pm-last D 10pm. Closed L Sat, D Sun, 26 Dec

Attention to detail shows throughout this little, stylish restaurant, from the quality of the seasonal, local ingredients to the breads, ice creams and petits fours, all prepared on the premises. In the country it may be, but the cooking has an urbane, mostly classic French orientation. Specialities include hot cheese soufflé with watercress and horseradish sauce with yoghurt, hay-baked jugged hare with rösti potato and rosemary scented sauce, and a bread-

and-butter pudding laced with Cointreau and oranges and finished with a brandy cream sauce. More idiosyncratic combinations are displayed in dishes such as locally reared veal poached in coconut milk, accompanied by ginger couscous and caramelised lychees, and pan-fried boned quails filled with truffle and crayfish tails enriched with a lemongrass scented sauce. As well as continental cheeses, there is an unusual savoury of baked brie with cucumber pickle. The wine list is notable for both range and balance, with ample choice by the glass.

Additional: Sunday L; Children welcome; 🌢 dishes
Seats: 60. Private dining rooms 30-12
Smoking: No-smoking area; air-conditioning
Credit cards: 💳 💳 💳 💳 💳 💳

Directions: 0.5 miles south of A31 Wimborne bypass on A349

WIMBORNE MINSTER,

Beechleas Hotel 🌸🌸

17 Poole Road BH21 1QA
Map 4: SZ09
Tel: 01202 841684
Fax: 01202 849344
Chef: Paulina Humphrey
Owner: Josephine McQuillan
Cost: *Alc* £21.60, fixed-price D £19.75 (3 courses). ☺ H/wine £9.95.
Times: D only, 7.30pm last D. Closed 24 Dec-mid Jan
Additional: Children welcome; 🌢 dishes
Seats: 25
Smoking: No smoking in dining room
Accommodation: 9 en suite
Credit cards: 💳 💳 💳

Beechleas is a fine Georgian house, just south of the town centre, within easy reach of the Minster and shops. It has an appealing restaurant, there's a delightful conservatory for the spring and summer months, and open fire burns in cooler weather. Produce from a nearby organic farm is used to good effect in carefully prepared dishes, often cooked in the Aga. The menu offers good choice yet is of a manageable length for the size of the restaurant. Beechleas pâté with Cognac and Madeira opened an inspection meal, followed by a well-balanced fresh fillet of salmon with lime and chive butter sauce. Desserts are a particular strength, and on this occasion, an apple meringue provided a good contrast between the tartness of the apple and the sweetness of the meringue. An iced light and dark chocolate parfait served with mocha sauce was also well reported.

Directions: On A349 at Wimborne

DURHAM, COUNTY

BEAMISH, Beamish Park Hotel 🌸🌸

A modern hotel, just a mile from the North of England Open Air Museum and a ten minutes' drive from the centre of Newcastle, Beamish Park offers a choice of restaurants. For informal meals there is the airy Conservatory Bistro for the likes of steaks, fishcakes, Cumberland sausages, and perhaps a spicily exotic red chicken and coconut curry. Serious eating is done in the country house-style dining room where the kitchen

Beamish Burn Road, Marley Hill, NE16 5EG
Map 12: NZ25
Tel: 01207 230666
Fax: 01207 281260
Chefs: Clive Imber
Owner: William Walker
Cost: Fixed-price D £22.50 (3 courses). ☺ H/wine £8.95.

Beamish Park Hotel

Times: Noon-last L 1.45pm/7pm-last D 9.30pm.
Additional: Bar food; Sunday L; Children welcome; ◑ dishes.
Seats: 40/70. Private dining room 12
Smoking: No smoking in dining room.
Accommodation: 47 en suite
Credit cards: 💳 📇 📇 💳 💳

Directions: Just off A6076 Newcastle to Stanley road

delivers contemporary ideas with plenty of interest. Note a summer meal which began with small pastry parcels of crab and a salad garnish dressed with black bean and sesame oil, and went on to a lightly grilled Orkney salmon served on a bed of saffron risotto accompanied by a tangy pesto dressing. The combination of flavours and textures in both dishes proved impressive. An 'honest' sticky toffee pudding with brandied prunes and fresh cream completed the meal.

DARLINGTON,
Hall Garth Country House ❀

A sixteenth-century house, with gabled wings of later date, Hall Garth is set in extensive grounds with a Victorian walled garden. Hugo's Restaurant offers a good choice with dishes such as rabbit stew with artichokes and tapenade croûtons, sea trout on tomato and leek compote, and items from the grill.

Coatham Mundeville DL1 3LU
Map 8: NZ21
Tel: 01325 300400
Fax: 01325 310083
Chef: Kevin Hacking
Cost: Alc £28, fixed-price L £11.95/D £21.95. ☺ H/wine £10.25.
Times: Last L 2pm/D 9pm. Closed L Sat, D Sun
Additional: Bar meals; Sunday L; Children welcome; ◑ dishes
Smoking: No-smoking area
Accommodation: 42 en suite
Credit cards: 💳 📇 📇 💳 💳

Directions: A1(M) exit 59 (A167) (Darlington), top of hill turn L signed Brafferton, hotel 200 yds on R

DARLINGTON, Headlam Hall Hotel ❀

A stone-built manor house dating mainly from the eighteenth century. Within, there's a classic interior with many period features. Dishes might include hors d'oeuvre of continental meats, seafood and salad, followed by fresh grilled turbot on a bed of fennel with peppercorns and lemon butter.

Smoking: No smoking in dining room
Accommodation: 28 en suite. **Credit cards:** 💳 📇 📇 💳 💳

Directions: 2 miles north off A67

Headlam, Gainford DL2 3HA
Map 8: NZ21
Tel: 01325 730238
Fax: 01325 730790
Chef: Mark Sayer
Owner: J H Robinson & family
Cost: Alc £22.50, fixed-price D £18. ☺ H/wine £7.
Times: D only, 7.30pm-9pm
Additional: Sunday L (noon-2pm); Children welcome; ◑ dishes

DURHAM, Bistro 21 ✿

The building was originally a farmhouse and latterly the County Hall, and the restaurant (part of Terence Laybourne's mini-empire) retains a rustic feel with whitewashed walls and wood and flagstone floors. Modern bistro dishes include a good fish soup with garlic croûtons, rouille and Gruyère; and confit of duck with braised butter beans and salad.

NEW

Aykley Heads House, Aykley Heads
DH1 5TS
Map 12: NZ24
Tel: 0191 384 4354
Fax: 0191 384 1149
Chef: Adrian Watson
Owners: Terence & Susan Laybourne
Cost: *Alc* £23, fixed-price L £11.50.
☺ H/wine £9.50.
Times: Last L 2pm/last D 10.30pm.
Closed Sun, Mon, Bhs
Additional: Children welcome;
dishes
Smoking: No smoking in dining room
Credit cards:

Directions: Off B6532 from Durham centre, pass County Hall on R and Dryburn Hospital on L; turn R at double roundabout into Aykley Heads

DURHAM, Royal County Hotel ✿✿

Old Elvet DH1 3JN
Map 12: NZ24
Tel: 0191 386 6821
Fax: 0191 386 0704
Chef: John Cruickshank
Owner: Swallow Hotels
Cost: *Alc* £25, fixed price L £14.50/D £23.50 (4 courses) ☺ H/wine £12.
Times: 12.30pm-last L 2.15pm/7pm-last D 10.15pm
Additional: Sunday L; Children welcome; dishes
Seats: 90
Smoking: No-smoking area
Accommodation: 150 en suite
Credit cards:

When the kitchen's on form at this riverside hotel, all is well. The menu in the County Restaurant steers a steady course between adventurous modern cooking and the sort of reliable dishes favoured by much of the local clientele. The set menu usually includes a roast carved from the trolley, as well as a selection of cold meats and salads. The *carte* ventures further afield with dishes such as pot-roasted guinea fowl on a casserole of foie gras and white beans with braised cabbage. Vegetarian dishes have a pronounced Asian accent – stir-fry asparagus with soy, ginger and black sesame seeds is typical. An unusual feature, these days, is a choice of flambé dishes such as strips of fillet of beef with shallots and wild mushrooms with braised rice, and cherries jubilee. Desserts include chocolate truffle torte with raspberry sauce, and bread-and-butter pudding with vanilla custard.

Directions: From A1(M) on to A690. Follow City Centre signs, straight ahead at 1st roundabout, L at 2nd, over bridge, L at lights, hotel on L

HARTLEPOOL,
Krimo's Restaurant ❀

Wide-ranging Mediterranean-inspired cooking, notably some interesting Algerian specialities, at this popular sea-front restaurant. Look out for baked mussels in cheesy leek sauce, Algerian vegetable stew, and chicken breast stuffed with garlic and parsley mousse with white wine and rosemary sauce. Attentive service.

Additional: No children under 8; ◑ dishes
Smoking: Air-conditioning
Credit cards: ▬ ▭ ▢

8 The Front Seaton Carew TS25 1BS
Map 8: NZ53
Tel: 01429 290022
Chef: Krimo Bouabda
Owners: Karen & Krimo Bouabda
Cost: *Alc* £20, fixed-price L £6.50/ D £11.95. ☺ H/wine £8.40.
Times: Last L 1.30pm/D 9pm. Closed L Sat, Sun, Mon, last 2 wks Aug

Directions: On A178 two miles from Hartlepool on the seafront

REDWORTH, **Redworth Hall** ❀❀

Near Newton Aycliffe DL5 6NL
Map 8: NZ22
Tel: 01388 772442
Fax: 01388 775112
Chef: Craig Nicholls
Owner: Tomorrows Leisure
Cost: Fixed-price D £32.95. H/wine £12.25
Times: D only, 7pm-last D 9.45pm. Closed Sun
Additional: Conservatory L&D; Sunday L; Children welcome; ◑ dishes
Seats: 24. Private dining room 18
Smoking: No smoking in dining room
Accommodation: 100 en suite
Credit cards: ▬ ▭ ▭ ▰ ▢ ▢

Set in 25 acres of grounds, this historic manor house now functions as a hotel, country club and leisure centre. On the food front, the main business takes place in the Blue Room restaurant which has been refurbished and stencilled by renowned Cornish artist, Lyn le Grice. The kitchen is obviously keen on elaboration and complexity: a tower of crab and pimento is served with tortellini of lobster and a rich shellfish jus, home-smoked medallion of beef is wrapped in pancetta topped with foie gras and presented with port jus, while fillet of pork is crowned with black pudding mousse, mille-feuille of wild mushrooms and a Madeira sauce. There are also simpler touches, as in the tender guinea fowl enjoyed by our inspector, which was accompanied by a rich sauce based on its juices and a garnish of root vegetables. To finish, lime tart served with a praline mille-feuille and chocolate sauce has also been praised.

Directions: From A1(M) take A68. Hotel is on A6072 (off A68) near Newton Aycliffe

ROMALDKIRK, **Rose and Crown** ❀❀

Dating from 1733 and still very much the hub of the village, the Rose & Crown has been lovingly nurtured by Christopher and Alison Davy. For more than eight years they have cared for the place and it shows. A huge stone fireplace, old oak beams and shuttered windows set the tone in the little bar, otherwise head for the oak-panelled dining room where the

Nr Barnard Castle
DL12 9EB
Map 12: NY92
Tel: 01833 650213
Fax: 01833 650828
Chefs: Christopher Davy, Dawn Stephenson
Owners: Christopher & Alison Davy

Rose and Crown

Cost: Fixed-price D £23 (4 courses).
☺ H/wine £9.50.
Times: D only, 7.30pm-9pm. Closed
D Sun, 25-26 Dec
Additional: Bar food; Sunday L (noon-
1.30pm); children welcome; ❸ dishes
Seats: 24
Smoking: No smoking in dining room
Accommodation: 12 en suite
Credit cards: ▬ ▬ ▬ ▬

daily four-course dinner menu shows a fondness for North
Country produce. A springtime inspection kicked off with a
heady casserole of monkfish and queenies, before smooth
parsnip and garlic soup, but the high point was a brilliant roast
loin of Yorkshire venison with a tip-top juniper sauce plus a
sweet pear tartlet. The repertoire also extends to fillet of
salmon with prawns, capers and nut brown butter and, of
course, roast rib of beef and Yorkshire pudding for Sunday
lunch. Strawberry and vanilla cheesecake makes a finely
crafted dessert. The creditable wine list begins adventurously
in the New World and ends in Europe.

Directions: On B6277 in the centre of the village, near the
church

RUSHYFORD,
Eden Arms Swallow Hotel

Rushyford DL17 0LL
Map 8: NZ22
Tel: 01388 720541
Fax: 01388 721871
Chef: Stephen Coldwell
Owners: Swallow Hotels, Vaux
Brewery
Cost: Alc £25-£30, fixed-price L
£11.50/ D £18.25. ☺ H/wine £9.
Times: Last L 2pm/D 10pm Closed L
Sat
Additional: Bar Food L; Sunday L;
Children welcome; ❸ dishes
Accommodation: 46 en suite
Credit cards: ▬ ▬ ▬ ▬ ▬ ▬

Well placed for visiting Durham, Beamish or the Dales, this
seventeenth-century coaching inn serves carefully prepared
food built around fresh produce. Starters can include smooth,
delicately flavoured duck liver parfait with onion marmalade,
sautéed crab, codling and potato cakes, or marinated pigeon
with oyster mushrooms, rocket salad and raspberry vinaigrette.
Main courses take in roast leg of lamb studded with garlic or,
more sumptuously, braised shank of lamb cooked with claret
and served with an abundance of roast vegetables, home-made
pork and veal sausage, or confit of tuna marinated in ginger
and soy sauce. Desserts take in a delicate chocolate and orange

mousse with chocolate sauce, or sticky toffee pudding with walnut butterscotch. There is a good range of wines on a list that includes modestly priced house wines, and wines by the glass.

Directions: From A1M/J60, follow A689 towards Bishop Auckland for 2 miles. Take 2nd exit at large roundabout, hotel is on L

STOCKTON-ON-TEES,
Parkmore Hotel ❀

An extensive selection of soundly cooked food are among the attractions at this extended Victorian house, set in its own grounds south of Stockton. Expect smoked trout pâté, lemon sole with cream and prawn sauce, and pan-fried pheasant with black cherry and orange sauce.

Times: Last L 2pm/D 9.30pm
Additional: Bar Food; Sunday L; Children welcome; ❹ dishes
Smoking: No smoking in dining room
Accommodation: 55 en suite
Credit cards: 🔳 🔳 🔳 🔳 🔳 🔳

636 Yarm Road Eaglescliffe
TS16 0DH
Map 8: NZ41
Tel: 01642 786815
Fax: 01642 790485
Chef: Dennis Ginsberg
Owners: Brian Reed
Cost: Fixed-price L £12.50/ D £16.75.
☺ H/wine £7.95.

Directions: On the A135 between Yarm and Stockton-on-Tees, almost opposite Eaglescliffe Golf Course

ESSEX

BRENTWOOD, Marygreen Manor ❀

Beamed ceilings and carved panelling set the mood in this handsome Tudor manor. The dining room is in the baronial hall, but the kitchen isn't rooted in the past. Start with spicy Thai soup and finish with hot raspberry soufflé. In between, try honey-glazed duck breast with lavender jus or baked lobster with spinach mousse.

Times: Last L 2.30pm/D 10.15pm
Additional: Snack menu L; Sunday L; Children welcome;
❹ dishes
Smoking: No smoking in dining room; air-conditioning
Accommodation: 33 en suite
Credit cards: 🔳 🔳 🔳 🔳 🔳 🔳

London Road CM14 4NR
Map 5: TQ59
Tel: 01277 225252
Fax: 01277 262809
Chef: Theresa Valentine
Owners: Paul Pearson
Cost: *Alc* £30, fixed-price L£15/D
£19.50. ☺ H/wine £10.95.

Directions: 1 mile from Brentwood town centre, 0.5 mile from M25/J28

BROXTED, Whitehall Hotel ❀❀

On a hillside overlooking the Essex countryside – yet only a few minutes' drive from Stansted Airport – this 600-year-old manor house lives and breathes Englishness. Low-beamed ceilings, leaded windows and blazing fires set the tone in the public rooms. Meals are served in the grandeur of the vaulted restaurant overlooking the Elizabethan walled garden. An

Church End Dunmow
CM6 2BZ
Map 5: TL52
Tel: 01279 850603
Fax: 01279 850385
Chef: Stuart Townsend
Owner: Sisyrinchiun Ltd

Whitehall Hotel

Cost: *Alc* £34, fixed-price L £16.50/D
£19 (3 courses). ☺ H/wine £13.50.
Additional: Sunday lunch; Children
welcome; ❸ dishes
Seats: 40. Private dining room 16
Smoking: No pipes and cigars
Accommodation: 25 en suite
Credit cards: ▬ ▨ ▨ ▨ ▨ ▨

extensive *carte* sits alongside a lighter, brasserie-style menu
and chef's selections. Expect anything from squid risotto and
tournedos of beef with foie gras and truffle essence, to deep-
fried Brie and breast of chicken in lemon sauce. A recent
inspection dinner began on a high note with a spectacularly
risen saffron and Gruyère cheese soufflé, moved on to roast
fillet of cod with grain mustard sauce, and concluded with a
perfectly caramelised apple and almond Pithiviers. Incidentals
such as home-made breads, amuse-bouches, sorbets and petits
fours suggest that this is a kitchen that takes its work seriously.

Directions: From M11/J8 follow signs for Stansted Airport and
then for Broxted

CHELMSFORD,
Pontlands Park Country Hotel ✿

West Hanningfield Road CM2 8HR
Map 5: TL70
Tel: 01245 476444
Fax: 01245 478393
Chef: Stephen Wright
Owner: Jason Bartella
Cost: *Alc* £25, fixed-price L&D £13.
☺ H/wine £9.95.
Times: Last L 2.30pm/D 10pm.
Closed L Mon & Sat, D Sun, 27 Dec-
30 Dec
Additional: Bar food; Sunday L;
Children welcome; ❸ dishes
Smoking: No pipes and cigars; air-
conditioning
Accommodation: 17 en suite
Credit cards: ▬ ▨ ▨ ▨ ▨ ▨

*Comfortable Victorian mansion with in an attractive Conservatory
Restaurant. A well-balanced carte offers an interesting choice,
perhaps chicken livers and asparagus risotto, tender honey and
apricot-glazed duck with apple sauce, and a light strawberry soufflé
with a refreshing strawberry coulis.*

Directions: From M25/J28 take A12 then A130; leave by 1st slip
road (Great Baddow) and take 1st turning L

COGGESHALL, **Baumann's** ✿

4-6 Stoneham Street, CO6 1TT
Map 5: TL82
Tel: 01376 561453
Fax: 01376 563762
Chefs: Mark Baumann, Jason Shaw
Owner: Baumanns Brasserie
Cost: A/c £23, fixed-price L £9.95. ☺
H/wine £8.75.
Times: Last L 2pm/last D10pm.
Closed L Sat, D Sun, Mon, 1st 2 wks
Jan

*There's a bright, breezy feel to this engaging brasserie. The
frequently changing menu is imaginative, with daily fish dishes
written on a roll of brown wrapping paper hung near the door.
Otherwise the choice might include down-to-earth dishes such as
bangers and mash with caramelised onion sauce or seared minute
steak with tomatoes, mushrooms and garlic.*

Additional: Sunday L; Children welcome; 🍴 dishes
Smoking: No cigars or pipes
Credit cards: 🔳 🔳 🔳 🔳 🔳 🔳

Directions: In centre of Coggeshall opposite the clock tower

COGGESHALL,
White Hart Hotel ✿✿

When Coggeshall's Guildhall was destroyed by fire in 1489,
this venerable inn became the principal meeting place for
visiting tradesmen and merchants. Today it continues as the
focal point of the town. Everything about the White Hart
speaks of England, yet the owners and chef are Italian and the
kitchen majors in old-style trattoria food. Pasta is made on the
premises, sauces are rich and cream-laden. Our inspector was
particularly pleased with gnocchi with broad beans and king
prawns as well as baked fillet of salmon with scallops and a
basil cream sauce, but the kitchen's output also extends to
asparagus risotto, chargrilled rump of marinated venison, duck
breast with apricot sauce, and veal cutlet with wild mushroom
sauce. Desserts such as Tia Maria gâteau come mainly from the
trolley. Lighter meals are also served in the lounge bar where
the mood is noticeably buoyant. Italian regional wines of good
pedigree top the international list.

Market End CO6 1NH
Map 5: TL82
Tel: 01376 561654
Fax: 01376 561789
Chef: Fausto Mazza
Owner: Mario Casella
Cost: A/c £25. H/wine £10.25. ☺
Times: Noon-last L 1.45pm/7pm-last
D 9.45pm. Closed D Sun
Additional: Bar food; Sunday L;
Children welcome; 🍴 dishes
Seats: 80. Private dining room 24
Accommodation: 18 en suite
Credit cards: 🔳 🔳 🔳 🔳 🔳

Directions: From the A12 towards Ipswich take the A120, L
towards Braintree; at B1024 crossroads turn L

DEDHAM, **Le Talbooth** ✿✿

Constable buffs will immediately recognise the sixteenth-
century former weavers cottage and toll house overlooking the
river from the famous paintings of Dedham Vale. Soufflé
aficionados will likewise home in on the house speciality
(soufflé Talbooth is made with Finnan haddock and

Dedham CO7 6HP
Map 5: TM03
Tel: 01206 323150
Fax: 01206 322309
Chef: Terry Barber
Owners: Gerald Milsom,
Paul Milsom

Le Talbooth

Cost: *Alc* £35, fixed-price L £17.50/D £22. ☺ H/wine £11.95.
Times: Noon-last L 2.15pm/7pm-last D 9.30pm. D Sun, summer only.
Additional: Sunday L; Children welcome; ◑ dishes
Seats: 75. Private dining room 30
Smoking: No pipes & cigars
Accommodation: 10 en suite (Maison Talbooth)
Credit cards:

mushrooms topped with cheese), but there is also a fine choice of other starters such as tea-smoked quail and terrine of foie gras and Suffolk ham. A main course of seafood nage, with red mullet, halibut, king prawns and mussels was impeccably cooked, but other typical choices might be monkfish tail bound with house-smoked bacon or local pigeon casserole cooked in Rhône wine with peeled grapes and wild mushrooms. The dessert menu also has some intriguing ideas, such as a mille-feuille of crunchy apple made with crisp layers of dried apple and caramelised chunks of fruit, and mulled wine winter pudding with clotted cream. Wines are well selected and mostly under £20, although there are some sound temptations to splash out.

Directions: 6 miles from Colchester: follow signs from A12 to Stratford St Mary, restaurant on L before vilaage

FELSTEAD, **Rumbles Cottage**

Braintree Road CM6 3DJ
Map 5: TL62
Tel: 01371 820996
Chef/Owner: E Joy Hadley
Cost: *Alc* £21.10, fixed-price L & D £13. H/wine £9.75
Times: L by request/7pm-last D 9pm. Closed Mon, 2 wks Feb
Additional: Sunday L only; Children welcome; ◑ dishes
Smoking: No-smoking area in dining room

A small, beamed cottage restaurant offering soundly cooked dishes such as breast of smoked chicken stuffed with banana slices and wrapped with bacon, and pan-fried tenderloin of pork with peaches and celery. For dessert try 'paw-paw dreamboat' – half a paw-paw filled with pineapple and kiwi fruit, and topped with a strawberry coulis.

Credit cards:

Directions: In centre of village, approached by A120 or A130. 15/20 minutes' from M11

GREAT DUNMOW,
Starr Restaurant

Market Place CM6 1AX
Map 4: TL62
Tel: 01371 874321
Fax: 01371 876337
Chef: Mark Fisher
Owners: Brian & Vanessa Jones, Terry & Louise George
Cost: *Alc* £27, fixed-price L&D £22. ☺ H/wine £11.
Times: 12.15-last L 2pm/7pm-last D 10pm. Closed L Sat, D Sun, 1st wk Jan

The big, white square building looks like a traditional market town inn, and that is just what it is, but the fifteenth-century beamed dining room comes as something of a surprise. The beautifully hand-written menu makes satisfying reading; home-made ravioli of rabbit is given depth with morels, crispy leeks and lardons of bacon, and pan-fried smoked salmon has added zest with a bulgar salad with fresh lime dressing. A main course of roast mallard is served on braised red cabbage with apples, walnuts and sultanas, and it seems a lively notion to pair fresh tuna with spaghetti puttanesca and fresh coriander sauce. The pan-fried turbot with a creamy velouté of peas and asparagus chosen by our inspector, however, proved a little heavy together with the accompanying fresh anchovy fritters, but apricot and frangipane sauce with spicy apricot compote was spot-on. The wine list includes some interesting bins, with a good range of everyday drinking and bottles to splash out on.

Additional: Bar food L; Sunday L; Children welcome; ◐ dishes
Seats: 56. Private dining rooms 12-36
Smoking: No smoking in dining room
Accommodation: 8 en suite
Credit cards: ▤ ▥ ▨ ▧ ▣ ▢

Directions: M11 exit 8, A120 7 miles eastward towards Colchester. In centre of small town

HARLOW, Churchgate Manor ❀

Churchgate Street CM17 0JT
Map 5: TL41
Tel/Fax: 01279 420246
Chef: Les Acreman
Owners: Manor Hotels
Cost: Alc £23.50, fixed-price L&D £18.95. ☺ H/wine £10.75.
Times: Last L 2pm/last D 10 pm (9pm Sun). Closed L Sat
Additional: Bar food L; Sunday L; Children welcome; ◐ dishes
Smoking: No smoking in dining room

Standing on the site of an earlier chantry house, the manor house (where the bar and restaurant are located), dates from the 1630s. Dishes might include baked sole in filo pastry with mushrooms and hot sauce tartare, and lamb roasted between hickory planks, with a honey and sherry sauce.

Accommodation: 85 en suite. **Credit cards:** ▤ ▥ ▨ ▣ ▢

Directions: Take A414 (Harlow) exit M11, turn R onto B183 at 4th roundabout, then L into village street; hotel past church, at bottom of hill

HARWICH, The Pier at Harwich ❀❀

The Quay
CO12 3HH
Map 5: TM23
Tel: 01255 241212
Fax: 01255 551922
Chef: Chris Oakley
Owner: The Pier at Harwich Ltd
Cost: Alc £35, fixed-price L £16.50/D £18. ☺ H/wine £9.95.
Times: Last L 2pm/D 9.30pm. Closed D 25 & 26 Dec
Additional: Sunday L; Children welcome; ◐ dishes
Smoking: No pipes or cigars
Accommodation: 6 en suite
Credit cards: ▤ ▥ ▨ ▧ ▣ ▢

The salty, bracing air whets the appetite for the fresh fish and shellfish landed right outside the window of this truly nautical set-up. The main first floor restaurant overlooks the quay and harbour and comes complete with ships wheel and bell, lots of shipping prints and maritime murals. Tried and tested favourites remain on the menu, which has taken on a new, lighter look and now includes gâteau of local cod and crabmeat with chive butter sauce and medallions of sautéed monkfish with papaya and red pepper salsa, as well as lobster with béarnaise sauce. A summer lunch of sauté of chicken livers in a creamy grain mustard and brandy sauce with forest mushrooms, fillet of sea bass, red wine sauce and whole roasted garlic cloves, and stem ginger and Advocaat syllabub was well received. On the ground floor is an informal, family-orientated bistro, the Ha'penny Pier, where the menu offers the likes of fish and chips and fish pie.

Directions: A12 to Colchester than A120 to Harwich town

MANNINGTREE, Stour Bay Café ❀

39-43 High Street CO11 1AH
Map 5: TM13
Tel: 01206 396687
Fax: 01206 395462
Chef: Sherri Singleton
Owners: David McKay, Sherri Singleton
Cost: Alc £16.95. H/wine £9.25. ☺
Times: Last L 2.30pm (Fri, Sat only)/last D 9.30pm (10pm Fri, Sat). Closed Sun, Mon, 2 wks Sept, 2 wks Jan
Additional: Children welcome; ◐ dishes

Californian cuisine is a 'magpie' style, taking ideas and influences from all over the place. Sherri Singleton's cooking follows this pattern while using local produce as much as possible. A strong bias towards seafood dishes – seared snapper fillet in Thai red curry sauce and grilled halibut fillet in saffron butter sauce with chives – is balanced by the chargrill for the likes of Deben duck breast and fillet steak.

Smoking: No-smoking area; no pipes and cigars; air-conditioning. **Credit cards:** ▤ ▥ ▨

Directions: Town centre (A317 from Colchester to Ipswich) – large green building in High Street

ROCHFORD, Hotel Renouf

Bradley Way SS4 1BU
Map 5: TQ89
Tel: 01702 541334
Fax: 01702 549563
Chef: Melvin Renouf
Owner: Derek Renouf
Cost: Alc £28.50, fixed-price L/D £15.50/£17.50. H/wine £9.50
Times: Last L 1.30pm/D 9.30pm. Closed L Sat, D Sun, 26-30 Dec
Additional: Sunday L; Children welcome; ♨ dishes
Smoking: Air-conditioning
Accommodation: 23 en suite
Credit cards: ▨▨ ▨▨ ▨▨ ▨▨ ▨ ▨

Charming family-run hotel offering worthwhile Anglo/French cooking. Starters might include prawn and smoked salmon strudel, pan-fried baby scallops with sun-dried tomatoes, and hot pork pâté wrapped in pastry. Pressed duck framboise (for two), and baked whole sea bass with fennel and Pernod sauce are highly recommended.

Directions: M25/J29, A127 into Rochford onto B1013

SAFFRON WALDEN,
Saffron Hotel

10-18 High Street CB10 1AY
Map 5: RL53
Tel: 01799 522676
Chef: David Robins
Owner: Richard Koch
Cost: Alc £18.
Additional: Bar food; Sunday L; Children welcome; ♨ dishes
Smoking: No-smoking area; air-conditioning
Accommodation: 17 en suite
Credit cards: ▨▨ ▨▨ ▨▨ ▨▨ ▨ ▨

Privately owned, town-centre hotel in a sixteenth-century listed building. Full meals are taken in the smart looking conservatory restaurant overlooking a tiny terrace. Dishes on the carte range from skewered medallions of monkfish with tomato and basil purée to fillet of lamb and apricot en croûte along with several chargrills.

Directions: Town centre – in the High Street

SOUTHEND-ON-SEA,
Schulers Hotel

The large restaurant at this family-run hotel has a loyal local following. The food is Swiss/German influenced, and our inspector particularly enjoyed the home-made brown bread, and

161 Eastern Esplanade, Southend-on-Sea, Essex, SS1 2YB
Map 5: TQ88
Tel: 01702 610172
Fax: 01702 466835

Schulers Hotel

Chef: Ben Allani
Owner: Manfred Schuler
Cost: Alc £25. Fixed-price L&D £10.
☺ H/wine £9.50.
Times: Last L 1.45pm/D 9.30pm.
Closed D Sun, L Mon.
Additional: Sunday L; Children
welcome; ◑ dishes
Smoking: No pipes or cigars
Accommodation: 9 (5 en suite)
Credit cards: 💳 💳 💳 💳 💳 💳

*an apple strudel. Look out for the likes of smoked salmon roulade
and fresh local skate as fish and seafood dishes are strengths of
the kitchen.*

Directions: From A13 or A127 into Southend, follow seafront
signs. Then E towards Thorpe Bay. Eastern Esplanade (E of pier).

TOLLESHUNT KNIGHTS,
Five Lakes Hotel ❀

 NEW

Colchester Road CM9 8HX
Map 5: TL91
Tel: 01621 868888
Fax: 01621 869696
Chef: Martin Carter
Owner: Abraham Bejerano
Cost: Alc £27.50, fixed-price D
£23.50. ☺ H/wine £11.50.
Times: 7pm-last D 10pm.
Closed D Sun
Additional: Sunday L only (12.30-
2.30); Children welcome; ◑ dishes
Smoking: No smoking in dining room
Accommodation: 114 en suite
Credit cards: 💳 💳 💳 💳 💳 💳

*Impressive contemporary hotel set in 320 acres of rolling
countryside. Cosmopolitan menus feature in the formal Camelot
Restaurant. A typical meal could take in baked goat's cheese soufflé
with walnut dressing, peppered pork fillet with ginger scented sauce,
and pear and almond tart for pudding*

Directions: Kelvedon exit A12 follow signs to Tiptree, over
staggered crossroads past jam factory, take L fork, approx 2
miles turn R at T junction.

WETHERSFIELD,
Dicken's Restaurant ❀❀

Oriental and Asian dishes pepper the otherwise broadly
modern European menu at this cottage restaurant in a sleepy
Essex village. On the one hand, there are crispy fried wun-tun
with spicy mango relish, and roasted monkfish and king prawns
on a stir-fry; on the other, Mediterranean fish soup with rouille
and croûtons, roast skate wing with Paris butter sauce and

The Green
CM7 4BS
Map 5: TL73
Tel/Fax: 01371 850723
Chef/Owner: W John Dicken
Cost: Alc £23.50, fixed-price
L £12/D £17.50. ☺
H/wine £8.25.

tenderloin of lamb on roasted parsnips and lentils. Game may be served either in the form of grilled terrine with lyonnaise potatoes and oyster mushrooms or as a seasonal pudding with braised leeks. Desserts largely stick to Anglo-Saxon favourites such as traditional bread-and-butter pudding, upside down caramelised pineapple and sultana pudding, and Bramley apple parfait on a stewed fruit compote.

Directions: From M11/Stanstead Airport take A120, bypass Gt Dunmow, towards Braintree. Turn L to Gt Saling then R towards Shalford. Wethersfield is next village

Times: 12.30pm-last L 2pm/7.30pm-last D 9.30pm. Closed Sun D, Mon, Tue
Additional: Sunday L; Children welcome; ❹ dishes
Seats: 60. Private dining room 18-36
Credit cards: ▇▇ ▀▀ ▀▀ ❰

GLOUCESTERSHIRE

ALVESTON,
Alveston House Hotel ✸

Alveston, Bristol, BS12 2LJ
Map 3: ST68
Tel: 01454 415050
Fax: 01454 415425
Chef: Julie Camm
Cost: Fixed-price D £17.50 (3 courses). ☺ H/wine £9.75.
Times: Last L 1.30pm/D 9.30pm
Additional: Bar food L; Children welcome; ❹ dishes
Accommodation: 30 en suite
Credit cards: ▇▇ ▀▀ ▀▀ ▀▀ ❰ ❰

Comfortable hotel handy for M4/M5, and Bristol, Bath and Gloucester. Well-reported food, served in Quincey's restaurant, could include warm salad of scallops, chicken suprême with a creamy Dijon mustard sauce served on a bed of fresh noodles, super vegetables, and sticky toffee pudding.

Directions: On A38 at Alveston, 3.5 miles N of M4/M5 junction

BIBURY, Swan Hotel ✸✸

Cirencester GL7 5NW
Map 4: SP10
Tel: 01285 740695
Fax: 01285 740473
Chef: Paul Mingo-West
Owners: Mr & Mrs A Furtek
Cost: Fixed-price D £24.50. ☺ H/wine £14.
Times: D only, 7.30pm-last D 9.30pm
Additional: Bar food; Sunday L only (noon-2.30pm); Children welcome; ❹ dishes
Seats: 60. Private dining room 30
Smoking: No smoking in dining room
Accommodation: 18 en suite
Credit cards: ▇▇ ▀▀ ▀▀ ❰

The Signet Dining Room is a particularly grand and richly decorated setting for a menu that is largely modern British, but with classical overtones. Starters might include spare-rib soup with flaked confit of pork belly, rillettes of guinea fowl wrapped in Savoy cabbage with a fresh tomato vinaigrette, or a warm scallop mousse on tangerine butter sauce topped with a seared scallop. Grilled Bibury trout with chives and citrus butter may feature amongst the main courses, along with roasted sea bass with braised chicory, chicken breast wrapped in Parma ham with creamed cabbage, green lentil and chorizo sauce, and a good Scotch ribeye steak with shallots and a rich Burgundy jus. The latter, cooked to order, was tender and served with rösti potatoes, aubergines, courgettes and a baby turnip 'so small it was still virtually a seed!' Rhubarb crème brûlée arrives elegantly in a small copper pan, but other choices might include Tatin of pineapple with lavender ice cream and iced banana parfait with a light toffee sauce and glazed banana.

Swan Hotel

Directions: On B4425 between Cirencester (7 miles) and Burford (9 miles). Beside bridge in centre of Bibury.

BIRDLIP, Kingshead House ✿

Cottagey little restaurant offering a cosy environment and capable cooking. Menus range from winter vegetable soup to brandade of smoked haddock, breast of chicken with spinach and a lemon and garlic sauce to salmon with puréed red beans and a red wine sauce, and apple and pear galette to mocha trifle with a coffee sauce.

Additional: Bar food L; Sunday L; Children welcome; ✿ dishes
Smoking: No pipes or cigars in dining room
Accommodation: 1 en suite. **Credit cards:** ▬ ▒ ▒ ▒

Directions: A417, then B4070 (Stroud) to village

Birdlip GL4 8JH
Map 3: SO91
Tel: 01452 862299
Chef: Judy Knock
Owners: Warren & Judy Knock
Cost: Alc £19 (L only, Tues to Fri), fixed-price D £25. H/wine £10.50
Times: Last L 1.45pm/D 9.45pm. Closed D Sun, Mon, L Sat, 25-27 Dec, 1 Jan

BLOCKLEY, Crown Inn ✿

High Street GL56 9EX
Map 4: SP13
Tel: 01386 700245
Fax: 01386 700247
Chef: Eric Tacheron
Owner: John Champion
Cost: Alc £25. H/wine £11.95. ☺
Times: Last L 2pm/D 10pm
Additional: Sunday L; Bar meals; Children welcome; ✿ dishes
Accommodation: 21 en suite
Credit cards: ▬ ▒ ▒ ▒ ▒

A sixteenth-century coaching inn built from mellow Cotswold stone and majoring in exposed beams and log fires. Meals in the formal Coach House restaurant have a modern flavour, with goat's cheese salad, smoked bacon, pine kernels and poached egg, or Irish oysters on a bed of seaweed and crushed ice, keeping things up-to-date.

Directions: A44 W from Moreton-in-Marsh, right on to B4479

BOURTON-ON-THE-WATER,
Dial House Hotel

The Chestnuts,
High Street GL54 2AN
Map 4: SP12
Tel: 01451 822244
Fax: 01451 810126
Chef: Kevin Chatfield
Owners: Lynn & Peter Boxall
Cost: Alc £19.50. H/wine £9.75. ☺
Times: Last L 2pm/Last D 9pm
Additional: Sunday L; Bar meals L;
No children under 10; ♨ dishes
Smoking: No smoking in dining
rooms
Accommodation: 10 en suite
Credit cards: ▨ ▨ ▨ ▨

A seventeenth-century building of Cotswold stone, fulfilling every romantic expectation with its two cosy dining rooms, inglenook fireplace, oak beams, flagged floors and candlelit tables. It also has a beautiful walled garden for summer meals. The modern English cooking takes in fish and game, plus some vegetarian dishes. Dinner in June produced fresh salmon fishcakes with a pink champagne and peppercorn butter sauce, medallions of pork sandwiched between a farce of apricot and pistachio on a Marsala and thyme sauce, and a fresh fruit crumble filled with seasonal red berries.

Directions: In village centre; A436 from Cheltenham, A40-A424 from Oxford

BUCKLAND, **Buckland Manor**

Broadway WR12 7LY
Map 4: SP03
Tel: 01386 852626
Fax: 01386 853557
Chef: Martyn Pearn
Owner: Roy & Daphne Vaughan
Cost: Alc £40, fixed-price L £27.50.
H/wine £11.50
Times: 12.30pm-last L
1.45pm/7.30pm-last D 9pm
Additional: Bar food L; Sunday L;
No children under 8; ♨ dishes
Seats: 40
Smoking: No smoking in dining room
Accommodation: 13 en suite
Credit cards: ▨ ▨ ▨ ▨ ▨ ▨

It's a stunning place. The medieval building, built of honey-coloured stone with mullioned windows, stands on a hillside in lovely gardens with a private entrance to the thirteenth-century church next door. There are fine views from every main room in the place. The dining room is in keeping with the country elegance of the rest of the hotel soft-pastel coloured panelling, comfortable padded chairs, paintings all around, splendid views of the Cotswold hills from the richly draped windows . Martyn Pearn's cooking is recognisably in the country house tradition with enough variation to give a little edge. It shows modern touches (ham hock and vegetable terrine with pease pudding, walnut oil and balsamic vinegar, shallow pan-fried John Dory served with honey and basil pickled aubergines and a raw tomato sauce), as well as a fondness for more traditional ideas (pâté of Landaise duck foie gras served with toasted brioche, paillard of Angus beef fillet, sauce Diane). A meal of shallow pan-fried scallops with chive beurre blanc and a scoop of tomato sorbet, followed by Angus beef fillet with braised Puy lentils and a good claret sauce, finishing with a warm lemon tart with blackcurrant sorbet and a sauce anglaise, showed all the hallmarks of a kitchen on top form, working with the best available produce. Indeed, seasonal vegetables, herbs and fruit can come from the Manor's own garden, as well as from the nearby Vale of Evesham. Small details such as the good canapés and home-made bread rolls are much appreciated, as is the professional service. The wine list, almost imperialist in its world-wide coverage, is also remarkable for impeccable sourcing and its tirelessly informative annotation. There is quality and interest in every section with fair pricing to be found throughout. New World blockbusters are well represented and those who choose to delve into the extensive Californian selection will be well rewarded, as will anyone who plumps for the much sought after St Hallets Old Block Shiraz from the Barossa at £24.50. A commendable proportion of bins are available in halves.

Directions: 2 miles SW of Broadway. Take B4632 signposted Cheltenham, then take turn for Buckland. Hotel is through village on R

CHARINGWORTH,

Charingworth Manor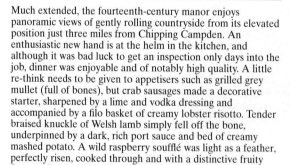

Much extended, the fourteenth-century manor enjoys panoramic views of gently rolling countryside from its elevated position just three miles from Chipping Campden. An enthusiastic new hand is at the helm in the kitchen, and although it was bad luck to get an inspection only days into the job, dinner was enjoyable and of notably high quality. A little re-think needs to be given to appetisers such as grilled grey mullet (full of bones), but crab sausages made a decorative starter, sharpened by a lime and vodka dressing and accompanied by a filo basket of creamy lobster risotto. Tender braised knuckle of Welsh lamb simply fell off the bone, underpinned by a dark, rich port sauce and bed of creamy mashed potato. A wild raspberry soufflé was light as a feather, perfectly risen, cooked through and with a distinctive fruity flavour. Good coffee comes with home-made chocolates.

Directions: From A429 Fosse Way take B4035 towards Chipping Campden, hotel is 3 miles on R

Chipping Campden GL55 6NS
Map 4: SP13
Tel: 01386 593555
Fax: 01386 593353
Chef: Mathew Laughton
Owner: English Rose Hotels
Cost: *A/c* £35.50, fixed-price L £17.50/D £32.50. H/wine £15
Times: 12.30pm-last L 2pm/7pm-last D 9.30pm
Additional: Bar food/lounge; Sunday L; Children welcome; ⍟ dishes
Seats: 48. Private dining room 30. Jacket & tie preferred
Accommodation: 26 en suite
Credit cards:

CHELTENHAM,

Charlton Kings Hotel ⍟ NEW

Small, friendly hotel with a pleasant modern-style restaurant. There is a daily fixed-price menu, offering dishes such as wild rabbit pie, chicken suprême in a white wine, mushroom and garlic sauce, and grilled lemon sole; plus a choice of home-made puddings.

London Road,
Charlton Kings
GL52 6UU
Map 3: SO92
Tel: 01242 231061
Fax: 01242 241900

Charlton Kings Hotel

Chef: Justin Higgs
Owner: Mr T Stuart
Cost: Fixed-price D £16.95. ☺
H/wine £8.90.
Times: Last L 1.45pm/last D 8.45pm
Additional: Sunday L; Bar meals;
Children welcome; ☺ dishes
Smoking: No smoking in dining room
Accommodation: 14 en suite
Credit cards: ■ ▦ ▦ ▦ ▣

Directions: From Cheltenham town centre, follow A40 direction
Oxford. Hotel on R at 2 miles.

CHELTENHAM, Le Champignon Sauvage Restaurant ❀❀❀❀

24 Suffolk Road GL50 2AQ
Map 3: SO92
Tel/Fax: 01242 573449
Chef: David Everitt-Matthias
Owners: David & Helen Everitt-
Matthias
Cost: Fixed-price L £18.50/D £30. ☺
H/wine £9.95.
Times: 12.30pm-last L 1.30pm/
7.30pm-last D 9.15pm.
Closed L Sat, Sun, Bhs, 10 days Xmas,
2 wks summer
Additional: Children welcome
Seats: 28
Smoking: No cigars or pipes;
air-conditioning
Credit cards: ■ ▦ ▦ ▦ ▣ ▣

Ten years on, David Everitt-Matthias is still cooking up a
storm, and his customers keep coming back for both the great
food and the unassuming and honest atmosphere. The
restaurant, which looks out over the street, comes in shades of
yellow and blue, the tables are well spaced, smartly laid and
the walls hung with impressively good pictures from the local
College of Art. It's actually one of those rare things, a
restaurant in which people visibly enjoy being, eating civilised
food, talking not rushing. Service is friendly, confident and
assured. An appetiser sets the tone of the French terroir-style
cooking: blanquette of butter beans with just the correct
amount of 'bite'. Our first course, breast of wood pigeon with a
watercress cream and a beetroot remoulade, was perfect –
pink, tender and richly flavoured meat with contrasting
dimensions of flavour. The choice of fish on the short *carte* is
often refreshingly unconventional; fillet of pollock with a lentil
and bacon salsa and red pepper jus is vibrant and deliciously
fresh, for example, and home-salted cod might be given an
unusually delicate treatment with parsnip purée and a light
carrot sauce. Other, more francophile main courses include
roasted loin of pork with red cabbage and roasted shallots, and
breast of Barbary duck with its leg formed into a small
cabbage, garnished with a confit of garlic and celeriac. Whilst
prune cake with prune and Armagnac ice cream is one dessert

that can be heartily recommended, it would be hard to resist the Arabian Nights flavourings of warm pistachio tart with an orange sorbet perfumed with liquorice. The well written and easy to use wine list offers six house wines under £15.50 and two dozen halves. The Maçon Uchizy, Dom Talmard 94 is well priced at £13.50, and the Côte du Frontonnais Ch La Colombière is worth trying at £12.75. At the other end of the scale Marc Brédif's Vouvray 55 is stunning and has a tag of £75.

Signature dishes: Meunière of skate, parsley cream and black butter; warm pistachio tart, roasted strawberries, orange sorbet; spiced breasts of Cotswold pigeon, beetroot barley risotto, light bitter chocolate jus; foie gras mousse, potato and turnip tortelloni.

Directions: South of town centre, near Boys' College on A40 (Oxford). Please phone for exact details

CHELTENHAM,
Cleeveway House &&

John and Susan Marfell have been in residence at this eighteenth-century Cotswold manor house for more than 30 years, and it continues to create a good impression. Meals are served by friendly, helpful staff in the attractive restaurant, decorated in pastel shades of blue with colourful prints dotted around the walls. The centrepiece of a recent inspection meal was superbly cooked rack of lamb with red onions and mint jelly, although the choice extends to rabbit provençal and fillet of turbot with brandy and lobster sauce. You might begin with cannelloni filled with leeks and Stilton or Parma ham with crème fraîche, and round things off with lemon tart with nice crisp pastry or one of the home made ice creams or sorbets. Complementing the food is a well chosen wine list with plenty of French stuff and a sprinkling from the New World.

Directions: A435 from Evesham, R at 2nd roundabout on Bishops Cleeve bypass

Bishops Cleeve GL52 4SA
Map 3: SO92
Tel: 01242 672585
Chefs: John Marfell, Susan Marfell
Owner: John & Susan Marfell
Cost: Alc £22. H/wine £9.50. ☺
Times: Noon-last L 1.30pm/7.30pm-last D 9.45pm. Closed D Sun, L Mon, Xmas
Additional: Bar food L; Sunday L; Children welcome; ☺ dishes
Seats: 36. Private dining room 16
Smoking: No pipes and cigars in dining room; air-conditioning
Accommodation: 3 en suite
Credit cards: ▦ ▦ ▦ ▧ ▢

CHELTENHAM,
81 Restaurant &&&

A name change denotes new owners at the former Epicurean – Nicola Stone and Fiorentino Izzo took over towards the end of 1996. Chef Jason Lynas, who under the old regime achieved three AA Rosettes, remains to head the brigade and reports suggest that the changeover has been seamless. Terrine of duck with foie gras and an apple and walnut dressing, or marinated salmon with fine herbs and a crab crème fraîche, with main courses of, say, roast lamb cutlets with tapenade farce and provençale vegetables, or soy and honey-glazed pig's trotters with crispy belly pork on ginger and five-spice jus, show that the kitchen is still flying the flag for modern British cooking. Lunch is good value, offering crab and spring onion risotto with caramelised squid and seafood jus, before confit of duck with butter beans, bacon and thyme, with rich chocolate mousse with poached pears and vanilla for dessert. Bread is good, the 'fruity variety excellent'. As an alternative to the smart setting of the restaurant, the downstairs bistro offers a

81 The Promenade GL50 1PJ
Map 3: SO92
Tel: 01242 222466
Fax: 01242 222474
Chef: Jason Lynas
Owners: Nicola Stone, Fiorentino Izzo
Cost: Alc £30, fixed-price L £15-£18 (2-3 courses). ☺ H/wine £11.50
Times: Noon-last L 2.30pm/7pm-last D 9.30pm (10pm Fri, Sat) Closed D Sun, Mon, 26 Dec-2 Jan, Bhs
Additional: Bistro & bar menus; Sun L; Children welcome; ☺ dishes
Seats: Restaurant 26, Bistro 36, Bar 24. Private dining room 14
Smoking: No smoking in restaurant
Credit cards: ▦ ▦ ▦ ▧ ▢

more informal atmosphere and the likes of chilled tomato and red pepper soup 'perfect for a hot day', baked fishcakes with a fine herb hollandaise and raspberry tart.

Directions: Centrally situated on Cheltenham's Promenade, behind Neptune's fountain

CHELTENHAM,

Golden Valley Thistle ❀

Gloucester Road GL51 0TS
Map 3: SO92
Tel: 01242 232691
Fax: 01242 221846
Chef: Ronnie Pharoah
Owner: Thistle Hotels
Cost: *Alc* £29.50, fixed-price L £15.50/D £22.50. ☺ H/wine £10.50.
Times: Last L 1.45pm/D-9.45pm (9.15pm Sun)
Additional: Bar food; Sunday L; Children welcome; ✿ dishes
Smoking: No-smoking area; air-conditioning
Accommodation: 124 en suite
Credit cards: ▨ ▨ ▨ ▨ ▨ ▨

Conveniently positioned for the M5, with good access to both Cheltenham and Gloucester, this modern hotel boasts a fine leisure centre and is popular with conference and business guests. Good honest cooking in a meal of suprême of salmon, rack of lamb set off with a lightly reduced sauce, and a chocolate roulade.

Directions: 2.5 miles from centre of Cheltenham on A40 (Gloucester). 1 mile M5/J11, towards Cheltenham (A40), 2nd exit off 1st roundabout.

CHELTENHAM,

The Greenway ❀❀❀

Shurdington GL51 5UG
Map 3: SO92
Tel: 01242 862352
Fax: 01242 862780
Chef: Peter Fairclough
Owners: David & Valerie White
Cost: *Alc* £29.50, fixed-price L £17/D £29.50. H/wine £13.50.

Beautiful gardens, flowers, views, stunning countryside, sumptuous comfort: this charming Elizabethan manor house has much going for it. David and Valerie White are rightly proud of their personally run hotel and people find the tranquil setting a tonic. Much approved too, is Peter Fairclough's

cooking of an innovative menu, one that always has a slight angle to it or something interesting. Creamy butter bean has morel tortellini and a tarragon oil; light mousse of wood pigeon a salad nantaise; pan-fried brill comes with braised leeks and a clam fish cream; roasted medallion of Cotswold venison with an apple and blackberry compote and a smoked bacon pommes Anna. The menu is kept short to ensure seasonality. In the conservatory restaurant, with its crisp fine linen, gleaming silver and glassware, a February dinner began with an amuse-bouche of well flavoured plum tomato soup before lightly sautéed veal kidneys with an excellent mushroom risotto, finished with freshly shaved Parmesan. After that, top quality sea bass, perfectly cooked on top of mashed potato with basil. A delicate vanilla sauce provided perfect balance. A chocolate soufflé only just missed the mark. Yet this is studied, daring cooking, with materials, methods, overall approach more than up to the mark. Service, by young staff, happily mixes professionalism with unpretentiousness. There's a fairly lengthy, well balanced wine list with some excellent first growths and *premier Cru* Burgundies, as well as a good range of New World, quite a few halves and some interesting pudding wines. An extensive list with many big name clarets and Burgundies and, unusually, a good range of quality German wines. Some popular New World selections offer value for money with several under £20. House wine at £13.50. Over a dozen vintage ports including a 1945. A large selection of champagnes.

Signature dishes: Roast rack of Welsh lamb with dauphinoise potato, seared foie gras and a Sauternes sauce; grilled fillet of sea bass with basil-creamed potato and a vanilla fish jus; roasted fillet of cod with a leek purée, crispy Parma ham and wild mushrooms on a morel cream sauce; pan-fried medallion of Scottish beef with shallot Tatin, étuvée of carrot and a port wine sauce

Directions: 2.5 miles south of Cheltenham on A46 (Stroud)

Times: 12.30pm-last L 2pm/7.30pm-last D 9.15pm. Closed L Sat
Additional: Sunday L; No children under 7; 🍴 dishes
Seats: 50. Private dining room 24
Smoking: No pipes and cigars
Accommodation: 19 en suite
Credit cards: ▆ ▆ ▆ ▆ ▆ ▆

CHELTENHAM,

Hotel on the Park 🏵🏵

Built in 1830, this listed Regency villa overlooking Pittville Park and close to the racecourse has a delightful sense of period charm, particularly in the dining room with its high ceilings and intricate cornice work. Guests can choose between a short daily menu or a more lengthy seasonal affair, both of which are fixed price. Chef Graham Mairs goes in for big bold flavours, as our inspector discovered when his taste buds were blasted by an appetiser of warm salmon mousse on soused onions. Seared scallops served on creamy chicory with vanilla jus proved to be a decoratively presented starter, while braised chump of lamb with olive polenta, tempura garlic and a thyme and flageolet cassoulet was another mix of strong flavours. To finish, a stunning 'deliberately scorched' apple, prune and Armagnac tart married well with a soothing orange Muscat ice cream. A substantial list of around 120 wines promises plenty of sound drinking from reliable sources.

38 Evesham Road GL52 2AH
Map 3: SO92
Tel: 01242 518898
Fax: 01242 511526
Chef: Graham Mairs
Owners: Graham Mairs, Donna Fox
Cost: Fixed-price D £21.50-£26. ☺
H/wine £9.75.
Times: Noon-last L 2pm/7pm-last D 9pm.
Additional: Bar meals L; Sunday L; No children under 8; 🍴 dishes
Seats: 28. Private dining room 16
Smoking: No smoking in dining room
Accommodation: 12 en suite
Credit cards: ▆ ▆ ▆ ▆ ▆ ▆

Directions: A435 (Evesham) from Cheltenham centre, hotel at 3rd lights opposite Pittville Park

CHELTENHAM,
Mayflower Chinese Restaurant ⊛

32-34 Clarence Street GL50 3NX
Map 3: SO92
Tel: 01242 522426/511580
Fax: 01242 251667
Chef: Mrs MM Kong, Mr CF Kong
Owner: The Kong Family
Cost: *Alc* £22.50, fixed-price L
£6.75/D £25. ☺ H/wine £8.95.
Times: Last L 1.45pm/D 10.30pm.
Closed L Sun, 24-26 Dec
Additional: Children welcome;
◔ dishes
Smoking: Air-conditioning
Credit cards: ▮▮ ▮▮ ▮▮ ▮▮ ▮ ▮

Directions: Town centre opposite
Eagle Star building

Slightly swish, family-run Chinese restaurant done out in 'Regency oriental' fashion. The long menu majors in Cantonese and Pekinese dishes with a sprinkling from Szechuan, and it's mostly familiar stuff. Wun tun soup, sizzling chicken, beef in oyster sauce and crispy aromatic duck are the sort of things to expect. Fresh jasmine tea, promising wines.

CHELTENHAM,
Regency House Hotel ⊛

A listed Regency terrace house, restored to retain its gracious period charm, situated in a quiet square just five minutes from the town centre. The dinner menu might offer twice-baked red Leicester and smoked salmon soufflé, followed by casserole of pork in a sauce flavoured with whole grain mustard.

Smoking: No smoking in dining room
Accommodation: 8 en suite
Credit cards: ▮▮ ▮▮ ▮▮

Directions: Clarence Square is in Pittville just N of town centre

50 Clarence Square GL50 4JR
Map 3: SO92
Tel: 01242 582718
Fax: 01242 262697
Chef: Barbara Oates
Owner: John & Barbara Oates
Cost: *Alc* £17.50, fixed-price L&D
£13. ☺
Times: Last L 2pm/D 7.45pm. Closed
D Sun
Additional: Children welcome;
◔ dishes

CHELTENHAM, # The Savoy ⊛⊛

Built as a gentleman's villa in Regency times, this privately owned hotel is very much in the old Cheltenham style. The interior is in keeping and many original features have been retained. In the attractive restaurant, a monthly fixed-price menu offers plenty of choice: have one, two or three courses from a range of dishes that might include chicken liver and prune pâté with onion marmalade, poached Scotch salmon with wilted spinach and chive cream sauce, and dark bitter chocolate tart with raspberry coulis. A test meal in May began with shallow-fried crab cakes with tiny fresh mussels and a delicate cream and tomato sauce, before straightforward sirloin steak au poivre with seasonal vegetables. To finish, summer pudding was just as it should be – juicy, sharp and refreshing. The short wine list includes some useful house selections.

Directions: M5/J11. Follow signs to town centre. Turn L into Bayshill Road, hotel is 300yds on L

Bayshill Road Montpellier GL50 3AS
Map 3: SO90
Tel: 01242 527788
Fax: 01242 226412
Chef: D Ostle
Owners: Mr & Mrs Yarker
Cost: *Alc* £15.95, Fixed-price D
£12.95 (2 courses). ☺ H/wine £9.95.
Times: D only, 6.30pm-9.30pm
Additional: Bar meals; Children
welcome; ◔ dishes
Seats: 30. Private dining rooms 10-60
Smoking: No-smoking area
Accommodation: 41 en suite
Credit cards: ▮▮ ▮▮ ▮▮ ▮

CHIPPING CAMPDEN,
Cotswold House

The Square GL55 6AN
Map 4: SP13
Tel: 01386 840330
Fax: 01386 840310
Chef: Raymond Boreham
Owners: Christopher & Louise Forbes
Cost: *Alc* £28, fixed-price D £18. ☺
H/wine £11.
Times: D only, 7.15pm-9.30pm.
Closed Xmas
Additional: Brasserie L&D; Sunday L;
Children welcome; ⑤ dishes
Seats: 42. Private dining room 20
Smoking: No smoking in dining room
Accommodation: 15 en suite
Credit cards: 🔲 💳 💳 📷 💳 🄲

Fish is a particularly good choice at this charming old house, overlooking a walled English garden. Griddled monkfish and sea scallops in a lime, ginger, basil and Vermouth sauce was fresh, light and full of flavour, for example. The choice, otherwise, runs to sliced breast of duck with cracked peppercorns, honey and a shallot confit, or poached suprême of corn-fed chicken with spinach and a tomato and coriander salsa. Spring cabbage with smoked bacon, broccoli with hollandaise and tomato purée and mashed carrot with coriander are amongst an imaginative vegetable selection. Lemon and vanilla bombe with griottine cherries steeped in brandy proved mouth-wateringly refreshing, tasting as good as it looked on the plate. Hard to choose though, when the list of desserts also includes a hot butterscotch soufflé with maple syrup and pecan brittle ice cream.

Directions: 1 mile N of A44 between Moreton-in-Marsh and Broadway on B4081

CHIPPING CAMPDEN,
The Malt House ⚜⚜

The Malt House is actually in Broad Camden, quieter than its more famous neighbour, and very much the quintessential English village with thatched cottages and orchards. The dining area has been moved, so that guests can now sit at individual tables instead of around a communal one. Booking, however, is essential for both residents and visitors. The menu is presented, discussed and the order taken by Julian Brown, who then goes and cooks it. There is a choice of three at each of the courses, and the whole menu changes nightly. A typical Saturday spring dinner included mille-feuille of Parmesan cracknell and asparagus, locally oak-smoked salmon with cucumber and avocado salsa, roast English duck with red onion and aubergine marmalade, seared pavé of venison with sweet potato lyonnaise and mushy peas. As well as an excellent selection of English and Irish cheeses, there was warm chocolate tart with home-made honey ice cream and treacle and ginger sponge with custard.

Broad Campden GL55 6UU
Map 4: SP13
Tel: 01386 840295
Fax: 01386 841335
Chef: Julian Brown
Owners: Mr N & Mr J Brown
Cost: Fixed-price D £24.50. H/wine
£16
Times: D only 7.30pm-last D 8.30pm.
Closed Tue, Wed, Xmas
Additional: No children under 2;
⑤ dishes
Seats: 20
Smoking: No smoking in dining room
Accommodation: 8 en suite
Credit cards: 🔲 💳 💳 📷 🄲

Directions: Entering Chipping Campden on A44, turn R for Broad Campden, follow four sharp turns to Malt House

CHIPPING CAMPDEN,

Noel Arms Hotel

The fourteenth-century coaching inn was built to serve visiting wool merchants to this historic Cotswolds town. The food takes a modern English tack in the formal oak-panelled restaurant. Typical are quenelles of salmon mousse set on a lobster and Cognac sauce, Loch Fyne salmon and smoked haddock soufflé and a saffron and tarragon sauce, marinated fillet steak with Thai spices and a timbale of scented rice. Many of the sauces are fruit-based – cranberry and orange comes with a suprême of chicken and pasta, lime and ginger combines with grilled loin of pork, and apple and mint partners half a roast duck. Desserts are pleasingly straightforward – chocolate fudge cake with clotted cream is a special favourite.

Directions: Town centre

High Street GL55 6AT
Map 4: SP13
Tel: 01386 840317
Fax: 01386 841136
Chef: Stuart Mallen
Owner: Noel Hotels Ltd
Cost: Fixed-price D £21.95. ☺
H/wine £10.25.
Times: D only, 7pm-9.30pm (9pm Sun)
Additional: Bar food; Sunday L (noon-2pm); Children welcome; ♨ dishes
Seats: 60. Private dining room 12
Smoking: No smoking in dining room
Accommodation: 26 en suite
Credit cards: 🖩 🖩 🖩 🖩 🖩 🖩

CHIPPING CAMPDEN,

Seymour House Hotel

Built from mellow Cotswold stone, the hotel dates from the early 1700s and includes one of the few original malt houses left in England. A grapevine grows strikingly in the centre of the restaurant, and in fine weather you can eat outdoors on the patio overlooking a 500-year-old yew tree. The *carte* has an interesting Italian dimension, with pasta specialities such as fusilli tossed with black cabbage, new season extra virgin olive oil and shaved Parmesan cheese, and regional Italian main courses such as wild boar steak with Barbera and a sweet red pepper and black olive ragout. Otherwise, choices might include salmon, vegetable and foie gras terrine with sauce vierge or medallions of veal with a wild mushroom and cream sauce. The menu also indicates healthy options, such as an unusual fillet of pork flavoured with fennel seeds served on a bed of cold-roasted sweet and sour vegetables, or broccoli and Stilton tartlet with a sun-dried tomato and leek fondue.

Directions: Town centre – along the High Street

High Street GL55 6AH
Map 4: SP13
Tel: 01386 840429
Fax: 01386 840369
Chef: Peter Clements
Owner: Seymour House Ltd
Cost: Fixed-price D from £20.95. ☺
H/wine £13.50.
Times: Noon-last L 2pm/7pm-last D 10pm
Additional: Bar food; Sunday L; Children welcome; ♨ dishes
Seats: 60. Private dining room 40
Smoking: No smoking in dining room
Accommodation: 16 en suite
Credit cards: 🖩 🖩 🖩 🖩 🖩

CIRENCESTER,

The Crown Of Crucis

Ampney Crucis
GL7 5RS
Map 4: SP00
Tel: 01285 851806
Fax: 01285 851735
Chef: Bill Leadbeater
Owner: Ken & Tessa Mills
Cost: *Alc* £16, fixed-price L £8.45. ☺
H/wine £7.40.
Times: Last L 2pm/D 10pm. Closed 25 Dec
Additional: Bar food; Sunday L; Children welcome; ♨ dishes
Smoking: No-smoking area; no pipes and cigars; air-conditioning
Accommodation: 25 en suite

On the edge of the village, with Ampney Brook running by, this
attractive Cotswold stone inn has a restaurant on two floors, joined
by a spiral staircase. Modern cooking brings potted prawns and crab
with lime and cognac butter, pot-roasted lamb with honey roasted
red onions and a piquant sauce, or pan-fried curried cod steak with
bananas and coriander.

Credit cards:

Directions: 3 miles E of Cirencester on A417 to Lechlade

CIRENCESTER, **Harry Hare's** ⊛

Vibrant, upbeat, with gutsy food, excellent wine and plenty of
attitude, all set in a seventeenth-century town house in a historic
street. Something-for-everyone from short snacks to three-course
blow-outs. Expect smoked haddock and bacon tart and bangers and
mash with sage and onion sauce.

Smoking: No-smoking area. **Credit cards:**

Directions: Opposite Cirencester Parish Church, in market place
at centre of town

3 Gosditch Street GL7 2AG
Map 4: SP00
Tel: 01285 652375
Fax: 01285 641691
Chef: Edward Portlock
Owners: Mark Stephens
Cost: Alc £19.50. H/wine £8.95. ☺
Times: 11am – last D 10.30pm.
Closed 1st wk Jan
Additional: Sunday L; Children
welcome; ❹ dishes

CIRENCESTER,
Kings Head Hotel ⊛

Four-centuries-old coaching inn complete with a secret passage in
the vaults and a reported ghost. Fixed-price menus offer a good
choice of straightforward dishes along the lines of chicken liver
parfait with Cumberland sauce, braised beef and Guinness with a
pastry crust, seafood and pasta gratin, plus a few old-school desserts.

Additional: Sunday L; Bar meals; Children welcome; ❹ dishes
Accommodation: 66 en suite
Credit cards:

Directions: In town centre opposite prominent church tower

Market Place GL7 2NR
Map 3: SP00
Tel: 01285 653322
Fax: 01285 655103
Chef: David Gilbert
Owners: Mr & Mrs Bannerman
Cost: Fixed-price D £14.95. ☺
H/wine £7.95.
Times: Last L 2pm/last D 9pm

CIRENCESTER, **Polo Canteen** ⊛

A pleasant brasserie-style restaurant, with exposed beams and
flooring dating back to the late 1700s. The fortnightly-changing carte
menu is based on modern ideas such as roasted salmon with mixed
peppers and sun-dried tomatoes, and braised breast of pheasant with
chestnut and red wine sauce.

Additional: Sunday L; Children welcome; ❹ dishes
Smoking: No-smoking area
Credit cards:

Directions: Just off Cirencester ring road, opposite Waitrose

29 Sheep Street
Map 4: SP00
Tel: 01285 650977
Fax: 01285 642777
Chef: Paul Welch
Owners: Paul & Carol Welch,
Tina & Brian Mussell
Cost: Alc £15. H/wine £8.95. ☺
Times: Noon-10pm

CIRENCESTER,
Stratton House Hotel ⊛

Attractive, seventeenth-century manor house, just a short walk from
the centre of town. Popular restaurant where the kitchen makes good
use of fresh, quality ingredients in dishes such as smoked haddock

Gloucester Road GL7 2LE
Map 3: SP00
Tel: 01285 651761
Fax: 01285 640024
Chef: Simon Walsh

herb pancake with cheese sauce, pork cooked with a smooth, glossy juniper sauce, and chocolate and kiwi cheesecake.

Smoking: No smoking in dining room
Accommodation: 41 en suite
Credit cards: ▨ ▨ ▨ ▨ ▨ ▨

Directions: From A419 (Cirencester), take A417 (Gloucester) for 0.5 mile.

Owners: Forestdale Hotels Ltd
Cost: *Alc* £22.50, fixed-price D £17.75. ☺ H/wine £9.45.
Times: D only, 7pm-last D 10pm
Additional: Bar food; Sunday L only (noon-2pm); Children welcome; ✪ dishes

CLEARWELL,
Tudor Farmhouse Hotel ✪

Dating from the thirteenth century, this splendid stone building retains many original features, notably in the charming period dining room. Imaginative menus feature fresh seasonal produce. Expect dishes such as fishcakes with lemon and dill mayonnaise, sage-stuffed pork tenderloin with mustard sauce, and duck with parsnip purée and cranberry jus.

Smoking: No smoking in dining room
Accommodation: 13 en suite
Credit cards: ▨ ▨ ▨ ▨ ▨

Directions: Leave Monmouth to Chepstow road at Redbrook, follow signs Clearwell, turn L at village cross, hotel on L

Near Coleford GL16 8JS
Map 3: SO50
Tel: 01594 833046
Fax: 01594 837093
Chef: Dean Wassell
Owners: Deborah & Richard Fletcher
Cost: *Alc* £22.20, fixed-price D £18.25. ☺ H/wine £8.50
Times: Last D 9pm. Closed L, Sun D (except BH) & Christmas
Additional: Children welcome; ✪ dishes

COLEFORD, Speech House ✪

Built as a hunting lodge for Charles II when he was riding in the heart of Forest of Dean. The beamed restaurant was originally the foresters' courtroom and is still used as a court four times a year. Quality produce and ingredients are used for a range of imaginative menus.

Smoking: No smoking in dining room
Accommodation: 14 en suite
Credit cards: ▨ ▨ ▨ ▨ ▨ ▨

Directions: On the B4226 halfway between Cinderford and Coleford

Forest of Dean GL16 7EL
Map 3: SO61
Tel: 01594 822607
Fax: 01594 823658
Chefs: Mark Barnett
Owner: Forte Hotels
Cost: Fixed-price D £21.95. ☺ H/wine £12.10.
Times: D only, 7pm-9pm
Additional: Bar food; Sunday L (noon-2pm); Children welcome; ✪ dishes

COLN ST ALDWYNS, New Inn ✪✪

Cirencester GL7 5AN
Map 4: SP10
Tel: 01285 750651
Fax: 01285 750657
Chef: Stephen Morey
Owner: Brian Evans
Cost: Fixed-price D £22.50. ☺ H/wine £9.75.
Times: Noon-last L 2pm (2.30pm Sun)/7.30pm-last D 9.30pm (9pm Sun)
Additional: Bar food; Sunday L; No children under 8 in restaurant; ✪ dishes
Seats: 36. Private dining room 20
Smoking: No smoking in dining room
Accommodation: 14 en suite

The New Inn was actually built as the result of a decree from Queen Elizabeth I that there should be a coaching inn within a day's travel of every town. Twenty monarchs later, it still looks as pretty as can be with its Cotswold-stone walls enveloped in creeper. Inspectors immediately warm to the genuine, friendly atmosphere within. A fixed-price menu of vivid modern dishes is served in the restaurant area: sea bass, skin-side up, on a mound of ratatouille with a thin jus flavoured with Chinese five spice made a good impression one evening in February, as did a caramelised lemon tart with pink and orange grapefruit segments on a pool of passionfruit juice. Elsewhere, the kitchen tries its hand with cappuccino of butter beans with truffle oil, crab and coriander cakes, and fillet of pork wrapped in bacon with a cider vinegar reduction. An equally promising menu is also offered in the Courtyard Bar, where similar dishes are bolstered by more gutsy 'pub grub' such as pork and leek sausages with bubble and squeak.

Credit cards: ■ ■ ■ ■ □

Directions: 8 miles E of Cirencester between Bibury (B4425) and Fairford (A417)

FOSSEBRIDGE, Fossebridge Inn

On the banks of the River Coln stands this charming inn. The bar dates from the fifteenth century, and there are oak beams, inglenook fireplaces and Yorkstone floors. There are fixed-price and pub food menus. Expect cream of cauliflower soup, salmon and cod fishcake in a lemon butter sauce, and apple and almond tart.

Seats: 50. Private dining room 14. **Accommodation:** 12 en suite
Credit cards: ■ ■ ■ ■ □

Directions: On A429 between Cirencester and Northleach

Northleach
Cheltenham GL54 3JS
Map 4: SP01
Tel: 01285 720721
Fax: 01285 720793
Chef: Kevin Hanks
Owners: Tim & Caroline Bevan
Cost: Fixed-price D £14.95. ☺
H/wine £8.95.
Times: Last L 2.30pm/last D 9.30pm
Additional: Bar meals; Sunday L;
Children welcome; ❸ dishes

GLOUCESTER,
Hatherley Manor Hotel

Down Hatherley Lane GL2 9QA
Map 3: SO81
Tel: 01452 730217
Fax: 01452 731032
Chef: David Gent
Cost: Fixed-price L £12.95/D £17. ☺
H/wine £10.50.
Times: Last L 2pm/D 9.30pm.
Closed L Sat
Additional: Bar food; Sunday L;
Children welcome; ❸ dishes
Smoking: No smoking in dining room
Accommodation: 52 en suite
Credit cards: ■ ■ ■ ■ ▣ □

40 acres of parkland surround this seventeenth-century manor house, a popular business hotel located just north of the city. Quality produce is used in creating the dishes featured on the fixed-price lunch and dinner menus. Typical dishes may include chicken pâté and salmon with hollandaise sauce.

Directions: From Gloucester take A38 towards Tewkesbury. Take R turn signed Down Hatherley

GLOUCESTER, Hatton Court

Upton Hill Upton St Leonards
GL4 8DE
Map 3: SO81
Tel: 01452 617412
Fax: 01452 612945
Owner: Hiscox family
Cost: Alc £30, fixed-price L £10-
£14.50/D £22.50. ☺ H/wine £9.95.
Times: Last L 2pm/D 10pm
Additional: Bar food; Sunday L;
Children welcome; ❹ dishes
Smoking: No smoking in dining room
Accommodation: 45 en suite
Credit cards: 📷 📷 📷 📷 📷 📷

*Beautifully preserved 300-year-old manor house with magnificent
views of the Severn Valley and surrounding countryside. The
kitchen delivers traditional English and modern French cooking
along the lines of chicken and wild mushroom boudin, herb-
crusted rack of lamb with garlic sauce, and toffee apple pie with
butterscotch sauce.*

Directions: Three miles from Gloucester on B4037

LOWER SLAUGHTER,
Lower Slaughter Manor 🏵🏵🏵

Lower Slaughter GL54 2HP
Map 4: SP12
Tel: 01451 820456
Fax: 01451 822150
Chef: Alan Dann
Owners: Mr & Mrs R Vaughan
Cost: Alc £39, fixed-price L £19.95 (3
courses). H/wine £17.50
Times: 12.15pm-last L
2.30pm/7.15pm-last D 9.30pm.
Additional: Sunday L; No children
under 10; ❹ dishes
Seats: 26. Private dining room 18.
Jacket & tie preferred
Smoking: No smoking in dining room
Accommodation: 15 en suite
Credit cards: 📷 📷 📷 📷 📷

A remarkable two-storey dovecote stands in the grounds of
this splendid Cotswold manor that started life as a convent.
The house (now Grade II listed) was largely rebuilt in 1658
and today it boasts everything from a delightful walled garden
to a swimming pool, putting green and croquet lawn. Since the
Vaughans took over as owners, and chef Alan Dann arrived in
1996, there have been noticeable improvements. The elegantly
furnished restaurant impresses with its stunning fabrics, fresh
flowers and comfortable seats, while the kitchen aims to dazzle
the palate. A fondness for fungi is a noticeable theme, whether
it be wild mushroom soup with grilled ceps, shallow-fried fillet
of brill on warm potato salad with sweet girolles and orange
butter sauce, or saddle of venison with parsley and garlic crust
with fondant potatoes and truffle sauce. The sheer finesse of it
all showed up perfectly in an elaborately fashioned starter of
pressed Devon crab and queen scallops served with crispy

vegetables marinated in teriyaki plus a roasted leek and
spinach sauce. Main courses such as loin of lamb with roasted
sweetbreads, cardamom and a mille-feuille of aubergine with a
Costa Rican coffee sauce represent big flavours and fine tuning
at their best. Desserts signal the start of a real firework display:
beautifully risen, delicate coconut and white rum soufflé
pointed up with a few iced grapefruit crystals, or tarte Tatin of
mango with green peppercorn ice cream, to name but two.
Alternatively, there are British Cheeses served with beetroot
chips and blue cheese tuiles. Service is dedicated and
professional to a fault.

Signature dishes: fresh langoustines bound in a light cream,
layered with tomato and served with truffle vinaigrette;
pressed Devon crab and queen scallops served with crispy
vegetables marinated in teriyaki, and a roasted leek and
spinach sauce; warm caramel sponge with rosemary ice cream;
terrine of foie gras, caramelised onion and apple served with
fig compote.

Directions: Off A429, signposted 'The Slaughters'. 0.5 miles
into village on R

MORETON-IN-MARSH,

Manor House Hotel ❀❀

Map 4: SP23
Tel: 01608 650501
Fax: 01608 651481
Chef: Richard Smith
Owner: Coraltrend Ltd
Cost: *Alc* £25, fixed-price L £10.95/D
£21.90 (4 courses). ☺ H/wine
£10.50.
Times: Noon-last L 2pm (2.30 Sun)/
7pm-last D 9.30pm (9pm Sun).
Additional: Sunday L; Bar food L;
Children welcome; ❸ dishes
Seats: 50. Private dining room 100
Smoking: No smoking in dining room
Accommodation: 39 en suite
Credit cards: ▬ ▨ ▨ ▧ ▣ ▢

Records show that this historic Cotswold manor was granted to
the Dean and Chapter of Westminster by Henry VIII in 1539,
and it has had a colourful history ever since. A sixteenth-
century priest's hole and haunted secret passage are two
features, and King George VI has numbered among twentieth-
century guests. Extensive refurbishment has taken place of late
and a talented new team is now in the kitchen. Fixed price
menus and a *carte* are offered in the Mulberry Restaurant. A
creamy risotto of sun-dried tomatoes garnished with asparagus
spears, followed by seared scallops on a bed of spinach
surrounded by saffron sauce and topped with julienne of
celeriac made a good impression both in terms of visual effect
and technique, while a vanilla rice pudding suggested that
traditional desserts are also handled with flair.

Directions: On main A429 Stow/Stratford Rd; at crossroads with
A44 Evesham/Oxford rd

MORETON-IN-MARSH,

Marsh Goose Restaurant

The Goose is located in a Cotswold-stone house of some character, comprising three dining areas decked out with paintings by local artists and heraldic coats-of-arms. Lunch is a popular occasion and our inspector began with slices of stuffed roast quail served with a salad of poached quails' eggs, nuggets of foie gras and a shallot dressing. The main course was a piece of grilled halibut with a decent herb crust and a red-wine sauce, although other choices might include pan-fried cod with onion and apricot compote and nutmeg butter sauce, or roast pork fillet with a spicy cashew and coriander sauce. Dinner brings some more ambitious offerings such as lobster salad with pickled cucumber, orange dressing and deep-fried herbs, or breast of guinea fowl with saffron risotto, sautéed chicken livers and a port and green peppercorn sauce. The well-chosen, reasonably priced wine list favours the output of small, quality conscious growers.

Directions: In the High Street opposite the war memorial

High Street GL56 0AX
Map 4: SP23
Tel: 01608 652111
Fax: 01608 652403
Chefs: Sonya Kidney, Rupert Staniforth
Owners: Sonya Kidney, Leo Brooke-Little, Gordon Campbell-Gray
Cost: Alc £30, fixed-price L £13.50/D £25. H/wine £9
Times: 12.30pm-last L 2.30pm/7.30pm-last D 9.45pm. Closed D Sun, Mon
Additional: Sunday L; Children welcome; dishes
Seats: 60.
Smoking: No smoking in dining room
Credit cards:

NAILSWORTH,

Egypt Mill Hotel   **NEW**

Tastefully converted seventeenth-century flour mill, with millstones, lifting equipment and working water wheels still in place. The 'fascinating' restaurant offers sound cooking. Look out for Stilton beignets with green mustard sauce, Cornish hake cutlets with chives, prawns and a lemon butter sauce, and raspberry crème brûlée.

Cost: Alc £17.50, fixed-price L £9/D £16.50
Times: Noon-last L 2pm/6.30-last D 9.45pm

Directions: On the A46

GL6 0AE
Map 3: ST89
Tel: 01453 833449
Fax: 01453 836098
Chefs: John Sanderson, Gary Phipps
Owners: SR & PJ Webb
Telephone for furtherdetails

NAILSWORTH,

Waterman's Restaurant   **NEW**

Old Market
GL6 0BX
Map 3: ST89
Tel: 01453 832808
Chef: Sarah Waterman
Owner: Sarah & John Waterman
Cost: Alc £22. H/wine £8.50. ☺

The sixteenth-century building has been many things over the years: mill, sweet shop, cake shop and art gallery. Sarah and John Waterman's restaurant consists of a couple of rooms, a huge fireplace, stacks of wine magazines, works by local artists, a

relaxed atmosphere, and simple cooking that shows imagination. Produce is well sourced – vegetables come from the Waterman's own organic allotment, game, meat, fish and cheese are local. The short, set-price menu changes on a monthly basis and could produce a light, creamy crab mousse, braised oxtail served with light herb dumplings in a rich gravy, Wiltshire venison medallions with celeriac purée and a port and orange sauce, and dark chocolate tart served with a light white chocolate sauce. Al fresco summer dining in the walled courtyard garden comes with a lions head fountain and trout stream. In winter, there are regular wine tasting and supper nights. The wine list has been chosen with some care and is reasonably priced.

Times: 7.30pm-last D 9.30pm.
Closed Sun, Mon
Additional: Sat L only (10am-last L 2pm); Children welcome; 🌢 dishes
Seats: 30. Private dining room 12
Smoking: No-smoking area, no pipes or cigars
Credit cards: ■ 📖 ☲ 🕉 🔊 🗐

Directions: Signposted off A46, in the centre of Nailsworth

NEWENT, Three Choirs Vineyard Restaurant ❁❁

Forming part of a successful 100-acre vineyard, complete with visitor centre and shop, this modern, pine-clad restaurant enjoys splendid views over vines and rolling countryside from large picture windows. Some exposed brick and a large fireplace give some character to the interior, while simple, padded chairs and plain tables topped with paper napkins create an informal look. The kitchen's philosophy is based on simple things well done, and translates as an interesting *carte* of traditional dishes with a modern twist. A satisfying spring meal began with a smooth, home-made chicken liver pâté with a distinct flavour, followed by beautifully tender braised beef in a rich red wine sauce with horseradish mash and fresh, crisp vegetables. To finish, home-made lemon and lime tart had good, sharp flavour. Also enjoyed were the warm home-made breads.

GL18 1LS
Map 3: SO28
Tel: 01531 890223
Fax: 01531 890877
Chef: Tony Warburton
Owners: Three Choirs Vineyards Ltd
Cost: *Alc* £15.25. H/wine £7.50. ☺
Times: Noon-2.30pm (Fri, Sat only)/7pm-last D 9.30pm. Closed 23 Dec-7 Jan
Additional: Children welcome; 🌢 dishes
Seats: 50. Private dining room 50
Smoking: No smoking establishment
Credit cards: ■ 📖 ☲ 🕉 🗐

Directions: On B4215, N of Newent

PAINSWICK, Country Elephant ❁❁

New Street GL6 6XH
Map 3: SO80
Tel/Fax: 01452 813564
Chef: Robert Rees
Owner: John Rees
Cost: *Alc* £28, fixed-price L £10 (2 courses)/D £13 (2 courses). ☺ H/wine £9.80.

Three years on, and standards remain high at this relaxed, unpretentious restaurant whose architectural history spans several centuries. The dining area is in the 'new' sixteenth century part, where large fireplaces create a sense of warmth and cosiness during the winter months. The set menu is short, concisely described and full of enticing ideas: grilled skate wing is served with Thai rösti and saffron butter; casserole of fresh snails comes with almonds, wild mushrooms, and a Chartreuse sauce; home-made vanilla marshmallow with coriander biscuits and griottine cherries. There are some interesting seasonal combinations, such as mousseline of scallops with broad beans, tomato and herb butter vinaigrette, as well as a timeless roast breast of duck served with confit leg, pommes fondant and a port sauce. The proprietor admits to an unashamed love of dessert wines – hence the excellent selection, both by the glass and bottle.

Directions: On the A46 between Stroud and Cheltenham

Times: Noon-last L 2pm/7pm-last D 10pm. Closed Sun, Mon, 1 wk Xmas
Additional: Sunday L (special occasions); Children welcome; ❸ dishes
Seats: 32
Smoking: No smoking in dining room
Credit cards: 🔳 🔳 🔳 🔳 🔳 🔳

PAINSWICK, **Painswick Hotel**

Kemps Lane Stroud GL6 6YB
Map 3: SO80
Tel: 01452 812160
Fax: 01452 814059
Chef: Jason Buck
Owner: Somerset & Hélène Moore
Cost: Alc £30; fixed-price L £14.75 (2 courses)/D £24.50. ☺ H/wine £10.50.
Times: Noon-last L 2pm/7.30pm-last D 9.30pm
Additional: Sunday L; Children welcome; ❸ dishes
Seats: 60. Private dining room 20
Smoking: No-smoking area
Accommodation: 20 en suite
Credit cards: 🔳 🔳 🔳 🔳 🔳

There is an emphasis on seafood, local game and Gloucestershire cheeses at this highly individual, Palladian-style hotel. Lobster (cold with lemon mayonnaise or Thermidor) and other shellfish comes from their own seawater tank. Whole grilled Dover sole is served with shallots and artichokes roasted with olive oil, and an equally imaginative treatment is given to roasted guinea fowl by matching it with honey and rosemary sauce and creamed celeriac. Hot crab fritters with a spicy pineapple and chilli vinaigrette, and lobster tortellini with roasted red peppers and a lemongrass sauce show an awareness of big city trends. Desserts, along the lines of honey and banana brûlée with a brandy snap basket filled with banana coulis and hazelnuts, tend to the elaborate. Arabica coffee arrives with home-made fudge.

Directions: Painswick is on A46, the Stroud/Cheltenham road. The turning into Kemps Lane is near the church

PETTY FRANCE, **Petty France Hotel**

Former dower house noted for winter-warming log fires in the public rooms, and an eighteenth-century regency-style restaurant with a romantic atmosphere and modern British cooking. Main courses might include wild mushroom risotto, pan-fried loin of lamb, and roast sea bass.

Smoking: No smoking in dining room
Accommodation: 20 en suite. **Credit cards:** 🔳 🔳 🔳 🔳 🔳 🔳

Directions: On the A46, 5 miles N of M4/J18

Petty France GL9 1AF
Map 3: ST78
Tel: 01454 238361
Fax: 01454 238768
Chefs: Jacqui Burton
Owner: WJ Fraser & VI Minnich
Cost: Alc £25. H/wine £11.95 ☺
Times: Last L 2pm/last D 9.30pm
Additional: Bar food; Sunday L; Children welcome; ❸ dishes

RANGEWORTHY,

Rangeworthy Court ❀

Church Lane Wotton Road BS17 5ND
Map 3: ST68
Tel: 01454 228347
Fax: 01454 228945
Chef: Peter Knight
Owners: Lucia & Mervyn Gillett
Cost: Alc £20, fixed-price L £12.50/D £18.50. ☺ H/wine £10.50.
Times: Last L 1.30pm/D 9pm
Additional: Bar Food; Sunday lunch; Children welcome; ✦ menu
Smoking: No smoking in dining room
Accommodation: 14 en suite
Credit cards: 🖻 🖻 🖻 🖻 🖻 🖻

A sixteenth-century creeper-clad manor house where the restaurant is the original courtyard now covered over with a flat roof. The fixed-price menu might offer stuffed lemon sole, or braised breast of pheasant in brown onion sauce. A separate vegetarian menu is also available.

Directions: Signposted off B4058, down Church Lane

STONEHOUSE, **Stonehouse Court** ❀

Imposing early seventeenth-century building set in six acres of secluded gardens, yet only a mile from the M5. It makes the perfect setting for a wedding, a service Stonehouse Court is licensed to perform. The kitchen is currently performing well, offering dishes prepared with skill and some dedication. A filo purse of tiger prawns and white crabmeat, with a salad of tomato confit, opened a summer dinner. Roast pork tenderloin came next, lean and tender, wrapped in streaky bacon with a thick foie gras sauce and garnished with apple crisps – accompanying vegetables were good. Pudding was a light, smooth-textured bread-and-butter pudding with rum soaked raisins, orange zest and sauce anglaise.

Stonehouse GL10 3RA
Map 3: SO80
Tel: 01453 825155
Fax: 01453 824611
Chef: Alan Postil
Owner: Pageant Hotels Ltd
Cost: Fixed-price D £19. H/wine £11.95.
Times: Last L 2.15pm/D 9.45pm
Additional: Bar food L; Sunday L; Children welcome; ✦ dishes
Smoking: No smoking in dining room
Accommodation: 36 en suite
Credit cards: 🖻 🖻 🖻 🖻 🖻 🖻

Directions: M5/J13/A419 (Stroud); 1.5 miles from M-way, 1 mile from Stonehouse

STOW-ON-THE-WOLD, **Fosse Manor** ❀

Cheltenham GL54 1JX
Map 4: SP12
Tel: 01451 830354
Fax: 01451 832486
Chef: Edward Turner
Owners: Mr R & Mrs Y V Johnstons
Cost: Alc £21, fixed-price L £13.95/D £19.95. ☺ H/wine £10.95.
Times: Last L 2pm/last D 9.30pm
Additional: Bar food; Sunday L; Children welcome; ✦ dishes
Smoking: No smoking in dining room
Accommodation: 20 en suite
Credit cards: 🖻 🖻 🖻 🖻 🖻 🖻

A friendly hotel with an elegant restaurant befitting a manor house. A salmon and sole terrine, filled with smoked quails' eggs on a dill mayonnaise, might be followed by rich venison, smoked bacon and haricot bean cassoulet. There is also a choice of steaks from the grill.

Directions: One mile S of Stow-on-the-Wold on the A429 (Cirencester)

STOW-ON-THE-WOLD,

Grapevine Hotel ✿✿

Sheep Street GL54 1AU
Map 4: SP12
Tel: 01451 830344
Fax: 01451 832278
Chef: Stephen Fitzpatrick
Owner: Mrs S Elliot
Cost: Fixed-price D £24 (3-courses).
☺ H/wine £9.25
Times: Noon-last L 2.30pm/7pm-last D 9.30pm
Additional: Bar food L only; Sunday L; Children welcome; ✇ dishes
Seats: 60. Private dining room 25
Smoking: No smoking in dining room
Accommodation: 22 en suite
Credit cards: ▦ ▦ ▦ ▦ ▦ ▦

Traditionalists will be well pleased with their cream of broccoli soup, shank of lamb braised on a bed of rosemary with parsnip and honey purée, and steamed ginger sponge with cinnamon custard. Irish stew, coq au vin, and chocolate profiteroles also feature amongst other old favourites on the lunchtime menu. But the more adventurous at this hospitable seventeenth-century market town hotel might prefer to go for rather more racy numbers such as chicken and oyster mushroom terrine drizzled with walnut oil, and monkfish tail cooked with leeks, shallots, chervil and smoked bacon, finished in a basil sauce. The conservatory restaurant is a particularly enchanting room with shutters, murals of the Tuscan countryside and a magnificent and prolific black Hamburg vine from which over 200 bunches of grapes are harvested every year.

Directions: Off Fosseway A429, take A436 Chipping Norton; 150 yards on R facing green

STOW-ON-THE-WOLD,

Old Farmhouse Hotel ✿

English farmhouse cooking is the appropriate fare at this 16th-century former farmhouse. The versatile menu encompasses a black pudding sandwich, and sausage and mash with three different local sausages and rich gravy. Major refurbishment of the restaurant will be completed for the currency of this Guide.

Smoking: No smoking in dining room. **Accommodation:** 13
Credit cards: ▦ ▦ ▦

Directions: One mile W of Stow-on-the-Wold, on B4068

Lower Swell GL54 1LF
Map 4: SP12
Tel: 01451 830232
Fax: 01451 870962
Chef: Michael Formstone
Owner: Erik Burger
Cost: *Alc* £19.50, fixed-price D £16.85. ☺ H/wine £8.50.
Times: Last L 2pm/Last D 9pm.
Closed 2 wks Jan
Additional: Sunday L; Bar meals; Children welcome; dishes

STOW-ON-THE-WOLD, Unicorn Hotel

Sheep Street GL54 1HQ
Map 4: SP12
Tel: 01451 830257
Chef: Anthony Harrison
Cost: Alc £22, fixed-price L £12.25/D
£19.95. ☺ H/wine £12
Times: Last L 2pm/last D 9.30pm
Additional: Sunday L; Bar meals;
Children welcome; ✪ dishes
Smoking: No smoking in dining room
Accommodation: 20 en suite
Credit cards: ▬ ▬ ▬ ▬ ▣ ▣

*Virtually unchanged in the last 300 years, this stone-built inn has oak
beams, huge stone fireplaces and Jacobean furniture. A meal from
the carte might begin with home-made fishcake with a white wine
sauce followed by suprême of guinea fowl on a bed of red cabbage.*

Directions: From A44 (Evesham) – about 4 miles out of
Chipping Norton take A436 to Stow

STOW-ON-THE-WOLD,
Washbourne Court Hotel ✿✿

Lower Slaughter
GL54 2HS
Map 4: SP12
Tel: 01451 822143
Fax: 01451 821045
Chef: Martin White
Owners: Roy & Daphne Vaughan
Cost: Alc £36.50, fixed-price L
£21.50/D £36.50. H/wine £16
Times: 12.30pm-last L
2.30pm/7.30pm-last D 9.30pm
Additional: Bar meals L; Sunday L;
No children under 10; ✪ dishes
Seats: 56. Private dining room 14
Smoking: No smoking in dining room.
Jacket & tie preferred
Accommodation: 28 en suite
Credit cards: ▬ ▬ ▬ ▬ ▣ ▣

A magnificent seventeenth-century building of honey-coloured
Cotswold stone, standing in four acres of grounds alongside the
River Eye. Traditional beamed ceilings, open log fires and
stone mullioned windows ensure that the original charm of the
place is retained. The restaurant features chintzy chairs,
wooden tables and quality Wedgwood crockery. The kitchen
produces impressive modern English dishes that show both
flair and imagination. Typical main courses include panaché of
Cornish fish and shellfish finished with a truffle and Madeira
cream, pan-fried breast of Herefordshire duckling with honey-
baked figs, spiced red cabbage and passion fruit sauce, and
marinated rump of Welsh lamb, pot roasted pink with celeriac
mash and a light tomato and tarragon stock. For vegetarians,
dishes such as baked tartlet of goat's cheese and asparagus are
available. The wine list is comprehensive.

Directions: Off A429 village centre by the river

STOW-ON-THE-WOLD,
Wyck Hill House Hotel

Wonderful views across the Windrush Valley add a special ingredient to dinner at this classic country house hotel in the heart of the Cotswolds. The modern British menu plays a pretty straight wicket with chargrilled cutlets of English lamb with home-made apple and mint jelly, but also includes more sophisticated items such as sea bass resting on a casserole of shellfish with a crab ravioli. Starters generally lack fuss – perhaps chilled ogen melon with fresh Greek figs or grilled king prawns wrapped in bacon served with a lemon-dressed salad and a garlic and herb marinade. Desserts that have been enjoyed include hot passion fruit soufflé and a dark chocolate tart with white chocolate mousse. The vast wine list offers over 200 bins with something to suit all pockets, a good number under £25. Some big names allow for a much more extravagant spend.

Directions: A424 (Burford) 1.5 miles from Stow

Burford Road GL54 1HY
Map 4: SP12
Tel: 01451 831936
Fax: 01451 832243
Chef: Ian Smith
Owner: Lyric Hotels
Cost: *Alc* £35, fixed-price L £16.95/D £35. H/wine £14.50
Times: 12.30pm-last L 2pm/7pm-last D 10pm (9pm Sun)
Additional: Bar meals L; Sunday L; children welcome; ❸ dishes
Seats: 60. Private dining room 40. Jacket & tie preferred
Smoking: No smoking in dining room
Accommodation: 30 en suite
Credit cards: 🔳 🔳 🔳 🔳 🔳 🔳

STROUD, # Ivy Restaurant ~~NEW~~

The atmosphere is welcoming and the food good at this listed, stone-faced country house, formerly Chris Oakes' eponymous restaurant. Good home-made bread was enjoyed with a carrot, fennel and apple soup, followed by chicken chasseur, and toasted almond mocha ice cream cake.

Additional: Sunday L; Children welcome; ❸ dishes
Smoking: No smoking in dining room
Credit cards: 🔳 🔳 🔳

Directions: From M5/J13 make for Cheltenham on Stroud ring road. At last roundabout turn R, then 1st L into Slad Road; the Ivy is 0.25 miles on L

169 Slad Road
Map 3: SO80
Tel: 01453 759950
Chef: Nicholas Ramplin
Owners: Mr & Mrs N Ramplin
Cost: *Alc* £20, set-price L £5/D £12.95. ☺ H/wine £8.75.
Times: Last L 2pm/last D 9.30pm.
Closed D Sun, Mon

TETBURY, # Calcot Manor

Calcot GL8 8YJ
Map 3: ST89
Tel: 01666 890391
Fax: 01666 890394
Chef: Michael Croft
Cost: *Alc* £22, fixed-price L £17/D £22 (3 courses). ☺ H/wine £12.50.

On the edge of Tetbury stands Calcot Manor. Public rooms have great charm; there are log fires, flagstone floors and exposed beams and, at the time of writing, a new restaurant was about to open. It is all a far cry from earlier, austere days when the collection of buildings (parts date from the

fourteenth century) was a farmhouse belonging to the Cistercians. The kitchen, however, ploughs a contemporary furrow, a style that has proved successful so far. Canapés and excellent home-made breads set the standard, and the kitchen thrives on combining the robust with the refined. This was apparent at a test meal that took in an accurately cooked smoked haddock and cheese soufflé, a simply conceived dish of fresh red bream served on top of roasted vegetables, and a spot on apple tart made exceptional by crisp pastry and well-caramelised apples and caramel ice cream. Coffee, served in front of the drawing room fire, came with home-made truffles. The wine list is comprehensive.

Directions: 4 miles W of Tetbury on A4135 close to intersection with A45

Times: Noon-last L 2pm/7pm-last D 9.30pm
Additional: Bar food; Sunday L; Children welcome
Seats: 70. Private dining rooms 12-40
Smoking: No smoking in dining room
Accommodation: 25 en suite
Credit cards: ▆ ▆ ▆ ▆

TETBURY, Close Hotel ❀❀❀

8 Long Street GL8 8AQ
Map 3: ST89
Tel: 01666 502272
Fax: 01666 504401
Chef: Stuart McLeod
Cost: *Alc* £29, fixed-price L £18.30/D £25.25 (3 courses). H/wine £13
Times: Noon-last L 2pm/7pm-last D 10pm
Additional: Bar food; Sunday lunch; No children under 7; ◑ dishes
Seats: 36. Private dining room 22
Accommodation: 15 en suite
Credit cards: ▆ ▆ ▆ ▆ ▆ ▆

Built in 1585 for a wealthy Cotswold wool merchant, the Close stands in the centre of town at the heart of the famous Royal Estates. Meals are served in the gracious dining room with its Adam ceiling and views of the delightful walled garden. New chef Stuart McLeod (ex-Washbourne Court, Stow-On-The-Wold) has settled in and reports suggest he is moving into top gear. The high points of a one inspection meal included perfectly cooked venison with parsnip purée and Madeira sauce, followed by a daring but finely executed white chocolate and grapefruit soufflé. Another dinner produced a Finnan haddock risotto of pronounced, smoky flavour, delicately wraped in bright spinach leaves to give some colour and differing texture, and topped by a tiny fillet of seared red mullet. John Dory proved exceptionally light and full-flavoured, and came with a compote of fennel and smoked beetroot butter sauce, and a strawberry soufflé with a powerfully flavoured mango ice cream was pronounced excellent. Otherwise the ambitious *carte* promises such things as warm marinated Cotswold rabbit with polenta and lavender jelly, pan-fried sea bream with a confit of spring onion, scallop mousse and sage gravy, and spiced apples with nutmeg pasta and liquorice ice. Staff are helpful and well-versed in old-fashioned courtesies. The wine list provides plenty of choice from Europe and the New World.

Directions: Centre of Tetbury – M4/J 17 or 18, follow signs

TETBURY, Hunters Hall Inn ❀

A sixteenth-century coaching inn with country-style decor, low beamed ceilings, roaring log fires in winter and a kitchen with a modern approach to food. Dishes might include smoked chicken and herb croûtons with blackberry dressing, and ballotine of pheasant with cranberry and wild mushroom sauce.

Smoking: No pipes or cigars in dining room
Accommodation: 12 en suite. **Credit cards:** 🟦 🟥 🟨 ⚡

Directions: From Tetbury take the A4135 towards Dursley

Kingscote GL8 8XZ
Map 3: ST89
Tel: 01453 860393
Fax: 01453 860707
Chef: Cyrille Portier
Owner: Old English Pub Company
Cost: Alc £20, fixed-price D £12.95
(2 courses). ☺ H/wine £7.75.
Times: Last L 2pm/last D 9.30pm
Additional: Sunday L; Bar meals;
Children welcome; 🍴 dishes

TETBURY, Snooty Fox ❀

Market Place GL8 8DD
Map 3: ST89
Tel: 01666 502436
Fax: 01666 503479
Chef: Stephen Woodcock
Cost: Fixed-price D £19.95. H.wine
£9.95. ☺
Times: Last L-2pm/D-9.30pm
Additional: Bar food; Sunday L;
Children welcome; 🍴 dishes
Smoking: No smoking in dining room
Accommodation: 12 en suite
Credit cards: 🟦 🟥 🟨 ⚡ 💳 🔲

Elegant, refurbished former coaching inn dating from the sixteenth century. An ambitious menu might highlight home-made mushroom soup with just a hint of sage, pan-fried loin of pork with mushroom risotto and creamy Stilton and chive sauce and, to finish, a glazed crème brûlée with griottine cherries.

Directions: Town centre opposite the Market Place

THORNBURY,
Thornbury Castle Hotel ❀❀❀

BS12 1HH
Map 3: ST69
Tel: 01454 281182
Fax: 01454 416188
Chef: Steven Black
Owner: The Baron of Portlethen

If it wasn't genuine, the privately owned sixteenth-century castle could have come straight out of a fairy tale, with its crenellated walls, oriel windows, tapestries, and heraldic shields. Ancestral portraits peer down from the oak-panelled dining-room, drinks are taken in the Grand Hall, reclining on expansive sofas and monarchical chairs. The kitchen cooks with a confidence to match the setting with techniques that are precise and polished: boned quail is stuffed with chervil mousseline and served with an asparagus velouté; griddled fillet of brill is matched with a tomato fondue, basil mash and a saffron and mussel sauce; whilst pot au feu of Aberdeen Angus beef fillet is given added richness with seared foie gras and a herb infused olive oil. Sometimes enthusiasm needs keeping in check. On one spring evening, for example, risotto appeared in three versions, albeit as tomato risotto with sautéed Cornish squid, ink risotto with roasted fillet of salmon, and watercress risotto as a stuffing for boned quail with champagne sauce. Desserts have been described as 'super'; highly recommended are the layers of chocolate blinis and chocolate mousse served with ginger sauce. The wine list is an immense tomb, with heavy emphasis on the old vintage clarets and *grand cru* Burgundies, although there are some good New World wines to be had for under £30.

Cost: Fixed-price L £16.50/D £34.50. H/wine £12
Times: Noon-last L 1.45pm/7pm-last D 9.30pm. Closed 3 days Jan
Additional: Sunday L; No children under 12; ✪ dishes
Seats: 60. Private dining rooms 14/28/20. Jacket & tie preferred
Smoking: No smoking in dining room
Accommodation: 18 en suite
Credit cards: 💳 💳 💳 💳 💳 💳

Directions: Bear left at bottom of High Street into Castle Street. The entrance is to left of St. Mary's Church

UPPER SLAUGHTER,
Lords of the Manor ✿✿✿

GL54 2JD
Map 4: SP12
Tel: 01451 820243
Fax: 01451 820696
Chef: John Campbell
Owners: Empire Ventures Ltd
Cost: *Alc* £50, fixed-price L £19.95/D £29.50. H/wine £15.95
Times: Noon-last L 2.30pm/7pm-last D 9.30pm
Additional: Bar food L, Sunday L; Children welcome; ✪ dishes
Seats: 60. Conservatory 30 + 9
Smoking: No smoking in dining room
Accommodation: 28 en suite
Credit cards: 💳 💳 💳 💳 💳

For 200 years, this beautifully preserved manor was home to the Witts family, rectors of the parish of Upper Slaughter; one Reverend F.E.B Witts was 'first Lord of the Manor' – hence the hotel's curious name. The building is idyllically situated on the edge of a dreamy Cotswold village with eight acres of parkland, lakes and gardens all around. In 1997, the hotel changed hands and chef John Campbell took up his position at the stoves, but an early test meal indicates that all is well and that the kitchen remains on course. Canapés, an appetiser of salmon terrine and ultra-fresh home-made breads made a good first impression, which was reinforced by the quality of a richly flavoured truffle, foie gras and lentil soup. As a main course, our inspector chose excellent seared scallops served on a chorizo and potato salad with a selection of tiny vegetables integrated into the dish. On this occasion, events concluded with a well risen apricot soufflé accompanied by apricot sauce and some refreshing liquorice ice cream in a filo basket. Complementing the *carte* is a daily Market menu of two or three courses (with suggested wines) that might run along the lines of duck confit with turnips and parsnips, loin of venison with creamed Savoy cabbage, wild mushrooms and pancetta, then pear and apple tarte Tatin. The cellar holds an extensive selection of fine wines.

Directions: Follow sign towards The Slaughters off A429. The restaurant is in centre of Upper Slaughter

WINCHCOMBE, Wesley House

High Street GL54 5LT
Map 4: SP02
Tel: 01242 602366
Fax: 01242 602405
Chef: Jonathan Lewis
Owners: Jonathan Lewis, Matthew Brown
Cost: Fixed-price D £26. H/wine £11.50
Times: Noon-2pm/7pm-9.30pm. Closed Sun, 14 Jan-12 Feb
Additional: Bar food L; Children welcome; ♨ dishes
Seats: 50
Smoking: No-smoking area
Accommodation: 5 en suite
Credit cards: ▨ ▨ ▨ ▨ ▨

The split-level restaurant, inside the charming, half-timbered early fifteenth-century building, is cosy and attractive. From a set-price two- or three-course menu, original dishes which stand out include tartare of salmon with citrus cream and pickled cucumber, and poached monkfish on a buttermilk pancake with asparagus ravioli. Savoury creamed pease pudding made a clever pairing with tender, well-flavoured boneless chump of Scottish lamb, whilst medallions of venison haunch are served with dauphinoise potatoes and sloe gin sauce. A set-lunch menu – maybe smoked salmon mousse with rocket salad, Indonesian chicken with pilau rice and chocolate torte – is extremely good value. Alternatively, there's a short but appetising choice of light lunch snacks in the bar – thick seafish bourride with garlic bread or fresh pasta with wild mushrooms and basil pesto – as well as morning coffee and afternoon teas. Throughout the year there are special dinners, feasts and festivities.

Directions: In the centre of Winchcombe on the main road

GREATER MANCHESTER

ALTRINCHAM, Bowdon Hotel

Well-maintained hotel handy for M56/J7 and Manchester Airport. The menu draws on both traditional and global influences. A well reported meal took in home-made fish pâté with tapenade, venison steak with a beetroot and horseradish sauce, and a peach and almond brûlée.

Additional: Sunday L; Bar meals; Children welcome; 🍴 dishes
Smoking: No-smoking area
Accommodation: 89 en suite
Credit cards: ▄▄ ▄▄ ▄▄ ▄▄ ▄▄ ▄▄

Langham Road Bowdon
WA14 2HT
Map 7: SJ89
Tel: 0161 9287121
Fax: 0161 9277560
Chef: Robert Conway
Owners: Lyric Hotels
Cost: *Alc* £24, fixed-price L £5.25 (1 course)/D £17.95. ☺ H/wine £10.50.
Times: Last L 2pm/D 10pm

Directions: Leave M56 at J7 signed Altrincham. At large roundabout take 3rd exit (Altrincham); at next traffic lights turn R into Park Rd. Hotel 1 mile on R

ALTRINCHAM, Juniper

21 The Downs Altrincham
WA14 2QD
Map 7: SJ89
Tel: 0161 9294008
Fax: 0161 9294009
Chef: Paul Kitching
Owners: Nora & Peter Miles
Cost: *Alc* £30, fixed-price L £14.95/D £25. H/wine £12.50
Times: Noon-last L 2pm/7pm-last D 9.30pm. Closed L Sat, Sun, L Mon
Additional: Children welcome
Seats: 50. Private dining room 14
Smoking: No pipes and cigars; air-conditioning
Credit cards: ▄▄ ▄▄ ▄▄ ▄▄ ▄▄

Juniper has turned out to be great news for Altrincham. Here is a restaurant that is in tune with the times, with bright modern decor, white walls punctuated by some striking pictures, flaglike wall hangings and luxuriant greenery. The atmosphere is eminently relaxed, thanks largely to staff who are slick and professional without seeming stuffy. The kitchen's speciality dish, Juniper fish soup (sea bass, codling, salmon and brill with herbs, olive oil and root vegetables) is a reminder that chef Paul Kitching loves cooking the fruits of the sea above all else. Lobster and haddock are turned into a mousse with boiled eggs, scallops might be chargrilled and served with tomato concasse and noodles, or sautéed with red wine and olive oil, while brill could be grilled with mustard mash or roasted and served with red pepper sauce and grilled aubergine. It's also worth taking note of the 'Gourmet Specials' – assiette of fish with Mediterranean vegetables, white beans and chive oil, for example. Our inspector, however, stayed with meat and game for a meal of razor-sharp flavours. Confit of chicken and aubergine terrine (a bold idea), had perfect balance and texture and was admirably set off by a 'sea-salty' vinaigrette, while a tender breast of guinea fowl came with pungent diced beetroot, crunchy sweet shallots and creamy parsley sauce. This is cooking with bags of enthusiasm.

It is also exact, deft and thoroughly contemporary. On this occasion, lunch finished with glazed lemon tart with a vivid citrus filling and a 'deliriously creamy' egg custard tart; as it was Shrove Tuesday, pancakes with honey ice cream were quickly added to the menu – a sure sign of keenness in the kitchen. The wine list makes a virtue of its relative brevity. The available bins are used with economy, breezing through regions and styles with ample choice in the under £20 bracket. There is some delving into the more mysterious varietals too with the pure Raffiate de Moncade of Pascal Lapevres, Béarn being a charming and pocket-friendly example.

Signature dishes: warm smoked salmon with creamy celeriac and vanilla; saddle of lamb with truffle and asparagus pancake; roast wild salmon with rhubarb and chicory; rice pudding soufflé.

Directions: A556 Chester-Manchester rd

ALTRINCHAM,
Woodland Park Hotel

Wellington Road
Timperley WA15 7RG
Map 7: SJ78
Tel: 0161 9288631
Fax: 0161 9412821
Chefs: Jeff Spencer
Owners: B N Walker
Cost: Alc £25, fixed-price D £16.95. H/wine £10.95
Times: Last L 1.55pm/D 9.55pm Closed Sun
Additional: Bar Food L; Children welcome; ♨ dishes
Smoking: Air-conditioning
Accommodation: 45 en suite
Credit cards: 🔲 📇 💳 📠 💷 ⚫

Friendly hotel serving good modern cooking in an elegant setting. A typical meal might begin with chargrilled goat's cheese with pine kernel and sunflower seed pesto, and continue with roast duck breast with orange and beetroot sauce.

Directions: Take A560 from town centre, turn L at 2nd lights, then L into Woodlands Parkway and R at 4-way junction into Wellington Road, hotel 100yds on L

BOLTON, Egerton House

The restaurant at this Victorian country house hotel has open views over landscaped gardens and moors. Typical dishes include a lightly spiced fresh mussel chowder and breast of Goosnargh pheasant on a sauce of baby onions, bacon lardons and wild mushrooms.

Times: Last L 1.45pm/D 9.30pm. Closed L Sat
Additional: Sunday L; Children welcome; ♨ dishes
Smoking: No smoking in dining room
Accommodation: 32 en suite
Credit cards: 🔲 📇 💳 📠 💷 ⚫

Blackburn Road
Egerton BL7 9PL
Map 7: SD70
Tel: 01204 307171
Fax: 01204 593030
Chef: Dale Edwards
Cost: Alc £30.85, fixed-price L £13/D £22. ☺ H/wine £11.95.

Directions: Hotel 3.5 miles N of Bolton on A666, in Egerton village

BURY, **Normandie Hotel** ●●●

The dedication and enthusiasm of Yves Champeau, who converted this former Pennine inn into a corner of France, lives on in Max and Susan Moussa. Set at the top of a winding lane with 'fantastic views over the north-west', the Normandie exists in its own world high above the massive spread of the Greater Manchester conurbation. 'I do like the old fashioned service,' commented one inspector. However, time moves on and Paul Bellingham's cooking does not fall into the former mould of classic French cooking. This can be seen in the repertoire of dishes that takes in up-to-the-minute ideas in starters such as smoked haddock soup with vegetable ravioli, and leek cannelloni filled with goat's cheese, followed by fillet of red bream with pesto mashed potatoes, and breasts of wood pigeon with a chicken mousse wrapped in savoy cabbage. In a meal of accurate composition, a chicken and pork sausage proved very light, well balanced by the excellent Madeira sauce. Then a bold main course of pithiviers of lamb sweetbreads, liver and kidney was set off by an exact rosemary sauce and by finely diced vegetables built into the dish. Rich hot chocolate fondant with 'super' banana ice cream and a light vanilla sauce showed the kitchen on top form. Not a vast wine list, but something for everyone; from the country wines starting at £12.75, through a good range French and New World wines under £20 – Aotea from New Zealand at £17.50, and Viognier Cuvée Cecile at £16.50. Some *premier cru* Burgundies top the bill at £50 and £60.

Signature dishes: Smoked haddock soup with vegetable ravioli; caramelised pear tart with crème fraîche sorbet; blanquette of monkfish with a dry vermouth sauce; breast of wood pigeon with a chicken mousse wrapped in Savoy cabbage.

Elbut Lane Birtle BL9 6UT
Map 7: SD81
Tel: 0161 7643869/7641170
Fax: 0161 7644866
Chef: Paul Bellingham
Owners: Max & Susan Moussa
Cost: *Alc* £25, fixed-price L £ 12.50/D £15. ☺ H/wine £9.95.
Times: Noon-last L 2pm/7pm-last D 9.30pm. Closed L Sat, Sun, one wk Easter, last wk Dec & 1st wk Jan
Additional: Children welcome; ❹ dishes
Seats: 50
Smoking: No pipes and cigars in dining room
Accommodation: 23 en suite
Credit cards:

Directions: From M66/J2, take A58 – Bury. After 100yds turn R into Wash Lane, then 1st R into Willow Street, R at B6222. After 1 mile L into Elbut Lane, then up hill 1 mile

MANCHESTER,
Copthorne Manchester ●

Part of the Salford Quays development, this modern hotel has two popular restaurants. A meal in Chandlers took in smoked salmon pancake mille-feuille, and grilled spiced chicken breast, with saffron risotto wild mushrooms and creamy mascarpone.

Additional: Bar meals; Children welcome; ❹ dishes
Accommodation: 166 en suite
Credit cards:

Directions: Close to M602

Clippers Quay, Salford Quays M5 2XP
Map 7: SJ89
Tel: 0161 873 7321
Fax: 0161 873 7318
Chef: Kenneth Tait
Owner: Chandlers Restaurant
Cost: *Alc* £25. H/wine £12.95. ☺
Times: Last L 2.15pm/last D10.15pm

MANCHESTER,
Holiday Inn Crowne Plaza ●●

Mr Rolls first met Mr Royce in this elegant Edwardian hotel, which is still fondly remembered as The Midland. The opulent French Restaurant is reckoned to be the best hotel dining room of its kind in the city and a new kitchen brigade has raised the standard of cooking a notch or two in recent months. An 'exceptionally good' test meal commenced impressively with an appetiser of lightly grilled turbot, before a classy terrine of goose liver served with an artichoke and

Peter Street M60 2DS
Map 7: SJ89
Tel: 0161 2363333
Cost: *Alc* £45
Times: 7pm-11pm. Closed Sun
Additional: Sunday L (Trafford Room); ❹ dishes
Seats: 50. Private dining room
Smoking: No-smoking area; air-conditioning

Holiday Inn Crowne Plaza

Accommodation: 303 en suite
Credit cards:

lobster salad with lemon vinaigrette. The main course was breast of duck with a wine sauce of Mercurey and Muscat grapes, although the menu also promises a mixed platter of chargrilled lamb, beef and baby chicken with Choron and Bordelaise sauces as well as steamed lobster with mango. Desserts include a fine crème brûlée. Guests are suitably cosseted by maitre d' Bruno Lucchi and attention to detail is of prime consideration. The wine list has some excellent clarets as well as more modest stuff from the New World.

Directions: City centre, opposite Central Reference Library

MANCHESTER, Little Yang Sing

Dim sum and daytime menus bring the crowds to this refurbished basement restaurant. The cooking shows its Cantonese roots with roast meats, casseroles and one-plate meals; also expect dishes such as steamed scallops, sliced duck with winter bamboo shoots, and lemon and honey chicken. Extensive vegetarian selection.

Credit cards:

Directions: Behind Piccadilly Plaza on the corner of George & Charlotte Street, on Metrolink route

17 George Street M1 4HE
Map 7: SJ89
Tel: 0161 2287722
Fax: 0161 2379257
Chef: Ting Chung Au
Owners: LYS Limited
Cost: Alc £16, fixed-price L £10/D £14. ☺ H/wine £7.95.
Times: Noon- last D 11.15pm. Closed 25 Dec
Additional: Children welcome; 🍴 dishes

MANCHESTER, Market Restaurant

104 High Street
M4 1HQ
Map 7: SJ89
Tel: 0161 8343743
Chefs: Mary-Rose Edgecombe, Paul Mertz, Dawn Wellens
Owners: Peter O'Grady, Anne O'Grady, Mary-Rose Edgecombe
Cost: Alc £22. H/wine £5.95. ☺
Times: D only, 6pm-last D 9.30pm. Closed Sun, Mon, Tue, 1 wk Xmas/Easter, most of Aug
Additional: Children welcome; 🍴 dishes
Seats: 46.
Smoking: Air-conditioning
Credit cards:

Two centuries ago this was the King Richard III pub and, more recently, catered for wholesalers from the nearby Smithfield

Market. Today, it is a distinctively decorated restaurant done out in a style echoing the 1950s, with lemon and dark green paintwork, tables fashioned from sewing machines and a clutter of period bric-à-brac all around. Seasonal menus plunder the globe for a repertoire that embraces everything from Thai sausages, Israeli mixed salad with tahini dressing, and spicy chicken breast stuffed with almonds and cashews to English spiced beef, Yorkshire rhubarb fool and Elizabeth Raffald's Seville orange custard (based on a recipe from the eighteenth-century Mancunian cook and recipe writer). House wine is served in 'old-style milk bottles', and the full list is a useful eclectic slate; also note the menu of Martinis and the fascinating collection of speciality bottled beers from far and wide.

Directions: On the corner of Edge St and High St, close to Craft Village. Nearest Metro station – High St

MANCHESTER, Mash & Air

A fully functioning micro-brewery cuts through the centre of all four floors of this converted mill in the city's Gay Village area. Mash serves designer pizzas from a wood-fired oven; Air is themed in sky and deep midnight blue colours and is more formal, although equally hyper-stylish. The kitchen seems to shoot from the hip – spraying ideas all over the place. A first course of excellent roasted Orkney scallops with crushed Jersey Royals and a creamy, rather bland, lemon confit sauce, was followed, on our inspection, by a first-class roast fillet of sea bass, paired with an ill-conceived cake of ramen noodles, wasabi broth lacking in horseradish bite and good pak choi. Rocket and Parmesan salad was no more than the sum of its two (undressed) parts. Pudding, a good pannacotta, did not try to impress, and as a result succeeded in so doing. Don't go without sampling some of the in-house beers (Mash and Air are both brewing terms).

40 Chorlton Street M1 3HW
Map 7: SJ89
Tel: 0161 6611111
Fax: 0161 6611112
Chef: Jason Atherton
Owner: Oliver Peyton
Cost: £26, fixed-price L £14.50. H/wine £11.50
Times: Noon-last L 2.45pm/6pm-last D 11.30pm. Closed L Sat, L Sun, L during July & Aug, Bhs
Additional: Children welcome; dishes
Seats: 140. Private dining room 14
Smoking: Air conditioning
Credit cards: ▓ ▓ ▓ ▓ ▓

Directions: City centre on corner of Chorlton Street/Canal Street

MANCHESTER,
Moss Nook Restaurant ❀❀

You're likely to see red, when you walk into this boudoir of a restaurant, improbably located alongside the airport runway. Red is the predominant colour – walls, carpet, chairs and drapes, and there's some pretty fine Bordeaux as well. Some might consider the pricey repertoire a little dated – lots of creamy, boozy sauces – and dishes over-garnished, but the restaurant retains a consistently loyal following. Perennial favourites include asparagus wrapped in fresh salmon served hot with béarnaise sauce, although the choice of first course also includes pan-fried chicken livers with crispy bacon and apples flamed with Calvados on a warmed salad. Grilled loin of venison is served pink, with a sultana and a pepper sauce, and a Madeira and truffle sauce makes a luxurious ensemble with fillet of British beef and mousse de foie gras. There are daily fish dishes, as well as a seven-course 'Menu Surprise', although this is by table only.

Ringway Road M22 5WD
Map 7: SJ89
Tel: 0161 4374778
Fax: 0161 4988089
Chef: Kevin Lofthouse
Owners: Derek & Pauline Harrison
Cost: Alc £35, fixed-price L £16.95 (5 courses)/D £29.95 (7 courses). H/wine £9.50
Times: Noon-last L 1.30pm/7pm-last D 9.30 pm. Closed L Sat, Sun, Mon, 2 weeks Xmas
Additional: No children under 12; dishes
Seats: 65
Accommodation: One bedroom cottage
Credit cards: ▓ ▓ ▓ ▓

Directions: Close to Manchester Airport – at junction of Ringway with B5166

MANCHESTER, **New Emperor**

A mix of traditional Chinese decor and modern furnishings appear at this likeable newcomer which faces the main square in Chinatown. It's big, occupying two floors, but always busy with a predominantly Chinese clientele. The menu is extensive, ambitious, and there's a good selection of one-bowl noodle dishes.

Smoking: Air-conditioning. **Credit cards:** ▨ ▨ ▨ ▧ ▣ ▢

Directions: Heart of Chinatown, near Manchester Piccadilly

52-56 George Street
Map 7: SJ89
Tel: 0161 2282883
Fax: 0161 2286620
Chef: Tommy Chan
Owner: Johnny Lee
Cost: *Alc* £14.50, fixed-price D £14.50. ☺ H/wine £9.95.
Times: Last L 1.40pm/D midnight
Additional: Sunday L; Children welcome; ◖ dishes

MANCHESTER, **Pearl City**

Large, first floor restaurant situated in the heart of Manchester's Chinatown. An extensive menu lists a wide range of Cantonese fare – beef dumpling with ginger and spring onion, duck with prawn meat and mushroom sauce – alongside a few Szechuan and Peking dishes.

Directions: In Chinatown

33 George Street M1 4PH
Map 7: SJ89
Tel: 0161 228 7683
Fax: 0161 237 9173
Telephone for further details

MANCHESTER, **Portland Thistle**

Well-equipped city-centre hotel, five minute's walk from Piccadilly station. Pride of place goes to Winston's restaurant where you can expect modern dishes along the lines of pan-fried scallops with Chinese spices and soy vinaigrette, smoked chicken with ratatouille and fillet of brill stuffed with sun-dried tomatoes. Calvados soufflé is a star dessert.

Smoking: Non-smoking area. **Accommodation:** 205 en suite **Credit cards:** ▨ ▨ ▨ ▧ ▣ ▢

Directions: Opposite Piccadilly Gardens

3-5 Portland Street M1 6DP
Map 7: SJ89
Tel: 0161 2283400
Fax: 0161 2286347
Chef: Neil Dominic Riley
Cost: *Alc* £35.50, fixed -price L £16.45/D £20.45. ☺ H/wine £10.50.
Times: Last L 2pm/D 10.30pm. Closed L Sat/Sun, Bhs
Additional: Bar food; Children welcome; ◖ dishes

MANCHESTER,
Simply Heathcotes

Having set the Lancashire scene alight with his cooking at Longridge, Paul Heathcote has now turned his attention to Manchester. This, his latest venture, is a testament to modern chic. Loud primary colours shout from the walls, Phillippe Starck furniture abounds, the floors are polished wood, the ceilings high. The set lunch menu is a best-selling bargain for the likes of warm salad of duck livers, pan-fried silver mullet with buttered spinach and red wine sauce, and glazed rice pudding. The full evening menu, which changes with the seasons, shows many of Heathcote's north-country trademarks – the 'salad of Lancashire cooked breakfast' (black pudding, mushrooms, haricot beans and poached egg), breast of Goosnargh corn-fed chicken with buttered cabbage glazed with Lancashire cheese – but there's also a global input. Brandade of salt cod comes on rounds of toast, baked ruby snapper is served with bouillabaisse and rouille, while chargrilled calves' liver is accompanied by an onion tart, mash and a classy red wine sauce. Desserts call into play such things as warm blueberry muffin with fennel ice cream, and bread-and-butter pudding.

Directions: M62/J17. Restaurant at the top end of Deansgate

Elliot House Jackson Row
151 Deansgate M3 3WD
Map 7: SJ89
Tel: 0161 8353536
Fax: 0161 8353534
Chef: Max Gnoyke
Owner: Paul Heathcote
Cost: *Alc* £22.50, fixed-price L £11.50/D £18.50. ☺ H/wine £10.75.
Times: 11.45am-last L 2.30-m/6pm-last D 11pm. Closed 25-26 Dec, 1 Jan
Additional: Bar meals L; Sunday L; Children welcome; ◖ dishes
Smoking: No pipes & cigars; air conditioning
Credit cards: ▨ ▨ ▨ ▧ ▢

MANCHESTER,
Victoria & Albert Hotel ✿✿

The building is a warehouse conversion on the banks of the
Irwell opposite Granada Studios, and much of the interior has
a 'television' theme. It's a different story, however, in the
Sherlock Holmes restaurant. A new brigade was still settling
when we visited, but the menus promise a lively blend of
French, Mediterranean and New World dishes. To begin there
might be marinated wild salmon with beetroot, five oriental
spices and lime water ice or pithiviers of seared duck livers,
spinach and garlic. Main courses tread a similar path with, say,
baked guinea fowl with a duo of boudin and grilled spring
vegetables or Scotch fillet of beef with roasted mustard kidneys
plus a ragoût of asparagus and salsify. Completing the picture,
you might find coconut and lime cheesecake with cinnamon
biscuit or warm chocolate soup with white chocolate sorbet.
The 100-strong wine list is a useful world-wide slate with a
decent selection of house recommendations.

Directions: Head for city centre and follow signs for Granada
Studio Tours. Hotel is opposite

Water Street M60 9EA
Map 7: SJ89
Tel: 0161 8321188
Fax: 0161 8342484
Chef: Paul Patterson
Cost: *Alc* £30, fixed-price L £20/D
£36. H/wine £15.
Times: Noon-last L 2.30pm/7.30pm-
last D 9.30pm. Closed L Sat, Sun
Additional: Sunday L; Children
welcome; ♦ menu
Seats: 80. Private dining room 30
Smoking: No-smoking area in dining
room; air-conditioning
Accommodation: 156 en suite
Credit cards: ▬ ▬ ▬ ▨ ▣

MANCHESTER, **Yang Sing** ✿✿

Arguably the best of its kind in Manchester and incessantly busy
seven days a week, Yang Sing flies the flag for Cantonese
cooking with bullish assertiveness. No wonder it attracts legions
of Chinese diners, business people and families. Most of the
action takes place in the basement dining room of this converted
'cotton building' and the kitchen maintains its reputation for
high quality dim sum. Recent successes have included carefully
executed spicy meat and cashew nut dumplings, paper-wrapped
king prawns tinged with coriander, and steamed beef balls with
ginger and spring onions. The massive menu also has a mighty
contingent of soups, noodles, casseroles and rice dishes
alongside fried chicken with straw mushrooms, braised duck
with seasonal greens and a curious-sounding (but wonderfully
flavoured) dish of squid in 'cheese sauce'. The Steamboat Room
on the ground floor specialises in 'da bin lao' (a Chinese version
of DIY fondues). Staff are exceptionally helpful.

Directions: Behind Piccadily Plaza. Princess Street is one-way.

34 Princess Street M1 4JY
Map 7: SJ89
Tel: 0161 2362200
Fax: 0161 2365934
Chef: Harry Yeung
Owner: Yang Sing Restaurants Ltd
Cost: H/wine £9.95. ☺
Times: Noon – last D 11pm.
Closed 25 Dec
Additional: Sunday L; Children
welcome; ♦ dishes
Seats: 140.
Main banqueting room 220.
Boardroom 30.
Magnolia Room 70.
Smoking: Air conditioning
Credit cards: ▬ ▬ ▬ ▨ ▣

MANCHESTER AIRPORT,
Bowdon Hotel ✿

See under ALTRINCHAM

MANCHESTER AIRPORT,
Etrop Grange ✿✿

A chauffeured limousine ride from Manchester Airport, Etrop
Grange plays on the fantasy of country living, despite the
proximity to the busiest airport in the North of England.
Nonetheless, the eighteenth-century core has been tastefully
extended into a modern, upmarket hotel, popular with both

Thorley Lane
M90 4EG
Map 7: SJ88
Tel: 0161 4990500
Fax: 0161 4990790
Chef: Hamish Deas
Owner: Regal Hotel Group

Etrop Grange

Cost: Fixed-price L £19.20/ D £29.75.
H/wine £11.50
Times: Noon-last L 2pm/7pm-last D
10pm. Closed L Sat
Additional: Bar Food L; Sunday L;
Children welcome; ♨ dishes
Seats: 60. Private dining room 6-85
Smoking: No-smoking area
Accommodation: 39 en suite
Credit cards:

executive travellers and honeymooners. The cooking is modern British and includes some interesting fish dishes such as ragout of prawns, mussels and crayfish tails with beansprouts, mange-touts and lemongrass sauce. Rillettes of duck with green peppercorns and spiced venison and herb rissoles with sweet and sour leeks number amongst the range of starters, alongside an interesting 60s dinner party update of Manx kipper and malt whisky parfait with toasted French bread. Various alcohol-based sauces include champagne cream sauce with roast breast of chicken, filled with Stilton and walnuts, Port wine sauce with calves' liver, and warm brandy sauce with a rich mincemeat terrine.

Directions: Off M56/J5. At main airport roundabout, take 1st L (to Terminal 2), then 1st R (Thorley Lane), 200yds on R

OLDHAM, Hotel Smokies Park ❀

A business/leisure hotel serving familiar international fare. Expect dishes such as pan-fried sirloin steak with a cream and brandy sauce, potato gnocchi with tomato, basil and fresh anchovies, and bread-crumbed escalope of veal filled with mozzarella and Parma ham.

Accommodation: 50 en suite. **Credit cards:**

Directions: On A627 btw Oldham and Ashton-under-Lyne

Ashton Road OL8 3HX
Map 7: SD90
Tel: 0161 624 3405
Fax: 0161 627 5262
Chef: Kevin Amesbury
Cost: Alc 21.50, fixed-price L
£3.50/D £14.95. ☺ H/wine £9.25.
Times: Last L 2.15pm/D 10.45pm
Additional: Sunday L; Children
welcome; ♨ dishes
Smoking: Air-conditioning

OLDHAM,
The Moorcock Restaurant ❀ NEW

Huddersfield Road Denshaw
OL16 3TG
Map 7: SD90
Tel: 01457 872659
Fax: 0161 6264683
Chef: Nigel Philip Skinkis
Cost: Alc £25, fixed-price D £12.95.
☺ H/wine £6.75
Times: Last L 2pm/last D 9.30pm
(Noon-8pm Sun). Closed Mon
Additional: Bar meals; Sunday L;
Children welcome; ♨ dishes
Smoking: No-smoking area
Credit cards: ▬ ▩ ⚞ €

Enthusiastic cooking from a keen, young chef at his family-owned restaurant, high on the moors. A wide-ranging choice repertoire features baked monkfish in sesame seeds with a warm dressing of tapenade, tomato, butterbeans, basil and garlic, alongside honey roast duck breast with an apple and tarragon sauce. An unusual feature is the choose your own salad dressing list.

Directions: J21/M62 follow signs for Newhey, then left for Denshaw

OLDHAM, White Hart Inn ❀❀

Refurbished with character intact, this 200-year-old inn has a brasserie with exposed stone walls and up-to-date ideas on the menu, and a restaurant geared towards formal dining with more put into presentation and service. Lunch in the brasserie comprised confit of duck leg with Parma ham and rucola salsa, a main course of salmon topped by a scallop with the coral intact, and served on a sweet garlic mash with a well-made sauce of wild mushrooms, and a fine crème brûlée with a thick, rich velvety texture.

Smoking: No smoking in dining room
Accommodation: 5 en suite
Credit cards: ▆▆ ▆▆ ▆▆ ▆▆ ▆

51 Stockport Road OL4 4JJ
Map 7: SD90
Tel: 01457 872566
Fax: 01457 875190
Chef: John Rudden
Owners: Charles Brierley, John Rudden
Cost: *Alc* £23, fixed-price L £8.50/D £22. ☺ H/wine £12.25.
Times: Last L 2.30pm/last D 9.30pm.
Additional: Bar food; Sunday L; Children welcome; ❹ dishes
Seats: 56. Private dining: 22

Directions: Take A669 for Oldham town centre; after going through Grotton turn immediate R after garage at top of hill – inn is 50 yards on L

RAMSBOTTOM,
The Village Restaurant ❀

16 Market Place BL10 9HT
Map 7: SD71
Tel: 01706 825070
Fax: 01706 822005
Chef: Ros Hunter
Owners: Ros Hunter, Chris Johnson
Cost: *Alc* £16.50 (L only), fixed-price L £6.50/D £19.50. ☺ H/wine £9.
Times: Last L 2.30pm/D at 8pm. Closed Sun D, Mon, Tue.
Additional: Sunday L at 1pm
Smoking: No smoking establishment
Credit cards: ▆▆ ▆▆ ▆▆ ▆▆ ▆ ▆

Two converted terraced cottages, dating from the 1820s, are the home of Ramsbottom Victuallers delicatessen and wine shop. In the upstairs restaurant, organic produce features widely, and a typical meal could consist of nettle shoot soup, braised beef steak, and sticky toffee pudding with custard.

Directions: From M66 northbound take J1 and follow signs to Ramsbottom. Restaurant in centre of village

ROCHDALE,

Nutter's ❀❀

Edenfield Road Cheesden Norden
OL12 7TY
Map 7: SD81
Tel/Fax: 01706 50167
Chef: Andrew Nutter
Owners: Rodney, Jean & Andrew
Nutter
Cost: *Alc* £26, fixed price D £29.50
(6 courses). ☺ H/wine £10.50.
Times: Noon-last L 2pm/7pm (6.45pm
Sat) – last D 9.30pm Closed Tue, 1st
2 wks Aug
Additional: Sunday L; Children
welcome; ❧ menu
Seats: 52
Smoking: No smoking in dining room
Credit cards: ▉ ▉ ▇ ▟ ▯

High up on the moors overlooking Lancashire's industrial
conurbations, Nutter's aims to be 'a top-flight restaurant
without the sometimes off-putting hauteur'. This is a family
business: father (an ex-butcher) is front-of-house/sommelier,
mother prepares the bills, daughter usually waits at tables
while Andrew holds sway in the kitchen. What is offered is a
version of Anglo-French cooking based on local supplies and
the world larder. Ravioli of chicken and sweet black bacon is
drizzled with tarragon and lemon grass dressing, beef fillet is
glazed with a wild mushroom and celeriac topping, while
Parmesan-crusted salmon is served on a mussel and coriander
chowder. If there is a signature dish, however, it is probably
crispy wun-tuns filled with Bury black pudding on a 'confetti'
of vegetables. Puddings are equally vibrant: griottine cherry
parfait with chewy pineapple fritters, pear and almond crumble
tart with marzipan ice cream. The list of around 100 wines
looks to France for most of its inspiration.

Directions: On the A680 between Rochdale and Edenfield

STANDISH,

Kilhey Court Hotel ❀❀

Chorley Road Wigan
WN1 2XN
Map 7: SD51
Tel: 01257 472100
Fax: 01257 422401

The quality of ingredients is impressively high at this much-
extended Victorian house, usefully close to the M6. Quality

Aberdeen Angus Cross comes from the impeccable herd of Donald Russell of Inverurie, poultry from Goosnargh and there is a well annotated list of first-class farmhouse cheeses. There are fashionable touches to dishes such as pan-fried fillets of red mullet crusted with rock salt on spaghetti of vegetables with virgin olive oil, risotto of roasted vegetables with sun-dried tomato dressing, and breast of duck with crisp vegetables, peppered white grape and ginger sauce. But there is the confidence, however, to offer classical minestrone soup, assiette of Scottish salmon and grilled whole Dover sole. The dessert menu is a little unbalanced – two pastry and ice-cream dishes, two hot puddings and two chocolate based ones – but maybe it doesn't matter too much when one of them is warm blueberry pie with honey ice cream.

Directions: On A5106 at Worthington.

Chef: Paul Davies
Owner: Kilhey Court Hotel
Cost: Alc £16, fixed-price L £12.95/D £22.95. ☺ H/wine £11.95.
Times: Noon-last L 2.30pm/7pm-last D 9.30pm (10pm Sat). Closed L Sat, D Sun
Additional: Sunday L; Children welcome; ◑ dishes
Seats: 90. Private dining room 12
Smoking: No smoking in dining room; air-conditioning
Accommodation: 62 en suite
Credit cards: ▨ ▨ ▨ ▨ ▨ ▨

HAMPSHIRE

ALRESFORD, Hunters ❀❀

Home-smoked trout with a watercress and horseradish salad and piquant dressing is an appropriate dish to find at this old coaching inn overlooking Broad Street, given the proximity of the Watercress Steam Railway Line. There are plenty of other good things to choose as well, from fillet of pork with spices and couscous on saffron and coriander sauce, to chump of lamb with roast ratatouille and thyme jus. A number of dishes rework old English concepts of spicing and flavouring – terrine of potted duck with apricot and clove chutney, saddle of rabbit with wild mushrooms and almonds on a sage sauce, fillet of beef accompanied by an ox kidney suet pudding with shallots in an ale sauce. There is a daily fish dish chalked on the blackboard, but a menu that features pastry in both vegetarian dishes may need a little re-thinking. For those who can't decide between the triple chocolate terrine or the glazed apple tart with toffee sauce and clotted cream, the assiette allows all the desserts to be sampled in miniature. The wine list has been particularly well selected for quality and value, and there is a decent choice by the glass.

Directions: Off A31 – in centre of Alresford

32 Broad Street SO24 9AQ
Map 4: SU53
Tel/Fax: 01962 732468
Chef: Andrew Sherlock
Owner: Martin Birmingham
Cost: Alc £25, fixed-price D £14.95. ☺ H/wine £8.95.
Times: Noon-last L 2pm/7pm-last D 10pm. Closed D Sun, 1 wk Xmas
Additional: Sunday L (winter only); Children welcome; ◑ dishes
Seats: 30. Private dining room 70
Accommodation: 3 en suite
Credit cards: ▨ ▨ ▨ ▨ ▨

ANDOVER, Esseborne Manor ❀

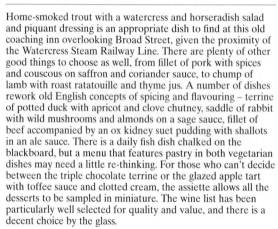

Map 4: SU34
Tel: 01264 736444
Fax: 01264 736725
Chef: Nicholas Watson
Owner: Ian Hamilton
Cost: Alc £25, fixed-price L/D £17. ☺ H/wine £13.
Times: Last L 2.30pm/D 9.30pm.
Additional: Sunday L; No children under 7; ◑ dishes
Smoking: No pipes and cigars
Accommodation: 14 en suite
Credit cards: ▨ ▨ ▨ ▨ ▨ ▨

Charming small country hotel. A delightful atmosphere is backed up by sharp cooking: rustic chicken and leek terrine, grilled fillet of brill on a base of spaghetti vegetables with brown butter, lemon and baby capers, and cinnamon pears with honey ice cream.

Directions: H/way between Andover & Newbury on A343, just N of Hurstbourne Tarrant

BARTON-ON-SEA, Cliff House

Welcoming family-run hotel that sits on top of a cliff overlooking the English Channel. There is always a curry on the menu, reflecting chef/proprietor James Simpson's time in the sub-continent. Otherwise, there is a traditional menu along the lines of lamb chops with mint sauce and grilled gammon with pineapple.

Additional: Bar Food; Sunday L; Children welcome; ❹ dishes
Smoking: No smoking establishment
Accommodation: 9 en suite
Credit cards: ▬ ▒ ▒ 🗀

Marine Drive West BH25 7QL
Map 4: SZ29
Tel: 01425 619333
Fax: 01425 612462
Chefs: James Simpson, Martin Cooper
Owners: James Simpson, Isobel Simpson
Cost: *Alc* from £18.50, fixed-price L £12.95/D £16.95. ☺ H/wine £8.50.
Times: Last L 1.45pm/D 8.45pm. Closed D Sun

Directions: Off A337 between Highcliffe and New Milton on far end of sea road

BASINGSTOKE, Audleys Wood

Alton Road RG25 2JT
Map 4: SU65
Tel: 01256 817555
Fax: 01256 817500
Chef: Paul Sutcliffe
Cost: *Alc* £31, fixed-price L £17.95/D £22. H/wine £13.85
Times: Noon-last L 1.45pm/7pm-last D 9.45pm. Closed L Sat, between 26-31 Dec.
Additional: Sunday lunch; Children welcome; ❹ dishes
Seats: 70.
Accommodation: 71 en suite
Credit cards: ▬ ▒ ▒ 🄳 🗀 🗀

The location of this extended Victorian country house hotel is splendidly bucolic: it overlooks some seven acres of wooded gardens with farmland beyond, but is just a short drive from Basingstoke. The kitchen delivers modern cooking, along the lines of galantine of monkfish and lobster, set amidst colourful leeks à la grecque, complete with saffron dressing, or terrine of rabbit and spiced apricots, served with courgette chutney and toasted walnut bread. This could be followed by grilled fillet of lamb with galette of potato and parsnip with a 'lovely' sweet red onion confit, or roast fillet of sea bass dressed on braised chicory with scallops, mussels, tiger prawns, peeled grapes and a red wine sauce. Puddings are definitely a hit. A hot chocolate pudding was cooked to perfection, served with a smooth, full-flavoured coffee bean sauce and a brandy snap basket of Baileys ice cream. The extensive wine list has some good-value French country wines and a wealth of halves.

Directions: M3/J6 & A339 (Alton). Hotel entrance is on R, one third of mile from Venture Roundabout.

BASINGSTOKE,
Basingstoke Country Hotel ❀

Nately Scures Hook Basingstoke
RG27 9JS
Map 4: SU65
Tel: 01256 764161
Fax: 01256 768341
Chef: Paul Haverson
Owner: Winchester Restaurant
Players Sports Bar & Diner

Popular business hotel with excellent facilities. Modern English cooking in typical main courses of fillet of monkfish with lentils, confit of duck with blackcurrant sauce and pan-fried fillet of Scottish beef with herbed dumplings.

Cost: Alc £20, Fixed-price L £15.25/D £21. ☺ H/wine £11.95.
Times: Last L 1.45pm/D 9.45pm. Closed L Sat, D Sun
Additional: Bar meals; Sunday L; Children welcome; ❀ dishes
Smoking: No cigars or pipes; air-conditioning
Accommodation: 100 en suite
Credit cards: ▰ ▰ ▰ ▰ ▰ ▰

Directions: On A30 between Nately Scures and Hook

BEAULIEU,
Beaulieu Hotel ❀

Beaulieu Road
Lyndhurst SO42 7YQ
Map 4: SU30
Tel: 01703 293344
Fax: 01703 292729
Chef: Phillip Cooper
Owner: Care Hotels plc

Country house hotel in a delightful setting in the heart of the New Forest. The restaurant makes the most of the views. Carefully cooked dishes may include carrot and orange soup, rack of lamb with brandy and apricot jus and a well-presented summer pudding.

Cost: Fixed-price D £18.50. ☺
Times: D only, 7pm-last D 8.45pm
Additional: Children welcome; ❀ dishes
Smoking: No smoking in dining room
Accommodation: 18 en suite
Credit cards: ▰ ▰ ▰ ▰ ▰ ▰

Directions: On the B3056 between Lyndhurst and Beaulieu, opposite railway station

BEAULIEU,
Montague Arms Hotel ❀❀

Palace Lane
Map 4: SU30
Tel: 01590 612324
Fax: 01590 612188
Telephone for details

Park alongside the donkeys and cows which graze around this charming, creeper-clad hotel. Inside, good locally sourced ingredients are used in a sound range of imaginative dishes. Bread is home-made and exceptionally good, and nibbles and petits fours all show serious intent. Rabbit confit with aubergine chips and filo, and red mullet and mushroom pithiviers with beurre blanc give an idea of the kitchen's range.

Directions: From Southampton take A326 (Fawley), follow signs to Beaulieu (B3054). The hotel is on L as you enter village

BROCKENHURST,
Carey's Manor ❀

Brockenhurst SO42 7RH
Map 4: SU30
Tel: 01590 623551
Fax: 01590 622799
Chef: Kevin Dorrington
Owner: Greenclose Ltd

An elegant country house hotel set in the heart of the New Forest. The restaurant – in yellows, golds and terracottas – offers a wide range of choices, either from the chargrill, vegetarian options, or classic dishes such as saddle of rabbit with Cointreau and juniper sauce.

Directions: M27/J1, follow signs for Lyndhurst and Lymington A337. Railway station 5 minutes from hotel

Carey's Manor

Cost: *Alc* £30, fixed-price L £13.75/D £21.95. ☺ H/wine £9.95.
Times: Last L 1.45pm/D 9.45pm
Additional: Sunday L; No children under 7; ♨ dishes
Smoking: No smoking in dining room
Accommodation: 79 en suite
Credit cards: 🔲 🔲 🔲 🔲 🔲 🔲

BROCKENHURST,

Forest Park Hotel ❀❀

NEW

Walkers and horsy types will find plenty to do around this informally run hotel in the heart of the New Forest. There are riding stables next door as well as an outdoor pool and sauna in the garden. The dining room has pleasant views of the grounds and here you can enjoy some capably prepared dishes from the set dinner menu. A recent inspection began well with a fish roulade wrapped around saffron mousse with a layer of spinach in between – which looked much like a Japanese sushi roll. The main course was fanned duck breast with lime and ginger topped with bean sprouts, while dessert consisted of bitter chocolate tart with a little pool of Grand Marnier sauce. Canapés and home-made petits fours are much appreciated.

Directions: From A337 to Brockenhurst turn into Meerut Road, follow road through Waters Green; at T junction turn R into Rhinefield Road

Rhinefield Road SO42 7ZG
Map 4: SU30
Tel: 01590 622844
Fax: 01590 623948
Chef: Matt Sherratt
Owner: Robin Collins
Cost: *Alc* £22, fixed-price L £12/ D £20. ☺ H/wine £10.
Times: Noon-last L 1.45pm/7pm-last D 9.30pm
Additional: Bar meals; Sunday L; Children welcome
Seats: 80. Private dining room 20
Smoking: No smoking in dining room
Accommodation: 38 en suite
Credit cards: 🔲 🔲 🔲 🔲 🔲

BROCKENHURST,

New Park Manor ❀❀

Lyndhurst Road SO42 7QH
Map 4: SU30
Tel: 01590 623467
Fax: 01590 622268
Chef: Matthew Tilt

Built in the sixteenth century and used as a hunting lodge by King Charles II, this is now a country hotel set in parkland

with its own equestrian centre. Meals are served in the oak-beamed Stag Head restaurant, which has its own terrace overlooking the gardens. The kitchen cooks to a menu of classic, French-based dishes along the lines of crepinette of beef and chicken mousse surrounded by wild mushrooms, carpaccio of venison with deep-fried celeriac and balsamic vinaigrette and 'diamonds' of sea bass with deep-fried fennel. Among the main courses you might find loin of lamb marinated in garlic and served en croûte, suprême of duck smoked over oak and tobacco, and sautéed king scallops served in a crisp pastry shell. For those who want to indulge, there's also a lavish 'menu gourmand' of chef's specialities. France is the main contender on the list of around 90 wines.

Directions: Turn of the A337 between Lyndhurst and Brockenhurst and follow the hotel signs.

Owner: Van Gelderen family
Cost: *Alc* £32.50, fixed-price L £17.50/D £29.50 (4 courses). ☺ H/wine £16.
Times: 12.30-last L 1.45pm/7pm-last D 9pm
Additional: Sunday L; No children under 7; ◑ dishes
Seats: 40. Private dining rooms 15-75
Smoking: No smoking in dining room
Accommodation: 21 en suite
Credit cards: 🔲 🔲 🔲 🔲 🔲 🔲

BROCKENHURST,

Le Poussin Restaurant ❀❀❀

Homage to the noble fowl is duly paid in the form of a variety of pictures hanging on the white walls of this intimate little no smoking restaurant. Chicken with wild mushrooms in a cream and herb sauce may also appear on the lunch menu, although the evening *carte* tends to more sophisticated variations such as creamed chicken sausage spiked with wild mushrooms served on wild rice. The use of fungi in both dishes is no coincidence – Alex Aitken has over the years searched for and located up to thirty different species of wild edible fungi in the nearby woods, all of which appear with seasonal regularity on the menus. The New Forest also provides game for dishes such as salad of chargrilled wood pigeon, roasted saddle of roe deer, and rabbit stuffed with morel mushrooms. Local fish and seafood may include scallops dived for by Alex himself, salmon from the Itchen and Test rivers, and crayfish trapped in local inland waters. The marshes and sea-shore also provide delicacies such as samphire, sea-beet, sea-kale and gulls' eggs. Menus change daily, and there are regular gourmet evenings, but all the cooking is distinguished by a belief that if the quality of the ingredients is good enough, things are best kept simple. A twice-baked cheese soufflé was superbly light in texture, pronounced in flavour, whilst a fillet of beautifully fresh halibut, sautéed and served on top of a bed of crunchy, bright green spring greens with butter sauce, also lived up well to its promise. Whilst dishes may have several elements, combinations are uncluttered – a trio of meats comprises rare fillet of beef, venison and pink lamb and is served with a reduced red wine sauce; oak smoked haddock comes on a potato salad topped with a soft poached egg. Desserts have a strong fruit bias – a warm rhubarb tart comes with pink rhubarb ice cream, hot soufflé of passionfruit is enhanced by a passionfruit sauce. The kitchen is astonishingly hard-working, marinating their own olives, and baking several varieties of bread rolls. Lunch and dinner are fixed price and are excellent value; as a result, booking is advised.

   Not surprisingly the wine list is predominantly French, with all European and New World wines listed under a section headed 'wines from other countries'. There is a good list of halves with over 30 on offer. Eight house wine are all priced under £12.50, are available by the glass, and offer good, easy drinking. Although most wines fall into the £20-£30 bracket, there is plenty of choice under £20.

The Courtyard Brookley Road SO42 7RB
Map 4: SU30
Tel: 01590 623063
Fax: 01590 622912
Chef: Alexander Aitken
Owners: Aitken Family
Cost: Fixed-price L £15 (2 courses)/D £22.50 (2 courses). H/wine £11
Times: Noon-last L 2pm/7pm-last D 10pm. Closed Mon, Tue
Additional: Sunday L; Children welcome; ◑ dishes
Seats: 24
Smoking: No smoking in dining room
Credit cards: 🔲 🔲 🔲 🔲

Signature dishes: Rabbit and wild mushroom sausage on pearl barley risotto; River Itchen salmon with marsh samphire and wild sorrel sauce; tagliatelle with wild New Forest mushrooms; haunch of venison braised in red wine like ox tail.

Directions: Village centre through an archway between two shops

BROCKENHURST,
Rhinefield House

Rhinefield Road SO42 7QB
Map 4: SU30
Tel: 01590 622922
Fax: 01590 622800
Owners: Virgin Hotels Ltd
Cost: *Alc* £35, fixed-price L £15.95/D £23.50 (4 courses). ☺
H/wine £12.50.
Times: Last L 2pm/last D 10pm
Additional: Bar food; Sunday L; Children welcome; ♨ dishes
Smoking: No smoking in dining room
Accommodation: 34 en suite
Credit cards: ■ ■ ■ ■ ■

A splendid mock-Elizabethan mansion deep in the heart of the New Forest. Popular for weddings and its 'murder mystery' weekends, Rhinefield House also enjoys a reputation for its sound Anglo/French cooking. Typical dishes include grilled trout with almonds and grapes, asparagus tortellini, and braised pheasant with port wine jus.

Directions: From M27/J1 follow signs to Lyndhurst, then take A35 to Christchurch. After 3 miles turn L to Rhinefield. Hotel approx 2 miles on R

BROCKENHURST,
Thatched Cottage ✿✿

Food is taken very seriously here, with three or four chefs, including Michiyo Matysik, on view in the kitchen cooking for just seven tables. The effort and commitment are obvious, sourcing is a strong point with specialist suppliers credited on the menu. A winter inspection meal produced one dish that was pronounced inspired – a simple puff pastry square topped with pear and melted slices of Irish Milleen cheese served with a pile of grapes and berries on the side. Of other dishes from the 'Taste of the New Forest' menu came venison consommé with wild mushrooms with a nice hint of real truffle aroma; a lobster dish with wild mushroom 'ragout'; rosemary, garlic and cinnamon crust on lamb; a good gin and pink grapefruit granité; three different kinds of home-made bread and simply steamed vegetables.

16 Brookley Road SO42 7RR
Map 4: SU30
Tel: 01590 623090
Fax: 01590 623479
Chef: Michiyo Matysik
Owners: Family Matysik
Cost: *Alc* £20. Fixed-price D £28.50. H/wine £12.50
Times: 12.30pm-last L 2pm/7.30pm-last D 9.30pm. Closed D Sun, Mon, Jan
Additional: L snacks; Sunday L; No children under 12
Seats: 20
Smoking: No smoking in dining room
Accommodation: 5 en suite
Credit cards: ■ ■ ■ ■

Directions: On A337 in Brockenhurst, turning before level crossing

BROCKENHURST,
Whitley Ridge Hotel ✿✿

Beaulieu Road SO4 7QL
Map 4: SU30
Tel: 01590 622354
Fax: 01590 622856
Chef: Russell Wootten
Owners: Mr & Mrs R Law
Cost: *Alc* £23, fixed-price D £20. ☺
H/wine £9.50.
Times: D only, 6.30pm-9pm.
Additional: Bar food L; Sunday L only
(Noon-2pm); Children welcome;
☻ dishes
Seats: 36. Private dining room 20
Smoking: No smoking in dining room
Accommodation: 14 en suite
Credit cards: 💳 💳 💳 💳 💳 💳

Built as a royal hunting lodge in the late eighteenth century,
but extended in Victorian times, wisteria-clad Whitley Ridge
now offers much in the way of home comforts. The restaurant
is done out in classical style with a large open fireplace and a
big bay window and terrace overlooking the secluded grounds.
The kitchen works to a well balanced menu that provides
plenty of interest without resorting to gimmickry. Starters
might include home-smoked duck with blackberry purée and
home-cured gravlax with lime salsa, while main courses could
range from Scotch fillet of beef with caramelised onion and
mushroom sauce to pan-fried fillet of sea bass 'Lymington'
(served with a fresh tomato and chervil sauce garnished with
black olives). Desserts are mostly textbook offerings such as
crème brûlée, French apple tart with Calvados custard and
souffléd chocolate pancakes. Plenty of dependable names
appear on the thoughtfully assembled wine list.

Directions: A337 (from Lyndhurst) turn L towards Beaulieu on
B3055, approx 1 mile.

BROOK, **Bell Inn** ✿

Lyndhurst SO43 7HE
Map 4: SU21
Tel: 01703 812214
Fax: 01703 813958
Chef: Malcolm Lugg
Owner: Brook Enterprises
Cost: *Alc* £15, fixed price D £24. ☺
H/wine £11.50.
Times: D 7.30pm-9.30pm
Additional: Bar L; Sunday L
(12.30pm-2.30pm)
Smoking: No smoking in dining room
Accommodation: 25 en suite
Credit cards: 💳 💳 💳 💳 💳 💳

Directions: M27/J1 (Cadnam) 3rd exit
onto B3078, signed Brook, 0.5 mile
on right

*Oak-beamed dining room of popular hotel and golf club where
local ingredients feature in modern dishes such as roast gurnard with
baked garlic and provençale sauce and delice of brill with samphire
and lemon beurre blanc. Flambéed peppered steak and crêpes
suzette add a retro touch to the menu.*

BUCKLERS HARD,

Master Builders House Hotel

Once the home of the master shipbuilder who oversaw the construction of the Navy's fleet during the great age of sail, this eighteenth-century building now features a light airy restaurant overlooking the Beaulieu River. Sound cooking at a March meal included mussels with tomato coulis, and a raspberry crème brûlée.

Accommodation: 23 en suite. **Credit cards:** ▄▄ ▒▒ ▄▄ ➵ ⊡ ⌐

Directions: Bucklers Hard is signposted from Beaulieu

Beaulieu SO42 7XB
Map 4: SU40
Tel: 01590 616253
Chef: Simon Berry
Owner: Lord Montagu of Beaulieu
Cost: *Alc* £20, fixed-price L/D £16. ☺
H/wine £9.95.
Times: Last L 2pm/D 9.30pm
Additional: Sunday L; Bar meals;
Children welcome; ◑ dishes
Smoking: No smoking in dining room

DENMEAD,

Barnard's Restaurant

There's a cosy intimacy about David and Sandie Barnard's likeable little restaurant and it makes an appropriately domestic setting for food that follows a well-tried path. Fresh ingredients are deployed judiciously, both on the *carte* and the good-value set menus. Typical starters might include a layered terrine of chicken and leeks or smoked salmon with scrambled eggs, while main courses could range from braised leg of lamb steak scented with rosemary and garlic or baked suprême of chicken stuffed with lobster served with a creamy lobster sauce spiked with tomato and cognac, to a daily fresh fish dish. Desserts are mostly stalwarts such as Marsala-soaked trifle, pancakes filled with chocolate custard and black cherries served on an Amaretto sauce, or glazed pineapple with coconut ice cream. The serviceable wine list has plenty of sound drinking at affordable prices.

Directions: Opposite village church, from A3M/J3/B2150 (Waterlooville)

Hambledon Road PO7 6NU
Map 4: SU61
Tel/Fax: 01705 257788
Chef: David Barnard
Owners: David & Sandie Barnard
Cost: *Alc* £12.50, fixed-price L
£8.50/D £15 (2 courses). ☺
H/wine £9.
Times: Noon-last L 1.45pm/7pm-last
D 9.45pm. Closed L Sat, Sun, Mon,
1 wk Xmas, 1 wk Aug
Additional: Bar meals L; Children
welcome; ◑ dishes
Seats: 40. Private dining room 34
Smoking: No-smoking area
Credit cards: ▄▄ ▒▒ ▄▄ ➵ ⊡ ⌐

EMSWORTH, **Julies**

Julies occupies a 300-year-old fisherman's cottage a short stroll from the harbour, and inside it sustains the domestic mood with old beams and warm pink colour schemes. The setting is homespun, but the kitchen works to a menu with plenty of invigorating touches. An enjoyable inspection meal in September began in complex style with steamed chive pancake filled with grilled chicken bound in a celeriac mousse spiced with cumin, all served on a green pepper and vodka sauce. A lot was happening in the main course too; note excellent crispy Aylesbury duck, steamed then pan-fried and served with creamy wild mushroom gnocchi and a honeyed sauce spiked with tayberries. At other times of the year you might find timbale of skate and Jerusalem artichoke with horseradish and mango compote, and local hare with rhubarb, caramelised red onion and filo pastry. Desserts range from spotted Dick and soufflés to chocolate roulade with a zesty pink grapefruit sauce. Around 40 well spread wines include seven house selections by the glass.

Directions: At Emsworth town centre, 1st R after Emsworth Square – South Street. Go l00 yds down towards the Quay. Restaurant on L facing main car park.

30 South Street PO10 7EH
Map 4: SU70
Tel: 01243 377914
Chef: Kevin Hartley
Owners: Mr & Mrs K Hartley
Cost: *Alc* £27.30, fixed-price L&D
£15.95. ☺ H/wine £8.95.
Times: Noon-last L 1.45pm/7pm-last
D 9.15pm. Closed L Sat, Sun, Mon,
2 wks Jan
Additional: Children welcome;
◑ dishes
Seats: 28. Private dining room 18
Credit cards: ▄▄ ▒▒ ▄▄ ➵

EMSWORTH, Spencers 🏵🏵

Real gas lighting and well-filled bookshelves give this cosy, first-floor restaurant bags of atmosphere. Staff are both friendly and efficient, and ply you with tasty, warm appetisers and freshly baked rolls. The monthly changing, modern French menu follows a similar format, with a choice of two, three or four courses. As well as a daily fish dish, there may be roast breast of duck with Puy lentils and braised red cabbage, or sautéed breast of pheasant wrapped in Parma ham together with the leg braised in red wine and apricots. Grills include calves' liver with lyonnaise sauce, and baby lamb cutlets served with lamb and Madeira sauce. Both starters and desserts include ever-popular dishes such as salmon gravad lax, rillettes of home-smoked trout, apple crumble and fresh fruit Pavlova. An appealing optional middle course might be baked black pudding and Irish champ.

36 North Street PO10 7DG
Map 4: SU70
Tel/Fax: 01243 372744
Chef: Denis Spencer
Owners: Denis & Lesley Spencer
Cost: Fixed-price D £22. ☺
H/wine £9.95.
Times: D only, 7.30pm-last D
10.30pm. Closed Sun, Mon, 25-26
Dec
Additional: No children under 12;
𝄐 dishes
Seats: 34. Private dining room 10
Credit cards: 💳 💳 💳 💳 💳 💳

Directions: Following A259 to Emsworth roundabout, turn L into North Street, restaurant is 0.5 mile on left.

EMSWORTH, 36 On The Quay 🏵🏵🏵

47 South Street PO10 7EG
Map 4: SU70
Tel: 01243 375592
Fax: 01243 375593
Chef: Ramon Farthing
Owners: Ramon & Karen Farthing
Cost: Fixed-price L £19/D £29.95
(4 courses). H/wine £13.50
Times: Noon-last L 1.45pm/7pm-last
D 9.45pm. Closed L Sat, Sun, L Mon,
5-18 Jan, 5-11 Oct
Additional: 𝄐 dishes
Seats: 40. Private dining room 10
Smoking: No-smoking area; no pipes
and cigars in dining room
Credit cards: 💳 💳 💳 💳 💳 💳

Chef Ramon Farthing (ex Harveys of Bristol) has now fully taken over the helm, and cooks to a consistently high standard with a single-minded formula that is all his own. The menu hints at the serious intent, and the cheese straws that sharpened the appetite for a winter's meal, along with an appetiser of skate, potato and leek terrine wrapped in Savoy cabbage with gazpacho 'sauce', were an impressive introduction. This is ambitious cooking, with the confidence to handle ingredients well. Creamed white haricot bean soup with truffle oil and chive cream was a sound concept, and was followed by a well-made tortellini of duck confit with peach vinegar sauce and stir-fry vegetable garnish. The main course, sea bass with creamed celeriac and fennel, was the star of the meal, featuring lovely fresh fish, as well as leeks, chanterelle mushrooms, potato and an inspired 'light roast chicken reduction'. The sound and satisfying meal was rounded off by a full-flavoured hot passion fruit soufflé, unusually but effectively contrasted with a cold, creamy chocolate sauce. The wine list is overwhelmingly francophile with plenty of mature class in red Bordeaux, less in Burgundy. The 'Rest of the World' selection verges on the token.

Directions: Last building on R in South Street, which runs from the Square in the centre of Emsworth

EVERSLEY,
The New Mill ◈◈

New Mill Road
RG27 0RA
Map 4: SU76
Tel: 0118 973277
Fax: 0118 9328780
Chef: Simon Smith
Owners: New Mill Restaurant Ltd
Cost: *Alc* £32, fixed-price L £10/D
£19.50. ☺ H/wine £9.95.
Times: Noon-last L 2pm/7pm-last D
10pm (Sun noon-9pm)
Additional: Grill Room L&D; Sunday
L, Children welcome; ◐ dishes
Seats: 80. Private dining rooms 40/20
Smoking: No pipes or cigars
Credit cards: ▬ ▬ ▬ ▼ ▣ ▫

The New Mill is actually very old, dating back to the sixteenth century, but it certainly keeps abreast of the times with a calendar-full programme of special events and a regular newsletter. The Riverside Restaurant looks out over the River Blackwater, and is the place for both upbeat modern British cooking such as Cajun halibut with mango, ginger and coriander salsa, and green lip mussels with ginger, lime, lemon grass and chillies, and classic sautéed lamb's kidneys in Madeira and sherry vinegar with cream and chiffonade of spinach, and roast marinated rump of lamb with dauphinoise potatoes and whole roast garlic. The chargrill comes into its own with fillet of beef on a garlic croûton and mustard glaze, and suprême of chicken with sorrel mayonnaise. There is more informal bistro eating in the Grill Room ('Desperate Dan's' sausage and mash with onion gravy is a firm favourite), and on the newly constructed terrace in summer.

Directions: From Eversley take A327 (Reading), cross river, turn L at cross roads into New Mill Road

FAIR OAK,
Noorani Restaurant ◈

Popular neighbourhood Asian restaurant decorated in grand style. An extensive menu offers a range of interesting dishes, including duck and imported fish such as ayre and boal. Good tandoori dishes, Parsi specialities and notable buffet lunches on Sundays and Mondays. Vegetarians are well catered for.

465 Fair Oak Road Eastleigh
Map 4: SU41
Tel: 01703 601901/3
Chef: K Miah, R Miah
Owner: Mrs M Meah, Mrs C Miah
Cost: *Alc* £15. H/wine £7.50. ☺
Times: Last L 2pm/last D 11.30pm.
Closed 25-26 Dec

Additional: Sunday L; Children welcome; ◐ dishes
Smoking: No-smoking area; air-conditioning
Credit cards: ▬ ▬ ▬ ▼ ▫

Directions: In village square opposite the war memorial

FAREHAM, **Lysses House Hotel**

Chargrilled meat and fish are a feature of the menu at this Grade II listed Georgian hotel. More elaborate dishes include the likes of grilled duck breast sliced and 'mingled' with filo pastry discs and roasted beetroot coated with a port wine sauce.

Additional: Bar Food; Children welcome; 🍴 dishes
Smoking: No smoking in dining room; air-conditioning
Accommodation: 21 en suite
Credit cards: ▨ ▨ ▨ ▨ ▨

Directions: From M27 exit 11 follow signs to Fareham town centre; hotel is at top of High Street

51 High Street PO16 7BQ
Map 4: SU50
Tel: 01329 822622
Fax: 01329 822762
Chef: Clive Wright
Cost: Alc £22.50, fixed-price L
£13.95/D £18.50. ☺ H/wine £9.35
Times: Last L 1.45pm/D 9.45pm.
Closed L Sat, Sun, Bhs, 24 Dec-2 Jan

FAREHAM, **Solent Hotel**

Although purpose-built and close to the motorway, there is an air of peaceful seclusion, helped by the surrounding mature trees and greenery – hence the name Woodlands restaurant. As well as chargrilled steaks and tuna, the reliable choice includes pan-fried salmon, roast fillet of cod and peppered tournedos of beef.

Additional: Bar food; Sunday L; Children welcome; 🍴 dishes
Smoking: No smoking in dining room; air-conditioning
Accommodation: 90 en suite
Credit cards: ▨ ▨ ▨ ▨ ▨

Directions: From M27/J9, follow signs to Solent Business Park & Whiteley

Solent Business Park Rookery Avenue
Whiteley PO15 7AJ
Map 4: SU50
Tel: 01489 880000
Fax: 01489 880007
Chef: Chris Taylor
Owners: Shire Inns Ltd
Times: Last L 1.45pm/last D 9.45pm.
Closed L Sat

FORDINGBRIDGE, **Ashburn Hotel**

Family-run hotel in a rural setting. Local produce is featured in dishes such as potted fresh salmon with fresh asparagus with French beans and smoked bacon, honey-roasted duck with port and honey sauce, or escalope of veal with a tomato and basil sauce.

Additional: Bar food; Sunday L; Children welcome; 🍴 dishes
Smoking: No smoking in dining room
Accommodation: 23 en suite
Credit cards: ▨ ▨ ▨ ▨ ▨

Directions: On the B3078

Damerham Road SP6 1JP
Map 4: SU11
Tel: 01425 652060
Fax: 01425 652150
Chefs: Geff Marsh, Mike Smith
Owners: Garry & Terri Robson
Cost: Alc £25, fixed-price D £15. ☺
H/wine £8.15.
Times: Last L 2pm/last D 9.30pm

FORDINGBRIDGE, **Hour Glass** ✺

Anglo-French cooking in a pretty, beamed thatched cottage. Breast of pigeon on a bed of lardons, potato and black pudding with a red wine sauce, pavé of turbot with scallops on black linguine, and hock of lamb, slow-braised for eight hours with rosemary, tomatoes and garlic, are amongst a choice of carefully prepared dishes.

Additional: Sunday L; No children under 5; 🍴 dishes
Smoking: No-smoking area
Credit cards: ▨ ▨ ▨

Directions: On main A338 (Salisbury/Ringwood road) just outside Fordingbridge

Burgate SP6 1LX
Map 4: SU11
Tel: 01425 652348
Chef: John Collins
Owners: John & Jean Collins
Cost: Fixed-price L £9.95/£11.95/D
£18.95. ☺ H/wine £9.95.
Times: Last L 1.45pm/D 9.30pm.
Closed D Sun, Mon, 1 wk Feb, 2 wks
Nov

FORDINGBRIDGE,

Lions Court Restaurant

A popular New Forest restaurant housed in an attractive seventeenth-century building complete with low beamed ceilings. The atmosphere is relaxed and informal, with Christine Williams providing friendly and attentive service. In the kitchen, Danny Wilson prepares simple but imaginative dishes with a good sense of balance and flavour. Typical starters include sautéed forest mushrooms and Somerset brie, folded in a crisp filo pastry parcel and served with a creamy shallot sauce, and chicken terrine with fresh walnut and olive rolls. Recommended main courses include a well-prepared dish of sliced fillet of Scottish beef, topped with watercress purée and served with mushroom jus, and a rich white and dark chocolate terrine. The short wine list features a number of reasonably-priced popular wines, with several good bottles from the New World.

29 The High Street SP6 1AS
Map 4: SU11
Tel: 01425 652006
Fax: 01425 657946
Chef: Daniel Wilson
Owners: Daniel Wilson, Christine Williams
Telephone for details

Directions: On A338, town centre, half way up High Street

FORDINGBRIDGE,

The Three Lions

At first glance, this converted Victorian farmhouse might seem like a village pub, but inside it tells a different story. The decor might be described as 'piney' with lots of soft touches, but it's the food that is the real attraction. Menus are written on blackboards that are hauled around from table to table in the bar, and the choice varies from day to day. Mike Womersley's cooking is based on a natural understanding of raw materials and local produce; his strength is to treat them simply, with energy, enthusiasm and respect. A recent inspection showed that fish is undoubtedly his forte. A starter of 'frighteningly fresh' scallops, lightly seared and served on dressed leaves tinged with sesame oil, lemon grass, coriander and a hint of chilli was reckoned to be a great dish. After that, our inspector was dazzled by the freshest and tastiest piece of brill he had ever eaten, steamed and served with a lemon beurre blanc scented with tarragon and set off with some sautéed New Forest fungi. Other choices from a typical day's offerings might be honey and spiced duck with quince and pears, and suprême of farm chicken with chanterelles. Desserts are real classics: superb chocolate sponge pudding with a liquid chocolate centre served with spot-on vanilla ice cream, and crème brûlée with star-anise bananas. A well chosen wine list with a front page of 16 'House Selection' bins offering prices under £20 – nine are served by the glass. The main section also has some good value – Ch du Vieux Parc Corbières (£14.50) is a rosé that can cope with a variety of dishes; Ch Picque Caillou won't disappoint at £22.50.

Stuckton SP6 2HF
Map 4: SU11
Tel: 01425 652489
Fax: 01425 656144
Chef: Michael Womersley
Owners: JM & SJ Womersley
Cost: *Alc* L £27, fixed-price L £13.50. ☺
Times: Noon-last L 2pm/7pm-last D 10pm.
Additional: Sunday L; Children welcome; ⓸ dishes
Seats: 60
Smoking: No smoking in dining room
Accommodation: 3 en suite
Credit cards: ▬ ▒ ▚ ⌐

Directions: In the village of Stuckton, near Fordingbridge, half a mile off the A338

HEDGE END,
Botleigh Grange Hotel ❀❀

Southampton
SO30 2GA
Map 4: SU41
Tel: 01489 787700
Fax: 01489 788535
Chef: Edward Denovan
Cost: *Alc* £22 Fixed price L £13.95/D
£18.50. ☺ H/wine £9.50.
Times: Noon-last L 2pm/7pm-last D
10pm. Closed L Sat
Additional: Bar food L; Sunday L;
No children under 6 months;
❀ dishes
Seats: 70. Private dining room 20
Smoking: No smoking in dining room
Accommodation: 41 en suite
Credit cards: ▉ ▉ ▉ ▉ ▉ ▉

The magnificent glass-domed restaurant looks out over
gardens and lakes. Pre-dinner drinks are served in the
adjoining wood-panelled cocktail lounge, along with a selection
of canapés. The cooking is skilful, and concerned enough about
the quality of the ingredients to list the name of local suppliers
at the end of the *carte*. The style is modern English-cum-
French, and adopts a pick-and-mix approach to contemporary
techniques: pan-fried smoked and fresh salmon with sarladaise
potato and horseradish cappuccino sauce, and tranche of
calves' liver with a 'cassoulet' sauce, Parma ham, button onions
and spaghetti of carrot are amongst a repertoire that also
includes brochette of monkfish with honey and sesame seeds,
couscous and ginger sauce, and braised shank of lamb in
orange, juniper and rosemary. Leave room for the baked
chocolate and hazelnut fondant with coffee ice cream.

Directions: On A334, 1.5 miles from M27 junc 7

HIGHCLERE,
Hollington Country House ❀❀

Woolton Hill Newbury
RG20 9XA
Map 4: SU46
Tel: 01635 255100
Fax: 01635 255075
Chef: Simon Rogan
Owners: Mr & Mrs John Guy

Hollington House is now owned and run in great style by
Australians, John and Penny Guy. Meals are served in the
grand oak-panelled dining room with views over the
countryside and gardens designed by Gertrude Jekyll. The high

point of a test meal was a large ball of superbly presented sweetbreads wrapped in Parma ham and set on an artichoke base with the leaves arranged around like the petals of a flower, accompanied by an 'ambrosia-like' turnip soubise. The menu is dominated by elaborate French dishes: terrine of pork knuckle with foie gras, boudin noir and sauce genoise, and roast John Dory 'a la royale' with a cannelloni of leeks, braised fennel and champagne velouté. Desserts are the likes of black cherry soufflé with Kirsch on a raspberry sabayon. The wine list begins in Australia and 29 impressive pages later it finally migrates as far as Tasmania. This is clearly a labour of love. One might have thought that offerings from the rest of the world might be something of an afterthought, but this is far from the case with good names and vintages on offer throughout.

Directions: Take A343 (Andover) from Newbury. Follow signs for Hollington Herb Garden, hotel is next door.

Cost: Alc £39, fixed-price L £19. H/wine £16.
Times: Noon-2pm/7pm-9.30pm
Additional: Sunday L; Children welcome; ⑨ dishes
Seats: 50. Private dining room 15
Smoking: No pipes & cigars; air-conditioning
Accommodation: 20 en suite
Credit cards: ▥ ▦ ▧ ▨ ▩

LIPHOOK,

Nippon-Kan at Old Thorns

Griggs Green GU30 7PE
Map 4: SU83
Tel: 01428 724555
Fax: 01428 725036
Chef: T Suzuki
Owner: London Kosaido Co Ltd
Cost: Alc £28, fixed-price L from £25/D £29. H/wine £10.50
Times: Noon-last L 2pm/7pm-last D 9pm. Closed 2nd wk Jan
Additional: Children welcome; ⑨ dishes
Seats: 36. Private dining room 96
Smoking: No pipes & cigars
Accommodation: 33 en suite
Credit cards: ▥ ▦ ▧ ▨ ▩ ▣

The combination of an 18-hole golf course and authentic Japanese cuisine is not such an unusual pairing at this smartly presented country hotel. A European restaurant (see entry below) offers a more conventional alternative. However, in the simple, minimalist decor of the Nippon-Kan, traditionally dressed waiting staff are happy to guide guests through a menu that specialises in teppan-yaki cooking, although the numerous set menus help the uncertain. A typical meal could take in appetisers of yakitori (chicken on a bamboo skewer with yakitori sauce), dobinmushi (clear soup), assorted sashimi, tonkatsu (pork cutlet), tempura of prawn and vegetables, and Japanese green tea-flavoured ice cream for dessert.

Directions: Approx 500 yds from Griggs Green exit off A3

LIPHOOK, Old Thorns Hotel

The much-extended hotel was once a fourteenth-century farmhouse, and original beams can still be seen in the lounge. The restaurant, however, is light, airy and thoroughly modern, and looks out over the 18-hole golf course. The Thorns Restaurant works hard to deliver up-to-the-minute dishes of

Griggs Green GU30 7PE
Map 4: SU83
Tel: 01428 724555
Fax: 01428 725036
Chef: Geoff Sutton
Owner: London Kosaido Co Ltd
Cost: Alc £28. H/wine £10.50 ☺

Old Thorns Hotel

Times: 12.15pm-last L 4pm/7pm-last D 9pm. Closed D Sun
Additional: Bar food L; Sunday L; Children welcome; ⊕ dishes
Seats: 45. Private dining rooms 96 & 40
Smoking: No pipes or cigars; air-conditioning
Accommodation: 33 en suite
Credit cards: ▄▄ ▄▄ ▄▄ ▄▄ ▄▄ ▄▄

orange-scented smoked chicken and celeriac with shredded chicory in a pine nut and balsamic dressing, or reworkings of traditional English classics such as leek, potato and mozzarella hot-pot, and strip of beef-tail fillet sautéed with flat mushrooms and chopped tomato in a sauce of mignonette pepper, onions and brown ale and served with bubble and squeak. Deep-fried boneless salmon cutlets on a bed of leek, white radish and carrot, glazed with honey, soy sauce and lemon, and fillet of codling baked in vegetable korma with prawns and served with 'pilaff' rice and poppadums, reflects the global outlook of a hotel that also includes a Japanese restaurant (see entry above for Nippon-Kan).

Directions: Approx 500 yds from Griggs Green exit off A3

LYMINGTON, Gordleton Mill ❀❀❀❀

Silver Street Hordle
SO41 6DJ
Map 4: 5739
Tel: 01590 682219
Fax: 01590 683073
Chef: Toby Hill
Owner: Mr WF Stone
Cost: Alc £42.50, fixed-price L £24.50/D £35. H/wine £17
Times: 12.30pm-last L 2.30pm/7.30pm-last D 9.30pm. Closed D Sun, Mon, 2 wks Nov
Additional: Sunday L; No children under 7; ⊕ dishes
Seats: 40. Private dining room 16-18
Smoking: No smoking in dining room; air-conditioning
Accommodation: 7 en suite
Credit cards: ▄▄ ▄▄ ▄▄ ▄▄ ▄▄ ▄▄

Stroll from the car park through the waterside gardens, past whitened trunks of Japanese maple, then over the footbridge towards the 300-year-old converted watermill (complete with its original sluice gates, weir and even a lily pond). In summer, it can feel like heaven to sit and sip champagne on the classic glazed terrace by the banks of the Avon, where fish jump and the mood is easy. Provence defines the decor in the restaurant, with its yellow stone walls, touches of terracotta stucco and arboreal artwork on the ceiling. Chef/manager Toby Hill worked out his apprenticeship with Raymond Blanc and his cooking style is born of the great master: 'sophistication without complexity, depth without heaviness', as one inspector observed. His technique is assiduous, but it never intrudes, never distracts from the essentials of each dish. As for the menu, it reads like a testament to '90s gastronomy: tartare of wild trout with pickled vegetables and caviar cream, mille-feuille of foie gras and roasted langoustine with baby fennel and sherry vinegar sauce, for example. But Hill is no mere plagiarist or imitator: his cooking sings with individual brilliance. Consider this: a terrine of meltingly soft rectangles of pink salmon and diced provençale vegetables, held together gently with strips of aubergine and gilded with baby tapenade croûtes and a saffron dressing. That is class. The quality of main courses is in the same league: top-quality local turbot is topped with fleshy poached scallops, drizzled with hollandaise on a bed of soft fennel and ringed by an intense rosemary jus, milk-poached endive and herb oil, while melt-in-the-mouth new season's lamb comes with provençale breadcrumbs, candied aubergine, asparagus and jus niçoise. Desserts are show-stoppers – to be expected from a man who was pastry chef at Le Manoir: smooth, sensual chocolate mousse in a serrated chocolate basket with two fine spun-sugar swords waving high, as well as a daringly timed chocolate soufflé with an intense red berry sauce and sorbet to accompany. This is food that thrills and invigorates the spirit. More wines are available here than on many a merchant's list. Depth and quality are accompanied by maturity (particularly in Bordeaux) and evidence of self-restraint when marking up. Not all the vintages are great but find a good wine from a relatively bad year, such as Château Pichon Longueville Lalande in 1981, and you'll be well rewarded. A thoughtful range of half-bottles are listed by region.

Signature dishes: Roast sea scallops with tomato sorbet and lemon vinaigrette; boudin of pheasant and truffle with wild rice, fumet of ceps; smoked wing-rib of Angus beef, parsley purée, sauce bordelaise.

Directions: Take A337 to Lymington, at railway bridge mini-roundabout go straight on then 1st R 1.5 miles

LYNDHURST, Crown Hotel ✸

High Street, SO43 7NF
Map 4: SU30
Tel: 01703 282922
Fax: 01703 282751
Chef: Stephen Greenhalgh
Owners: Mr & Mrs AJS Green
Cost: A/c £26, fixed-price D £17. ☺
H/wine £10.20
Times: D only, 7.30pm-9.30pm
Additional: Bar food; Sunday L
(12.30pm-2pm); Children welcome;
♨ dishes
Smoking: No smoking in dining room
Accommodation: 39 en suite
Credit cards: ▬ ▦ ▦ ☒ ▣ ℂ

The façade may be 100-years-old, but the cooking at this well-established, traditional hotel has a more modern outlook. Fillet of fresh salmon, samphire and smoked salmon cream, and breast of duck marinated in soy, honey and ginger are set amongst old favourites such as roast leg of lamb and sugar-baked ham.

Directions: Top end of Lyndhurst High Street, opposite church

LYNDHURST, **Parkhill Hotel**

Beaulieu Road
SO43 7FZ
Map 4: SU30
Tel: 01703 282944
Fax: 01703 283268
Chef: Richard Turner
Owners: Mr & Mrs Topham
Cost: *Alc* £30, fixed-price L £16/D
£27.50 (4 courses). ☺ H/wine
£11.50.
Times: Noon-last L 2pm/7pm-last D
9pm
Additional: Bar food L; Sunday L;
No children under 1; ✪ dishes
Seats: 80. Private dining room 50
Smoking: No smoking in dining room
Accommodation: 20 en suite
Credit cards: ■ ▦ ▦ ▣ ▢

Deer are frequently seen grazing alongside this charming New
Forest hotel, adding the final touch to this tranquil away-from-
it-all setting. The *carte* is structured around sound English
classics – cured Denhay Farm ham with a piccalilli dressing and
sultana bread, light duck liver parfait laced with orange and
brandy served with a home-made quince preserve, grilled
Dover sole with lemon flavoured fish cream, and traditional
Chateaubriand (for two) with a 'bouquetier' of vegetables and
a Madeira sauce. Daily specials might include seared peppered
salmon with niçoise salad and a warm gazpacho dressing, or
pot-roasted chicken filled with a cured ham and prune mousse
set on a bed of Puy lentils. Desserts stick to the tried and tested
with warm plum and almond tart with butterscotch sauce and a
tulip basket of seasonal and exotic fruits with Chantilly cream.

Directions: From Lyndhurst take B3056 (Beaulieu), hotel signed
1 mile on R. From Southampton take A35 (Lyndhurst)

MIDDLE WALLOP, **Fifehead Manor**

Stockbridge SO20 8EG
Map 4: SU23
Tel: 01264 781565
Fax: 01264 781400
Chef: Andrew Poole
Owners: Roy & Lesley Bishop-Milnes
Cost: Fixed-price L £19/D £25.
H/wine £9
Times: Last L 2pm/D 9.30pm.
Closed 1 wk after Xmas
Additional: Bar food; Sunday L;
Children welcome; ✪ dishes
Seats: 30. Private dining room 14
Smoking: No smoking in dining room
Accommodation: 14 en suite
Credit cards: ■ ▦ ▦ ▩ ▢

As manor houses go, Fifehead is a real old stager, with a
history dating back to Saxon times. Ancient details abound,
especially in the dining room which occupies the original main
hall of the place. A new kitchen team is in confident mood and
the result is a repertoire of deftly crafted modern dishes based
on quality ingredients. Technically there's a lot going on in, say,
paupiette of Fjordling smoked salmon filled with its own
mousse, cucumber salad, keta and a saffron water vinaigrette,

or a pressed terrine of duck confit and foie gras studded with whole caramelised shallots with a garnish of potato brunoise and a scattering of lentils; the latter our inspector's choice. Main courses maintain the momentum – roast fillet of cod with a seared spicy curry crust on a bed of lentils and ham lardons with a basil oil and red pepper coulis, or roast breast of guinea fowl en cocotte with garden peas and morels plus sauce auoffera, for example. Puddings are in the classic mould of gâteau opera with a slice of chocolate marquise. Wines are mostly French with a token showing from other countries.

Directions: On the A343, 5 miles S of Andover

MILFORD-ON-SEA,

Rocher's Restaurant

Alain and Rebecca Rocher have been in residence at this classy little village restaurant for almost a decade, and the place continues to flourish. Chintz curtains, gilt mirrors and dark green upholstered chairs give the classically decorated dining room a touch of elegance. Table d'hôte and 'gastronomic dinner' menus (priced for two or three courses) promise highly competent French cooking with a noticeable bias towards fish. Fillet of turbot is immaculately presented on a bed of fennel with a classic beurre blanc, pan-fried scallops are seasoned with garlic butter, perfectly timed brill comes with a delicately spiced curry sauce. Away from fish, you might find venison pie topped with flaky pastry, fillet of beef with a coarse-grain mustard sauce, or breast of duck with raspberry vinegar sauce. To finish, hot chocolate gâteau with coffee ice cream was a 'molten winner' for our inspector, and crème brûlée has been given the thumbs-up. The broadly based wine list leans heavily towards France, although the New World is not ignored; half bottles show up well.

69/71 High Street SO41 0QG
Map 4: SZ29
Tel: 01590 642340
Chef: Alain Rocher
Owners: Alain & Rebecca Rocher
Cost: Fixed-price L £14.50/D £23.50. ☺ H/wine £9.50.
Times: D only, 7.15pm-9.45pm. (D Sun only Bhs). Closed Mon, Tue
Additional: Sunday L (12.15pm-1.45pm); No children under 7
Seats: 26
Smoking: No pipes or cigars in dining room
Credit cards: ▀ ▒ ▒ ▀ 💷 🅖

Directions: On the B3058 3 miles S-W of Lymington

MILFORD ON SEA,

South Lawn Hotel ⊛

Lymington Road SO41 0RF
Map 4: SZ29
Tel: 01590 643911
Fax: 01590 644820
Chefs: Ernst Barten & David Gates
Owners: Ernst & Jennifer Barten
Cost: Alc £22.10, fixed-price L £11.85/D £18.50. ☺ H/wine £10.25.
Times: Last L 1.45pm/D 8.45pm. Closed L Mon, 20 Dec-16 Jan
Additional: Sunday L; ◑ dishes
Smoking: No smoking in dining room
Accommodation: 24 en suite
Credit cards: ▀ ▒ 🅖

Directions: A337 from Lymington, L after 3 miles on to B3058; hotel 1 mile on R

Tranquil, chintzy hotel on edge of the New Forest. Local fish is particularly recommended; lemon sole with prawns and dill, and cod fillet poached and served in a cheesy cream sauce are amongst a carefully cooked choice, which also includes lamb diable, chicken Kiev and curried prawns with basmati rice.

MILFORD ON SEA, Westover Hall

Park Lane SO41 0PT
Map 4: SZ29
Tel: 01590 643044
Fax: 01590 644490
Chef: Roberto Musetti
Owners: Stewart Mechem, Nichola & Robert Musetti
Cost: Alc £22, fixed-price L&D £20. ☺ H/wine £10.50
Times: Last L 1.45pm/last D 9pm
Additional: Bar food; Sunday L; Children welcome; ❹ dishes
Smoking: No smoking in dining room
Accommodation: 12 en suite
Credit cards:

This Victorian mansion, 200 yards from the beach with wonderful views, rich oak panelling and dramatic stained glass, makes an atmospheric setting in which to enjoy classical Italian cooking. Look out for artichoke vinaigrette, breast of pheasant wrapped in Parma ham, medallions of veal with a Marsala sauce, and woodcock with rich red wine sauce and sage polenta.

Directions: Turn off A337 onto B3058; hotel a few 100 yds W of Milford on Sea

NEW MILTON,
Chewton Glen Hotel

Christchurch Road BH25 6QS
Map 4: SZ29
Tel: 01425 275341
Fax: 01425 272310
Chef: Pierre Chevillard
Owner: Martin Skan
Cost: Alc £45, fixed-price L £23.50/D £45. H/wine £15
Times: 12.30pm-last L 1.45pm/7.30pm-last D 9.30pm
Additional: Bar meals L; Sunday L; ❹ dishes
Seats: 120. Private dining rooms 100. Jacket & tie preferred
Smoking: No smoking in dining room; air-conditioning
Accommodation: 52 en suite
Credit cards:

A curious concept: at Chewton Glen, certain dishes on the *carte* are given a star in order to indicate that they are low in calories, bringing a touch of modern austerity to a meal at this rather hushed, luxurious country house hotel, health and country club, where gentlemen need to be politely told to wear a jacket and tie. Most of the lengthy *carte* is, however, rooted in modern French cooking. It's a style which relishes the juxtaposition of luxury items with more down-to-earth ingredients, as in braised pork cheeks and local lobster with baby vegetables flavoured with coriander and lemon grass, or oven-baked fillet of turbot coated with shallots and fresh breadcrumbs with a light curry and mussel sauce. The solidly Francophile pot-roasted French squab pigeon served on buttered cabbage with mushroom ravioli and a brandy jus, and crispy leg of duck confit on braised lentils with a light jus, are

balanced by starred items on the menu, directing the eye immediately towards vegetarian dishes of ragout of fresh morel mushrooms and asparagus braised with Gewürztraminer wine, and fresh linguini with fresh tomato compote flavoured with pesto. Despite the ambition and undoubted skill, the cooking can at times drift off-balance – our inspector decided, for example, that a lobster and coriander sauce rather overpowered an otherwise excellent ravioli of langoustine, and that a caramelised banana tart lacked sufficiently tangy taste, although a 'scrumptious' rum and raisin ice cream came happily to the rescue. Service, throughout the meal, was immaculate, well-paced and visibly enthusiastic. The masterly wine list of over 500 bins is a tribute to tireless and inspired compilation. As much effort has gone into searching out affordable excitement from the less esteemed regions as in assembling majestic columns of the good and the great from the classic French estates. There is a distinctly open-minded approach with the South of France, Australia, California and New Zealand all being well represented, and plenty of good drinking available for under £25. Customers are actively encouraged to ask for advice and with a list of this depth, it would be wise to do so.

Directions: On A35 (Lyndhurst) turn R through Walkford, then 2nd left into Chewton Farm Road.

OLD BURGHCLERE,

The Dew Pond Restaurant

The pair of former drover's cottages that make up this rambling restaurant date from the sixteenth century, and the whole place is imbued with a homely charm brought about by the limitations of small rooms and an old fashioned decor that is strong on pink damask. Keith Marshall works hard in the kitchen, producing dishes that come from a classic repertoire based on well sourced ingredients, sound technique and clear flavours. An early summer inspection dinner opened with a signature dish of gâteau of crab that came with gazpacho sauce and spiced tomato sorbet, and went on to an excellent saddle of roe deer, sliced over a confit of shallots and roast tomatoes that had been scented with thyme, a separate croustade of wild mushrooms, and a nicely flavoured port and stock reduction. Pudding was a classic lemon tart with a coulis of raspberries and a caramelised sugar top. Attention to small details is spot on with both bread and petits fours receiving praise. Wines are grouped according to style: oaked, unoaked, light, weighty. Some interesting bottles and nothing too wildly expensive, with over two dozen half-bottles under £14.25. Stag's Leap Chardonnay is a good buy at £24.50, and their red at £28 is a good match for the many games dishes which feature here. Four house wines from Europe and Australia are a good safe bet at £11.95.

Signature dishes: Best end of new season lamb with garlic and rosemary; fillet of beef with wild mushrooms and Madeira

Directions: Six miles south of Newbury. Take the Burghclere turn off A34 (Winchester), and follow signs for Old Burghclere

Newbury RG20 9LH
Map 4: SU46
Tel/Fax: 01635 278408
Chef: Keith Marshall
Owners: Keith & Julie Marshall
Cost: Fixed-price D £25.
H/wine £11.95
Times: D only, 7pm-D 10pm.
Closed Sun, Mon, 2 wks Jan, 2 wks Aug
Additional: No children under 5; dishes
Seats: 45. Private dining room 20
Smoking: No smoking in dining room
Credit cards: ▆ ▆ ▆ ▆

PORTSMOUTH,

Bistro Montparnasse ❀❀

The cosy bistro in the centre of Swansea was carved out of a former Victorian town house. It is hugely popular, not just with locals, but with travellers catching the ferry to France. Terracotta walls, cream table linen and fresh flowers create a cheerful setting for a seasonally changing modern menu, supported by a blackboard list of fish specialities. Home-made breads are a hit, certainly with one inspector, who sampled ciabatta, rye, and a good crusty white. That test meal included leek and bacon tart with some balsamic-dressed mixed leaves, turbot with a saffron and shallot butter sauce, garnished with fleurons (pastry shapes) and spinach, and accompanied by some good fresh vegetables. Bread-and-butter pudding terrine to finish, served with blueberry coulis and vanilla ice cream.

Directions: Follow brown tourist signs to D Day Museum. Turn L opposite museum (Avenue de Caen). At 1st road junction look for somewhere to park. Bistro across road on R.

103 Palmerston Road PO5 3PS
Map 4: SU60
Tel/Fax: 01705 816754
Chef: Gillian Scott
Owners: Peter Moore, Gillian Scott
Cost: *Alc* £25, fixed-price D £14.90. ☺ H/wine £10.50.
Times: D only 7pm-10pm.
Closed Sun, Mon, Xmas, Bhs
Additional: Children welcome; ◑ dishes
Seats: 40. Private dining room 25
Smoking: No pipes and cigars in dining room
Credit cards: ▆▆ ▆ ▆ ▆ ▆

RINGWOOD,

Moortown Lodge Hotel ❀❀

Speciality of the house, at this relaxed, family-run hotel on the edge of the New Forest, is 'Floating Cheese Island', a light cheese soufflé. This makes a fine start to a short, well-judged, dinner-party style menu that might also include game pie made with local venison, red wine sauce and puff pastry, or pan-fried tenderloin of pork cooked in cider with cream and apples. The trio of starters always includes a freshly made soup and a salad, perhaps home-smoked duck breast with seasonal leaves or bacon and Stilton. Sirloin steak is simply grilled and served with fresh herb butter, although this carries a supplement. Main courses are served with a selection of fresh market vegetables, and there is a choice of tempting home-made puddings, as well as a selection of British cheese.

Directions: From Ringwood town centre take B3347 towards Christchurch for about 1.5 miles

244 Christchurch Road BH24 3AS
Map 4: SU10
Tel: 01425 471404
Fax: 01425 476052
Chef: Jilly Burrows-Jones
Owners: Jilly & Bob Burrows-Jones
Cost: Fixed-price D £17.95 (3 courses), £20.95 (4 courses). ☺ H/wine £8.95.
Times: D only, 7pm-last D 8.30pm.
Closed Sun (non-residents), Xmas – mid Jan
Additional: Children welcome; ◑ dishes
Seats: 24
Smoking: No smoking in dining room
Accommodation: 6 rooms (5 en suite)
Credit cards: ▆▆ ▆ ▆

RINGWOOD,

Tyrrells Ford Country House ❀

Avon, New Forest, BH23 7BH
Map 4: SU10
Tel: 01425 672646
Fax: 01425 672262
Owner: Mr Ivan Caplan
Cost: *Alc* £24, fixed-price L £15.95/D £19.95. ☺ H/wine £10.95.
Times: Last L 2pm/D 9.30pm
Additional: Bar food; Sunday L; Children welcome; ◑ dishes
Smoking: No smoking in dining room
Accommodation: 16 en suite
Credit cards: ▆▆ ▆ ▆ ▆ ▆ ▆

No watching the waistline allowed here – lamb cutlets pan-fried with cream, mustard seed and basil sauce, medallions of best beef fillet in a rich Stilton and port sauce and seafood thermidor are amongst the main courses at this restful and charming country house hotel. And that's before the selection of home-made desserts, puddings, sweet pies and cream cakes!

Directions: M27/A31 to Ringwood, B3347 3 miles south to Avon

ROMSEY, **Bertie's**

Once the women's workhouse, Bertie's is situated close to the centre of the old market town. The restaurant is cosy and intimate, and the theme is P G Wodehouse's hapless hero Bertie Wooster, complete with framed cartoons and gilt mirrors; there's also a separate bar area. At a summer meal the first course, game terrine, came set on a full flavoured port and redcurrant jelly with a tarragon mayonnaise. Grilled John Dory – a 'fish special' from the daily blackboard menu – was of excellent quality, accurately cooked and served on a bed of wild mushrooms with a well-made butter sauce. The pudding, baked American cheesecake, had a light biscuit base with a heavier white chocolate and hazelnut filling and a thick chocolate fudge sauce.

Directions: 200m from Broadlands' gate in the centre of town

The Hundred
Map 4: SU32
Tel/Fax: 01794 830708/507507
Chef: Michael Weir
Owner: David Birmingham
Cost: *Alc* £23, fixed-price D £9.95 (2 courses). ☺ H/wine £9.50.
Times: Noon-last L 2pm/6.30pm-last D 10pm. Closed Sun
Additional: Bar food L; Children welcome; ❹ dishes
Seats: 50
Smoking: No-smoking area in dining room
Accommodation: 5 en suite
Credit cards: ▀▀ ▀▀ ▀▀ ▀▀ ▀▀ ▀▀

ROMSEY, **Old Manor House Restaurant**

21 Palmerston Street
SO51 8GF
Map 4: SU32
Tel: 01794 517353
Chef: Mauro Bregoli
Owners: Esther & Mauro Bregoli
Cost: *Alc* £25, fixed-price L £17.50/D £19.50. ☺ H/wine £11.50.
Times: Noon-last L 2pm/7pm-last D 9.30pm. Closed D Sun, Mon, 1 wk Xmas-New Year
Additional: Sunday L; Children welcome; ❹ dishes
Seats: 45. Private dining room 20
Smoking: No pipes and cigars
Credit cards: ▀▀ ▀▀ ▀▀ ▀▀ ▀▀

This is a beautifully restored Tudor building complete with beams, a mighty inglenook and patio for alfresco dining during the summer months. If that sounds quintessentially English and thoughts of roast beef or steak and kidney pie come to mind, you are in for a very pleasant surprise. Mauro Bregoli is an Italian who clings to his roots and works industriously to preserve some of his country's culinary traditions. 'We endeavour to use local fish and produce; most of the time we succeed', says a note on the menu. When he is not making his own coppa (cured neck of pork), spicy cotechino sausage (which is served hot with lentils) or curing and smoking bresaola in the Manor House chimney, Mauro is likely to be out shooting game in the New Forest, fishing on the Test, or foraging for wild fungi. Assorted mushrooms turn up in a risotto, they get a look in with wild boar cutlet and confit of cabbage and appear in the creamy wine sauce served with fillet of beef. Pasta, quite naturally, is home made. The earthiness shows in dishes such as tagliatelle with Parma ham and peas, and Italian sausage with Parmesan mash, but there's also a lighter Mediterranean undercurrent as well. A lasagne of aubergines and courgettes with ricotta and mascarpone found favour with one inspector, as did delicate parcels of salmon cleverly filled with creamed leeks drenched with a caper water vinaigrette. Other evocative ideas might include carpaccio of foie gras and walnuts, barbecued eel steak with salsa verde, and grilled squid on a bed of salad with pine kernels. Desserts are classic confections such as bitter chocolate mousse with passion fruit coulis and warm apple tart, as well as more unexpected offerings like roasted figs with vanilla ice cream. Espresso coffee is deep and strong, and petits fours good. Scots-born Esther Bregoli is an outgoing hostess with a natural flair for looking after guests.

Signature dishes: Grilled sea bass with fresh herbs; grilled escalope of roe deer with onion confit and spiced fruit.

Directions: Opposite the entrance to Broadlands Estate

ROTHERWICK, Tylney Hall ❀ ❀

Tylney Hall is Victorian grandeur personified. The Grade II listed mansion stands in 66 acres of glorious parkland and gardens, originally laid out by Gertrude Jekyll and currently being restored to their original glory. Lakes and ornamental fountains provide a pleasing prospect. Inside, the handsome Oak Room makes a splendid setting for refined modern cooking based on top-notch ingredients. Seared scallops might be served with a salad of French beans, bacon, hazelnuts and parsley or, impressively, with a fruity courgette relish. Our inspector was also quick to praise a tender 'gâteau' of well-hung lamb served with rosemary jus and a tomato brunoise. Otherwise you might encounter grilled red mullet with fennel confit, balsamic vinegar and lobster dressing, and Gressingham duck with bean shoots and spinach accompanied by a soy and sesame dressing. Desserts could range from crème brûlée to brochette of fruit on a chocolate couscous with pear purée.

Directions: M3/J5 take A287 (Newnham). From M4/J11 take B3349 (Hook), at sharp bend L (Rotherwick), L again and L in village (Newnham), 1 mile on R.

Rotherwick, Hook
RG27 9AZ
Map 4: SU75
Tel: 01256 764881
Fax: 01256 768141
Chef: Stephen Hine
Cost: *Alc* £40, fixed-price L £13-£21/D £31. ☺ H/wine £12.85.
Times: 12.30pm-last L 2pm/7.30pm-last D 9.30pm
Additional: Sunday L; Bar meals L; Children welcome; ❹ dishes
Seats: 120. Jacket & tie preferred
Smoking: No smoking in dining room
Accommodation: 110 en suite
Credit cards: ▆ ▆ ▆ ▆ ▆ ▆

SILCHESTER, Romans Hotel

A Lutyens-style property, in a historic village, sympathetically converted to provide up-to-date facilities, yet retaining the atmosphere and period detail of an Edwardian country house. Dishes range from pan-fried breast of chicken in Cajun spices with fried rice to boiled silverside of beef on caper sauce.

Smoking: No smoking in dining room
Accommodation: 25 en suite
Credit cards: ▦ ▦ ▦ ▣ ▢

Directions: In village centre

Little London Road RG7 2PN
Map 4: SU66
Tel: 01189 700421
Fax: 01189 700691
Chef: Kevin Pearson
Owners: Mr & Mrs Tuthill
Cost: Alc £24, fixed-price L&D £18.
☺ H/wine £11.35.
Times: Last L 2pm/D 9.30pm. Closed L Sat, 26 Dec-2 Jan
Additional: Bar meals; Sunday L; Children welcome; ❸ dishes

SOUTHAMPTON, The Boathouse

Having worked his way through heavyweight restaurants and country house hotels, Ian McAndrew has settled into this nautically decorated brasserie overlooking Hythe marina. Gone is the intense 'nouvelle' style of the past, in its place is a more direct, no-frills approach with the emphasis on up-front flavours. The menu is a typically jazzy selection of dishes for the 90s: salad of black pudding with chorizo and poached egg, confit of duck with smooth pesto mash, and fillet of salmon with wilted rocket and couscous are typical, but you can also get soups, open sandwiches and pasta. Additional 'chef's recommendations', are reminders of McAndrew's love of fish and game: fillet of brill with a nage of shiitake mushrooms, loin of venison on a celeriac and parsnip purée, for example. Desserts are equally in tune with the mood of the place: textbook versions of crème brûlée, rhubarb crumble, chocolate marquise with pear sorbet, and so on. Forty wines offer exactly what this kind of food demands.

Directions: M27 exit 2 A326 (Fawley). Left to Hythe, in Marina Village

29 Shamrock Way Hythe Marina Village SO45 6DY
Map 4: SU41
Tel: 01703 845594
Fax: 01703 846017
Chef: Ian McAndrew
Owner: Leisure Great Britain (Oakley) Ltd
Cost: Alc £22. Fixed price L £10.50 (2 courses). ☺ H/wine £9.
Times: Noon-last L 2.30pm/7pm-last D 10pm. Closed D Sun, all Mon, 2 weeks Jan
Additional: Bar meals L; Sunday L; Children welcome; ❸ dishes
Seats: 50. Private dining room 12
Smoking: Air-conditioning
Credit cards: ▦ ▦ ▩ ▢

SOUTHAMPTON,
De Vere Grand Harbour

West Quay Road SO15 1AG
Map 4: SU66
Tel: 01703 633033
Fax: 01703: 633066
Chef: David Hewlett
Owner: De Vere Hotels
Cost: Alc £30, fixed-price L £15.50/D £24.50 (4 courses). ☺ H/wine£10.75.
Times: Last L 2.15/7.30pm-last D 10.15pm
Additional: Sunday L; Bar meals; Children welcome; ❸ dishes
Smoking: No smoking in dining room; air-conditioning
Accommodation: 172 en suite
Credit cards: ▦ ▦ ▦ ▩

A striking modern hotel overlooking the old city walls. Allertons, the more formal of its two restaurants, provides elaborate dishes from an extensive carte, such as terrine of lambs' sweetbreads with foie gras, pistachio nuts and toasted brioche, and glazed duck breast with rhubarb, roasted fig and green peppercorn sauce.

Directions: In 'old town' area, just S of city centre

SOUTHAMPTON, Kuti's Brasserie ❀

Venison, duck, Bangladeshi fish (ayre, hilsha, boal) and ethnic vegetables such as mustard greens and tinda (baby pumpkin) jazz up the long menu in this smart Indian restaurant. There's also a full range of curry house stalwarts such as lamb tikka, chicken dupiaza and king prawn patia. Breads are particularly successful.

Additional: Sunday L; children welcome; ❹ dishes
Smoking: Air-conditioning
Credit cards: ■■ ■■ ■■ ➡ ▣ ▢

Directions: In old part of city near Ocean Village and Docks

37-39 Oxford Street
Map 4: SU41
Tel: 01703 221585/333473
Fax: 01703 233025
Chefs: R Miah, K Miah, B Arman
Cost: Alc £15; Fixed price L £8.50.
H/wine £7.50
Times: Last L 2pm/D 11.30pm Closed
25-26 Dec

SOUTHSEA, Queens Hotel ❀

An elegant late Victorian hotel that has dominated the seafront since 1898, and offers panoramic views to the Isle of Wight. The menu shows ambition, especially in dishes such as seared scallops with lentils and bacon, and a well-executed stir-fry of scampi with spring onions, ginger and tomato concasse.

Smoking: No smoking in dining room
Accommodation: 90 en suite
Credit cards: ■■ ■■ ■■ ➡ ▣ ▢

Directions: Follow signs to Southsea seafront. Hotel opposite war memorial

Clarence Parade PO5 3LJ
Map 4: SU06
Tel: 01705 822466
Fax: 01705 821901
Chef: Eddie Rolf
Owners: Mr W Shufflebottom,
Mrs P Shufflebottom
Cost: Alc £22, fixed-price L £14.75/D
£17.75. ☺ H/wine £10.60.
Times: Last L 2pm/D 9.45pm
Additional: Sunday L; Bar meals;
Children welcome; ❹ dishes

SWAY, String of Horses ❀

Gillian Reardon has overseen this country hotel on the fringes of the New Forest for more than 14 years and the place continues in its own way. In the beamed, candlelit restaurant you can try Anglo-French dishes along the lines of smoked chicken salad with raspberry dressing, and breast of duckling in brandy and peppercorn sauce.

Smoking: No-smoking area; no pipes & cigars
Accommodation: 7 en suite
Credit cards: ■■ ■■ ■■ ➡ ▣ ▢

Directions: From B3055 turn R over station bridge, 2nd L into Mead End Road, 350 yds on L

Mead End Road SO41 6EH
Map 4: SZ39
Tel/Fax: 01590 682631
Chef: Julio Frias Robles
Owner: Gillian A Reardon
Cost: Alc £24.50, fixed price D
£18.95 (4 courses). ☺ H/wine £11.50.
Times: D only, 7pm-last D 8.30pm.
Closed Mon, Tue
Additional: Sunday L (12.30pm-
1.30pm); No children under 16;
❹ dishes

WICKHAM, Old House Hotel ❀❀

Do not be fooled by the beautifully preserved, classic Georgian exterior; this is really an *auberge romantique* run by Francophiles and specialising in French regional cooking. Both the bar and restaurant have a rustic French character, with the set-price menus written in concise French (with English sub-titles). Typical starters include smoked haddock glazed with a fruity curry sabayon, fresh salmon finely chopped with lime juice, shallots and chives, and a salad of sliced mango, avocado and continental salad leaves. A meal in July started with stuffed courgettes with cream and mustard sauce, was followed by a succulent piece of turbot, served with a vibrant sauce of capers, olives and black beans and finished with a dark chocolate mousse flavoured with honey and coffee. Other

The Square PO17 5JG
Map 4: SU51
Tel: 01329 833049
Fax: 01329 833672
Chef: Nicholas Harman
Owners: Richard & Annie Skipwith
Cost: Fixed-price L&D £27 (3
courses). H/wine £12.75
Times: 12.15pm-last L 1.45pm/7pm-
last D 9.45pm. Closed L Sat & Mon,
Sun, 2 wks Xmas, 1 wk Easter, 2 wks
July/Aug
Additional: Bar food L; Children
welcome; ❹ dishes
Seats: 40. Private dining room 14

Old House Hotel

Smoking: No pipes and cigars in dining room
Accommodation: 12 en suite
Credit cards: ■ ■ ■ ■

desserts, from an impressive list, include passion fruit crème brûlée, and fresh pineapple pan-fried in butter and topped with maple ice cream. While the wine list is biased towards France, it also features a good selection from the New World.

Directions: In the centre of Wickham, 3 miles N of Fareham at junction of A32/B2177

WINCHESTER, Harvey's ❀❀

31b The Square SO23 9EX
Map 4: SU42
Tel: 01962 843438
Telephone for details

Persevere, and make or fight your way through the crowded, rather raucous wine bar on the ground floor to the restaurant upstairs. There you'll find an attractive, airy haven of a room decorated in bright pastels, with a menu on the same fresh theme. At lunch-time, things are kept relatively simple with bistro-style local sausages and mashed potato, or smoked salmon fish cakes with parsley beurre blanc. In the evening things get a bit more adventurous, with the likes of game terrine with onion and red pepper chutney, and tender medallions of beef with roasted sweet garlic and port jus. If the apple strudel is as good as it was on our last visit, then it is worth the twenty minute wait.

Directions: In The Square, which runs parallel to the pedestrianised High Street

WINCHESTER,
Hotel du Vin & Bistro ❀❀

14 Southgate Street SO23 9EF
Map 4: SU42
Tel: 01962 841414
Fax: 01962 842458

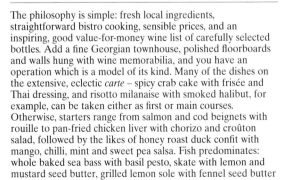

Chef: James Martin

The philosophy is simple: fresh local ingredients, straightforward bistro cooking, sensible prices, and an inspiring, good value-for-money wine list of carefully selected bottles. Add a fine Georgian townhouse, polished floorboards and walls hung with wine memorabilia, and you have an operation which is a model of its kind. Many of the dishes on the extensive, eclectic *carte* – spicy crab cake with frisée and Thai dressing, and risotto milanaise with smoked halibut, for example, can be taken either as first or main courses. Otherwise, starters range from salmon and cod beignets with rouille to pan-fried chicken liver with chorizo and croûton salad, followed by the likes of honey roast duck confit with mango, chilli, mint and sweet pea salsa. Fish predominates: whole baked sea bass with basil pesto, skate with lemon and mustard seed butter, grilled lemon sole with fennel seed butter

Owners: Robin Hutson, Gerard Basset
Cost: *Alc* £50. H/wine £10
Times: Noon-last L 1.30pm/7pm-last D-9.30pm
Additional: Sunday L; Children welcome; ❀ dishes
Seats: 45. Private dining room 48
Smoking: No pipes or cigars
Accommodation: 23 en suite
Credit cards: ■ ■ ■ ■ ■ ■

and charred limes. Try an original tarte Tatin of pineapple with black pepper, or chargrilled bananas with toffee sauce and vanilla ice cream for dessert.

Directions: M3/J11, at roundabout 3rd exit (St Cross & Winchester). Continue along Southgate Street 2 miles, hotel on L just before town centre

WINCHESTER, **Hunters**

A light, airy city-centre restaurant offering popular, brasserie-style dishes at lunchtime and a good-value carte and fixed-price dinner menu. The emphasis is on sound, modern British cooking, and well-priced house wines, plus half a dozen by the glass.

Additional: Children welcome; ♨ dishes
Smoking: No-smoking area
Credit cards: ▬ ▒ ▒ ▒ ▒ ▒

Directions: Towards top of the City just off High Street, 200 yards from Theatre Royal & Library car park

5 Jewry Street SO23 8RZ
Map 4: SU42
Tel/Fax: 01962 860006
Chef: Simon Cox
Owner: David Birmingham
Cost: *Alc* £23, fixed-price D £9.95.
☺ H/wine £9.50.
Times: Last L 2pm/last D 10pm.
Closed Sun, 25-30 Dec

WINCHESTER,
Lainston House Hotel ❀❀

Sparsholt SO21 2LT
Map 4: SU42
Tel: 01962 863588
Fax: 01962 776672
Chef: Friedrich Litty
Cost: *Alc* £35, fixed-price L £19/D £35 (6 courses). H/wine £15.
Times: 12.30pm-last L 2pm/7pm-last D 10pm
Additional: Bar food L; Sunday L; Children welcome; ♨ dishes
Seats: 70. Various private dining rooms. Jacket & tie preferred
Smoking: No pipes and cigars
Accommodation: 38 en suite
Credit cards: ▬ ▒ ▒ ▒ ▒ ▒

The spectacular avenue of English lime trees immediately commands the eye from the dining room at this fine William and Mary period country house hotel. The *carte* shows a considered, expert hand on the helm, and is classically based without appearing old-fashioned. On the contrary, dishes such as poached monkfish tail with provençale tian, clams and cockles with saffron, and pan-fried black pudding with salad roquette, Parmesan curls, crispy Serrano ham and sherry dressing have quite a contemporary air. Confidence shows in technically challenging dishes such as sole and salmon sausage with wilted spinach and caviar cream, noisette of venison wrapped with potato and celeriac, served with apple and pear fondant and surrounded by its own jus, as well as in sophisticated desserts such as raspberry croquant with a fondue of rhubarb and a compote of citrus.

Directions: Three miles from the centre of Winchester, off the A272 road to Stockbridge. Signposted.

WINCHESTER, **Nine the Square**

An attractive restaurant situated opposite the cathedral offering good food in a choice of settings. The ground floor has the atmosphere of a wine bar while the first floor is more intimate, though the menu is the same. The wine list covers a good range, many available by the glass.

Directions: Situated in the main square of the city, just outside the grounds of the cathedral and opposite the museum

The Square, SO23 9HA
Map 4: SU42
Tel: 01962 864004
Fax: 01962 879586
Telephone for details

WINCHESTER,
Old Chesil Rectory

Built in 1450 and reputedly one of the oldest buildings in Winchester, the Old Rectory thrives on character, with oak beams and inglenook fireplaces aplenty. Polished wooden tables, leaded lights and wooden floors set the tone downstairs; linen cloths add a touch of formality on the first floor. Fixed-price lunches feature hearty dishes such as confit of duck with carrot and orange purée, or free-range chicken breast with black pudding and Calvados sauce. Evening meals move up a notch for langoustine and scallop raviolo with a shellfish and saffron bisque, medallions of venison and pigeon breasts and rich game sauce and grilled ribeye of beef with salsa verde. Puddings are a high point: prune and Armagnac ice cream has been particularly pleasing, otherwise you might try syrup and orange sticky sponge or banana and Malibu mousse with chocolate sorbet and mango sauce. Ten well-chosen wines by the glass front the catholic list.

Directions: From King Alfred's statue at the bottom of The Broadway, cross the small bridge and turn R; the restaurant is to the R, just off mini roundabout

1 Chesil Street SO23 8HU
Map 4: SU42
Tel: 01962 851555
Fax: 01962 869704
Chefs: Nicholas Ruthven-Stuart, Nicola Saunders
Owners: Nicholas & Christina Ruthven-Stuart
Cost: Fixed-price L £15-£20 (2-3 courses)/D £28 (3 courses). H/wine £9.95
Times: Noon-last L 2pm/7pm-last D 9.30pm. Closed Sun & Mon, 2 wks Xmas, 2 wks summer
Additional: Children welcome
Seats: 55. Private dining 20
Smoking: No-smoking area; no pipes or cigars in dining room
Credit cards: 🔳 🔳 🔳 🔳 🔳

WINCHESTER, **Royal Hotel**

Popular hotel tucked away in a quiet street in the centre of historic Winchester. The conservatory dining room offers an interesting menu of well-prepared English dishes, and in the summer months guests can enjoy a barbecue lunch in the walled garden. Service is courteous and professional.

Directions: Take one-way system through Winchester, turn R off St George's Street into St Peter Street. Hotel on R

Saint Peter Street SO23 8BS
Map 4: SU42
Tel: 01962 840840
Fax: 01962 841582
Chef: Mr C McBride
Owners: Mr & Mrs AF Smith
Cost: Fixed-price L £9.75/D £21.25. ☺ H/wine £12.95.
Times: Last L 2.15pm/D 9.30pm
Additional: Bar meals L; Sunday L; Children welcome; 🍴 dishes
Seats: 90. Private dining rooms 120
Smoking: No smoking in dining room; air-conditioning
Accommodation: 75 en suite
Credit cards: 🔳 🔳 🔳 🔳 🔳

WINCHESTER, **Wessex Hotel**

Imaginative cooking at this large modern hotel, especially of fresh fish and seafood. Grilled scallops came with a fine dill and saffron sauce, and well flavoured turbot with a confit of roast vegetables and a delicate lobster sauce. Summer pudding made a memorable dessert.

Directions: City centre close to cathedral

Paternoster Row SO23 9LQ
Map 4: SU42
Tel: 01962 861611
Fax: 01962 841503
Telephone for details

WINCHESTER, **Wykeham Arms**

Tucked away in the oldest part of the city, between the college and the cathedral, stands this attractive, atmospheric old pub. Good food in generous portions – perhaps mackerel fillets with garlic new potatoes, bacon and chilli salsa, or Aberdeen Angus steaks.

Additional: Bar Food L; No children under 14; ◑ dishes
Smoking: No-smoking areas
Accommodation: 13 en suite
Credit cards: ■ ▦ ▦ ⚛ ⚏ ▯

Directions: Head S out of city along Southgate Street. Take 3rd turning L into Canon Street, inn on R at end.

75 Kingsgate Street SO23 9PE
Map 4: SU42
Tel: 01962 853834
Fax: 01962 854411
Chefs: B Watson, G Strickland, H McLane
Owners: Graeme & Anne Jameson
Cost: *Alc* £17, fixed-price L £8. ☺
H/wine £9.25.
Times: Last L 2.30pm/D 9pm.
Closed 25 Dec

HEREFORDSHIRE

BRIMFIELD, **Poppies Restaurant**

As we went to press Carole Evans informed us that she had sold The Roebuck and further plans have yet to be finalised.

LEDBURY, **Feathers Hotel**

High Street HR8 1DS
Map 3: SO73
Tel: 01531 635266
Fax: 01531 632001
Chef: John Capaldi
Owner: Mr David Elliston
Cost: *Alc* £19.50. ☺
Times: Last L 2pm/last D 9.30pm
Additional: Sunday L; Children welcome; ◑ dishes
Smoking: No pipes and cigars
Accommodation: 11 en suite
Credit cards: ■ ▦ ▦ ⚛ ⚏ ▯

Centuries old timber-framed inn standing proudly in the centre of the High Street. Quills Restaurant is more formal, and there is also a brasserie, Fuggles. The varied menu with modern overtones includes crab terrine with orange, roast Herefordshire sirloin with red wine and thyme gravy, and spiced coconut lamb cutlets.

Directions: Ledbury is on A449/A438/A417, and the hotel is prominent on the main street

LEDBURY, Hope End Country House Hotel

The ornate but delightful old Georgian house, once the childhood home of Elizabeth Barrett Browning, is surrounded by 40 acres of restored eighteenth-century listed parkland. Pride of place, however, goes to the large walled kitchen garden, historic hothouse and orchards which are the source of the wonderfully fresh produce Patricia Hegarty uses in her traditional English cooking. The short, set-price *carte* is carefully constructed; smoked haddock pancakes, light and bursting with flavour, accompanied by a mild curry sauce, for example, is followed by a lean and tender best end of lamb served with a red wine gravy and redcurrant jelly. A simple but good selection of vegetables might consist of carrot batons, boiled and diced beetroot and riced potatoes. Elderflower sorbet or individual, creamy bay leaf custards with caramel cream and pralines may feature amongst the puddings. Other typical dishes include buttercup pumpkin soup, roast free-range chicken with sweet pepper and paprika sauce and baked fillet of Tweed salmon with lovage sauce – but it all depends on the season and what's growing in the garden.

Directions: From the centre of town, take B4214 Bromyard road, then 1st R after railway bridge, signed. Entrance on L

Hope End HR8 1JQ
Map 3: SO73
Tel: 01531 633613
Fax: 01531 636366
Chef: Patricia Hegarty
Owners: John & Patricia Hegarty
Cost: Fixed-price D £30 (3 courses). H/wine £8
Times: D only, 7.30pm-8.30pm. Closed late Dec- early Feb
Additional: 🍴 dishes
Seats: 24
Smoking: No smoking in dining room. Jacket & tie preferred
Accommodation: 8 en suite
Credit cards: ▭ ▭ ▭ ▭

LEOMINSTER, The Marsh Country Hotel

Eyton HR6 0AG
Map 3: SO45
Tel: 01568 613952
Chef: Jacqueline Gilleland
Owners: Jacqueline & Martin Gilleland
Cost: Fixed-price D £24.75. H/wine £10.50
Times: D only, 7.30pm-last D 8.30pm. Closed 3 wks Jan
Additional: Sunday L only (12.30pm-2pm); 🍴 dishes
Seats: 24
Smoking: No smoking in dining room
Accommodation: 4 en suite
Credit cards: ▭ ▭ ▭ ▭

Jacqueline and Martin Gilleland have worked hard as custodians and restorers of this historic fourteenth-century timber framed building. The interior is a delight and their garden is a joy throughout the year, with its 30 kinds of herbs, plentiful fruit and vegetables, and even a wildlife pond and a stream. Calm and tranquillity prevail. Jacqueline's fixed-price menus make full use of what the garden can deliver, as well as drawing on abundant local produce. The highlight of a recent inspection was breast of Hereford duck fanned on a heap of glorious creamed braised cabbage, accompanied by a duck liver tartlet and raspberries. Starters might include glazed eggs on a bed of leeks with watercress sauce or brill and scallop mousse with smoked mussels, while desserts could feature gingerbread pudding served on puréed banana and

accompanied by stewed rhubarb tinged with sweet cicely.
The eclectic wine list includes a trio from nearby Bodenham,
plus a few organics.

Directions: Two miles N/W of Leominster. Follow signs for
Eyton and Lucton

ROSS-ON-WYE, Chase Hotel ❀

Gloucester Road HR9 5LH
Map 3: SO52
Tel: 01989 763161
Fax: 01989 768330
Chef: Kenneth Tait
Owners: Camanoe Estates Ltd
Cost: Fixed-price L £12.50/D £25.
H/wine £9.25
Times: Last L 2pm/last D 9.45pm.
Closed L Sat

*Georgian mansion set in extensive grounds yet within walking
distance of the town centre. An inspection dinner in spring took in
chicken and sweetcorn soup, braised lamb shank with provençale
vegetables and a rosemary sauce, and red berry crème brûlée with a
home-made orange sorbet.*

Additional: Bar food L; Sunday L; Children welcome;
❀ dishes
Smoking: No pipes & cigars
Accommodation: 38 en suite
Credit cards: 🟦 🟦 🟦 🟦 🟦 🟦

Directions: From town centre follow B4260 towards Gloucester,
hotel 200yds on R

ROSS-ON-WYE,
Glewstone Court Hotel ❀

Glewstone HR9 6AW
Map 3: SO52
Tel: 01989 770367
Fax: 01989 770282
Chef: Christine Reeve-Tucker
Owners: Christine & William Reeve-
Tucker
Cost: Fixed-price D £24. ☺
H/wine £9.
Times: Last L 2pm/last D 9.30pm.
Closed 25-27 Dec
Additional: Bar food; Sunday L;
Children welcome; ❀ dishes

*Accomplished cooking in a lovely old Georgian house filled with an
eclectic collection of pictures, prints and china. Grilled loin of
venison steak is served with a damson gin jus on a rösti, and fillet of
English sea bass with sea asparagus and lemon butter. Leave room
for some 'boozy' Italian trifle.*

Smoking: No pipes and cigars in dining room
Credit cards: 🟦 🟦 🟦 🟦 🟦

Directions: From Ross Market Place take A40/A49
(Monmouth/Hereford) over Wilton Bridge. At roundabout L onto
A40 (Monmouth/S Wales), after 1 mile R for Glewstone

ROSS-ON-WYE, **The Royal Hotel**

Former coaching inn boasting commanding views over the River Wye. Traditional dishes are given a new look in pan-fried lamb cutlets with green-pea mousse, roast shallots and Madeira jus, and roast tenderloin of pork coated in sesame seeds and served with a tomato and garlic compote.

Additional: Bar meals L; Sunday L (12.30pm-2pm); Children welcome; ✦ dishes
Smoking: No smoking in dining room
Accommodation: 40 en suite
Credit cards: ▬ ▬ ▬ ▬ ▬ ▬

Directions: Midway between Gloucester and Hereford; situated in Ross-on-Wye town centre

Palace Pound, HR9 5HZ
Map 3: SO52
Tel: 01989 565105
Fax: 01989 768058
Chef: Paul Brady
Owners: The Royal Hotel (Forte UK)
Cost: Fixed-price D £19.95. ☺
H/wine £11.70.
Times: D only, 7pm-9.30pm.

RUCKHALL, **Ancient Camp Inn** ✸✸

You can truly feel as if you can see forever from the windows of this old inn, which looks down on the River Wye from a remote, high hillside. The beamed and stone-flagged bar serves real ale, and there are open fires both here and in the dining room. The dinner menu changes nightly – our inspector dined well off haggis in pastry with wild mushroom sauce, medallions of beef with mushrooms and truffles and a fine home-made lemon and lime cheesecake. Good ingredients are allowed to speak for themselves, and combinations such as Welsh rack of lamb with leek and mint, chicken suprême with a capsicum sauce, and fresh smoked haddock with quail egg mousse are simple but effective. Game is popular – maybe pheasant with spinach and pine nuts, or venison terrine with pistachio and redcurrant jelly. There are always plenty of takers for the Camp sticky toffee pudding with vanilla ice cream, but damson cheese and apple crumble would also be a nice, old-fashioned choice.

Directions: Take A465 (Abergavenny road) from Hereford. Turn R to Ruckhall and Belmont Abbey; inn is 2.5 miles along road

Nr Eaton Bishop
HR2 9QX
Map 3: SO54
Tel: 01981 250449
Fax: 01981 251581
Chef: Ewart McKie
Owners: Pauline & Ewart McKie
Cost: Alc £25. H/wine £8.50. ☺
Times: Noon-last L 2pm/7pm-last D 9pm. Closed D Sun, Mon , 1st 2wks Jan
Additional: Bar food L only; Sunday L; ✦ dishes
Seats: 40. Private dining room 40
Smoking: No smoking in dining room; air-conditioning
Accommodation: 5 en suite
Credit cards: ▬ ▬ ▬

ULLINGSWICK, **The Steppes** ✸✸

The listed fourteenth-century building is welcoming and cheerfully decorated. Its pluses include a dining room rich in oak beams, the original red and black tiled floor still intact, and a magnificent inglenook fireplace draped in local hops – 'a

Hereford HR1 3JG
Map 3: SO54
Tel: 01432 820424
Fax: 01432 820042
Chef: Tricia Howland
Owners: Henry & Tricia Howland

romantic setting for dinner by candlelight,' mused one lone inspector. The menus – one fixed-price standard menu, the chef's daily special, and a set four-course dinner – bristle with bright ideas. A typical example might be wild boar and juniper-berry pâté with Melba toast, followed by noisettes of Welsh lamb with paloise sauce and spinach bouchées, then a pudding of iced Drambuie mousse, and a selection of cheeses to finish. Dishes from the standard menu range through pork leg forestière, with brandy, cream and mushrooms, seafood casserole, with fresh salmon, cod, prawns and mussels in a creamy dill sauce, and Thai vegetables with lemon grass.

Cost: Fixed-price D £24 (4 courses).
☺ H/wine £6.95.
Times: D only, 7.30pm-last D 9pm
(Booking essential)
Additional: No children under 12;
🍴 dishes
Seats: 12. Jacket & tie preferred
Smoking: No smoking in dining room
Accommodation: 6 en suite
Credit cards: ▬ ▦ ▭ ▨ ▣

Directions: Off the A417 Gloucester to Leominster road

WALTERSTONE,
Allt-yr-Ynys Hotel ֎֎

Some of the buildings that make up this hotel date from 1550, and the massive beams, oak panelling and moulded ceilings are all authentic features. The house stands in 16 acres of woods and grounds, and its name, which means 'hill of the island', refers to the fact that it is surrounded by two rivers. The repertoire is enticing and takes vegetarianism in its stride; vegetarian dishes are flagged in the main menu and might include roasted shallot and artichoke tart with tomato and basil sauce. At a summer meal the kitchen won approval for very rare carpaccio of beef, beautifully presented and full of flavour, and fresh diper-caught scallops nicely seared and served with charred provençale vegetables – aubergine, courgette, tomato and black olives. Summer fruit crêpe for pudding proved large, light, refreshing and generously filled with strawberries and redcurrants.

Walterstone,
Hereford
HR2 0DU
Tel: 01873 890307
Fax: 01873 890539
Chef: Alan Robinson
Owner: Howard Williams
Cost: Fixed-price L £17.50/D £24.50
(3 courses). ☺ H/wine £8.50.
Times: 12.30pm-last L 2.15pm/7pm-last D 9.15pm. Closed Mon L
Additional: Sunday L; Children welcome; 🍴 dishes
Seats: 30. Private dining room 12
Smoking: No smoking in dining room
Accommodation: 20 en suite
Credit cards: ▬ ▦ ▭ ▨

Directions: 7 miles NE of Abergavenny, off A465

WEOBLEY,
Ye Olde Salutation Inn ֎֎

Market Pitch HR4 8SJ
Map 3: SO45
Tel: 01544 318443
Fax: 01544 318216
Chef: Mark Green
Owners: Mr & Mrs C Anthony
Cost: Alc £22. Fixed-price L £10 (3 courses). ☺ H/wine £8.25.
Times: Noon-last L 2pm/7pm-last D 9pm. Closed Sun, Mon, 25 Dec
Additional: Bar food 7 days; Sunday L; 🍴 dishes
Seats: 40.
Smoking: No smoking in dining room
Accommodation: 4 en suite
Credit cards: ▬ ▦ ▭ ▨ ▣ ▢

The spire of the 900 year old church dominates the black and white timbered medieval village, which is all set in a frame of gently wooded hills; it is very 'olde worlde' and goes down well with the tourists. At Ye Olde Salutation Inn the beams, timbers, log fires and drunken floors make an immediate, welcoming impact whether one is planning a simple bar snack or heading for the restaurant. The latter has been extended since our last visit but otherwise remains unchanged, continuing to offer a repertoire that veers between the traditional roast loin of lamb with a redcurrant and thyme flavoured sauce, and guinea fowl with its own stock flavoured with port wine and sage, to the modern invention of a warm salad of queen scallops flavoured with red pepper, lime and coconut or tenderloin of pork coated in Chinese-style spices with spring onion and orange. Leave room for the fine selection of local cheeses.

Directions: Down hill into village, take 1st R, then 2nd R

HERTFORDSHIRE

BISHOP'S STORTFORD,
The Mill at Gaston Green

A century-old working watermill, now home to the Mill Restaurant and the Granary. The more formal of the two, the Mill offers dishes such as roasted cod with shrimp gravy, lamb kidneys in grain mustard and beef stew and dumplings. The Granary features chargrilled steaks and several fish dishes.

Times: Last L 2.15pm/D 10.15pm. Closed Mon, L Sat, D Sun
Additional: Sunday L; Children welcome; 🍴 dishes
Credit cards: ▰ ▰ ▰ ▰ ▰

Directions: Off A1060 to Hatfield Heath

Old Mill Lane,
Gaston Green,
Little Hallingbury,
CM22 7QT
Map 4: TL52
Tel: 01279 726554/726914
Fax: 01279 722110
Chef: David Copoersmith
Owners: Oatmarsh Ltd
Cost: *Alc* £19, fixed-price L £10/D £16. ☺

ELSTREE, Edgwarebury Hotel

Barnet Lane WD6 3RE
Map 4: TG19
Tel: 0181 9538227
Fax: 0181 2073668
Chef: Chris Fisher
Cost: Fixed-price L&D £24-£30. ☺
H/wine £10.45.
Times: 12.30pm-last L 2.30pm/7pm-last D 10pm
Additional: Sunday L;
Children welcome; 🍴 dishes
Seats: 65. Private dining rooms 18 + 40
Smoking: No-smoking area
Accommodation: 47 en suite
Credit cards: ▰ ▰ ▰ ▰ ▰ ▰

Anyone with stars in their eyes will enjoy dining at this mock Tudor mansion, favourite theatrical 'digs' for many actors working at Elstree Studios nearby. If the celebrity count is low, then there is compensation in the shape of impressively presented dishes such as risotto of smoked bacon with Parmesan and tomato oil, grilled fillet of sea bass with mussels, spinach and shellfish butter sauce, nage of Cornish seafish with fennel, or roast rump of lamb with peas and mash. Luxury ingredients take a bow for supporting roles in ragout of goose with foie gras and morels, and pot-roasted duck with wild mushrooms and Périgord truffles. Sauces deserve a special credit. As well as a fixed-price menu, there is a 'Plain and Simple' menu, priced per item, which welcomes back old favourites such as leek and potato soup, grilled whole lemon sole, poached Tay salmon and chargrilled beef.

Directions: Access from Ml/J4 & 5, M25/J19 & 23, Barnet Lane is signed Elstree & Aldenham

HADLEY WOOD,
West Lodge Park Hotel ❀

Impressive Regency-style hotel set in peaceful parkland, owned by the same family for over 50 years. The Cedar restaurant has lovely garden views and offers an ambitious menu that takes in salmon and dill mousseline wrapped in lemon sole with watercress mayonnaise, and braised leg of lamb with apricot stuffing in a rosemary and red wine sauce.

Smoking: No smoking in dining room; air-conditioning
Accommodation: 45 en suite
Credit cards: 🔲 🔲 🔲 🔲 🔲

Cockfosters Road Hadley Wood
Barnet EN4 0PY
Map GtL: C5
Tel: 0181 4408311
Fax: 0181 4493698
Chef: Peter Leggat
Owners: The Beale family
Cost: Fixed-priced L £21.95/ D £24.95. ☺ H/wine £12.50.
Times: Last L 2pm/D 9.45pm
Additional: Bar Food; Sunday L; Children welcome

Directions: 1 mile S of M25 exit 24 on the A111; 1 mile from Cockfosters & Hadley Wood stations

HEMEL HEMPSTEAD,
The Bobsleigh Inn ❀

Successfully blending modern and traditional architecture, this improving hotel offers high standards of hospitality and service. Prime ingredients, including meat from the owner's butchery, produce an appealing range of dishes – perhaps shellfish soup and pork fillet stuffed with apricots and prunes with Armagnac sauce.

Additional: Bar meals; Children welcome; 🍴 dishes
Smoking: No pipes or cigars
Accommodation: 44 en suite
Credit cards: 🔲 🔲 🔲 🔲 🔲 🔲

Hempstead Road Bovingdon
HP3 0DS
Map 4: TL00
Tel: 01442 833276
Fax: 01442 832471
Chef: Stuart Ambury
Owners: Celia Derbyshire, Arthur Rickett
Cost: *Alc* £25, set L £14.95/D £18.95. ☺ H/wine £11.50.
Times: Last L 2pm/D 9.30pm. Closed Sun, Mon L, 26 Dec-Jan 4

Directions: From Hemel Hempstead take A4251 past station, L at Swan (B4505 to Chesham), 2 miles on L.

SAWBRIDGEWORTH, The Shoes ❀❀

In Victorian times, this attractive old building was a coaching inn, now it's a pleasant eating place serving the local neighbourhood well. The owners moved here from their original premises in High Ongar, but their style and menus continue in much the same vein. Good value fixed-price lunches (of two or three courses) feature creditable dishes such as pork terrine with piccalilli, accurately timed fillet of salmon with oriental stir-fried prawns and a spot-on hot orange soufflé with marmalade anglaise poured in afterwards. The *carte* ventures into the more heady realms of shallot tarte Tatin with pan-fried chicken livers and balsamic vinegar, seared scallops with black pudding and creamed garlic potatoes, and pan-fried

52 Bell Street CNM21 9AN
Map 4: TL41
Tel: 01279 722554
Chef: Mark Green
Owners: Lyndon Wootton, Peter & Doreen Gowan
Cost: *Alc* £25, fixed-price L £8.50-£11/D£17. ☺H/wine £10.25.
Times: Noon-last L 2pm/7pm-last D 9.30pm. Closed L Sat, Sun, L Mon, 2 wks Aug, 2 wks after Xmas, Bh Mon
Additional: Children welcome; 🍴 dishes
Seats: 60

fillet steak with grilled onion polenta and tomato jus. Service is professional but friendly, and the wine list offers a fair range at reasonable prices.

Directions: From M11/J7 take A414 (Harlow); continue as road becomes A1186 (Bishop's Stortford). Sawbridgeworth is midway between Harlow and Bishop's Stortford

The Shoes

Smoking: Separate no-smoking area
Credit cards: ▉ ▉ 🗫 🗫 💳

ST ALBANS, Noke Thistle

Watford Road AL2 3DS
Map 4: TL10
Tel: 01727 854252
Fax: 01727 841906
Chef: Andrew Stickings
Owner: Thistle Hotels
Cost: *Alc* £30, fixed-price L £19.50/D from £23. ☺ H/wine £11.25.
Times: Last L 1.45pm/D 9.45pm. Closed L Sat, 27-31 Dec
Additional: Sunday L; Children welcome; ⌗ dishes
Smoking: No pipes and cigars; air-conditioning
Accommodation: 111 en suite
Credit cards: ▉ ▉ ▉ 🗫 💳 💳

The hotel is set in open countryside on the edge of St Albans, and its main restaurant, Bertie's, has a good local reputation. The highlight of a test meal was a Welsh goat's cheese gâteau, of excellent texture and flavour, followed by chicken breast with a prawn and basil mousse.

Directions: On A4O5, Watford road; from M25/J21A, 1st roundabout, turn L

ST ALBANS,
Sopwell House Hotel ⌗⌗

The grace, colour and style of architecture reflect the time when the building and surrounding land was owned by the Mountbatten family. Within, there is a choice of various lounges, a popular modern conference centre, and two restaurants; snacks and light dishes are offered in the Brasserie, formal meals in the Magnolia Conservatory restaurant. In the latter, terrine of chicken liver and foie gras

Cottonmill Lane Sopwell AL1 2HQ
Map 4: TL10
Tel: 01727 864477
Fax: 01727 844741
Chef: Warren Jones
Cost: *Alc* £45, fixed-price L £17.50/D £23.50. ☺ H/wine £12.95.
Times: 12.30pm-3pm/7.30pm-10pm. Closed L Sat, D Sun

Sopwell House Hotel

Additional: Bar food; Sunday L;
Children welcome; ❹ dishes
Seats: 120. Private dining rooms up to
350. Jacket & tie preferred
Smoking: No smoking in dining room
Accommodation: 92 en suite
Credit cards: ▨ ▨ ▨ ▨ ▨ ▨

with a Cumberland sauce, mille-feuille of salmon with glazed
new potatoes and asparagus spears, or fillet of beef on a potato
galette with Savoy cabbage, oyster mushrooms and a tarragon
jus, show a kitchen working well within the modern idiom
without resorting to wild ideas. Careful construction was
evident at an early summer dinner that took in roasted scallops
with marinated vegetables and basil vinaigrette, suprême of
guinea fowl with pearl barley risotto and celeriac ravioli, and
pear tart.

Directions: On London road from St Albans follow signs to
Sopwell, over mini-roundabout, hotel is on L

TRING,
Rose and Crown Hotel

High Street HP23 5AH
Map 4: SP91
Tel: 01442 824071
Fax: 01442 890735
Chef: Greig Barnes
Owners: Mr and Mrs C E Wilson
Cost: *Alc* £22.63, fixed-price L
£12.95/D £19.95. ☺ H/wine £9.75.
Times: Last L 2pm/D 9.45pm
Closed D Sun
Additional: Bar food; Sunday L;
Children welcome; ❹ dishes

*Built by the Rothschild family as a coaching inn in 1904, this
imposing Tudor-style hotel offers imaginatively cooked food in the
attractive, split-level Carriages Restaurant. The extensive carte may
list creamed fennel and herb soup, salmon with apple purée, cider
sabayon and sage sauce, and iced nougat parfait.*

Smoking: No-smoking area in dining room
Accommodation: 27 en suite
Credit cards: ▨ ▨ ▨ ▨ ▨ ▨

Directions: Just off A41 between Aylesbury and Hemel
Hempstead, 1.5 miles from Tring station

WARE,
Marriott Hanbury Manor 🌼🌼🌼

Thundridge SG12 0SD
Map 5: TL31
Tel: 01920 487722
Fax: 01920 487692
Chef: Robert Gleeson
Cost: *Alc* £40, fixed-price L £23.50/D
£31.50. H/wine £19.50
Times: 12.30pm-last L
2.30pm/7.30pm-last D 9.30pm
Additional: Bar food; Sunday L;
No children under 8 at dinner
Seats: 45. Private dining room 20.
Jacket & tie preferred at D

The nineteenth-century baronial grandeur of the panelled Oak
Hall does not prepare the visitor for the creamy white elegance
of the Zodiac Restaurant, originally designed as a summer
drawing room for the Hanbury family by Sir Ernest George,
architect of Claridges. The name comes from the signs of the
zodiac carved into the ceiling; the culinary stars are now in the
hands of ex-Dorchester chef Robert Gleeson. The *carte* at this
international, executive country-club hotel is suitably lengthy,
luxurious and expensive, with separate fish and soup listings.
Dishes are priced in words, not numbers – perhaps fifty eight
pounds for Beluga caviar with blinis and vodka, seems less

Marriott Hanbury Manor

Smoking: No smoking in dining room
Accommodation: 96 en suite
Credit cards:

damaging to the expense account than £58. Other grand
classics include soufflé suissesse, terrine of chicken and foie
gras with wild mushrooms and truffle vinaigrette, roast pavé of
turbot with spinach, baby leeks and grain mustard sauce, and
braised haunch of venison in red wine with celeriac purée,
chestnuts and roast vegetables. There are modern classics in
the repertoire, dishes such as cappuccino of langoustine, red
mullet with aubergine caviar and basil, and noisette of
monkfish with basil risotto and porcini mushrooms. Ingredients
are of the highest standard – sauté of black leg chicken comes
with young leeks, carrots, girolles and champagne and tarragon
cream, for example. Vegetarian meals are prepared on request.
Simpler meals are served either in The Conservatory,
overlooking the 18 hole championship golf course, or the
brasserie-style Vardon's.

Directions: On A10 just 12 miles N of M25/J25

KENT

ASHFORD, **Eastwell Manor** ❀❀❀

Eastwell Park Boughton Lees
TN25 4HR
Map 5: TR04
Tel: 01233 219955
Fax: 01233 635530
Chef: Ian Mansfield
Owner: Mr T F Parrett
Cost: *Alc* £39.50, fixed-price L
£16.50/D £28.50. H/wine £15
Times: Noon-last L 2pm/7.30-last D
9.30pm
Additional: Bar food; Sunday L;
Children welcome; ❸ dishes
Seats: 65. Private dining room 45-70
Smoking: No smoking in dining room
Accommodation: 23 en suite
Credit cards:

Settings do not come much grander than this. Eastwell Manor,
an awesome Jacobean-style edifice, nestles in 62 acres of
magnificently laid out grounds which form part of a 3,000 acre
estate. It should come as no surprise that the place claims royal
connections: Queen Victoria and King Edward VII were
frequent visitors and a Queen of Rumania was born in the

house. Today the Manor plays heavily on its past, but is highly sought after for all kinds of occasions and meetings. The dining room is a resplendent 'baronial hall' complete with oak panelling, chandeliers and leaded windows: a pianist tinkles at the baby grand, service involves the ritual lifting of cloches. Ian Mansfield's cooking is in tune with all of this, although he has a lightness of touch and a thoroughly modern view of things gastronomic. His menus follow the seasons and his style is typified by dishes such as warm quail and boudin blanc with leeks in a black truffle vinaigrette (which might be offered as an amuse bouche), seared scallops with beetroot jus, Bramley apple and ginger purée, or roast sea bass with crushed new potatoes, courgettes, fennel and tomatoes. The highlight of a recent inspection, however, was a 'tremendous' dish consisting of pan-fried fillet and leg confit of rabbit with sautéed liver and heart, accompanied by spears of fresh asparagus, baby vegetables and a leek risotto. It was simply dazzling. As you might expect, desserts aim for heart-stopping accomplishment: iced chocolate truffles with a chocolate box filled with orange confit was triumphantly rich, otherwise there might be blueberry tart with lemon grass ice-cream or mille-feuille of strawberries, mascarpone, vanilla and Kirsch. Some lusty mark-ups mean that it is quite possible to spend over £15 on some characterless wines but there's plenty of worthwhile drinking for an extra fiver or so, particularly from the New World. Dip into New Zealand for the vibrant Palliser Estate Sauvignon Blanc at £23.50.

Directions: M2O/J9 follow A251 Faversham, hotel on L after Kennington. From Canterbury, A28 to Ashford L turn to Boughton Lees.

BIDDENDEN,
Ristorante da Claudio ❀❀

West House High Street TN27 8AH
Map 5: TQ83
Tel: 01580 291341
Chef/Owner: Claudio Covelli
Cost: *Alc* £16, fixed-price L&D £14.95. ☺ H/wine £9.80.
Times: Noon-last L 2.30pm/7pm-last D 10.30pm. Closed D Sun, Mon, 1 wk Jan/May/Oct
Seats: 40
Credit cards: 🟦 🟦 🟦 🟦 🟦 🟦

First-rate pan-fried fillet of sea bass with a lime-flavoured sauce was the centrepiece of an enjoyable meal at this Italian restaurant set in a fifteenth-century timber-framed building with original oak beams and a huge fireplace. Our inspector thoroughly approved of a rich fish soup, more in the French style than the Italian, but none the worse for that, and an apricot tart with almond frangipane and home-made vanilla ice cream. The *carte* is relatively short, but contains some interesting regional Italian cooking such as sweet and sour duck, rabbit casserole with anchovies, garlic and white wine, and cannoli biscuits alla Siciliana (with ricotta and candied fruit filling). Seafood tagliatelle, roast peppers with mozzarella cheese and fillet of lamb in a rosemary and garlic sauce are more familiar mainstream dishes, but look out for the daily specials. Italian wines are very reasonably priced and include some good vintage Barolo.

Directions: On High Street

BRANDS HATCH,
Brandshatch Place ❀❀

Fawkham DA3 8NQ
Map 5: TQ56
Tel: 01474 872239
Fax: 01474 879652
Chef: Alan White

The views of the racing paddock might have inspired the rather daring, high-octane menu at this country house hotel. Ideas such as chargrilled marinated vegetables with Stilton and balsamic ripple ice cream and roast pepper essence, roast loin of lamb, seared kidney and sweet bread pudding, and seared cod fillet with lobster risotto, poached egg and caviar might be rather risky in the wrong hands, but a test drive of a cannon of roe deer with bitter chocolate sauce made it through the chequered flag with ease. A delicately flavoured first course of tortellini and seared scallops with leeks and vanilla jus would have been more of a contender if the pasta had not been quite so thick. Armagnac parfait with prune and Earl Grey syrup arrived with a fabulous barley sugar twist with poppy seeds. Burnt vanilla custard with Ovaltine ice cream, however, may be just the thing to ensure a good night's rest before the big race, particularly on top of a sampling of the wine list put together by John Hoskins, an award-winning Master of Wine.

Directions: Off A20, M25/J3, follow signs for Circuit then Fawkham; 2nd turn R after motorway bridge

Owners: Arcadian Hotels
Cost: Alc £25, fixed-price L £14.95/D £19.95. ☺ H/wine £12.50.
Times: 12.30pm-last L 1.45pm/7pm-last D 9.15pm. Closed L Sat, L Bh Mon
Additional: Sunday L; Children welcome; ❸ dishes
Seats: 60. Private dining room 30-40
Smoking: No smoking in dining room
Accommodation: 41 en suite
Credit cards: 🖃 🖃 🖃 🖃 🖃

BROADSTAIRS,

Royal Albion Hotel ❀

Albion Street
CT10 1LU
Map 5: TR36
Tel: 01843 862481
Fax: 01843 861509
Chef: Steven Watson
Owners: John, David & Peter Roger
Cost: Alc £22, fixed-price L £11/ D £15.50. ☺ H/wine £8.50.
Times: Last L 2pm/D 9.30pm Closed Sun D, 27-30 Dec
Additional: Sunday L; Children welcome; ❸ dishes
Smoking: No-smoking area
Credit cards: 🖃 🖃 🖃 🖃 🖃

Marchesi's is two doors down from this favourite seafront hotel. Established in 1886, it continues to woo Kent holidaymakers with safe and sound continental cooking. Seafood shows up well, otherwise there might be asparagus with hollandaise, honey-glazed duck breast and fillet steak with red wine sauce and wild mushrooms. Personal service, impressive wines.

Directions: Town centre – down High Street, turn right into Albion Street 50 yards on R

CANTERBURY,

Canterbury Hotel ❀❀

Within walking distance of the city centre, one enters this small hotel through a wrap-around car park, but is soon charmed by the place's plain-spoken simplicity. A tiny bar, a bright, sunny yellow dining room, some fresh flowers and pleasant, accommodating staff auger well. French chef Jean-Luc Jouvente was trained classically, latter years have been spent in the south of France, and his repertoire, therefore, is very much neo-classical French cuisine with an emphasis on technique and sauces. Accuracy and refinement do seem to be on offer,

71 New Dover Road
CT1 3DZ
Map 5: TR15
Tel: 01227 450551
Fax: 01227 780145
Chef: Jean Luc Jouvente
Owners: Mr & Mrs F Bevan
Cost: Alc £17.50, fixed-price L £10.50/D £15.50. ☺ H/wine £7.95.
Times: Last L 2pm/D 10pm

evinced by a spring lunch that took in smoked chicken terrine, pan-fried noisettes of swordfish with a basil sauce and deep-fried courgettes, and supreme of chicken stuffed with langoustines and served with buttered spinach and a light curry sauce. Home-made ravioli with langoustine sauce were also sampled and were good. Tiramisu was outstanding, but strong competition was offered by a tarte Tatin.

Additional: Bar meals L; Children welcome; 🍴 dishes
Seats: 65
Accommodation: 26 en suite
Credit cards: ▆ ▆ ▆ ▆

Directions: On A2, Dover road

CANTERBURY, Ebury Hotel ✿

Family-run hotel quietly situated in pretty gardens just outside the city centre. The food is good. Cream of mussel soup with julienne of vegetables and light curry seasoning, Thai chicken with rice pilaff, and strawberry shortbread, from a carte that shows a modish global influence, as well as a fondness for chargrilling.

Additional: Children welcome; 🍴 dishes
Smoking: No-smoking area
Accommodation: 15 en suite
Credit cards: ▆ ▆ ▆ ▆ ▆

65-67 New Dover Road CT1 3DX
Map 5: TR15
Tel: 01227 768433
Fax: 01227 459187
Chef: Henry Leach
Cost: *Alc* £13.50. H/wine £8.50. ☺
Times: D only, 7pm-8.30pm

Directions: Follow ring road around Canterbury. Turn into New Dover Road (signed for Dover), past Safeways, over traffic lights. Hotel on R.

CANTERBURY, Falstaff Hotel ✿

Beamed fifteenth-century inn built to accommodate pilgrims, and set by the impressive Westgate. Modern travellers to this historic city can sample chicken liver parfait, pan-fried guinea fowl with wild mushroom and red wine sauce, plus a tangy lemon tart.

Additional: Bar meals; Sunday L; Children welcome; 🍴 dishes
Smoking: No smoking in dining room
Accommodation: 24 en suite
Credit cards: ▆ ▆ ▆ ▆ ▆ ▆

St Dunstans Street CT2 8AF
Map 5: TR15
Tel: 01227 462138
Fax: 01227 463525
Chef: Anthony Drewe
Owner: Regal Hotels
Cost: *Alc* £16, fixed-price L&D £14. ☺ H/wine £9.95.
Times: Last L 2pm/last D 9.45pm

Directions: Turn into St Peters Place off the A2, pass Westgate Towers into St Dunstans St, hotel on right

CANTERBURY,

Ristorante Tuo e Mio ✿

Long-standing Italian serving traditional trattoria dishes. A meal in April featured a spicy fish soup, fettucine with smoked salmon and cream sauce, and gnocchi tartufo with a mushroom and truffle sauce. Service comes with the usual banter from the pepper mill wielding waiters!

Additional: Sunday L; Children welcome; 🍴 dishes
Smoking: No cigars or pipes
Credit cards: ▆ ▆ ▆ ▆ ▆ ▆

16 The Borough CT1 2DR
Map 5: TR15
Tel: 01227 761471
Chefs: M Orietti, J Mula
Owner: R P M Greggio
Cost: *Alc* £25, fixed-price L £13.50. ☺ H/wine £8.50.
Times: Last L 2.30pm/D 10.45pm Closed Mon, L Tue, last 2 wks Feb, last 2 wks Aug

Directions: Opposite King's School

CRANBROOK, **Kennel Holt Hotel**

Goudhurst Road TN17 2PT
Map 5: TQ73
Tel: 01580 712032
Fax: 01580 715495
Chef: Neil Chalmers
Owners: Neil & Sally Chalmers
Cost: Fixed-price L & D £22.50-
£27.50(3/4 course). H/wine £12
Times: 12.30pm-last L
1.30pm/7.30pm-last D 9pm.
Closed D Sun, all Mon, L Sat,
3 wks Jan
Additional: Sunday L (Oct-March);
No children under 10; ⊕ dishes
Seats: 25. Private dining room 16
Smoking: No smoking in dining room
Accommodation: 10 en suite
Credit cards: ¡ ™ # ¶ •

*Relaxing, family-run Elizabethan manor house set in five lovely acres.
Beams, oak panelling and log fires characterise the intimate restaurant.
An interesting fixed-price menu, from chef/proprietor Neil Chalmers,
may offer fishcake with lemon and coriander sauce, monkfish with
bean and chorizo casserole and tarte Tatin. Good wine list.*

Directions: On A262 1 mile from A229 crossroad, 3 miles from
Goudhurst towards Cranbrook

CRANBROOK, **Soho South**

Stone Street TN17 3HF
Map 5: TQ73
Tel: 01580 714666
Fax: 01580 715653
Chef: Nigel Tarr
Owner: Nigel & Linnea Tarr
Cost: Alc £19.80. H/wine £8.30. ☺
Times: 11am – 4pm, 6.30pm – last D
9pm. Closed Sun, Mon, D Tues
Additional: Children welcome;
⊕ dishes
Seats: 30
Smoking: No pipes & cigars
Credit cards: ■ ■ ▓ ▢

Nigel and Linnea Tarr's stylish restaurant is in an ancient
building dating from 1560 that was originally part of a Flemish
weaving factory. Now it has been transformed into a smart,
open-plan eating place with natural wood floors, oak beams
and exposed brick walls; shelves of home-made pickles,
vinegars, dried fungi and potted fruit add a touch colour. A
short, all-day 'bistrot' menu offers good value in the shape of
fish soup with croûtons, coq au vin and Irish stew with parsley
dumplings. In the evening there's a weekly-changing *carte* that
shows a touch more ambition: cold confit of pork belly comes
with Arrac-flavoured lentils and plum chutney, chargrilled loin
of veal is accompanied by honey-glazed pear, olive oil and
Parmesan mash and seared leeks, while guinea fowl might be
pot-roasted with rum and served on tagliatelle with wild
mushrooms. A lively choice of desserts includes lemon
syllabub with candied peel, fresh figs and almond ice cream,
and iced Grand Marnier soufflé. The shortish wine list is
bolstered by some serious vintages for moneyed enthusiasts.

Directions: In town centre, opposite
Barclays Bank, 50 metres from tourist
info centre & church

DEAL,
Dunkerleys Restaurant ❀❀

Smart Victorian, sea-front town house, refurbished and
extended into the building next door to create a bar and a
long, narrow restaurant that has one wall mirrored to give the
impression of size, the other covered in large panels with
pencil sketches of local people and scenes. The kitchen shows
ambition and puts a lot of effort into the cooking. Go for the
carte as this offers some inspired dishes with a light modern
outlook. Chicken liver parfait, roast sea bass on a bed of oyster
mushrooms, beurre blanc sauce with tomato and herbs, good
fresh vegetables, and an excellent cinnamon brûlée made up
one well liked inspection meal. Otherwise, there's grilled
Dover sole, filleted skate wing with capers, turned cucumber
and pesto sauce, as well as crab bisque or prawn cocktail. Ice
creams and sorbets are home-made.

Directions: Turn off A2 onto A258 to Deal – 100 yds before
Deal Pier

19 Beach Street CT14 7AH
Map 5: TR35
Tel: 01304 375016
Fax: 01304 380187
Chef: Stephen Harvey
Owners: Ian & Linda Dunkerley
Cost: *Alc* £22.50, fixed-price lunch
£9.50. ☺ H/wine £8.25.
Times: Last L 2.30pm/D 10pm
Closed D Sun, Mon, 5-19 Jan
Additional: Bar meals; Sunday L;
Children welcome; ◑ dishes
Smoking: No-smoking area;
air-conditioning
Accommodation: 6 en suite
Credit cards: ▰ ▰ ▰ ▰ ▱ ▱

DOVER, Wallett's Court ❀❀❀

The Oakleys run Wallett's Court their way, and it is very much
a hands-on operation for the whole family. The lovely
Jacobean manor house has an old-style dining room with
views onto mature gardens, although in summer the
conservatory dining room comes into its own when drinks can
be taken on the terrace. The individualistic cooking of Chris
Oakley is based on a classic approach, is built around big,
bold flavours and employs the finest materials. The intentions
are not complicated, methods may be direct but they are
never crude. Thus Kentish wild boar appears as pan-fried
fillets in a creamy green peppercorn sauce with caramelised
Cox's apples, and a brace of whole roasted quails come with a
Madeira sauce and a compote of new season's rhubarb. A
winter dinner produced game terrine with pumpkin chutney,
crab cakes with ginger on a light pimento sauce with stir-fried
assorted peppers, and a lemon tart. On another occasion a
gratin of Cromer crab came with avocado, was topped with
grilled goat's cheese, and served with a roasted pepper salad,
whilst new seasons Romney Marsh lamb was baked with fresh
rosemary and served with a mushroom duxelle and potato
rösti.
   Signature dishes: Mad March hare jugged in red wine with
creamed potatoes; fillets of Dover sole Leonora; Whitstable
rock oysters and queen scallops braised in saffron sauce with a
concasse of roasted peppers; baked haunch of Wadhurst Park
venison in a ginger wine sauce with Kentish cherries.

Directions: From A2 take A258 (Dover/Deal) 1st R to St
Margarets, hotel on R

West Cliffe St Margarets-at-Cliffe
CT15 6EW
Map 5: TR34
Tel: 01304 852424
Fax: 01304 853430
Chef: Christopher Oakley
Owners: The Oakley Family
Cost: *Alc* D £25.
Times: 7pm-last D 8.30pm.
Closed 1 wk Xmas
Additional: Sunday L (noon-2pm);
Children welcome; ◑ dishes
Seats: 60. Private dining room 34
Smoking: No smoking in dining room
Accommodation: 12 en suite
Credit cards: ▰ ▰ ▰ ▰ ▱ ▱

EDENBRIDGE,
Honours Mill Restaurant ❀

An old mill with a small bar and an upstairs restaurant supporting a
wealth of original beams. A test meal produced well made onion
tartlets, good home-made white rolls, smoked haddock and dill

87 High Street
TN8 5AU
Map 5: TQ44
Tel: 01732 866757
Chef: Martin Radmall

sausage with a mild curry sauce, sautéed magret of duck, confit of duck, foie gras mash and raspberry vinegar sauce, and caramelised rice pudding with roasted apples and an apple caramel sauce.

Additional: Sunday L; Children welcome on Sundays
Credit cards: 〓 〓 〓 〓

Directions: Town centre, southern end of High Street, just N of the bridge

Owners: Neville, Duncan, Giles Goodhew
Cost: Fixed-price L (Tue-Fri only) £15.50/D (Tue-Fri only) £26. ☺ H/wine £10.15.
Times: Last L 2pm/last D 10pm. Closed L Sat, D Sun, Mon, 2 wks Xmas

FAVERSHAM, Read's ✿✿✿

'We are aware of the limitations of the front exterior', writes Rona Pitchford, 'and concentrate our efforts on the inside and back of the restaurant, which has a beautiful view over the Belmont Valley.' It's twenty years since the Pitchfords took over this former supermarket and transformed it into one of the best restaurants in Kent, and David Pitchford's cooking continues to go from strength to strength. The style is carefully considered, fresh produce soundly sourced, and not one ingredient is used because it is currently fashionable, but because it works well within the framework of ideas. There is a certain refined richness. In duck liver parfait with toasted brioche, a salad of mixed leaves and a three mustard dressing, for example, or fillet of Whitstable codling with a fresh crabmeat crust on a bed of leaf spinach with a Chardonnay sauce, and ribeye of Aberdeen Angus beef served with crispy onions, Cumbrian air-dried ham and field mushrooms and peppercorn sauce, the richness is self-evident, but then so is the competence. There is an enthusiasm for grouping elements of a dish: lightly smoked Scottish salmon goes out with a partner of smoked salmon mousse, a pork cutlet is paired with a black pudding mousse, bacon braised Savoy cabbage and balanced by caramelised Cox's orange pippins. Desserts range from marinated orange segments glazed in a Grand Marnier sabayon with home-made almond ice cream to a chocoholics anonymous of mousse, marquise, sorbet, truffle cake and white chocolate ice cream. Heaven. Service, by young, smartly uniformed staff, is pleasant and well-supervised by Rona Pitchford. The full wine list runs to over 250 bins and as each has at least some description, the abbreviated *carte* of 40 or so of the more reasonable items is a thoughtful addition. Louis Latour's stylish Ardèche Chardonnay at £14 and Gigondas from Domaine Saint Gayan at £17 are evidence that one may not feel the need to delve deeper.
Signature dishes: Romney Marsh lamb with Mediterranean vegetables, garlicky potatoes; sea scallops on Jersey royal potatoes with fresh asparagus and white truffle oil; breast of pheasant on a bed of braised red cabbage, prune and bacon rolls, gaufrette potatoes; hot apricot soufflé with almond ice cream.

Directions: M2/J6, turn L onto A2, then L into Brogdale Road, signposted Painters Forstal 1.5 miles S of Faversham

Painters Forstal ME13 0EE
Map 5: TR06
Tel: 01795 535344
Fax: 01795 591200
Chef: David Pitchford
Owners: Rona & David Pitchford
Cost: *Alc* £34, fixed-price L £16.50/D £20. ☺ H/wine £14.
Times: Noon-last L 2pm/7pm-last D 10pm. Closed Sun, Mon, Bhs
Additional: Children welcome; ♨ dishes
Seats: 40. Private dining room 20
Smoking: No pipes or cigars
Credit cards: 〓 〓 〓 〓 〓

FOLKESTONE, **Paul's Restaurant**

The secret of longevity, if Paul's is anything to go by, is sound bistro cooking. A lengthy choice ranges from fillets of sea bass steamed on a bed of leeks, mushrooms and lemon juice, to braised lamb neck fillet with a rich, creamy whole grain mustard and onion sauce. Desserts are served from the trolley. An extensive and well-priced wine list reflects the eponymous Paul's considerable personal interest in the subject.

Credit cards: ▬ ▦ ▩ ▧

Directions: Opposite Sainsburys, 50 yds from bus station

2A Bouverie Road West CT20 2RX
Map 5: TR23
Tel: 01303 259697
Fax: 01303 226647
Chefs: Paul & Penny Hagger, Darren Byer
Owners: Paul & Penny Hagger
Cost: *Alc* £18.95, fixed-price L £4.95 (1 course + coffee). ☺ H/wine £8.95
Times: Last L 2.30pm/last D 9.30pm. Closed Xmas (3 days)
Additional: Sunday L; Children welcome; ⚫ dishes

FOLKESTONE, **Sandgate Hotel**

The marriage of English hospitality with French flair is a felicitous one at this small, personally run seafront hotel and restaurant. La Terrasse, as its name suggests, opens onto a terrace that looks towards France, as do chef/patron Samuel Gicqueau's masterful classic dishes, outstanding pâtisserie and well-crafted sauces. This is a kitchen of serious gastronomic intent, displayed in the context of an interesting (French-written) *carte* and competitively priced set menu. A winter inspection meal showed a typically high level of technical skill. Canapés of salmon tartlette, crab toast and tiny gougères, plus a choice of excellent home-made bread rolls, were followed by caille pressé – beautifully moist terrine of quail layered with foie gras, served with crab-apple jelly and mixed leaves coated with walnut dressing. This fine first course was matched by a main one of tender, succulent monkfish and baby beetroot, turnip, fennel, leek and carrot with beurre blanc. The dessert, moelleux chocolat, however, stole the show – sinfully rich and dark chocolate with an almond cream and verbena ice cream. Richly-flavoured cafetière coffee with petits fours can be taken in the stylish yellow and blue dining-room, hung with oil paintings of French scenes, the comfortable lounge/bar, or in fine weather, on the terrace. Not surprisingly, the serious, well-balanced wine list is mostly French, and it is worth taking advice from the knowledgeable manager, M. Joel.

Signature dishes: Coquilles St Jacques lardées de poitrine fumée sur un coussin d'epinards au beurre d'orange; ecrevisses glacées de sauce Nantua gratinée; raviolis de homard de la Baie de Hythe et beurre a l'estragon; ballotine de foie gras au torchon et gelée au Sauternes.

Directions: On the A259 coastal road in Sandgate, between Hythe and Folkestone

The Esplanade CT20 3DY
Map 5: TR13
Tel: 01303 220444
Fax: 01303 220496
Chef: Samuel Gicqueau
Owners: Samuel Gicqueau, Zara Jackson
Cost: *Alc* £35, fixed-price L/D £18.50 (3 courses). H/wine £11.50
Times: Noon-last L 1.30pm/7pm-last D 9.30pm. Closed Sun D, Mon, mid Jan-mid Feb
Additional: Children welcome; ⚫ dishes
Seats: 24.
Smoking: No smoking in dining room
Accommodation: 15 en suite
Credit cards: ▬ ▦ ▦ ▩ ▧ ▧

HYTHE, **Imperial Hotel** ❀

A magnificent Victorian building set in 50 acres of prime seafront. Carefully prepared dishes, making good use of fresh ingredients, are served in the informal bistro and in the well-appointed restaurant. At inspection, the latter yielded a well-made monkfish mousse, breast of duck with honey sauce and a good summer pudding.

Accommodation: 100 en suite. **Credit cards:** ▬ ▦ ▦ ▩ ▧ ▧

Directions: M20/J11/A261 to Hythe; follow signs to Folkestone, turn R into Twiss Rd opposite Bell Inn towards seafront

Princes Parade CT21 6AE
Map 5: TR13
Tel: 01303 267441
Fax: 01303 264610
Chef: Michael Rieder
Cost: *Alc* £30, fixed-price L £16/D £22. ☺ H/wine £12.50.
Times: Last L 2pm/last D 9.30pm. Closed L Sat
Additional: Bar food; Sunday L; Children welcome; ⚫ dishes
Smoking: No smoking in dining room

HYTHE, **Stade Court Hotel**

Built in 1938 on the seafront, just yards from the shingle beach, Stade Court offers sound hospitality and some promising cooking in the smartly appointed restaurant. Dishes enjoyed at inspection included ravioli of crab, tender roast duck with Calvados sauce and warm apple tart.

Additional: Sunday L; Bar meals; Children welcome;
🍴 dishes
Smoking: No-smoking area
Accommodation: 42 en suite
Credit cards: 🌑 🌑 🌑 🌑 🌑 🌑

Directions: M20, J11 on A261

West Parade
CT21 6DT
Map 5: TR13
Tel: 01303 268263
Fax: 01303 261803
Chef: Kevin Lea
Owner: Marston Hotels
Cost: *Alc* £26, set L £12.50/D £16.95.
☺ H/wine £9.10
Times: Last L 2pm/D 9pm (9.30pm Fri & Sat)

IVY HATCH, **The Plough**

A splendid village pub with a good local trade and a conservatory restaurant. The carte runs alongside a separate fish and seafood menu, which has a growing reputation. A huge bowl of 'meaty' fish soup had a lovely rich flavour, followed by wonderfully fresh red mullet with Cajun spices.

Additional: Bar meals; Sunday L; Children welcome; 🍴 dishes
Smoking: No pipes & cigars; air conditioning
Credit cards: 🌑 🌑 🌑 🌑

Directions: In village centre

Coach Road Ivy Hatch Sevenoaks
TN15 0NL
Map 5: TQ55
Tel/Fax: 01732 810268
Chef: Daniel Humbert
Owner: Six Bells Limited
Cost: *Alc* £18. H/wine £9.50.
Times: Last L 2pm/D 10pm. Closed D Sun

LENHAM, **Chilston Park**

Map 5: TQ85
Tel: 01622 859803
Fax: 01622 858588

This is a most extraordinary place, a cross between an antique collector's emporium and an eccentric theatrical stage set; even the staff dress up. The cooking derives inspiration from the setting, and the main menu is continually evolving, although popular favourites are retained. There's a minimum charge for dinner, and you are encouraged to opt for the six-course menu which includes soup and 'water ice'. Dishes are described with a suitably flourish – 'mosaic of guinea fowl studded with blueberries, enhanced with ginger and rosemary, complemented with a balsamic and truffle oil'. The cooking, however, is well-crafted and brings out the flavours of good quality ingredients. Desserts are less effusively announced, and as well as the likes of iced orange and mint parfait presented on a pool of apricot purée, there is an annotated, thoughtful British cheese menu.

Directions: Telephone for directions

LENHAM, **The Lime Tree**

The setting is a fourteenth-century building in the main square. Within, there are plenty of beams, high back carvery chairs, round tables, fresh flowers and no less than two open fires. The menu, in French with English subtitles, offers a repertoire that is mainstream French in style, with a few modern touches here and there. However, the cooking has shown signs of unevenness, with a dinner in January contrasting 'unappetising straight from the fridge' vol au vents with good, home-made ravioli, correctly cooked, and filled with a ricotta and spinach

8-10 The Limes
The Square ME17 2PL
Map 5: TQ75
Tel: 01622 859509
Fax: 01622 850096
Chef: Musa Kivrak
Owners: Mr & Mrs Kivrak
Cost: Fixed-price L £16.95/D £20.95 (3 courses). H/wine £10.95
Times: Noon-last L 1.30pm/7pm-last D 10pm. Closed D Sun, L Mon & Sat

farce on a creamy tomato and basil sauce. The main dish of monkfish served on a wild mushroom and onion base with a simple, creamy white wine sauce was also workmanlike, even if the panache of vegetables on the side were unevenly cooked. Nougat ice cream proved a good mix of fruit and flavour.

Directions: Off the A20. 5 miles from M20

Additional: Sunday L; Children welcome; ◑ dishes
Seats: 60. Private dining room 24. Jacket & tie preferred
Smoking: No pipes and cigars in dining room
Accommodation: 10 en suite
Credit cards: ▨ ▨ ▨ ▨ ▨ ▨

LITTLEBOURNE,
Bow Window Inn ✤

50 High Street CT3 1ST
Map 5: TR25
Tel: 01227 721264
Fax: 01227 721250
Chef: R W Steinmetz
Owners: Mr and Mrs R W Steinmetz
Cost: Alc £15.50. H/wine £8.50. ☺
Times: Last L 1.45pm/D 9pm.
Additional: Bar food; Sunday L; Children welcome; ◑ dishes
Smoking: No smoking in dining room
Accommodation: 9 en suite
Credit cards: ▨ ▨ ▨ ▨ ▨

A 300-year-old country cottage hotel complete with oak beams, a huge Kentish fireplace, and a picturesque village setting. Dishes might include pan-fried magret of duck with mango and Amaretto sauce, and strips of beef fillet, veal and scampi in a creamy curry sauce with apple and banana.

Directions: Take A257 from Canterbury towards Sandwich: Littlebourne is approximately 3 miles E of the city

LITTLEBOURNE, King William IV ✤

4 High Street CT3 1ST
Map 5: TR25
Tel/Fax: 01227 721244
Chefs: Aaron Goldfinch, Nick Perkins
Owners: Paul and Lynn Thurgate
Cost: Alc £14.50, fixed-price L £9.95. ☺ H/wine £7.
Times: Last L 2pm/last D 9.30pm
Additional: Bar food L; Sunday L; No children under 10; ◑ dishes
Accommodation: 7 en suite
Credit cards: ▨ ▨ ▨ ▨ ▨

The bar and restaurant at this 200-year-old inn are decorated with local hops and brasses and all the tables are polished wood with fresh flowers and candles. Dishes include braised wild rabbit with orange and juniper berries, and stir-fried duck breast with bean shoots and baby sweetcorn.

Directions: On A257 3 miles E of Canterbury

MAIDSTONE, **Russell Hotel**

136 Boxley Road ME14 2AE
Map 5: TQ85
Tel: 01622 692221
Fax: 01622 762084
Chef: Brian Mulrooney
Cost: A/c £20, fixed-price L & D
£13.95. ☺ H/wine £9.75
Times: Last L 2.30pm/ D 9.30pm.
Closed Sun L
Additional: Bar meals; Children
welcome; ☺ dishes
Smoking: No-smoking area
Accommodation: 42 en suite
Credit cards:

*Personally run Victorian house in two acres of grounds on the edge
of town. A wide-ranging Anglo/French carte promises coarse
chicken liver pâté, spinach noodles with spring vegetables, crisp-
skinned duck breast with Cassis sauce, and monkfish with cream
and pimento sauce. To finish there might be coffee cheesecake.*

Directions: Telephone for directions

MAIDSTONE, **Tanyard Hotel**

Built in the fourteenth century, Tanyard has been through a
number of transformations. Originally a yeoman's house, by
the seventeenth century the property was being used as a
tannery. In Victorian times it was used as cottages for the local
farm, and until the 1980s it was a private home. The restaurant
retains many of the original features of the yeoman's house:
timber frame, ragstone walls and flagstone floors.
Endorsements for chef/proprietor Jan Davies continue for her
refreshingly uncomplicated, accomplished cooking. The style
takes in starters of roasted red peppers with cherry tomatoes
and mozzarella cheese, salad of smoked venison, pine nuts
and mango, and smoked haddock and broccoli filo tart. The
highlight of a July meal was a dish of duck, served with a
bitter orange sauce and locally grown carrots and new
potatoes. This was followed by a Kent cherry clafoutis (vanilla
flavoured egg custard dotted with baked red cherries and
marinated in Kirsch). Freshly baked rolls – made with
pumpkin seeds, sun-dried tomatoes or walnuts – are
recommended.

Wierton Hill
Boughton
Monchelsea
ME17 4JT
Map 5: TQ85
Tel: 01622 744705
Fax: 01622 741998
Chef/Owner: Jan Davies
Cost: Fixed-price L £22.50 (3
courses)/D £27.50 (4 courses).
H/wine £10.50.
Times: Noon-last L 1.30pm/7pm-last
D 9pm. Closed L Mon, L Tue, L Sat,
2 wks Jan
Additional: Sunday L;
No children under 6; ☺ dishes
Seats: 28
Smoking: No smoking in dining room
Accommodation: 6 en suite
Credit cards:

Directions: Turn off B2163 at Cock
Pub nr Boughton Monchelsea

ROCHESTER,

Bridgewood Manor Hotel

A modern aspect and great facilities belie the distinctly Gothic interior of this hotel not far from the ancient Pilgrims Way. Eye-catchers include a stone fireplace retrieved from a Yorkshire mill owner's house and artefacts from old churches, although the focal point is the classical courtyard. Squires Restaurant echoes the Gothic theme, and here you can order from a choice of menus, supplemented by seasonal specialities and a buffet. The kitchen team is gaining confidence and the cooking shows some adventurous, assured touches. Artichoke mousse with a beetroot dressing is a clever idea, although our inspector was more impressed by a complex dish of well-timed red mullet combined with choucroute flavoured with juniper and cumin and served with a rösti with lemon grass. Desserts are seasonal things like pear gratin glazed with poire William sabayon and a blackberry sorbet; the separate cheese menu is also worth exploring. The 100-strong wine list covers the globe.

Bridgewood Roundabout
Maidstone Road ME5 9AX
Map 5: TQ76
Tel: 01634 201333
Fax: 01634 201330
Chef: Jean-Claude MacFarlane
Owner: Marston Hotels
Cost: A/c £35, fixed-price L £17/D £24 (3 courses). ☺
Times: 12.30pm-last L 1.30pm/7pm-last D 9.45pm. Closed L Sat
Additional: Sunday L; Bar meals; Children welcome; ◑ dishes
Seats: 80. Private dining room 25-40
Smoking: No smoking in dining room
Accommodation: 100 en suite
Credit cards: ▨ ▨ ▨ ▨ ▨ ▨ ▨

Directions: Adjacent to roundabout on A229

ROCHESTER, **The Limehouse**

327 High Street ME1 1DA
Map 5: TQ76
Tel: 01634 813800
Fax: 01634 819489
Chefs: Phil Bedford, Paul Wood
Owners: Mr A Auger, R Ebanks
Cost: A/c £20. H/wine £9.50.
Times: Noon-last L 2pm/6.30pm-last D 9.30pm (7pm-11pm Sat). Closed Sun, 26 Dec, 1 Jan, some Bhs
Additional: Bar meals L; Children welcome; ◑ dishes
Seats: 45. Private dining room 40
Smoking: No smoking in dining room
Credit cards: ▨ ▨ ▨ ▨ ▨

Simple brasserie-style restaurant with paintings and sculptures by local artists, distressed walls and no-cloth wooden tables. The global menu mixes and matches flavours, ideas and traditions: salmon and seaweed sushi flavoured with green mustard and served with soy sauce, roast whole onion filled with spiced minced lamb with sultanas and pine nuts, breast of chicken filled with a bacon and mushroom farce wrapped in puff pastry and served with a Madeira sauce. Service by a young and cheerful staff is attentive, but some inconsistencies have been noted in the cooking. No complaints about an accurately cooked red snapper served on wilted leaf spinach and topped with good tapenade and a light balsamic and honey dressing, but a spicy fish broth lacked any real piscine depth of flavour and a lemon tart, despite a good zesty flavour and creamy texture, was let down by poor pastry.

Directions: From town centre, follow signs to Chatham; restaurant is on L past railway station next to North Foreland pub.

ROYAL TUNBRIDGE WELLS,

Royal Wells Inn ❀❀

For almost three decades, David and Robert Sloan have been in residence at this delightful hotel situated high above the town. There are stunning views of the common from the windows of the original Victorian conservatory, which now serves as the main dining room. The *carte* and daily fixed-price menus are bolstered by fish specials such as goujons of monkfish in sherry and saffron or sea bass served on warm potato and bacon salad. On the meaty side of things you might find guinea fowl in Cassis or flash-fried calves' liver with balsamic vinegar. Twice-baked Stilton soufflé with chive sauce makes a good start and you could finish with crème brûlée with quince conserve. A blackboard menu is also offered in the Brasserie. The wine list offers a good spread of reasonably priced bottles with an increasing fondness for the New World.

Directions: Situated 75 yards from the junction of the A21 and A264

Mount Ephraim TN4 8BE
Map 5: TQ53
Tel: 01892 511188
Fax: 01892 511908
Chef: Robert Sloan
Owners: David & Robert Sloan
Cost: *Alc* £24, fixed-price L £ 10.50 (2 courses)/D £21.50 (3 courses). ☺
H/wine £9.75.
Times: 12.30pm-last L 2.15pm/7.30pm-last D 10pm. Closed Sun, D Mon. 24-25 Dec
Additional: Bar food; Sunday L (Wells Brasserie); Children welcome; 🍴 dishes
Seats: 45. Private dining room 20
Accommodation: 19 en suite
Credit cards: 💳 💳 💳 💳 💳 💳

ROYAL TUNBRIDGE WELLS,

Signor Franco ❀❀   NEW

The location, above a chemist's shop, may be pedestrian, but once up the stairs (lined with signed celebrity photos), it's a different story. Bright, airy, with magnificent floor to ceiling arched windows from the conservatory at Hever Castle, this is a little bit of Italy in the middle of Kent. The waiters are informative and attentive, overseen by the utterly charming Franco himself. An extensive menu runs through all the traditional favourites – tuna, beans and onion salad, minestrone, king prawns with butter, garlic and chilli for starters, plus a choice of nearly twenty pastas. Main courses include monkfish with lemon and white wine, chicken breast with mozzarella cheese, aubergine and tomato sauce, veal escalope with Parma ham and sage and osso buco. A first course of warm baby artichokes with sun-dried tomatoes, herbs, balsamic and olive oil dressing, was beautifully tender and fresh, a good lead-in to a main course of meaty Italian sausage served on fresh broad beans with pan-fried polenta. Our inspector then chose a light but rich chocolate mousse from the desserts which also include tiramisu, cassata and zabaglione (for two, and not at weekends).

Directions: Near Tunbridge Wells train station

5a High Street
Map 5: TQ53
Tel: 01892 549199
Fax: 01892 541378
Chef: Giuseppe Miramba
Owner: Franco de Tommaso
Cost: *Alc* £30. H/wine £9.50. ☺
Times: 12.30pm-last L 2.45pm/6.30pm-last D 11pm. Closed Sun
Additional: Children welcome; 🍴 dishes
Seats: 45
Smoking: No pipes or cigars; air-conditioning
Credit cards: 💳 💳 💳 💳 💳

ROYAL TUNBRIDGE WELLS,

The Spa Hotel ❀

Mount Ephraim
TN4 8XJ
Map 5: TQ53
Tel: 01892 520331
Fax: 01892 510575
Chef: Edward Heasman
Owners: Goring family
Cost: *Alc* £20, fixed-price L £14.50/D £19. ☺ H/wine £9.50.
Times: Last L 2.30pm/D 9.30pm. Closed L Sat
Additional: Sunday L; Bar meals; Children welcome; ❸ dishes
Smoking: No-smoking area; no cigars or pipes
Accommodation: 74 en suite
Credit cards: ▆ ▆ ▆ ▆ ▣ ▢

A pianist plays in the elegant Georgian restaurant on Friday and Saturday nights, creating a relaxing atmosphere in which to enjoy some sound Anglo-French cooking. Try wild boar terrine with warm wild mushroom salad, followed by roast rack of lamb stuffed with rosemary and apple farce.

Directions: On A264 leaving Tunbridge Wells towards East Grinstead

ROYAL TUNBRIDGE WELLS, **Thackeray's**

House Restaurant ❀❀

85 London Road TN1 1EA
Map 5: TQ53
Tel/Fax: 01892 511921
Chef/Owner: Bruce Wass
Cost: *Alc* £32, fixed-price L £12 (2 courses)/D £24.50 (3 courses). H/wine £11.85
Times: 12.30pm-last L 2pm/7pm-last D 10pm. Closed D Sun, Mon
Additional: Sunday L; Children welcome; ❸ dishes
Seats: 50. Private dining room 10 + 35
Smoking: No pipes and cigars in dining room
Credit cards: ▆ ▆ ▆ ▢

William Makepeace Thackeray once lived in this seventeenth-century tile-hung building, but since the mid-1980s it has been the domain of Bruce Wass. These days, serious gastronomic business takes place in the peach-coloured ground floor dining room hung with paintings. Set lunches and mid-week menus provide alternatives to the *carte*, which treads a path through ham hock and leek terrine with corn salad and truffle oil, grilled sea bass with saffron and capers, and calves' liver with sweet and sour onions. Ingredients are sought out with care: Trelough duck breast from Herefordshire is peppered and served with an Armagnac sauce, organic lamb fillet comes with haricot beans, dried tomato and garlic fritters, while the sea yields anything from gurnard to carpet shell clams. Desserts can include apricot, walnut and ginger toffee pudding or coconut parfait with exotic fruit salad. A clutch of cask strength malt whiskies, several Calvados and eaux de vie – not to mention around a dozen bottled beers from around the world – bolster the impressively strong wine list.

Directions: At corner of London Road/Mount Ephraim Road overlooking Common, 2 mins from hospital

SEVENOAKS,
Royal Oak Hotel ❀

An inn since the seventeenth century, this well-established town-centre hotel offers abundant atmosphere and charm within its informal bistro and partly panelled restaurant. New blood in the kitchen is raising standards with carefully prepared modern British cooking.

Additional: Bar Food; Sunday L; Children welcome; dishes
Accommodation: 40 en suite
Credit cards: 🃏 💳 💳 💳 💳 💳

Directions: M25/J5; at far end of High Street, opposite Sevenoaks school, walking distance from the town centre

Upper High Street TN13 1HY
Map 5: TQ55
Tel: 01732 451109
Fax: 01732 740187
Chef: Andrew Cullum
Owners: Brook Hotels
Cost: *Alc* £21, fixed-price L £15.95/D £19.95. ☺ H/wine £8.95.
Times: Last L 2.30pm/D 9.30pm

SISSINGHURST, Rankins ❀❀

The white weatherboard building was originally two cottages. After a spell as the village saddlers, the property became the agreeable, oak-beamed restaurant it is today. The short, eclectic, seasonal menu displays an enthusiasm for extracting the maximum flavour from quality ingredients, and combinations are kept uncomplicated. Parsnip and Chinese five-spice soup and leeks vinaigrette with Parma ham and shallots may be followed by boned, grilled chicken leg with salsa verde and lemon butter sauce or fresh pasta ribbons with smoked haddock, fresh cod, skate and mussels. The same simple philosophy applies to the desserts – poached dried fruits with orange and spices and crème fraîche, lemon tart with Jersey cream and coffee fudge pudding with coffee ice cream. There is also a cheese of the week to be sampled.

Directions: Village centre, on R on A262 (Ashford)

TN17 2JH
Map 5: TQ73
Tel: 01580 713964
Chef: Hugh Rankin
Owners: Hugh & Leonora Rankin
Cost: Fixed-price D £26. H/wine £8.50.
Times: D only, 7.30pm-last D 9pm. Closed D Sun, Mon, Tue, 1 wk Sept
Additional: Sunday L (noon-1.30pm); Children welcome; dishes
Seats: 20
Credit cards: 🃏 💳 💳

WESTERHAM, Kings Arms Hotel ❀

Map 5: TQ45
Tel: 01959 562990
Fax: 01959 561240
Chef: Terry Howland
Owners: Angela & Barrie Hallett
Cost: *Alc* £23. H/wine £11.50. ☺
Times: Last L 2.30pm/D 10pm
Additional: Bar food; Sunday L; Children welcome; dishes
Smoking: No pipes and cigars; air-conditioning
Accommodation: 17 en suite
Credit cards: 🃏 💳 💳 💳 💳 💳

Attractive, comfortably appointed Georgian coaching inn located in the town centre. Opening out onto the terrace and garden, the Conservatory restaurant offers an imaginative carte that may feature clam chowder followed by beef fillet with Madeira and horseradish sauce, with white chocolate mousse with winter berry stew for pudding.

Directions: On A25, in the centre of Westerham

WHITSTABLE,
Whitstable Oyster Fisher Co

Lively, atmospheric fish restaurant right on the beach, set in an old holding building for oysters awaiting dispatch to London. Simple decor. There's a cinema on the first floor, and a tidal tank underneath the restaurant that supplies water for shellfish purification. Whitstable oysters, of course, and the cooking lets the lovely fresh seafood speak for itself.

Additional: Bar food; Sunday L; Children welcome; 🍴 dishes.
Accommodation: 8 en suite
Credit cards: 🟦 🟦 🟦 🟦

Directions: On High Street, follow one-way then 1st L.

Horsebridge Beach,
Whitstable, Kent,
CT5 1BU
Map 5: TR16
Tel: 01227 276856
Fax: 01227 770666
Chef: Nikki Billington
Owner: Whitstable Oyster Fisher Co.
Cost: Alc £25
Times: Last L 2pm/D 9pm Closed D Sun, Mon except June-Sept

WYE, **Wife of Bath** ✿

4 Upper Bridge Street TN25 5AW
Map 5: TR25
Tel: 01233 812540
Fax: 01233 813630
Chef: Robert Hymers
Owner: John Morgan
Cost: Alc £22, fixed-price L £8.75/D £22. ☺ H/wine £9.95.
Times: Last L 2.30pm/D 10.00pm. Closed Sun & Mon, 1 wk Jan
Additional: Children welcome; 🍴 dishes
Smoking: No pipes or cigars in dining room
Accommodation: 6 en suite
Credit cards: 🟦 🟦 🟦 🟦 🟦

Converted from the village doctor's house over 30 years ago, this charming restaurant-with-rooms still retains the atmosphere of a private house. The menu is short and ideas are modern, culled from far and wide. Home-made noodles with a mussel and cockle cream sauce, and roast Kent duckling with a blood orange sauce are typical.

Directions: Just off the A28 Ashford to Canterbury Road

LANCASHIRE

BILLINGTON, **Foxfields Hotel** ✿

Purpose-built modern hotel handily placed for the M6 as well as the Ribble Valley. A new head chef offers plenty of capably prepared dishes including seared smoked salmon with potato and dill salad, lamb shank with potato and parsnip hash browns, roast duck with apple fritters and lime sauce, and banana and vanilla cream pudding.

Accommodation: 44 en suite
Credit cards: 🟦 🟦 🟦 🟦 🟦

Directions: From A59 follow sign for Whalley, hotel is 0.5 mile on R

Whalley Road BB7 9HY
Map 7: SD73
Tel: 01254 822556
Fax: 01254 824613
Chef: Alex Coward
Owners: Lyric Hotels
Cost: Alc £20, fixed-price L £6.95/ D £17.95. ☺ H/wine £10.50.
Times: Last L 2pm/D 9.45pm Closed L Sat
Additional: Bar Food; Sunday L; Children welcome; 🍴 menu
Smoking: No smoking in dining room. Air-conditioning

BLACKBURN, **Millstone Hotel** 🏵

A country hotel in a small village setting with an attractive oak-panelled restaurant. An interesting choice of dishes includes potted duck with spiced pears and mixed leaves, and loin of Pendle lamb topped with chicken and mint mousse. Desserts range from crème caramel to sticky toffee pudding.

Church Lane Mellor BB2 7JR
Map 7: SD62
Tel: 01254 813333
Fax: 01254 812628
Chef: Adrian Sedden
Cost: Alc £24, fixed-price L £13.50/D £21. ☺ H/wine £10.95.
Times: Last L 1.45pm/D-9.30pm. Closed L Sat
Additional: Bar food; Sunday L; Children welcome; 🍴 dishes
Smoking: No smoking in dining room
Accommodation: 24 en suite
Credit cards: ▇ ▧ ▨ ▩ 🄿 🄲

Directions: M6/J31, follow A677 (Blackburn) for 2 miles. Turn L (Mellor), follow road to top of hill, hotel is on R.

BLACKPOOL, **September Brasserie** 🏵🏵

Fish and chips is as much a Blackpool experience as a trip up the Tower; once, however, is enough for most, and the serious food lover should thereafter make their way to the North Pier, cross the road, and climb the stairs over the hairdresser's to the small, first-floor restaurant that shares its floor space with the tiny galley kitchen. Individual and eclectic ideas, enthusiasm and undeniable ability come together in a short, snappy menu – our inspector found a main course of sea bass stuffed with a mousse of queenies impressively fresh and well-flavoured. Other lively, free-ranging dishes might be poached halibut fillet with ink spätzli and wasabi vinaigrette, saddle of wild boar with mushroom and seaweed sauce, and free-range bison bourguignonne with buckwheat pilaff. Desserts, such as chocolate bread-and-butter pudding and fresh rhubarb crumble, are more homely-sounding but equally enjoyable. Unusually, the restaurant welcomes BYO diners (£5 corkage fee); otherwise check out the interesting seasonal wine selections or, if possible, order in advance from the reserve list held by Pagendam Pratt and Bibendum.

Directions: 200 yards from the promenade, adjacent to the Cenotaph

15-17 Queen Street FY1 1PU
Map 7: SD33
Tel: 01253 23282
Fax: 01253 299455
Chef: Michael Golowicz
Owners: Michael Golowicz, Pat Wood
Cost: Alc £13 (L)/£20 (D), fixed-price D £16.95 (3 courses). H/wine £9.90. ☺
Times: Noon-lastL 1.45pm/7pm-last D 9.30pm. Closed Sun, 2 wks summer, 1 wk winter
Additional: Children welcome; 🍴 dishes
Seats: 40
Smoking: No-smoking area; no pipes and cigars
Credit cards: ▇ ▧ ▨ 🄿

CHIPPING, **Gibbon Bridge Hotel** 🏵

Enthusiastically-run hotel with splendid views across open countryside as well as award-winning gardens. The dinner menu features both modern and traditional English dishes. Expect roast guinea fowl with blackcurrant sauce, couscous parcels filled with roast vegetables and goat's cheese, and simply cooked fresh fish.

Accommodation: 30 en suite
Credit cards: ▇ ▧ ▨ ▩ 🄿 🄲

Directions: In village turn R at T junction for Clitheroe, hotel at 0.75 mile

PR3 2TQ
Map 7: SD74
Tel: 01995 61456
Fax: 01995 61277
Chef: Mrs Grace Holland
Owner: Janet Simpson
Cost: Alc £22, fixed-price L £14/D £20. H/wine £9. ☺
Times: Last L 1.30pm/D 8.30pm
Additional: Sunday L; Children welcome; 🍴 dishes

LANCASTER, **Lancaster House**

A genuine northern welcome awaits guests at this modern hotel, built in open countryside next to Lancaster University. There's also a northern flavour to the dishes served in the split-level restaurant. Start, perhaps, with a 'seafood harvest' followed by fillet of pork sautéed with bean sprouts and served with Wensleydale cheese sauce.

Smoking: No smoking in dining room; air-conditioning
Accommodation: 80 en suite
Credit cards: ▆ ▆ ▆ ▆ ▆ ▆

Directions: M6/J33, take A6 North, through village of Galgate and hotel 0.5 mile on R. Turn R onto Green Lane 100m before traffic lights

Green Lane Ellel LA1 4GJ
Map 7: SD57
Tel: 01524 844822
Fax: 01524 844766
Chef: Ian Benville
Owner: English Lakes Hotels
Cost: Alc £22.50, fixed-price L £10.95. ☺ H/wine £9.95.
Times: Last L 2.30pm/last D 9.30pm
Additional: Bar food; Sunday L; Children welcome; ◑ dishes

LANGHO, **Northcote Manor** ❀❀❀

Northcote Road nr Blackburn
BB6 8BE
Map 7: SD73
Tel: 01254 240555
Fax: 01254 246568
Chef: Nigel Haworth
Owners: Nigel Haworth, Craig Bancroft
Cost: Alc £34, fixed-price L £15/D £37. H/wine £12.50
Times: Noon-last L 1.30pm/7pm-last D 9.30pm (10pm Sat/9pm Sun)
Additional: Sunday L; Children welcome; ◑ dishes
Seats: 100. Private dining room 40
Smoking: No smoking in dining room
Accommodation: 14 en suite
Credit cards: ▆ ▆ ▆ ▆ ▆ ▆

Like his near neighbour, Paul Heathcote, chef Nigel Haworth clings doggedly to his north country roots and his cooking is a blistering rendition of new Lancashire cuisine with a touch of 'hip'. The setting for these displays of culinary fireworks is a Victorian red-brick manor in a corner of the Ribble Valley close to Pendle Hill. Inside, the dining room is in keeping with the origins of the house – chandeliers hung from the high ceilings, bright pictures on the walls, and so on. The foundation of Haworth's craft is what the region can proudly produce: that could mean anything from an emblematic starter of black pudding and buttered pink trout with mustard and watercress sauce, or a plate of tiny Lancashire delicacies, to the extraordinary Lancashire cheese ice cream served with a brilliant, light apple crumble soufflé. Some dishes on the menu suggest that the kitchen is intent on breaking new ground or at least keeping up with the pack leaders. Perfectly 'scorched' Orkney scallops are laid on deep-green spinach with sweet and sour cherry tomatoes and a pool of tomato water; the effect is visually stunning, the flavour absolutely superb. In less revolutionary vein, inspectors have also raved about wonderfully frothy Cajun crab chowder and local Goosnargh duckling, roasted and braised to keep the flesh tender and juicy, then delicately arranged on caramelised endive with rhubarb and juniper juices. Other successes have included grilled sea bass with deep-fried leeks, a herby potato purée and red wine jus, as well as an assiette of lamb featuring sautéed sweetbreads with mint pesto, kidney in a spinach samosa, saddle and best end (although the accompanying couscous was reckoned to be rather overbearing). To finish, the selection of six Lancashire cheeses is worth noting – in case anyone needed reminding what county they were in. French staff provide astute, courteous service.

Directions: From M6/J31 take A59, follow signs for Clitheroe. At first traffic lights L onto Skipton/Clitheroe Rd for 9 miles. L into Northcote Rd. Hotel on R.

LONGRIDGE, Paul Heathcotes Restaurant ❀❀❀❀

104-106 Higher Road PR3 3SY
Map 7: SD63
Tel: 01772 784969
Fax: 01772 785713
Chef: Paul Heathcote, Andrew Barnes
Owner: Paul Heathcote
Cost: Alc £45, fixed-price L £22.50/D £38 (6 courses). H/wine £14.50
Times: Noon-last L 2pm (Fri, Sun only)/7pm-last D 9.30pm. Closed Mon
Additional: Sunday L; Children welcome; ❹ dishes
Seats: 60. Private dining room 18
Smoking: No smoking in dining room
Credit cards: ▉ ▉ ▉ ▉ ▉ ▉

Even the most practised of professional stomachs can flag towards the end of Paul Heathcote's ten-course 'Signature Menu', although our inspector gamely struggled through to reach a just dessert. In Heathcote's case, this means bread-and-butter pudding with apricot coulis and clotted cream, 'the best I've ever eaten, and by god, I finished it!'. Heathcote now has solid teams in place at his two satellite brasseries (see Manchester and Preston entries), and as a result is able to spend more time at Longridge. This is a very traditional restaurant with a split-level dining-room, heavily draped tables, and a comfortable lounge with deep sofas. Staff are correctly drilled, but their ingrained Northern sense of hospitality cuts through any of the icy attitude often found at this level of cuisine. Canapés give the first hint of the Heathcote style, with some potted shrimp croûtes and a miniature cottage pie taking pride of place. Breads come in six varieties including sage and onion, black pudding and sun-dried tomato. A sliver of pan-fried foie gras may be served with an onion and thyme potato cake, onion marmalade and Madeira sauce, while truffles flavour both the mashed potatoes that accompany breast of Goosnargh corn-fed chicken with veal sweetbreads and wild mushrooms, and the smoked chicken and celeriac soup. Another soup, a chilled sparklingly clear tomato juice, with no hint of colour but a real, sweet, acid intensity of flavour, with a chiffonade of basil and spring vegetables, was a magnificent way to reinvent the wheel. Goosnargh poultry triumphs again, though, in a duckling main course, when variations on a theme include pairing it with buttered potatoes, caramelised apples and jasmine scented juices, or with fondant potato, a dumpling of leg meat and herbs and an orange and cardamom sauce. Top-notch petits fours and good espresso round off the whole experience. It's still Lancashire's finest. The wine list here needs to be approached with some caution. There is plenty of good drinking to be had, but the best bins of this mixed bunch need to be carefully plucked from the surrounding mediocrity. Alsace, Rhone, Australia and the U.S., are areas displaying the greatest consistency and hence offering the most favourable odds for a worthwhile selection.

Signature dishes: Black pudding on a bed of crushed potatoes, baked beans and bayleaf sauce; breast of Goosnargh duckling, buttered potatoes, dumpling of its leg, prunes, in its own juices; rack of spring lamb, hot-pot potatoes, baby vegetables, lentils, rosemary juices; bread-and-butter pudding, clotted cream, compote of dried apricots.

Directions: Follow signs for Golf Club & Jeffrey Hill. Higher Road is beside White Bull Pub in Longridge.

PRESTON,

Heathcote's Brasserie ❀❀

There was a time when the queue on a Saturday night could be two hours long – the introduction of reservations must be a welcome relief to the citizens of Preston. 'It's got a great buzz and would not be out of place in London' was one inspector's enthusiastic response to Paul Heathcote's lively brasserie. It has much to recommend it. A polished wood floor, simple white decor, glass, and impressive 'wavy modern' mural running the length of the room creates an up-market look; the brasserie-style menu reflects Paul Heathcote's modern British style. An autumn meal opened with what the inspector thought would be a light appetiser of savouries – 'something to nibble on whilst deciding what to eat' – but what quickly appeared was almost a meal in itself: some 'really nice' deep-fried risotto, crostini, shredded carrot, chicken wings, black pudding, potato salad, french beans in oil with nuts and olives. This was followed by chargrilled calves' liver on top of a wedge of herb polenta, mushrooms, bacon, 'almost caramelised' onion, and a nice 'lip-smacking' jus. The bread-and-butter pudding, scented with orange, was rich with a definite orange tang. There is a good selection of reasonably priced wines, available by the glass and bottle, although no half-bottles. The location in the town centre means that during the day parking is at a premium.

Directions: Town centre

23 Winkley Square
Map 7: SD52
Tel: 01772 252732
Fax: 01772 203433
Chef: Lawrence Dodds
Owner: Paul Heathcote
Cost: Alc £25, fixed-price L £8.50 (2 courses). H/wine £10.25
Times: Noon-last L 2.15pm/7pm (Sat/Sun 6pm) last D 10.30pm. Closed 25 Dec, 1 Jan
Additional: Bar food; Sunday lunch; Children welcome; ⓓ dishes
Seats: 90
Smoking: No pipes or cigars; air-conditioning
Credit cards: 🔳 📇 📇 🔛 ⓖ

PRESTON,

Preston Marriott Hotel ❀❀

Originally a Victorian house set in 11 acres of pleasing gardens and woodland, this is now a business-oriented hotel which has been given a thorough dose of refurbishment of late. The cooking here is straight and true, and the short carte offered in the Broughton Park restaurant includes impressive offerings along the lines of pressed terrine of duck with foie gras and potato served on a spiced couscous and mushroom salad, fillet of turbot stuffed with smoked salmon and Lancashire cheese, and breast of duckling with paprika-roasted onions and potato plus a sauce of preserved 'vine fruits'. Al dente vegetables are impeccably handled and desserts might feature honey parfait with sauce anglaise or a gâteau of Baileys ice cream with

Garstang Road Boughton PR3 5JB
Map 7: SD52
Tel: 01772 864087
Fax: 01772 861728
Chef: Neil McKevitt
Owner: Whitbread Hotel Company
Cost: Alc £25, fixed-price L £13.50/D £18.95. ☺ H/wine £10.95.
Times: Noon-last L 1.45pm/7pm-last D 9.45pm. Closed L Sat
Additional: Bar food; Sunday L; Children welcome; ⓓ dishes
Seats: 60. Private dining room 16
Smoking: No smoking in dining room

Preston Marriott Hotel

Accommodation: 98 en suite
Credit cards:

crème brûlée and fresh raspberries. Breads are also praiseworthy. Around 60 wines offer plenty of choice and dependable drinking.

Directions: M6/J32, follow A6 towards Garstang. Hotel approx. 600 yds

SLAIDBURN, Parrock Head

Low beams and open fires create a relaxed atmosphere in the restaurant of this converted seventeenth-century farmhouse that is surrounded by open fells and valleys. . Dishes such as chicken breast filled with Camembert with a light pimento and Cinzano sauce, and a crisp, tangy lemon tart have been well reported.

Accommodation: 9 en suite
Credit cards: ▆▆ ▆▆ ▆▆ ▆

Directions: Take B6478 to Slaidburn; L by village pub up Woodehouse Lane, hotel drive 1 mile on L

Nr Clitheroe BB7 3AH
Map 7: SD75
Tel: 01200 446614
Fax: 01200 446313
Chef: David Gibbons
Owner: Terry Hesketh
Cost: Fixed-price L £5-£15/ D £19.75. ☺ H/wine £9.
Times: Last L 2pm/last D 9pm. Closed Jan
Additional: Bar food L; Sunday L; Children welcome; ❹ dishes
Smoking: No smoking in dining room

THORNTON,
The Victorian House ❀❀

The house is a genuine piece of Victoriana dating from 1896, although the interior has been re-designed with a Provençale/Mediterranean theme. Most attention is now focused on the informal atmosphere of Didier's bistro – particularly at lunchtime when a wide range of individually priced dishes are offered. In the evening there's also the option of a four-course dinner in the original Victorian dining room. The cooking might be described as robust international with leanings towards France and an occasional modern twist. Creamy wild mushroom risotto, and roast monkfish with tagliatelle and aïoli, are typical starters before a soup such as minestrone or Cullen skink. Main courses take in everything from butterfly prawns and queen scallops in lobster sauce to grilled kangaroo steak with béarnaise sauce, while desserts could feature French apple tart with Calvados sauce. Some decent wines by the glass show up on the adequate list.

Directions: M55 Kirkham exit – follow A585 (Fleetwood), then Thornton at roundabout, continue towards Fleetwood, turn R at church

FY5 4HF
Map 7: SJ38
Tel: 01253 860619
Fax: 01253 865350
Chef: Didier Guerin
Owners: Mr & Mrs D Guerin
Cost: Alc £15, fixed-price L £8. ☺ H/wine £6.95.
Times: Noon-last L 2pm/6pm-last D 10pm.
Additional: No children under 6; ❹ dishes
Seats: 65. Private dining room 16
Smoking: No pipes & cigars
Credit cards: ▆▆ ▆▆ ▆▆ ▆

UPHOLLAND,
Holland Hall Hotel ✿✿

6 Lafford Lane Skelmersdale
WN8 0QZ
Map 7: SD50
Tel: 01695 624426
Fax: 01695 633433
Chef: Nigel Smith
Owners: Mr & Mrs Rathbone
Cost: *Alc* £22.50, fixed-price D
£19.95. H/wine £8.95
Times: D only, 6.30pm-10pm
Additional: Bar food; L Sun & Fri
(noon-3.45pm) ;
No children under 10; ✿ dishes
Seats: 55. Private dining room 35
Smoking: No-smoking area
Accommodation: 35 en suite
Credit cards: 🔲 🔲 🔲 🔲 🔲 🔲

Chef Nigel Smith of 'Ready Steady Cook' fame directs operations with great style at this well established hotel. For instance, there is a choice of seven home-made breads, including tomato, cheese and fennel, all 'very moreish'. The menu shows an admirable use of local produce, which gives a good flavour of the area (a magnificent part of Lancashire), with black pudding, salmon from the River Lune, and Goosnargh duck and corn-fed chicken making regular appearances. The kitchen is prepared to look back to such classics as soufflé Arnold Bennett (with smoked haddock, Gruyère cheese, poached egg, spinach and balsamic dressing), and Caesar salad, as well as updating ideas such as shoulder of lamb, slowly braised, and served with roasted root vegetables glazed with a horseradish sabayon and delicate minted lamb jus lie. Raspberry crème brûlée has been well reported.

Directions: 2 minutes drive from M6/J26. Take A577 (Upholland), turn R into Lafford Lane

WRIGHTINGTON, High Moor Inn ✿✿

High Moor Lane WN6 9QA
Map 7: SD51
Tel: 01257 252364
Fax: 01257 255120
Chef: Darren Wynn
Owners: James Sines, John Nelson
Times: Noon-last L 2pm/5.30pm-last
D 10pm
Additional: Bar food L; Sunday L;
Children welcome; ✿ dishes
Seats: 100
Smoking: No smoking in dining room
Credit cards: 🔲 🔲 🔲 🔲 🔲 🔲

The old stone building on the moors dates back to 1642, and there are still remnants of the past in the original oak beams, Yorkshire stone floors and log fires that set the tone in the bar and dining room. There is plenty of flexibility about this set-up, with the option of set menus and a keenly priced 'Early Doors' menu (5.30-7pm) in addition to the *carte*; at lunchtime you can even get sandwiches and baguettes. Thai spiced salmon fish cake with pickled ginger and cucumber salad impressed as a starter, but the repertoire also embraces crayfish and coriander risotto, and duck terrine with sweet fig relish. Fish and chips with home-made mushy peas is a firm favourite with the regulars, otherwise you might stay in hearty mood with braised boneless oxtail with bubble and squeak, or court fashion with fillet of cured salmon with mussel and smoked salmon bouillon. Bread and butter pudding cooked in a pastry case makes an unusual finish. The well chosen wine list includes an intriguing 'connoisseur's selection'.

Directions: M6/J27, follow sign to Parbold, after hospital turn R into Robin Hood Lane, 1st L into High Moor Lane

WRIGHTINGTON,
Wrightington Hotel

The Wrightington is a modern hotel with exceptional leisure facilities situated close to junction 27 of the M6 near Wigan. A strong sporting theme runs through the hotel; the restaurant, for instance, is called Blazers, and the adjoining bar displays sporting bric-à-brac and pictures. Food is thoroughly modern in concept too, quality is good and the kitchen is careful not to overstretch itself. Inspection yielded a good, smooth chicken and asparagus terrine wrapped in Savoy cabbage and served with a small salad. This was followed by excellent steamed suprême of Tay salmon, the flavour, colour and texture spot on, with a well judged, delicate tarragon and white wine sauce. Dessert was exceptional, a very light sticky toffee pudding with dates and served with a butterscotch sauce. Prices are reasonable. Wine choice is limited, but inexpensive; there are few halves.

Directions: From M6/J27, drive 0.25 mile towards Parbold. 200yds past church, fork R. Hotel is 100yds on R.

NEW

Moss Lane, Standish WN6 9PB
Map 7: SD51
Tel: 01257 425803
Fax: 01257 425830
Chefs: Ian Snape, Jeff Nugent
Owner: Davie Whelan
Cost: Fixed-price L £9.95 (3 courses)/D £17.50 (4 courses). ☺ H/wine £8.
Times: 12.30pm-last L 2pm/7pm-last D 9.30pm. Closed L Sat
Additional: Sunday lunch (carvery); Children welcome; ⬤ dishes
Seats: 70
Smoking: No pipes or cigars in dining room
Accommodation: 47 en suite
Credit cards: ▆ ▆ ▆ ▆ ▆ ▆

LEICESTERSHIRE

EAST MIDLANDS AIRPORT,
The Donington Thistle ⬤

Remarkably peaceful, yet situated at the gateway to East Midlands Airport. The Sherwood Restaurant with its atmosphere 'reminiscent of a Spanish hacienda' makes a good setting for the likes of galantine of duck studded with foie gras, salmon in puff pastry with mint and strawberry sauce, and honey and Drambuie parfait.

Smoking: No smoking in dining room
Accommodation: 110 en suite
Credit cards: ▆ ▆ ▆ ▆ ▆ ▆

Directions: At East Midlands International Airport, 1 mile from M1/J23A/24 and A42(M) Birmingham link road

Derby DE74 2SH
Map 8: SK42
Tel: 01332 850700
Fax: 01332 850823
Chef: Ronnie Wyatt-Goodwin
Owner: Thistle Hotels
Cost: *Alc* £37, fixed-price L £15/D £19.95/£21. H/wine £10.50. ☺
Times: Last L 2pm/D 10pm. Closed Sat lunch
Additional: Bar food; Sunday L; Children welcome; ⬤ dishes

HINCKLEY,

Sketchley Grange Hotel

Sketchley Lane, Burbage LE10 3HU
Map 4 : SP49
Tel: 01455 251133
Fax: 01455 631384
Chef: Colin Bliss
Owner: Nigel Downes
Cost: Fixed-price L £11.95/ D £18.95
(5 courses). ☺ H/wine £9.50.
Times: Last L 2.30pm/D 9.45pm
Closed D Sun, L Sat
Additional: Bar Food; Sunday L;
Children welcome; ☺ dishes
Smoking: No smoking in dining room.
Air-conditioning
Accommodation: 38 en suite
Credit cards: ▨ ▨ ▨ ▨ ▨ ▨

An extended country house hotel that's set in peaceful landscaped gardens just minutes from the M69. Fixed-price menus and a carte offer the likes of ragout of woodland mushrooms or smoked salmon roulade, breast of chicken Wellington or casserole of game with glazed shallots and herb dumplings. Extensive wine list with fair prices.

Directions: From M69/J1 take B4109, at mini roundabout turn L, then 1st R

LEICESTER,

Belmont House Hotel

De Montfort Street LE1 7GR
Map 4: SK50
Tel: 0116 2544773
Fax: 0116 4070804
Chef: Mark Crockett
Owners: Bowie family
Cost: Fixed-price L £9.95/D £18.50.
H/wine £9.50. ☺
Times: Last L 2pm/D 9.50pm.
Closed L Sat, D Sun, 25 Dec-2 Jan
Additional: Bar meals; Sunday L;
Children welcome; ☺ dishes
Smoking: No-smoking area
Accommodation: 65 en suite
Credit cards: ▨ ▨ ▨ ▨

Owned by the Bowie family for more than 60 years, and located at the end of tree-lined New Walk, this hotel is a natural asset to the city. Formal meals are served in the conservatory-style Cherry Restaurant, where the menu features foie gras parfait, mustard-crusted rack of lamb, and baked salmon in filo with lemon butter sauce.

Directions: From railway station, first R off A6 southbound

LEICESTER, **The Tiffin** ☺

Lively modern Indian with contemporary westernised decor and a conservatory extension. The menu is a familiar trawl through chicken tikka, fish masala, lamb badam pasanda and the like, plus

1 De Montfort Street LE1 7GE
Map 4: SP60
Tel: 0116 2470420/2553737
Fax: 0116 2625125
Chef: Mohammed Ali

The Tiffin

Owners: Pravin Parmar
Cost: *Alc* £18, fixed-price L&D £18.
☺ H/wine £10.
Times: Last L 2pm/D 11pm. Closed L
Sat, Sun, 4 days Xmas, Bhs
Additional: Children welcome;
🍴 dishes
Seats: 60. Private dining room 35
Smoking: No-smoking area
Credit cards: 🔲 🔲 🔲 🔲 🔲 🔲

*baltis and dishes cooked in a tawa. Incidentals such nan bread and
pilau rice are up-to-the-mark.*

Directions: Near railway station on the corner of De Montfort
Street and London Road (A6)

LEICESTER, Time Out Hotel ❀

*The ground floor areas of the hotel have been refurbished, giving a
Colonial-style feel to Hunters Restaurant. Expect modern English
cooking with a Mediterranean twist – dishes such as fish soup with
rouille, and rump of lamb with olive oil mash.*

Additional: Bar Food; Sunday L; Children welcome; 🍴 dishes
Smoking: Air-conditioning
Accommodation: 25 en suite. **Credit cards:** 🔲 🔲 🔲 🔲 🔲 🔲

Directions: Off the A426, 3 miles S of Leicester

Enderby Road Blaby LE8 4GD
Map 4: SP60
Tel: 0116 2787898
Fax: 0116 2781974
Chef: Carl Swingler
Owner: Regal Hotels Plc
Cost: *Alc* £26.50, fixed-price L £12/
D £16.95. ☺ H/wine £9.80.
Times: Last L 2.30pm/D 10pm.
Closed L Sat

MARKET HARBOROUGH,
Three Swans ❀

*Historic connections and up-to-the-minute facilities are all part of
this refurbished sixteenth-century coaching inn. Formal meals are
eaten in the elegant Swans restaurant where classic and modern
dishes such as turkey terrine with cranberry sauce and gazpacho are
prepared from good ingredients.*

Additional: Bar food; Sunday L; No children under 8; 🍴 dishes
Smoking: No-smoking area; no pipes or cigars; air-conditioning
Accommodation: 36 en suite. **Credit cards:** 🔲 🔲 🔲 🔲 🔲 🔲

Directions: Follow High Street S through town centre; hotel is
on R at traffic lights

21 High Street LE16 7NJ
Map 4: SP78
Tel: 01858 466644
Fax: 01858 433101
Chef: Richard Payne
Owner: Richard MacKay
Cost: *Alc* £28.70, fixed-price L
£12.95/D £18.95. ☺ H/wine £10.95
Times: Last L 2.15pm/last D 10.15pm.
Closed D Sun, Bh Mon

MELTON MOWBRAY,
Stapleford Park ❀❀

This is a delightful stately home, surrounded by an estate of
500 acres comprising woods, parkland, fishing lake, stables,
church, and gardens originally laid out by Capability Brown.
Within, the public rooms are sumptuous, with gleaming
mahogany panelling, walls crowded with paintings, while each

Stapleford LE14 2EF
Map 8: SK71
Tel: 01572 787522
Fax: 01572 787651
Owner: Peter De Savaray
Cost: Fixed-price L £19/D £37.50.
H/wine £16

bedroom has been individually designed by an individual or company ranging from David Hicks to Coca Cola. Meals are served in the Old Kitchen (an impressive sixteenth-century stone room with roaring log fire), but on busier evenings the grand Grinling Gibbons room comes into its own. Quality and skill were evident in a meal that took in crispy ravioli filled with peppered goat's cheese, with mesclun greens and a warm pesto dressing, suprême of Scottish salmon, flavoured by a whisky and maple syrup marinade, served with a handful of large scallops set on spinach, and caramelised chocolate and banana tart with clotted cream.

Directions: Follow Melton ring road A607 (Grantham) onto B676, 4 miles turn R signed Stapleford

Times: 12.30pm-last L 2pm/7pm-last D 9.30pm
Additional: Bar food L; Sunday L; No children under 9; ❹ dishes
Seats: 60 + 30. Private dining room 26 +12. Jacket & tie preferred
Smoking: No smoking in dining room
Accommodation: 51 en suite
Credit cards: ▨ ▨ ▨ ▨

QUORN, **Quorn Country Hotel**

Charnwood House
Leicester Road
LE12 8BB
Map 8: SK51
Tel: 01509 415050
Fax: 01509 415557
Chef: David Wilkinson
Owner: JN Brankin-Frisby
Cost: *Alc* £29, Fixed-price L £ 12/D £20. ☺ H/wine £10.
Times: Last L 2pm/D 9.30pm. Closed L Sat
Additional: Bar meals; Sunday L; children welcome; ❹ dishes
Accommodation: 20 en suite
Credit cards: ▨ ▨ ▨ ▨ ▨ ▨

A quintessential English country house with landscaped gardens sweeping down to the river's edge. The Orangery Brasserie offers a distinctive contemporary style of cooking, the Shire Restaurant has a more traditional approach. A good choice of vegetarian dishes is always available, roast pepper and couscous bake, for example.

Directions: Off A6 in village centre

QUORN, **Quorn Grange**

Country house in extensive grounds where hospitality is a cornerstone. Locally sourced ingredients are put to good effect in breast of pigeon and partridge with a salad dressed with thyme and Madeira, smoked goose with beans and herb salad, and medallions of pork fillet rolled in peppercorns and served with prunes and Armagnac sauce.

Additional: Bar foodL ; Sunday L; Children welcome L only; ❹ dishes
Smoking: No smoking in dining room
Accommodation: 15 en suite
Credit cards: ▨ ▨ ▨ ▨ ▨ ▨

Directions: Turn off B591 Quorn High Street into Wood Lane, signed Swithland

88 Wood Lane LE12 8DB
Map 8: SK51
Tel: 01509 412167
Fax: 01509 415621
Chef: Gerard Stacey-Midgley
Owner: Jeremy Lord, Dagma Lord
Cost: *Alc* £25, fixed-price L £9.85 (2 courses)/D £18.95 (3 courses). ☺ H/wine £9.
Times: Last L 2pm/D 9.30pm. Closed L Sat, 26 Dec – 1 Jan

ROTHLEY, **Rothley Court Hotel** ❀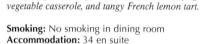

Splendid eleventh-century manor with its own chapel and six acres of grounds edged by the river. Menus in the Thomas Babington restaurant offer imaginative dishes such as scallops with mille-feuille of asparagus, rack of marinated lamb with a flageolet bean and vegetable casserole, and tangy French lemon tart.

Smoking: No smoking in dining room
Accommodation: 34 en suite
Credit cards: ▩ ▩ ▨ ▨ 🄿 🄒

Directions: From M1/J21A follow A46 for 7 miles. Turn onto A6 (Loughborough) and follow signs to Rothley. Hotel is 1 mile out of village

Westfield Lane
LE7 7LG
Map 8: SK51
Tel: 0116 2374141
Fax: 0116 2374483
Chef: Wayne Leonard
Owner: Forte
Cost: Alc £21.50, fixed-price L
£14.50/D £21.50. ☺ H/wine £12.50.
Times: Last L 2pm/last D 9.30pm
Additional: Sunday L; Bar meals;
Children welcome; ⬥ dishes

LINCOLNSHIRE

BECKINGHAM,
Black Swan Restaurant ❀❀

Set in a heavily beamed sixteenth-century building by the banks of the river Witham, this long-serving cottagey restaurant has a solid reputation both with locals and outsiders. Meals are served by white-gloved waiters in a setting of pink linen and fresh flowers; to the rear is an open patio for summer evenings. Anton Indans' dinner menus are an intriguing blend of traditional classics bolstered by ideas from the Mediterranean, California and the Far East. Seafood soup is flavoured with lemon, orange and basil, chicken breast is cooked in green Thai curry sauce, escalope of pork is coated in Parmesan batter and accompanied by tagliatelle. To finish, the kitchen might offer Christmas pudding soufflé with brandy sauce as a seasonal novelty, otherwise expect Mocha mousse with butterscotch sauce, apple and blackberry tart and the like. Sunday lunch is a popular family occasion – particularly as children under 11 eat free of charge ('one per adult')

Directions: 5 miles from Newark, A17 (Sleaford), 1st R & R again in village

Hillside LN5 0RF
Map 8: SK85
Tel: 01636 626474
Chef: Anton Indans
Owner: Mr & Mrs A Indans
Cost: Alc £22, fixed-price L £13.55.
☺ H/wine £8.60
Times: Noon-last L 2pm/7pm-last D
10pm. Closed D Sun, Mon, 1 wk Feb,
2 wks Aug
Additional: Sunday L; Children
welcome; ⬥ dishes
Seats: 35. Private dining room 12-26
Smoking: No smoking in dining room
Credit cards: ▩ ▨ ▨ 🄒

BELTON,
Belton Woods Hotel ❀

An impressive conference/leisure hotel not far from Grantham. A good range of carefully prepared dishes is available in the Manor restaurant – typical starters include warm salad of pigeon and pine kernels, grilled goat's cheese with roast peppers and aubergines, and smoked venison with rocket and figs.

Additional: Children welcome; ⬥ dishes
Smoking: No-smoking area; air-conditioning
Accommodation: 136 en suite
Credit cards: ▩ ▩ ▨ ▨ 🄿

Directions: Telephone for directions

Grantham NG32 2LN
Map 8: SK94
Tel: 01476 593200
Fax: 01476 574547
Chef: Mark Hotchkins
Cost: Alc £20 – £30, fixed-price D
£21. ☺ H/wine £9.95.
Times: D only, 7pm – last D 9.45pm.
Closed Sun

CLEETHORPES, **Kingsway Hotel** 🌸

Long-running seafront hotel that has been in the Harris family for four generations. Typical dishes from the dinner menu might include home-cured gravlax, lamb cutlets with pâté-stuffed mushrooms and port sauce, and roast sirloin of beef carved from the trolley. Desserts are freshly made in-house.

Additional: Bar Food (not Sun); Sunday L; No children under 5; 🌶 dishes
Smoking: No smoking in lounge
Accommodation: 52 en suite
Credit cards: 🔳 🔳 🔳 🔳 🔳

Directions: At junction of A1098 and sea front

Kingsway DN35 0AE
Map 8: TA30
Tel: 01472 601122
Fax: 01472 601381
Chef: Ivon Trushell
Owners: Mr & Mrs Harris & Sons
Cost: Alc £25, fixed-price L £13.25/ D £16.50. ☺ H/wine £9.75.
Times: Last L 2pm/D 9pm
Closed 25-26 Dec

GRANTHAM, **Harry's Place** 🌸🌸🌸

The roadside location belies the depth and charm of Harry's Place. 'This is a take your time, forget your worries sort of place', enthused one inspector of Harry and Caroline Hallam's tastefully restored old town house. Decorated in rich, warm tones, the tiny ten-seater restaurant has a homely feel. There are just three polished-wood tables, one for larger parties, old china butter dishes, bone-handled cutlery, and masses of fresh flowers. At a mid-winter lunch, the sheer quality and dedication of this simple place was seen immediately in canapés of freshly cooked tartlets of English goat's cheese, and Harry Hallam's own rich, nutty, rustic granary bread. Just two dishes are offered at each course, suitable for the size and style of the restaurant. Large, plump Orkney king scallops came lightly seared with a vibrant sauce of mango, lime, ginger and basil, its counterpart, a celeriac soup, was delicately flavoured. Then a wonderful winter dish of breast of free-range, corn-fed chicken, roasted with bacon and lentils and served with a sauce of white wine, Madeira and sage. A fillet of very fresh monkfish was lightly cooked with mussels, saffron, white wine, and came with home-made herb fettucine, leeks, mushrooms and cream. Apricot and Cognac soufflé offered wonderful flavours, with a generous dash of alcohol, and caramel mousse brûlée served with fruits and berries and a little coulis, was almost perfection. The wine list offers a good range, and wines by the glass are of notable quality. Booking is essential.
Signature dishes: Filleted loin of Devon spring lamb, served with baby broad beans and a sauce of white wine, tarragon and rosemary; terrine of River Dee wild salmon, with lemon, green peppercorns, fresh herbs, green leaves and truffle oil dressing; young Yorkshire grouse, roasted with bacon, sage and thyme, and served with a sauce of Madeira and cognac; Lincolnshire salt marsh teal with lentils, rosemary and Madeira.

Directions: On the B1174 2 miles NW of Grantham

17 High Street Great Gonerby NG31 8JS
Map 8: SK93
Tel: 01476 561780
Chef: Harry Hallam
Owners: Harry & Caroline Hallam
Cost: Alc £42.50.
Times: 12.30pm-last L 2pm/7pm-last D 9.30pm. Closed Sun, Mon, 25-26 Dec, Bhs
Additional: No children under 5
Seats: 10
Smoking: No smoking
Credit cards: 🔳 🔳 🔳

HORNCASTLE,
Magpies Restaurant 🌸🌸 NEW

Small, family-owned restaurant set in a charming row of cottages on the edge of town. Low ceilings characterise the two cosy lounges and the elegantly furnished, L-shaped dining room where candlelight and soft piped jazz music enhance the

71-75 East Street LN9 6AA
Map 8: TF26
Tel: 01507 527004
Fax: 01507 524064
Telephone for details

relaxed atmosphere. Mum runs front of house, whilst chef brothers Matthew and Simon Lee produce some excellent dishes on their extensive dinner menus. Cooking shows sound skill and flavours are clear and fresh. 'Delightfully' presented dishes sampled at a recent test meal included a delicious, frothy mushroom cappuccino, followed by crab ravioli with langoustine sauce, and roast fillet of beef with roasted shallots, parsley purée and a 'wonderful' Madeira sauce. To finish our inspector enjoyed a superb tarte Tatin simply served with home-made vanilla ice cream, Good global list of wines.

Directions: 0.5 mile from Horncastle on A158 towards Skegness

LINCOLN, Wig and Mitre ✺

29 Steep Hill LN2 1LU
Map 8: SK97
Tel: 01522 535190
Fax: 01522 532402
Chefs: P Vidic, G Aitkinhead, P Dodd, M Cheseldine
Owners: Michael & Valerie Hope
Cost: Alc £18.50, fixed-price L/D by arrangement. ☺ H/wine £10.
Times: 8am-11pm. Closed Dec 25
Additional: Bar food; Sunday L; Children welcome; ◑ dishes
Credit cards: 🔲 🔲 🔲 🔲 🔲 🔲

Flexibility is the watchword in this marvellously renovated medieval building. Downstairs is the bar (complete with beer garden), upstairs is the restaurant. Menus change twice daily and you can order anything you like. The range embraces everything from toasted crumpets to tiramisu, with confit of duck and chicken breast in Stilton sauce in between.

Directions: Close to cathedral, castle and car park at top of Steep Hill

LOUTH, Kenwick Park Hotel ✺✺

Kenwick Park LN11 8NR
Map 8: TF38
Tel: 01507 608806
Fax: 01507 608027
Chef: Paul Harvey
Owner: Mr SD Flynn
Cost: £24.50, fixed-price L & D £18.50 (4 courses). ☺ H/wine £10.95
Times: Noon-2pm/7pm-last L 9.45pm
Additional: Bar food; Sunday L; Children welcome; ◑ dishes
Seats: 44. Private dining room 24.
Jacket & tie preferred
Smoking: No smoking in dining room
Accommodation: 24 en suite
Credit cards: 🔲 🔲 🔲 🔲 🔲 🔲

The Fairway Restaurant, named after the 18-hole golf course that can be seen from the dining room, is part of a hotel and leisure club. The kitchen is strong on modern ideas and dishes such as pan-fried fillet of rainbow trout with red onion, garlic and almond butter, noisettes of English lamb glazed with port and sherry and served with deep-fried courgettes, and saddle of local rabbit with roasted garden vegetables, show the range. Vegetarian dishes, as well as home-made pasta, are always available. An inspection meal featured monkfish tails with a tangy and sweet orange butter sauce, seafood and ginger chowder, and roasted darne of salmon in a juniper berry sauce. Dessert was a good crème brûlée, served with acacia honey and a scoop of cinnamon ice cream. The 'Keepers' bar, which also overlooks the golf course, serves a good range of bar meals and real ales in a more relaxed and informal setting.

Directions: Take A631 from Market Rasen

STALLINGBOROUGH,
Stallingborough Grange ⊛⊛

Built in the eighteenth century as a country house – complete with thatched roof, pleasant gardens and a pond – the Grange is a popular, family-run hotel geared largely to the business community. Snacks can be eaten in the Tavern Bar, but the really serious business takes place in the traditional wood-panelled restaurant. A test meal in May suggested that the kitchen can handle quite complex dishes with a degree of flair and artistry. To start, a boudin of salmon and tarragon nestling on a celeriac rösti with creamed leeks and lemon butter sauce was reckoned to be 'a super sausage'. This was followed by loin of lamb rolled in rosemary and sliced onto a first-rate compote of fennel and sweet roasted peppers, while an individual apricot and brandy bread-and-butter pudding served with brown bread and cinnamon ice cream concluded proceedings successfully. The wine list has global appeal with some particularly interesting French bins from lesser known sources; the selection of unblended single vineyard Cognacs from Mme. Raymond Ragnaud, Le Château, Ambleville is also worth noting.

Riby Road DN37 8BU
Map 8: TA11
Tel: 01469 561302
Fax: 01469 561338
Chef: Neal Burtwell
Owners: Mr & Mrs G W Feeney
Cost: Fixed-price D £21.95. ☺
H/wine £8.80.
Times: 6.30pm-last D 10pm
Additional: Sunday L
Seats: 42. Private dining room 120.
Jacket & tie preferred
Smoking: No-smoking area; no pipes & cigars
Accommodation: 32 en suite
Credit cards: 🔳 🔳 🔳 🔳 🔳 🔳

Directions: On A1173 between Riby crossroads and Stallingborough village

STAMFORD, George of Stamford ⊛

Splendid sixteenth-century coaching inn featuring an elegant oak-panelled restaurant, and a flower-filled courtyard for summer meals. Traditional roasts vie with more ambitious dishes on the essentially modern British menu. The wine list is outstanding and has won awards for its excellent Italian range.

Accommodation: 47 en suite

Directions: From A1 take B1081 to Stamford. Follow road to traffic lights, hotel on L

St Martins PE9 2LB
Map 8: TF00
Tel: 01780 755171
Fax: 01780 757070
Chef: Chris Pitman
Owner: Lawrence Hoskins
Cost: Alc £30, fixed-price L £13.50-£16.50. H/wine £8.95
Times: Noon-11pm
Additional: Bar food; Sunday L; Children welcome; 🄯 dishes; Jacket & tie preferred

MABLETHORPE,
Grange & Links Hotel ⊛

Sea Lane
Sandilands LN12 2RA
Map 9: TF58
Tel: 01507 441334
Fax: 01507 443033
Chef: Christina Harrison
Owners: Eva & Robert McGahon
Cost: Alc £20. H/wine £8. ☺
Times: Last L 1.30pm/last D 8.45pm
Additional: Bar food; Sunday L; Children welcome; 🄯 dishes
Accommodation: 30 en suite
Credit cards: 🔳 🔳 🔳 🔳 🔳 🔳

Directions: Follow signs to Sandilands from Sutton-on-Sea

A friendly seaside hotel, popular with golfers and families with children. Good home cooking, served in the traditional dining room, has an emphasis on seafood. Lobster dishes require 24-hours notice, there's always a home-made terrine of the day, and a range of steaks.

WINTERINGHAM,
Winteringham Fields ❀❀❀❀

Winteringham DN15 9PF
Map 8: SE92
Tel: 01724 733096
Fax: 01724 733898
Chef: Germain Schwab
Owner: Annie & Germain Schwab
Cost: *Alc* £42, fixed-price L £17.50/D
£28. H/wine £12.50
Times: Noon- last L 1.30pm/7.15pm-
last D 9.30pm. Closed L Sat, Sun, L
Mon, 1-9 Aug, 24 Dec- 9 Jan
Additional: Children welcome;
❀ dishes
Seats: 35. Private dining room 10
Smoking: No smoking in dining room
Accommodation: 7 en suite
Credit cards: ▬ ▬ ▬ ▰

Germain and Annie Schwab have created a European-style
oasis of comfort, good food and hospitality that frankly takes
some beating. Their small country hotel is full of charming
Victoriana, elegant swagged curtains, pretty mirrors and
Annie's hand-made dried flower garlands. The quality of
produce is impeccable, and much now comes from their walled
garden, with Grimsby not far away, plus a network of hand-
picked sources all around the region. Annie has polished her
team of staff into a super-professional crew, who temper
unflagging attentiveness with friendly Northern smiles. The
place runs like clockwork and it is little wonder guests from
Europe think nothing of flying in just to dine here. To say
Swiss-born Germain is hands-on is an understatement – quite
simply if he is not there the restaurant closes. His style is based
on traditional methods, applied with a light touch and a
modern twist. An amuse-bouche of petit salé of pork en croute
with a haricot vert sauce and peeled feves was an excellent
contrast of clean, rich flavours. Typical dexterity and
imagination was shown with a first course of cassoulette of
squid, the body slow-braised and tender, the tentacles crispy
and the sauce full of intense, shellfish bisque flavour. An
unctuously rich, mouth-watering main course of pork cheeks
braised in a rich winey jus with crisped, wafer-thin Ventreche
bacon, Gruyère polenta, button onions, mushrooms and turned
carrots, also showed a deft hand with slow cooking techniques.
The cheese trolley is a theatrical turn in its own right, with
great British, French and Swiss cheeses in prime condition,
served with dried fruit, nuts, malt bread, biscuits and celery.
Desserts show Annie's professional skills as a pâtissier, and our
inspector could not fault a quite perfect rice crème brûlée of
velvety texture, served with poached rhubarb and ginger. An
extensive, well balanced wine list with six house wines at £13,
seven wines of the month under £20, an interesting section of
Swiss wines (worth a try as they are rarely seen), and some top
quality Austrian wines. There's good informative text on lesser
known wines plus all the top French, sound Italian and
Australasian sections, and quite range of Chilean and
Argentinean wines.

Directions: Village centre, off the A1077, 4 miles S of Humber
bridge.

MERSEYSIDE

BIRKENHEAD, **Beadles**

Monthly changing hand-written menus highlight a short selection of soundly cooked dishes on offer at this relaxed and informal restaurant in the heart of Oxton village. Expect guinea fowl and bacon terrine with cranberry relish, followed perhaps by chargrilled beef fillet with port and redcurrant sauce and rhubarb tart.

Additional: No children under 7
Credit cards: ▄▄ ▄▄ ▄▄

Directions: Centre of Oxton village

15 Rosemount Oxton L43 5SG
Map 7: SJ38
Tel: 0151 653 9010
Chef: Bea Gott
Owners: Roy & Bea Gott
Cost: H/wine £8.
Times: D only, 7.30pm-9pm.
Closed Sun, Mon, Tue, 2 wks Feb,
1 wk July/Aug

BIRKENHEAD, **Bowler Hat Hotel**

Highly popular hotel much used for business, weddings and functions. Specialities from the international menus might include a trio of smoked fish, honey-roast rack of lamb with flageolet beans and duck with Grand Marnier and orange sauce with glazed kumquats, followed by strawberry cheesecake.

Additional: Bar meals; Sunday L; Children welcome; ◑ dishes
Accommodation: 32 en suite
Credit cards: ▄▄ ▄▄ ▄▄ ▄▄ ▄▄ ▄▄

Directions: M53/J3 (Birkenhead) follow sign for Oxton Village, hotel on L

2 Talbot Road Oxton L43 2HH
Map 7: SJ38
Tel: 0151 652 4931
Fax: 0151 653 8127
Chef: Ian Brown
Owner: Regal Hotel Group plc
Cost: *Alc* £22, Fixed-price L £12.95/D
£17.95. ☺ H/wine £9.45.
Times: Last L 2pm/D 9.30pm
Closed L Sat

BIRKENHEAD, **Capitol**

24 Argyle Street Hamilton Square
L41 6AE
Map 7: SJ38
Tel: 0151 647 9212
Fax: 0151 647 3793
Chef: Yan Tam
Owner: Steve Tam
Cost: *Alc* £15, fixed-price L £6/ D
£15. ☺ H/wine £9.
Times: Last L 1.45pm/D 11pm
Closed L Sat, L Sun, 25-26 Dec
Additional: Children welcome;
◑ dishes
Smoking: Air-conditioning
Credit cards: ▄▄ ▄▄ ▄▄ ▄▄ ▄▄

Popular Chinese restaurant that informally doubles as a Chinese art gallery. The generally reliable Cantonese cooking includes tender beef with ginger and spring onions, and chicken with cashew nuts, yellow bean sauce, celery and water chestnuts to give some welcome crispness. French bread and butter, we assume, is a regional idiosyncracy.

Directions: Town centre, at the corner of Hamilton Square

LIVERPOOL, Becher's Brook

One of the attractions of this popular restaurant is its location close to the city's two cathedrals, theatres and university. The setting is a listed Georgian townhouse with a basement bar and a dining room with bare floorboards and brick walls festooned with bundles of fresh herbs and ethnic artwork – mostly Native American. Lunch and pre-theatre menus are good value and the kitchen takes care over supplies: grilled Arctic char, tasted at inspection, had been air-freighted from Iceland the previous day. The cooking is modern international, with a few oriental gestures, especially among the starters, for example, leek and mushroom wun-tuns with sesame and soy butter or lobster salad with sweet and sour pickled onions, ginger and rice wine vinaigrette. Main courses tend to be more robust: braised lamb shank is served on mash with roasted parsnips and green beans, baron of rabbit comes with black pepper, button mushrooms, shallots and bacon on wild rice. To finish, a rich chocolate pyramid garnished with diced poached pear has been favourably received. The wine list is a well-chosen, world-wide slate.

29a Hope Street L1 9BQ
Map 7: SJ38
Tel: 0151 7070005
Fax: 0151 7087011
Chefs: David Cooke, Gerard Mogan
Owners: Mr & Mrs D Cooke ☺
Cost: Alc £25, fixed-price L £16.
H/wine £11.50.
Times: Noon-last L 2.30pm/5pm-last D 10pm. Closed L Sat, Sun, Xmas 1-14 Aug
Additional: No children under 7; ◑ dishes
Seats: 38
Smoking: No-smoking in dining room or lounge
Credit cards: all major cards accepted

Directions: From M62 follow signs for City Centre and Catholic Cathedral. L into Mount Pleasant Rd, then L again into Hope St. Restaurant is 100yds on L

SOUTHPORT, Royal Clifton Hotel

A long-established hotel with a prominent promenade position. Modern English dishes are served in the restaurant – guests can choose from either the daily set menu or the popular carte. A March meal included a starter of Parma ham wrapped with asparagus, and a main dish of venison noisettes with red wine sauce.

Promenade PR8 1RB
Map 7: SD32
Tel: 01704 533771
Fax: 01704 500657
Chef: Peter Kershaw
Cost: Alc £20, fixed-price D £16.50. ☺ H/wine £7.95.
Times: D only, 6.30pm-9.30pm.
Additional: Bar meals; Sunday L (12.30pm-3pm); Children welcome; ◑ dishes
Seats: 100

Smoking: No-smoking area; no cigars or pipes; air-conditioning
Accommodation: 108 en suite
Credit cards: ▪️▬▬🔲▪️

Directions: M6/J26, take M58 (Southport), exit at J3. Follow A570 through Ormskirk – hotel on Southport promenade.

THORNTON HOUGH,
Thornton Hall Hotel

Neston Road Wirral L63 1JF
Map 7: SJ38
Tel: 0151 3363938
Fax: 0151 3367864
Chef: Neil McKevitt
Owners: Mr & Mrs Thompson
Cost: Alc £30, fixed-price L £9.95/D £20.50. ☺ H/wine £10.95.
Times: 12.30pm-last L 2.15pm/7pm-last D 9.30pm. Closed L Sat, 25-26 Dec
Additional: Bar food; Sunday L; Children welcome; ◑ menu
Seats: 50. Private dining room 25
Smoking: No-smoking area
Accommodation: 63 en suite
Credit cards: ▪️▬▬▪️

Billed as 'Wirral's country hotel', this solid-looking mansion was built by an eighteenth-century shipping magnate from Liverpool. Stained glass windows and impressive oak panelling are features of the hall, while the restaurant (housed in the old music room) is notable for its leather ceiling inlaid with mother-of-pearl. A typical dinner might commence with ballotine of duck liver with asparagus and an orange and redcurrant dressing, or seared Oban scallops marinated in Thai fish sauce with lime and ginger before, say, rack of Welsh lamb with lemon and rosemary crust, or pan-fried maize-fed poussin with a hotch-potch of vegetables. Desserts could include white chocolate terrine with blackcurrant nectar, or apple crumble with vanilla custard, and the menu also advertises 'British countryside and guest cheeses'. The hotel's own blend of coffee comes with home-made sweetmeats. France is the big player on the wine list.

Thornton Hall Hotel

Directions: M53/J4 onto B5151. Turn R at first crossroads – B5136 (Thornton Hough). Hotel just past village centre on L

NORFOLK

ATTLEBOROUGH,

Sherbourne Hotel

NEW

Sound modern cooking based on prime ingredients at this small, family-run hotel. Home-made bread and soups are backed up by daily fish dishes, the likes of roast duck with red onion marmalade and kumquat sauce or fillet of lamb with whisky and horseradish cream, with caramelised lime tart for dessert.

Smoking: No smoking in dining room
Accommodation: 8 rooms (6 en suite)
Credit cards:

Directions:: At Parish Church follow signs for A11 to Norwich. Hotel is 200yds on R

8 Norwich Road NR17 2JX
Map 5: TM09
Tel: 01953 454363
Fax: 01953 453509
Chef: Christopher Seddon
Owners: Ann & Richard Holden
Cost: Alc £17. H/wine £8.50. ☺
Times: Last L 2pm/last D 9.30pm
Additional: Bar meals; Sunday L; Children welcome; ◑ dishes

BARNHAM BROOM,

Barnham Broom Hotel

With its extensive range of sporting, leisure and conference facilities, this golfing hotel offers plenty to both its corporate and leisure guests. Dishes served in the restaurant could include pan-fried fillet of lamb in a port wine sauce, and saddle of Norfolk hare with oyster mushrooms and straw potatoes.

Smoking: No smoking in dining room
Accommodation: 53 en suite
Credit cards: ▦ ▦ ▦ ▦ ▣ ▣

Directions:: From Norwich head E on A47 (Swaffham/Kings Lynn). After 9 miles turn L towards Barnham Broom

Barnham Broom NR9 4DD
Map 9: TG11
Tel: 01603 759393
Fax: 01603 758224
Chef: David Bell
Cost: Alc ££25, fixed-price D £16.25. ☺ H/wine £9.25.
Additional: Sunday L; Bar meals; Children welcome; ◑ dishes

BLAKENEY, **Morston Hall**

Dating from the seventeenth century, Morston Hall stands in lovely, well-tended gardens in a small, coastal village close to National Trust owned Blakeney Point. The restaurant, full of fresh flowers and paintings, opens into the conservatory, and is decorated in jewel-coloured shades of red and blue. The fixed-price, four-course menu (no choice until dessert), is both well-balanced and skilfully executed; good quality ingredients are intelligently handled and interesting combinations are enthusiastically explored. Grilled apple boudin with sautéed mixed wild mushrooms and whole grain sabayon might precede a delicately-flavoured steamed salmon mousse served on wilted spinach leaves with a tomato butter. The main course – perhaps roast breast of duck, served pink with rosemary scented jus – comes with a good selection of vegetables. Cinnamon and beer-battered pear beignets with caramel sauce and warm chocolate tartlet with pistachio ice cream are typical of the imaginative approach to desserts. A June dinner opened with an appetiser of leg of corn-fed chicken with a morel jus, then a starter of grilled vegetables with guacamole. Fricassée of fishes took in lobster cappuccino, a panaché of four different locally landed fish on 'squeaky' al dente leeks with a delicately flavoured, frothy lobster broth, pan-fried salmon, steamed turbot, pan-fried monkfish, and moist slip lemon sole. Roasted breast of honeyed duck came on fondant potato with French beans, young carrots and a rich duck jus – a very simple, clean-cut dish. Dessert was coffee cream served with a sorbet of local strawberries alongside a crisp brandy snap basket with a superb strawberry sorbet. Details throughout are highly commendable, from the tiny lemon tart with cafetière coffee to the particularly delicious black olive bread rolls. The wine list offers a good selection of cross-level priced bottles.

Directions:: On A149 (King's Lynn/Cromer) 2 miles W of Blakeney in the village of Morston.

Morston NR25 7AA
Map 9: TG03
Tel: 01263 741041
Fax: 01263 740419
Chef: Galton Blackiston
Owner: Galton & Tracy Blackiston, Justin Fraser
Cost: D £26 (4 courses). ☺ H/wine £9.50.
Times: 7.30pm-8pm. Closed Jan
Additional: Sunday L (£15, 12.30pm-1pm); Children welcome; ✦ dishes
Seats: 40
Smoking: No smoking in dining room
Accommodation: 6 en suite
Credit cards: 🔳 🔳 🔳 🔳 🔳

BURNHAM MARKET,
Hoste Arms Hotel

The Green PE31 8HD
Map 9: TF84
Tel: 01328 738777
Fax: 01328 730103
Chef: Stephen David
Owner: Paul Whittome
Cost: Alc £18.50. H/wine £8.95. ☺
Times: Noon-last L 2pm/7pm-last D 9.15pm
Additional: Bar food; Sunday L; Children welcome; ✦ dishes
 Seats: 160. Private dining room 36
Accommodation: 20 en suite
Credit cards: 🔳 🔳 🔳 🔳

This 'great market town local inn' overlooking the Georgian village green seems to have everything going for it. Regular live jazz, monthly art exhibitions, a splendid buzzy atmosphere and cooking that is on-the-up are just some of its attributes. No wonder the place gets packed. One menu is now served throughout the bar and restaurant and local fish gets top billing. Excellent turbot on a near-perfect spinach and pine kernel risotto was the highlight of a recent test meal but you might also find, say, plates of Burnham Norton oysters, catfish with fettucine and red pepper vinaigrette, and baked hake with Savoy cabbage, potato purée and veal jus. Away from the sea, the kitchen can also produce anything from pan-fried foie gras on toasted brioche with braised oxtail and orange sauce, and deep-fried Thai meatballs with noodles and hot and sour sauce, to chargrilled rump steak and chips. Prune and Armagnac parfait or warm plum and almond tart are typical desserts. East Anglian real ales and plenty of wines by the glass make for affordable drinking.

Directions: In the centre of the village

CAWSTON, Grey Gables Hotel ❀

Peaceful former rectory in five acres, providing discreet hospitality and wholesome food. Traditional English and regional French dishes, prepared from fresh local produce, feature on the set-price dinner menu. Dishes sampled at inspection included delicately cooked plaice and succulent lamb cooked with orange and ginger.

Accommodation: 8 en suite
Credit cards: 🔳 🔳 🔳

Directions: 1 mile S of Cawston village, near Eastgate

Norwich Road NR10 4EY
Map 9: TG12
Tel & Fax: 01603 871259
Chef: Rosalind Snaith
Owners: James & Rosalind Snaith
Cost: Fixed-price D £18. ☺
H/wine £8.50.
Times: D only, 7pm-9pm.
Closed 24,25,26 Dec
Additional: No children under 5;
🍴 dishes
Smoking: Air conditioning

DISS, Salisbury House ❀❀

84 Victoria Road IP22 3JG
Map 5: TM18
Tel/Fax: 01379 644738
Chef: Barry Davies
Owners: Mr & Mrs B Davies
Cost: *Alc* (bistro) £17, fixed-price D
£24.95. ☺ H/wine £7.95.
Times: 12.15pm-last L
1.45pm/7.15pm-last D 9pm.
Closed Sat L, Sun, Mon, 1 wk Xmas,
2 wks summer
Additional: Children welcome;
🍴 dishes
Seats: 36. Private dining room 20.
Jacket & tie preferred in restaurant
Smoking: No smoking in dining room
Accommodation: 3 en suite
Credit cards: 🔳 🔳

Salisbury House wears two hats. Light lunches are served in the bistro, a bright, sunny yellow room that was originally a storeroom for the nearby windmill. Here, a monthly menu of vibrant dishes encompasses everything from pork and garlic sausages with bubble and squeak, or Italian meatballs on tagliatelle, to delicately flavoured red mullet mousseline with lemon butter sauce, and breast of guinea fowl stuffed with wild mushroom mousse, served on Puy lentils. Desserts tend to be things like Armagnac parfait with Agen prunes in Earl Grey syrup. The restaurant offers a more formal repertoire, and meals are priced according to the number of courses taken: sautéed scallops with bacon, pan-fried fillet of pork with roasted peppers and pesto vinaigrette, and coffee bavarois with Tia Maria sauce are typical. The wine list is a well-balanced selection with several halves and plenty of affordable drinking.

Directions: On A1066
(Thetford/Scole) 0.25 mile E of Diss
town centre

ERPINGHAM, **Ark Restaurant**

In a rambling old brick and flint cottage in a small village off the beaten track, but close to the sea, the Kidds' restaurant enjoys a well-deserved reputation. Sheila Kidd is a self-taught cook and a disciple of Elizabeth David, whose influence is discernible in dishes such as fillet steak with a caramelised red wine and Cassis sauce, and wild mushroom lasagne made with home-made herb pasta. Local produce is a pronounced feature, as can be seen in a meal that opened with fresh Cromer crab, orange salad and an avocado sauce, and went on to spiced braised pheasant with walnuts and onions. The extensive garden produces flowers and vegetables in season. Desserts are all home-made and include fresh apricot frangipane tart, honey nougatine ice cream, and a selection of British cheeses from Neal's Yard dairy. There is a good wine list featuring an interesting selection of half-bottles, and personal tasting notes by Michael Kidd.

Directions: Off the A140m 4 miles N of Aylsham

Norwich NR11 7QB
Map 5: TG20
Tel: 01263 761535
Fax: 01263 587455
Chefs: Sheila Kidd
Owners: Sheila & Mike Kidd
Cost: Alc £24, fixed-price D £23.50. ☺ H/wine £8.
Times: D only, 7pm-9.30pm. Closed D Sun, Mon, 25-30 Dec, Tue from Oct-Easter.
Additional: Sunday L only (12.30pm-2pm); Children welcome; ❹ dishes
Seats: 30. Private dining room 8
Smoking: No smoking in dining room
Accommodation: 3 rooms
Credit cards: None

GREAT YARMOUTH, **Imperial Hotel**

North Drive NR30 1EQ
Map 5: TG50
Tel: 01493 851113
Fax: 01493 852229
Chef: Stephen Duffield
Owner: Roger Mobbs
Cost: Alc £20.50, fixed-price L £11.50/D £18.50. ☺ H/wine £12.
Times: Last L 2pm/D 10pm. Closed L Sat
Additional: Bar meals; Sunday L; No children under 5; ❹ dishes
Smoking: No-smoking area
Accommodation: 39 en suite
Credit cards: ▆ ▆ ▆ ▆ ▆ ▆

A spacious and well appointed hotel on the quieter North Beach, a short walk from the bright hurly-burly of the main promenade. A wide choice of dishes is served in the Rambouillet Restaurant, ranging from a simple chargrilled pepper steak, to the more exotic pan-fried fillet of turkey zingara with mozzarella and fresh tagliatelle.

Directions: On the seafront 100 yards N of Britannia Pier

GRIMSTON,
Congham Hall Hotel

Forty acres of grounds including a fascinating herb garden with more than 100 varieties – not to mention a walled flower garden and even a cricket pitch – are among the attractions at this lovely Georgian manor house. The Orangery Restaurant is appropriately decked out with trailing plants and, of course, a miniature orange tree. Light lunches can be as straightforward as a goat's cheese tartlet with provençale vegetables or a BLT, but dinner is altogether more ambitious. To start there might be a gratin of Kings Lynn brown shrimps layered with richly flavoured, crisp Parmesan biscuits or beautifully limpid

Lynn Road King's Lynn PE32 1AH
Map 9: TF72
Tel: 01485 600250
Fax: 01485 601191
Chef: Stephanie Moon
Owners: Christine & Trevor Forecast
Cost: Alc £25, fixed-price L £17.50/D £32. ☺ H/wine £12.75.
Times: 12.30pm-last L 2pm/7.30pm-last D 9.15pm. Closed L Sat
Additional: Bar food; Sunday lunch; No children under 12; ❹ dishes

Congham Hall Hotel

Seats: 50. Private dining room 16
Smoking: No smoking in dining room
Accommodation: 14 en suite
Credit cards: ▆▆ ▆ ▆ ▆

consommé of Peking duck (the real thing) with mango and spring onion wun-tuns. For main course, saddle of venison, cooked pink with a thin herb crust, preserved blueberries and sauce Bercy impressed one inspector, although the choice extends to shank of lamb with olive mash and parsley jus or steamed halibut with oyster tortellini and lemon grass butter. Hot chocolate cake is a richly flavoured dessert, well complemented by cardamom ice cream in a tuile basket. Plentiful halves and wines by the glass appear on the well-chosen list.

Directions: 6 miles N/E of King's Lynn on A14, turn R toward Grimston. Hotel is 2.5 miles on L; don't go to Longham.

HETHERSETT, Park Farm Hotel ❀

NR9 3DL
Map 5: TG10
Tel: 01603 810264
Fax: 01603 812104
Chef: Adam Hodge
Owners: Mr P Gowing & Partners
Cost: *Alc* £25, fixed-price L £12/ D £17. ☺ H/wine £9.50.
Times: Last L 2pm/D 9pm
Additional: Bar Food; Sunday L; Children welcome; ⚫ dishes
Smoking: No smoking in dining room
Accommodation: 38 en suite
Credit cards: ▆▆ ▆ ▆ ▆ ▆ ▆

The hotel is in a secluded setting surrounded by pastureland and mature gardens, and the restaurant is part of the original Georgian house – intimate and tastefully decorated. Game sausage was the highlight of a recent meal, which might be followed by lobster, noisette of wild boar, or leek Wellington.

Directions: 5 miles S of Norwich on B1172 (the old A11)

HOLT, Yetman's ❀❀

37 Norwich Road NR25 6SA
Map 9: TG03
Tel: 01263 713320
Chef: Alison Yetman
Owners: Peter & Alison Yetman
Cost: Fixed-price D £25.50.

Rural Norfolk can offer some surprises, not least the unique and personal service offered by Peter Yetman, and the contemporary British cooking of partner Alison – 'enthusiastically sampled by the eclectic clientele, where nose rings sit happily beside business suits'. The two small dining rooms in this low-beamed cottage are bright, and filled with an abundance of fresh flowers. At a test meal home-made rolls 'were so good I barely had an appetite after polishing off three – mint, cheese and olive', but the appetite came back for a 'perfect' twice-baked cheese soufflé, and chargrilled rack of lamb came with a gratin of tomatoes and was described as 'another winner'. Pudding was toasted fresh apricot pancakes with a creamy sauce. The wine list is sensible, makes no apologies for being biased towards Sauvignon Blanc, which admirably suits Alison's food style, and is very reasonably priced.

Times: D only, 7.30pm-9pm. Closed D Mon (in winter),Tue
Additional: Sunday L (12.30pm-1.30pm); Children welcome; 🌢 dishes
Seats: 32. Private dining room 12/18
Smoking: No smoking in dining room
Credit cards: ▆ ▆ ▆ ▆ ▆

Directions: Village centre

KING'S LYNN, Rococo

The sun shines all year round in the bright, yellow dining room at this busy seventeenth-century cottage restaurant in the Old Town. Anyone in doubt, though, as to the contemporary nature of the cooking need only take one glance at the menu, where items such as couscous and goat's cheese, confit and tapenade, rocket and black pudding, are clues to the kitchen's orientation. Although there are a few familiar inclusions, chicken liver and foie gras parfait, breast of duck with Puy lentils, smoked bacon and shallots, sticky toffee pudding with anglaise sauce, for example, there are also some confident ideas that deserve wider appreciation. Look out for crispy tongue salad with five herb dressing, and lamb sweetbreads with cumin-scented couscous and chilled yoghurt and mint relish. Lunch times revolve around a set-priced *carte* and a selection of simpler dishes along the lines of sausages and creamy mash and Caribbean jerk chicken.

11 Saturday Market Place PE30 5DQ
Map 9: TF62
Tel/Fax: 01553 771483
Chef: Nick Anderson
Owners: Nick & Anne Anderson
Cost: Fixed-price L £13.50/D £27.50 (3 courses). H/wine £12.95
Times: Noon-last L 1.30pm/7pm-last D 10pm. Closed Sun, L Mon
Additional: Children welcome; 🌢 dishes
Seats: 40
Smoking: No pipes and cigars in dining room
Credit cards: ▆ ▆ ▆ ▆ ▆ ▆

Directions: Follow signs to The Old Town, next to Tourist Information

NORWICH,

Adlard's Restaurant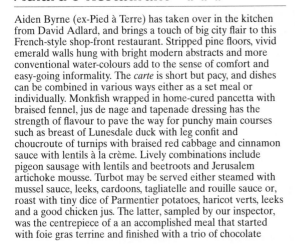

Aiden Byrne (ex-Pied à Terre) has taken over in the kitchen from David Adlard, and brings a touch of big city flair to this French-style shop-front restaurant. Stripped pine floors, vivid emerald walls hung with bright modern abstracts and more conventional water-colours add to the sense of comfort and easy-going informality. The *carte* is short but pacy, and dishes can be combined in various ways either as a set meal or individually. Monkfish wrapped in home-cured pancetta with braised fennel, jus de nage and tapenade dressing has the strength of flavour to pave the way for punchy main courses such as breast of Lunesdale duck with leg confit and choucroute of turnips with braised red cabbage and cinnamon sauce with lentils à la crème. Lively combinations include pigeon sausage with lentils and beetroots and Jerusalem artichoke mousse. Turbot may be served either steamed with mussel sauce, leeks, cardoons, tagliatelle and rouille sauce or, roast with tiny dice of Parmentier potatoes, haricot verts, leeks and a good chicken jus. The latter, sampled by our inspector, was the centrepiece of a an accomplished meal that started with foie gras terrine and finished with a trio of chocolate

79 Upper St Giles Street NR2 1AB
Map 5: TG20
Tel: 01603 633522
Fax: 01603 617733
Chefs: Aiden Byrne, David Adlard
Owners: David & Mary Adlard
Cost: Fixed-price L £19/D £32. H/wine £9.50
Times: 12.30pm-last L 1.45pm/7.30pm-last D 10.45pm. Closed Sun, L Mon, 1 wk after Xmas
Additional: Children welcome; 🌢 dishes
Seats: 40
Smoking: No pipes and cigars in dining room
Credit cards: ▆ ▆ ▆ ▆ ▆ ▆

soufflé, dark chocolate ice cream, and chocolate mousse.
A lengthy wine list with lots of interest. Argentine house red
sounds fun at £9.50; 20 'Beginnings', as opposed to bin ends,
offer good value, most under £16; Vina Casablanca, Sauvignon
Blanc offers a change from New Zealand at £15. Intriguing is
wine described as 'Rubbish' and selling at £5 a bottle!

Signature dishes: Rack of English lamb with grilled
Mediterranean vegetables and thyme sauce; warm smoked
salmon with tart of quails eggs, citrus beurre blanc; tarte Tatin
of pears with ginger ice cream.

Directions: City centre, 200 yards behind City Hall

NORWICH, **Brasted's** ✿✿

8-10 St Andrews Hill NR2 1AD
Map 5: TG20
Tel: 01603 625949
Fax: 01603 766445
Chef: Adrian Clarke
Owner: John Brasted
Cost: *Alc* £25. H/wine £10.85. ☺
Additional: Children welcome;
✿ dishes
Seats: 24
Credit cards: ▦ ▦ ▦ ▦ ▦ ▦

The tiny bar-cum-entrance at this side-street restaurant is full
of inviting clutter and worn rugs, reminiscent of a country
house study. The dining room is lined with heavy striped fabric
and is full of fresh flowers and well used china that has
mellowed with age – 'one feels really comfortable here'. A
veritable rabbit warren of tiny passageways lead to the upstairs
kitchen where Adrian Clarke beavers away, producing dishes
that show a complete understanding of modern trends, but
taken in step with what he knows. Thus Thai crab cakes, grilled
Mediterranean vegetables tossed with a salsa verde, and a
baked spaghetti cake flavoured with pancetta, Parmesan and
cream might appear as starters, but they are balanced by such
stalwarts as soft herring roes served on toast and twice-baked
cheese soufflé. The house speciality is a real blast-from-the-
past beef Stroganoff, and there's also steak and kidney
pudding, lamb's liver and bacon, and roast pheasant served
with game chips, bread sauce and fried breadcrumbs. The wine
list has all the hallmarks of an enthusiast, with many fine
vintages for those wanting to push the boat out.

Directions: City centre, close to the Castle & Cathedral,
between London Street and St Andrews Street

NORWICH, **By Appointment** ✿

27-29 St George's Street NR3 1AB
Map 5: TG20
Tel: 01603 630730
Chef: Timothy Brown
Owners: Timothy Brown,
Robert Culyer
Cost: *Alc* £26.10 ☺ H/wine £8.90
Times: D only, 7.30pm-9.30pm.
Closed Sun, Mon

*Sumptuously decorated with period antiques and bold colours, this
intimate restaurant enjoys a pleasant location within a row of
sixteenth-century merchant's houses. A short blackboard menu lists
the competently cooked dishes on offer. Expect salmon and prawn
mousse, wild boar with caramelised apples and Calvados, and pear
frangipane tart.*

Additional: No children under 12; ✿ dishes
Smoking: No smoking in dining room
Accommodation: 4 en suite
Credit cards: ▦ ▦ ▦ ▦

Directions: City centre, from St Andrews Hall, down St
George's Street, into Colegate then 1st R into courtyard

NORWICH, **Cumberland Hotel** ✿

212-216 Thorpe Road NRJ 1TJ
Map 9: TG21
Tel: 01603 434550/60
Fax: 01603 433355
Chef: Craig Robinson

*A warm, welcoming place featuring a South African themed
restaurant. The carte and set menus include a mixture of English
and French dishes with an emphasis on fresh fish. Look out for*

chargrilled red snapper with a vanilla and champagne butter, and steamed turbot on a bed of pasta, asparagus and sun-dried tomatoes.

Smoking: No smoking in dining room
Accommodation: 25 en suite
Credit cards:

Directions: 1 mile E of city centre on A47 to Yarmouth. Nr rail station & football ground

Owner: Michael A Price
Cost: *Alc* £22.50, fixed-price L £10.95/D £17.95. ☺ H/wine £10.95.
Times: Last L 1.15pm/D 9.15pm. Closed Sun, 26 Dec-2 Jan
Additional: Bar meals; No children under 12; ◢ dishes

NORWICH, Femi's ❀

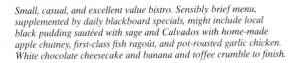

Small, casual, and excellent value bistro. Sensibly brief menu, supplemented by daily blackboard specials, might include local black pudding sautéed with sage and Calvados with home-made apple chutney, first-class fish ragoût, and pot-roasted garlic chicken. White chocolate cheesecake and banana and toffee crumble to finish.

Credit cards:

Directions:: City centre. 200 yds from Castle and Cathedral. Behind Anglia Television.

42 King Street NR1 1PD
Map 5: TG20
Tel: 01603 766010
Chef/Owner: Mr Femi Abodunde
Cost: *Alc* £20, fixed-price L £10/D £13.50. ☺ H/wine £6.95.
Times: Last L 2pm/D 9.45pm. Closed Sun, Mon, 24-31 Dec
Additional: Children welcome; ◢ dishes
Smoking: No-smoking area; no pipes & cigars

NORWICH, Greens Seafood Restaurant ❀

Only the freshest seafood is served in this cosy dining room complete with warm green decor and informal back bar. Cooking is a welcome mix of traditional and modern ideas with oriental twists. Meat-eaters are not forgotten – our inspector sampled a crisp confit of duck with parsley mash, haricot beans, sausage, bacon and a rich sauce.

Smoking: No pipes & cigars; air conditioning
Credit cards:

Directions: Near St John's RC Cathedral

82 Upper St Giles Street NR2 1LT
Map 5: TG20
Tel: 01603 623733
Fax: 01603 615268
Chef/Owner: Dennis William Crompton
Cost: *Alc* £25, fixed-price L £16. ☺ H/wine £9.20.
Times: Last L 2pm/last D 10.30pm. Closed L Sat, Sun, Mon, 2wks Xmas
Additional: Bar meals L; No children under 9; ◢ dishes

NORWICH, Marco's Restaurant ❀❀

Still going strong after more than 25 years, Marco's has become a fixture of the Norwich restaurant scene. The setting is an elegant Georgian building in the centre of the city, where Marco Vessalio produces authentic regional Italian dishes. Starters include a range of unusual antipasti dishes, thin slices of cured wild boar, served with mozzarella cheese and olive oil, or *penne all'abbruzzese* – quill-shaped pasta with chillies, garlic, pancetta and Pecorino cheese – and smoked Scottish salmon and light potato pancakes. The Genoan *buridda di pesce,* an enormous dish of halibut, prawns, monkfish, turbot and brill (depending on market availability), served with a simple salad, is highly recommended. Other main courses include breast of Norfolk pheasant, served with a light apple brandy cream sauce, fillet of local beef with a Rubesco red wine sauce, and scallops of chicken breast with sage and Parma ham. The impressive wine list covers all regions of Italy.

Directions: City centre: from market place facing Guildhall, turn R then L into Pottergate

17 Pottergate NR2 1DS
Map 5: TG20
Tel: 01603 624044
Chef/Owner: Marco Vessalio
Cost: *Alc* £26, fixed-price L £14. ☺ H/wine £9.50
Times: Noon-last L 2pm/7pm-last D 10pm. Closed Sun, Mon, Xmas, Bhs
Additional: Children welcome; ◢ dishes
Seats: 22
Smoking: No smoking in dining room
Credit cards:

NORWICH,

Pinocchio's Restaurant ❀

Traditional Italian cooking and good jazz are the main attractions at this informal, café-style brasserie. Beyond lunchtime and early evening bargain blackboard menus, a sound carte lists traditional spaghetti carbonara alongside grilled red snapper with pesto coulis and crispy duck with Italian mash and Siciliana sauce.

Smoking: No-smoking area
Credit cards: ▆▆ ▆▆ ▆▆ ▆▆ ▆

Directions: From City centre follow Castle Meadow to traffic lights, 1st L into Bank Plain, leads to St Benedict's Street

11 St Benedicts Street NR2 4PE
Map 5: TG20
Tel: 01603 613318
Fax: 01603 765377
Chef: Pino Longardo
Owners: Nigel & Jayne Raffles
Cost: *Alc* £15, fixed-price L £5 (2 courses). ☺ H/wine £7.
Times: Last L 2pm/D 11pm.
Closed Sun, 25-26 Dec
Additional: Children welcome; ✿ dishes

NORWICH,

St Benedicts Restaurant ❀

Thriving town-centre bistro noted for cheerful service and adventurous food at affordable prices. Big blackboard menus list a good range of dishes that reflect modern ideas and quality raw ingredients. These may include Thai-style prawn fishcakes, venison with celeriac and wild mushroom purée, and baked lemon cheesecake.

Smoking: No-smoking area; no pipes and cigars
Credit cards: ▆▆ ▆▆ ▆▆ ▆▆ ▆▆ ▆

Directions: At city end of St Benedicts. Nearest car park Duke Street (day), on street (evening).

9 St Benedicts NR2 4PE
Map 5: TG20
Tel/Fax: 01603 765377
Chef: Nigel Raffles
Owner: Nigel & Jayne Raffles
Cost: *Alc* £15.95, fixed-price L from £5. ☺ H/wine £7.95.
Times: Last L 2pm/D 10pm.
Closed Sun. Mon, 25 Dec-2 Jan
Additional: Children welcome; ✿ dishes

NORWICH, **Sprowston Manor** ❀❀

The setting, on the outskirts of Norwich, allows this smart nineteenth-century manor house all the space it needs for extensive conference, leisure and health spa facilities. The kitchen offers a well-rounded choice of menus, including one for vegetarians, based on a style that is best described as discreet modernism. There's an admirable restraint about rillettes of duck with Madagascan peppers and a redcurrant sauce, or poached seafood sausage with Noilly Prat fish cream. Griddled fillet of English beef with confit of shallots and Burgundy wine sauce, and noisettes of lamb with a timbale of aubergine, pesto and a sweet garlic jus, show a firm sense of balance. The extensive, well annotated wine list majors in France but covers most wine producing countries. Prices are reasonable and there is a decent selection of half-bottles.

Directions: Take A1151 (Wroxham), follow signs to Sprowston Park

Sprowston Park Wroxham Road NR7 8RP
Map 5: TG20
Tel: 01603 410871
Fax: 01603 423911
Chef: John Curtis
Owner: Manor Hotels
Cost: £28, fixed-price L&D £19.95. ☺ H/wine £13.
Times: 12.30-last L 1.45pm/7pm-last D 9.45pm. Closed L Sat
Additional: Bar food L; Sunday L; ✿ dishes
Seats: 120. Private dining room 10-100
Smoking: No smoking in dining room; air-conditioning
Accommodation: 94 en suite
Credit cards: ▆▆ ▆▆ ▆▆ ▆▆ ▆▆ ▆

NORWICH,

The Wildebeest Arms ❀❀

A local watering hole for more than a century, now an up-beat bar/restaurant providing sustenance for locals and visitors out of Norwich. African kitsch and tasteful carpets decorate the

Norwich Road Stoke Holy Cross NR14 8QJ
Map 5: TG20
Tel: 01508 492497
Chef: Eden Derrick

yellow walls, delicate flower arrangements are set in old milk churns, the floors are polished wood, tables are hued slabs from tree trunks. Eden Derrick learned his craft at Adlards (see entry, Norwich) and he knows his stuff. Accurately griddled polenta is served on mixed mushrooms with tomato, rocket and an olive oil dressing, or you might begin with curried mussel risotto perked up with coriander and spring onion. Main courses are equally in tune with the times: grilled cod with a carrot and coriander purée and a perfect aïoli was a hit with our inspector, otherwise the choice ranges from pan-fried chicken breast on a spicy pear purée with cinnamon sauce and deep-fried sage to home-made duck, plum and brandy sausage with ginger-scented cabbage and port wine sauce. Desserts could include a technically accomplished chocolate tart with zingy orange custard and creamy vanilla ice. The wine list is a typically eclectic slate from Adnams.

Directions: A140 (Ipswich), under southern by-pass. Turn L into last exit before Dunston Hall and follow road into Stoke Holy Cross

Owners: Henry Watt, Andrew Wilkins
Cost: Alc £20, fixed-price L £12. ☺
H/wine £8.95.
Times: Noon-last L 2pm/7pm-last D 9.45pm. Closed 25 Dec
Additional: Sunday L; Children welcome; ◑ dishes
Seats: 60-70
Smoking: No-smoking area
Credit cards:

SWAFFHAM, Romford House

At one end of Swaffham's busy main street stands Romford House. The beamed restaurant's comfortable atmosphere is home to the cooking of chef Jane Mitchell. Typical starters include sautéed chicken livers on a potato and thyme pancake, tagliatelle with smoked salmon, mushroom and pine nuts, with roasted duck breast, marinated in honey, ginger and mustard for main course.

Smoking: No-smoking area
Credit cards: ▬ ▭

Directions: 16 miles from Kings Lynn, on the main Market Place

5 London Street PE37 7DD
Map 9: TF80
Tel: 01760 722552
Chef/Owner: Jane Mitchell
Cost: Alc £20. H/wine £8.25. ☺
Times: Last L 2pm/D 10pm. Closed Sun, L Mon
Additional: Children welcome; ◑ dishes

SWAFFHAM, Strattons

The striking decor is inspired by the building itself, an eighteenth-century Palladian villa. There is much to see and appreciate, though the atmosphere remains friendly and informal. The restaurant is painted saffron yellow, with a mural of nearby Blickling Hall, as well as paintings of food and dressers of china and silver. The menu is built around local produce. At a test meal, bacon and avocado salad was found to be a modest description for the riot of shoots and greenery, including salad burnet, rocket, marjoram and oregano, that accompanied the perfectly ripe avocado and sauté of bacon and mushrooms. A deep wedge of turkey, ham and mushroom pie followed, with a rich shortcrust and light savoury sauce. Cherry and almond flan completed the meal, with vanilla ice cream and the liquor of home-grown cherries bottled in alcohol. There is also a well-chosen wine list embellished by hand with pictures and verse.

Directions: North end of Market Place, turn into Ash Close and restaurant straight ahead

4 Ash Close PE37 7NH
Map 9: TF80
Tel: 01760 723845
Fax: 01760 720458
Chefs: Vanessa Scott, Margaret Cooper
Owners: Les & Vanessa Scott
Cost: Alc £25, fixed-price D £25 (4 courses). H/wine £11.
Times: D only, 7pm-last D 8.45pm. Closed 25-26 Dec
Additional: Children welcome; ◑ dishes
Smoking: No-smoking establishment
Accommodation: 6 en suite
Credit cards: ▬ ▭ ▰ ▭

THORPE MARKET,
Elderton Lodge Hotel

Cromer NR11 8TZ
Map 9: TG24
Tel: 01263 833547
Fax: 01263 834673
Chef: Tim Turner
Owners: Christine & Martin Worby
Cost: *Alc* £23.50, fixed-price L
£7.95/D £16.50. ☺ H/wine £8.50.
Times: Last L 2pm/D 9pm.
Additional: Bar food L only; Sunday
L; No children under 6 ; ❹ dishes
Smoking: No smoking in dining room
Accommodation: 11 en suite
Credit cards: 🔳 🔳 🔳 🔳 🔳 🔳

An Edwardian shooting lodge overlooking Gunton deer park, once a favourite haunt of King Edward VII. Today it maintains its sporting links with a menu featuring a wealth of local seasonal game. Typical main courses could include roasted wood pigeon with sage and red wine jus, and chargrilled venison liver with onion gravy.

Directions: Off A149 Cromer/North Walsham rd, 1 mile S of village

TITCHWELL,
Titchwell Manor ✿

Local fish and game figure prominently on the menu at this charming family-run hotel a short walk from the saltings and the sea. In the Garden Restaurant you could sample such things as roast baby squid with avocado salsa, mussel chowder, and haunch of Sandringham venison with juniper, port and elderberry gravy.

Smoking: No smoking in dining room
Accommodation: 17 en suite
Credit cards: 🔳 🔳 🔳 🔳 🔳 🔳

Directions: on the A149 coast road between Brancaster and Thornham

Brancaster PE31 8BB
Map 9: TF74
Tel: 01485 210221
Fax: 01485 210104
Chef: Adam Wright
Owners: Margaret & Ian Snaith
Cost: Fixed-price D £24 (4 courses).
☺ H/wine £12.50.
Times: Last L 2pm/D 9.30pm
Additional: Bar Food; Sunday lunch;
Children welcome; ❹ dishes

WELLS-NEXT-THE-SEA,
Moorings Restaurant ✿✿

The hallmark of this extremely popular, compact and casual eating place is enthusiasm – for good, local ingredients, and for stimulating ideas culled from here, there and everywhere. Venison terrine is given a shot in the arm with an interesting spiced compote of wild mushrooms plus pistachios for texture, and Louisiana crabcakes are superbly creamy and fresh-tasting, served with tomato tartare sauce and salsa. One of the strengths, using the favoured location to the full, is fish – try seared sea bass steak with a mild oriental vinaigrette, smoked haddock basquaise, or sea trout steaks with a mild ginger and orange zest sauce. Amongst the starters are smoked mullet

6 Freeman Street NR23 1BA
Map 9: TF94
Tel: 01328 710949
Chef: Carla Phillips
Owners: Bernard & Carla Phillips
Cost: *Alc* £25, fixed price L&D £25.
☺ H/wine £8.50.
Times: 12.30pm-last L
1.30pm/7.30pm.
Closed Tue, Wed, L Thurs
Seats: 30
Smoking: No smoking in dining room
Credit cards: None

Moorings Restaurant

pâté, local cockles served with shallot vinaigrette and three sorts of herring. Vegetables merit roll-call honours – sea spinach just picked off the shoreline, turnips in spiced red wine, slow-cooked leeks with currants, excellent mashed potatoes. Booking is essential.

Directions: Off A149 coast road, 50 yds W of the quay

WYMONDHAM,
Number Twenty Four

Enthusiastic owner/chef Richard Hughes continues to produce reliable and confidently cooked food at this friendly restaurant located in a row of black and white Victorian cottages. Shellfish bisque, rack of herb-crusted lamb with Dubonnet jus, and marmalade and whisky sponge pudding are typical choices.

Additional: Children welcome; ❸ dishes
Smoking: No cigars or pipes
Credit cards: ▬ ▭ ▬ ▭

Directions: Town centre opposite war memorial

24 Middleton Street NR18 0BH
Map 5: TG10
Tel/Fax: 01953 607750
Chef: Richard Hughes
Owners: Richard & Sue Hughes
Cost: *Alc* £20, fixed-price L £8. ☺
H/wine £7.95.
Times: Last L 2.30pm/D 9.30pm.
Closed Sun, Mon, D Tues, 24-30 Dec,
1 wk Easter

WYMONDHAM,
Wymondham Consort Hotel

Small, friendly hotel with a stylish restaurant serving sound Anglo/French cooking. A recent inspection meal consisted of good chicken and mushroom soup with home-made granary rolls, chicken korma with perfectly cooked saffron rice and an excellent crème caramel with a fresh fruit coulis to finish.

Smoking: No smoking in dining room
Accommodation: 20 en suite
Credit cards: ▬ ▭ ▬ ▬ ▭ ▭

Directions: A11 (M11) 9 miles S of Norwich. Turn off at B1172 Wymondham/Morley. At traffic lights turn L into town centre and L again

28 Market Street NR18 0BB
Map 5: TM29
Tel: 01953 606721
Fax: 01953 601361
Chef: Grace Fiddaman
Owners: C & G Fiddaman
Cost: *Alc* £20, fixed-price L £10.95/D
£15.95. ☺ H/wine £8.95
Times: Last L 2pm/D 9.30pm
Additional: Sunday L; Bar meals;
Children welcome; ❸ dishes

NORTHAMPTONSHIRE

CASTLE ASHBY, **Falcon Hotel** ✿

A sixteenth-century country cottage-style hotel with intimate dining room and large terrace for alfresco summer dining. Modern Anglo/French dishes such as braised shank of lamb with Cumberland sauce, and tagliatelle with mixed mushrooms are offered. Engaging staff do much to make guests feel at home.

Additional: Bar meals; Sunday L; No children under 10 at D; ✤ dishes
Accommodation: 16 en suite
Credit cards: ▬ ▭ ▭ ▬ ▭

Directions: From A428 (Northampton-Bedford) turn off at Castle Ashby sign, hotel 1.5 miles ahead

NN7 1LF
Map 4: SP85
Tel: 01604 696200
Fax: 01604 696673
Chef: Neil Helks
Owners: Josephine & Neville Watson
Cost: *Alc* £22, Fixed-price L&D £19.50. ☺ H/wine £8.95.
Times: Last L 1.30pm/D 9.30pm

HELLIDON,
Hellidon Lakes Hotel ✿

Spacious hotel with spectacular sweeping views over landscaped grounds and lakes. The kitchen delivers modern British cooking along the lines of crisp potato baskets filled with crab, or lamb's liver with shallot and parsley jus, and baked cod on a light chive cream. For dessert try the excellent hazelnut parfait with fresh raspberry coulis.

Smoking: No pipes & cigars
Accommodation: 45 en suite
Credit cards: ▬ ▭ ▭ ▬ ▭ ▭

Directions: 1.5 miles off A361 at Charwelton, follow signs for Golf Club

Daventry NN11 6LN
Map 4: SP55
Tel: 01327 262550
Fax: 01327 262559
Chef: Graham Reeves
Owners: G S & J A Nicoll
Cost: *Alc* £25, fixed-price D £18.95. ☺ H/wine £9.75.
Times: Last L 2pm/D 9.30pm
Additional: Bar food; Sunday L; No children at D; ✤ dishes

HORTON,
French Partridge Restaurant ✿✿

David and Mary Partridge have been incumbents at this sixteenth-century coaching inn since 1963, and they work to a true and trusted formula. He is a cook of the old school – listing Kenneth Bell, George Perry-Smith and others among his contemporaries; his wife is as charming a hostess as you could wish for. The kitchen continues to deliver four-course menus that are rooted in the French bourgeois tradition, although it may spread its wings farther afield. The classics remain: quails' eggs in pastry with hollandaise, braised lamb shank with haricot beans, and, of course, roast partridge with Anna potatoes. But there are also more up-to-the-minute touches, as in a salad of cod ceviche, or baked mussels with couscous. Cuisine ancienne dominated a recent inspection: chicken liver parfait with brioche, feuilleté of seafood with chive cream (a 'blast from the past'), roast suckling pig with a tartlet of crabapple jelly, then iced orange soufflé meringue with Cointreau marinated oranges.

NN7 2AP
Map 4: SP85
Tel: 01604 870033
Fax: 01604 870032
Chef: David Partridge
Owners: David & Mary Partridge
Cost: D only, fixed-price D £26 (4 courses). H/wine £11
Times: 7.30pm-last D 9pm. Closed Sun, Mon, 2wks Xmas, 2 wks Easter, 3wks July/Aug
Seats: 50
Smoking: No smoking in dining room
Credit cards: None

Directions: On B526, village centre, 6 miles from Northampton

KETTERING, **Kettering Park Hotel** ⊛

Imaginative menus combined with lively modern cooking continue to please visitors to Langberry's Restaurant at this purpose-built hotel, conveniently located just off the A14. Typical dishes may include Thai-style fishcakes, rack of lamb with shallot tart, and lemon poached pear with caramel sauce.

Smoking: No smoking in dining room
Accommodation: 90 en suite (120 en suite from Nov 1997)
Credit cards: 💳 💳 💳 💳 💳 💳

Directions: A14/J9 – hotel on that roundabout

Kettering Parkway NN15 6XT
Map 4: SP87
Tel: 01536 416666
Fax: 01536 416171
Chef: Darren Winder
Owner: Shire Inns
Cost: Alc £25, fixed-price L £12.95/D £22. ☺ H/wine £9.95.
Times: Last L-1.45pm/D-9.30pm. Closed L Sat
Additional: Bar food; Sunday L; Children welcome; 🍴 dishes

MARSTON TRUSSELL,
The Sun Inn ⊛

Enjoying a good local following, this traditional village inn offers comfortable accommodation, a cosy bar and a pretty restaurant serving inventive dishes. A recent inspection meal highlighted decent fishcakes with a chive flavoured beurre blanc and perfectly cooked duck with morels and broad beans.

Accommodation: 20 en suite
Credit cards: 💳 💳 💳 💳 💳

Directions: 0.5 mile off A4304, 3 miles W of Market Harborough

Main Street LE16 9TY
Map 4: SP68
Tel: 01858 465531
Fax: 01858 433155
Chef: Mark Smith
Owners: Mr Furber, Mr Raven
Cost: Alc £20. H/wine £8.95. ☺
Times: Last L 2.15pm/last D 9.30pm
Additional: Bar meals; Sunday L; Chilren welcome; 🍴 dishes

NORTHAMPTON,
Swallow Hotel ⊛

Custom-built business hotel complete with its own self-contained management centre. Eat in either the Italian-style La Fontina or the more formal Spires Restaurant. Inspectors have praised crispy aromatic duck with pancakes and plum sauce, as well as herb-crusted monkfish with provençale sauce, and apple and almond tart.

Smoking: Non-smoking area; air conditioning
Accommodation: 120 en suite
Credit cards: 💳 💳 💳 💳 💳

Directions: M1/J15, follow A508 then A45 (Wellingborough). L at roundabout signposted Delapre Golf Complex. Hotel on R

Eagle Drive NN4 7HW
Map 4: SP86
Tel: 01604 768700
Fax: 01604 769011
Chef: David Bishop
Cost: Alc £28, fixed-price L £21
Additional: Bar meals; Sunday L; Children welcome; Vegetarian dishes
Times: Last L 2pm/last D 9.45pm. Closed L Sat, Bhs

ROADE, **Roadhouse Restaurant** ⊛

Former ale house now a smart village restaurant serving a short fixed-price lunchtime menu and select evening carte. Unfussy modern British cooking exhibits well-executed dishes such as seared fillet of halibut with ginger and lime sauce, chicken stuffed with herbs with wild mushroom sauce, and apple and almond tart.

Smoking: No pipes & cigars in dining room
Credit cards: 💳 💳 💳 💳 💳

Directions: M1/J15 (A508 Milton Keynes) to Roade, L at mini-roundabout, 500yds on L

16 High Street NN7 2NW
Map 4: SP75
Tel: 01604 863372
Chef: Christopher Kewley
Owners: Christopher & Susan Kewley
Cost: Alc £24.50. Fixed-price L £16. ☺ H/wine £10.
Times: Last L 1.45pm/last D 9.30pm. Closed L Sat & Mon, D Sun
Additional: Sunday L; Children welcome

TOWCESTER, **Vine House**

Built over 300 years ago from local limestone, Vine House is in many ways an archetypal country-cottage restaurant with rooms. There's something immediately relaxing about the whole set-up, from the moment you sit down for drinks and canapés in the sitting room. Julie Springett oversees out front, while Marcus heads the kitchen. His menu changes daily, his repertoire is seasonal and his style is true modern British – which means sweet-cured gammon terrine with home-made mustard pickle as well as jellied prawns and smoked haddock with warm parsley and dill sauce. But there's also great judgement and skill in abundance – as in grilled red mullet on a strongly tomato tapenade surrounded by drizzles of home-made pesto. Confit of duck is a real winner, whether it comes with buttered marrowfat peas and truffles or with sweet roast garlic and a crystal clear rosemary sauce. Puddings might range from sticky toffee pudding to rhubarb jelly with crisp hazelnuts, almonds and passion fruit.

100 High Street Paulersbury
NN12 7NA
Map 4: SP64
Tel: 01327 811267
Fax: 01327 811309
Chef: Marcus Springett
Owners: Julie & Marcus Springett
Cost: Fixed-price L £16/D £23.50 (3 courses). H/wine £9.95.
Times: 12.30pm- last L 1.30pm (Thurs/Fri only)/7.30pm- last D 9.30pm. Closed Sun, 2 wks from 24 Dec
Additional: Children welcome
Seats: 45. Private dining room 12
Smoking: No smoking in dining room
Accommodation: 6 en suite
Credit cards: ■■ ▨▨

Directions: 2 miles S of Towcester, signposted from the A5

NORTHUMBERLAND

BERWICK,
Marshall Meadows Hotel ✸

An elegantly decorated Georgian country house set in wooded grounds flanked by farmland. The restaurant is a two-tier affair – a traditional ground floor room and an attractively panelled upper extension. There is a daily menu and a chef's speciality selection offering chargrilled wild boar and fillet of English ostrich.

Smoking: No smoking in dining room
Accommodation: 19 en suite
Credit cards: ■■ ▨▨ ▨▨ ▨

Berwick-Upon-Tweed TD15 1UT
Map 12: NT95
Tel: 01289 331133
Fax: 01289 331438
Chefs: Ian Frost, Steve McNamara
Owners: Mr & Mrs BR Worsell
Cost: Alc £25, fixed-price L £7/D £18. ☺ H/wine £8.
Times: Last L 2pm/D 9.30pm
Additional: Sunday L;
Children welcome; ❤ dishes

Directions: Just off the A1 N of Berwick

BLANCHLAND,
Lord Crewe Arms Hotel ✸

Dating from medieval times when it was a lodging house for monks, this historic house now features a well-run restaurant that overlooks the gardens. Expect sound English cooking of dishes such as rack of lamb with mustard and herb crust, roast breast of duck with black cherries, and carrot and cashew nut loaf.

Additional: Bar food; Sunday L (12.30pm-2pm); Children welcome; ❤ dishes
Accommodation: 20 en suite
Credit cards: ■■ ▨▨ ▨▨ ▨ ▨

Nr Consett Co Durham DH8 9SP
Map 12: NY95
Tel: 01434 675251
Fax: 01434 675337
Chef: Ian Press
Owners: Alec Todd, Peter Gingell, Ian Press
Cost: Alc £21. H/wine £13
Times: D only, 7pm-9.15pm

Directions: 10 miles S of Hexham on B6306

CHOLLERFORD, George Hotel

Charming hotel, situated where the old Roman road crosses the River Tyne, with its own terraced gardens running down to the water's edge. The Riverside Restaurant makes the most of the setting: large picture windows take in the whole view. The kitchen bases its three menus – fixed-price, a *carte* and a 'Gourmet' menu – around local and regional produce. Curried velouté of Scottish mussels, chicken liver parfait with red onion marmalade, or feuilletté of roasted rabbit with summer vegetables and jus of coriander, or even oysters poached in champagne are some of the starters. Main courses include braised shank of English lamb with root vegetables and rosemary jus, roast breast of duck served with pommes fondant and French beans in a delightful bitter sweet sauce, roast beef forestière, or cold ballotine of salmon with herb fromage and toasted brioche. Hot raspberry and white chocolate soufflé is highly recommended. Wines include house varieties, several from the New World, and a connoisseurs' choice which includes three good vintage clarets and special selections from Burgundy, Australia, New Zealand, Chile and Germany.

Hexham NE46 4EW
Map 12: NY96
Tel: 01434 681611
Fax: 01434 681727
Chef: Martin Strangward
Owner: Swallow Hotels Ltd
Cost: Alc £24, fixed-price L from £13.50/D £24. ☺
Times: Noon-last L 2pm/6.30pm-last D 9.30pm
Additional: Lounge menu L; Sunday L; Children welcome; ⑤ dishes
Seats: 90. Private dining room 50. Jacket & tie preferred
Smoking: No-smoking area
Accommodation: 46 en suite
Credit cards: 🟦 🟦 🟦 🟦 🟦 🟦

Directions: From A6079 take B6318. 400 yds on opposite side of river

CORNHILL-ON-TWEED, Tillmouth Park Hotel

TD12 4UU
Map 12: NT83
Tel: 01890 882255
Fax: 01890 882540
Chef: David Jeffrey
Owner: Stever Investments
Cost: Alc £14.65, fixed-price D £25. H/wine £9
Times: Last L 1.45pm/D 8.45pm
Additional: Sunday L; Bar meals; Children welcome; ⑤ dishes
Accommodation: 14 en suite
Credit cards: 🟦 🟦 🟦 🟦

Directions: On A698 3 miles E of roundabout at Cornhill-on-Tweed

Magnificent late-Victorian mansion set in mature grounds beside the River Till. Emphasis is on fresh local produce. A typical meal may feature smoked Teviot Dale chicken with lemon mayonnaise, trio of stuffed Border lamb cutlets with port and rosemary jus and chocolate mousse.

HEXHAM, Beaumont Hotel

The restaurant on the first floor of this popular hotel overlooks the park and has superb views of the seventh-century abbey and its grounds. The kitchen delivers a mix of standard and innovative dishes ranging from smoked chicken with spicy tomato sauce, and roast guinea fowl with lemon thyme, to red mullet served on black olive, anchovy and caper purée.

Smoking: No smoking in dining room
Accommodation: 23 en suite
Credit cards: 🟦 🟦 🟦 🟦 🟦 🟦

Directions: Town centre hotel just up from the Abbey

Beaumont Street NE46 3LT
Map 12: NY96
Tel: 01434 602331
Fax: 01434 606184
Chef: Anthony Miller
Owners: Martin & Linda Owen
Cost: Alc £20, fixed-price D £17.75. ☺ H/wine £8.95.
Times: Last L 2pm/D 9.45pm. Closed 25 Dec
Additional: Bar food L; Sunday L; Children welcome; ⑤ dishes

MORPETH, **Longhirst Hall** ✿

Longhurst NE61 3LL
Map 12: NZ28
Tel: 01670 791348
Fax: 01670 791385
Chef: Colin Bowden
Owner: Longhirst Hall Ltd
Cost: *Alc* £19.95, fixed-price L
£11.95/ D £16.50. ☺ H/wine £9.95.
Times: Last L 1.45pm/D 9.45pm.
Closed L Sat
Additional: Sunday L; Bar meals;
Children welcome; ✪ dishes
Smoking: No-smoking area; no pipes
and cigars
Accommodation: 75 en suite
Credit cards: ▀▀ ▀▀ ▀▀ ▀▀ ▀▀ ▀▀

Built in 1826 for a local coal magnate, this country mansion is now a lavish hotel complex set in 75 acres, which includes a lake. Menus are peppered with lively ideas such as a pyramid of oyster mushrooms and cherry tomatoes with fennel mousse, salmon coulibiac with tarragon and lobster sauce, and chocolate truffle marquise with liquorice sauce.

Directions: 2 miles NE of Morpeth on the B1337 Widdrington road

NOTTINGHAMSHIRE

LANGAR, **Langar Hall** ✿

Langar NG13 9HG
Map 8: SK73
Tel: 01949 860559
Fax: 01949 861045
Chefs: Toby Garratt, Nick Aeillo
Owner: Imogen Skirving
Cost: Fixed-price L&D £15. ☺
H/wine £11.
Times: Last L 1.45pm/last D 9.45pm.
Closed D Sun
Additional: Sunday L;
Children welcome; ✪ dishes
Smoking: No smoking in one dining
room
Accommodation: 10 en suite
Credit cards: ▀▀ ▀▀ ▀▀ ▀▀

The Skirving family home since 1837, now a delightful hotel hard by the village church and offering views over gardens and medieval fish ponds. Home-made asparagus soup, juicy calves' liver with smooth mustard mashed potato and caramelised onions, and nougatine parfait constituted one well reported meal.

Directions: Off A46 and A52, in village centre (behind church)

NOTTINGHAM, **Ginza**

Smart modern neighbourhood restaurant offering a unique blend of Japanese cuisine and Oriental culture. An extensive menu specialises in good set meals, notably the sizzling teppan-yaki dishes that are

393-395 Mansfield Road NG5 2FW
Map 8: SK53
Tel: 0115 9691660/9691716
Fax: 0115 9691660
Chefs: Roy Cheung, Richard Wan

*cooked in front of diners. Also featured, a traditional ebi tempura –
lightly battered king prawns with vegetables.*

Additional: Sunday L; Children welcome; ❹ dishes
Credit cards: 🔳 🔳 🔳 🔳 🔳 🔳

Directions: From Nottingham's Victoria Centre follow A60
(Mansfield road) just past Sports Ground and Moat House

NOTTINGHAM, Hotel Des Clos

*Riverside hotel, recommended for its tranquil setting and friendly
atmosphere. Inventive cooking of quality ingredients encompasses
seared scallops with warm oyster sabayon, fillet of beef topped with
foie gras with Pinot Noir sauce, and Le Gavroche baked lemon tart
with an orange cream. Superb French wine list.*

Credit cards: 🔳 🔳 🔳 🔳 🔳 🔳

Directions: M1/J24, follow A453 (Nottingham) 10 miles. Cross
River Trent, follow signs to Old Lenton Lane Industrial Estate. At
roundabout L, immediate L again. Follow lane down to river

NOTTINGHAM, Sonny's

'Bright, airy and modern', is how Sonny's describe themselves
and our inspector was not one to disagree. The busy brasserie,
set in a chic, pedestrianised shopping street, attracts a lively
mix of shoppers and business suits. The formula follows the
modern approach of its London parent, informal but attentive
service, stridently modern menu but with enough of a local
accent to give a sense of individuality. Graeme Watson picks
and chooses ideas, pulling influences from far and wide:
mussels in Thai broth, blackened sirloin steak with Cajun
butter, chargrilled Barnsley chop with apple, jalapeño and mint
jelly, all make an appearance. A test meal, taken on a cold and
miserable November day, produced an enthusiastic report for
rich, thick, intensely flavoured fish soup, tender, succulent
braised lamb shank with Parmesan polenta 'just waiting to
soak up the juices' although, incongruously, served with
tomato mashed potatoes or fries – 'apparently the locals
demand it'. Home-made vanilla ice came with warmed, slightly
bitter chocolate sauce to take the edge off.

Directions: City centre, close to Market Square and Victoria Centre

SOUTHWELL,
Vineyard Café & Bistro NEW

*Low beamed ceilings, rustic wooden floors and wine memorabilia
characterise this relaxing town-centre bistro. Fresh food is
competently cooked by enthusiastic chef/owner Tim Hooton. At
inspection the short evening carte produced a full flavoured fish
soup, succulent cod with lemon butter sauce and crème brûlée.*

Smoking: No smoking in dining room. Air conditioning
Credit cards: 🔳 🔳 🔳 🔳 🔳 🔳

Directions: In the main street

Owner: Derek Hung
Cost: *Alc* £15-£18, fixed-price L £8/D
£15. ☺ H/wine £8.85.
Times: Last L 1.30pm/last D 10.30pm.

Old Lenton Lane NG7 2SA
Map 8: SK53
Tel: 0115 9866566
Fax: 0115 9860343
Chef/Owner: John Abbey
Cost: *Alc* £28; fixed-price L £13.95-
£16.95. ☺ H/wine £9.50.
Times: Last L 1.45pm/last D 9pm.
Additional: Sunday L; Children
welcome; ❹ dishes
Smoking: No pipes & cigars
Accommodation: 10 en suite

3 Carlton Street Hockley NG1 1NL
Map 8: SK54
Tel: 0115 9473041
Fax: 0115 9507776
Chef: Graeme Watson
Owner: Ms R Mascarenhas
Cost: *Alc* £20; fixed-price L £11.95
(3 courses). ☺ H/wine £8.95.
Times: Noon-last L 3pm/7pm-last D
10.30pm. Closed Bhs
Additional: Sunday lunch;
Children welcome; ❹ dishes
Seats: 75
Smoking: No pipes and cigars;
air-conditioning
Credit cards: 🔳 🔳 🔳 🔳

12 King Street NG25 0EN
Map 8: SK75
Tel: 01636 816573
Chef: Tim Hooton
Owners: Tim & Sharon Hooton
Cost: *Alc* £20, fixed-price L £12.95.
☺ H/wine £9.95.
Times: Last L 2.30pm/D 9.30pm.
Closed Sun & Mon
Additional: No children under 6;
❹ dishes

OXFORDSHIRE

ABINGDON, **Merry Miller**

The name presumably refers to the fact that the building was originally a granary, and new owners have done an impressive job in refurbishing the interior. The place retains its original beams, low ceilings and old York paving stones – although scrubbed pine tables laid with fresh flowers and church candles add a contemporary note. Snacks and real ales are available at the bar although the kitchen is clearly capable of higher things; innovative cuisine remains the order of the day. The menu promises such things as feuilleté of Mediterranean vegetables with feta cheese, tomato salsa and fried polenta, honey-roast duck breast with jasmine tea and lime sauce, and chargrilled halibut with roasted peppers and saffron rice, alongside Miller's Pie and haggis 'bitok' on a potato and swede rösti. Desserts could include chocolate mille-feuille or choux beignets with cinnamon ice cream.

Directions: From Abingdon take A415 (Marcham), turn 1st R then 2nd R to Cothill

Cothill OX13 6JW
Map 4: SU49
Tel: 01865 390390
Fax: 01865 390040
Chef: Kier Miekle
Owner: Merry Miller Ltd
Cost: *Alc* £17.50, fixed-price L £9.95/£13.95 (2/3 courses). ☺
H/wine £7.50
Times: Noon-last L 2.30pm/7pm-last D 9.30pm
Additional: Bar meals L; Sunday L; Children welcome; ☺ dishes
Seats: 100. Private dining room 50
Smoking: No smoking in dining room; air-conditioning
Credit cards: ▨ ▨ ▨ ▨

BANBURY, **Whately Hall Hotel**

A spacious seventeenth-century coaching inn overlooking Banbury Cross offering both modern-inspired and traditional English dishes. At a meal in January, our inspector enjoyed braised oxtails with caramelised onions, followed for dessert by a beautifully presented chocolate teardrop with a compote of berries.

Smoking: No smoking in dining room
Accommodation: 72 en suite
Credit cards: ▨ ▨ ▨ ▨ ▨ ▨

Directions: On A423 at Banbury Cross

Banbury Cross OX16 0AN
Map 4: SP44
Tel: 01295 263451
Fax: 01295 271736
Chef: Marcus Renzi
Owner: Forte
Cost: Fixed-price L £13.25/D £21.50. ☺ H/wine £12.50.
Times: Last L 2pm/D 9.30pm. Closed L Sat
Additional: Bar food; Sunday L; Children welcome; ☺ dishes

BANBURY, **Wroxton House**

Built from three old cottages, with a clock tower wing and conservatory lounge, Wroxton House makes a comfortable hotel. The restaurant offers the likes of chicken liver and green peppercorn parfait, roast sirloin of beef with a shallot and Madeira sauce and sweet onion relish, and almond and cherry tart with crème anglaise.

Smoking: No smoking in dining room
Accommodation: 32 en suite
Credit cards: ▨ ▨ ▨ ▨ ▨ ▨

Directions: On A422 to Stratford, 3 miles from M40/J11

Wroxton St Mary OX15 6QB
Map 4: SP44
Tel: 01295 730777
Fax: 01295 730800
Chef: Hylton Bradley
Owner: Spring Hotels
Cost: *Alc* £25, fixed-price L £15.50/D £22.50. ☺ H/wine £10.
Times: Last L 2pm/D 9.30pm
Additional: Bar food, Sunday L; Children welcome; ☺ dishes

BURFORD,
The Angel at Burford

Sound Anglo-French cooking in a sixteenth-century beamed inn. Eat in the bar, the walled garden or the pretty candlelit restaurant. Typical dishes might include dariole of lemon sole and lobster with

14 Witney Street OX18 4SN
Map 4: SP21
Tel: 01993 822438
Fax: 01993 822714
Chef: Christophe Arcalis

carrot coulis, rosettes of lamb with coriander and sweetbreads on a pepper and redcurrant sauce, and crème brûlée with pineapple.

Accommodation: 3 en suite. **Credit cards:**

Directions: Turn R (signposted Widford) off A40 just before Burford. Inn is on L a few yds before High St

BURFORD, **The Bay Tree** ⚜

Built in traditional style from local stone, The Bay Tree is an attractive inn ideally situated for exploring the Cotswolds. At inspection, both a bruschetta of plum tomatoes and wild mushrooms with pesto, and rabbit in red wine sauce topped with puff pastry, were praised.

Smoking: No smoking in dining room
Accommodation: 22 en suite
Credit cards:

Directions: Off main street in centre of Burford

Owners: Mr & Mrs J. R. Harrington
Cost: *Alc* £28. H/wine £10.25 ☺
Times: Last L 2.30pm/last D 9.30pm
Additional: Sunday L; Bar meals;
No children under 14; ❹ dishes
Smoking: No smoking in dining room

12-14 Sheep Street OX18 4LW
Map 4: SP21
Tel: 01993 822791
Fax: 01993 823008
Chef: Mark Gilberthorpe
Owner: Pageant Hotels
Cost: *Alc* £30, set L £12.95/D £19.95.
☺ H/wine £10.95.
Times: Last L 1.55pm/D 9.25pm
Additional: Sunday L; Bar meals;
Children welcome; ❹ dishes

BURFORD,
Cotswold Gateway Hotel ⚜ NEW

Prominently positioned at the top of Burford's picturesque High Street, this attractive stone hotel makes an ideal Cotswold base. Noted for its hospitality, it offers traditional cooking with a modern twist in the period restaurant. Typical dishes may include courgette and rosemary soup, pork with mustard cream sauce, and chocolate marquise.

Accommodation: 21 en suite
Credit cards: ▉ ▥ ▤ ⧕ ▣ ⊆

Directions: On A40 roundabout at Burford

Cheltenham Road OX18 4HX
Map 4: SP21
Tel: 01993 822695
Fax: 01993 823600
Chef: Tony Phizacklea
Owner: Mr J Ford
Cost: *Alc* £16.95. H/wine £8.90. ☺
Times: Last L 3pm/last D 9.30pm
Additional: Bar meals; Sunday L;
Children welcome; ❹ dishes
Smoking: No pipes & cigars;
air conditioning

BURFORD, **Inn For All Seasons** ⚜

The Barringtons OX18 4TN
Map 4: SP21
Tel: 01451 844324
Fax: 01451 844375
Chef/Owner: Matthew R Sharp
Cost: Fixed-price L £12.50/D £16.50
(both 4-course). ☺ H/wine £10.75.
Times: Last L 2.30pm/last D 10pm.
Closed 25-26 Dec
Additional: Sunday L; Bar meals;
Children welcome; ❹ dishes
Smoking: No-smoking area;
air-conditioning
Accommodation: 10 en suite
Credit cards: ▉ ▥ ▤ ⧕

Directions: On the A40 at The Barringtons, 3 miles from Burford & 17 miles from Cheltenham

A seventeenth-century coaching house, kept in period style, with log fires, beams and original stonework. From a wide choice of dishes, tomato and basil soup came piping hot in its own tureen, followed by a generous portion of grey mullet, but the pudding of nougat terrine was the highlight.

BURFORD, Lamb Inn

Centuries of history are etched into the beams, mullioned windows and stonework of this classic Cotswold inn. Roses and honeysuckle entwine the walls and there's a pretty cottage garden for sunny days. Dinner is served by candlelight in the elegant Regency-style dining room, where menus are fixed-price for two or three courses. The repertoire changes daily, and dishes sampled by one inspector suggested a sure hand in the kitchen. Smoked haddock and salmon soufflé was served with spring onion cream, perfectly pink noisettes of lamb were presented on a parsnip and thyme rösti with a port jus, while prune and Armagnac crème brûlée made a good finish. At other times you might find, say, duck and pheasant pâté with black pudding, and pan-fried fillet of sea bass with fennel and Pernod sauce, not to mention several worthwhile British cheeses. Light lunches are served in the bar. The lengthy wine list will not intimidate with its prices.

Directions: 1st L as you descend the High Street

Sheep Street OX18 4LR
Map 4: SP21
Tel: 01993 823155
Fax: 01993 822228
Chef: Pascal Clavaud
Owners: Richard & Caroline de Wolfe
Cost: Fixed-price D £24 (3 courses). ☺ H/wine £10.
Times: D only, 7pm-9pm.
Closed 25-26 Dec
Additional: Bar meals L (not Sun); Sunday L (12.30pm-2pm); Children welcome; 🌢 dishes
Seats: 50
Smoking: No smoking in dining room
Accommodation: 15 en suite
Credit cards: 🔲 🔤 🔃 📵

CHARLBURY, The Bell Hotel 🏵

Built in 1700, and right in the centre of the ancient town of Charlbury, this historic inn attracts a loyal local following. Snacks are served in the bar, while the restaurant menu moves into the modern realms of confit of chicken with soured white cabbage, fillets of plaice with parsley and caper mash, and dark chocolate and rum brûlée.

Additional: Bar meals; Sunday L; Children welcome; 🌢 dishes
Smoking: No smoking in dining room
Accommodation: 14 en suite
Credit cards: 🔲 🔤 🔃

Directions: Town centre

Church Street OX7 3PP
Map 4: SP31
Tel: 01608 810278
Fax: 01608 811447
Chef: D Naylor
Owner: Mr WK Vickers
Cost: Alc £15, fixed-price L £9.95. ☺ H/wine £9.95.
Times: Last L 2.30pm/D 9.30pm

CHINNOR,

Sir Charles Napier

'Well, is it a pub or a restaurant?' Thus ran the thoughts of one inspector who had been drawn to this casual country inn surrounded by beechwoods and fields, by the food put out by Sardinian chef Batiste Tolu. This is serious cooking even if the setting is quirky – unmatching old chairs, modern sculpture. The menu changes frequently, and in addition to a set three-course menu, there is a wide range of *carte* choices. Torn between fish soup with rouille, wild mushroom risotto, griddled scallops with sorrel and bacon, or steamed whole Cornish crab, our inspector opted for the oriental influence that came through in crab cakes with lime and coriander served with avocado purée, crispy duck ('and yes, it came very crispy') cooked with lime, ginger and soy sauce, with papaya salsa, and lime again in a lime and ginger crème brûlée. There's a wide range of wines with some hundreds of top vintages spanning the globe, over twenty dessert wines on offer, and thirty half-bottles.

Directions: M40/J6 follow Chinnor; there turn R at roundabout. Carry on straight up hill to Spriggs Alley

Spriggs Alley OX9 4BX
Map 4: SU70
Tel: 01494 483011
Chefs: Batiste Tolu, David Jones
Owner: Julie Griffiths
Cost: Alc £24.50, fixed-price L £14.50/D £15.50. ☺ H/wine £11.
Times: Noon-2.30pm/7pm-10pm.
Closed D Sun, Mon
Additional: Sunday L; Bar meals L; No children under 7 at D; 🌢 dishes
Seats: 75. Private dining room 45
Smoking: No-smoking area; air-conditioning
Credit cards: 🔲 🔤 🔃 📵

CHIPPING NORTON, **Morel's**

NEW

Local restaurant offering fair French cooking in casual surroundings. Dishes range from mille-feuille of frogs' legs with gazpacho coulis and tomato confit, to Barbary duck with couscous in a cabbage leaf, to braised camel with home-made pasta. Finish with the likes of apple beignet with crème anglaise and apple Calvados.

Additional: Sunday L only (noon-2pm); ❹ dishes
Smoking: No smoking in dining room
Credit cards: ▰ ▰ ▰ ▰

Directions: Immediately before town centre entering on A44 Oxford/Banbury road, on rd to Evesham.

2 Horsefair OX7 5AQ
Map 4: SP32
Tel: 01608 641075
Chef: Fabrice Morel
Owners: Fabrice & Rachel Morel
Cost: Fixed-price D £20.85. ☺
H/wine £8.95.
Times: 7pm- last D 9.30pm.
Closed D Sun, Mon, from 2 Jan for
3 wks, 1 wk Sept

CLANFIELD,

Plough at Clanfield ❀❀

Bourton Road OX18 2RB
Map 4: SP20
Tel: 01367 810222
Fax: 01367 810596
Chef: J Lyons
Owners: John & Rosemary Hodges
Cost: *Alc* £27.50, fixed-price L
£16.50/D £18.80. ☺ H/wine £12.95.
Times: Noon-last L 2pm/7pm-last D
9.30pm. Closed 27-30 Dec
Additional: Bar food; Sunday L;
No children under 12; ❹ menu
Seats: 40. Private dining room 10
Smoking: No smoking in dining room
Accommodation: 6 en suite
Credit cards: ▰ ▰ ▰ ▰ ▰ ▰

Full of character and original features, this is the quintessential Elizabethan hostelry. The cooking, however, is more mod Brit than olde worlde. The short, set-priced menu changes frequently and is accompanied by superb home-baked bread. Starters might include an original crab and prawn empanada with pickled garlic remoulade or a rather fabulous-sounding pheasant and foie gras broth with gribiche croûton. This may be followed by fashionable numbers such as roasted Cornish cod with a purée of Jerusalem artichoke and parsley jus, or roast breast of magret duck with wild mushroom risotto and coriander jus. When it comes to desserts, though, the star turn has to be the flamboyant chocolate voodoo cake – moist, layered chocolate sponge crowned with what only can be described as toffee totem poles. Lunch is a particular bargain at £16.50.

Directions: Village centre, on A4095 between Faringdon & Witney, easy reach of A40 and A420

DEDDINGTON,
Dexters Restaurant ❀❀

Market Place OX15 0SE
Map 4: SP43
Tel: 01869 338813
Fax: 01993 778267
Chef/Owner: Jamie Dexter-Harrison
Cost: *Alc* £25, fixed-price L £11/D £19.95. ☺ H/wine £9.50
Times: Noon-last L 2.15pm/7pm-9.15pm.
Additional: Sunday L; Children welcome; ◑ dishes
Seats: 40
Smoking: No pipes and cigars in dining room
Credit cards: ▬ ▬ ▬ ◻

The local art group are a prolific lot, judging by the number of paintings they have hanging on the yellow coloured walls. There's more artwork in the hand-written menu listing modern British dishes along the lines of duck confit wrapped in Parma ham on mustard mash with red wine and thyme, and grilled red mullet salad with lime and coriander and marinated mushrooms. Ideas are pacy but intelligently restrained- pork fillet on grilled peppers and aubergine with sage oil and Cumberland sauce, for example, or warm banana and rum tart with caramel sauce and vanilla ice cream. Vegetarians are well provided for with warm goat's cheese salad with grilled vegetables and sherry vinegar, and roast shallot and artichoke tart with sauce vierge. At lunch there may be good, old-fashioned pork and chive sausages on mashed potato with onion gravy, plus bread-and-butter pudding. Irish cheeses are served with russet apples and oatcakes. Reservations are strongly recommended for Sunday lunch.

Directions: Village centre, A4260 from Banbury; L at lights

DEDDINGTON,
Holcombe Hotel ❀

High Street OX15 0SL
Map 4: SP43
Tel: 01869 338274
Fax: 01869 337167
Chef: Mr Alan Marshal
Owners: Mr & Mrs C Mahfoudh
Cost: *Alc* £25, fixed-price L £19.50. ☺ H/wine £12.95.
Times: Last L 1.30pm/D 9.30pm
Additional: Bar meals; Sunday L; Children welcome; ◑ dishes
Smoking: No smoking in dining room
Accommodation: 16 en suite
Credit cards: ▬ ▬ ▬ ▬ ◻

Seventeenth-century Cotswold stone hotel with a good reputation for family hospitality and atmosphere. Menus run along the lines of smoked duck terrine with cranberry coulis, and baked red mullet with lemon and herb butter, while desserts range from summer pudding to prune and Armagnac tart.

Directions: On A4260 btw Banbury & Oxford. M40/J11 – follow A4260 (Adderbury) 7 miles, hotel is on R at traffic light

DORCHESTER-ON-THAMES,
White Hart Hotel ❀❀

High Street
OX10 7HN
Map 4: SU59
Tel: 01865 340074
Fax: 01865 341082
Chef: Robert Kerr
Owner: Raceoak Ltd

An architecturally interesting, timbered coaching inn (with parts dating from 1691, others much earlier), the White Hart holds centre stage in this trendy Thameside village. The place functions as an inn-with-rooms and one menu operates throughout the bar and Hartes Restaurant. The repertoire changes with the seasons: in summer you can expect, say, roasted garlic and asparagus salad with orange and cardamom oil, crown of corn-fed chicken with basil risotto and vegetable lyonnaise, or sea bass with mixed greens, crème fraîche and langoustine. Our inspector enjoyed 'really good' timbale of pickled brisket flaked and pressed into a tower, topped with capers and served with Oxford sauce, followed by paupiettes of sole and crab with lemon balm sauce and a side dish of vegetables all cooked to a turn. To finish, poached pear in Curaçao with rhubarb sorbet and apricot coulis proved to be 'a riot of colour'. Cheerful, casual staff keep things ticking over. The wine list is commendable for its realistic prices.

Directions: In village centre

Cost: Alc £20, fixed-price D £15. ☺ H/wine £9.50.
Times: Noon-2pm/7pm-last d 9.30pm (9pm Sun)
Additional: Bar meals; Sunday L; Children welcome; ♨ dishes
Seats: 80. Private dining room 50
Smoking: No-smoking area
Accommodation: 19 en suite
Credit cards:

GORING,
The Leatherne Bottel ❀❀

RG8 0HS
Map 4: SU68
Tel: 01491 872667
Fax: 01491 875308
Chef: Keith Read
Owner: Keith Read
Cost: Alc £40. H/wine £12.50.
Times: 12.15pm-2pm/7.15pm-9pm.
Closed D Sun, 25 Dec
Additional: Sunday L; ♨ dishes
Seats: 50 (75 river terrace).
Private dining room 12
Smoking: No pipes in dining room
Credit cards: ▬ ▬ ▬

A cottage-style restaurant in an idyllic setting, decorated with some elegance and style. There is a choice of a brief lunch menu, featuring salads and pizza, or a more extensive, eclectic dinner menu, with definite oriental influences – nori seaweed, ginger and lemon grass appear regularly. Typical starters include potted shrimps with chilli jelly and toast fingers, mussels in a chicken and saffron broth, served with a bowl full of preserved lemons, and Caesar salad with fresh anchovies and croutons. Main courses could include lambs' tongues and sweetbreads with shell pasta, smoked ham and lavender, or roast duck with fresh local vegetables. Desserts range from sticky toffee pudding to brandy snap baskets filled with cream and strawberries. On sunny summer days, pre-dinner drinks can be enjoyed in the flower-filled garden, overlooking the water.

Directions: M4/J12 or M40/J6, signed off B4009 Goring-Wallingford

GREAT MILTON, Le Manoir
Aux Quat' Saisons ❀❀❀❀❀

Church Road
OX44 7PD
Map 4: SP60
Tel: 01844 278881
Fax: 01844 278847

Raymond Blanc's mellow, fifteenth-century country house hotel revolves around the restaurant, and the place is busy. Finding a seat before dinner in the drawing rooms (plenty of deep-cushioned sofas, chintz, fresh flowers, lots of magazines, all in keeping with the style of the house) can be difficult, although there are staff to pull up the odd chair. The several dining rooms all smack of quality – the flowers, the polished silver, decent glass – and the view across the garden is stunning. 'It feels decadent, special, as if there is a surprise in store.' The guests are smart, cosmopolitan, with plenty of expense accounts around. Clive Fretwell has left and Jonathan Wright taken over but, under the guidance of Raymond Blanc, the whole place remains well organised and disciplined; it shows in the quality and execution of the food. A 'superb' baby scallop that had been marinated in lime juice was the highlight of a great selection of canapés, and augured well for the meal to come. That summer inspection dinner never missed a beat. It opened with asparagus spears (with a superb hollandaise), cassolette with morels, and foie gras mille-feuille, each element placed separately on an oblong dish, to be eaten in the order described. It was a clever dish in terms of building up flavours from the lightest and cleanest to the heaviest and richest. Main course was an accomplished 'vibrantly fresh' pan-fried fillet of sea bass and langoustine, with red pepper coulis and coriander. This was served with aubergine filled with tomato, the lightest fennel, and deep-fried polenta. Pudding was a caramelised William pear (cooked with ginger and butterscotch) in a sweet puff pastry feuilleté with 'the most stunning' lime sorbet and a crème anglaise. It is nice to note that children are made very welcome too, they even have their own menu. Service is slick, polished and professional in the old style, but it's not stuffy, and 'it is great to have a friendly, helpful and fun sommelier'.

Chefs: Raymond Blanc, Jonathan Wright
Owner: Raymond Blanc
Cost: Fixed-price L £29.50 (not Sun)/D £69
Times: 12.15pm-last D 2.15pm/7.15pm-last D 10.15pm
Additional: Sunday L; Children welcome; 🍴 dishes
Seats: 120. Private dining room 46
Smoking: No-smoking area; air-conditioning (Conservatory)
Accommodation: 19 en suite
Credit cards: ▆ ▆ ▆ ▆

Directions: From M40/J7 follow A329 towards Wallingford. At 1 mile turn R, signposted Great Milton Manor

HENLEY-ON-THAMES,

Red Lion Hotel ❀

There's a sensible, flexible approach to eating at the Regency-style Regatta Brasserie. Here you can order rack of lamb with brioche crust and fresh cherries, terrine of sardine and tomato with olive parsley dressing, coronation chicken baguette, and Caesar salad, in the knowledge that everything is of the same reliably high standard.

Additional: Bar Food; Sunday L; Children welcome; 🍴 menu
Smoking: No-smoking area
Accommodation: 26 en suite
Credit cards: ▆ ▆ ▆ ▆ ▆

Directions: On the right when entering Henley by the bridge

Hart Street RG9 2AR
Map 4: SU78
Tel: 01491 572161
Fax: 01491 410039
Chef: Stuart Robbins
Owners: Miller family
Cost: Alc £17.50. H/wine £10.95. ☺
Times: Last L 2.30pm/D 9.30pm

HORTON-CUM-STUDLEY,

Studley Priory ❀❀

Dinners at this ancient Elizabethan manor are priced by the main course, inclusive of a choice of starter and dessert, so for pan-fried breast of Aylesbury duckling on swede purée with a lime and redcurrant sauce at £29.75, you get tartlet of chicken livers in a brandy and wild mushroom sauce glazed with foie gras, and hot apple soufflé with Calvados ice cream thrown in

Oxford
OX33 1AZ
Map 4: SP51
Tel: 01865 351203
Fax: 01865 351613
Chef: Peter Hewitt
Owners: Parke family
Cost: Alc £25. H/wine £16

Times: Noon-last L 1.45pm/7.30pm-last D 9.30pm
Additional: Bar meals L; Sunday L; Children welcome; 🐾 dishes
Seats: 60. Private dining room 34
Smoking: No smoking in dining room
Accommodation: 19 en suite
Credit cards: 💳 💳 💳 💳 💳

as well. The menu displays all the terminology of modern British cooking, with confits, pestos, tapenades, cassoulets and shavings of Parmesan at almost every turn. Nonetheless, good ingredients are imaginatively handled – roast Scottish scallops with Chablis sauce and ribbons of deep-fried vegetables, for example, and pot-roast Studley Wood pheasant served on a bed of vegetable cassoulet with juniper and blueberry sauce.

Directions: At top of hill in the village

KINGHAM,
The Mill House Hotel 🏵🏵

Chipping Norton
OX7 6UH
Map 4: SP22
Tel: 01608 658188
Fax: 01608 658492
Chef: Ali Hussain
Owners: Sheila & John Parslow
Cost: *Alc* £30, fixed-price D £22.75. ☺ H/wine £10.70.
Times: Last L 2.30pm/D 9.30pm
Additional: Bar food; Sunday L; Children welcome; 🐾 dishes
Smoking: No smoking in dining room
Accommodation: 23 en suite
Credit cards: 💳 💳 💳 💳 💳 💳

Delightful small hotel, a lovingly restored and extended former mill set in seven acres of gardens, complete with trout stream. The restaurant, all Cotswold quaint and cottagey charm, offers imaginative, well-balanced menus that may feature Thai fish broth, and pistachio and wild mushroom stuffed quail with thyme sauce. A June dinner highlighted a good asparagus and wild mushroom risotto, lamb fillet with ginger-flavoured chick peas, red cabbage sauce that was 'alive with flavour', and perfect creamed potatoes with spring onion, and a 'best I've ever had' blackberry soufflé with a rich, clearly flavoured blackberry sauce and superb home-made yoghurt ice cream.

Directions: On B4450, on southern outskirts of Kingham village

KINGSTON BAGPUIZE, **Fallowfields Country House** ❀

An elegant seventeenth-century house featuring an intimate dining room with winter log fires. House party-style dining – guests are introduced to each other before dinner, but sit at their own tables to enjoy serious cooking based on local, and some home-grown, produce. Expect orange-glazed saddle of lamb, and roasted halibut in a sorrel and vermouth sauce.

Accommodation: 10 en suite. **Credit cards:** 🟦 🟦 🟦 🟦

Directions: From A34 at Abingdon take A415 (Witney). At mini-r/bout in Kingston Bagpuize turn L. Fallowfields is one mile on L

Faringdon Road
Kingston Bagpuize OX13 5BH
Map 4: SP49
Tel: 01865 820416
Fax: 01865 821275
Chef/Owner: Peta Lloyd
Cost: Alc £27, fixed-price D £31.
H/wine £13
Times: D only, 7.30pm-last D 9pm.
Closed D Sun
Additional: No children under 10;
🌀 dishes
Smoking: No smoking in dining room

MIDDLETON STONEY, **Jersey Arms Hotel** ❀

Bicester OX6 8SE
Map 4: SP52
Tel: 01869 343234
Fax: 01869 343565
Chef: Douglas Parrott
Owners: Donald & Helen Livingston
Cost: Alc £21. H/wine £9.50 ☺
Times: Last L 1.45pm/D 9.30pm
Closed D Sun
Additional: Bar Food; Sunday L;
Children welcome; 🌀 dishes
Smoking: No smoking in dining room
Accommodation: 16 en suite
Credit cards: 🟦 🟦 🟦 🟦 🟦 🟦

Centuries old, but still going strong, this charming Cotswold-stone inn continues as a purveyor of honest sustenance. Full meals are served in the oak-panelled dining room, where the menu ranges from French onion soup and pastas to casseroled rabbit and fillet of pork on braised red cabbage. Crème brûlée is a typical sweet.

Directions: On B430, 3 miles from Bicester, 10 miles N of Oxford

MINSTER LOVELL, **Lovells at Windrush Farm** ❀❀❀

This thoroughly charming farmhouse restaurant, decorated in muted shades of Wedgwood blue and grey, cleverly provides three simple rooms for guests too replete from the ornate seven-course dinners to drive home. Marcus Ashenford is a chef with excellent skills who knows how to build well-conceived dishes without any unnecessary flourishes. Proceedings may commence with squares of Welsh rarebit with home-made rhubarb chutney, followed by tartlet of braised onion and sage topped with sautéed foie gras on a bed of caramelised endive with roasted pistachio nuts and a Cabernet Sauvignon vinegar sauce. Soup might be a stunningly simple leek and potato or crab bisque with tortellini of crab and tarragon. Pan-fried fillet of brill is baked with a spring onion mousse, gratinated with pesto and brioche crumbs on a bed of

Old Minster Lovell OX8 5RN
Map 4: SP31
Tel: 01993 779802
Fax: 01993 776212
Chef: Marcus Ashenford
Owner: Lovells Windrush Farm Ltd
Cost: Fixed-price L £23 (5 courses)/D
£37 (7 courses)
Times: L for 1pm (Sun & Fri only)/D
for 7.45pm. Closed D Sun, Mon, Jan
Additional: Sunday L; Children
welcome; 🌀 dishes
Seats: 18
Smoking: No smoking in dining room
Accommodation: 3 en suite
Credit cards: 🟦 🟦 🟦 🟦 🟦

braised leeks accompanied by a tomato dressing, then it's onto
roasted breast of wild mallard duck with home-made duck
sausage on creamed celeriac, crushed parsnips with deep-fried
spring greens and a cassis sauce. Cheese, then pear poached in
red wine and grenadine caramelised and served with cinnamon
ice cream with vintage balsamic vinegar wraps things up in the
baroque, sophisticated style with which the whole thing began.

Directions: From the Witney-Minster Lovell road, take the first
turning to the Old Minster

MOULSFORD, **Beetle & Wedge**

Ferry Lane
Wallingford
OX10 9JF
Map 4: SU58
Tel: 01491 651381
Fax: 01491 651376
Chefs: Richard Smith, Robert Taylor
Owners: Kate & Richard Smith
Cost: Dining Room – fixed-price L
£27.50/D £35. H/wine £12.95.
Boathouse – *Alc* £25-£27.
Times: 12.30pm-last L 2pm/7pm-last
D 10pm. Closed D Sun, Mon (Dining
room).
Additional: Bar food (Boathouse);
Sunday L; Well behaved children
welcome
Seats: 25 (Dining Room) 60
(Boathouse). Private dining room 12-
60
Smoking: No smoking in dining room
Accommodation: 10 en suite
Credit cards: ▆ ▆ ▆ ▆ ▆ ▆

The restaurant of this Thames-side hotel offers the works:
literary links (this is the former home of Jerome K Jerome),
river views and fine cooking (tip-top freshness on a menu that
changes daily according to market availability). Chef-patron
Richard Smith cooks fish notably well – a main course of hake
with tomato, fennel and samphire was exceptionally good,
accompanied by broccoli, puréed celeriac and rösti potatoes.
Sweet and savoury soufflés feature regularly, perhaps
Cointreau with raspberry sauce or Stilton with wild mushroom
sauce ladled in at the table from a little copper pan. The simply
described *carte* treads a careful path between modern British
and classical French; as such, it may include both a warm
scallop salad with grilled potatoes and balsamic vinegar, and
grilled fillet steak with snails, garlic and baby onions. There is
also a sprinkling of traditional English dishes, such as hot
rhubarb crumble with organic cream. The Boathouse is a more
informal dining area; the wide selection of dishes range from
pork and parsley terrine with piccalilli, to wing of skate with
black butter and capers, plus selections from the chargrill. An
enthusiastically francophile wine list is tempered by a
smattering of New World and a splash of quality Tuscans.
French whites are a strength with Grippat in Rhône and
Vincent in Burgundy being notably good value. There is a
declared encouragement here to ask for assistance and given
the limited annotation this would be a wise approach. Take
advantage also of the 'dipstick' option, allowing measured
consumption of half or more of a full bottle.
Signature dishes: Grilled escalope of wild salmon with fresh
English asparagus and new potatoes; suprême of local
pheasant with cream, Cognac and button onions; whole
partridge with cabbage, foie gras and truffle sauce.

Directions: In the village, turn towards the river via Ferry Lane.

OXFORD, **Bath Place Hotel**

Oxford's city walls are largely long gone, but a small section still makes up part of the split-level dining-room wall in this seventeenth-century cottage hotel and restaurant tucked away between two ancient colleges. There are historical links to Thomas Hardy, King Edward VII, Dorothy L Sayers, Richard Burton and Elizabeth Taylor, but these days the visitors come as much for the imaginative cooking as for the colourful anecdotes. A pan-fried fillet of red mullet with rocket salad, pesto, shaved Parmesan and white Italian truffle, was slightly top-heavy on the olive oil dressing, but a main course of pan-fried breast of mallard with confit of Brussels sprouts and griottine cherries in a griottine and game sauce was prepared with care and evident skill. A superb dessert of white and dark chocolate mousse filled with chocolate eggs with dark chocolate sorbet and butterscotch sauce was equally well appreciated. Although there is a set price menu for lunch and dinner, note that many dishes carry a supplement, and at lunch an extra amount is charged for bread, canapés and petits fours. The interesting wine list is usefully arranged by style.

Directions: City centre, opposite Holywell Music Room, between Hertford & New College

4/5 Bath Place Holywell Street
OX1 3SU
Map 4: SP50
Tel: 01865 791812
Fax: 01865 791834
Chef: Jeremy Blake O'Connor
Owners: Kathleen & Yolanda Fawsitt
Cost: Alc £35, fixed-price L £14-£17.50/D £29.50. H/wine £11.95
Times: Noon-last L 2pm/7pm-last D 10pm. Closed D Sun, Mon, L Tues
Additional: Sunday L; Children welcome; ✪ menu
Seats: 32
Smoking: No smoking in dining room; air-conditioning
Accommodation: 12 en suite
Credit cards: 🃏🃏🃏🃏🃏

OXFORD,
Cotswold Lodge Hotel

Popular family-run Victorian hotel within walking distance of the city centre. Well prepared, imaginative cooking may include terrine of game mousseline with Oxford sauce, and salmon and scallop roulade with sea asparagus and saffron sauce.

Smoking: No smoking in dining room
Accommodation: 50 en suite. **Credit cards:** 🃏🃏🃏🃏

Directions: Take A4165 (Banbury Road) off A40 ring road, hotel 1.5m on left.

66A Banbury Road OX2 6JP
Map 4: SP50
Tel: 01865 512121
Fax: 01865 512490
Chef: Garin Chapman
Owners: Mr & Mrs K Peros
Cost: H/wine £9.50. ☺
Times: Open for L/6.30pm-last D 10.30pm
Additional: Bar meals; Children welcome; ✪ dishes

OXFORD, **Liaison** ✪

Popular Chinese specialising in dim-sum. Choices could include steamed dumplings, turnip cakes and 'cha siu bao' – fluffy white bread mounds filled with a sweet pork mixture. Also look out for sizzling chicken cooked with green pepper, and roast pork 'cheung fun'.

Directions: Behind main shopping centre

29 Castle Street
Map 4: SP50
Tel: 01865 242944
Chef: Mr Lo
Owner: Timmy Yt Tsang
Cost: Alc £20, fixed-price D £15. ☺ H/wine £7.50
Telephone for further details

OXFORD, **Munchy Munchy** ✪✪

Munchy Munchy, as the name suggests, is not your average Chinese restaurant. The simple decor, bright orange and gold painted walls, quarry-tiled floor and well-spaced pine tables and chairs, forms a backdrop to Ethel Ow's idiosyncratic cooking, an interpretation of the dishes of South-East Asia. The dominant influence is Sumatran Padang cuisine, but China, Thailand and Malaysia are also represented. The menu changes on a daily basis, no starters or side dishes are offered,

6 Park End Street
OX1 1HH
Map 4: SP50
Tel: 01865 245710
Chef: Ethel Ow
Owners: Tony & Ethel Ow
Cost: Alc £15. H/wine £7.45. ☺
Times: Noon-2pm/5.30pm-10pm.
Closed Sun, Mon, 2 wks Aug, 2 wks Dec

and there are just six or seven main dishes described in a straightforward what-you-read-is-what-you-get manner. A duck dish, for instance, with fresh tarragon, juniper berries, coriander seeds, fresh lime leaves in ruby port and crushed cranberries. Or you might find tender, spicy lamb with nutmeg, marjoram, celery seeds, chives and 'daun-kare' curry leaves in a sour cream sauce. Or fillet of brill in a spicy broth that complemented the fish well, served with mayonnaise and white wine. To drink there are bottled beers, unusual teas and a few inexpensive wines.

Directions: W of city centre, between Nuffield College & the station

Additional: No children under 6 Fri/Sat D. ⓓ dishes
Seats: 60
Smoking: No-smoking area; no pipes and cigars
Credit cards: ▄▄ ▦ ▦ ▇ 🗎

OXFORD, Le Petit Blanc ❀❀

'Words like fresh, busy, noisy, buzzing, popular, polished, sparkling, fun, low-key, modern and cosmopolitan all spring to mind', noted an inspector in garrulous mood. This all-day brasserie is Raymond Blanc's homecoming to Oxford. A former piano shop in Jericho has been given the Conran treatment: glass frontage, high stools at the bar, an abstract mural of the city on one wall. Service is 'blue jean casual'. Holding centre stage is the open-plan kitchen, with a Molteni spit-roasting grill as the prime source of heat and interest. The something-for-everyone menu is a flexible, up-to-the-minute slate encompassing pastas, salads, plenty of fish and more gutsy offerings such as chargrilled ribeye steak with herb and mustard sauce. Added to that are breakfasts, afternoon teas, and even a special children's menu. Successes from recent meals have included a terrine of duck, liver and fennel with beetroot dressing, cream of butternut squash soup, and an exemplary risotto of morels with crusty Parmesan. The wine list has a good spread to suit all palates and pockets.

Directions: From centre of Oxford, up St Giles, L down Little Clarendon and R at end into Walton Street

71-72 Walton Street OX2 6AG
Map 4: SP50
Tel: 01865 510999
Fax: 01865 510700
Chef: Stuart Busby
Owner: Raymond Blanc (Blanc Restaurants Ltd)
Cost: Fixed-price L £14. ☺ H/wine £9.95.
Times: Noon-last L 3.30pm/6.30pm-last D 11pm. Closed 25 Dec
Additional: Sunday L; Children welcome; ⓓ dishes
Seats: 115. Private dining room 16
Smoking: No-smoking area; air-conditioning
Credit cards: ▄▄ ▦ ▦ ▇ 🟦 🗎

OXFORD, Randolph Hotel ❀

A city landmark, built in 1864, and popular with generations of town and gown. In Spires Restaurant – a magnificent room festooned with crests of Oxford colleges – sample ambitious dishes such as scallops with lemon polenta and thyme butter, mint-crusted venison, spätzli and sloe gin, and iced coffee and Kahlua parfait with vanilla sauce.

Accommodation: 109 en suite. **Credit cards:** ▄▄ ▦ ▦ ▇ 🟦 🗎

Directions: At corner of Beaumont St and Magdalen St, opposite Ashmolean Museum

Beaumont Street OX1 2LN
Map 4: SP50
Tel: 01865 247481
Fax: 01865 791678
Chef: Geoff Balharrie
Owner: Forte Hotels (Granada)
Cost: Alc £35, fixed-price L £12/D £30. H/wine £18
Times: Last L 2pm/last D 10pm
Additional: Bar meals; Sunday L; Children welcome; ⓓ dishes
Smoking: No-smoking area; no pipes & cigars

OXFORD, Whites

As we went to press we heard from Michael Llewellyn-White that he was giving up the lease on Whites in Turl Street, and relocating the restaurant to 19 High Street, Woodstock, Oxford OX20 1TE. Tel 01993 812872/fax 01993 813754. The style of the new Whites will remain the same. Whites in Oxford achieved two AA Rosettes in last year's Guide.

SHIPTON-UNDER-WYCHWOOD,

Lamb Inn ❀

Popular seventeenth-century Cotswold stone inn sporting character bars with open fires and a low-beamed restaurant offering a fixed-price dinner menu noted for its country cooking and use of fresh local ingredients. Look out for the impressive lunchtime buffet – home-cooked ham, salmon, lobster – and good desserts like bread-and-butter pudding.

Smoking: No smoking in dining room
Accommodation: 5 en suite
Credit cards: ▬ ▭ ▱ ▨ ▢

Directions: In village centre

High Street OX7 6DQ
Map: 4 SP21
Tel: 01993 830465
Fax: 01993 832025
Chef: John McGarrigle
Owners: Michael & Jenny Eastick
Cost: *Alc* £25, fixed-price D 21. ☺
H/wine £9.95.
Times: Last L 2pm/last D 9.45pm
Additional: Bar meals; Sunday L;
No children under 12; ❹ dishes

SHIPTON-UNDER-WYCHWOOD,

Shaven Crown Hotel ❀

Fascinating old building, originally a retreat for medieval monks and later used as a hunting lodge by Good Queen Bess. Snacks and real ales are served in the bar, more formal meals in the dining room. Gravlax, fillet of beef with basil, olives and capers, and chocolate truffle torte are typical dishes.

Smoking: No smoking in dining room
Accommodation: 9 en suite
Credit cards: ▬ ▭ ▱ ▨ ▣ ▢

Directions: On A361, village centre, 4 miles N of Burford

OX7 6BA
Map 4: SP21
Tel: 01993 830330
Fax: 01993 832136
Chefs: Stanley Ryder
Owners: Robert & Jane Burpitt
Cost: Fixed-price D £18.50. ☺
H/wine £8.50.
Times: Last L 2pm/D 9pm
Additional: Bar Food; Sunday L;
Children welcome; ❹ dishes

STEEPLE ASTON,

Hopcrofts Holt ❀

Creeper-clad 500-year-old coaching inn serving ambitious French menu. 'Jambon persille de bourgonne', suprême of chicken stuffed with crab meat and served on a langoustine butter with sun-dried tomatoes, and a spot-on nougat glace with 'bits of ginger confit' show the range.

Smoking: No smoking in dining room
Accommodation: 88 en suite
Credit cards: ▬ ▭ ▱ ▨ ▣ ▢

Directions: Follow A426 through Kidlington towards Deddington. Hotel on R at traffic lights.

Map 4: SP42
Tel: 01869 340259
Fax: 01869 340865
Chef: Pascal Parize
Owners: Hopcrofts Holt Hotel
Cost: *Alc* £24, Fixed-price L £10.50/D £19. ☺ H/wine £9.45.
Times: Last L 2.15pm/D 9.45pm.
Closed L Sat
Additional: Bar Food; Sunday L;
Children welcome; ❹ dishes

STONOR, **Stonor Arms** ❀❀

'Bags of historic charm' defines the mood in the Stonor Arms – a modest inn/hotel at the heart of a picture-postcard village. The Blades Bar is a popular local haunt, while those wanting food can choose between the formal setting of mahogany tables and antique paintings in the dining room or the more informal atmosphere of the two hop-festooned, flower-filled conservatories overlooking the walled garden. The short *carte* offers plenty for vegetarians – polenta fritters with sweet and

Near Henley-on-Thames RG9 6HE
Map 4: SU78
Tel: 01491 638866
Fax: 01491 638863
Owner: Stonor Hotels Ltd
Cost: *Alc* £25, fixed-price L £10 (2 courses)/D £25 (3 courses). ☺ H/wine £10.50.
Times: Noon-last L 2pm/7pm-last D 9.30pm.

Stonor Arms

Additional: Bar meals; Sunday L; children welcome; dishes
Seats: 55. Private dining room 18 +12
Smoking: No pipes and cigars
Accommodation: 10 en suite
Credit cards:

sour sauce, or pancakes stuffed with wild mushrooms and hazelnuts. The kitchen has a way with sauces, whether they are used to accompany roast turbot and braised fennel, or heartwarming steak and kidney pudding. There's also a fair choice when it comes to desserts – 'suitably sharp' lemon tart, Armagnac parfait with poached pears, and steamed ginger sponge, for example. The wine plunders Chile, Canada, the Lebanon and others for reliable drinking across the range.

Directions: In centre of village

THAME, Spread Eagle Hotel

Redoubtable 400-year-old coaching inn which made its name in the 1920s when it was run by innkeeper John Fothergill. In the eponymous pine-panelled restaurant, guests have a choice of menus including special selections from, say, China and Italy. Elsewhere expect old-school dishes such as salmon in a paper bag, and roast leg of lamb.

Accommodation: 33 en suite
Credit cards: ▬ ▬ ▬ ▬

Directions: M40/J6 from S, J8 from N. Town centre on A418 Oxford to Aylesbury road

Cornmarket OX9 2BW
Map 4: SP70
Tel: 01844 213661
Fax: 01844 261380
Chef: Michael Thomas
Owners: Mr & Mrs DML Barrington
Cost: *Alc* £23.95, fixed-price L £17.95/D £21.95. ☺ H/wine £9.45.
Times: Last L 2pm/D 10pm (9pm Sun). Closed 25-30 Dec
Additional: Bar meals; Sunday Children welcome; dishes

WALLINGFORD, Shillingford Bridge NEW

Enjoying a unique Thameside setting, this popular, extended inn provides freshly prepared food in its traditional chandeliered restaurant. The good selection of dishes may feature pan-fried mushrooms in spicy herb and tomato butter, chicken stuffed with cream cheese, and apricot crème brûlée.

Shillingford
OX10 8LZ
Map 4: SU68
Tel: 01865 858567
Fax: 01865 858636
Telephone for details

WALLINGFORD, Springs Hotel NEW

Most of the tables in the pretty dining-room overlook the lake and island from large picture windows. Service is very professional and smooth, the staff courteous and friendly. There are Dover sole and steaks for the traditional-minded (at the table next to our inspector, all four diners ordered the mixed grill), but there are also more innovative dishes as well.

Wallingford Road
North Stoke OX10 6BE
Map 4: SU68
Tel: 01491 836687
Fax: 01491 836877
Chef: Phil Wilkins
Owner: Springs Hotel (Thames Valley) Ltd

An intense smoked chicken consommé, served with Puy lentils floating in the bottom and a mushroom ravioli, made a good start to the meal, but the main dish of pan-fried halibut with Chinese five-spice served on cucumber tagliatelle with a ginger and carrot sauce, would have worked better without the spicing. Extra vegetables come at extra cost. Lemon tart was attractively arranged on the plate with a portion of lime sorbet and a pool of Seville orange chutney (a fancy name for marmalade with raisins, was how our inspector described it!)

Cost: H/wine £12
Times: 12.30pm-last L 2pm/7pm-last D 9.45pm
Additional: Bar meals; Sunday L; Children welcome; ❹ dishes
Seats: 80. Private dining room 22-26
Smoking: No pipes & cigars
Accommodation: 30 en suite
Credit cards: 💳 💳 💳 💳 💳 💳

Directions: From A4130 to Wallingford take A4074 (Reading); over first roundabout, turn R on B4009 (Goring). Hotel 1 mile on R

WANTAGE, **Foxes**

Charming cottage-style restaurant with convenient town-centre location. Lunch and dinner revolve around a daily changing set-price menu. Scallop mousse with fresh mussels and a light scallop sauce, confit of duck, and pan-fried fillet of sea bream with a wild mushroom sauce are backed up by the likes of prune parfait with a chocolate sauce.

Smoking: No smoking in dining room. **Credit cards:** 💳 💳 💳

Directions: 50 yds from Market Square on A338 Newbury/Reading rd

8 Newbury Street OX12 8BS
Map 4: SU38
Tel/Fax: 01235 760568
Chef: Karen Sweeney
Owners: Karen Sweeney, Nicholas Offen
Cost: Fixed-price L £15/D £25. H/wine £10.
Times: Last L 1.30pm/D 9.30pm. Closed Sun, Mon, L Sat
Additional: Children welcome; ❹ dishes

WESTON-ON-THE-GREEN,
Weston Manor Hotel

Imposing fifteenth-century manor house standing in 13 acres of gardens and grounds. Popular with the business community its offers impressive conference facilities and enjoyable English cooking in the magnificent vaulted restaurant, complete with minstrels gallery and original panelling.

Directions: 2 mins from M40/J9 via A34 (Oxford) to Weston-on-the-Green; hotel in village centre

Oxford OX6 8QL
Map 4: SP50
Tel: 01869 350621
Fax: 01869 350901
Telephone for details

WOODSTOCK, **Bear Hotel** ❀❀

Park Street, OX20 1SZ
Map 4: SP41
Tel: 01993 811511
Fax: 01993 813380
Chef: Ian Morgan
Cost: *Alc* £25.95, fixed-price L £16.95 (3 courses). H/wine £13.50
Times: 12.30pm-last L 2.15pm/7pm-last D 9.45pm
Additional: Bar food L; Sunday L; Children welcome; ❹ dishes
Seats: 76. Private dining room 28
Smoking: No smoking in dining room
Accommodation: 44 en suite
Credit cards: 💳 💳 💳 💳 💳

History is etched deep into this seven-centuries-old coaching inn that holds pride of place in Woodstock's market square.

There are echoes of the past in the exposed stone walls, heavily beamed ceilings and ancient staircase, but there's nothing archaic about the food served in the attractive, spacious restaurant. Lunch menus change weekly, dinner varies with the season. Up-to-the-minute ideas such as avocado and prawn gâteau with gazpacho sauce, and crispy Gressingham duckling on a purée of roasted vegetables with a carefully reduced sour cherry sauce, appear alongside more classic offerings like ravioli of smoked salmon mousse, grilled Dover sole and stuffed breast of chicken with Marsala sauce. Bringing up the rear are desserts ranging from chocolate mousse to strawberry and champagne shortbread. Staff are keen and eager to please. The wine list is a wide-ranging global slate, with some decent house selections and several half-bottles to boot.

Directions: Town centre, facing the market square

WOODSTOCK, The Chef Imperial

Complete with an ornamental pond and modern decor, this friendly high street Chinese specialises in Cantonese and Szechuan cuisine. From an extensive menu look out for good steamed scallops with garlic and spring onions, wun tun soup (prawn dumplings in a pleasant broth) and succulent crispy duck with plum sauce.

Smoking: No-smoking area; air-conditioning
Credit cards:

Directions: In main street of Woodstock

22 High Street OX20 1TF
Map 4: SP41
Tel: 01993 813593
Fax: 01993 813591
Chef: Mr P C Wong
Owner: Alan Tse Loong Shek
Cost: Alc £18, fixed-price L from £5.95/D £15. ☺ H/wine £8.50.
Times: Last L 2.30pm/last D midnight.
Closed 25-27 Dec
Additional: Sunday L buffet; Children welcome; ✤ dishes

WOODSTOCK, Feathers Hotel

Market Street
OX20 1SX
Map 4: SP50
Tel: 01993 812291
Fax: 01993 813158
Chef: David Lewis
Owners: Simon Lowe, Howard Malin, Andrew Leeman
Cost: Alc £30. Fixed-price L £16.50. H/wine £11.75
Times: 12.30pm-last L 2.15pm/7.30pm-last D 9.15pm
Additional: Bar food L (D Mon-Fri only); Sunday lunch; Children welcome; ✤ dishes
Seats: 60. Private dining room 20

A really super little hotel with lots of quality and character. The historic seventeenth-century building with its wood-panelling, steep, narrow stairways, antique furnishings and log fires, provides restful surroundings. But there is nothing retro about the kitchen which produces cooking that is comfortably modern British and shines with honest flavours. A test meal, taken on Halloween 'but thankfully free of any themed nonsense', featured delicately handled chargrilled swordfish with tuna spring rolls, soy sauce and ginger, the latter flavours working particularly well with the tuna. Breast of free-range chicken came sliced on white and squid-ink coloured fettucine, with oyster mushrooms, glazed shallots and crisp rösti sauced with a not too overpowering grain mustard hollandaise.

Pudding was a simple and effective cooked cheesecake served with pistachio anglaise and a compote of black cherries. There's a decent selection of half-bottles and wines by the glass on a wide-ranging list.

Directions: Town centre

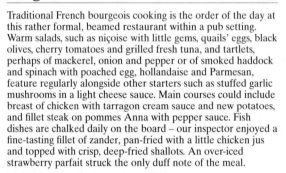

WOODSTOCK,

Kings Head Inn ❀❀

Traditional French bourgeois cooking is the order of the day at this rather formal, beamed restaurant within a pub setting. Warm salads, such as niçoise with little gems, quails' eggs, black olives, cherry tomatoes and grilled fresh tuna, and tartlets, perhaps of mackerel, onion and pepper or of smoked haddock and spinach with poached egg, hollandaise and Parmesan, feature regularly alongside other starters such as stuffed garlic mushrooms in a light cheese sauce. Main courses could include breast of chicken with tarragon cream sauce and new potatoes, and fillet steak on pommes Anna with pepper sauce. Fish dishes are chalked daily on the board – our inspector enjoyed a fine-tasting fillet of zander, pan-fried with a little chicken jus and topped with crisp, deep-fried shallots. An over-iced strawberry parfait struck the only duff note of the meal.

Smoking: No pipes and cigars in dining room; air-conditioning
Accommodation: 16 (15 en suite)
Credit cards: ■ ▦ ▨ ▧ 🄿 🄴

NEW
Chapel Hill Wootton OX20 1DX
Map 4: SP50
Tel/Fax: 01993 811340
Chef: Olivier Broyer
Owners: Mr & Mrs Tony Fay
Cost: Alc £20. H/wine £9.95. ☺
Times: Noon-last L 2pm/7pm-last D 9.45pm
Additional: Bar meals; Sunday L; ⓓ dishes
Seats: 36
Smoking: No smoking in dining room
Accommodation: 3 en suite
Credit cards: ■ ▦ ▧ 🄴

Directions: On A44 2 miles N of Woodstock turn R to Wootton. The Inn is located near church in Chapel Hill

RUTLAND

NORMANTON,

Normanton Park Hotel ❀

Normanton Park is built around a recently restored Georgian stable block – all that remains of the original Hall and its vast estate. The Orangery restaurant overlooks Rutland Water, a haven for boating and fishing enthusiasts. Here you can enjoy sound British home-cooking in elegant surroundings.

Smoking: No pipes or cigars
Accommodation: 23 en suite. **Credit cards:** ■ ▦ ▧ 🄴

Directions: South shore of Rutland Water near Edith Weston

Rutland Water
South Shore LE15 8RP
Map 4: SK90
Tel: 01780 720315
Fax: 01780 721086
Chef: Paul Huxtable
Owners: Jane Hales, Robert Reid
Cost: Alc £25.30, fixed-price D £15.
☺ H/wine £8.75.
Times: Last L 2.15pm/D 9.45pm
Additional: Bar meals; Sunday L; Children welcome; ⓓ dishes

OAKHAM, **Barnsdale Lodge** ❀

A seventeenth-century farmhouse, with an Edwardian-style restaurant and conservatory overlooking Rutland Water. A good range of freshly cooked, classic English dishes includes vegetarian options and desserts for diabetics. The new bakery ensures a fresh supply of delicious breads and pastries.

Accommodation: 30 en suite
Credit cards: ■ ▦ ▧ 🄴

Directions: Two miles outside town on A606 to Stamford

The Avenue Rutland Water LE15 8AH
Map 8: SK80
Tel: 01572 724678
Fax: 01572 724961
Chefs: Robert Knowles, Patrick Taylor
Owner: Robert Reid
Cost: Alc £25. H/wine £9.95. ☺
Times: Last L 2.30pm/D 9.45pm.
Closed D 25 Dec
Additional: Bar meals; Sunday L; Children welcome; ⓓ dishes
Smoking: No smoking in dining room

OAKHAM, **Hambleton Hall** 🏵🏵🏵🏵

Hambleton LE15 8TH
Map 8: SK80
Tel: 01572 756991
Fax: 01572 724721
Chef: Aaron Patterson
Owners: Tim & Stefa Hart
Cost: *Alc* £54, fixed-price L £14.50 (2
courses)/D from £35. H/wine £15
Times: Noon-last L 2pm/7pm-last D
9.30pm
Additional: Sunday L; Children
welcome; 🍴 dishes
Seats: 60. Private dining rooms 20
Smoking: No pipes and cigars in
dining room
Accommodation: 15 en suite
Credit cards: 🔲 🔲 🔲 🔲 🔲 🔲

Hambleton Hall is to many the archetypal country house hotel.
The setting alone, with Rutland Water as a backdrop, is idyllic,
but the hotel itself is an exercise in taste and style from both
designer Nina Campbell and proprietors Tim and Stefa Hart.
Public areas range from a clubby bar, a drawing room with
stunning views over the lake, to the opulent, smart restaurant
complete with silk wall coverings. In the kitchen Aaron
Patterson's style continues to evolve and is showing even
greater signs of maturity. He is a very good cook. A winter
meal exemplified some of his skills, revealing that some of the
earlier fussiness has disappeared and a little more restraint and
assurance is coming through. Flavours, especially, are allowed
to sing. An amuse-bouche of deeply flavoured parsnip soup
was followed by a raviolo of wild mushrooms with girolles and
a truffle oil sabayon of white beans, with a moist chicken
mousse binding the fungi; a 'refined' salad niçoise came with
chargrilled tuna; a 'great' Bresse pigeon was cooked en cocotte
with fondant potatoes and roasted garlic; an assiette of desserts
demonstrated superb technical skills in the pastry work- lemon
tart with crisp pastry and a tang to the correctly textured
filling, a superb tear drop of chocolate mousse topped with a
quenelle of raspberry sorbet, and a caramel globe of blown
glass-like sugar filled with vanilla cream. That same winter
menu majored in seasonal game, with loin of local hare
wrapped in puff pastry with a port sauce, roast saddle of fallow
buck with a port and red wine sauce and braised loin of rabbit
with a little pie of its leg meat and a grain mustard sauce,
superbly balanced by traditional luxuries such as mille-feuille
of pan-fried foie gras with roasted endive and a Madeira and
lentil sauce, and whole roasted lobster with baby vegetables
and basil-flavoured tortellinis. It is worth noting that lesser
details, such as bread, canapés and petits fours, can hardly be
bettered. Staff are superb and offer really skilled service,
although it is a touch formal.

The wine list combines serious intent with some welcome
concessions to accessibility. Particularly bright is the user
friendly range of thirty or so 'wines of the moment',
recommended as drinking well and categorised by price. For
those who wish to delve deeper, there is quality throughout,
but the greatest interest lies in white Burgundy where the
grandeur of Corton-Charlemagne and Mersault is matched by
some chipper selections from the Chalonnaise and
Mâconnaise.

Signature dishes: A light chicken and foie gras mousse with a
fricassee of morel mushrooms; tails of fresh langoustines with a

chilled essence of tomato and basil; caramelised apple tart with a compote of blackberries and vanilla ice cream; simply roasted woodcock with a mille-feuille of crispy potatoes.

Directions: From A1 – A606 Oakham. After 8.4 miles take turning signed Hambleton/Egleton only. Hotel on R in main street of Hambleton village

OAKHAM, Whipper-In Hotel 🏵

The Market Place LE15 6DT
Map 8: SK80
Tel: 01572 756971
Fax: 01572 757759
Chef: James Butterfill
Owner: Brook Hotels
Cost: *Alc* £26.50, fixed-price L £9.95/D £16.50. ☺ H/wine £8.50.
Times: Last L 2.30pm/D 9.30pm

Fashionably refurbished seventeenth-century hotel with an atmospheric beamed restaurant. Modern menus promise the likes of open wild mushroom ravioli with chive butter sauce, herb-crusted salmon with spring onions and saffron essence, and desserts such as iced chocolate and orange parfait.

Additional: Bar food; Sunday L; Children welcome; 🍴 dishes
Accommodation: 24 en suite
Credit cards: ▬ ▦ ▦ ▦ 🔅 🄖

Directions: In the market place, town centre

STRETTON, Ram Jam Inn 🏵

Great North Road LE15 7QX
Map 8: SK92
Tel: 01780 410776
Fax: 01780 410361
Chef: Chris Ansell
Owner: Tim Hart
Cost: *Alc* £16, fixed-price L £7.95. ☺ H/wine £9.
Times: Noon-last D 10pm.
Closed 25 Dec
Additional: Bar Food; Sunday L; Children welcome; 🍴 dishes

Stylish landmark hostelry on A1 offering an up-market menu that embraces everything from toasted goat's cheese croûton fingers with salad to grilled duck breast with sautéed fennel potatoes and a mirabelle plum sauce, and a duo of chocolate mousse terrine with black cherry coulis and pistachio ice cream. Informal atmosphere, attentive service.

Smoking: No smoking in dining room
Accommodation: 7 en suite
Credit cards: ▬ ▦ ▦ ▦ 🔅 🄖

Directions: On N/bound carriageway of A1, 8 miles N of Stamford; S/bound exit Oakham B668, follow signs under bridge to inn.

UPPINGHAM, Lake Isle Hotel 🏵🏵

High Street East LE159PZ
Map 4: SP89
Tel: /Fax: 01572 822951
Chef: David Whitfield
Owners: David & Claire Whitfield
Cost: Fixed-price L £9.50/D £21.50. ☺ H/wine £8.95.
Times: Last L 1.45pm/D 9.30pm
Closed L Mon
Additional: Sunday L; children welcome; 🍴 dishes
Accommodation: 12 en suite
Credit cards: ▬ ▦ ▦ ▦ 🔅

To find the entrance to this attractive town house, you need to penetrate the floral displays in the courtyard at the back. Inside, a rustic, cottagey mood prevails, with a Welsh dresser

and sturdy pine tables dotted around the panelled dining room. Proprietor David Whitfield is now more regularly involved in the kitchen and our inspector thought the cooking had benefited from his presence. Daily fixed-price menus provide a interesting mix of modern British dishes with robust French provincial overtones and a few Mediterranean gestures. Typically capable offerings could include white fish soup with rice and saffron, a croûte of polenta topped with sun-dried tomatoes and goats' cheese on an unusual orange and toasted almond sauce, and stuffed breast of guinea fowl with a well-balanced sauce of lime and hazelnuts. Chocolate marquise makes a rich finale, and cheeses are 100% British. The wine cellar has been nurtured over the years and now runs to 300 bins, of which 100 are half-bottles.

Directions: Town centre, on foot via Reeves Yard; via Queen Street by car

SHROPSHIRE

BRIDGNORTH, **Haywain**

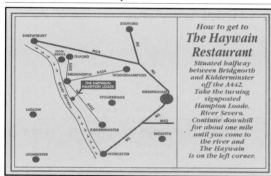

How to get to
The Haywain
Restaurant
Situated halfway between Bridgnorth and Kidderminster off the A442. Take the turning signposted Hampton Loade. River Severn. Continue downhill for about one mile until you come to the river and The Haywain is on the left corner.

Hampton Loade
WV15 6HD
Map 7: SO79
Tel: 01746 780404
Fax: 01746 780533
Chef: Paul Lacey
Owner: David Browning
Cost: Fixed-price D £19.75 (7 courses), Sat D £23.95 (8 courses).
H/wine £7.65
Times: D only from 7.30pm.
Closed D Sun, Mon
Additional: Sunday L; Children welcome; ❸ dishes
Seats: 50. Jacket & tie preferred
Smoking: No smoking in the dining room; air-conditioning
Credit cards: ▊ ▊ ▊ ▊

Of the three set menus, at this homely, rural restaurant, the seven-course 'Nostalgia Gourmet Menu' set some of us sighing with thoughts of roast duck à l'orange and cutlets d'agneau en croute, although medallions of ostrich might only be a stroll down memory lane for ex-pats or former colonial administrators. The 'Royal Gourmet Menu' is a bit of a blow-out starting with soup, then a plate from the cold table, succulent spare ribs, sorbet and a main course, such as poussin rôti chasseur or a daily fish dish, followed by home-made desserts, cheeses and grapes, coffee and friandises. If that all seems too much, then the 'Petit Gourmet Menu' offers much the same in an abbreviated version – soup and main course, or main course and sweet, but also including the Haywain cheese dip and 'lashings' of coffee. Sunday lunch is very good value at £12.95 per person (and children under 10 at £6.50). Afterwards go down to the Severn and look at the last river ferry still to use cable.

Directions: Off the A442, halfway between Bridgnorth and Kidderminster, in the village by the river

CHURCH STRETTON, Mynd House

Little Stretton SY6 6RB
Map 7: SO49
Tel: 01694 722212
Fax: 01694 724180
Chef: Janet Hill
Owners: Robert & Janet Hill
Cost: Fixed-price D £26. ☺
H/wine £10.
Times: D only, 7.30pm- last D 8.45pm. Closed Jan, 2 wks summer
Additional: Bar food L (12.30-2); Children welcome; dishes
Seats: 18; private dining room 10
Smoking: No smoking in dining room
Accommodation: 7 en suite
Credit cards:

Small village hotel converted from an Edwardian house (the restaurant is open to non-residents though space is limited). A house speciality is Shropshire 'Hoggit' pie, an ancient recipe using year-old lamb and damsons. Other options might be Mediterranean-style cod or vegetable Kiev.

Directions: Village centre, 0.5 mile off A49 on B4370 (Little Stretton)

CLEOBURY MORTIMER, Redfern Hotel

DY14 8AA
Map 7: SO67
Tel: 01299 270395
Fax: 01299 271011
Chef: Jamie Bailey
Owners: Jon & Lis Redfern
Cost: *Alc* £16.50, fixed-price L £5.55/D £17.75 (5 courses). ☺
H/wine £6.95.
Times: Last L 2.30pm/D 9.15pm
Additional: Bar meals L; Sunday L; Children welcome; dishes
Smoking: No smoking in dining room

Loaves of home-baked bread are put on every table and home-cured hams hang from the beams in the bistro-style, country restaurant. The kitchen deals in no-frills cooking along the lines of Greek-style mushrooms, braised shoulder of lamb and mustard-crusted halibut, followed by cold desserts. Similar food is also available in the coffee shop.

Accommodation: 11 en suite. **Credit cards:**

Directions: Midway on A4117 btw Kidderminster and Ludlow. For Kidderminster leave at M5/J3

DORRINGTON, Country Friends Restaurant

Shrewsbury SY5 7JD
Map 7: SJ40
Tel: 01743 718707
Chef: Charles Whittaker
Owners: Charles & Pauline Whittaker
Cost: Fixed-price L&D £26.
H/wine £10.50
Times: Noon-last L 2pm/7pm-last D 9pm (9.30pm Sat). Closed Sun, Mon, 2 wks beginning July
Additional: Bar food L; Children welcome; dishes
Seats: 45
Smoking: No smoking in dining room
Accommodation: 3 rooms, 1 en suite
Credit cards:

Pauline and Charles Whittaker have clocked up more than 13 years in residence at their seventeenth-century half-timbered house, and they are still driven by enthusiasm. Their formula of a short fixed-price menu priced according to the number of courses still operates in the evening, while lunch is a *carte* of lighter dishes. Customers taking dinner in the pink restaurant overlooking the garden might be treated to starters such as spinach fettucine with smoked salmon, or marinated quail with peanuts, while varied main courses could take in everything from chicken breast with wild mushroom ravioli and Madeira sauce, or fillet steak with boudin blanc and mustard sauce, to a daily fish dish depending on supplies from the market. Rounding things off are desserts such as pear timbale with caramel sauce, and summer pudding with elderflower ice cream; otherwise choose British cheese or Welsh rarebit.

Directions: On A49 in centre of village, 6 miles S of Shrewsbury

LUDLOW, Dinham Hall ❀❀

By The Castle SY8 1EJ
Map 7: SO57
Tel: 01584 876464
Fax: 01584 876019
Chef/Owner: Mr JP Mifsud
Cost: Fixed-price L £10.50/D £27.50
(5 courses). ☺ H/wine £10.50.
Times: 12.30pm-last L 2pm/7pm-last
D 9 pm
Additional: Sunday L; No children
under 12; ❹ dishes.
Seats: 30. Private dining room 24
Smoking: No smoking in dining room
Accommodation: 12 en suite
Credit cards: ▆ ▆ ▆ ▆ ▆ ▆

The setting is a rather grand eighteenth-century mansion set in landscaped lawns and gardens hard by Ludlow's ancient castle. Inside, there's an air of elegance about the place bolstered by smart, efficient and friendly staff. Fixed-price lunches can run to three courses, dinner to five, and the style is very much in the country hotel idiom, with a luxurious undercurrent. Grilled smoked haddock comes on a bed of tomato and basil, pan-fried duck breast is served with a compote of rhubarb and ginger, salmon is wrapped in filo pastry and accompanied by asparagus. To finish, expect concoctions such as hot chocolate pudding with home-made ice cream, cappuccino parfait with coffee sauce, or strawberry and Grand Marnier parfait crème brûlée. Eight house wines top the well-spread list of around 70 bins.

Directions: Town centre, off Market Place, by the Castle

LUDLOW, The Feathers at Ludlow ❀

Impressive seventeenth-century timbered-framed building offering spacious, well appointed accommodation, friendly staff and soundly cooked food. Both carte and fixed-price menu list interesting dishes, perhaps smoked bacon and barley broth, followed by grouper with saffron cream, and apple and pecan nut tart.

Smoking: No smoking in restaurant
Accommodation: 39 en suite.
Credit cards: ▆ ▆ ▆ ▆ ▆ ▆

Bull Ring SY8 1AA
Map 7: SO57
Tel: 01584 875261
Fax: 01584 876030
Chef: Simon Thyer
Owner: Regal Hotel Group plc
Cost: *Alc* £25, fixed-price L £13.50/D
£16.95. ☺ H/wine £9.75.
Times: Last L 2pm/D 9pm
Additional: Bar meals L only; Sunday
L; Children welcome; ❹ dishes

Directions: In centre of Ludlow, which is signposted off A49

LUDLOW,

The Merchant House 🏵🏵🏵

62 Lower Corve Street SY8 1DU
Map 7: SO57
Tel/Fax: 01584 875438
Chef: Shaun Hill
Owners: Shaun & Anja Hill
Cost: Fixed-price L & D £26.
H/wine £12.50
Times: 12.30pm-last L 2pm (Fri-Sat only)/7pm-last D 9pm.
Closed Sun, Mon, 1 wk Xmas, 7-10 days late spring, early summer
Seats: 24
Smoking: No smoking in dining room
Credit cards:

The Merchant House is small, but stylish in its own way: there's a black and white frontage, beams and standing timbers in the restaurant, and a small cosy *olde worlde* lounge that is very traditionally furnished. Here Shaun Hill cooks in an impressive and single-minded manner. His is a simple approach, although a country house feel from his previous life at Gidleigh Park does come through, the food is honest, not messed about, and ingredients are very well chosen and married. The formula is straightforward, menus are fixed-price and daily changing, a choice of four at each course based on whatever fish, meat and vegetable were best that day. From a winter lunch there were parallels to be drawn with Simon Hopkinson (ex Bibendum) and Rick Stein (The Seafood Restaurant) – that the food is the point, not presentation or fripperies. First came a signature dish from Gidleigh days, sautéed scallops with lentil and coriander sauce – first-rate seafood and a sauce that was lightly curried, the fresh tasting coriander contrasting with the earthy lentils. The main course, a great piece of rack of lamb, had 'super flavour and succulent', served with some roughly chopped vegetables (fennel, carrots and green beans) a spot-on lamb jus and a potato and olive cake that worked well with the meat. Pudding was a chocolate pithiviers, the excellent chocolate filling deeply rich and satisfying. Petits fours are a tiny selection but well made, breads are great: a super buttermilk roll, and some good granary with lots of seeds and grain. Anja Hill runs front of house with great aplomb.

Messy wine list, red and white sections but no other order, countries, prices, halves all muddled in together. House wines are £12.50, house Champagne Drappier £22, approx. 12 halves. Some good country wines available for under £20 and some interesting New World – Big House Red, Californian from Ca del Sol offers a big Chateauneuf type wine for £16.50.

Directions: Town centre, next to Unicorn pub

LUDLOW, **Oaks Restaurant** 🏵🏵🏵

Impressive seventeenth-century coaching inn with much original character, a warm, relaxing atmosphere and hosts who play their part with enthusiasm. In the lounge bar Mrs Adams chats with guests, hands out menus and serves canapés while

17 Corve Street SY8 1DA
Map 7: SO57
Tel: 01584 872325
Chef/Owner: Ken Adams
Cost: Fixed-price D £22. ☺
H/wine £10.

Ken Adams slaves over a hot stove. The style is modern, and this translated, one summer evening, into smoked salmon rolled around its mousse with potato and chive salad and a hint of horseradish, all set on finely diced red onions with sushi vinegar and hazelnut oil and topped with salmon eggs; grilled sea bass with scallops with basil sauce was also tried. The centrepiece was a light smoked fillet of Aberdeen Angus, nicely flavoured, on a smooth carrot purée and served with morels and a light port sauce, its counterpart, a sautéed breast of chicken came with St Georges' mushrooms and a contrasting lemon, thyme and garlic butter sauce. To finish, pistachio crème brûlée with smooth vanilla ice cream and a good, well kept British cheese selection, served with walnuts, grapes, celery and walnut bread.

Directions: Town centre, bottom of hill below Feathers Hotel

Times: D only, 7pm – last D 9.30pm. Closed D Mon, 1 wk spring, 1 wk autumn
Additional: No children under 8; 🄳 dishes
Seats: 30. Private dining room 16
Smoking: No smoking in dining room; air conditioning
Credit cards: ▬ ▧

LUDLOW, Overton Grange ❀❀

The wooden pillars supporting the fireplace in the oak-panelled Edwardian dining room reputedly come from Oliver Cromwell's four-poster bed. Apocryphal or not, it's a good story to speculate on before getting down to more serious matters, such as whether to choose the slow-cooked shoulder of Welsh lamb with garden pea risotto and roast carrot sauce, or the roast wild duck with celeriac dauphinoise, button onions, broad beans and poivrade sauce. Pork is organic and comes with cep and potato tartlet. A southern European flavour also adds a distinctive note – fillets of black sea bream are served with traditional caldo verde broth, chorizo and coriander, fish broth with mussels and olive oil. Excellent farmhouse cheeses, mostly local, are listed on a separate menu and served with home-made chutney and treacle bread. The only problem then is to decide between this and puddings such as rich chocolate tart with griottine cherry ice cream. The serious approach to food is reflected in the wine list, which also represents tremendous value.

Directions: On B4361 off A49.

Hereford Road SY8 4AD
Map 7: SO57
Tel: 01584 873500
Fax: 01584 873524
Chef: Adrian Jones
Owner: Grange Hotels Ltd
Cost: Alc £20, fixed-price L £12.50/D £16.50 (3 courses). ☺ H/wine £10.
Times: Noon-last L 2.15pm/7pm-last D 9.15pm
Additional: Sunday L; Bar meals; Children welcome; 🄳 dishes
Seats: 35. Private dining room 100
Smoking: No smoking in the dining room
Accommodation: 16 en suite
Credit cards: ▬ ▧ ▨ ▨ ▣

MARKET DRAYTON, Goldstone Hall ❀❀

Goldstone TF9 2NA
Map 7: SJ63
Tel: 01630 661202
Fax: 01630 661585
Chef: Carl Fitzgerald Bloomer
Owners: J Cushing, H Ward
Cost: Alc £24, fixed-price L £14.50 (3 courses)
Times: Noon-2.30pm/7.30pm-10pm. Closed D Sun
Additional: Sunday L; Children welcome; 🄳 dishes
Seats: 50. Private dining room 20
Smoking: No cigars or pipes
Accommodation: 8 en suite
Credit cards: ▬ ▧ ▨ ▨ ▣ ▣

In 1390 Hugh de Golstan concocted his new English home from a traditional French recipe: take several acres of fresh countryside, add a cellar stocked with fine wines, a well seasoned chef and a four-poster bed and resist every temptation to stir. This time-honoured recipe, according to the current 'squire', guarantees perfect results. Food is a vital ingredient at Goldstone Hall, where the kitchen puts a strong emphasis on quality produce and true flavours. Typical starters could be seared chicken livers with sherry cream sauce and black pudding, or Goldstone gravad lax with coarse dill mustard sauce. Main courses offer more robust fare, with rack of lamb, stuffed with Stilton and rosemary, or whole red mullet baked with Moroccan chermoula marinade. Puddings range from crème brûlée to steamed chocolate pudding. There are regular themed evenings, and the chef also holds master classes, where guests can learn the art (and eat the results) of good cooking.

Directions: From A529, 4 miles S of Market Drayton, follow signs for Goldstone Hall Gardens

MUCH WENLOCK, **Raven Hotel** ❀

30 Barrow Street TF13 6EN
Map 7: SO69
Tel: 01952 727251
Fax: 01952 728416
Chef: Paul Goring
Owner: Raven Hotel (Wenlock) Ltd
Cost: *Alc* £23.
Times: Last L 2pm/D 9.15pm
Closed 25 Dec
Additional: Bar Food L; Sunday L;
❸ dishes
Smoking: No smoking in dining room
Accommodation: 15 en suite
Credit cards:

Characterful former coaching inn with original features, pleasant courtyard, kitchen herb garden, and a determined effort being made to provide good contemporary cooking. Expect collops of monkfish with Thai cabbage salad, hay-baked loin of lamb with black pudding, and bread and butter pudding.

Directions: Town centre

NORTON, **Hundred House Hotel** ❀❀

Bridgnorth Road
Shifnal TF11 9EE
Map 7: SJ70
Tel: 01952 730353
Fax: 01952 730355
Chef: Stuart Phillips
Cost: *Alc* £25. H/wine £10
Times: Noon-last L 2.30pm/6pm-last
D 9.30pm
Additional: Bar food; Sunday L;
Children welcome; ❸ dishes
Seats: 80. Private dining room 35
Smoking: No pipes or cigars; air-conditioning
Accommodation: 10 en suite
Credit cards:

Four members of the Phillips family run this enticingly idiosyncratic Georgian inn. Sylvia Phillips shows green-fingered talent in the enchanting gardens; her expertise also extends to the paintings on the walls, the patchwork and fabrics, and the bunches of dried herbs that add to the beguilingly eccentric charm of the place. Son Stuart heads the team in the kitchen, and the cooking has brasserie overtones with plenty of lively ideas. Menus are interchangeable and you can eat in the bar or restaurant from a repertoire that encompasses everything from unusual soups (such as chicken, chilli and noodle), bruchetta and Caesar salad to roast monkfish with asparagus and a morel risotto and cassoulet of local wild boar. Nursery favourites like lemon meringue pie or treacle tart with custard for dessert. Real ales are tip-top and the wine list has plenty of decent stuff by the glass.

Directions: Midway between Bridgnorth/Telford on A442, 15 mins from M54/J4

Hundred House Hotel

OSWESTRY, **Old Mill Inn**

Converted old mill set in 12 acres within the remote Candy Valley. Home-grown vegetables and herbs feature on the blackboard specials and short carte served throughout the inn. Recommended are duck livers with port wine sauce, herb-crusted rack of lamb, and sticky toffee pudding.

Smoking: No smoking in dining room; air-conditioning
Accommodation: 5 bedrooms
Credit cards: ▬ ▭

Directions: From A5 follow B4579 signed Trefonen; after Ashfield take 1st R towards Llansillin then 1st R again.

Candy Llanforda SY10 9AZ
Map 7: SJ22
Tel: 01691 657058
Chef: David Atkinson
Owners: David & Sharon Atkinson
Cost: *Alc* £11. H/wine £6.95. ☺
Times: Last L 2.30pm/D 9.30pm. Closed 25 Dec D
Additional: Bar meals; Sun L; Children welcome; 🍴 dishes

OSWESTRY, **Wynnstay Hotel**

Church Street SY11 2SZ
Map 7: SJ22
Tel: 01691 655261
Fax: 01691 670606
Chef: Les Simpson
Owner: Mr B Woodward
Cost: *Alc* £20. H/wine £8.25. ☺
Times: D only, 7pm-last D 9.30pm
Additional: Bar food; Sunday L only (noon-2pm); Children welcome; 🍴 dishes
Seats: 40. Private dining room

The Wynnstay was once a well known posting house on the Liverpool to Cardiff route. The building is Georgian in style and boasts its own walled bowling green, as well as a fitness and leisure centre where one can work up an appetite for some Italian cooking with an international twist. Typical starters include beef carpaccio with Parmesan flakes, melon with Parma ham, and Italian bread topped with artichoke hearts, olives, onions and mozzarella. Pasta dishes range from tortellini with butter, sage and Parmesan, to cannelloni filled with spinach and ricotta cheese. Recommended main courses include breast of chicken with pan-fried polenta, basil and tomato sauce, oven-baked trout with almonds and butter, and devilled kidneys with mushrooms and Madeira wine served on a bed of rice. The wine list concentrates on sound, dependable drinking from familiar sources.

Directions: In centre of town, opposite church

SHIFNAL, **Park House Hotel** ❀❀

Created from a pair of seventeenth-century country residences, this sympathetically extended hotel is ever improving. There's also a touch of elegance about the Silvermere Restaurant, with its high ceilings, ornate plasterwork and long windows overlooking the grounds. The kitchen is capable of delivering accomplished dishes with noticeable technical skill and assurance. Witness a recent lunchtime inspection that included a terrine of chicken and hazelnut wrapped in bacon served with a sharp tomato and herb vinaigrette, followed by an accurately poached fillet of plaice filled with a salmon mousseline accompanied by cucumber and dill sauce. Dinner heralds more complex specialities such as braised mini-shoulder of lamb on a bed of creamed turnip and red lentils garnished with onion marmalade, or steamed fillet of sea bass with couscous and a sweet red pepper coulis. Desserts are mostly well-tried offerings like glazed lemon tart and hot banana and syrup sponge pudding.

Directions: From M54/J4 take A464 through Shifnal; hotel is 200 yards after railway bridge

Accommodation: 27 en suite
Credit cards: 🔲 🔲 🔲 🔲 🔲

Park Street TF11 9BA
Map 7: SJ71
Tel: 01952 460128
Fax: 01952 461658
Chef: Graeme Shaw
Owner: MacDonald Hotels plc
Cost: Alc £28, fixed-price L £12.50/D £20.95 (4 courses). ☺ H/wine £9.95.
Times: Noon-last L 2pm/7pm-last D 9.45pm. Closed Sat L
Additional: Bar food; Sunday L; Children welcome; ♦ dishes
Seats: 45; Private dining room to 180
Smoking: No smoking in dining room
Accommodation: 54 en suite
Credit cards: 🔲 🔲 🔲 🔲 🔲 🔲

SHREWSBURY,
Albright Hussey Hotel ❀❀

Ellesmere Road
SY4 3AF
Map 7: SJ41
Tel: 01939 290571/290523
Fax: 01939 291143
Chefs: Martin Galley, Lawrence Otteburn
Owner: Franco Subbiani
Cost: Alc £25, fixed-price L £12.50/D £19.50 (4 courses). ☺ H/wine £9.75.
Times: Noon-last L 2.15pm/7pm-last D 10.15pm

Black swans swim in the moat of this timber-framed Tudor house surrounded by four acres of gardens complete with fountains and specially chosen shrubs. Meals are served in the fine beamed restaurant, where fixed-price menus supplement a *carte* that is in the modern British mould of home-cured carpaccio and avocado with black olive vinaigrette, or flaked duck meat with oranges sandwiched in a crisp potato galette. Main courses are in the same vein: pork fillet wrapped around a piece of asparagus with a nicely spiced pink peppercorn sauce, roast monkfish in bacon with mustard and tarragon sauce, marinated best end of lamb served with a timbale of creamed spinach and a spearmint glaze, and so on. Warm marinated seasonal fruits appear among the sweets, alongside cheeses and home-made pâtisserie. The wines list runs to around 140 bins with a good spread of prices across the range.

Directions: On A528, 2 miles from centre of Shrewsbury

Additional: Sunday L;
No children under 7; ❹ dishes
Seats: 80. Private dining room 50.
Jacket & tie preferred
Smoking: No smoking in dining room
Accommodation: 14 en suite
Credit cards: ▬ ▦ ▦ ▧ ▨ ▧

TELFORD, Holiday Inn ❀

Japanese teppan-yaki cooking is a novel feature of proceedings in Courts Restaurant, where guests prepare their own dishes at the table, on hot stones. Otherwise expect sashimi, sukiyaki and tempura. British menus provide alternatives in the shape of chicken livers with pink peppercorns and Madeira, salmon in shellfish sauce, and tournedos of beef.

Smoking: No-smoking area; air-conditioning
Accommodation: 100 en suite
Credit cards: ▬ ▦ ▦ ▧ ▨ ▧

Directions: M54/J4 (Telford East), follow signs for town centre; then 2nd exit off St Quentin roundabout

St Quentin Gate TF3 4EH
Map 7: SJ60
Tel: 01952 292500
Fax: 01952 291949
Chef: Stephen Poole
Owner: Mr B Gray, Telford Hotels Ltd
Cost: Alc £29.85, fixed-price L
£10.50/D £15.95. ☺
Times: Last L 2.30pm/last D 9.30pm.
Closed L Sat
Additional: Bar food; Sunday L;
Children welcome; ❹ dishes

TELFORD, Madeley Court ❀❀

There is a choice for visitors to this Elizabethan manor house. The main restaurant is in the Great Hall, which is said to date from the thirteenth century, with its lofty ceilings, mural and magnificent fireplace. The alternative is the cosy cellar brasserie, offering a complete contrast in atmosphere and extending the range of the dishes on offer. On one hand, typical choices from the restaurant *carte* are stuffed escalope of venison with almond, thyme and lemon set on a casserole of creamed beetroot, and mixed seafood sausage on a purée of celeriac and parsnip with a saffron and parsley sauce. On the other hand, Expressions Brasserie offers a vegetarian choice, perhaps tomato and Pecorino tartlet, and healthy eating dishes such as wok-fried sirloin of beef seasoned with ginger, lime leaf, garlic and sesame noodles. There is plenty of more robust fare too, including roast rack of pork with baked onion pudding.

Directions: From M4/J4 procede on A442 to Kidderminster. At roundabout, marked by ornamental pit shaft, turn L. Hotel 0.25 mile on L.

TF7 5DW
Map 7: SJ60
Tel: 01952 680068
Fax: 01952 684275
Chef: Rosemary Mclean
Owner: Lyric Hotels
Cost: Alc £25, fixed-price L&D
£14.95. ☺ H/wine £10.50.
Times: Noon-last L 2.30pm/7pm –
last D 9.45pm.
Additional: Bar food; Sunday L;
Children welcome; ❹ dishes
Seats: 57. Private dining room 200
Smoking: No-smoking area, no pipes
or cigars in dining room
Accommodation: 47 en suite
Credit cards: ▬ ▦ ▦ ▧ ▨ ▧

WORFIELD, Old Vicarage Hotel

No rosette award this year as changes in the kitchen occurred as we were going to press. John Williams, who earned the Old Vicarage three AA Rosettes, has left and his place taken by Richard Arnold (ex Lake Hotel, Llangammarch Wells, see entry Wales). However, although we cannot comment on the cooking, we felt the wine list deserved special mention. This is what our wine writer made of it: Adventurous, balanced and democratically priced, this wine list has much to commend it. For once, Bordeaux can be approached with confidence offering ready to drink vintages from quality producers at

Bridgnorth WV15 5JZ
Map 7: SO79
Tel: 01746 716497
Fax: 01746 716552
Chef: Richard Arnold
Owners: P & C Iles
Cost: Fixed-price L £19/D £27.50.
H/wine £13.50
Times: 7pm-last D 8.30pm
Additional: Sunday L (noon-last L
1.45pm); Children welcome;
❹ dishes

Old Vicarage Hotel

Seats: 40. Private dining room 16.
Jacket and tie preferred
Smoking: No smoking
Accommodation: 14 en suite
Credit cards: ▨ ▨ ▨ ▨

exemplary prices. Similar virtues are apparent across the globe with selections displaying verve, imagination and generosity throughout. Not much is above £30, and most less than £20. A welcome instance of being spoilt for choice with little chance of being disappointed.

Directions: From Wolverhampton take A454 Bridgnorth Road; from M54/J4 take A442 towards Kidderminster.

SOMERSET

AXBRIDGE, **Oak House Hotel** ❀

The Square Axbridge BS26 2AP
Map 3: ST45
Tel: 01934 732444
Fax: 01934 733112
Chef: Martin Ball
Owners: Amanda &
Anthony Saint Claire
Cost: *Alc* £15.50. H/wine £6.75. ☺
Times: Noon-last L 2.15pm/7pm-last
D 9.15pm
Additional: Bar food L; Sunday L;
Children welcome; dishes
Smoking: No-smoking area; air-
conditioning
Accommodation: 10 en suite
Credit cards: ▨ ▨ ▨ ▨ ▨

Blackboards advertise a range of bistro-style dishes in this relaxed hotel overlooking the town square. Typical offerings might include sautéed chicken livers en croute with Madeira sauce, fillet of gurnard with basil and garlic, and sliced bananas in hot rum and cream sauce.

Directions: On E side of town square

BATH, **Bath Spa** ❀❀

The magnificent Georgian building and surrounding gardens overlook the city, offer extensive leisure facilities, and surprisingly for a grand hotel, has a welcoming attitude to children that is backed up by nursery facilities. Within, the

Sydney Road BA2 6JF
Map 3: ST76
Tel: 01225 444424
Fax: 01225 444006
Chef: Jonathan Fraser
Owner: Forte Hotels

Vellore Restaurant (the more formal of the hotel's two restaurants), is superb; once a ballroom it has been converted into a splendid restaurant, huge 'but somehow you don't feel overwhelmed'. There's crisp linen, gleaming silver, pretty flowers at each table, a 'switched on' sommelier and 'smiling French and Italian waiters', and the food is good, light and fresh in its approach. A 'great' starter of fresh asparagus and chervil soup was followed by 'a really delicious' tapenade baked chicken breast, basil, linguine, plum tomato and onion confit, whilst a Jamaican banana tart with toffee sauce and rum and raisin ice cream was simply described as 'heaven'.

Directions: From A4 turn L onto A36 Warminster, R at mini roundabout and pass fire station, turn L into Sydney Place

BATH, Cliffe Hotel ❀

A converted nineteenth-century country house with glorious views across the Avon Valley. The restaurant is bright and spacious, while summer meals are possible on the patio outside. Main courses include whole grilled trout with smoked bacon and crème fraîche, and pan-fried fillet of beef with spinach and Stilton.

Accommodation: 11 en suite
Credit cards: ▨▨ ▨▨ ▨▨ ▨▨ ▨

Directions: From A36 take B3108 (Bradford-on-Avon), turn R before railway bridge, follow to Limpley Stoke. Hotel on brow of hill

BATH, Clos du Roy ❀❀

'A delightful little restaurant; close to the theatre; set upstairs with an attractive balustrade overlooking the surrounding shops; decor follows a musical theme with instruments and musical notes adorning the walls.' Thus run the notes of one inspector who also remarked that the restaurant was fully booked on a Monday lunchtime. Phillipe Roy is firmly in control, although cooking less these days, retaining a strong influence over the menus: a fixed-price lunch of two or three courses, pre-theatre, dinner at £16.50 and £19.50, as well as a *carte.* Modern ideas abound. Pan-fried medallions of monkfish tail come with a herb pancake and red grape butter sauce; roast breast of wild goose with its own leg confit and peppercorn sauce; noisettes of English lamb are wrapped in a

Bath Spa

Cost: *Alc* £47, fixed-price D £35. ☺ H/wine £18.50.
Times: 12.30pm-last L 1.30pm/7pm-last D 9.30pm
Additional: Bar meals; Sunday L; Children welcome; ❹ dishes
Seats: 80. Private dining room 20. Jacket & tie preferred
Smoking: No smoking in dining room
Accommodation: 98 en suite
Credit cards: ▨▨ ▨▨ ▨▨ ▨▨ ▨▨ ▨

Crowe Hill Limpley Stoke BA3 6HY
Map 3: ST76
Tel: 01225 723226
Fax: 01225 723871
Chef: Richard Okill
Owners: Richard & Barbara Okill
Cost: *Alc* £19, fixed-price L £15. ☺ H/wine £9.25.
Times: Last L 2pm/D 9.30pm
Additional: Sunday L; Bar meals
Smoking: No smoking in dining room

1 Seven Dials
Saw Close BA1 2EN
Map 3: ST76
Tel: 01225 444450
Fax: 01225 404044
Chefs: David Ollivrin, Phillipe Roy
Owners: Phillipe & Emma Roy
Cost: *Alc* £21, fixed-price L £8.95 (2 courses)/D £19.50 (3 courses). ☺ H/wine £8.95.
Times: Noon-last L 2.30pm/6pm-last D 10.30pm.
Additional: Sunday L; Children welcome; ❹ dishes
Seats: 85. Jacket and tie preferred

Clos du Roy

Smoking: No-smoking area; no pipes and cigars
Credit cards:

paste of carrot and served with a peppermint jus. Amongst the desserts an egg bread and caramelised pear mille-feuille served with honey and ginger sauce catches the eye. The wine list will not break the bank.

Directions: Next to Theatre Royal

BATH, Combe Grove Manor ❀❀

Brassknocker Hill Monkton Combe BA2 7HS
Map 3: ST76
Tel: 01225 834644
Fax: 01255 834961
Chef: Martin John Horsley
Owner: Chia Group
Cost: *Alc* £40, fixed-price L £19.50/D £30 (3 courses). H/wine £14
Times: Noon-last L 2pm/7pm-last D 9.30pm
Additional: Bar food; Sunday L; No children under 7
Seats: 40. Private dining room 18
Smoking: No smoking in dining room
Accommodation: 40 en suite
Credit cards:

After taking in the tennis, jogging trails, pool, gym, aerobics and golf driving range at this extended, eighteenth-century manor-cum-leisure hotel, appetites are bound to be sharpened for a good plate of meat and three veg – transformed in the panoramic Georgian restaurant into pot-roasted fillet of beef with pumpkin mash, roasted shallots, jardinière vegetables and orange and cinnamon jus. Other dishes typical of the complex, sophisticated (and rather effusively described) style are Tatin of fresh scallops placed on buttered baby leeks served with a tomato and saffron nage, crispy skinned sea bass placed on a bean salsa enhanced with a warm gazpacho dressing and roquette pesto, saltimbocca of chicken on glazed Roma tomatoes and basil compote, garlic confit and lobster oil, and bread-and-butter pudding flavoured with Amaretto and served with coffee bean sauce.

Directions: A4 from Bristol to roundabout (Newton St Loe), 2nd exit for Combe Down (5 miles). At Combe Down continue for 1.5 miles, hotel entrance on R

BATH, The Hole in the Wall Restaurant 🏵🏵

16 George Street BA1 2EH
Map 3: ST76
Tel/Fax: 01225 425242
Chef: Eric Lepin
Owners: Chris & Gunna Chown
Cost: Alc £22.50; fixed-price L
£11.50/D £22.50. ☺ H/wine £9.50.
Times: Noon-last L 2pm/6pm-
10.30pm.
Additional: Sunday L;
Children welcome; 🥄 dishes
Seats: 70
Smoking: No-smoking area; air-
conditioning
Credit cards: 🟦 🟥 🟨 🄲

What impresses about this redoubtable restaurant is its heritage, and the way in which its most famous incumbent, George Perry-Smith, played a pivotal role in the development of new British cuisine. Appropriately, a sample of his 1969 menu is on show at the entrance. The scene of the action is an intimate basement room with coir matting on the floors, boldly coloured banquettes, Sussex weave chairs and a fireplace holding centre stage. The menu takes a thoroughly modern view of things and it promises a great deal. Starters could range from warm salad of quail with red onion marmalade and truffle dressing to scallop and lentil soup with coriander, while main courses take in such things as pan-fried red mullet with sauerkraut and a herb nage, noisettes of lamb with ratatouille, fondant potato and rosemary sauce or Hereford duck breast with rösti and a griottine sauce. Desserts are capably prepared offerings such as strawberry gratin with a sabayon and excellent white chocolate ice cream.

Directions: Town centre. George Street is at top end of Milsom Street

BATH, The Moody Goose 🏵🏵🏵 NEW

7A Kingsmead Square BA1 2AB
Map 3: ST76
Tel: 01225 466688
Chef: Stephen Shore
Owners: Stephen & Victoria Shore
Cost: Alc £25, fixed-price L & D
£13.50. ☺ H/wine £10
Times: Noon-2.30pm/6pm-10pm.
Closed Sun
Additional: No children under 7;
🥄 dishes
Seats: 35
Smoking: No-smoking area
Credit cards: 🟦 🟥 🄳 🄲

Going down the steps to this basement restaurant, it is only natural to anticipate a dimly lit cellar wine bar within. Preconceptions lie scattered on the threshold. The clean lines, breezy freshness of the decor and the visible enthusiasm of the staff announce loudly there is a bright new act in town. Stephen and Victoria Shore wanted a slightly off-beat, memorable name, so when they purchased the large pottery goose with a face like thunder that stands in the centre of the restaurant, the Moody Goose was born. The cooking displays vitality, but is elegantly understated, based on mainly local ingredients with fish coming up from Brixham. A terrine of duck confit, Parma ham and carrots for example, had a purposeful sweetness from being cooked in Sauternes, then matched with a spirited sherry vinaigrette. Duck is cooked in various ways – perhaps as a meaty terrine with relish or, as an alternative confit, with caramelised apple, spiced red cabbage and balsamic vinaigrette. Just the right amount of resistance was put up by a braised shank of lamb with rosemary, before it fell off the bone into a serious sauce enriched with red wine, Madeira, onion, wild mushrooms and some fine ratatouille. Pot-roasting is another favoured technique – wild rabbit was beautifully tender, and on a scorching summer's day, worth every bead of sweat! A warm pear and almond clafoutis turned out to be an individual tartlet, served straight from the oven with home-made vanilla ice cream and vanilla sauce. The wine list contains around 50 interesting bins, with a pleasing choice by the glass.

The Moody Goose

Directions:

BATH, No 5 Bistro ❀❀

'A smashing little place to eat', enthused an inspector. Outstanding personal hospitality from owner Charles Home is one of its greatest assets, but everything pleases. The setting is classic bistro – polished elm floors, stripped walls hung with arty posters, big plants dotted around – and the kitchen goes about its work meticulously, offering daily specials in addition to a cosmopolitan *carte*. Lamb rissoles with a garlic and rosemary sauce share the billing with grilled prawns cooked with lemon grass, chilli coriander and balsamic vinegar, fillets of pork are served on sage-flavoured parsnip purée with a caramelised apple and cider sauce, while braised haunch of venison is cooked Burgundian style with baby onions, bacon and mushrooms in a red wine sauce. Desserts such as rice pudding with stewed rhubarb brûlée, or prune and Armagnac tart are alternatives to organically produced ice creams. Imported bottled beers line up alongside the decent selection of wines. Note that you can bring your own (without corkage) on Monday and Tuesday evenings.

Directions: 30 yds from Pulteney Bridge towards Laura Place

5 Argyle Street BA2 4BA
Map 3: ST76
Tel: 01225 444499
Fax: 01225 318668
Chef: Stephen Smith
Owners: Stephen Smith, Charles Home
Cost: *Alc* £21. H/wine £8.50. ☺
Times: Noon-last L 2.30pm/6.30pm-last D 10pm (10.30pm Fri, 11pm Sat). Closed Sun, L Mon, Dec 24-29
Additional: Children welcome, ❀ dishes
Seats: 35
Smoking: No pipes & cigars
Credit cards: ▬ ▬ ▬ ▬ ▢ ▢

BATH, Olive Tree at The Queensberry Hotel ❀❀

The hotel is an attractively restored Bath-stone house dating from 1770, with a ground floor lounge and bar opening out onto the courtyard garden. Downstairs, however, it's another world. The Olive Tree restaurant is done out in contemporary style with menus to match. Chargrilled monkfish with cucumber and mango Thai relish, and Gressingham duck breast with its leg braised with plums and elderberry vinegar

Russel Street BA1 2QF
Map 3: ST76
Tel: 01225 447928
Fax: 01225 446065
Chef: Mathew Prowse
Owners: Stephen & Penny Ross
Cost: *Alc* £27, fixed-price lunch £12.50/D £19. ☺
H/wine £10.50.

Olive Tree at
The Queensberry Hotel

Times: Noon-last L 2pm/7pm-last D
10pm. Closed Sun L, 1wk Xmas
Additional: Children welcome.
🍴 dishes
Seats: 50
Smoking: No smoking in dining room;
air-conditioning
Accommodation: 22 en suite
Credit cards: 🔳 🔳 🔳 🔳

represent the two extremes of the gastronomic spectrum. In between, there are also plenty of Mediterranean ripples: saffron risotto with rocket, grilled courgettes and Parmesan, for example. Our inspector opted for the no-choice fixed-price menu and was impressed with the results. A thin slice of smoked haddock was served on a heap of wilted spinach surrounded by blobs of sun-dried tomato purée, while chargrilled chicken breast was carved over Savoy cabbage with garlic and pancetta. Desserts could include a plum and almond tart bursting with natural flavours. Wines of the month back up the carefully assembled list.

Directions: 100 yds north of Assembly Rooms in Lower Lansdown

BATH, Priory Hotel ❀❀

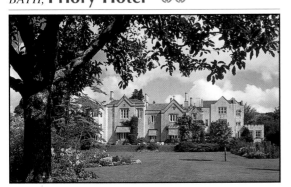

Weston Road BA1 2XT
Map 3: ST76
Tel: 01225 331922
Fax: 01225 448276
Chef: Michael Collom
Cost: *Alc* £18, fixed-price L £14.50/D
£29. H/wine £13
Times: 12.30pm-last L 2pm/7pm-last
D 9.30pm
Additional: Sunday L;
No children under 8; 🍴 dishes
Seats: 75. Private dining room 120
Smoking: No smoking in dining room
Accommodation: 29 en suite
Credit cards: 🔳 🔳 🔳 🔳 🔳 🔳

Gothic windows and open fireplaces testify to the age of this grand Georgian country mansion, set in four acres of grounds, a short drive from the centre of Bath. Formal meals are served in the smart Gothic Room overlooking the gardens, and long-serving chef Michael Collom continues to offer a menu of French dishes that is mostly in the classic style. Inspection began with a pleasing chicken and celeriac soup garnished with shavings of fried celeriac, then moved on to roast loin of lamb, cooked as requested, and served prettily on chargrilled red, yellow and green peppers surrounded by a black olive jus. As a finale, there was a seductive chocolate tart with a thick, rich filling garnished with oranges. Other options on the short *carte* might be game terrine with autumn fruit chutney, roast

Gressingham duck with apple and cinnamon galette, and grilled salmon with lemon and ginger sauce.

Directions: At the top of Park Lane, on W side of Victoria Park, turn L into Weston Rd; 300 yds on L

BATH,
Rajpoot Tandoori Restaurant ❀

4 Argyle Street BA2 4BA
Map 3: ST76
Tel: 01225 466833/464758
Fax: 01225 444527
Chefs: H Zerauguai, M Ali
Owners: Ahmed & Mahmud Chowdhury

Bath's long-standing Indian restaurant, offering a range of tandoori, Mughlai and Bengali dishes in a conventional sub-continent listing. Bhona ghost (tender lamb cooked with tomatoes and herbs) has been well received, with chicken tikka and tandoori paratha showing fair cooking.

Cost: Alc £20, fixed-price L £6.95/D £18.95. ☺ H/wine £8.95.
Times: Last L 2.30pm/ D 11pm. Closed 25-26 Dec
Additional: Children welcome; 🍴 dishes
Seats: 90. Private dining rooms 30 & 14. Jacket and tie preferred
Smoking: Air-conditioning. **Credit cards:** 💳 💳 💳 💳 💳 💳

Directions: Near city centre, by Pulteney Bridge

BATH, ## Royal Crescent ❀❀❀

16 Royal Crescent BA1 2LS
Map 3: ST76
Tel: 01225 823333
Fax: 01225 339401
Chef: Steven Blake
Owner: John Tham
Cost: Alc L £18.50, fixed-price L £14.50 (2 courses)/D £33. H/wine £15.50
Times: 12.30pm-last L 2pm/7pm-last D 9.30pm (Sat 10pm)
Additional: Sunday L; Children welcome; 🍴 dishes
Seats: 60. Private dining room 32
Smoking: No smoking in dining room; air-conditioning
Accommodation: 42 en suite
Credit cards: 💳 💳 💳 💳 💳

The historic, gloriously proportioned Georgian setting demands a degree of formality. Most diners here are residents, which adds an air of discreet privilege to the enjoyment of Steven Blake's Anglo-French cooking. Until now, the Dower House, across a neat, pretty garden behind the main house ('but not good in the rain'), has served as the hotel restaurant. As we went to press a new dining room, situated in the main part of the hotel, was opened, but Steven Blake remains in charge of the brigade. Our inspection meal, however, was taken in the Dower House shortly before this occurred. Typical of Blake's style are tranche of salmon with an oyster and chive cream, guinea fowl with braised red cabbage, red mullet with an olive and thyme butter sauce, and, our inspector's choice, tournedos of beef with creamed spinach and red wine jus. But an oriental touch frequently creeps in, from appetisers of light vegetable samosas, and sea scallop wrapped in filo pastry with sir-fried vegetables, to the spicy flavours layered into a duck breast served on duck confit. Desserts take in caramelised banana, strawberry coulis, coconut, lime, chocolate and natural yogurt, or a simpler raspberry soufflé. A fairly traditional wine list concentrates heavily on French and Italian classics, with some New World selections, and is divided into red and white sections. Some good regional wines can be found for under £20 and the five house wines range from £13-19. A range of over twenty half-bottles offers some interesting options including some from the New World.

Signature dishes: Cannelloni of crab, sautéed langoustines and lemon grass butter; chargrilled asparagus with lardons, scallops and Parmesan shavings; rump of lamb with couscous and niçoise vegetables; venison with spätzli, Cabernet Sauvignon vinegar jus.

Directions: In city centre follow signs to Royal Crescent

BATH, Woods Restaurant

Handy for the Assembly rooms in the heart of Bath, this popular restaurant takes up the ground floors of five Georgian houses. The atmosphere is generally relaxed, and there is a 'fantastic buzz' as people get down to enjoying the excellent Anglo/French dishes featured on the *carte* and set-price menus. Our inspector chose a starter of chicken liver parfait with 'big flavours' and a 'lovely smooth texture', which came with a mixed leaf garnish and pickled vegetables, and followed with a main course of salmon fillet with a sauce of pancetta, thyme and cream. Other main dishes to look out for include breast of chicken stuffed with sun-dried tomato and tapenade mousse and served with a claret jus, and for non-meat eaters, a crispy filo parcel of wild mushrooms and pistachio with port and Stilton sauce. The concise wine list comes with useful tasting notes and includes a number of wines available by the glass.

Directions: Opposite the Assembly Rooms

9-13 Alfred Street BA1 2QX
Map 3: ST76
Tel: 01225 314812
Fax: 01225 443146
Chef: Miss Leigh Davidson
Owners: Mr & Mrs Price
Cost: *Alc* £14-£19, fixed-price L £6/D £10. ☺ H/wine £9.
Times: Noon – last L 3pm/6pm – last D 11pm. Closed D Sun, 25-26 Dec
Additional: Sunday L; Children welcome; ♿ dishes
Seats: 100. Private dining room 40
Smoking: No cigars or pipes
Credit cards:

BECKINGTON, Woolpack Inn

Bath BA3 6SP
Map 3: ST85
Tel: 01373 831244
Fax: 01373 831223
Chef: Mark Nacehia
Owner: Old English Pub Co plc
Cost: *Alc* £25. H/wine £9.95. ☺
Times: Noon-last L 1.50pm/7pm-last D 9.50pm (9pm Sun).
Additional: Bar food; Sunday L; No children under 5; ♿ dishes
Seats: 60. Private dining room 18
Smoking: No-smoking area
Accommodation: 12 en suite
Credit cards:

Occupying a central position in the village, just a short drive from the city of Bath, the Woolpack is a traditional sixteenth-century coaching inn, complete with stone-flagged floors, beams and open fires. The atmosphere is friendly and relaxed and there is a choice of eating places: the bar for light snacks, the Oak Room for more substantial meals, and the Garden Room which leads to an inner courtyard. Menus are innovative with modern English, French and Oriental influences, supported by an interesting list of wines and a selection of real ales. A winter meal began with a good chicken liver pâté, followed by a main course of turbot accompanied by perfectly cooked vegetables. The contrast between sweet, crunchy crumble and the sharpness of apple made for a memorable pudding.

Directions: Village centre. Beckington recently by-passed. On A36 (Bath – Southampton) near junction with A361.

BRENT KNOLL,

Woodlands Hotel

Delightful little family-run hotel whose elevated position promises glorious views of the surrounding countryside with Burnham-on-Sea in the distance. Simplicity is the keynote in the kitchen with honest clear flavours very much in evidence. Modern ideas abound, as in gratin of goat's cheese with smoked ham and apricot coulis, roast sea bass on a bed of spring onion and ginger with saffron broth, or roast rack of English lamb with a crispy Italian herb crust. An autumn inspection dinner kicked off with smoked breast of chicken served with a creamy satay sauce, went on to tender fillet of pork on a bed of creamed leek with a grain mustard sauce, and finished with a sweet, rich nougatine parfait.

Hill Lane TA9 4DF
Map 3: ST35
Tel/Fax: 01278 760232
Chef/Owner: Keith Trevor Gibson
Cost: Alc £25. H/wine £7.95. ☺
Times: D only, 6pm-9.30pm.
Closed Xmas-New Year
Additional: No children under 8; ❸ dishes
Seats: 40. Private dining room 14
Smoking: No smoking in dining room
Accommodation: 6 en suite
Credit cards: ▬ ▤ ▨ ▣

Directions: From A38 take 1st turn L into village, then 5th turn R into Church Lane, 1st L into Hill Lane; hotel on R at 250yds

BRUTON, **Truffles Restaurant**

Deep blues and gold give the restaurant, converted from a seventeenth-century mill cottage, a sophisticated look. It is well matched by a monthly changing menu that is modern British but enthusiastically includes influences from both the Pacific Rim and the Mediterranean. Emphasis is placed on sourcing good ingredients – saddle of local roasted rabbit is served with a wild mushroom and pistachio sauce, medallions of seared Brixham monkfish with avocado pearls and shellfish bisque, while starters might include chicken and herb galantine with a pâté centre wrapped in 'Dorset Parma ham' served with a Cumberland sauce, as well as a salad of spring leaves topped with slices of Somerset smoked chicken and mango strips with Parmesan croûtons. Unusual ice creams include home-made fig with a chocolate shortbread biscuit and creamy lemon sauce. Dorset biscuits and grapes go well with the West Country cheeses.

95 High Street BA10 0AR
Map 3: ST63
Tel/Fax: 01749 812255
Chef: Martin Bottrill
Owners: Denise & Martin Bottrill
Cost: Fixed-price L £13.50/D £21.95. ☺ H/wine £9.50.
Times: D only, 7pm-last D 9pm.
Closed D Sun, Mon, 2wks end of Jan
Additional: Sunday L (Noon-2pm); No children under 5; ❸ dishes
Seats: 20
Smoking: No pipes & cigars
Credit cards: ▬ ▤ ▨

Directions: Bruton centre, at start of one-way system, on L

CASTLE CARY,

The George Hotel ✿

A *fifteenth-century hotel with thatched roof, bay windows and honest home cooking. An inspection meal started with Maston Magna mushrooms stuffed with crab and glazed with cheese sauce. Steak and mushroom pie followed, and for dessert, oranges in Grand Marnier with a light sorbet.*

Market Place BA7 7AH
Map 3: ST72
Tel: 01963 350761
Fax: 01963 350035
Chef: Martin J Barrett
Owners: Sue & Greg Sparkes
Cost: Alc £19. H/wine £8. ☺

The George Hotel

Times: Last L 2pm/last D 9pm
Additional: Sunday L; Bar meals; Children welcome; dishes
Smoking: No cigars or pipes
Accommodation: 15 en suite
Credit cards:

Directions: From A303 take A371 at Wincanton to Castle Cary.
Centre of town

CHEDDAR, Oak House

See Axbridge, Somerset page 486

CHELWOOD, Chelwood House

*New owners at this imposing 300-year-old country house make good
use of fresh local produce in dishes such as venison sausages with
mash and onion gravy, magret of duck with fruits of the forest sauce
and cheese soufflé. Try the crème brûlée for dessert.*

Bristol BS18 4NH
Map 3: ST66
Tel: 01761 490730
Owners: Jean-Jacques Fontaine,
Sue Allen
Telephone for further details

Directions: On A37 between Clutton and Pensford, 200yds
from Chelwood roundabout

DULVERTON, Ashwick House

*You may have to check directions to this pleasant Edwardian
country house set in the wilds of Exmoor, but you won't want to
check out. The cooking majors in simply prepared, fresh quality
ingredients, and home-made soups, bread and locally grown
vegetables have won praise. Good reports too of lamb in red wine
sauce and dark chocolate and Amaretto torte.*

Dulverton TA22 9QD
Map 3: SS92
Tel/Fax: 01398 323868
Chef/Owner: RA Sherwood
Cost: Fixed-price L £12.75/D £22
(5-courses). ☺ H/wine £8.
Times: D only, 7.15pm- 8.30pm

Additional: Sunday L (12.30pm-1.45pm); No children under 8;
 dishes
Smoking: No smoking in dining room
Accommodation: 6 en suite
Credit cards: None

Directions: From M5/J27 follow signs to Dulverton, then take
B3223 Lynton road and turn L after second cattle grid

DUNSTER, **Exmoor House Hotel**

12 West Street TA24 6SN
Map 3: SS94
Tel: 01643 821268
Fax: 01643 821267
Chef: Karan Howell
Owner: David & Karan Howell
Cost: Fixed-price D £24.50 (5 courses). ☺ H/wine £7.95.
Times: Last L 2pm/last D 8pm. Closed D Sun, Mon
Additional: Bar food; Sunday L; No children under 13; ✿ dishes
Smoking: No smoking establishment
Accommodation: 6 en suite
Credit cards: 💳 💳 💳 💳 💳

The choice may be limited but is compensated by excellent ingredients, sound cooking skills and flair. Carrot and orange soup might be followed by crevettes with garlic mayonnaise, rich beef and kidney ragout, and tarte Tatin with cinnamon ice cream. Long Clawston Stilton is served with herb scones.

Directions: To Dunster on A396, off High Street, 75yds from church

EXEBRIDGE, **Anchor Inn Hotel**

On late summer evenings, guests at this seventeenth-century coaching inn on the banks of the river Exe can watch the salmon as they battle their way upstream. Within, the Stable Restaurant offers simple, traditional English cooking, dishes such as pan-fried fillet of local trout with toasted almonds, and Scotch sirloin steak topped with Stilton.

Smoking: No-smoking area; no pipes and cigars
Accommodation: 8 en suite. **Credit cards:** 💳 💳 💳

Directions: M5/J27, through Tiverton to Exebridge

Dulverton TA22 9AZ
Map 3: SS92
Tel: 01398 323433
Fax: 01398 323808
Chef: Stephen Richards
Owners: Mr & Mrs J Phripp
Cost: Fixed-price D £22 (5 courses). ☺ H/wine £7.95.
Times: Last L 2pm/D 9pm
Additional: Bar food; Sunday L; Children welcome; ✿ dishes

EXFORD, **Crown Hotel**

Park Street TA24 7PP
Map 3: SS83
Tel: 01643 831554/5
Fax: 01643 831665
Chef: Andrew Dixon
Owners: Michael Bradley, John Atkin

Every village should have a place like the Crown, although its unique style is hard to define. Essentially a smart country hotel in character, with a formal evening restaurant, there's also the

adjoining village pub where there's real ale and an extensive blackboard menu for both lunch and dinner. Andrew Dixon presides over both sides of this operation with imaginative style and not inconsiderable skills, producing balanced and appealing menus. A March lunch in the bar comprised a fresh salmon fish cake with ginger and spring onion, chicken breast with mushroom risotto, and crème brûlée with a wonderful paper-thin biscuit and a properly crunchy top. Dinner in the restaurant of, say, tortellini of foie gras with mustard celeriac and a wild mushroom cream, pan-fried fillet of sea bass on an avocado salsa and an olive oil dressing, and a red fruit soup with champagne, reveals a chef well versed in the modern idiom.

Cost: Alc £35, fixed-price D £22. ☺
H/wine £9.90.
Times: Noon-last L 2pm (bar only)/7pm-last D 9.30pm (restaurant)
Additional: Bar food; Sunday L; Children welcome; ♨ dishes.
Seats: 36. Private dining room 18
Smoking: No pipes or cigars in dining room
Accommodation: 17 en suite
Credit cards: ▬ ▦ ▧ ▩ 🄵

Directions: Village centre facing the green

FARRINGTON GURNEY,
Country Ways Hotel ❀

Marsh Lane BS18 5TT
Map 3: ST75
Tel: 01761 452449
Fax: 01761 452706
Chef/Owner: Janet Richards
Cost: Alc £23. H/wine £8.50. ☺
Times: D only, 7pm-8.45pm
Closed Sat, Sun
Additional: ♨ dishes

Dating back nearly 300 years, this attractive, creeper-clad hotel is personally-run by enthusiastic owners. Freshly prepared food is served in the split-level dining room. The evening carte may offer carrot and coriander soup, John Dory with tomato and herb sauce, and summer pudding with red berry coulis.

Smoking: No smoking in dining room
Accommodation: 6 en suite. **Credit cards:** ▬ ▦

Directions: From village take A362 to Midsomer Norton, then 1st R into Marsh Lane. Hotel next to Farrington Golf Club

FROME, The Talbot Inn ❀

Mells BA11 3PN
Map 3: ST74
Tel: 01373 812254
Fax: 01373 813599
Chef: Mark Jones
Owner: Roger Elliot
Cost: Alc £16. H/wine £7.25. ☺
Times: Last L 1.45pm/last D 9.45pm
Additional: Sunday L; Bar meals; Children welcome; ♨ dishes
Smoking: No-smoking area

The home of the nursery rhyme character 'Little Jack Horner', this fifteenth-century coaching inn is set in lovely Mendip countryside. The beamed restaurant is hung with hops and furnished with stripped pews and an assortment of tables. Sound cooking takes in the likes of chicken liver pâté and individual game pies.

Accommodation: 7 en suite. **Credit cards:** ▬ ▧ ▩ 🄿 🄵

Directions: From M5/J23, follow Wells & Shepton Mallet towards Frome. Before Frome turn L to Mells.

HINTON CHARTERHOUSE,
Homewood Park ❀❀❀❀

Bath BA3 6BB
Map 3: ST75
Tel: 01225 723731
Fax: 01225 723820
Chef: Gary Jones
Owners: Gueuning-Fentum family
Cost: Alc £45, fixed-price L £20.
H/wine £14
Times: Noon-last L 1.30pm/7pm-last D 9.30pm
Additional: Bar food; Sunday L; Children welcome; ♨ dishes
Seats: 50. Private dining room 30

Modern, stylish presentation is the order of the day at this elegant yet unstuffy country house hotel. Gary Jones has thoroughly established his own style of imaginative cooking with the emphasis on the quality of ingredients, rejecting unnecessary fuss and clutter. Thus, breast of Trelough duck is perfectly matched with celeriac and Calvados sauce, and Cornish turbot needs nothing more than to be simply poached in a saffron and garlic bouillon. A selection of doll's house canapés – a tiny chicken satay, half a quail's egg on a croûton with horseradish, and a smooth salmon mousse also on a croûton – is served on a plate decorated with natural green

Homewood Park

Smoking: No smoking in dining room
Accommodation: 19 en suite
Credit cards: ▆ ▆ ▆ ▆ ▆ ▆

leaves. Freshly baked breads are a particular pleasure; try the walnut and the crusty saffron rolls. One starter, ravioli lined with spinach, filled with Parmesan risotto and a soft, free-range egg, surrounded by a smooth and fine bread sauce laced with pesto, was described as 'memorable'. That same meal moved on to a civet of sea fish of tremendous quality and clear flavours. Other fine main courses have included braised pig's trotter stuffed with sweetbreads and black pudding with garlic mashed potato, spring greens, parsley and caper cooking juices – visually stunning, and delicately prepared – and chump of West Country lamb served on a bed of creamed young broad beans flavoured with smoke-house bacon, garden herbs, salsify and rosemary essence. Highlights of another meal were an amuse-bouche of roasted scallop on mashed potato defined by a thin coating of spinach, a 'brilliant' confit of foie gras sliced onto brioche with well flavoured aspic jelly flavoured with bay leaf, tiny fried fillets of sea bass with crisp skin, roasted fennel and tomato – 'cracklingly fresh fish' in a dish that was very much French classical in feel but done with a light touch, and a spot-on mille-feuille of strawberries with a subtle rosemary ice cream. Opinions have been divided on other puddings, but a chocolate and banana 'moon' (sponge, banana mousse, light milk and dark bitter chocolate sauces, white chocolate sorbet) certainly zapped the eye with an appearance 'like something from outer space', and the recipient fully appreciated a witty chestnut macaroon and vanilla ice cream 'Sous Bois'. Tiramisu is made with mascarpone, Tia Maria and a strongly flavoured espresso sauce.

A competent wine list offers good names in France, although both red Bordeaux and Burgundy tend to the youthful. There are representatives from all the usual areas with some of the best value to be found in South Africa.

Speciality dishes: Roast chump of West country lamb with broad beans and bacon; tartare of lightly curried tuna with yoghurt, mango and cucumber; squab pigeon roasted with wild mushrooms and a red wine jus; hot chocolate and almond soufflé 'pudding' with frangelico ice cream

Directions: 5 miles south-east of Bath off A36, turning marked Sharpstone

HOLFORD, Combe House Hotel

Deep in the heart of the Quantock Hills, this charming seventeenth-century house enjoys a peaceful setting in the beautiful surroundings of Butterfly Combe. A short, simple menu with an emphasis on fresh

Nr Bridgwater TA5 1RZ
Map 3: ST14
Tel/ Fax: 01278 741382
Chef: Lynn Gardner
Owner: Richard Bjergfelt

ingredients is served in the beamed restaurant. Look out for hearty home-made soups and delicious fruit pies with clotted cream.

Accommodation: 19 en suite
Credit cards:

Directions: M5/J24 (A39 Bridgwater) towards Minehead. Turn L up lane between Holford Garage and Plough Inn

Cost: Fixed-price D £17.75. ☺
Times: 7.30pm-last D 8.30pm
Additional: Bar meals L only (noon-2pm); Children welcome; ♨ dishes
Smoking: No smoking in dining room

HUNSTRETE,

Hunstrete House Hotel ❀❀❀

Chelwood BS18 4NS
Map 3: ST66
Tel: 01761 490490
Fax: 01761 490732
Chef: Clive Dixon
Owners: Mr & Mrs Fentum
Times: Noon-last L 2pm/7pm-last D 9.30pm
Additional: Bar meals; Sunday L; Children welcome; ♨ dishes
Seats: 70.
Private dining room 30 + 18
Smoking: No smoking in dining room
Accommodation: 23 en suite
Credit cards:

Hunstrete is the epitome of gentrified Englishness: the house itself – an eighteenth-century country residence – is set in 92 acres of deer park and woodland on the fringes of the Mendip Hills. This classical backdrop is mirrored by the interior, which is lavishly furnished with antiques, original paintings and fine porcelain. The heart of the place is its dining room which opens onto an attractive courtyard for summer evenings. The hotel changed ownership in March 1997 and it is also all-change in the kitchen. Clive Dixon (ex-Lords of the Manor, Upper Slaughter, see entry), moved here with his entire brigade and brought with him a prodigious talent for powerful modern cooking. This is food that is capable of hitting the taste buds head-on. Those familiar with Dixon's style will pick up many echoes on his current menu: the potato and chorizo salad served with seared scallops, the home-salted cod, here paired with Indian spiced sweetbreads, jus of Sauternes and coriander, and that fondness for foie gras, which appears in a soup with lentils and truffles, and as a sauce for blade of Aberdeenshire beef on buttered cabbage with crisp potatoes. An inspection visit a few weeks after the new team had settled in proved that the set-up had quickly found its feet. An appetiser of fish soup with plenty of depth was fine, if a little gimmicky, but the kitchen moved into its stride for a ravioli of langoustines with a langoustine dressing and a purée of lentils that provided plenty of earthy contrast to the crustacean delicacy. Breast of 'kindly reared' Trelough duck from Herefordshire was cooked daringly pink with a good crisp skin, while the accompanying tian of potato and confit and the sauce of honey and vanilla displayed skill and invention aplenty. The finale was another Dixon signature dish: a near-perfect fine apple tart with a gloriously unctuous caramel sauce and a sultana and Calvados ice cream. The well-annotated wine list matches the food admirably.

Directions: On A368 – 8 miles from Bath

ILCHESTER, Ilchester Arms ✿

Eighteenth-century creeper-clad inn dominating the village square. Stone-flagged floors and open fires characterise the cosy bars and separate dining room. An extensive evening carte, enhanced by daily blackboard specials, may list freshly prepared dishes such as Stilton and broccoli soup and herb-crusted rack of lamb with rosemary jus.

Accommodation: 8 en suite
Credit cards: ▆▆ ▆▆ ▆▆

Directions: just off A30 in village centre

The Square BA22 8LN
Map 3: ST52
Tel: 01935 840220
Fax: 01935 841353
Chef: Bill Austin
Owner: T & MC Finlay
Cost: *Alc* £22.50. H/wine £8.75
Times: L from noon/D 7pm-10pm
Additional: Sunday L; Bar meals;
Children welcome; ✿ dishes
Smoking: No pipes or cigars

MINEHEAD, Periton Park Hotel ✿✿

Built as a gentleman's country residence in 1875, Periton Park stands in its own wooded grounds high on the northern edge of Exmoor. Caring owners Richard and Angela Hunt have managed to ensure that up-to-the-minute facilities like a meeting room and helipad don't impinge on the mood of civilised tranquillity that is such a feature of the place. Menus change with the seasons, and the kitchen makes a laudable effort to support local producers. Exmoor goat's cheese is rolled in bread crumbs, roasted and served on salad leaves with hazelnut vinaigrette, while slices of venison are fried in butter and presented with a cranberry sauce. Other typical dishes might include spiced chicken liver salad, pan-fried halibut with a peppered crust and a warm lime and coriander vinaigrette, and Gressingham duck with apple and Stilton sauce. To finish, cinnamon and apple tart has passed with flying colours. Look for the house whites from the local Bagborough vineyard on the impressive list.

Middlecombe TA24 8SW
Map 3: SS94
Tel/Fax: 01643 706885
Chef: Angela Hunt
Owners: Richard & Angela Hunt
Cost: Fixed-price D £21.50. ☺
H/wine £8.95.
Times: D only, 7pm-last D 9pm.
Closed Jan
Additional: No children under 12;
✿ dishes
Seats: 24. Private dining room 16
Smoking: No smoking in dining room
Accommodation: 8 en suite
Credit cards: ▆▆ ▆▆ ▆▆ ▆▆ ▆

Directions: Off A39 signposted
Porlock & Lynmouth. Hotel about
1 mile on left

MONTACUTE, Kings Arms Hotel ✿✿

It's easy to forget about the rest of the world in front of a roaring log fire in this sixteenth-century inn, in a perfect picture book village. Especially when enjoying a menu that offers smoked halibut with warm dill sauce and individual beef Wellington with truffle sauce. A touch of luxury comes in other dishes, such as a trio of raviolis (lobster, oysters and langoustines), served with a caviar sauce, but there is also deep-fried cod fillet in a beer batter with gherkin and caper butter nage, and roasted noisettes of lamb loin with braised Savoy cabbage and redcurrant sauce to keep the balance.

Bishopstow TA15 6UU
Map 3: ST41
Tel: 01935 822513
Fax: 01935 826549
Chef: Mark Lysandrou
Owners: Karen & Jonathan Arthur
Cost: Fixed-price L £9.50 (2
courses)/D £19.50. ☺ H/wine £10.
Times: Noon-last L 2pm/7pm-last D
9pm. Closed D Sun
Additional: Bar food; Sunday L;
Children welcome; ✿ dishes

There is also a daily fish dish. As well as the more formal Abbey restaurant, the Pickwick Bar serves a good range of food that includes grilled pork chop with apple and sage sauce, fish pie topped with a cheese and herb breadcrumb crust and curry with poppadums and tit-bits.

Directions: Take A3088 roundabout off A303; inn is in village centre, next to church

Seats: 60. Private dining room 16
Smoking: No smoking in dining room
Accommodation: 15 en suite
Credit cards: ▆▆ ▆▆ ▆▆

NAILSEA, **Sweet Bartley's Bistro**

2 King's Hill BS19 2AU
Map 3: ST47
Tel: 01275 858348
Chef: Paul Baker
Owner: Gillian Howard
Cost: Fixed-price D £12.50. ☺
H/wine £7.25.
Times: D only, 6.30pm-last D 10.30pm. Closed D Sun, Mon, seasonal holidays
Additional: Sunday L (11.30am-3pm); Children welcome; ♨ dishes
Smoking: No-smoking area
Credit cards: ▆▆ ▆▆ ▆▆

There's been a change of name and a bright new look at the former Howard's Bistro. Two small rooms provide a cosy setting with gold cloths, candles and flowers, and the blackboard menu includes fillet of salmon with a peppercorn crust and vermouth sauce, and chicken breast with asparagus cream sauce.

Directions: In old village near West End shopping precinct

NUNNEY, **George at Nunney**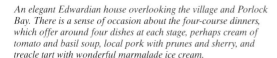

11 Church Street BA11 4LW
Map 3: ST74
Tel: 01373 836458
Fax: 01373 836565
Chef: Caroline Filder
Owners: David & Marjorie Page
Cost: *Alc* £18, Fixed-price L £5 (1 course). ☺ H/wine £7.
Times: Last L 2pm/last D 9.30pm
Additional: Bar food; Sunday L; No children under 14; ♨ dishes

Seventeenth-century coaching inn directly opposite the ruins of Nunney's medieval castle. As well as commendable bar meals, the kitchen offers restaurant food with plenty of imaginative touches. Chicken and coriander consommé, fillet steak topped with mozzarella and served with port sauce, and grilled swordfish piri-piri are typical offerings.

Accommodation: 9 en suite. **Credit cards:** ▆▆ ▆▆ ▆▆ ▆

Directions: Take A361 Frome to Shepton Mallet road and turn off in village centre, opposite medieval castle

PORLOCK, **Oaks Hotel** ✿

Doverhaye TA24 8ES
Map 3: SS84
Tel/Fax: 01643 862265
Chef: Anne Riley
Owners: Tim & Anne Riley
Cost: Fixed-price D £24. ☺ H/wine £9.50.
Times: D only, 7pm-8.30pm.
Additional: Bar meals L
Smoking: No smoking in dining room

An elegant Edwardian house overlooking the village and Porlock Bay. There is a sense of occasion about the four-course dinners, which offer around four dishes at each stage, perhaps cream of tomato and basil soup, local pork with prunes and sherry, and treacle tart with wonderful marmalade ice cream.

Accommodation: 9 en suite. **Credit cards:** ▆▆ ▆▆ ▆▆ ▆

Directions: At bottom of Dunstersteepe Road, on L, on entering Porlock from Minehead

SHEPTON MALLET,
Bowlish House

The pale yellow and white dining-room of this imposing
eighteenth- century house is just the place to wind down at the
end of a hectic week. The modern British menu has choices to
suit all tastes, not forgetting vegetarians. The food is
beautifully presented, from the tiny canapé of prosciutto,
Parmesan and lamb's lettuce offered at the beginning of the
meal to the home-made petit fours served with coffee.
Ingredients are impeccable – duck breast with strawberry and
pink peppercorn sauce, baked cod fillet with Thai spiced sauce,
wild mushroom soufflé glazed with garlic cream and toasted
goat's cheese with salad leaves, herbs and walnut oil were all
appreciated to the full on our inspection visit. Desserts,
including a tart lemon semi-freddo, and 'yummy' orange cream
with caramelised oranges, were all up to the same high
standard as the rest of the meal. The wine list is an extensive,
award-winning selection that includes a lovely Cloudy Bay
from New Zealand and the excellent Château Musar from the
Lebanon.

Bowlish BA4 5JD
Map 3: ST64
Tel/Fax: 01749 342022
Chef: Linda Morley
Owners: Linda & Bob Morley
Cost: Fixed-price D £22.50 (3
courses). H/wine £9.45.
Times: D only, 7pm-9.30pm.
Closed 1 wk winter, 1 wk spring
Additional: Sunday L (1st Sun of
month); Children welcome; ⬤ dishes.
Smoking: No smoking in dining room
Accommodation: 3 en suite
Credit cards: ▬ ▨ ▨

Directions: 0.25 mile from town centre on A371 Wells road

SHEPTON MALLET,
Brottens Lodge ⬤

*A great little restaurant with a couple of rooms for overnight guests.
Decent country house cooking is served in the charming dining
room. Typical main courses include plaited trout fillets marinated in
orange and lemon juice, and pork escalopes with Dolcelatte cheese,
fresh asparagus and Marsala sauce.*

Seats: 36. Private dining room 8
Smoking: No cigars or pipes
Accommodation: 3 en suite
Credit cards:

Doulting BA4 4RB
Map 3: ST64
Tel: 01749 880352
Fax: 01749 880601
Chef: Santa Checkley
Owners: Roger & Santa Checkley
Cost: Alc £21, fixed-price D £16.50.
☺ H/wine £8.50.
Times: L by arrangement/7pm – last D
9.30pm. Closed Sun, Mon
Additional: Children welcome;
⬤ dishes

Directions: From Frome take A361 (Shepton Mallet). Turn L
after Abby Narn pub – hotel signposted

SHEPTON MALLET,
Charlton House Hotel ⬤⬤⬤

This is country living made real – literally a showcase of classic,
rich, romantic English style, designed by a company that has
stamped its discreet little tree logo on bags hanging from
fashionable international shoulders. The seventeenth-century
house (owned by the founders of the Mulberry Design
Company) has been decorated using the Mulberry Home
Collection of fabrics, furnishings, china and glassware. Chef
Trevor Brooks, however, goes for a more modern look in The
Mulberry Restaurant – although extra vegetables and potatoes
can be ordered on a concession to appetites enlarged by
country air. As well as a seasonal *carte*, there is a daily
changing set lunch and dinner menu, and although the choice
is not extensive, it is clearly described and sensibly constructed.
Fashionable ingredients play their part in crab cake with

Charlton Road BA4 4PR
Map 3: ST64
Tel: 01749 342008
Fax: 01749 346362
Chef: Trevor Brooks
Owners: Mr & Mrs Roger Saul
Cost: Alc £34, fixed-price L £18.50/D
£28.50. H/wine £12.50
Times: 12.30pm-last L 2pm/7.30pm-
last D 9.30pm
Additional: Bar meals; Sunday L;
No children under 7; ⬤ dishes
Seats: 60. Private dining room 35
Smoking: No smoking in dining room
Accommodation: 17 en suite
Credit cards: ▬ ▨ ▨ ▧ ▨ ▨

roasted tomato couscous, mango and onion salsa and langoustine oil, for example, as do fashionable techniques in the likes of terrine of duck confit with wood-oven roasted peppers, artichoke heart and salami. A first course of chicken liver parfait packed a punch with great, smooth consistency and a pungent slice of truffle. Good Scottish turbot made a fine main course, with plump, vibrant mussels and asparagus, served in a mussel, dill, crème fraîche and lemon juice broth that just hit the right note. Tender and perfectly cooked venison saddle with port and peppercorn sauce, figs and celeriac mash followed, and a robust sausage made from the leg added extra muscle to another main course of guinea fowl with crisp Savoy cabbage and coriander-spiced lentils.

Signature dishes: Rack of spring lamb with aubergine galette, tomato confit and a thyme jus; wild salmon with Cajun spices, wasabi butter and oriental rice pilaff; carpaccio of venison with a tempura of wild mushrooms; hot apple charlotte with cinnamon ice cream.

Directions: M4/J 17, follow A350 S. At Trowbridge join A361. Hotel is located 1 mile before Shepton Mallet on L

SHEPTON MALLET,

Shrubbery Hotel

Commercial Road BA4 5BU
Map 3: ST64
Tel: 01749 346671
Fax: 01749 346581
Chefs: Christopher West, Rachel Harris
Owner: Christopher West
Cost: *Alc* £20, fixed-price L £13.95/D £14.95. ☺ H/wine £8.05.
Times: Last L 2pm/last D 9pm. Closed D Sun
Additional: Bar meals; Sunday L; Children welcome; 🍴 dishes
Smoking: No smoking in dining room
Accommodation: 7 en suite
Credit cards: ▆▆ ▆▆ ▆▆ ▆▆ ▆▆ ▆▆

Once the home of an eighteenth-century wool merchant, now a 'smashing little hotel' with elegant decor and great service. An excellent gratin of mussels was the highlight of one inspection; other choices are roast duck breast glazed with marmalade and served with plum confit, supreme of chicken with watercress and Vermouth sauce.

Directions: Situated on main A361 through town, near police station

SHIPHAM,

Daneswood House Hotel

David and Elise Hodges have been at the helm of this hospitable Edwardian house (originally a homeopathic health hydro) for more than two decades, and their personable presence continues to enliven proceedings. The views over the Severn Estuary towards Bristol and Wales are as breathtaking as ever. The kitchen is solidly on course with the cooking built

Chuck Hill Winscombe BS25 1RD
Map 3: ST45
Tel: 01934 843145
Fax: 01934 843824
Chefs: Ian White & Elise Hodges
Owners: Mr & Mrs Hodges
Cost: Fixed-price D £23.95 (3 courses). ☺ H/wine £9.95.

Daneswood House Hotel

Times: Noon-last L 2pm/7pm-last D
9.30pm. Closed L Sat, Dec 26-Jan 4
Additional: Sunday L;
Children welcome; 😊 dishes
Seats: 50. Private dining room 8-30.
Jacket and tie preferred
Smoking: No smoking in dining room
Accommodation: 12 en suite
Credit cards: 🔲 🔲 🔲 🔲 🔲 🔲

around a daily fixed-price menu of two or three courses along the lines of thinly sliced salmon with a butter sauce zinged with fresh lime juice, rack of lamb, cooked pink, and served on a bed of garlicky Puy lentils, and a first rate bread-and-butter pudding made with brioche and accompanied by a rich custard topped with an apricot glaze. Home-made bread rolls and petits fours are also sound. The wine list is impressive for its content and presentation.

Directions: On A38 Bristol/Bridgwater, just outside the village

SIMONSBATH,
Simonsbath House Hotel ❀

Minehead TA24 7SH
Map 3: SS73
Tel: 01643 831259
Fax: 01643 831557
Chef: Sue Burns
Owners: Mike & Sue Burns
Cost: Fixed-price D £22.50 (5 courses). ☺ H/wine £8.25.
Times: D only, 7pm-8.30pm.
Closed Dec-Jan
Additional: No children under 10

Dating from 1654, this was the first house to be built in the forest of Exmoor. The dining room is elegant in cool green, the tables laid with bone china and crystal. Imaginative dishes are prepared from fresh local ingredients, including deep fried Somerset Brie and trout with lemon and herbs.

Smoking: No smoking in dining room
Accommodation: 7 en suite
Credit cards: 🔲 🔲 🔲 🔲 🔲 🔲

Directions: Situated on B3223 in the village

STON EASTON,
Ston Easton Park ❀❀❀

Bath BA3 4DF
Map 3: ST65
Tel: 01761 241631
Fax: 01761 241377
Chef: Mark Harrington
Owner: Peter & Christine Smedley
Cost: Alc £39.50, fixed-price L £26 (3 courses)/D £39.50 (4 courses).
H/wine £16.50
Times: 12.30pm-last L 2pm/7.30pm-last D 9.30pm
Additional: Sunday L; Bar meals L;
No children under 8; 😊 dishes
Seats: 45. Private dining room 26.
Jacket and tie preferred
Smoking: No smoking in dining room

'Grand' is the word that springs to mind when describing this dramatic Palladian mansion and its wondrous classical parkland laid out by Humphrey Repton. Whether you are relaxing in the saloon, taking coffee by the fire in the library, or enjoying dinner in the main dining room, all around are exceptional architectural features and fine furnishings. Peter and Christine Smedley own and run the place as their special corner of gentrified England, while chef Mark Harrington does the business in the kitchen. Canapés (perhaps a tiny chorizo tartlet, angels on horseback and a Stilton palmier) set the tone, while petits fours and pâtisserie emphasise the serious approach to things. In between, the kitchen deploys home-grown and local produce with real confidence. The fixed-price menu might begin with something as exquisitely simple as

Ston Easton Park

Accommodation: 21 en suite
Credit cards:

vegetable broth delicately tinged with tarragon, or something as overtly luxurious as roulade of foie gras with Sauternes jelly and brioche. Fish comes next (perhaps fillet of red mullet with red pesto and tapenade), followed by a handful of main courses ranging from ragout of seafood (although this was paired with a rather thin and unconvincing lemon butter sauce at inspection), roast rump of Welsh lamb with chargrilled vegetables and basil jus, or saddle of wild rabbit roasted in a coat of Parma ham. Desserts are out of the top drawer – first-rate lemon and raspberry soufflé proved its worth in terms of featherlight texture and clean flavours; alternatively, you might pick iced mascarpone cheese torte with warm poached strawberries and passionfruit coulis. The seriously endowed, aristocratic wine list makes for great reading, if you allow time to peruse its pages; expect everything from keenly priced house wines by the glass to top-class vintages, including a fair contingent from the New World.

Directions: On A37 from Bristol to Shepton Mallet, about 6 miles from Wells.

TAUNTON, Castle Hotel ❀❀❀❀

Castle Green TA1 1NF
Map 3: ST22
Tel: 01823 272671
Fax: 01823 336066
Chef: Phil Vickery
Owners: The Chapman family
Cost: Fixed-price D from £23.
H/wine £11.25
Times: 12.30pm-last L
2.30pm/7.30pm-last D 9pm
Additional: Sunday L;
Children welcome; ❹ dishes
Seats: 60. Private dining room 24.
Jacket and tie preferred
Smoking: No smoking in dining room
Accommodation: 36 en suite
Credit cards:

The mature, wisteria-clad façade makes an awe-inspiring first impression, especially when in full bloom. There is an immediate sense of style throughout the lavishly decorated interior, full of intimate little corners in which to give the *carte* the serious study it warrants. Phil Vickery is justly lauded for menus that prove imagination is far from lacking in the British kitchen, should anyone still doubt it. Local ingredients and suppliers are given due credit, and most produce derives from a carefully sourced network of regional suppliers; Mrs Montgomery's renowned Cheddar, for instance, comes straight from the farm. At his best, Vickery cooks with impressive subtlety and accuracy – pan-fried sea trout with saffron pasta ribbons, leaf spinach and chive cream was the highlight of an inspection meal, along with a selection of rhubarb desserts that restored all faith in this much maligned and misused garden perennial (smooth sorbet in a tiny brandysnap tuile, a 'quite divine' rhubarb crumble in a tiny, very crisp, very thin pastry shell, rhubarb parfait and the poached fruit itself). Saffron is a favourite spice, adding colour and aroma to a glazed crab and tomato tart, the mayonnaise that accompanies deep-fried sole, and the syrup that cuts a vanilla blancmange with shortbread, as well as the couscous alongside a first course of steamed lobster and crab sausage with roasted artichokes. If there is any criticism to be made, it is that at times there is an overpowering intensity of flavour. In a first course of smoked chicken stock with plum tomatoes, fennel and basil oil, the base was full-flavoured to the point of overload, the thin layer of basil oil floating on the top adding little to the dish, with the fennel undetectable amongst strips of underripe tomato. Nonetheless, this is cooking of considerable quality, whether sampled from the more elaborate of the two set menus, or from the less inexpensive one which includes 'simpler' dishes such as chicken liver parfait with salad leaves and brioche toast, or roast fillet of salmon with braised aubergines, new potatoes and rocket. The dining room is peaceful and pretty in pink and eau-de-nil, with overhead chandeliers and paintings and prints by contemporary artists.

A lengthy wine list but not daunting. Short selection at the beginning presents a selection of 20 under £20, there are some 30 half-bottles, and the main list offers some well priced drinking with a huge choice under £25. Try a unique white, Ch Bouscasse, a Pacherenc sec from Brumont at £21.25. Ch de Sours Rosé is good at £14.30, or Le Volte, Tenuta del Ornellaia, an excellent Bordeaux-style red at £21.50.

Signature dishes: Braised shoulder of lamb with thyme, garlic and spring vegetables; seared salmon with a spice crust, couscous and spring onion crème fraîche; mulberry tart with vanilla ice cream; potted game with spiced pears; baked egg custard tart with nutmeg ice cream.

Directions: Town centre follow directions for Castle & Museum

Castle Hotel

TAUNTON, Farthings Hotel ❀

Charming, personally-run Georgian hotel in a peaceful village close to Taunton and the M5. An interesting, frequently changing dinner menu is built around an innovative use of local produce. Expect carrot and orange soup, succulent lamb noisettes with redcurrant and port jus, and an excellent lemon sponge pudding.

Additional: Bar food L; No children under 13
Smoking: No smoking in dining room
Accommodation: 8 en suite
Credit cards: ▆ ▆ ▆ ▆ ▆

Hatch Beauchamp TA3 6SG
Map 3: ST22
Tel: 01823 480664
Fax: 01823 481118
Chef: Jason Harmer
Owners: Mr & Mrs E Sparkes, Mr & Mrs E Tindall
Cost: Fixed-price D £18.50. ☺
H/wine £8.95.
Times: Last L 1.30pm/D 8.30pm.
Closed Sun, New Year

Directions: Village centre, just off A358 between Taunton (M5/J25) & Ilminster

TAUNTON,

Meryan House Hotel

Charming period house set in its own grounds yet only a mile from the centre of Taunton. Well-reported food takes in potato and herb pancake; Gruyère soufflé with a rich Parmesan cream; rack of lamb with herb crust and fresh tomato sauce; breast of duck with fresh oranges and lemon and orange sauce; blackberry and apple crumble.

Smoking: No smoking in dining room
Credit cards: ▬ ▒ ⚡ ▭

Directions: From Taunton/A38 direction Wellington. After 1 mile (the cremetorium) take 1st R signed Bishops Hull Rd. Hotel is 600 yds.

Bishops Hull TA1 5EG
Map 3: ST22
Tel: 01823 337445
Fax: 01823 322355
Chef: Mrs C Clark
Owners: Mr & Mrs N Clark
Cost: Fixed-price D £17. ☺
H/wine £9.
Times: 7.30pm – last D 8.30pm.
Closed 26 Dec-3 Jan
Additional: Sunday L only (12.30-2pm); Children welcome; 🍴 dishes
Seats: 24. Private dining room 12

TAUNTON,

Mount Somerset Hotel ❀❀

Henlade TA3 5NB
Map 3: ST22
Tel: 01823 442500
Fax: 01823 442900
Chef: Freddie Blandin
Owner: Mount Somerset Hotel Ltd
Cost: Fixed-price L £15.95/ D £24.50 (4 coiurses). ☺ H/wine £9.50.
Times: Noon-last L 1.45pm/7pm-last D 9.45pm
Additional: Sunday L; Children welcome; 🍴 dishes
Seats: 40. Private dining rooms 18-30
Accommodation: 11 en suite
Credit cards: ▬ ▒ ▭ ⚡ ▣ ▭

Classic Regency mansion, magnificently furnished, set in sweeping parkland overlooking the Quantock and Blackdown Hills, yet within a few miles of the M5/J25. The kitchen tries hard to produce imaginative food and this year's reports have noted more confidence. A well received winter dinner took in chicken liver parfait with brioche and grape chutney, parsnip, swede and apple soup, fillet of halibut on a bed of bubble and squeak with a white wine and butter sauce, and banana and toffee tart. Another meal, taken in early summer, consisted of a vegetable terrine with horseradish cream, tender beef fillet with red wine sauce, and a good strawberry bavarois for pudding.

Directions: 3 miles SE of Taunton. From M5/J25 take A358 (Chard), turn R in Henlade (Stoke St Mary), then L at T-junction, hotel entrance 400yds R

TAUNTON, **Nightingales** ❀❀

A 'smashing little restaurant', enthused an inspector after visiting this cluster of converted farm buildings out in the country. The mood inside is elegantly rustic with an air of comforting domesticity, both in the little bar where canapés are

Bath House Farm Lower West Hatch TA3 5RH
Map 3: ST22
Tel/Fax: 01823 480806
Chef: Sally Edwards
Owners: Margaret & Jeremy Barlow

Nightingales

Cost: Fixed-price D £21. ☺
H/wine £9.50.
Times: D only Fri, Sat, 7.30pm-last D
9pm.
Closed 2 wks Feb
Additional: Sunday L (12.30pm-last L
2pm); Children welcome; ✇ dishes
Seats: 40
Smoking: No smoking in dining room
Credit cards: ▬ ▭ 🛪 🄶

eaten and in the pretty white-walled dining room. Opening
times may be restricted – dinner on Friday and Saturday night
plus lunch on Sunday – but the kitchen takes its work seriously.
There's a sunny Mediterranean feel to dishes like fresh
linguine with roasted vegetables, pesto and shaved Parmesan
or 'harmoniously balanced' fillet of lamb with minted couscous,
tapenade and a roasted tomato and anchovy dressing. Other
influences surface in, say, cod and spring onion fishcakes with
crème fraîche tartare sauce, and griddled duck breast
marinated in soy, ginger and orange, served with crispy fried
noodles and leeks. Desserts could include a huge wine glass
filled with rhubarb and strawberries poached in a vanilla and
ginger syrup topped with vanilla ice cream. The value for
money extends to the lively wine list.

Directions: From M5/J25 take A358 (Ilminster). Restaurant is
4 miles at bottom of hill on L after traffic lights

WELLINGTON, **Bindon House** ❁❁ NEW

A wonderful country house hotel, facing the Blackdown Hills.
The Wellesley Restaurant makes a strong designer statement,
and the cooking is full of style. To begin at the beginning, there
are canapés, home-made bread rolls and an appetiser the size
of a starter; in our case, diced cooked lamb wrapped in a lattice
of carrot with lamb jus. The actual starter, three crab sausages
in a filo basket filled with moist lobster risotto and set on a
lime and basil dressing, was also a generous portion. Classical
training shows in dishes such as fillet of Cornish sea bass
stuffed with shallots and dill on a citrus butter sauce, individual
beef Wellington and crisp potato, on a thyme and olive sauce,
and roast chump of lamb with pomme fondant and a port
infusion. Herbs are used in unexpected ways – a lavender
infusion flavours best end of lamb wrapped in leek and carrot,
and basil is paired with raspberry in a hot soufflé served with
raspberry ice.

Directions: Telephone for directions

Map 3: ST12
Tel: 01823 400070
Fax: 01823 400071
Chef: Patrick Robert
Owners: Mark & Lynn Jaffa
Cost: *Alc* £30, fixed-price L £20/D
£27.50. H/wine 310
Times: Noon-last L 1.45pm/7.30pm-
last D 9.45pm
Additional: Bar meals; Sunday L;
Children welcome; ✇ dishes
Seats: 35
Smoking: No smoking in dining room
Accommodation: 12 en suite
Credit cards: ▬ ▭ ▭ 🛪 🄳 🄶

WELLS,
Ancient Gate House Hotel ❁

*Set within the cathedral close and dating from the fourteenth
century, this small character hotel serves quality Italian food*

20 Sadler Street BA5 2RR
Map 3: ST54
Tel: 01749 672029
Fax: 01749 670319

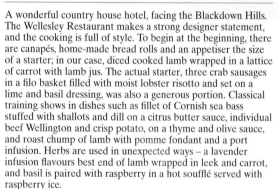

Ancient Gate House Hotel

Chef: Luigi Abis
Owners: Mr & Mrs Franco Rossi
Cost: Alc £16.50, fixed-price L
£6.90/D £13.75. ☺ H/wine £10.50.
Times: Last L 2pm/D 10pm
Additional: Sunday L; Bar meals L;
Children welcome; ◑ dishes
Smoking: No smoking in dining room
Accommodation: 9 bedrooms;
7 en suite
Credit cards: ▨ ▨ ▨ ▨ ▨ ▨

alongside English inspired dishes in the attractive Rugatino
Restaurant. Traditional Italian choices range from typical antipasti
and pasta dishes to good value fish and meat specialities.

Directions: The corner of Cathedral Green and
Sadler Street

WELLS, The Fountain

1 St Thomas Street BA5 2UU
Map 3: ST54
Tel: 01749 672317
Fax: 01749 670825
Chef: Julie Pearce
Owners: Adrian & Sarah Lawrence
Cost: Alc £15, fixed-price L £7.75
(not Sun). ☺ H/wine £7.95.
Times: Last L 2pm/D 10pm.
Closed Dec 25-26
Additional: Sunday L; Bar meals;
Children welcome; ◑ dishes
Credit cards: ▨ ▨ ▨ ▨ ▨

Parsnip soup, salmon with saffron and dill sauce, and chicken and
smoky bacon salad with pine kernels made up a recent meal at The
Fountain, a welcoming town inn just up the road from Wells
cathedral. Meals can be taken in the comfortably worn bar, or in the
more formal dining room upstairs.

Directions: At junction of A371 & B3139 in city centre, 50 yds
from cathedral

WELLS,
The Market Place Hotel ❀❀

BA5 2RW
Map 3: ST54
Tel: 01749 672616
Fax: 01749 679670
Chef: Tony Smith
Owner: Charles Garrard
Cost: Alc £22, fixed-price D £22. ☺
H/wine £9.50.
Times: 12.30pm-last L 2pm/7pm-last
D 9.30pm
Additional: ◑ dishes

Built five centuries ago by a certain Bishop Bekynton, this
fixture of the Wells scene stands in the lee of the city's
venerable cathedral. Today, guests can eat alfresco in the
courtyard garden or in the main restaurant, which has been
decorated to evoke a Scandinavian atmosphere. The fixed-
price dinner menu shows flair and imagination across the
board. Boudin of salmon with marinated scallops and
cucumber, and consommé of oxtail with herb dumplings and
port are typical starters, while main courses could feature, say,

seared tuna steak with vierge dressing and spinach ravioli, whole roast wood pigeon with glazed button onions and Cassis, and pan-fried Gressingham duck breast with crushed potatoes, olives and Madeira jus. The wine list is short and to-the-point.

Seats: 50. Private dining room 80
Smoking: No pipes and cigars
Accommodation: 34 en suite
Credit cards: ■ ▨▨ ▨▨ ⊠ ⊠

Directions: A39 – A371. In centre of town, down one way system. Directly in front of Conduit in Market Square

WESTON-SUPER-MARE,
Commodore Hotel

A friendly hotel with direct access to the nearby beach. An extensive menu is served in Alice's, a smart dining room named after a cosmopolitan Malibu restaurant. Try chicken Caribbean, served with fresh slices of mango and coated with coconut, or perhaps broccoli and walnut Mornay.

Smoking: No pipes or cigars
Accommodation: 18 en suite
Credit cards: ■ ▨▨⊠ ⊠

Directions: 1.5 miles N from town along coast toll road

Beach Road Sand Bay
Kewstoke BS22 9UZ
Map 3: ST36
Tel: 01934 415778
Fax: 01934 636483
Chef: David Williams
Cost: Alc £15, fixed-price L £11.95.
☺ H/wine from £7.30.
Times: D only, 7pm-9pm.
Closed 24 Dec–2 Jan
Additional: Sunday L (noon-2.30pm);
Bar meals; Children welcome;
⬤ dishes

WILLITON, Curdon Mill ✿

'*Inspired English with a flash of continental' is the cooking on offer at Curdon Mill, a converted sandstone watermill with the river flowing through the garden and tumbling over the waterwheel. Dishes include rack of lamb with redcurrant gravy, or Aga-roast Gressingham duck with orange and Cognac sauce.*

Yellow TA4 4LS
Map 3: ST04
Tel: 01984 656522
Fax: 01984 656197
Chef: Daphne Criddle
Owners: Richard & Daphne Criddle
Cost: Alc £19.50, fixed-price D £19.50. ☺ H/wine £7.80.
Times: 6pm-last D 9pm. Closed L except Sun
Additional: Sunday L (noon-2.30pm);
No children under 8; ⬤ dishes
Smoking: No smoking in dining room
Accommodation: 6 en suite
Credit cards: ■ ▨▨ ▨▨ ⊠

Directions: From A358 take Yellow & Stogumber turning. Hotel 1 mile on L

WILLITON,
White House Hotel ✿✿✿

It needs a great deal of staying power to carry on for 30 years, running the show and cooking everything yourselves, but Dick and Kay Smith have done just that. Their enthusiasm for the business has never waned. Their policy of closing from early November to mid-May no doubt helps to re-charge the batteries before the season gets under way and it's back to the kitchen for dinners seven nights a week. Little changes in their friendly white-shuttered Georgian hotel, which reminded one inspector of 'a Mediterranean artist's retreat' and the formula

Long Street TA4 4QW
Map 3: ST04
Tel: 01984 632306/632777
Chefs/Owners: Dick & Kay Smith
Cost: Fixed-price D £29.50.
Times: D only, 7.30pm-last D 8.30pm. Closed early Nov-mid May
Additional: Children welcome
Seats: 26
Smoking: No smoking in dining room

White House Hotel

Accommodation: 12 rooms
Credit cards: None

of a three-course fixed-price menu remains. This may not be the cutting edge of '90s cuisine, but the cooking is wholly consistent and ingredients are chosen with impeccable care. Meals always begin with a soup, perhaps leek and potato or chilled beetroot and fennel, the latter impressing with its beautiful magenta colour and stunning clarity of flavour. First courses could be the fixture dish of soufflé suissesse or seared scallops with tomato and basil vinaigrette, while main courses tend to divide equally between meat and fish: old English Charter pie or roast fillet of local spring lamb with purée soubise on the one hand, turbot baked with button mushrooms and Noilly Prat or a fine piece of spanking fresh sea bass in crisp buttery pastry with a zingy sorrel sauce to cut through the richness on the other. To finish there is generally a quartet of puddings to choose from, for example home-made shortbread layered with crème fraîche and sliced strawberries, or peaches in wine. Details such as 'incredibly simple' warm mini-pizzas to start and 'super' fudge with coffee show that this is a kitchen that cares.

An informative, well balanced wine list that makes compulsive reading; it inspires enthusiasm. Daunted by the main list? Two pages of particularly interesting wines have been picked out, half of them under £25. A strong Rhône section with wines from Robin Yapp – where wines carry higher price tags but are well worth it. A vast array of halves including some older vintages

Signature dishes: roast monkfish stuffed with pine kernels, green olives and garlic served with a purée of potatoes and chives; chargrilled marinated breast of wood pigeon with beetroot salad; roast local Gressingham duck with damson sauce; crêpes normande.

Directions: On the A39 in the centre of village

WINSFORD, Royal Oak Inn ✿

A twelfth-century thatched inn with oak beams and open fireplaces, in a quintessentially English village setting. Dishes might include roast leg of Exmoor lamb with gravy and apple mint jelly, duck and venison pie with a rich red wine sauce, or whole trout, grilled and served with prawn butter.

Credit cards: 🟦 🟦 🟦 💳 ℂ

Directions: From M5/J27 take A396 (Minehead) 20 miles turn L to Winsford, then L in village

Minehead TA24 7JE
Map 3: SS93
Tel: 01643 851455
Fax: 01643 851009
Chefs: Laetitia Brown & David Sylvester
Cost: *Alc* £25, fixed-price L £13.50/D £18.50. ☺ H/wine £10.
Times: D, 7.30pm-9.15pm
Additional: Bar L (noon-2pm); Sunday L; Children welcome; 🍴 dishes
Accommodation: 14 en suite

WINSFORD, Savery's at Kerslake House ⊛⊛

Earthy, intelligent cooking with big flavours is the order of the day at this charming fifteenth-century malthouse, now a little country house hotel. Tuck into satisfying dishes such as venison braised in port wine with grilled polenta and crisp, smoked bacon, and entrecôte of prime English beef with a forest mushroom and Madeira sauce. Meat predominates, but there is also a fresh, daily fish choice. A first course of chicken liver parfait with toasted brioche had perfect texture, and Parmesan biscuits with baby leeks and sun-dried tomatoes were a spot-on combination of Mediterranean flavours. Desserts are equally accomplished, especially a passion fruit tart with pineapple and lime sorbet, whilst terrific white chocolate ice cream lifted a simple tuile basket filled with fresh raspberries into a new league. After dinner, relax in a deep armchair in front of the inglenook fireplace or, in summer, in the pretty, private garden.

Halse Lane TA24 7JE
Map 3: SS93
Tel/Fax: 01643 851242
Chefs: John Savery, Nicky Plumb
Owners: Patricia Carpenter, John Savery
Cost: Alc £27
Times: D only, 7.15pm-9pm. Closed Sun, Mon
Additional: No children under 15; ⓭ dishes
Seats: 30
Smoking: No smoking in dining room
Accommodation: 7 en suite
Credit cards: ▤ ▤ ▤ ▤

Directions: From A396 follow signs to Winsford and Exford. Enter Winsford and turn L at garage. On the R past the Royal Oak Inn

WITHYPOOL, Royal Oak Inn ⊛

TA24 7QP
Map 3: SS83
Tel: 01643 831506
Fax: 01643 831659
Chef: Jill Tapp
Owners: Mr & Mrs Howard
Cost: Alc £27.50, fixed-price D £22. ☺ H/wine £9.90.
Times: D only, 7pm-9.30pm. Closed Xmas & New Year
Additional: Sunday L; Bar meals; ⓭ dishes
Smoking: No cigars or pipes
Accommodation: 8 en suite
Credit cards: ▤ ▤ ▤ ▤ ▤ ▤

Beamed ceilings and log fires create a welcoming atmosphere at this traditional village inn, which dates back 300 years. Quality local ingredients are used in dishes such as escalope of venison filled with chestnuts, smoked bacon and onions, and tenderloin of Somerset pork, with roasted apples and cider sauce.

Directions: From M5/J27, A361 to South Molton junction. Turn R to North Molton, then follow signs to Withypool

WIVELISCOMBE, Langley House ⊛⊛

A day out on nearby Exmoor will sharpen appetites for the nightly changing, fixed-price, four-course dinner, served country house style at this attractive, family-run hotel, with everyone gathering in the drawing-room at 8pm for an 8.30pm start. Dessert pear marinated in walnut oil with a herb cheese savoury is a particularly popular starter, followed, perhaps, by a fish course of roasted sea bass with provençale breadcrumbs on a bed of leeks with a thyme beurre blanc, using the abundance of fresh herbs and vegetables from the walled

Langley Marsh TA4 2UF
Map 3: ST02
Tel: 01984 623318
Fax: 01984 624573
Chef: Peter Wilson
Owners: Peter & Anne Wilson
Cost: Fixed-price D £29.85 (4 courses). H/wine £12.50
Times: D only, 7.30pm-last D 8.30pm
Additional: No children under 7; ⓭ dishes

kitchen garden. After a main course such as mignons of Somerset lamb (cut from the saddle) with young spinach and port wine sauce, there is a choice of dessert, when it's a close call between the likes of elderflower and elderberry syllabub, icky sticky pudding with toffee sauce and artisan cheeses served with walnut and banana bread. The impressive wine list features over 140 wines, with an emphasis on the Bordeaux region.

Seats: 20. Private dining room 16
Smoking: No smoking in dining room
Accommodation: 8 en suite
Credit cards: ▬ ▬ ▬

Directions: Off B3277 0.5 miles from Wiveliscombe on Langley Marsh Rd

WOOKEY HOLE, Glencot House

Glencot Lane
BA5 1BH
Map 3: ST54
Tel: 01749 677160
Fax: 01749 670210
Chef: Danny Cannon
Owner: Jenny Attia
Cost: Alc £21.50, fixed-price D £26.50. ☺ H/wine £8.70.
Times: D only, 6.45pm-8.30pm
Additional: Bar meals D; Children welcome; ⑤ dishes
Smoking: No smoking in dining room
Accommodation: 13 en suite
Credit cards: ▬ ▬ ▬

A fine Jacobean-style Victorian mansion with grounds sweeping down to the river, making a peaceful retreat with plenty to offer. A meal in the oak-panelled dining room might feature a timbale of mushrooms and chicken, followed by roast rack of lamb stuffed with apricots, with a sweet port sauce.

Directions: In village, turn L at sign for hotel after pink cottage on hill brow

WOOLVERTON,
Woolverton House NEW

An impressive early nineteenth-century rectory, sympathetically converted into a small hotel, set in some two acres of grounds. The fixed-price menu offers a short choice of dishes cooked in provincial French style. Expect French onion soup, Chateaubriand, monkfish armoricaine and iced zabaglione for pudding. Well chosen list of wines.

Additional: No children under 8; ⑤ dishes
Smoking: No smoking in dining room
Accommodation: 14 en suite
Credit cards: ▬ ▬ ▬ ▢

Bath BA3 6QS
Map 3: ST75
Tel: 01373 830415
Fax: 01373 831243
Chef: Marina Terry
Owners: Mr & Mrs Terry
Cost: Fixed-price D £13.95. ☺ H/wine £8.95.
Times: D only, 7.30pm-9.30pm.
Closed Sun

Directions: On the A36 7 miles south-east of Bath

YEOVIL, Little Barwick House

Barwick Village BA22 9TD
Map 3: ST51
Tel: 01935 423902
Fax: 01935 420908
Chef: Veronica Colley
Owners: Christopher & Veronica Colley
Cost: Fixed-price D £19.90-£24.90 (2-4 courses). H/wine £11.90
Times: D only, 7pm-last D 9pm. Sun residents only. Closed Xmas-New Year
Additional: Children welcome; dishes
Seats: 40. Private dining room 18. Jacket and tie preferred
Smoking: No smoking in dining room; air-conditioning
Accommodation: 6 en suite
Credit cards:

Set in some three acres of delightful gardens on the edge of the village, Christopher and Veronica Colley's beguiling Georgian dower house functions perfectly as a restaurant with rooms. Veronica's cooking is reckoned to be the main attraction for visitors and her style is refreshingly unshowy. Fish from Lyme Bay, local meat and seasonal game all make an appearance on her short, well-balanced menus. The repertoire changes daily and meals are priced for two or four courses. Home-baked breads are a star turn, soups such as spicy vegetable are heartwarming, while main courses could range from a 'pie of the week' or Thai roast guinea fowl to chargrilled medallions of pork with a tangy caramelised apple and onion marmalade. To finish, our inspector drooled over a brittle butter biscuit filled with Amaretto ice cream and served with a fruity plum coulis. There is plenty of interesting drinking to be found on the well-spread wine list.

Directions: Turn off A371 Yeovil/Dorchester opposite Red House pub, 0.25 mile on L

YEOVIL, Yeovil Court Hotel ✿

West Coker Road BA20 2NE
Map 3: ST51
Tel: 01935 863746
Fax: 01935 863990
Chef: Howard Mosley
Owner: Brian Devonport
Cost: A/c £11.50. H/wine £8.90. ☺
Times: Last L 1.45pm/D 9.45pm Closed L Sat /D Sun
Additional: Bar meals; Sunday L; Children welcome; dishes
Smoking: No smoking in dining room
Accommodation: 26 en suite
Credit cards:

Between the blackboard specials, the carte and vegetarian menus, there's an extensive selection of dishes offered at this attractive Georgian-style restaurant. Fish, meat and game served with carefully prepared sauces are usually featured, along with straightforward steaks. Puddings include steamed syrup and lemon sponge.

Directions: On A30 2.5 miles W of town centre

STAFFORDSHIRE

ACTON TRUSSELL, Moat House

Restored seventeenth-century timbered building with extensive grounds overlooking the Staffs & Worcs Canal. Now a busy dining pub/restaurant offering consistently good standards of cooking and efficient service. Dishes include salmon and sole mousse, herb-crusted rack of lamb with port and redcurrant sauce, and crème brûlée.

Credit cards: ▨▨▨▨▨▨

Directions: M6/J13 head towards Stafford, Ist R to Acton Trussell; Moat House by church.

ST17 0RJ
Map 7: SJ91
Tel: 01785 712217
Fax: 01785 715344
Chef: Bob Peagram
Owners: John & Mary Lewis
Cost: *Alc* £25, fixed-price L £12.95/D £14.95. H/wine £9.45. ☺
Times: Last L 2pm/D 9.30pm.
Closed Sun D
Additional: Sunday L; Bar meals; Children welcome; dishes
Smoking: No smoking in dining room

BURTON-UPON-TRENT,
Riverside Hotel

Charming modernised inn standing on the banks of the River Trent. The popular restaurant enjoys fine river views and offers a good range of freshly prepared dishes. A recent test meal highlighted a well-made cheese and thyme soufflé, followed by seared sea bream, and pear clafoutis for pudding.

Directions: Off A5121 to Burton

Riverside Drive
Branston DE14 3EP
Map 8: SK22
Tel: 01283 511234
Fax: 01283 511441
Chef: Stephen Sander
Cost: *Alc* £22, fixed-price D £17.50
Times: Last L 2pm (Sun 2.20pm)/D 10pm (Sun 8.30pm). Closed Sat L
Telephone for further details

NEWCASTLE-UNDER-LYME,
Deansfield Hotel

Small, family-run Victorian town hotel that retains many original features. A recent inspection meal produced soundly cooked dishes of juicy pan-fried scallops, lamb fillet with chervil stuffing and a piquant sauce, with an excellent chocolate mousse with lemon tart to finish.

Accommodation: 11 en suite. **Credit cards:** ▨▨▨

Directions: M6 J15 follow A34 to town centre, turn right into The Avenue (City General Hospital), Lancaster Road third on left.

98 Lancaster Road ST5 1DS
Map 7: SJ84
Tel/Fax: 01782 619040
Chef: David Evans
Owners: David & Susan Evans
Cost: *Alc* £23, fixed-price L £11/D £25 (6 courses). ☺ H/wine £9.75.
Times: Last L 1.30pm/D 9.15pm.
Closed Sun, L Mon, 25-26 Dec
Additional: Children welcome; dishes

SUFFOLK

ALDEBURGH, Regatta Restaurant

Seaside murals, pennants and nautical blue and white colour schemes define the mood. Fish is a strong suit, whether roast fillet of local cod crusted with tandoori spices and served with onion jam or grilled skate with black olives and capers. Alternatives appear in the shape of warm pigeon and bacon salad, and spicy lamb meatballs.

Smoking: No-smoking area. **Credit cards:** ▨▨▨▨

Directions: Town centre

171 High Street IP15 5AN
Map 5: TM45
Tel/Fax: 01728 452011
Chef: Robert Mabey
Owners: Robert & Johanna Mabey
Cost: *Alc* £15. H/wine £7.50. ☺
Times: Noon-3pm/7pm-midnight.
Closed Mon, Tues (low season)
Additional: Bar food; Sunday L; Children welcome; dishes

BIDLESTON, **The Bow Window**

Quaint beamed restaurant occupying a sixteenth-century building in the picturesque market square. Well-presented dishes, prepared from fresh ingredients, include a perfectly cooked lamb fillet wrapped in spinach, ham and puff pastry with port and thyme gravy, and rhubarb sponge with stem ginger custard.

Additional: Sunday L (noon-2pm); Children welcome; ◑ dishes
Smoking: No smoking in dining room
Credit cards: ▬ ▬ ▬

Directions: In main street on B1115 between Stowmarket and Hadleigh

116 High Street IP7 7EB
Map 5: TL94
Tel/Fax: 01449 740748
Chef: Hilary Pixton
Owners: Hilary & Eric Pixton
Cost: *Alc* £18.20, fixed-price D £13.95. ☺ H/wine £8.95.
Times: D only 7pm-9pm (Fri & Sat only), other days by prior arrangement. Closed 24-30 Dec

BROME, **Cornwallis Arms**

Superb setting – a sixteenth-century dower house with yew topiary and a small lake. The kitchen serves the likes of smoked halibut salad with mustard and dill dressing, and local free-range guinea fowl with port jus, smoked bacon and wild mushrooms, the latter picked by the chef, a keen mycologist. Cask-conditioned ales from the hotel's own micro-brewery are another speciality.

Eye IP23 8AJ
Map 5: TM17
Tel: 01379 870326
Fax: 01379 870051
Chef: Kim Hatch
Owner: St Peter's Brewery Co Ltd
Cost: *Alc* £25, fixed-price L £14.95. ☺ H/wine £8.95.
Times: Last L 2pm/D 9.30pm.
Additional: Sunday L; Bar meals; No children under 1; ◑ dishes
Smoking: No-smoking area
Accommodation: 11 en suite
Credit cards: ▬ ▬ ▬ ▬ ▣ ▢

Directions: Just off A140 at Brome, midway between Norwich & Ipswich

BURY ST EDMUNDS, **Angel Hotel**

Angel Hill IP33 1LT
Map 5: TL86
Tel: 01284 753926
Fax: 01284 750092
Chef: Denis Grouille
Owner: Mrs Mary Gough

Dating from 1452 and still very much the hub of the town, the creeper-clad Angel has seen some refurbishment of late. Even so, its heart remains firmly entrenched in the Regency restaurant overlooking the historic Abbey Gate. The kitchen

takes its work seriously and the French-inspired *carte* clings to the classic tradition for most of its ideas. Baked salmon is wrapped in filo pastry and topped with a delicate broccoli mousse, roast rack of lamb is finished with fresh truffle jus, saddle of Denham venison comes with sweet-cured bacon and a raspberry vinegar reduction. Desserts are also in the time-honoured vein of dark chocolate marquise and Grand Marnier soufflé glacé. Informal, brasserie-style meals are served in the dramatic setting of the vaulted twelfth-century undercroft. The wide ranging wine list has a good spread from the Old and New World.

Cost: Alc £29, fixed-price L £13 (2 courses)/D £20 (3 courses). ☺ H/wine £9.75.
Times: 12.30pm-last L 2pm/7.15pm-last D 9.45pm. Closed D Sun
Additional: Brasserie; Sunday L; Children welcome; ✿ dishes
Seats: 45. Private dining room 20
Smoking: No smoking in dining room
Accommodation: 42 en suite
Credit cards: 🗖 🗖 🗖 🗖 🗖 🗖

Directions: Town centre, close to Tourist Information

BURY ST EDMUNDS,
Ravenwood Hall ❀

Rougham IP30 9JA
Map 5: TL86
Tel: 01359 270345
Fax: 01359 270788
Chef: David White
Owner: Craig Jarvis
Cost: Alc £27.95, fixed-price L £19.75/D £27.95. ☺
Times: Last L 2pm/D 9.30pm
Additional: Sunday L; Bar meals; Children welcome; ✿ dishes
Smoking: No smoking in dining room
Accommodation: 14 en suite
Credit cards: 🗖 🗖 🗖 🗖 🗖 🗖

Warm welcome, cheerful service, relaxed bar and formal restaurant – a splendid room with carved timbers and a huge Tudor fireplace – are all part of the charm of Ravenwood. Expect a mix of traditional and modern cooking; grilled mackerel with gooseberries, or sirloin steak topped with Stilton, for example.

Directions: 3 miles E of Bury on A14, signposted to Rougham

FRESSINGFIELD,
Fox & Goose Inn ❀❀

'A place of great character', comments an inspector of this typical village inn where the emphasis is firmly on food. Bare boards and brickwork, oak beams and log fires and a lovely view of the church (it used to be the church eating house, opened to stop the congregation eating in church) all add to the charm. A winter meal opened with baguettes sandwiched with a good tapenade, then spicy curried crab cakes served with a simple, rustic sauce of black olives, tomato and balsamic vinegar. Pan-fried monkfish came next, top-quality fish, served with a well seasoned parsnip purée with nutmeg. Only sticky toffee pudding showed some slippage in quality – it was oversweet and served in a 'sea' of caramel sauce. The wine list is concise, covering Europe and the New World.

Nr Diss IP21 5PB
Map 5: TM27
Tel: 01379 586247
Fax: 01379 586688
Chef: Max Dougal
Owners: Mr & Mrs T O'Leary
Cost: Alc £30, fixed-price L £9.50 (2 courses)/D £17.50. ☺ H/wine £13.50
Times: Noon-2pm, 7pm-9.30pm. Closed Mon, Tue, 25-26 Dec, 1 Jan
Additional: Bar meals; Sunday L; Children welcome: ✿ dishes
Smoking: No smoking in dining room
Credit cards: 🗖 🗖 🗖 🗖

Directions: A140 & B1118 (Stradbroke) L after 6 miles – in village centre by church

HINTLESHAM,
Hintlesham Hall ❀❀❀

IP8 3NS
Map 5: TM04
Tel: 01473 652334
Chef: Alan Ford
Owner: David Allan
Cost: *Alc* £36, fixed-price L £19.50.
D £25. H/wine £12.50
Times: Noon-last L 1.45pm/7pm-last
D 9.30pm. Closed L Sat
Additional: Sunday L;
No children under 9; ❀ dishes
Seats: 100. Private dining rooms 14-
40. Jacket and tie preferred
Smoking: No smoking in dining room
Accommodation: 33 en suite
Credit cards: ▬ ▦ ▦ ▣ ℂ

A resplendent Georgian façade, unmistakable Elizabethan
chimney stacks, and even a splendid carved oak staircase from
the Stuart period might seem architecturally and historically
confusing. In fact, this magnificent house was built in the 1570s
by Thomas Timperley, grandson of the 3rd Duke of Norfolk.
Today, it ranks as one of England's most gracious country
hotels, the epitome of gentrified style and elegance, set in over
175 acres of Suffolk countryside. Meals are either served in the
Parlour with its polished pine panelling and portraits of 'crusty
old aristos', or the Salon – a magnificent high ceilinged room
that oozes luxury. Alan Ford's cooking is evolving away from
creamy richness and weighty flavours towards a lighter style,
although his technique is precise and as razor-sharp as ever.
Meals begin with a selection of tiny, intricate canapés – a filo
basket with watermelon and avocado salsa, a gravlax and
caviar barquette and so on. Menus follow the seasons. In
spring you might find brochette of scallops with couscous salad
and a vanilla and ginger dressing or rack of lamb with olive oil
and basil crust and tapenade sauce, while winter might usher in
duck confit with grilled courgette and sweet pepper salad or
medallions of pork with wild mushrooms and tarragon jus. An
inspection dinner one May evening started in style with a lamb
and rabbit terrine with a base of chicken set on a broad bean
purée with a bean and tomato salsa. Then came a ragout of
lobster and monkfish (again, first-class raw materials) with
perfectly timed asparagus and baby vegetables, although it was
felt the nage itself lacked depth. To finish, strawberries
marinated in Cassis served with a strawberry and crème fraîche
ice cream emphasised the new, healthier approach to things.
Young suited waiters and floral-skirted waitresses serve
professionally.
   The wine list is lengthy, but there are two pages of 'House
Selections', most under £20, and of nine quality wines served
by the glass, there are Bollinger and Ch Palmer 88 at £14.
Country Wine section offers well priced easy drinking (under
£14), but there are some classy wines at the other end of the
scale. Over 60 halves.

Directions: 5 miles west of Ipswich on the A1071 Hadleigh
road.

IPSWICH, **Belstead Brook Manor**

Country house hotel, on the edge of Ipswich, with modern
extensions and a restaurant divided into small intimate rooms.
Substantial dishes include Belstead Manor pot (sautéed mushrooms,
bacon and onion in a brandy and cream sauce glazed with
Cheddar), and summer fruit pudding.

Smoking: No smoking in dining room
Accommodation: 76 en suite
Credit cards:

Directions: Take A1214 exit at main A12/A14 interchange then
3rd exit at 1st roundabout; after bridge take 1st L

Belstead Brook Park
Belstead Road IP2 9HB
Map 5: TM14
Tel: 01473 684241
Fax: 01473 681249
Chef: Alex Honeywell
Owners: Manor Hotels
Cost: *Alc* £25, fixed-price L&D
£18.50. ☺ H/wine £9.80.
Times: Last L 2pm/last D 11pm
Additional: Bar meals; Sunday L;
Children welcome; ♨ dishes

IPSWICH, **Marlborough Hotel**

Henley Road IP1 3SP
Map 5: TM14
Tel: 01473 257677
Fax: 01473 226927
Chef: Simon Barker
Owners: Gough family
Cost: *Alc* £28, fixed-price L £14.50/D
£18.50. ☺ H/wine £9.25.
Times: 12.30pm-last L 2pm/7.30pm-
last D 9.30pm. Closed L Sat
Additional: Bar food; Sunday L;
Children welcome; ♨ dishes
Seats: 60. Private dining room 40
Smoking: No smoking in dining room
Accommodation: 22 en suite
Credit cards:

At night, the gardens of this welcoming, family-run hotel are
illuminated for the benefit of diners; inside, the eclectic,
impressive cooking also lights up the plate. Pre-dinner drinks
are taken amidst the modern sculptures in the upbeat, brightly
coloured bar that sets the tone for a meal full of robust
ingredients and big ideas. A warm salad of duck, black pudding
and Toulouse sausage was served on mixed leaves with a
pungent balsamic dressing; fillet of cod in filo with coriander,
ginger and yellow bean sauce was equally precisely cooked,
and impressed with a well-judged balance of flavours. Other
dishes have a more familiar ring – honey grilled duck breast
with apples and Calvados, pan-fried lamb's liver with bacon,
caramelised onions, garlic-mashed potatoes and Madeira jus.
Vegetarians are well looked after with an asparagus, roast
pepper and pine nut cheesecake amongst a wider than usual
choice. Admirable desserts include crêpes with apple and
blackcurrant and iced vanilla parfait.

Directions: Take A12/14 (Felixstowe & Yarmouth), R at lights at
brow of hill, hotel is 500 yds on R

IPSWICH, **The Old Boot House**

No spelling error, but an idiosyncratic name for an engaging
country restaurant. In fact, it's so far from anywhere, one
wonders how the place is always as busy as it is. The drawback
is that service can be very slow as a result, but it's worth the
wait for free-wheeling British cooking that embraces both

Shotley
IP9 1EY
Map 5: TM14
Tel: 01473 787755
Chef: Ian Chamberlain
Owners: Ian & Pamela Chamberlain
Cost: *Alc* £20. H/wine £7.95. ☺

seafood gumbo with spicy sausage, slow-cooked peppers and okra and haggis tart topped with slices of lamb tenderloin on a pool of rosemary-flavoured pan juice gravy. The penchant for unusual pairings generally works well – red mullet stuffed with crab, for example, was an unexpected hit. Sauces are also a strength, and mussel pancakes with a creamy sauce, grilled breast of chicken with spinach and blue cheese sauce, and venison meatloaf with green peppercorn sauce, all depend on ability in this department. Desserts include a very 'yummy' treacle tart and an irresistible hot-baked banana and praline strudel with home-made prune and Cognac ice cream.

Directions: 7 miles SE of Ipswich on the B1456, through Chelmondiston and 0.25 mile beyond Shotley. Sign on R

Times: L from noon/D from 7pm. Closed Sun D, Mon
Additional: Sunday L; Children welcome
Seats: 45
Smoking: No smoking in dining room
Credit cards:

IPSWICH, St Peter's Restaurant ✿✿

This outpost of Robert Mabey's trio of Suffolk eating houses has taken on an uncompromising Italian flavour of late with a menu that encompasses everything from home-cured bresaola and hand-made pasta to spumoni Amaretti and cassata with candied fruit. To start there might be Tuscan bean soup with Parmesan or a salad of char-grilled Mediterranean vegetables garnished with tiny sage leaves and served on warm pianina (flat bread cooked in a skillet). Main courses continue the emphatic regional theme with coarse-chopped spicy lamb meatballs with tomato and basil sauce on al dente tagliatelle, Roman fish brodetto with saffron and garlic crostini, and peppered fillet steak with vin santo and raisin sauce plus roasted Italian potatoes. To finish, our inspector plumped for baked pears with Marsala and cinnamon sauce with a quenelle of mascarpone on the side. Complementing the food is a judiciously selected wine list from Lay & Wheeler that naturally focuses on Italy without ignoring other countries.

Directions: St Peter's Street runs through the centre of the town. Restaurant at S end opposite Novotel

35-37 St Peter's Street IP1 1XP
Map 5: TM14
Tel/Fax: 01473 210810
Chef: Nigel Ramsbottom
Owners: Robert & Johanna Mabey
Cost: Alc £15. H/wine £7.50. ☺
Times: Noon-last L 2pm/7pm-last D 10pm. Closed Sun, Mon
Additional: Children welcome; ✿ dishes
Seats: 85. Private dining room 20
Smoking: No-smoking area
Credit cards:

IPSWICH, Scott's Brasserie ✿   NEW

A wine bar/brasserie on three levels; the bar at street level, the main restaurant at mid level and a second dining area on the top floor. The menu has cosmopolitan influences and there's a stamp of originality to dishes such as Bermuda fish chowder with chilli liquor and black rum.

Additional: Bar meals; Children welcome; ✿ dishes
Smoking: No pipes or cigars in dining room
Credit cards:

Directions: Near Buttermarket shopping centre, close to Cox Lane and Foundation Street car parks

4A Orwell Place IP4 1BB
Map 5: TM14
Tel: 01473 230254
Fax: 01473 218851
Chef: Scott L Davidson
Owners: Charles Lewis, Scott Davidson
Cost: Alc £25, fixed-price L £18/D £25. H/wine £9.95
Times: Last L 2.30pm/last D 10pm. Sun, D Mon

IXWORTH,
Theobalds Restaurant ✿✿

The virtues of Theobalds twice-baked cheese soufflés are regularly extolled by visitors to this town-centre restaurant

68 High Street IP31 2HJ
Map 5: TL97
Tel/Fax: 01359 231707
Chef: Simon Theobald

Theobalds Restaurant

Owners: Simon & Geraldine Theobald
Cost: Alc £26.50, fixed-price L £10 (2 courses). ☺
Times: Noon-last L 1.30pm/7.15pm-last D 9.15pm. Closed L Sat, D Sun, Mon, 2 wks Aug
Additional: Sunday L; Children welcome; ♨ dishes
Seats: 36
Smoking: No smoking in dining room
Credit cards: ■ ■ ■ ■

housed in a quaint, beamed, sixteenth-century building. Sweetbreads also appear frequently on the *carte*, deep-fried with creamy noodles, and scallops come pan-fried and served in a crispy, pastry case with a spinach and Vermouth sauce. Although some dishes have an indulgent, endearingly old-fashioned air, whole Dover sole served with champagne and saffron sauce, iced Grand Marnier soufflé, for example, others, such as roast baby guinea fowl with redcurrant sauce flavoured with ginger and lime, and pan-fried fillet of John Dory on a bed of aubergines marinated in honey and vinegar with a tomato and basil sauce, strike a lighter, more contemporary note. Good local ingredients are used to advantage in full-frontal dishes such as fillet of Suffolk hare wrapped in bacon with braised lentils and red wine sauce. In summer, there are three patio tables for alfresco dining. An excellent wine list includes four top-rate dessert wines by the glass.

Directions: 7 miles from Bury St Edmunds on A143 Bury/Diss road

LAVENHAM, Angel Hotel ✿

Market Place CO10 9QZ
Map 5: TL94
Tel: 01787 247388
Fax: 01787 248344
Chefs: Michael Pursell, Chris Boyle
Owners: Roy & Anne Whitworth, John Barry
Cost: Alc £16. H/wine £7.95. ☺
Times: Last L 2.15pm/last D 9.15pm. Closed 25-26 Dec
Additional: Bar food; Sunday L; Children welcome; ♨ dishes
Smoking: No-smoking area
Accommodation: 8 en suite
Credit cards: ■ ■ ■ ■ ■

Begun in 1390 and extended in 1520, this medieval building retains many original features, including an inglenook fireplace and an Elizabethan window. The hotel is popular locally for its daily menu of appealing dishes such as duck terrine with Cumberland jelly, steak and ale pie, and sticky toffee pudding.

Directions: Take A143 from Bury and turn onto A1141 after 4 miles; hotel is on Market Place, off High Street

LAVENHAM, The Great House

The historic building may boast a typically English inglenook fireplace but the place is a little piece of France, with food, wines and charming French staff. Consider moules marinière with fresh fat mussels in a light sauce, followed perhaps by duck confit served on a bed of creamed leeks.

Additional: Sunday L; Bar food L; Children welcome; ❹ dishes
Accommodation: 4 suites
Credit cards: ▬ ▦ ▦ ▧ ▣

Directions: In Market Place (turn into Market Lane from High Street).

Market Place CO10 9QZ
Map 5: TL94
Tel: 01787 247431
Fax: 01787 248007
Chef: Regis Crepy
Owners: Mr & Mrs Crepy
Cost: Alc L £13.95/D £25,
fixed price L £9.95-£12.95/D £16.95.
☺ H/wine £9.50.
Times: Last L 2.30pm/D 9.30pm.
Closed Mon L,
Sun-Mon D (ex residents) & 3 wks Jan

LAVENHAM, The Swan 🏵🏵

High Street CO10 9QA
Map 5: TL94
Tel: 01787 247477
Fax: 01787 248286
Chef: Andrew Barrass
Owner: Forte Heritage Hotels
Cost: Alc £38, fixed-price L £15.95/D £24.95. H/wine £13.50
Times: 12.30pm-last L 2pm/7pm-last D 9.30pm
Additional: Bar food; Sunday L; Children welcome; ❹ dishes
Seats: 70. Private dining room 40
Smoking: No smoking in dining room
Accommodation: 46 en suite
Credit cards: ▬ ▬ ▦ ▦ ▧ ▣ ▣

Lavenham is the best preserved medieval village in England, and the half-timbered Swan dates back to the fifteenth century. A minstrels' gallery, open fires and beautiful courtyard gardens give bags of atmosphere, which adds to the enjoyment of the fresh, seasonal cooking. The gastronomic menu has a suitable degree of gravitas – lobster soup is laced with Cognac and oyster mushroom strudel is set on a rich Madeira and truffle sauce. There are alcoholic notes throughout – braised whole Dover sole and lobster are glazed with a champagne sauce, breast of duck with Calvados and apples, and roast saddle of venison and cranberry compote is interestingly served with a sloe gin sauce. The set dinner menu is a little more conservative, but still very tempting with, for example, warm chicken liver salad, crispy bacon and toasted pine nuts and fresh smoked salmon fishcakes with crispy spinach and citrus butter sauce amongst the starters, and fillet of lamb with black cherry and Marsala sauce and sirloin of beef baked in brioche typical of main courses.

Directions: In the centre of the village on the A1141

LONG MELFORD,
Chimneys Restaurant 🏵🏵

Keeping company with antique shops and *olde worlde* pubs, this sixteenth-century timbered house looks every inch the part with its blackened beams, brick fireplaces and brass

Hall Street CO10 9JR
Map 5: TL84
Tel: 01787 379806
Fax: 01787 312294
Chef: David Clarkson

Chimneys Restaurant

Owners: Sam & Zena Chalmers
Cost: Fixed-price D £17.50-£27.50.
☺ H/wine £10.50.
Times: Noon-last L 2pm/7pm-last D
9.30pm. Closed D Sun
Additional: Sunday L;
Children welcome; ⚬ dishes
Seats: 50
Credit cards: ▮▮ ▮▮ ▮▮

furnishings. But there's nothing too homespun or rustic about the cooking; the kitchen takes its work seriously and dishes are fashioned with great attention to visual detail. A recent inspection dinner began with a terrine of guinea fowl with a vivid, bright red Cumberland sauce flecked with fine strands of orange zest. The main course was breast of Suffolk chicken filled with a lemon and garlic mousseline, accompanied by a circle of excellent boulangère potatoes, although the choice extends to, say, fillet of cod wrapped in smoked salmon with pesto and tomato, or roast fillet of pork with rosemary and thyme. To finish, an individual raspberry delice with fresh raspberry sauce has been favourably well received. The list of around seventy wines is a racy collection from around the globe.

Directions: On main street of Long Melford village

LONG MELFORD,
Countrymen Restaurant At The Black Lion Hotel ✸

The Green CO10 9DN
Map 5: TL84
Tel: 01787 312356
Fax: 01787 374557
Chef: Stephen Errington
Owners: S & J Errington
Cost: Alc £24, fixed-price L £7.75/D
£15.75. ☺ H/wine £8.50.
Times: Last L 1.45pm/D 9.30pm.
Closed D Sun, Mon, Jan
Additional: Bar food; Sunday L;
Children welcome; ⚬ dishes
Smoking: No smoking in dining room
Accommodation: 9 en suite
Credit cards: ▮▮ ▮▮ ▮▮ ▮▮ ▮

Themed wine evenings are particularly popular at this welcoming family-run hotel. Choose fillet of lamb with rosemary and redcurrant or braised duck breast with Puy lentils in the restaurant or, in the bistro, robust Italian specialities such as shank of cured ham braised in wine and fresh herbs.

Directions: On the village green in Long Melford

LONG MELFORD,
Scutchers Restaurant

Westgate Street CO10 9DP
Map 5: TL84
Tel: 01787 310200/310620
Telephone for details.

Scutchers is a lively bistro-style place, with a small bar, split-level dining room and brightly coloured curtains and walls. Lightly seared queenies on melting tomatoes scented with basil and tapenade made an enjoyable starter, tender and moist with lively, contrasting flavours. Our inspector followed this with pan-fried medallions of pork with red cabbage – the quality of the meat underlined by a well-crafted sauce – served with spring onion potato mash and accurately cooked vegetables. For dessert, the decadent-sounding warm bread-and-butter-pudding with apricot sauce and clotted cream ice cream.

Directions: About a mile from Long Melford on the road to Clare

LOWESTOFT, Ivy House Farm NEW

Ivy Lane
Oulton Broad NR33 8HY
Map 5: TM59
Tel: 01502 501353
Fax: 01502 501539
Chef: Richard Pye
Owners: Caroline Sterry, Paul Coe
Cost: *Alc* £29, fixed-price L £17.95/D £19.95. ☺ H/wine £8.95.
Times: Last L 1.45pm/last D 9.30pm

Eighteenth-century, timbered and thatched barn in a pastoral setting. A sense of adventure permeates the cooking – sample dishes include cream of aubergine and wild mushroom soup with mixed pepper and chickpea salsa, and roast fillet of brill and king scallops on arborio rice flavoured with basil surrounded by a black squid ink sauce.

Additional: Bar meals L; Sunday L; Children welcome; ❹ dishes
Smoking: No smoking in dining room
Accommodation: 12 en suite
Credit cards: ▬ ▬ ▬ ▅ ▤ ▮

Directions: From Lowestoft – follow A146 (Norwich). Hotel approx 0.25 mile after junction to A1117 (Ipswich), over small railway bridge.

MILDENHALL, Riverside Hotel NEW

Mill Street IP28 7DP
Map 5: TL77
Tel: 01638 717274
Fax: 01638 715997
Telephone for details

Built in 1720, the personally-run Riverside Hotel enjoys a delightful position on the banks of the River Lark. Opening on to the gardens and river, the charming restaurant offers carefully prepared food and good-value house wines. Expect Roquefort cheesecake with marinated pear, lamb with redcurrant sauce and summer fruit meringues.

Directions: Telephone for directions

NAYLAND, Martha's Vineyard

18 High Street
Nayland CO6 4JF
Map 5: TL92
Tel: 01206 262888
Chef: Larkin Rogers
Owners: Christopher Warren, Larkin Rogers
Cost: Fixed-price L&D £21. ☺ H/wine £11.95.
Times: D only (Thu-Sat), 7.30pm-last D 9.30pm. Closed 2wks winter, 2 wks summer

The name gives the game away – otherwise, the discovery of a restaurant serving modern American food in this traditional country area, might come as rather a surprise (albeit a very pleasing one). The sixteenth-century, Grade II listed, former grocer's shop is a fine example of Suffolk village vernacular architecture, but the cooking is new wave rather than *Olde Englande*. The menu, either two or three courses, is short but punchy; leek and English goat's cheese tart with mixed lettuce or seared monkfish on warm flageolet beans and bacon with garlic salad may be amongst the starters, a number of which, such as Brazilian fish stew with lime, coriander, chipotle pepper and coconut, can be taken either as first or main courses. Collops of venison with Madeira sauce may be followed by baked mocha custard with pinwheel biscuits, or the very un-American warm sticky toffee pudding.

Directions: On the High Street of Nayland, a village about 6 miles north of Colchester on the A134

NAYLAND, White Hart Inn ❀❀

The menu has all the hallmarks of quality one might expect from a Roux-backed establishment, including their own label house wine and champagne from a cellar exposed underneath a glass floor. The medieval coaching inn, once frequented by Gainsborough and Constable, is now serving up a tempting selection of dishes including breast of wood pigeon with oyster mushrooms and baby onions, and roast fillet of cod wrapped in bacon with red wine and thyme sauce. The English farmhouse revisited style is typified by old fashioned pork terrine with piccalilli, salmon fishcake with tartare butter, and grilled pork chop with sage and grainy mustard butter from the grill. When it comes to puddings, there's nothing too fancy either – apple crumble with custard, perhaps, or poached pear in red wine with pistachio ice cream.

Directions: In the centre of village

NEWMARKET, The Chifney Restaurant at Tattersalls ❀❀

Racing enthusiast David Allan, owner of Hintlesham Hall (see entry) made a bold decision to open this restaurant in the heart of Tattersalls Sales Paddock, and the signs are good. Punters are, however, warned to avoid the place on sales days when the crowds descend and a simpler style takes over. Chef Paul Murfitt worked at The Pink Geranium, Melbourn (see entry) before changing horses. His style is classic, but with ambitious modern overtones. Fixed-price lunches are fantastic value for dishes such as a crisp tartlet filled with hot braised red onions and slices of mousse-like boudin blanc, chargrilled chicken breast on tagliatelle with a cinnamon butter sauce dotted with diced ginger, and nutty nougatine layered with coconut mascarpone and caramelised banana. The *carte* moves up a gear for, say, pot au feu of baby guinea fowl in a

---

Additional: Sunday L (12.30pm-2pm); Children welcome; ❹ dishes
Seats: 41. Private dining room 14
Smoking: No smoking in dining room
Credit cards: ▬ ▬

High Street CO6 4JF
Map 5: TL94
Tel: 01206 263382
Fax: 01206 263638
Chef: Mark Prescott
Owners: Mark Prescott, Michel Roux
Cost: *Alc* £18, fixed-price L £16. ☺
H/wine £9.50.
Times: Noon-last L 2pm/6.30pm-last D 9.30pm. Closed 26 Dec, 1-2 Jan
Additional: Bar food L; Sunday L;
Children welcome; ❹ dishes
Seats: 65. Private dining room 48
Credit cards: ▬ ▬ ▬ ▬ ▣ ▣

Park Paddocks
The Avenue CB8 9AU
Map 5: TL66
Tel: 01638 666166
Fax: 01638 666099
Chef: Paul Murfitt
Owner: David Allan
Cost: *Alc* £25, fixed-price L £15.75.
☺ H/wine £8.35-££9.60.
Times: Noon-last L 2.30pm/7pm-last D 10pm. closed D Sun, Mon
Additional: Bar meals L; Sunday L;
Children welcome; ❹ dishes
Seats: 70. Private dining room 30-100
Smoking: No-smoking area
Credit cards: ▬ ▬ ▬ ▬ ▣ ▣

marjoram-scented consommé, and roast chump of lamb on piperade couscous with a fumet of sage. The wine list is a sprightly canter through France and the New World.

Directions: Centre of Newmarket. Enter Park Paddocks from The Avenue, which is a turning off High St near Jockey Club

NEWMARKET, Heath Court Hotel ✿

Modern red-brick hotel at the bottom of one of the horse training gallops. Fashionable mix of classic dishes and popular trends mixes duck terrine with spiced chicken served on coconut flavoured couscous, and braised casserole of lamb with winter vegetables and herb bread dumplings.

Additional: Bar food; Sunday lunch; Children welcome; ✪ dishes
Smoking: No-smoking area
Accommodation: 41 en suite
Credit cards: 💳 💳 💳 💳 💳 💳

Directions: Off town centre – turn R at clock tower into Moulton Road

Moulton Road CB8 8DY
Map 5: TL66
Tel: 01638 667171
Fax: 01638 666533
Chef: Paul Rolt
Owner: Heath Court Investments Ltd
Cost: *Alc* £18.50. H/wine £9.50. ☺
Times: Last L 1.45pm/last D 9.30pm.
Closed L Sat

SOUTHWOLD,
Crown at Southwold ✿

The Adnams foodie flagship attracts punters in droves. Wines without compare, fish from the North Sea boats, and an atmosphere of classless bonhomie are the reasons for coming here. Bar and restaurant menus promise contemporary assemblages along the lines of sautéed squid with Chinese greens, chilli and garlic oil; lamb cutlets with Puy lentils and thyme mash, and mango and lime syllabub.

Seats: 22. Private room 20
Smoking: No smoking in dining room
Accommodation: 12 (9 en suite)
Credit cards: 💳 💳 💳 💳 💳 💳

Directions: Take A1095 from A12; hotel at top of High Street, just before Market Place

90 High Street IP18 6DP
Map 5: TM57
Tel: 01502 722275
Fax: 01502 727263
Chef: Simon Reynolds
Owner: Adnams Hotels
Cost: Fixed-price L £13.50/D £18.50.
☺ H/wine £8.95.
Times: Last L 1.30pm/last D 9.30pm.
Closed 1st or 2nd 2 wks Jan
Additional: Bar food; Sunday L;
Children welcome; ✪ dishes

SOUTHWOLD, Swan Hotel ✿

Grand old Southwold. A mere beach pebble's throw from The Crown (see above) but light years away in style and conduct, the stately Swan glides on. Bar lunches are noteworthy, afternoon teas de rigueur, and full menus veer between roast leg of lamb with garlic cloves and redcurrant sauce and grilled fillets of sea bass with a pesto crust on a potato and bacon salad. Exemplary wines from the Adnams list.

Smoking: No smoking in dining room
Accommodation: 45 en suite
Credit cards: 💳 💳 💳 💳 💳 💳

Directions: Take A1095 off A12; follow High Street into Market Place, hotel on left

Market Place IP18 6EG
Map 5: TM57
Tel: 01502 722186
Fax: 01502 724800
Chef: Chris Coubrough
Owner: Adnams Hotel
Cost: Fixed-price lunch £15.50/D from £21. ☺ H/wine £6.95.
Times: Last L 1.45pm/last D 9.30pm.
Closed L Mon-Fri Jan-Mar
Additional: Bar food L; Sunday L;
No children under 5yrs; ✪ dishes
Seats: 66. Private dining room 46

SUDBURY, Mabey's Brasserie

The decor in this branch of Robert Mabey's mini-empire of Suffolk eating houses is pure provincial brasserie, with wooden tables, bench seating and the open-plan kitchen in full view. Not surprisingly, the menu and additional daily specials are written up on a blackboard; the accent is emphatically eclectic. Starters might range from Welsh rarebit with mango chutney to warm oyster mushroom and artichoke salad with balsamic dressing, while main courses plunder the globe for teriyaki cod fillet with Chinese noodles, pot au feu of silverside with root vegetables, and roast lamb steak with rosemary sauce and steamed couscous. To finish, British cheeses and 'Grandma's hot syrup pudding' share the billing with Italian cassata and excellent warm chocolate tart with a creamy butterscotch sauce. Service is suitably friendly and informal. The wine list from Lay & Wheeler does its job by providing quality and value for money in equal measure.

47 Gainsborough Street CO10 7SS
Map 5: TL84
Tel/Fax: 01787 374298
Chef: Guy Alabaster
Owners: Robert & Johanna Mabey
Cost: Alc £15. H/wine £7.50. ☺
Times: Noon-last L 2pm/7pm-last D 10pm. Closed Sun, Mon
Additional: Children welcome; ⓓ dishes
Seats: 60-70
Smoking: No-smoking area; air-conditioning
Credit cards:

Directions: 150 yards from Market Hill, next to Gainsborough House Museum

SUDBURY, Red Onion Bistro NEW

A converted Victorian meeting hall with a vibrant, lively atmosphere, a sheltered garden, and a self-selection wine room. The food is honest, full of flavour, with influences as varied as Chinese and classic French. Recommended dishes are fish soup, twice-baked cheese soufflé, and pear and almond tart.

Additional: Children welcome; ⓓ dishes
Smoking: No pipes or cigars
Credit cards: ▬ ▬ ▬ ⓒ

57 Ballingdon Street CO10 6DA
Map 5: TL84
Tel: 01787 376777
Fax: 01787 883156
Chef: Darren Boyles
Owners: Gerry & Jane Ford
Cost: Alc £15, fixed-price-price L £7.50/D £9.75. H/wine £7.25. ☺
Times: Last L 2pm/last D 9.30pm. Closed Sun, Bh Mon

Directions: On A131 Chelmsford road out of Sudbury

WOODBRIDGE, Captain's Table ⊛

A long-established seafood restaurant, decked out with nautical paraphernalia. Tony Prentice captains the kitchen, producing dishes such as mixed seafood grill of monkfish, salmon and brill, served with a tangy purée of mango and lime, and fillet of halibut with prawns in a white wine and coriander sauce.

Additional: Bar meals; Children welcome; ⓓ dishes
Smoking: No smoking in dining room
Credit cards: ▬ ▬ ▬ ▬ ⓟ ⓒ

3 Quay Street IP12 1BX
Map 5: TM24
Tel: 01394 383145
Chef/Owner: Tony Prentice
Cost: Alc £22.50, fixed-price L/D £12.95. H/wine £9.95. ☺
Times: Last L 2pm/D 9.30pm. Closed Sun, Mon, last 2 wks Feb

Directions: From A12, pass garden centre on L. Quay St is opposite station & theatre; restaurant 100 yds on L

WOODBRIDGE, Seckford Hall Hotel NEW

Imposing Elizabethan manor house set in peaceful gardens. Period features abound, notably in the formal restaurant which offers competent classic French cooking with innovative modern touches. Expect scallops with garlic, lemon grass and coriander, guinea fowl stuffed with morel mousse, and tropical fruit terrine. Good wine list.

IP13 6NU
Map 5: TM24
Tel: 01394 385678
Fax: 01394 380610
Telephone for details

YAXLEY, Bull Auberge 🏵

A fifteenth-century roadside hostelry with a wealth of beams and exposed brickwork, and rather striking with its deep yellow and dark green table linen. Influences are diverse, the range of dishes including rillettes de canard, blackened redfish with okra and banana, Irish rock oysters, and mascarpone brûlée.

Additional: Sunday L; Bar meals; Children welcome; 🅰 dishes
Smoking: No smoking in dining room; air-conditioning
Credit cards: ▬ 📇 📇 🔨 🖭 🄲

Directions: Adjacent to A140 (Norwich to Ipswich) on junction B1117 to Eye

Ipswich Road IP23 8BZ
Map 5: TM17
Tel/Fax: 01379 783604
Chef: John Stenhouse
Owners: Dee & John Stenhouse
Cost: *Alc* £23, fixed-price D £15. ☺
H/wine £9.
Times: Last L 2pm/last D 9.30pm.
Closed D Sun

YOXFORD, Satis House Hotel 🏵

Eighteenth-century listed house set in three acres of parkland. Expect a warm welcome and both European and Malaysian food carefully prepared with fresh produce. Our inspector enjoyed the authentic Kenduri feast – chicken and lime leaf soup, spicy beef with coconut and chicken baked with coriander, chilli, ginger and lemon grass.

IP17 3EX
Map 5: TM36
Tel: 01728 668418
Fax: 01728 668640
Telephone for details

SURREY

BAGSHOT, Pennyhill Park 🏵🏵🏵

London Road GU19 5ET
Map 4: SU96
Tel: 01276 471774
Fax: 01276 473217
Chef: Karl Edmunds
Cost: *Alc* £45, fixed-price L £21.50/D £32. H/wine £14.50
Times: 12.30pm-2.30pm/7.30pm-11pm
Additional: Bar food L; Sunday L; Children welcome; 🅰 dishes
Seats: 45. Private dining room 80
Smoking: No smoking in dining room
Accommodation: 90 en suite
Credit cards: ▬ 📇 📇 🖭

The original creeper-clad Victorian building, surrounded by fine, formal gardens and terraces, has been much extended over the years, and a second more informal restaurant currently in the pipeline. The beamed, mock Tudor dining room is formal but comfortable, with a mix of banquette and armed tapestry chairs, fresh flowers and linen-fold panelling at one end. Weather permitting, there is a terrace for alfresco eating. Karl Edmunds, having come through a year in which his kitchen was devastated by fire, cooks with a clear French accent, mostly in the classical style. Pan-fried foie gras with crispy celeriac and a truffle jus, avocado and bacon salad with shallot dressing, poached fillet of turbot on a bed of seafood risotto with sauce Jacqueline and fillet of beef with roasted vegetables, glazed with honey and served with a horseradish

cream sauce may be followed by desserts such as hot blackberry soufflé with Bramley apple sorbet or a dark chocolate 'teardrop' filled with a duo of chocolate mousse and griottine cherries. Dishes seem more restrained, in terms of elements and combinations, than in past years – the most excess comes in a main course of pan-fried fillet of venison, served on a tartlet of creamed potatoes and pan-fried spätzli with a fresh cranberry and venison jus, although desserts such as wafers of coffee meringues layered with a Baileys cream show a fondness for sweet liqueurs. One eye-catching idea is a toad in the hole made with chicken sausages in a Yorkshire pudding batter on a bed of creamed potatoes and spring onion, served with a sage and onion sauce.

Directions: On A30 between Bagshot and Camberley

CAMBERLEY, Frimley Hall ❀

Handsome Victorian manor house, with grand staircase, wood panelling and stained glass windows. Traditional English dishes are served in the formal Wellington restaurant – expect venison steak with cranberry and brandy sauce, roast beef and Yorkshire pudding, and baked avocado with spinach and cheese.

Smoking: No smoking in dining room
Accommodation: 66 en suite
Credit cards: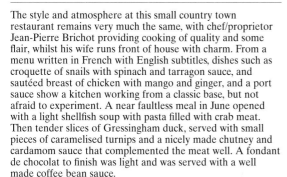

Portsmouth Road GU15 2BG
Map 4: SZ96
Tel: 01276 28321
Fax: 01276 691253
Chef: Marc Legros
Owner: Forte (UK)
Cost: Alc £24.60, fixed-price L £15/D £19.95. ☺ H/wine £13.75.
Times: Last L 2pm/D 9.30pm
Additional: Sunday L; Bar meals; Children welcome; ❹ dishes

Directions: M3/J3, take A322 (Bracknell) then second L onto A30 (Camberley). After 2 miles join A325, take 5th on R, then R into Lime Avenue

CLAYGATE, Le Petit Pierrot ❀❀

The style and atmosphere at this small country town restaurant remains very much the same, with chef/proprietor Jean-Pierre Brichot providing cooking of quality and some flair, whilst his wife runs front of house with charm. From a menu written in French with English subtitles, dishes such as croquette of snails with spinach and tarragon sauce, and sautéed breast of chicken with mango and ginger, and a port sauce show a kitchen working from a classic base, but not afraid to experiment. A near faultless meal in June opened with a light shellfish soup with pasta filled with crab meat. Then tender slices of Gressingham duck, served with small pieces of caramelised turnips and a nicely made chutney and cardamom sauce that complemented the meat well. A fondant de chocolat to finish was light and was served with a well made coffee bean sauce.

4 The Parade KT10 0NU
Map 4: TQ16
Tel: 01372 465105
Fax: 01372 467642
Chef: Jean-Pierre Brichot
Owners: JP & A Brichot
Cost: Fixed-price L £18.95/£21.75. ☺ H/wine £9.75
Times: From 12.15pm/from 7.15pm. Closed L Sat, Sun, 1 wk after Xmas, 1 wk in summer
Additional: No children under 8; ❹ dishes
Seats: 32
Smoking: No pipes; air-conditioning
Credit cards:

Directions: Village centre, 1 mile from Esher

DORKING, The Burford Bridge ❀

Box Hill inspired both Keats and Wordsworth, and visitors to this smart hotel can still marvel at the landscape. Menus range from Chateaubriand to kangaroo, with potted sardines and swordfish, roast venison, red cabbage and sauce soubise, and banoffee pie ice cream also in the repertoire. Eat in the Emlyn Room or alfresco in summer.

Box Hill RH5 6BX
Map 4: TQ14
Tel: 01306 884561
Fax: 01306 880386
Chef: Graham Barlow
Owner: Forte – The Burford Bridge
Cost: Alc £32. H/wine £13.50. ☺
Times: Last L 2.30pm/D 9.30pm

The Burford Bridge

Additional: Bar meals; Sunday L; Children welcome; ❸ dishes
Smoking: No smoking in dining room
Accommodation: 48 en suite
Credit cards: ▦ ▦ ▦ ▦ ▣ ▣

Directions: M25/J9 – A24 S for 4 miles towards Dorking. Hotel on roundabout with directions towards Box Hill

DORKING, **Partners West Street** ❀❀

A change of ownership and a new man in the kitchen but the sixteenth-century building remains much as before with its oak beams, earthy colour schemes and interesting artwork on the walls. Starters on the *carte* might include carpaccio of lamb with marinated and roasted Mediterranean vegetables with sunny flavours shining through in main courses such as roasted duck breast and confit of leg with orange and jasmine tea sauce. By contrast, classic ideas surface in the shape of baked lemon sole filled with crab mousse served with sauce vierge or pavé of Scotch beef with dauphinoise potatoes, creamed parsley and balsamic jus. Desserts take in everything from chargrilled fruit salad with lemon bavarois to a chocolate teardrop filled with white chocolate mousse served with bitter orange sauce. Around 50 wines globe trot in search of quality.

2,3 & 4 West Street RH4 1BL
Map 4: TQ14
Tel: 01306 882826
Chef: James Tea
Owner: Irmgard Bland
Cost: *Alc*: £30. H/wine £11. ☺
Times: Noon-last L 2pm/7pm-last D 10pm. Closed D Sun, Tue, Jan
Additional: Sunday L
Seats: 70. Private dining room 20
Smoking: No-smoking area
Credit cards: ▦ ▦ ▦ ▦ ▣ ▣

Directions: Town Centre – Guildford end of High Street

EGHAM, **Runnymede Hotel** ❀

Windsor Road
TW20 0AG
Map 4: TQ07
Tel: 01784 436171
Fax: 01787 436340
Chef: Laurence Curtis
Cost: *Alc* £24. H/wine £12.95. ☺
Times: Last L 3pm/D 9.45pm Closed L Sat, D Sun
Additional: Bar menu; Sunday L; Children welcome; ❸ dishes
Smoking: No-smoking area; air-conditioning
Accommodation: 171 en suite
Credit cards: ▦ ▦ ▦ ▣

The riverside setting and easy access to the M25 are big pluses at this popular business hotel. In the elegant restaurant, the views onto the Thames form a backdrop to dishes such as salmon fishcakes with saffron sauce, confit of duck with red wine gravy and plum chutney, and warm pear and almond tart, vanilla ice cream and crème anglaise.

Directions: On A308 Windsor road from M25/J3

EPSOM, Le Raj ❀❀

211 Firtree Road KT17 3LB
Map 4: TQ26
Tel: 01737 371371
Fax: 01737 211903
Chef/Owner: Enam A Ali
Cost: *Alc* £20.
Times: Noon-last L 2.15pm/6pm-last
D 10pm. Closed 25 & 26 Dec
Additional: Sunday L; Children
welcome; ❀ dishes
Seats: 48
Smoking: Air-conditioning
Credit cards: 🔳 🔳 🔳 🔳 🔳 🔳

This Bangladeshi restaurant is nothing if not enterprising; one of their most innovative ideas has been to launch the world's first flying restaurant, serving an Indian banquet whilst flying over the sights of London, or else combining a low-level, champagne-fuelled flight with dinner back in Epsom. Their greatest coup, however, was in sending a takeaway to Los Angeles. Although there are familiar dansak, bhoona, and madras dishes on the menu, they are freshly cooked without the use of ghee. Specials, either regional or the original creations of chef-proprietor Enam Ali, include lamb mince meat cooked in mustard oil with fenugreek, coriander and ginger, and Dhaka-style slow-cooked lamb biriany. Ingredients are of dependably high quality, and Bangladeshi freshwater fish is either served as a cutlet with garlic and coriander or as a main course with fresh herbs. There is home-made naan bread baked in the tandoor, plus their own pickles and chutney.

Directions: Off the A217, near the racecourse.

ESHER,
Good Earth Restaurant ❀

A popular Chinese decorated in pine and red lacquer with marble floors. Enjoyable dishes from the extensive menu include Cantonese stir-fried Dover sole, with spring onions, water chestnuts and Chinese mushrooms, and Mandarin fillet steak, sizzling with tender pieces of beef stir-fried with yellow bean and tangy fruit sauce.

Additional: Children welcome; ❀ dishes
Smoking: No pipes or cigars; air-conditioning
Credit cards: 🔳 🔳 🔳 🔳 🔳 🔳

14-18 High Street KT10 9RT
Map 4: TQ16
Tel: 01372 462489
Fax: 01372 465588
Chef: AH Sing
Owner: Holland Kwok
Cost: *Alc* £28, fixed-price L £12. ☺
H/wine £9.50.
Times: Last L 2.30pm/last D 11pm.
Closed Xmas

Directions: Sandown Park end of High Street

EWELL, C'est la Vie ❀

A sixteenth-century listed building with low beamed ceilings, wood floors and a large fireplace. The short set menu features classic French dishes such as roast red mullet with creamed saffron sauce, grilled tournedos of beef with red wine and shallot sauce, and broiled salmon fillet with pastry lattice and leek fondue.

17 High Street
KT17 1SB
Map 4: TQ26
Tel: 0181 3942933
Fax: 0181 7867123
Chef: Lionel Jouanet
Owners: Clive & Jackie Lane

C'est la Vie

Cost: Alc £20, fixed-price L £8.75/D £14.75 (4 courses). ☺ H/wine £9.25.
Times: Last L 2.30pm/D 10pm

Additional: Sunday L; Children welcome; ❹ dishes
Smoking: No-smoking area; air-conditioning
Credit cards: ▀ ▦ ▦ ▚ ▣ ▯

Directions: Village 1 mile from Epsom towards Kingston. Restaurant is opp. Lloyds Bank

FARNHAM, Bishop's Table Hotel ❀❀

27 West Street GU9 7DR
Map 4: SU84
Tel: 01252 710222
Fax: 01252 733494
Chef: Douglas Hull
Owner: Mr K Verjee
Cost: Fixed-priced L&D £18.50. ☺ H/wine £10.
Times: Last L 1.45pm/D 9.45pm Closed 26 Dec-4 Jan
Additional: Sunday L; Children welcome; ❹ menu
Seats: 50. Private dining room 18
Smoking: No cigars or pipes
Accommodation: 17 en suite
Credit cards: ▀ ▦ ▦ ▚ ▣

Once used as a training school for the clergy – hence the name – this charming Georgian town house now functions as a family-run hotel with an up-and-coming restaurant. The dining room, with its pretty Dutch blinds at the windows and views of the walled garden, is run with impeccable polish and professionalism. It makes a fine setting for cooking that shows a surprising degree of skill and restrained invention. Our inspector was bowled over by a brilliant wild salmon and caper berry mousse served on deep-fried watercress with a Montpelier butter sauce, but the kitchen is also capable of other creative flashes such as oxtail and wild mushroom soup, a salad of marinated tuna loin coated in fresh herbs, and saddle of venison on a bed of sweet potato purée with a well-judged pink peppercorn sauce. To finish, fresh peach and raspberry gratin has been enthusiastically received, although the choice extends to apple and pecan strudel with clotted cream, and caramelised oranges laced with brandy and served with coconut ice cream and fresh mint. The wine list offers around three dozen carefully selected bins from well-respected sources.

Directions: In the centre of the town

GODALMING, Inn on the Lake

Set in two acres of splendid landscaped gardens overlooking a lake, this stylish country house-style inn serves good snacks in the pubby bar and a modern British carte in the Lake View Restaurant. Expect teriyaki-style beef, wild mushroom risotto, spicy chicken with bean sprouts and peaches, and summer pudding.

Smoking: No pipes and cigars
Accommodation: 21 en suite
Credit cards: ▬ ▥ ▭ ▚ ◨ ▫

Ockford Road GU7 1RH
Map 4: SU94
Tel: 01483 415575
Fax: 01483 860445
Chef: Wayne Hatenboer
Owner: MG & JE Cummings
Cost: Alc £22. H/wine £9.95. ☺
Times: Last L 1.45pm/last D 9pm.
Closed D Sun, D 26 Dec
Additional: Bar food; Sunday L;
Children welcome; ◑ dishes

Directions: From A3 (Guildford) take A283 (Milford). At traffic lights turn L onto A3100. After 1.5 miles, go under railway bridge, hotel is on R

GUILDFORD,

Angel Posting House

91 High Street GU1 3DP
Map 4: SU94
Tel: 01483 564555
Fax: 01483 533770
Chef: Anthony O'Hare
Owner: Gordon Wigginton
Cost: Alc £25, fixed-price lunch
£15/D £18.50. ☺ H/wine £10.50.
Times: Noon-last L 2.30pm/7pm-last
D 10pm
Additional: Sunday L; Children
welcome; ◑ dishes
Seats: 42. Private dining room 70.
Jacket and tie preferred at D
Smoking: No-smoking area; air-
conditioning
Accommodation: 21 en suite
Credit cards: ▬ ▥ ▭ ▚ ◨ ▫

Historic town centre coaching inn where a Jacobean fireplace and a seventeenth-century 'parliament' clock are among the original features to be found in cosy public areas. The thirteenth-century stone-vaulted, tapestry-hung restaurant is the setting for Tony O'Hare's sound cooking. The sheer industry in the kitchen is evident in the several varieties of their own bread rolls, the petits fours and, as was noted at a winter dinner, the 'especially good' canapés: hot chicken beignet, smoked salmon tartlet, fresh foie gras, duck pâté. At that same meal a lobster and basil raviolo came with a decent creamy lobster and brandy sauce, maize-fed chicken with smoked ham and truffle in the stuffing and ginger and lapsang souchong tea in the sauce; accompanying vegetables were excellent – spinach wrapped leek and tomato parcel on rösti, carrot (both a mousse and turned), cauliflower and broccoli florets. Sabayon-glazed winter fruits proved to be a good selection of sliced fruits. Valet parking for lunch guests as the High Street is pedestrianised between 10am and 4pm.

Directions: In town centre (one way street)

GUILDFORD, Gate Restaurant

The warm Mediterranean colours make this small restaurant seem light and airy, despite its size. Owned by a local wine company, there is the bonus of an interesting and changing wine list, and probably few other places where you're likely to find cru Beaujolais as house wine. The cooking is modern, free-wheeling and the *carte* is balanced and well-priced. With easy going individuality, it picks its way between the likes of braised rabbit, spiced couscous with apricots and harissa sauce, tuna fish with three-bean salad, salsa verde and lemon, and pot-roasted pheasant with choucroute, parsley and garlic. Vegetable crisps seem to be something of a signature – mushroom risotto sported crisp parsnip fronds, seafood spring rolls with sweet and sour sauce had a bundle of deep-fried beetroot strands, and there was even a crispy, citrus zest on the dessert of gypsy toast with citrus fruit and cardamom. The set lunch is an unmissable bargain.

Directions: In a passageway just off the main High Street in central Guildford

3 Milkhouse Gate GU1 3EZ
Map 4: SU94
Tel: 01483 576300
Fax: 01483 455068

Chef: Steven Dray

Owner: Liz Reid
Cost: *Alc* £25, fixed-price L £8.95 (2 courses). ☺ H/wine £10.95
Times: Noon-last L 2.30pm/7pm-last D 10.30pm. Closed Sun, Xmas-New year, last 2 wks Aug
Additional: Children welcome; ✪ dishes
Seats: 50
Smoking: No-smoking area; air-conditioning
Credit cards: 🔲 🔲 🔲 🔲

GUILDFORD, The Manor ✿

Quietly situated in nine acres of mature grounds, the Manor offers a good choice of typically English dishes, plus a varied vegetarian selection, in its panelled restaurant. A dinner in March started with confit of quail with warm brioche and was followed by delicious noisettes of lamb with a tangy redcurrant jus.

Directions: M25/J10 – A3 (Ripley) to W Clandon, up hill, hotel is on L

Newlands Corner GU4 8SE
Map 4: SU94
Tel: 01483 222624
Fax: 01483 211389
Telephone for details

HASLEMERE, Fleur de Sel ✿✿✿

The setting is Surrey, in a trio of 300-year-old listed cottages set up on a high pavement in a very English village, but everything else about this restaurant is French through and through. Chef/proprietor Michel Perraud hails from Noirmoutier, which is also the source of the eponymous 'fleur de sel' (high quality sea salt). Pastel blues and yellows create a summery mood in the dining room, where customers are treated to some top-flight cooking in the modern classical style. Meals begin with unusual rolls such as pistachio, or tomato and bacon, and there's no doubting the kitchen's technical expertise when it comes to handling meat and fish or creating fulsome sauces. Starters might include a warm chicken mousseline with blue cheese and walnuts providing contrast, texture and bite, crab ravioli served in vegetable consommé, or a slice of foie gras served on a flat rösti roundel with a fruity, sticky elderberry sauce. Moving on you might find daube de boeuf with another excellent sauce, this time laced with Beaujolais. Alternative centrepieces are the likes of roast Scotch salmon and scallops with squid-ink sauce, lamb cutlets topped with wild mushroom soufflé, and braised and boned oxtail with baby vegetables. The best way to experience desserts is to order the 'farandole' – lots of 'lovely mouthfuls' on one plate: our inspector singled out a 'super' little chocolate cake with a liquid centre, creamy nougatine mousse, mini-crème brûlée, some marron purée and a quenelle of Drambuie cream. Otherwise try, say, mille-feuille of bananas with caramel sauce, or shortcrust biscuits with pear sabayon.

23-27 Lower Street GU27 2NY
Map 4: SU94
Tel: 01428 651462
Fax: 01428 661568
Chef/Owner: Michel Perraud
Cost: Fixed-price L £9.50/£12.50 (2-3 courses)/D £12.50/£16.50 (mid week only). ☺ H/wine £11.
Times: Noon-last L 2pm/7pm-last D 10pm. Closed L Sat, D Sun, Mon, 2 wks summer.
Additional: Sunday L; Children welcome; ✪ dishes
Seats: 50
Smoking: No pipes and cigars in dining room
Credit cards: 🔲 🔲 🔲 🔲 🔲

Signature dishes: Lobster and scallop terrine served with leek sabayon; breast of chicken filled with sweet peppers, wrapped in crisp potatoes; roast crispy duck with honey and ginger sauce; iced terrine of glazed fruits with honey and figs.

Directions: In the town centre, turn R at the top of High St

HASLEMERE,
Lythe Hill House ❀❀

Petworth Road
GU27 3BQ
Map 4: SU94
Tel: 01428 651251
Fax: 01428 644131
Chef: Roger Clarke
Cost: *Alc* £28; fixed-price D £17.50 (2 courses). ☺ H/wine £11.75
Times: D only 7.15pm – last D 9.15pm. Closed Mon
Additional: Bar food; Sunday lunch (12.15pm-2.15pm); Children welcome; ✦ dishes
Seats: 60. Private dining room 24
Smoking: No smoking in dining room
Accommodation: 40 en suite
Credit cards: ■ ■ ■ ■ ■ ■

Lythe Hill has been created out of a cluster of historic buildings set in twenty acres of fine grounds that include a bluebell wood and several lakes. Chef Roger Clarke has been here a long time, getting on for 20 years, and he presides over the oak-panelled Auberge de France restaurant, set in the original house (there is another restaurant in the main building). 'Oodles of character, of course,' sums up one inspector, ' being set in a fourteenth-century black and white timbered building featuring lots of low beams and mellow wood panelling.' The menu, in French with English subtitles, embraces modern ideas, offering the likes of warm tartlet of plum tomato and goat's cheese, medallion of ostrich garnished with a sauté of Mediterranean vegetables, fresh and accurately grilled brill served with coriander and lentil cream and topped with a fan of cooked banana, and a chocolate and Tia Maria brûlée to finish.

Directions: 1 mile E of Haslemere on B2131 off A286

HERSHAM, The Dining Room ❀

10/12 Queens Road KT12 5LS
Map 4: TQ16
Tel: 01932 231686
Cost: *Alc* £17.50, fixed-price L/D £12.75. ☺ H/wine £9.50.
Times: Last L 2.30pm (3pm on Sun)/D 10.30pm. Closed L Sat, D Sun, 24 Dec-3 Jan, Bh Mon
Additional: Sunday L; Children welcome; ✦ dishes
Smoking: No cigars or pipes; air-conditioning
Credit cards: ■ ■ ■ ■ ■

Charming restaurant housed in two Victorian cottages. The small but stylish menu takes in duck and damson pie in rich black sauce, tender strips of chicken sizzled with Cajun spices and peppers, and lamb steak with Rutland Ale gravy. Alfresco meals (under the dappled shade of the secluded patio) are a real pleasure.

Directions: From A3 at Esher take A244 (Walton-on-Thames); turn L into Hersham at Barley Mow pub/roundabout; restaurant is off village green

HORLEY, Langshott Manor ❀

Pretty-as-a-picture small Elizabethan manor house, now a hotel of enormous charm and comfort. The fixed-price dinner, served in the beamed dining-room, offers a concise choice of dishes, but be sure to leave room for the delicious desserts and/or the excellent farmhouse cheeses.

Additional: Bar meals D; Sunday L; No children under 10; ❸ dishes
Seats: 25. Private dining room 12
Smoking: No smoking in dining room
Accommodation: 9 en suite
Credit cards: 🁢 🁢 🁢 🁢 🁢 🁢

Ladbroke Road RH6 9LN
Map 4: TQ24
Tel: 01293 786680
Fax: 01293 783905
Chef: Colin Gibbons
Owners: Christopher, Geoffrey & Patricia Noble
Cost: Fixed-price L £24/D £32.50. H/wine £12
Times: Noon-last L 1.30pm/7pm-last D 9.15pm. Closed L Sat, 25-30 Dec

Directions: From A23 Horley, take Ladbroke Road turning off Chequers Hotel roundabout, 0.75 mile on R

NUTFIELD, Nutfield Priory ❀❀

Redhill RH1 4EN
Map 4: TQ35
Tel: 01737 822066
Fax: 01737 823321
Chef: Stephen Cane
Owner: Arcadian Hotels (UK) Ltd
Times: Noon-last L 2pm/7pm-last D 10pm. Closed L Sat, Dec 26-30
Additional: Bar meals; Sunday L; Children welcome; ❸ dishes
Seats: 60. Private dining room 6-30
Smoking: No smoking in dining room
Accommodation: 60 en suite
Credit cards: 🁢 🁢 🁢 🁢 🁢 🁢

Nutfield is a remarkable piece of work – a flamboyantly designed Victorian folly complete with intricate carved wood, pierced stonework and crenellated battlements. There's even a smartly restored pipe organ in the lounge, and the views stretch for miles over the Downs. The Cloisters Restaurant was designed to copy the cloisters of the Palace of Westminster: it makes a novel setting in which to sample food that is in the classic French tradition, but light with it. Presentation is very busy: grilled baby squid is served on a buttery, herb-tinged risotto, while roast lamb with a tarragon jus comes with prettily shaved carrots and leeks, a small rösti and creamed artichoke heart. Other offerings from the menu might include daube of venison with roasted apples and foie gras, and pan-fried scallops with fondant potatoes and balsamic jus, while poached pear with praline cream makes a typically rich but dainty sweet. Master of Wine John Hoskins is the driving force behind the irresistibly fascinating wine list.

Directions: On A25 1 mile east of Redhill

REIGATE, **Bridge House Hotel**

The hotel's perched high on top of Reigate Hill and its Mediterranean-style restaurant overlooks miles of countryside. The Med influence extends to the menu with dishes such as breast of chicken with mozzarella and finely cut peppers, and cannelloni pancake filled with asparagus and mushrooms.

Smoking: No pipes & cigars in dining room
Accommodation: 39 en suite
Credit cards:

Directions: M25/J8 (Reigate), A217 under footbridge and then on R

Reigate Hill RH2 9RP
Map 4: TQ25
Tel: 01737 246801
Fax: 01737 223756
Chef: David Dunn
Owner: Onesto Lanni
Cost: Alc £30, fixed-price L £16/D £21. ☺ H/wine £11.50.
Times: Last L 2.15pm/D 10pm
Additional: Sunday L; Children welcome; ❸ dishes

REIGATE, **The Dining Room**

One has the sense of dining in a private club at this first floor restaurant, brightly hung with still life pictures. The short but lively menu is almost Californian in its eclectic explorations – seared tuna with roasted tomatoes, coriander and lime pesto, and fried goat's cheese fondants with tomato-chilli jam, for example. Chilli, in fact, seems a favourite way of enlivening flavours, as in chilli roast lamb with provençale vegetables and roasted garlic vinaigrette, and roast breast of chicken with garlic, sage and chilli oil and provolone shavings. Expensive ingredients are given a refreshingly insouciant treatment (wok-fried baby lobster with coriander, lime and spicy noodles), while more mundane ones get a lift (barbecued pork chop, braised cabbage and mustard mash). Desserts are generally more conservative, but a passionfruit curd tart with Italian meringue caught the eye and the imagination.

Directions: First floor restaurant on Reigate High Street

59a High Street RH2 9AE
Map 4: TQ25
Tel: 01737 226650
Chef: Anthony Tobin
Owner: Paul Montalto
Cost: Alc £30, fixed-price L £7.50/D £13.95 (2 courses). ☺ H/wine £8.50.
Times: Noon-last L 2pm/7pm-last D 10pm. Closed L Sat, Sun, Xmas, Easter, 2 wks summer
Additional: Children welcome; ❸ dishes
Seats: 50
Smoking: No smoking in dining room; air-conditioning
Credit cards:

RIPLEY,
Michels' Restaurant

13 High Street GU23 6AQ
Map 4: TQ05
Tel: 01483 224777
Fax: 01483 222940
Chef: Erik Michel
Owners: Erik & Karen Michel
Cost: Alc £38, fixed-price L £21/D £23 (4 courses). H/wine £12
Times: 12.30pm-last L 1.30pm/7.30pm-last D 9pm. Closed L Sat, D Sun, Mon, 1 wk Jan, 2 wks Aug
Seats: 45-50. Private dining room 12
Credit cards:

Erik Michel's eponymous restaurant occupies a Georgian house in the centre of town, and inside it is boldly decorated with the proprietor's own paintings – which he finds time to create when he is away from the kitchen. His cooking is generally technically accomplished, ideas are bright, presentation artful. Typically complex starters might include sliced new potatoes with garlic mayonnaise and mussels 'drowned' in a saffron-tinged vegetable consommé, or white crab meat on julienne of courgettes with roasted tomatoes surrounded by a crab coral sauce and a chiffonade of oven-dried vegetables. Main courses inhabit similar territory – steamed sea bass with a butter sauce pointed up with lemon grass, basil and tomatoes accompanied by deep-fried shrimps or pork fillet wrapped in a cabbage leaf and baked with roast garlic and a sage-flavoured Madeira sauce. Top of the tree as regards desserts is probably a warm chocolate fondant cake with ginger ice cream, although rum baba filled with crème pâtissière and fresh fruit accompanied by passion fruit sorbet has also been well received. A concise wine list offers nine well chosen house wines under £14, all available by the glass – look no further than Les Chemins de Bassac (Vin de Pays d'Oc) at £12.75. A particularly good rosé is Costières de Nîmes at £11.75. The New World section covers Australia, New Zealand, Chile and South Africa, with some good drinking at under £20 – note New Zealand's Nobilo Estate Sauvignon at £16.35, and a Yaldara Shiraz at £14.25.

Directions: Take M25/J8 towards Guildford. First exit to Ripley just past lights on R

SHERE, Kinghams ❀❀

Shere is a picturesque village, full of historic buildings, including Kinghams, a charming seventeenth-century cottage with beamed ceilings and walls. There are crisp white cloths and tapestry upholstered chairs, and a relaxed and cheerful atmosphere. The menu is fairly short but does not lack interest, and the cooking stays comfortably within its limits. Starters include pressed chicken, Parma ham and leek terrine, and a warm salad of cheese beignets with walnut dressing. A blackboard lists the daily fish dishes, otherwise there is an attractive choice of meat ones, such as roast pheasant breast served on sage and apricot stuffing with cranberry gravy and parsnip chips, roast loin of lamb topped with a fresh herb soufflé crust, or rib steak either chargrilled or with various sauces. Vegetarians can opt for the leek and pepper crumble on spiced carrot sauce. Our inspection ended particularly well with a freshly baked caramelised mango flan served with first-rate vanilla ice cream.

Directions: From Dorking follow A25; from Guildford follow A246 then A25

Gomshall Lane GU5 9HB
Map 4: TV14
Tel: 01483 202168
Chef: Paul Baker
Owners: Paul Baker, Jason Baker
Cost: *Alc* £22, fixed-price L&D £10.95 (2 courses, not D Fri/Sat). ☺
H/wine £9.50.
Times: Noon-last L 2.30pm/7pm-last D 10pm. Closed D Sun, Mon, 25-26 Dec, Bhs
Additional: Sunday L; Children welcome; ❸ dishes
Seats: 44. Private dining room 26
Smoking: No-smoking area; no pipes and cigars
Credit cards: 🖿 🖿 🖿 🖿 🖿

SOUTH GODSTONE,
La Bonne Auberge ❀❀

The setting may seem like a quintessentially English country house with 14 acres of grounds complete with a two-acre lake, but the cooking is rooted in the French tradition. A choice of fixed-price menus supplements the *carte* and the kitchen seems

Tilburstow Hill
Godstone RH9 8JY
Map 5: TQ34
Tel: 01342 892318
Fax: 01342 893435
Chef: Mark Cheeseman

La Bonne Auberge

Owner: Antoine L S Jalley
Cost: Alc £20, fixed-price L £16/D
£18.90. ☺ H/wine £10.50.
Times: Noon-last L 1.45pm/7pm-last
D 9.45pm. Closed D Sun, Mon,
25-26 Dec, 1 Jan
Additional: Sunday L; Children
welcome; ♦ dishes
Seats: 86. Private dining room 30
Smoking: No cigars or pipes in dining
room
Credit cards: ▬ ▦ ▦ ▧ ▣ ▢

particularly adept at balancing flavours. An inspection meal
provided some happy combinations in the shape of spinach
and cep filo tart topped with Roquefort and a poached egg, as
well as crispy aromatic duck breast with a subtly judged vanilla
and chervil jus. Other typical dishes from the repertoire might
include ragout of queen scallops and mussels with a tomato
salsa, pan-fried fillet of beef with rosemary and garlic and roast
lamb cutlets with asparagus mousse and a tomato and tarragon
fondue. Raspberry bavarois makes a stylishly presented finale
and coffee comes with decent petits fours. The wine list is a
heavyweight collection of around 130 bins with a
predominantly French bias – although the New World does get
a look in.

Directions: M25/J6 – A22 (Godstone) turn right after Bell pub

STOKE D'ABERNON,
Woodlands Park ❀

Woodlands Lane KT11 3QB
Map 4: TQ15
Tel: 01372 843933
Fax: 01372 842704
Chef: James Chapman
Owner: Arcadian International Hotels
Cost: Alc £25.30, fixed-price L
£14.95/D £20.50. ☺ H/wine £11.50.
Times: Noon-last L 2.30pm/7.30pm-
last D 9.30pm (10pm Sat). Closed L
Sat, D Sun, Bhs
Additional: Bar food; Sunday L;
Children welcome; ♦ dishes

*An attractive Victorian mansion with an impressive Grand Hall. As
well as the Oak Room Restaurant, which serves dishes such as roast
fillet of pork with candied apples and Calvados sauce and breast of
duck with fig sauce and poached pears, there is more informal
dining in Langtry's Bar and Brasserie.*

Seats: 30. Private dining room 10-270. Jacket & tie preferred
Accommodation: 59 en suite. **Credit cards:** ▬ ▦ ▦ ▧ ▣ ▢

Directions: On the A245 between Leatherhead and Cobham,
close to M25/J10

TADWORTH, Gemini ❀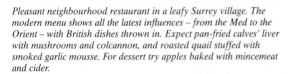

Pleasant neighbourhood restaurant in a leafy Surrey village. The modern menu shows all the latest influences – from the Med to the Orient – with British dishes thrown in. Expect pan-fried calves' liver with mushrooms and colcannon, and roasted quail stuffed with smoked garlic mousse. For dessert try apples baked with mincemeat and cider.

Additional: Sunday L; Children welcome for L; ❹ dishes
Smoking: No cigars or pipes
Credit cards: ▆ ▆ ▆ ▆ ▆

Directions: M25/J8, on roundabout turn R to Sutton, on 3rd roundabout take 2nd exit to Tadworth, At traffic lights turn R, restaurant is on L.

28 Station Approach
Map 4: TQ25
Tel: 01737 812179
Chef/Owner: Robert Foster
Cost: Alc £24.50, fixed-price L £14.50/D £24.50. ☺ H/wine £8.95.
Times: Last L 2pm/D 10pm. Closed D Sun, Mon, L Sat,

THAMES DITTON, Avant Garde ❀

When Avant Garde opened in the late summer 1996 it hit the ground running, serving a mix of reworked classic French dishes at reasonable prices. Look out for monkfish noisettes with smoked haddock mousse, roasted duck magret served on a lemon and peppercorn sauce, and fillet of beef wrapped in bacon.

Additional: Children welcome; ❹ dishes
Credit cards: ▆ ▆ ▆ ▆ ▆

Directions: 5 mins from Hampton Court Palace

75 High Street KT7 0SF
Map GtL: B1
Tel: 0181 398 5540
Chef/Owner: Frederick Dervin
Cost: Alc £18, set L £5.50/D £12.50. ☺ H/wine £8.50.
Times: Last L 2.30pm/D 10pm. Closed D Sun

WEYBRIDGE,
Oatlands Park Hotel ❀

Ample choice at this large hotel includes Dublin Bay prawns poached in dry Vermouth with avocado and smoked ham in a pastry case, and half a Surrey duckling with a cherry and Kirsch sauce. Sizzling steak on a granite stone is an intriguing addition to the menu, as is the imaginative effort with vegetables.

Additional: Bar food; Sunday L; Children welcome; ❹ dishes
Smoking: No pipes & cigars
Accommodation: 128 en suite
Credit cards: ▆ ▆ ▆ ▆

Directions: Through town, up Monument Hill, L into Oatlands Drive. Hotel on L.

146 Oatlands Drive KT13 9HB
Map 4: TQO6
Tel: 01932 847242
Fax: 01932 821413
Chef: John Hayes
Owner: Oatlands Investments Ltd
Cost: Alc £27, fixed-price L £17/D £19.50. ☺ H/wine £11.50.
Times: Last L 2pm/D 10pm. Closed L Sat, some L Bhs, between Xmas-New Year

Entries in this Guide are based on reports filed by our team of professionally trained, full-time inspectors.

WEYBRIDGE, **The Ship Thistle**

Monument Green KT13 8BQ
Map 4: TQ06
Tel: 01932 848364
Fax: 01932 857153
Chef: Gary Smith
Owner: Thistle Hotels
Cost: Alc £25, fixed-price L £10.75-£13.75/D £17.95. ☺ H/wine £11.45.
Times: Last L 1.45pm/D 9.45pm
Additional: Sunday L; Bar meals; Children welcome; ◑ dishes
Smoking: No smoking in dining room; air-conditioning
Accommodation: 39 en suite
Credit cards: ▬ ▒ ▒ ▒

Charming town centre hotel noted for warm hospitality and good service. L'Escales Restaurant offers promising food from a young, keen brigade. Typical choices from the carte may include tomato and mozzarella terrine with pesto vinaigrette, followed by sea bass stuffed with fennel with a lemon beurre blanc.

Directions: Town centre – M25/J11, or A3/J10

SUSSEX EAST

ALFRISTON,
Moonraker's Restaurant

It's business as usual at this attractive sixteenth-century cottage restaurant located in the centre of a historic village. The consistently high standard of service, ingredients and cooking is reflected in a fixed-price menu that changes according the season. Dishes that have been enjoyed at inspection include quail's egg in duck and orange pâté and Sussex smoky – a selection of smoked fish in white sauce, topped with gratinated Cheddar cheese – as well as main courses such as rack of lamb with redcurrant sauce and a tartlet of mint jelly, roasted escalope of salmon with dill and lemon butter and Hungarian beef goulash. Lemon sponge with orange sauce and crème brûlée might be amongst the short selection of desserts, followed by fresh filtered coffee.

High Street BN26 5TD
Map 5: TQ50
Tel: 01323 870472
Chef: Mark Goodwin
Owners: Norman & Angelica Gillies
Cost: Alc £20, fixed-price D £12.95-£15.95. H/wine £8.95
Times: 7pm-last D 9.45pm
Additional: Sunday L;
No children under 8; ◑ dishes
Seats: 48. Private dining room 20
Smoking: One dining room no smoking; no pipes or cigars
Credit cards: ▬ ▒ ▒ ▒

Directions: Alfriston signposted from A27 between Brighton and Eastbourne

BATTLE, **Netherfield Place** ❀❀

Built in the 1920s, this mock-Georgian country house is set amid 300 acres of tranquil parkland between Netherfield and Battle. Long-serving owners, the Colliers, care for the place well and the atmosphere remains eminently civilised. The kitchen makes good use of local produce as well as the harvest from the hotel's own gardens and the menus offer plenty of

Netherfield TN33 9PP
Map 5: TQ71
Tel: 01424 774455
Fax: 01424 774024
Chef: Clinton Webb
Owners: Helen & Michael Collier
Cost: Alc £30, fixed-price L £13.95/D £25 (4 courses). ☺ H/wine £8.95.

Netherfield Place

Times: 12.30pm-last L 2pm/7pm-last
D 9.30pm. Closed 2wks Jan
Additional: Bar food; Sunday L;
No children under 4; ♨ dishes
Seats: 75. Private dining room 40
Smoking: No pipes or cigars in dining
room
Accommodation: 14 en suite
Credit cards:

interesting possibilities. Marinated saddle of Ashburnham venison is served with juniper berry sauce, breast of local pheasant is pot-roasted with vegetables and thyme, while shank of Sussex lamb is served on parsnip purée. To start there might be wild mushroom soup with Madeira, or fillets of sole on a well-cooked olive risotto with beurre blanc, while desserts range from caramelised lemon tart to chocolate roulade with raspberry coulis. Home-baked breads, canapés and petits fours are well up-to-the-mark. The extensive wine list puts its faith in dependable growers from all parts of the globe.

Directions: M25/J5 – A21 (Hastings) to A2100 for Netherfield; hotel is on L after 1.5 miles

BATTLE,

PowderMills Hotel ☺☺

In the eighteenth century, PowderMills was part of a gunpowder factory making the finest in Europe, now the setting couldn't be more tranquil: 150 acres of wooded, lake-dotted grounds, with a stone-balustraded bridge leading to the extended, wisteria-clad mansion. A light, airy theme dominates the conservatory-style Orangery Restaurant – complete with marble floor and cushioned wicker chairs – which forms the backdrop to Paul Webbe's restrained modern cooking. The style is simple, flavours are clear and presentation attractive. An inspector was impressed by a good plum confit that lifted pork rillettes, and by the well-balanced aromatic sauce that came with a magret of duck with confit of leg on a stir-fry of

Powdermill Lane
TN33 0SP
Map 5: TQ71
Tel: 01424 775511
Fax: 01424 774540
Chef: Paul Webbe
Owners: Douglas & Julie Cowpland
Cost: Alc £25, fixed-price L £15 (3
courses). ☺ H/wine £9.95
Times: Noon-last L 2pm/7pm-last D
9pm
Additional: Bar food L only; Sunday
lunch; No children under 10;
♨ dishes
Seats: 100. Private dining room 16.
Jacket & tie preferred
Smoking: No-smoking area in dining
room
Accommodation: 35 en suite
Credit cards:

bean sprouts and spring onion. Pudding was a caramelised Bramley apple tart, cooked to order, and rather meagre on the butterscotch and Calvados sauce, but the addition of sweetened cream cheese was a good idea. Canapés and petits fours are home-made, as is the bread, which is outstanding.

Directions: Past Battle Abbey toward Hastings, 1st turn R into Powdermill Lane just before Battle train station; hotel is on R after 1 mile.

BRIGHTON, Black Chapati

The setting is an arcade of shops just off Preston Circus, a few minutes from the centre of town. Inside it is reminiscent of a café: black-topped tables crammed close together, white walls and bright lights are the sum total of the decor. What matters, however, is the radically inclined food. Stephen Funnell describes his cooking as 'evolved Asian', in fact it's a risky, maverick view of Far Eastern cuisine seen through western eyes. Ideas are garnered mercilessly from India, China, Thailand and Japan, ingredients are stirred in the cultural melting pot, the result is a menu of dishes that refuse to be pigeonholed. Bhel pooris and Keralan vegetarian thalis are reminders of the early days of the Chapati, but the current crop of dishes might extend to steamed mussels with lemon grass, Thai basil and udon noodles, roast leg of salt duck with Chinese greens and fried rice, and rack of lamb with aubergine stew and couscous. Desserts return to the occident for lemon tart with crème fraîche, and dark chocolate ice cream with a brandy snap. A handful of wines and beers provide decent drinking, but rare ciders are the real cult offerings.

Directions: Directions are complex. Readers are advised to use a local map

12 Circus Parade New England Road BN1 4GW
Map 4: TQ30
Tel: 01273 699011
Chef/Owners: Stephen Funnell, Lauren Alker
Cost: Alc £20. H/wine £9.50. ☺
Additional: Children welcome; ⓓ dishes
Times: 7pm-last D 10.30.pm. Closed Sun, Mon, 2 wks Xmas, 2 wks July
Seats: 30
Smoking: No pipes or cigars in dining room
Credit cards: 🔲🔲🔲🔲🔲

BRIGHTON, Brighton Thistle

Large modern hotel occupying a prime seafront location. Comfortable public areas are enclosed under an attractive atrium. In the Noblesse Restaurant, ambitious modern cooking takes in cream of mussels with saffron and poached watercress, and pork fillet with Parma ham, sweetbreads and tarragon sauce.

Directions: On the seafront

King's Road BN1 2GS
Map 4: TQ30
Tel: 01273 206700
Fax: 01273 820692

Chef: David Veal
Owner: Thistle Hotels
Cost: Fixed-price L £18.50/D £26.50. H/wine £12.50
Times: Last L 2pm/D 9.45pm. Closed L Sat, Sun, Mon
Additional: Bar food; Sunday L; No children under 5; ⓓ dishes
Smoking: No-smoking area in dining room
Accommodation: 204 en suite
Credit cards: 🔲🔲🔲🔲🔲🔲

BRIGHTON, La Marinade

Small restaurant owned and run by the charming Vincent Lhuillery, almost as a one-man show. His daily-changing, hand-written carte features classic French dishes such as langoustines served with mushrooms and crème d'anis sauce, poached brill fillet with beurre rouge, and roasted pigeon with honey.

Smoking: Non-smoking area. **Credit cards:** ▉ ▉ ▉ ▉ ▉ ▉

Directions: From Palace Pier take direction of Marina, turn L at Royal Sussex Hospital sign, then first L

77 St George Road BN2 1EF
Map 4: TQ30
Tel/Fax: 01273 600992
Chef/Owner: Vincent Lhuillery
Cost: Fixed-price L £12.80/D £18.50.
☺ H/wine £9.80
Times: Last L 2pm/D 10pm.
Closed D Sun, Mon
Additional: Sunday L;
No children under 1; ❹ dishes
Seats: 26

BRIGHTON, One Paston Place

Since taking over as owners, Mark and Nicole Emmerson have put their stamp on this popular Brighton address. The trademark 'Langan' pictures have gone, and the pale yellow room now features a mural depicting a view from the conservatory. Gilt-framed mirrors hang on one wall, balloon-back chairs are grouped around crisply clothed tables. Nicole is an accomplished hostess, Mark cooks. His modern menu has a forthright French accent and his repertoire changes constantly. A 'raviolo' of scallop mousse and langoustine tails with fond d'artichaut made an excellent start to one meal, while main courses could range from fillet of sea bass on a bed of spicy couscous with vegetable beignets to pavé of calves' liver with salsify and thyme. The quality of the desserts shows in the expert assiette gourmande sampled by our inspector: mini-versions of coconut brûlée, unctuous toffee tartlet, passionfruit sorbet and others. A handful of New World wines and fine vintages bolster the mainly Gallic list.

Directions: Just off the seafront about halfway between the Palace Pier and the Marina

1 Paston Place BN2 1HA
Map 4: TQ30
Tel: 01273 606933
Fax: 01273 675686
Chef: Mark Emmerson
Owners: Mark & Nicole Emmerson
Cost: *Alc* £28, fixed-price L £16.50 (3 courses). H/wine £9.40
Times: 12.30pm-last L 2pm/7.30pm-last D 10pm. Closed Sun & Mon, 1st two weeks Jan & Aug
Additional: No children under 5; ❹ dishes
Seats: 45
Smoking: No pipes or cigars in dining room; air-conditioning
Credit cards: ▉ ▉ ▉ ▉ ▉ ▉

BRIGHTON, Terre à Terre

7 Pool Valley BN1 1NJ
Map 4: TQ30
Tel: 01273 729051
Fax: 01273 327561
Chefs: Paul Morgan, Lawrence Glass
Owners: Philip Taylor,
Amanda Powley
Cost: *Alc* £17. H/wine £8.75. ☺
Times: Noon – last D 10.30pm.
Closed 25-26 Dec
Additional: Children welcome;
❹ dishes
Smoking: No-smoking area
Credit cards: None

Influences are global at this vegetarian restaurant, and there's lots of interest and flavour. Choose tapas if you want to taste your way around the menu. Ricotta, lemon and parsley dumplings were well received, as was the individual apple and cinnamon charlotte. Look out for good breads and notable organic wines.

Directions: Town centre near Cannon cinema, close to Palace Pier

BRIGHTON, Whytes ❀❀

Ian and Jane Whyte continue to please the crowds in their converted fisherman's cottage just off the seafront. She supervises the front of house in charmingly hospitable fashion while he cooks. Their menu changes every few weeks to take account of fresh produce, and the kitchen generally has some locally caught fish on offer. Grilled brill with soft red peppers and chives in a cream sauce pleased our inspector, but the repertoire also extends to, say, ragout of corn-fed chicken with Pernod, basil and mussels, and crispy roast duckling with a caramelised grapefruit and pink peppercorn sauce. Starters range from salmon and coriander fishcakes with home-made tomato ketchup to pan-fried pigeon breast and peach salad, while desserts (which are recited at the table) could feature chocolate marquise with 'lovely' caramelised oranges. A fair number of half-bottles support the serviceable wine list.

Directions: On the Brighton-Hove border, Western St is off the seafront, 1st R after the Norfolk Resort Hotel

33 Western Street BN1 2PG
Map 4: TQ30
Tel: 01273 776618
Chef: Ian Whyte
Owners: Ian & Jane Whyte
Cost: Fixed-price D £19.50.
H/wine £8.70
Times: D only, 7pm - 9.30pm.
Closed Sun, Mon, end Feb for 2 wks
Additional: ❹ dishes
Seats: 36. Private dining room 16
Smoking: No cigars or pipes in dining room
Credit cards: ▬ ▬ ▬

EASTBOURNE,
The Downland Hotel ❀❀

A photographic family tree of the owners holds pride of place in the bar of this intimate, personable hotel – along with a display of military helmets. Patrick Faulkner cooks, while his wife Stephanie provides warm hospitality out front. The kitchen produces everything from breads and nibbles to the marzipan chocolate served with good cafetière coffee. There is plenty of skill in evidence here and the cooking shows invention without resorting to gimmickry. A typically sound inspection began with ballotine of chicken stuffed with ginger, served on rocket, with apple and cider dressing, and concluded in fine style with a stunningly good orange and elderberry brûlée. In between you might find medallions of venison on a croûton cunningly topped with lentil purée, steamed fillet of pike with crispy pasta and lemon butter sauce, or grilled fillet of beef with polenta rösti and Stilton sauce. The wine list is peppered with popular and familiar names.

Directions: On A2021 about 0.5 mile from the town centre

37 Lewes Road BN21 2BU
Map 5: TV69
Tel: 01323 732689
Fax: 01323 720321
Chef: Patrick Faulkner
Owners: Patrick & Stephanie Faulkner
Cost: Alc £25, fixed-price D £17.50.
☺ H/wine £9.50.
Times: D only, 6.30pm-9pm.
Closed Sun, Mon, 26-30 Dec
Additional: No children under 10;
❹ dishes
Seats: 35
Smoking: No cigars and pipes in dining room
Accommodation: 14 en suite
Credit cards: ▬ ▬ ▬ ▬ ▬

EASTBOURNE,
Grand Hotel, Mirabelle ❀❀

A majestic piece of Victorian architecture, unassailably grand, is this aptly named hotel which stands at the western end of the seafront before the steep ascent to Beachy Head. The stylish Mirabelle is all soft colours, high ceilings, and the formal service of food that is as elegant as the surroundings. Standards remain high. Dishes such as warm salad of smoked quail or pithiviers of lambs' sweetbreads, followed perhaps by assiette of lamb (peppered loin, medallion and cutlet topped with a herb mousseline), or vegetable pie with roasted celeriac, candied onions and morel cream sauce, give an idea of the style. There's always a good choice of seafood. The pudding problem is easily solved by plumping for ménage à trois (three

King Edward Parade BN21 4EQ
Map 5: TV69
Tel: 01323 410771
Fax: 01323 412233
Chef: Keith Mitchell
Owner: De Vere Hotels
Cost: Alc £35, fixed-price L £18.50/D £31. H/wine £11.75
Times: 12.30pm-last L 2pm/7pm-last D 9.30pm. Closed Sun, Mon, 2 wks Jan, 2 wks Aug
Additional: Bar food; Sunday L; Children welcome;
❹ dishes

Grand Hotel, Mirabelle

Seats: 40. Private dining room 300.
Jacket and tie preferred
Smoking: No smoking in the dining
room; air-conditioning
Accommodation: 164 en suite
Credit cards: ■ ■ ■ ■ ■

small desserts served as one), or a trio of dark, milk and white
Belgian chocolate desserts.

Directions: On the seafront at the western end of town

FOREST ROW,

Ashdown Park Hotel ❀❀

Wych Cross RH18 5JR
Map 5: TQ43
Tel: 01342 824988
Fax: 01342 826206
Chef: John McManus
Owner: Ashdown Park Hotel
Cost: *Alc* £32, fixed-price L £21/D
£31. H/wine £13.75.
Times: 12.30pm-last L 2pm/7.30pm-
last D 9.30.pm (10 pm Sat.)
Additional: Bar meals L; Sunday L;
Children welcome; ◑ dishes.
Seats: 100. Private dining room up to
150
Smoking: No cigars or pipes in dining
room
Accommodation: 95 en suite
Credit cards: ■ ■ ■ ■ ■ ■

The setting is an absolute joy: a sprawling Victorian mansion
standing in 186 acres of grounds complete with secret gardens,
woodland trails, streams and ornamental lakes teeming with
Koi carp. The house (once a convent) also has its own chapel
with stained glass windows and a fully working organ. Meals in
the elegant Anderida Restaurant begin with a fine selection of
canapés, then a choice of menus provides plenty in the way of
imaginative ideas based on sound technique. A 'smartly done'
crab tartlet with fried squid rings and a bright red pimento
sauce impressed at inspection, as did marinated rump of lamb
served with 'meaty' Puy lentils, a rösti and port wine sauce.
Other options might include chargrilled John Dory with a
casserole of mussels, saffron and kumquats, and roast pigeon
breasts with a sweetcorn and thyme pancake and peppercorn
cream. To finish, seared custard with rhubarb ice cream and
shortbread biscuits was reckoned to be clever and
appropriately seasonal. The well-annotated wine list leans
heavily towards France.

Directions: From A22 at Wych Cross take Hartfield turning, hotel
is 0.75 mile on R

FRANT, **Bassetts Restaurant**

Sixteenth-century building where atmospheric surroundings are created by low oak beams and a bottle-filled fireplace. The restaurant is split level with a comfortable adjoining lounge and bar area. Expect braised pigeon with herb dumplings and sautéed root vegetables, or poached halibut with hazelnut mousseline and vermouth butter sauce.

Times: Last L 1.30pm/D 9pm. Closed Sun, Mon, last wk Jan, first wk Feb
Additional: Children welcome; ⊕ dishes
Smoking: No smoking in dining room
Credit cards: ▬ ▬

Directions: Opposite the village church

35 High Street TN3 9DT
Map 5: TQ53
Tel: 01892 750635
Fax: 01892 750913
Chef: D Morey
Owners: N Mott, K Sinclair
Cost: Fixed-price L £16/D £26.50.
H/wine £9.25

HAILSHAM, **Boship Farm Hotel**

Set in attractive grounds and offering a relaxed and congenial atmosphere, this extended farmhouse serves an interesting range of well presented dishes in the traditional, candlelit dining room. Typical choices may include duck galantine with orange and cranberry compote and monkfish wrapped in bacon with lemon hollandaise.

Directions: On A22 at Boship; junction of A22/A267/A271

Lower Dicker BN27 4AT
Map 5: TQ50
Tel: 01323 844826
Fax: 01323 843945
Telephone for details

HAILSHAM, **The Olde Forge**

Small, cottagey hotel with a cosy beamed bar and candlelit restaurant. The cooking is sound, honest and fresh and includes some traditional French favourites such as trout amandine and steak chasseur. A typical meal could be mushroom soup, poached salmon hollandaise, and a fresh fruit roulade to finish.

Smoking: No pipes or cigars
Accommodation: 7 rooms
Credit cards: ▬ ▬ ▬ ▬ ▬ ▬

Directions: On A271, 2.5 miles from Lower Dicker roundabout towards Bexhill.

Magham Down BN27 1PN
Map 5: TQ50
Tel/Fax: 01323 842893
Chef: Jean Daniels
Owner: J Bull
Cost: *Alc* £18, fixed-price D £15. ☺
H/wine £8.
Times: D only 7pm- 9.30pm.
Closed 25 Dec-2 Jan
Additional: Sunday L only (noon-last L 1.45pm); Children welcome; ⊕ dishes

HASTINGS & ST LEONARD'S,
Beauport Park

Fine Georgian manor house surrounded by 40 acres of formal gardens and parkland. However, the Garden Restaurant, where the staff are dressed in Victorian costume, serves thoroughly modern British cooking. Dishes range from pan-fried loin of lamb with fried aubergine to thin slices of veal flamed with mushrooms and cream.

Smoking: No smoking in dining room; air-conditioning
Accommodation: 23 en suite
Credit cards: ▬ ▬ ▬ ▬ ▬ ▬

Directions: On main A2100, 3 miles from both Hastings and Battle

Battle Road TN38 8EA
Map 5: TQ80
Tel: 01424 851222
Fax: 01424 852465
Chef: Duncan Biggs
Owner: Harvest Hotels Ltd
Cost: *Alc* £28, fixed-price L £16/D £21. ☺ H/wine £9.50.
Times: Last L 2pm/last D 9.30pm
Additional: Bar food; Sunday L; Children welcome; ⊕ dishes

HASTINGS & ST LEONARD'S,

Röser's Restaurant ✤✤✤

64 Eversfield Place TN37 6DB
Map 5: TQ80
Tel/Fax: 01424 712218
Chef: Gerald Röser
Owners: Gerald & Jenny Röser
Cost: *Alc* £35, fixed-price L £18.95/D
£21.95. ☺ H/wine £10.95.
Times: Noon-last L 2pm/7pm-last D
10pm. Closed L Sat, Sun, Mon, 2 wks
Jan & Jun
Additional: Children welcome;
🌢 dishes
Seats: 30. Private dining room 30
Smoking: No pipes and cigars
Credit cards: 🁢 🁢 🁢 🁢 🁢 🁢

Röser's is housed in an unprepossessing Victorian terrace
within sight of Hastings pier. Inside is a panelled dining room
with patterned fabrics and curtains at the windows overlooking
the esplanade. This is a tightly-run ship: German-born Gerald
Röser plus one apprentice in the kitchen, wife Jenny
overseeing the front of house with amiable hospitality. The
strength of the cooking is its clarity and simplicity; there is no
desire to over embellish, or to get sidetracked into cluttering
the plate with gestures that seek to impress. Two dishes from a
recent inspection show what Röser is about: Rye Bay scallops
surrounded by a light creamy sauce that zinged with saffron
flavour without going over the top, and smoke-roasted salmon
(almost 'sooty' in flavour) with a gloriously refined
Gewürztraminer sauce. Raw materials matter here, as do the
seasons. Röser has a passion for fungi, and mycological
treasures are peppered throughout the repertoire: pickled wild
mushroom salad with roast wood pigeon breast, a soup of
Jerusalem artichokes with slivers of earthy fresh truffles
(courtesy of Franco Taruschio at the Walnut Tree Inn,
Llandewi Skirrid), for example. Fish – much of it from the
Hastings boats – might include turbot with cream of
ratatouille, chargrilled sea bream with Puy lentils, or roast
monkfish with fennel and langoustine stock, while meat could
run to wild boar (perhaps cured in port, then smoked by Röser
himself) alongside best end of Romney Marsh lamb marinated
in olive oil, garlic, ginger and rosemary. Among the desserts is
a signature dish – lightly poached slices of Granny Smith apple
held together with a Calvados-infused crème pâtissière, lightly
caramelised on top and served on swirls of butterscotch sauce.
The vast tome of a wine list is not entirely centred on France,
although the great producers of Bordeaux, Burgundy and
Rhône are there in abundance. The inclusion of an impressive
range from Moselle is a bold stroke and there is plenty of
excitement in Italy too, with well priced Chianti from Ruffino
and the sumptuous Ornellaia from Antinori.
Signature dishes: Apple mille-feuille with a butterscotch
sauce; chargrilled sea bass with olives and capers; wild
mushroom salad with chanterelles, ceps and fresh truffle
dressing; pike soufflé with smoked salmon and dill dressing.

Directions: On the seafront, opposite Hastings pier.

HERSTMONCEUX,
Sundial Restaurant

A French-style auberge in the heart of Sussex. For thirty years Guiseppe Bertoli and his French wife Laure have run this cottage-restaurant, serving up a few Italian favourites along with inventive interpretations of classic French dishes to both loyal regulars and new customers. Guiseppe's repertoire is extensive, his skill with sauces worth stressing. Set-price menus, plus a five-course 'surprise gourmandaise', supplement the lengthy *carte*, while daily specials provide even more choice. At a meal in March, quenelles of scallops and monk fish came with lobster sauce and parsnip purée. This was followed by loin of Scotch salmon, served with two poached eggs and hollandaise sauce. Other, typical main courses could include roast crispy duckling with strawberry sauce, tender sirloin steak with peppercorns and brandy, and lightly fried langoustines in pastry. The lengthy wine list features mainly French bottles, plus a number from the Italian regions.

Directions: In centre of village, on A271

Hailsham BN27 4LA
Map 5: TQ81
Tel: 01323 832217
Chef: Giuseppe Bertoli
Owners: Giuseppe & Laure Bertoli
Cost: A/c £31.50, fixed-price L £19.50/D £26.50. ☺ H/wine £12.25
Times: Noon-last L 2pm (2.30pm Sun)/7pm-last D 9.30pm. Closed D Sun, Mon, from Xmas-20 Jan, Aug 10 – 1st wk Sep
Additional: Sunday L; Children welcome; ♨ dishes
Seats: 40. Private dining room 22
Smoking: No smoking in dining room
Credit cards: ▆ ▆ ▆ ▆ ▆ ▆

HERSTMONCEUX,
White Friars Hotel ❀

The panelled Ashburnham Restaurant at this former medieval hall offers a varied carte and fixed-price menu. Sound cooking may be highlighted by seafood terrine with tomato and shallot salsa, followed by roast quail stuffed with apricot and pistachio mousse. To finish try the prune and Armagnac parfait.

Smoking: No smoking in dining room
Accommodation: 20 en suite
Credit cards: ▆ ▆ ▆ ▆ ▆ ▆

Directions: 2m east on A271

Boreham Street BN27 4SE
Map 5: TQ81
Tel: 01323 832355
Fax: 01323 833882
Chef: Duncan Englefield
Owners: Clive & Antony Williams
Cost: A/c £23, fixed-price L £9.50/D £19.50. ☺ H/Wine £9.50.
Times: Last L 1.50pm/D 8.50pm (Fri & Sat 9.20pm)
Additional: Sunday L; Bar meals; Children welcome; ♨ dishes

HOVE, Quentin's

Quentin and Candy Fitch have built up a strong local following in their agreeable little restaurant in a busy parade of shops. The mood inside is pleasantly relaxed as customers sit at scrubbed pine tables and gaze at the modern 'foodie' prints on the walls. Quentin smokes his own salmon and makes admirable use of local seafood for a monthly menu that is French with distinct Oriental overtones. His personal style showed up well in a recent inspection that began with salmon, basil and chilli fishcakes with Cumberland sauce, followed by corn-fed chicken breast served on a rösti with flageolet beans, wilted greens and a mustard and bay sauce. Menus might also feature anything from beef teriyaki kebabs and Thai vegetable curry to sautéed calves' liver and peppered duck breast with blackberry sauce. Desserts include a fine version of crème brûlée tinged with saffron, as well as Hungarian hazelnut torte and apricot and Madeira parfait. Six house wines by the glass head the short, affordable list.

Directions: On the south side of Western Road between Brunswick Square and Palmeira Square

42 Western Road BN3 1JD
Map 4: TQ30
Tel: 01273 822734
Chef: Quentin Fitch
Owners: Quentin & Candy Fitch
Cost: Fixed-price L £5.95 (1 course)/D £17.95. ☺ H/wine £8.50.
Times: Noon-last L 2pm/7pm-last D 10pm. Closed Sat, Sun, Mon
Additional: Children welcome; ♨ dishes
Seats: 28. Private dining room 22
Smoking: No pipes and cigars in restaurant; air-conditioning
Credit cards: ▆ ▆ ▆ ▆ ▆ ▆

JEVINGTON, **Hungry Monk** ✿✿

Nr Eastbourne BN26 5QF
Map 4: TQ60
Tel/Fax: 01323 482178
Chefs: Claire Burgess, Lucy Baldwin
Owners: Sue & Nigel Mackenzie
Cost: Fixed-price D £23.50. ☺
H/wine £9.
Times: D only, 7pm – last D
10.15pm. Closed Bhs, 24-26 Dec
Additional: Sunday L (noon-2.30pm)
Seats: 40. Various private dining
rooms
Smoking: No smoking in dining room;
air-conditioning
Credit cards: ▨

Nigel and Sue Mackenzie claim to have invented the 'banoffi' pie, and this much imitated dessert still appears on the menu of their long-serving restaurant. The 500-year-old flint house was originally a monastic retreat, and there are still echoes of the past in the oak beams and antiques that set the tone in the candlelit dining room. Seafood from the Newhaven boats might appear in the shape of a croustade of four fish with spinach, or fillet of sea bream with red wine and shallot sauce. Elsewhere the kitchen makes use of local ingredients for a world-wide menu that takes in such things as Thai beef, sweet potato, spring onion and coriander cake with curried tomato sauce, and pigeon breasts stuffed with foie gras and mushrooms served with Armagnac sauce and braised Savoy cabbage. In addition to 'banoffi' pie, the line-up of desserts is likely to range from, say, caramelised apple and Calvados syllabub to pineapple tarte Tatin with crème fraîche. Bacchus wine from nearby Barkham Manor vineyard appears on the well-spread list of reasonably priced tipples.

Directions: Follow the A22 towards Eastbourne. Turn R on to the B2105. The restaurant is between Polegate and Friston

LEWES, **Shelleys Hotel** ✿✿

High Street BN7 1XS
Map 5: TQ41
Tel: 01273 472361
Fax: 01273 483152
Chef: Allen Sperring
Owner: Thistle Hotels
Cost: Alc £30, fixed-price L
£13-£17/D £25. H/wine £11.50
Times: Last L 2.15pm/D 9.15pm
Additional: Bar Food L; Sunday L;
Children welcome; ♨ dishes
Smoking: No smoking in dining room
Accommodation: 19 en suite
Credit cards: ▨ ▨ ▨ ▨ ▨ ▨

It was an inn in the sixteenth century, but is now a pleasant town house hotel with the dining room overlooking a peaceful garden; the style is elegant yet relaxed. The menu format of a list of seasonal specialities supplementing the fixed-price menu works well. There is a serious attitude to the food, and the menu reflects this, but generally does not stray too far from recognised combinations. Sussex bouillabaisse of locally caught fish, home-cured gravad lax flavoured with dill and gin, and chargrilled lamb's liver with a morel and spring onion gravy, show the range. An early summer dinner highlighted a well made chicken and guinea fowl parfait with pieces of duck foie gras, oyster mushrooms and baby leeks, poached turbot with pak choi, fennel and star anise beurre blanc, with some 'unadvertised' marsh samphire coming as a 'nice touch', and pine nut and praline tart, which came with a whisky and honey ice cream.

Directions: Town centre

NEWICK, Newick Park

A stunning dessert, croustillant of chocolate with pistachio ice cream, pistachio cream and a vanilla sauce, was the star of our inspector's meal at this beautiful Georgian house with views over parkland, lake and river. The dining-room is in the former ballroom, and has panelled walls, intricate mouldings and a large marble open fireplace, and guests can choose from either a set five-course gourmet menu or the carte. Grilled lobster on leaf spinach with a pea ragout, and veal cutlet with a panaché of root vegetables, gratin dauphinoise and a rich veal jus, both did justice to the quality of their ingredients. Much of the latter is supplied locally – an assiette of South Downs lamb, for example, is served on a bed of pearl barley risotto with its own jus. Canapés, appetisers and petits fours are all expertly and freshly made.

BN8 4SB
Map 5: TQ42
Tel: 01825 723633
Fax: 01825 723969
Chef: Jason Neilson
Owners: Michael & Virginia Childs
Cost: Alc £30, fixed-price L £17.50/D £25. H/wine £8.70
Times: 12.15pm-last L 2.15pm/7pm-last D 10pm. Closed D Sun
Additional: Sunday L; Children welcome; ✿ dishes
Seats: 45. Private dining room 14-45. Jacket and tie preferred
Smoking: No smoking in dining room
Accommodation: 13 en suite
Credit cards: ▬ ▨ ▨ ▨ ⬚

Directions: From Newick on A272 between Haywards Heath/ Uckfield, turn S on Church Road, at end of road turn L. Hotel 0.25 mile on R

PEASMARSH, Flackley Ash Hotel

Rye TN31 6YH
Map 5: TQ82
Tel: 01797 230651
Fax: 01797 230510
Chef: Dale Skinner
Owners: Clive & Jeanie Bennett
Cost: Fixed-price L from £9.50/D £21. ☺ H/wine £9.95.
Times: Last L 1.45pm/last D 9.30pm
Additional: Bar food; Sunday L; Children welcome; ✿ dishes
Smoking: No smoking in dining room
Accommodation: 32 en suite
Credit cards: ▬ ▨ ▨ ▨ ▣ ⬚

Home-made desserts, preserves and cakes were all highly praised at our last inspection meal at this friendly Georgian hotel. Main courses were well-reported too. Typical dishes include grilled fillet of haddock with watercress sauce, roast Romney Marsh lamb with apple and mint jelly, and filo parcel of sea bass with sorrel sauce.

Directions: M25/J5, take A21 (Flimwell), turn L on to A268 (Peasmarsh)

RYE, Landgate Bistro

Grilled fillet of eel with watercress sauce, lamb's sweetbreads sautéed with ginger and coriander, and chump of English lamb with butter beans, bacon and basil are typical of the enterprising menu in this much-liked, beamed bistro. Honest cooking, casual attentive service, backed by a short list of reasonably priced wines.

5-6 Landgate TN31 7LH
Map 5: TQ92
Tel: 01797 222829
Chef: Toni Ferguson-Lees
Owners: Nick Parkin & Toni Ferguson-Lees
Cost: Alc £22, fixed-price D £14.90 (Tue-Thu only) ☺
Times: D only, 7pm-last D 9.30pm. Closed Sun, Mon
Additional: Children welcome; ✿ dishes

Seats: 30
Smoking: No pipes & cigars
Credit cards: ▬ ▨ ▨ ▨ ▣ ⬚

Directions: From the High Street head towards the Landgate. The bistro is in a row of shops on L

RYE, The Mermaid Inn ❀

An ancient, timbered inn up a narrow, cobbled street, serving a classic Anglo-French mix of dishes. Roast best end of English lamb with redcurrant and rosemary sauce, and grilled suprême of Scotch salmon with buttered prawns, spring onions and lemon are typical of the daily changing, four-course menu.

Times: Last L 2pm/ last D 9.15pm
Additional: Bar food; Sunday L; children welcome; ❹ dishes
Accommodation: 28 en suite
Credit cards: ▆▆ ▆▆ ▆▆ ▆▆ ▆ ℂ

Directions: Town centre. Car park through archway

Mermaid Street TN31 7EU
Map 5: TQ92
Tel: 01797 223065
Fax: 01797 225069
Chef: Matthew Varty
Owners: Robert Pinwill,
Judith Blincow
Cost: Alc £21, fixed-price L £14.95/D
£23. ☺ H/wine £9.85.

SEAFORD, Quincy's ❀❀

The front room of this pleasant, family-run restaurant used to be a cobblers shop, and owners Ian and Dawn Dowding have imbued the place with a certain domesticity. Warm colour schemes, illuminated pictures and bookcases add to the atmosphere. Fish from Newhaven is the main attraction on the seasonal fixed-price menus, but the kitchen also takes on board dishes such as Moroccan artichoke and almond soup, and goat's cheese and sun-dried tomato baked in puff pastry. Main courses are equally eclectic with roast saddle of venison coming with chestnuts, apples and smoked bacon, while quail is stuffed with saffron tabouleh and served with wild mushroom and Madeira sauce. Desserts range from grilled apricots with Amaretto and crème fraîche, to treacle tart with clotted cream. Four 'great wines' front the extensive wine list, which plunders the globe in search of quality.

Directions: From the A259 turn into Broad Street (opposite Caffyns Garage) then L into old High Street. Restaurant is 50 metres up on R

42 High Street BN25 1PL
Map 5: TQ40
Tel: 01323 895490
Chef: Ian Dowding
Owners: Ian & Dawn Dowding
Cost: Fixed-price D £22.45. ☺
H/wine £9.25.
Times: D only, 7pm-10pm.
Closed D Sun, Mon
Additional: Sunday L (noon-2pm);
Children welcome; ❹ dishes
Seats: 28
Smoking: No-smoking area
Credit cards: ▆▆ ▆▆ ▆▆

UCKFIELD, Buxted Park ❀❀

The imposing Georgian mansion is the works: 300 acres of stunning Sussex countryside, a wealth of original architectural features, stylish decor, and an original Victorian orangery where the restaurant is housed. Here, muslin softens the light from the glass roof, and tall windows overlook the putting green. The hotel is Thai owned and this influences the menu slightly, although the kitchen works hard to produce food that is of broader interest, taking in ideas from everywhere, and cooking standards are high. A spring dinner opened with good 'nibbles' – a hot filo 'purse' filled with smoked salmon and goat's cheese, and a chicken and mango tartlet. Then 'a super dish' of local rabbit and sage pithiviers that came with a rich and intensely reduced sauce based on black olives, sun-dried tomato and tarragon jus. Lemon sorbet was home-made with lots of zest, and was followed by paupiette of lemon sole and salmon with basil and a 'rather good' lobster butter sauce. To finish, chocolate bread-and-butter pudding with a sauce anglaise – ' a good idea that worked'.

Directions: Turn off A22 Uckfield By-pass (London-Eastbourne road), then take A272 to Buxted. Cross set of traffic lights, entrance to hotel is 1 mile on R

Buxted TN22 4AX
Map 5: TQ42
Tel: 01825 732711
Fax: 01825 732770
Chef: Glenn Purcell
Owner: Buxted Park Country
House Ltd
Cost: Alc £30, fixed-price L £14.50/D
£25 (4 courses). H/wine £11.75
Times: Noon-last L 1.30pm/7pm-last
D 9.15pm. Closed L Sat
Additional: Sunday L; Bar meals;
Children welcome; ❹ dishes
Seats: 65. Private dining room 120
Smoking: No smoking in dining room
Accommodation: 44 en suite
Credit cards: ▆▆ ▆▆ ▆▆ ▆▆ ℂ

UCKFIELD,
Hooke Hall, La Scaletta ❀❀

250 High Street TN22 1EN
Map 5: TQ42
Tel: 01825 766844
Fax: 01825 768025
Chef: Michele Pavanello
Owners: Juliet & Alister Percy
Cost: A/c £25, fixed-price L £9.75 (2
courses).☺ H/wine £10.75
Times: Noon – last L 2pm/7.15pm –
last D 9pm. Closed L Sat, all Sun,
2 wks Feb
Additional: No children under 10;
🍴 dishes
Seats: 30. Private dining room 20
Smoking: No smoking in dining room
Accommodation: 9 en suite
Credit cards: 🖷 🖷 🖷 🖷

Italy has come to Uckfield in the shape of this elegant Queen
Anne town house. La Scaletta wears a well upholstered, stylish
look – all warm tones and walls covered with pictures, plates
and hangings. Michele Pavanello cooks an essentially north
Italian menu that changes every two months. The repertoire is
a step up from traditional trattoria fare and value for money is
excellent, especially at lunch. Marinated beef, smoked salmon,
Roman salami, and grilled aubergines with smoked scamorza
cheese might appear as antipasti, and there could be tagliatelle
with duck and walnut sauce, or a risotto of scampi, broad
beans and pesto sauce from the *primi piatti* section (also
available as a main course). Fish and meat dishes might include
brill fillet with green asparagus and shellfish dressing, or
casserole of wild boar with polenta. Mango mousse with
banana sauce gives a light finishing touch. The wine list is
predominantly Italian with a small French selection.

Directions: Northern end of High Street.

UCKFIELD, Horsted Place ❀❀❀

Grand is an understatement for this magnificent example of
Gothic revivalist architecture, designed by Pugin and built
around 1850 by George Myers. It is surrounded by a 1,000 estate
which now includes the East Sussex National Golf Club, and
inside it is full of elegantly proportioned rooms and there is a
particularly fine staircase. The dining room has raspberry
coloured wallpaper with discreet paintings on the walls, and a
semi-private area at one end known as 'The Justices'. Allan
Garth's cooking has evolved slowly over the years; he is not one
for showy gestures, although saucing is one of his great
strengths, with strong, complex flavours to the fore. Smoked
haddock and asparagus are served on fresh noodles, medallions
of pork come with a tian of pork, prunes and hazelnuts, while
saddle of rabbit is filled with shallots, brioche and lime leaves
and set on shiitake mushrooms. A recent inspection began
confidently with 'particularly moreish' amuse-gueules including
a skewer of spicy minced lamb, a filo purse of goat's cheese, and
a prawn and vegetable fritter. To start, plump seared scallops
with cubes of Jerusalem artichoke and an intense hot lobster
dressing proved outstanding. This was followed by accurately
pink rump of lamb on a pile of mash with sprigs of wild garlic

Little Horsted TN22 5TS
Map 5: TQ42
Tel: 01825 750581
Fax: 01825 750459
Chef: Allan Garth
Owner: Granfel Holdings Ltd
Cost: A/c £35, fixed-price L £16.95/D
£28.50. H/wine £12.50
Times: Noon-last L 2pm/7.30pm-last
D 9.15pm
Additional: Bar food; Sunday L;
No children under 12; 🍴 dishes
Seats: 40. Private dining room 24
Smoking: No smoking in dining room
Accommodation: 17 en suite
Credit cards: 🖷 🖷 🖷 🖷 🖷 🖷

554 SUSSEX, EAST – WEST **ENGLAND**

strewn over it and a well-made rosemary jus, unusual accompaniments included a mould of couscous with sun-dried tomatoes and mushrooms. To finish, pear and almond with slices of wine-poached pear, cold anglaise sauce and vanilla ice cream; otherwise there is a choice of British farmhouse cheeses. A broad brush of a wine list traverses the globe sweeping up some familiar and well-loved names from most regions. House wines have an intelligent emphasis on the southern French revival, and the extensive list of half-bottles offers genuine choice.

Signature dishes: noisette of lamb on asparagus and minted hollandaise; grilled fillet of sea bass on a salad of roasted vegetables and tomato dressing; raspberry strudel pastry; breast of pheasant wrapped in bacon and thyme, served with a purée of parsnips.

Directions: Two miles South of Uckfield on the A26

WILMINGTON, Crossways Hotel ✿✿

Surrounded by good walking country close to the South Downs Way and in the shadow of the Long Man of Wilmington, this white-fronted Georgian hotel makes an ideal basecamp for travellers. David Scott and Clive James run the place with infectious enthusiasm and take care with what happens in the kitchen. Bread, sorbets and ice creams are made on the premises, many ingredients are organically grown and fish varies from day to day. Typical dishes from the four-course dinner menu might include duck and pheasant galantine, steamed bacon pudding with tomato sauce and roast Gressingham duck served with sun-dried cranberry and kumquat sauce. Local Southdown lamb also appears, perhaps casseroled with peanuts in a mild curry sauce. Desserts include such things as banana brandy snap filled with crème chantilly and topped with butterscotch caramel sauce. The wine list is worth perusing: in particular note the selection from English vineyards as well as the French contingent.

Nr Polegate BN26 5SG
Map 4: TQ42
Tel: 01323 482455
Fax: 01323 487811
Chefs: David Stott & Juliet Anderson
Owners: David Stott & Clive James
Cost: Fixed-price D £25.95. H/wine £9.95
Times: D only, 7.30pm-last D 8.45pm. Closed Sun, Mon, Jan
Additional: No children under 12; ✇ dishes
Seats: 24
Smoking: No smoking in dining room
Accommodation: 7 en suite
Credit cards: 🔲 🔲 🔲 🔲 🔲

Directions: A27, 2 miles W of Polegate

SUSSEX WEST

AMBERLEY, Amberley Castle ✿✿

A chunk of authentic medievalism in the Sussex countryside overlooking the Weald and downland. The edifice itself dates back to the eleventh century and comes complete with a massive gate house (complete with a working portcullis), high curtain walls and battlements. White peacocks strut their stuff in the grounds and the interior is packed with treasures, from an ancient oubliette to garde robes (the last word in fourteenth-century sanitation). Meals are served in the Queens Room restaurant, an atmospheric room with its barrel-vaulted ceiling and lancet windows. The 'Castle Cuisine' menu picks up on the historic theme by offering carefully researched old English recipes such as brawn with piccalilli and spiced fig chutney or black cap pudding with lavender ice cream. Other

Arundel BN18 9ND
Map 4: TQ01
Tel: 01798 831992
Fax: 01798 831998
Owners: Martin & Joy Cummings
Cost: Alc £40, fixed-price L from £10/D £27.50. H/wine £13.95
Times: Noon-last L 2pm/7pm-last D 9.45pm
Additional: Sunday L; No children under 10; ✇ dishes
Seats: 30. Private dining room 48. Jacket and tie preferred
Smoking: No smoking in dining room
Accommodation: 15 en suite

Amberley Castle

Credit cards:

menus reflect more modern ideas: featherlight langoustine flan (actually a mousse) with coriander; scallops and coriander comes studded with mussels; lamb cutlets are wrapped in caul with a herby forcemeat stuffing and served with a mint flavoured rösti and a deep sticky sauce. Desserts range from strawberry brûlée to mille-feuille of chocolate mousse and praline meringue with pistachio custard. A heavyweight list of more than 250 wines casts its net wide in search of quality.

Directions: Off the B2139 between Amberley and Houghton villages.

ARUNDEL,

Burpham Country Hotel

A one-time rectory, dating from 1750, facing due south with glorious downland views. The menu has a Swiss influence, manifest in 'butterleberli' – pan-fried strips of calves' liver, and schnitzel of pork fillet, breadcrumbed, pan-fried and topped with ham, peppers and cheese. Rösti is a favourite accompaniment.

Old Down Burpham BN18 9RJ
Map 4: TQ00
Tel: 01903 882160
Fax: 01903 884627
Chef: Neal Findley
Owners: George & Marianne Walker
Cost: Fixed-price D £20. ☺ H/wine £9.50.
Times: D only, 7.30pm-last D 8.45pm. Closed Sun, Mon, 2 wks Jan
Additional: No children under 10; ❹ dishes
Smoking: No smoking in dining room
Accommodation: 10 en suite
Credit cards:

Directions: 3 miles NE of Arundel, off A27

ARUNDEL, George & Dragon

Nearly 400 years old, although externally (white painted brick, bow windows, flowering baskets), it looks younger, the George and Dragon lies in a peaceful village at the end of a three-and-a-half mile no-through-road four miles from Arundel. The pleasant, intimate dining room is only open for dinner (plus Sunday lunch) but bar meals at every session (except Sunday evening) are recommended. The cooking is modern and ambitious with a distinct Mediterranean slant, although it also looks to the English past for inspiration. The menu is

Burpham BN18 9RR
Map 4: TQ00
Tel: 01903 883131
Fax: 01903 883341
Chefs: Gary Scutt, Kate Holle, David Futcher
Owners: James Rose, Kate Holle
Cost: Fixed-price D £16.50-£19.50 (2-3 courses). ☺ H/wine £9.25
Times: D only, 7.15pm-last D 9.45pm. Closed 25 Dec

refreshingly short and might feature lemon scented scallops with vegetable spaghetti and a chervil beurre blanc, mussel and saffron soup lightly flavoured with fennel and curry, roast rack of lamb with champ and apricot sauce, and sautéed lambs' kidneys with a sherry cream sauce and a wild rice timbale. The dessert trolley is a splendid affair loaded with the likes of lime meringue pie, and banoffee pie with slices of fresh banana on top of the 'toffee' on a lovely crushed-biscuit base. Be warned, lashings of cream is a hallmark of desserts here.

Additional: Bar food; Sunday L (12.15pm-2pm); No children under 8; 🍴 dishes
Seats: 36.
Smoking: No pipes in dining room
Credit cards: ▬ 🖩 🖩 📇 📇

Directions: 2.5 miles up no-through road signposted Burpham off A27, 1 mile E of Arundel

ARUNDEL, Norfolk Arms Hotel ⚜

An eighteenth-century town-centre coaching inn (built by the tenth Duke of Norfolk), and retaining a traditional atmosphere. The extensive restaurant menu offers freshly prepared dishes. On a recent visit, smoked haddock with cheese sauce was followed by tender stir-fried lamb with noodles, and pears in red wine.

Smoking: No smoking in dining room
Accommodation: 34 en suite
Credit cards: ▬ 🖩 🖩 📇 📇 📇

Directions: In Arundel High St

High Street BN18 9AD
Map 4: TQ00
Tel: 01903 882101
Fax: 01903 884275
Chef: Neil Jack
Owner: Forestdale Hotels
Cost: Alc £17, fixed-price L £9.95. ☺
H/wine £8.95.
Times: Last L 1.45pm/last D 9.45pm
Additional: Bar meals; Sunday L;
Children welcome; 🍴 dishes

ARUNDEL, The Swan Hotel ⚜

A Grade II listed building restored to its original Victorian elegance, the Swan offers a good range of dishes in its candlelit restaurant. Options might include crevettes and sole served on a quenelle of spinach and leek, or pork marinated in oriental spices, wrapped in Parma ham and roasted.

Accommodation: 15 en suite
Credit cards: ▬ 🖩 🖩 📇 📇 📇

Directions: Town centre

27-29 High Street BN18 9AG
Map 4: TQ00
Tel: 01903 882314
Fax: 01903 883759
Chef: Michael Collis
Owners: John Ryan, Steven Lowson
Cost: Alc £25, fixed-price L/D £12.95. ☺ H/wine £7.95.
Times: Last L 2.30pm/D 9.30pm
Additional: Sunday L; Bar meals;
No children under 5; 🍴 dishes

BILLINGSHURST, The Gables ⚜⚜

Picture postcard pretty, The Gables is a fifteenth-century beamed cottage with low black beams and plenty of character. Rebecca Illes looks after guests with great charm and vivacity, while her husband, Nick, works tirelessly in the kitchen, producing self-assured, confident cooking that takes in classic favourites as well as more modern offerings. Prime pork fillet, sautéed with spinach, garlic and cream, might appear alongside grilled fillet of salmon with a twist of lemon and freshly-made hollandaise sauce, or chargrilled Scotch fillet with roasted shallots, bacon and a rich red wine sauce. There's a large selection of fish dishes, including the likes of a simply-grilled Dover sole, and steaks, perhaps a Chateaubriand for two with béarnaise sauce. The wine list, although short, deserves a mention – there are some very good domaine bottled red and white Burgundies, plus some historic *cru classé* Bordeaux. Weekends are busy, so it's advisable to book early.

Directions: On A29 just S of Billingshurst

Parbrook RH14 9EU
Map 4: TQ02
Tel: 01403 782571
Fax: 01403 784094
Chef: Nick Illes
Owners: Nick & Rebecca Illes
Cost: Fixed-price L £17.50/D £23. ☺ H/wine £10.
Times: 12.15pm-last L 1.30pm/7.15pm-last D 9pm.
Closed L Sat, D Sun, Mon
Additional: Sunday L
Seats: 52
Smoking: No pipes & cigars in dining room
Credit cards: ▬ 🖩 🖩 📇
Directions: On the A29 just south of Billingshurst

BOSHAM, **Millstream Hotel**

Set beside a mill stream, this former malthouse is now home to the modern English cooking of Bev Boakes. The seasonal set-price menu makes good use of local produce such as fresh fish, game and poultry. Expect pan-fried breast of duck with prunes and Calvados sauce, and roast fillet of beef Wellington, with wild mushroom sauce.

Bosham Lane PO18 8HL
Map 4: SU80
Tel: 01243 573234
Fax: 01243 573459
Chef: Bev Boakes
Owner: John Wild
Cost: Fixed-price L £13.50/D £19.50.
☺ H/wine £9.75.
Times: Last L 2pm/D 9.30pm
Additional: Bar food L; Sunday L;
Children welcome; ❹ dishes
Smoking: No smoking in dining room;
air-conditioning
Accommodation: 33 en suite
Credit cards:

Directions: Take A259 exit from
Chichester roundabout and in village
follow signs for quay

BRACKLESHAM,
Cliffords Cottage Restaurant

Tony and Brenda Shanahan's sixteenth-century thatched cottage deservedly lives up to its name, with lots of old blackened beams hung with horse brasses, wheelback chairs, shiny black-topped tables and a real log fire blazing during the winter months. He cooks, she runs the front of house. The menu holds few surprises, being in the sound Anglo-French mould of avocado mousse with smoked salmon and prawns, grilled Dover sole and herb-crusted rack of lamb with redcurrant and orange sauce. The results on the plate, however, are admirable – witness an inspection dinner of poached egg on ratatouille, followed by slices of Barbary duck breast on a bed of apple and onion with plum sauce, plus a nicely judged crème caramel to conclude proceedings. Around three dozen eminently affordable wines provide the back up.

Directions: On B2179 Birdham/Bracklesham road

Bracklesham Lane PO20 8JA
Map 4: SZ89
Tel: 01243 670250
Chef: Tony Shanahan
Owners: Tony & Brenda Shanahan
Cost: 7pm-last D 9pm. Closed Mon,
Tues, D Sun, 1st 2 wks Nov
Additional: Sunday lunch only
(12.30pm-3.30pm);
No children under 5; ❹ dishes
Seats: 28
Smoking: No-smoking area; no pipes
and cigars; air-conditioning
Credit cards:

CHICHESTER, **Comme Ça**

The Navets' appealing restaurant continues to draw endorsements from our inspectors. Decor is charming, with the original restaurant – elaborate stencilling on the walls, hops hung from the ceiling beams – added to (since our last inspection) by an extension with pitched ceiling, bare brick, more hops and a lovely little terrace and garden beyond. A summer lunch produced cauliflower vichyssoise, shrimps and mussels in a filo purse with an intense saffron and chive jus, and succulent chicken in an interesting sauce flavoured with coconut milk and vanilla, accompanied by particularly good vegetables. Pudding was a passionfruit mousse on a coconut 'sponge' with strawberry coulis and sauce anglaise. Staff are notably smart, efficient and pleasant.

Directions: On the A286 near Festival Theatre

67 Broyle Road PO19 4BD
Map 4: SU80
Tel: 01243 788724
Fax: 01243 530052
Chef: Michel Navet
Owners: M & J Navet
Cost: Alc £21, fixed-price L £17.45 (3
courses). ☺ H/wine £9.65.
Times: Noon-last L 2pm/6pm-last D
10.30pm. Closed D Sun, Mon, 25
Dec
Additional: Bar food L; Sunday L;
Children welcome; ❹ dishes
Seats: 75. Private dining room 40
Smoking: No smoking in dining room
Credit cards:

CHICHESTER, Little London

Pleasant restaurant named after the part of town in which it is set. Ambitious modern cooking from a chef who is trying hard. Boudin de pintard, with spicy cabbage noodles with warm soy sauce, smoked haddock and chive timbale with curry beurre blanc, monkfish with colcannon rösti and sauce vierge, rice pudding and nutmeg ice cream show the range.

Additional: Children welcome; 🕭 dishes
Smoking: No-smoking area; no pipes and cigars
Credit cards: ■ ▒ ▒ ▒ ▒ ▒

Directions: From A27 follow signs to centre of town; Little London is off East Street

38-39 Little London PO19 1PL
Map 4: SU80
Tel: 01243 530735
Fax: 01243 533011
Chef: Shane Beaton
Owners: Philip Cotterill, Thierry Boishu
Cost: *Alc* £28.50, fixed-price L £12.50/D £15.50. ☺ H/wine £9.50.
Times: Last L 2.30pm/D 10.30pm.
Closed Sun, 26 Dec, 1 Jan

CHICHESTER, The Ship Hotel

Owned by Admiral Sir George Murray in Napoleonic times, this historic hotel retains many original features including a unique cantilevered Adam staircase. Murray's restaurant is the setting for roasted tomato consommé, seared medallions of monkfish with chive butter sauce, and duck with roast peppered pineapple.

Smoking: No smoking in dining room
Accommodation: 34 en suite
Credit cards: ■ ▒ ▒ ▒ ▒ ▒

Directions: From Festival Theatre roundabout turn into North Street. Hotel on L, car park at rear

North Street PO19 1NH
Map 4: SU80
Tel: 01243 778000
Fax: 01243 788000
Owner: First Secured Hotels Ltd
Cost: *Alc* £23, fixed-price D £17.50.
☺ H/wine £9.
Times: Last L 2pm/D 9.30pm
Additional: Bar food; Sunday L; Children welcome; 🕭 dishes
Seats: 43. Private dining rooms 18/70

CHILGROVE, White Horse Inn

Built as a hostelry in 1745, and looking for all the world like a row of flint cottages, the White Horse keeps up appearances with its bow windows and wisteria-clad walls. The bar still feels like a genuine pub and beyond are several dining areas like varnished wooden tables. Bar lunches and suppers represent the informal side of things, while fixed-price menus operate in the restaurant. Game is a regular fixture in season, but the kitchen is always capable of delivering plenty of interesting stuff across the board. Breast of Barbary duck on a bed of leaf spinach served in a filo basket with nutmeg sauce, and supreme of chicken filled with mango and served with a fruity curry sauce, are typical of the repertoire, and there are always fish specials, which are recited verbally. Home-made ice creams and sorbets are alternatives to the list of desserts. Whilst enormity is not always the measure of a good wine list, the depth and rigour on offer here amounts to a breathtaking accomplishment. Page after page resonates with the greatest achievements of the wine making world. Tall lists of vintages from the likes of Château Cheval-Blanc, Château Lafite-Rothschild and Romanée-Conti are the mighty pillars on which the list is built, but housed within are collections from South Africa, California and especially Germany that combine in an assembly of bins as impressive as any in the country.

Directions: On the B2141 between Chichester and Petersfield

Chichester PO18 9HX
Map 4: SU81
Tel: 01243 535219
Fax: 01243 535301
Chef: Neil Rusbridger
Owners: Barry Phillips, Neil Rusbridger
Cost: Fixed-price L £19.50/D £23.50 (4 courses). ☺ H/wine £11.50.
Times: Noon-last L 2pm/6pm-last D 9.30pm. Closed D Sun, Mon, Feb, 1 wk Oct
Additional: Bar food; Sunday L; 🕭 dishes
Seats: 70. Private dining room 12
Smoking: No-smoking area; air-conditioning
Accommodation: 5 en suite
Credit cards: ■ ▒ ▒ ▒ ▒

CLIMPING, Bailiffscourt Hotel ⊛⊛

Littlehampton
BN17 5RW
Map 4: SU90
Tel: 01903 723511
Fax: 01903 723107
Chef: Frank Eckermann
Owners: Mr & Mrs Goodman
Cost: Fixed-price D £32.50.
H/wine £14
Times: 12.30pm-last L 2.15pm/7pm-last D 9.30pm. Closed D 25-26 Dec
Additional: Bar food L; Sunday L; Children welcome; ⊕ dishes
Seats: 50. Private dining room 80.
Jacket and tie preferred
Smoking: No smoking in dining room
Accommodation: 27 en suite
Credit cards: ▬ ▬ ▬ ▬ 🔲 🔲

It may appear architecturally correct 'medieval' in every detail, but Bailiffscourt was built as an impressively researched folly by Lord Moyne in 1927. It is, as the brochure proclaims 'the genuine fake'. Original building materials and antiques were salvaged from far and wide and the house is an evocative mix of old stone windows, heavy iron-studded doors, ancient arches and other judiciously chosen details. A new team in the kitchen is clearly making a serious effort. Meals in the appealing beamed dining room might feature such dishes as roulade of chicken with foie gras and pistachio nuts on a tomato vinaigrette, suprême of guinea fowl in a Calvados sauce with glazed apples, and gratin of Scottish salmon and lobster with chervil. To finish, the hot soufflé of the day (in this case a well judged lime and honey version) created a good impression, otherwise you might find a duo of white and plain chocolate mousses on coconut anglaise or baked vanilla cream with mango and ginger.

Directions: W of Littlehampton off the A259, signposted Bailiffscourt

COPTHORNE,

Copthorne London Gatwick ⊛⊛

Copthorne Way
RH10 3PG
Map 5: TQ33
Tel: 01342 714971
Fax: 01342 717375
Chef: Richard Duckworth

The house speciality is a tempting-looking roast prime rib of beef with Yorkshire pudding, served from a silver-domed trolley. Otherwise, the Lion D'Or restaurant in this sprawling

but well-run hotel, offers a measured choice of modern European dishes such as a trio of salmon, marinated, grilled and smoked with a horseradish cream, or suprême of chicken rolled in honey and sesame seeds presented on a port wine gravy. Seared red mullet with couscous, salad and watercress demonstrated the kitchen's ability to deliver precise, controlled flavours, as did a fillet of pork with grain-mustard sauce, mushroom duxelle and tagliatelle. Caramel and apple cake with liquorice ice-cream and toffee sauce turned out to be a surprisingly good combination. Full strength espresso is served in a glass beaker. Low ceilings, exposed beams and lots of cosy corners, plus the bulwark of 100 acres of gardens and woodlands, help protect the traveller against all thoughts of airport congestion and M25 grid-lock.

Owner: Millenium & Copthorne Hotels
Cost: *Alc* £25, fixed-price L £18.50/D £22.50.☺ H/wine £12.95.
Times: Noon-last L 2.30pm/7pm-last D 10pm. Closed L Sat, Sun
Additional: Bar food; Sunday L (Brasserie); Children welcome; ♨ dishes
Seats: 50; private dining room 10
Smoking: Air-conditioning
Accommodation: 227 en suite
Credit cards:

Directions: From M23/J10 follow A264 signed East Grinstead; take 3rd exit off 1st roundabout

CRAWLEY, Holiday Inn London – Gatwick West ✺

Busy airport hotel featuring the formal 'Colonnade' restaurant. Recently introduced menus include dishes with Mediterranean and Far Eastern influences. Expect main courses such as braised shank of lamb with red pepper mash and basil, piri piri marinated chicken with turmeric rice, and whole roast aubergine with pastry trellis.

Smoking: No-smoking area; air-conditioning
Accommodation: 217 en suite
Credit cards: ▬ ▦ ≈ ≋ ▣ ℂ

Directions: M23/J10, take A2011 (Horsham & Crawley). Hotel at junction of A23 & A264

Langley Drive RH11 7SX
Map 4: TQ23
Tel: 01293 529991
Fax: 01293 515913
Chef: David Woods
Owner: Holiday Inn Gatwick (UK Ltd)
Cost: *Alc* £20, fixed-price L £12.50/D £18.50.☺ H/wine £9.
Times: D only, 7pm-last D 9.45pm. Closed D Sun
Additional: Sunday L (noon-2pm); Children welcome; ♨ dishes

CUCKFIELD, Ockenden Manor ✺✺

Ockenden Lane
RH17 5LD
Map 4: TQ32
Tel: 01444 416111
Fax: 01444 415549
Chef: Geoff Welch
Owners: Mr & Mrs Sandy Goodman
Cost: Fixed-price L £19.50/D £31. H/wine £13.50
Times: 12.30pm-last L 2pm/7.30pm-last D 9.30pm

A sixteenth-century 'country town house' set in nine acres of grounds, with a beguiling atmosphere reinforced by open fires, beams in the bar, a pretty drawing room and a fine garden for summer drinks. Main meals are served with a degree of friendly formality in the oak-panelled restaurant, which also boasts a splendid hand-painted ceiling. South Coast fish shows up strongly on the *carte* (there's also a separate menu devoted to shellfish). Expect robust bisque of Chichester crab and

Cornish mussels with saffron and cognac, and fillet of brill with asparagus and orange butter sauce, alongside locally bred duck with a well-made honey and ginger sauce, or roast haunch of Ashdown venison served on a celeriac and potato rösti with raspberry vinegar and butter sauce. Desserts could include iced elderflower soufflé on apricot coulis, banana clafoutis and sticky toffee pudding. France is the main contributor to the carefully assembled wine list.

Additional: Sunday L;
Children welcome; ✿ dishes
Seats: 45. Private dining room 14/75.
Jacket & tie preferred
Smoking: No smoking in dining room
Accommodation: 22 en suite
Credit cards: 🟦 📧 📧 📧 📧 📧

Directions: Village Centre, off main street

EAST GRINSTEAD,

Gravetye Manor Hotel 🌸🌸🌸

East Grinstead RH19 4LJ
Map 5: TQ33
Tel: 01342 810567
Fax: 01342 810080
Chef: Mark Raffan
Owner: Peter Herbert
Cost: Alc £45, fixed-price L £24/D £30. H/wine £15
Times: 12.30pm-last L 2pm/7.30pm-last D 9.30pm. Closed 25 Dec D
Additional: Sunday L;
No children under 7
Seats: 56. Private dining room 16.
Jacket & tie preferred
Smoking: No smoking in dining room
Accommodation: 18 en suite
Credit cards: 🟦 📧 📧 📧

Gravetye was one of the first of the country house hotels and it remains an exemplar of all that such a hotel should be. It helps, of course, to start with a splendid Elizabethan stone manor house, set in 1000 acres. The flower-filled rooms have a timeless quality with mellow oak panelling and some very fine ceilings. One of the most impressive features, however, is the excellent standard of hospitality and unobtrusive professional service. In the kitchen, Mark Raffan uses first-rate raw materials including some fresh produce from the hotel's walled kitchen garden, and the carafes of water offered at the table come from their own spring. Gravetye can also boast its own smokehouse, which provides excellent salmon. The style of cooking is sophisticated. On our inspection visit, the star dish was the starter – artichoke heart filled with a very soft, almost runny mousse topped with some lovely foie gras and surrounded by trompette mushrooms in a Madeira butter laced with truffle vinaigrette. This was followed by Hebridean scallops with crab cakes, on a little pile of leeks and surrounded by piles of pesto purée, and Gravetye traditional apple pie, served with vanilla ice-cream or local double cream. Most of the wines on the lengthy list need a friendly bank manager. However, with close study, there are a few to be found for under £30, most of them in the Australia/New Zealand section. Salice Salentino Riserva is a rich, concentrated wine at £19.50, and Goldwater, a good New Zealand Chardonnay, is weighty but balanced at £19. France is covered in great depth – the range of over 40 champagnes sets the scene.

Directions: Off B2028, 2 miles SW of East Grinstead

FINDON,
Findon Manor Hotel

High Street BN14 0TA
Map 4: TQ10
Tel: 01903 872733
Fax: 01903 877473
Chef: Stanley Ball
Owners: Mike & Jan Parker-Hare
Cost: Fixed-price L £15.95/D £17.95.
☺ H/wine £9.75.
Times: Noon-last L 2pm/7pm-last D 9pm
Additional: Sunday L; Bar meals; No children under 12; ⚘ dishes
Seats: 45. Private dining room 30
Smoking: No-smoking area; no pipes & cigars
Accommodation: 11 en suite
Credit cards: 💳 💳 💳 💳 💳

Faggots are an old-fashioned homely dish, so it was apt, perhaps, that the highlight of an inspection meal at this former nineteenth-century rectory was a particularly fine main course of faggot of oxtails and lambs' sweetbreads with glazed onions and sherry vinegar sauce. Quite a number of the dishes on offer have a gutsy appeal – stuffed pig's trotter, Madeira and thyme jus with truffle oil, and traditional French-style cassoulet Languedoc, for example, whilst salmon and sea scallop mousse with asparagus, lemon grass and vanilla-scented fish sauce, and a pink champagne and summer-fruit terrine with a cider and caraway sabayon show an interest in experimenting with flavours. The fine, home-made pâtisserie is eye-catchingly decorative, service is attentive but not over-formal, wines are good value and there is also an extensive choice of bar food in the cosy, real ale Snooty Fox bar.

Directions: 500 metres off the A24 in Findon village, 3 miles N of Worthing.

GATWICK AIRPORT, London
Gatwick Airport Hilton

RH6 0LL
Map 4: TQ23
Tel: 01293 518080
Fax: 01293 528980
Chef: Ken Paterson
Cost: *Alc* £31.15, fixed-price L&D £23.75. ☺ H/wine £13.75.
Times: Last L 2.30pm/D 10.15pm. Closed L Sat
Additional: Bar food; Sunday L; Children welcome; ⚘ dishes
Smoking: No-smoking area; air-conditioning
Accommodation: 550 en suite
Credit cards: 💳 💳 💳 💳

Directions: Within Gatwick Airport complex at South Terminal

A full-size replica of 'Jason', the bi-plane of Amy Johnson, hangs suspended above the lounge-bar in the atrium of this large airport hotel. Serious dining takes place in the Garden Restaurant, not a place to choose for decor, for it is rather rambling with cushioned rattan chairs and looks out onto a central courtyard (into which the glass walled swimming pool extends). A new menu taking in a mix of Oriental and Occidental influences, as well as a repertoire of classic dishes, seems particularly suited to the cosmopolitan clientele, and the effort taken in the kitchen is very evident. Up-beat offerings at an inspection meal took in straw mushroom bouillon with baby bok choy and coriander and flavoured with sesame oil and soya sauce, cinnamon-cured duck breast with plantain mash with citrus juice and foie gras vinaigrette, and plum tart with crème anglaise.

GOODWOOD, Marriott Goodwood Park Hotel ❀❀

Chichester PO18 0QB
Map 4: SU80
Tel: 01243 775537
Fax: 01243 520120
Chef: Gary Foster
Owner: Marriott Goodwood Park Hotel
Cost: Alc £30, fixed-price D £20. ☺
Times: Noon-last L 1.45pm/7pm-last D 9.45pm. Closed L Sat
Additional: Bar food; Sunday L; Children welcome; ❸ dishes
Seats: 90. Private dining room 120
Smoking: No smoking in dining room
Accommodation: 94 en suite
Credit cards: ■ ▦ ▦ ▧ ▣ ▯

Directions: 3 miles NE of Chichester. From Portsmouth head E along A27, staying S of Chichester. Signposted within area

As the name suggests, this hotel/country club/golf course is set in Goodwood Estate and it makes much of its location – although people are also drawn by the food. A pleasing inspection meal commenced with an exceptionally light chicken liver parfait served with dressed leaves and brioche. This was followed by intense confit of duck with a first-class, boldly flavoured sauce, and proceedings concluded with tarte Tatin. The kitchen is also capable of delivering carpaccio of tuna with a morel dressing, as well as punchier ideas such as braised rabbit with marrow dumplings, boiled collar of bacon with braised pearl barley and a Dijon mustard sauce, and plum pudding with rum sauce. Lighter meals are also served in the Waterbeach Grill. The wine list is a heavyweight tome supplied by Lay & Wheeler with an abundance of half-bottles from around the world.

HORSHAM, Random Hall Hotel ❀

It's all very 'olde worlde' at this sixteenth-century hotel restaurant, with its tapestries, iron candelabras, beams, and flagstone and wooden floors. There are also two fine fireplaces, where ducks are spit roasted in winter. Other main courses range from monkfish soufflé to steak and kidney pudding.

Additional: Bar food; Sunday L; No children under 6; ❸ dishes
Smoking: No-smoking area
Accommodation: 15 en suite
Credit cards: ■ ▦ ▦ ▧ ▯

Directions: 4 miles W of Horsham, 15 miles SW of Gatwick Airport

Stane Street
Slinfold RH13 7QX
Map 4: TQ13
Tel: 01403 790558
Fax: 01403 791046
Chef: Jonathan Gettings
Owner: Nigel Evans
Cost: Alc £19.50, fixed price L £10/D £19.35. ☺ H/wine £9.95.
Times: Last L 2pm/D 10pm.
Closed 27 Dec-5 Jan

HURSTPIERPOINT, Boles

117 High Street BN6 9PU
Map 4: TQ21
Tel: 01273 833452
Chef: Anne-Michele Bole
Owner: Michele Bole
Cost: Alc £25. H/wine £7.95. ☺
Times: Weekday L by prior booking,
7.30-last D 9.30pm. Closed D Sun,
Mon, 1 wk Feb, 2 wks Aug-Sept
Additional: Sunday L (12.30pm-2pm);
Children welcome; ⬥ dishes
Smoking: No-smoking area in dining
room
Credit cards: ▬ ▭ ▭

There's a warm rustic feel to this High Street restaurant, which comprises two rooms plus a brick-floored patio for summer meals. Live music is a regular Saturday night event. Recommended dishes have included a fillet of lamb on celeriac rösti with a port and redcurrant sauce, and a zesty lemon tart.

Directions: In town centre, half way along High Street

LANCING, Sussex Pad Hotel ❀❀

Old Shoreham Road BN15 0RH
Map 4: TQ10
Tel: 01273 454647
Fax: 01273 453010
Chef: Paul Hornsby
Owner: Wally Pack
Cost: Alc £22, fixed-price L & D from
£16.50. ☺ H/wine £10.50
Times: Noon-last L 2pm/7pm-last D
10pm. Closed 25-26 Dec
Additional: Bar food; Children
welcome; ⬥ dishes
Seats: 40.
Smoking: No smoking in dining room
Accommodation: 18 en suite
Credit cards: ▬ ▬ ▭ ▰ ▣ ▯

There's plenty of seafood fresh from Shoreham Harbour at Ladywells Restaurant, within this well-run inn. Dishes are cooked to order, and the excellent fish choice ranges from fillets of black sea bream with red and green peppers, aubergine, courgettes and orange sauce to turbot on a sweet potato galette with a dill and Vermouth sauce. More classic fish cookery takes in skate beurre noir and grilled Dover sole with butter and fresh garden herbs. The majority of the starters – crab soup with lemon grass and mild chillies and oysters Florentine, for example – are also based around fish and shellfish, and salmon is oak-smoked and hand-carved in their own smoke house. Non-fish eaters might prefer knuckle of ham simmered in fine spices, basted in honey and cinnamon and spiked with cloves, then roasted, or a roast best end of Southdown lamb. Desserts include the nostalgic Paris Brest, as well as traditional bread-and-butter pudding.

Directions: On the A27 between Shoreham & Lancing, opposite Shoreham Municipal Airport & by Lancing College

LOWER BEEDING,

Jeremy's at the Crabtree

The daily-changing menu at this roadside pub-cum-restaurant displays the internationalism currently the norm in British cooking. Luckily, the kitchen knows what it is about, and is able to handle genres as disparate as Moroccan lamb casserole with olives, lemon, parsley and couscous, curried fish on spiced rice with coconut, fresh coriander and yoghurt dressing, and seared tuna with chilli, lime and coriander on egg noodles, cucumber, mouli relish and wasabi cream, with equal facility. More mainstream dishes might include grilled fillet of smoked haddock on braised fennel with a poached egg, pan-fried pork chop with ginger and honey, caramelised red onions and mashed swede, and the ever popular toffee pudding. Sunday lunch may include lemon sole on dill polenta with a chive butter sauce, as well as roast rib of beef with Yorkshire pudding and a rich red wine gravy. Home-made walnut bread comes as an 'extra'. The non-smoking dining room has a rather more formal atmosphere, the smoking room is cosier with oak beams, but there are open fires in both.

Brighton Road RH13 6PT
Map 4: TQ22
Tel: 01403 891257
Fax: 01403 891606
Chefs: Jeremy Ashpool, Pia Walters
Owner: Jeremy Ashpool
Cost: *Alc* £19, fixed-price L £10.50 (2 courses)/D £23.50. H/wine £10
Times: 12.30pm-last L 2.30pm/7.30pm-last D 9.30pm. Closed D Sun, 25 Dec
Additional: Bar food L; Sunday L; Children welcome; ❸ dishes
Seats: 45.
Smoking: No-smoking area
Credit cards: 🔳 🔳 🔳 🔳 ▢

Directions: 4 miles SE of Horsham on A281 Brighton road

LOWER BEEDING,

South Lodge Hotel

Brighton Road Horsham RH13 6PS
Map 4: TQ22
Tel: 01403 891711
Fax: 01403 891766
Chef: Timothy Neal
Owners: Mr G Pecorelli – Exclusive Hotels
Cost: *Alc* £40.50, fixed-price L £16.50 (3 courses)/D £25-£32 (3-5 courses). ☺ H/wine £14.50.
Times: 12.30pm-last L 2.30pm (3pm Sun)/7.30pm-last D 10pm (10.30pm Fri, Sat)
Additional: Bar food; Sunday L; Children welcome; ❸ dishes
Seats: 40. private dining room 2-80
Smoking: No smoking in dining room
Accommodation: 39 en suite
Credit cards: 🔳 🔳 🔳 🔳 ▢ ▢

An ancient camellia holds pride of place on the south-facing terrace of this splendidly restored Victorian mansion. And that's not all, some 260 varieties of rhododendron flourish in the expansive grounds. The hotel has a stylishly comfortable bar and lounge for drinks, but the main action takes place in the aptly named Camellia restaurant with its hand-carved oak panels and views of the South Downs. There is a very serious intent about Tim Neal, an enthusiastic cook who makes use of local game and some fine organic beef for a menu that is a convincing blend of traditional and modern. Duck terrine is set in green cabbage leaves and served with crabapple jelly, tranche of turbot is topped with lobster mousse. Elsewhere, you might find anything from sautéed veal kidneys in puff pastry to Thai-spiced breast of chicken interleaved with gingered pasta. As an accompaniment look for the mash and fungi of the day. A summer dinner opened with asparagus and watercress soup that had 'plenty of flavour', then came a monkfish, a whole piece grilled and then sliced and topped with rocket and fines herb salad and surrounded by a lemony

beurre blanc – a good dish that worked well. Warm rhubarb came with a good sauce anglaise and vanilla ice cream. Other desserts such as Bramley apple soufflé show skill and variety and there are some decent English cheeses too. The sound wine list includes about half a dozen by the glass.

Directions: At junction of A279 (Horsham) and A281, turn onto the Cowfold/Brighton road. Hotel is 0.5 mile on R

MIDHURST, Angel Hotel ❀❀❀

There is a sense of time travel at this old coaching inn, which conceals its Tudor origins behind a Georgian facade. A setting for some of the scenes in the early novels of H.G. Wells, it has a mellow atmosphere, enhanced by careful restoration. The Cowdray Room is smartly furnished, with posies of fresh flowers on each table; staff are trimly turned out in dark jackets. Darren Tidd took over as Head Chef at the beginning of 1997, and comes with experience of a clutch of top-flight kitchens. His style emphasises light sauces, using quality ingredients cooked in a way that maximises their full flavours without the need for overpowering garnishes. Typically, chargrilled scallop salad with chilli dressing, may be followed by nage of shellfish with baby vegetables on a Sauternes butter sauce, and sablé of raspberries with raspberry coulis and a cluster of fresh berries. Flavours can be unexpectedly subtle – fillet of sea bass, served on a bed of julienne of celeriac and mange-touts with a sauce of chives and caviar turned the initial scepticism of our inspector into agreeable surprise. The menu choice is short, and on the whole well thought out, although a sample menu showed its limitations when three out of four main meat dishes included a bird of one sort or the other – clover honey roast duck with apple charlotte and truffle sauce, breast of free-range chicken with braised Savoy cabbage, garlic confit and a tarragon cream sauce, and roast Norfolk pigeon with lentil du Puy, trompet mushrooms and a galette potato. The assiette of desserts is a good way to sample the range – our selection included a crème brûlée, freshly baked lemon tart, chocolate cheesecake with walnuts, and a raspberry sorbet on a bed of chocolate flakes. Yet more chocolate arrived with the coffee, along with nutty nougat and home-made shortbread. More informal meals are served in the rustic-looking beamed bar, where the menu includes popular dishes such as deep-fried whiting with tartare sauce, and chargrilled calves' liver and bacon with onion sauce. Wines cover most regions, with depth and reliability being the watchwords in France and some excitement to be found in the New World. Drodsty Hof's South African Chenin Blanc and Montes' Chilean Malbec are reasonably priced examples of the latter. Thirty odd half-bottles provide ample variety.

North Street GU29 9DN
Map 4: SU82
Tel: 01730 812421
Fax: 01730 815928
Chef: Darren Tidd
Owners: Peter Crawford-Rolt, Nicholas Davies
Times: Noon-last L 2pm/7.30pm-last D 10pm
Additional: Sunday L; No children under 5; ◑ dishes
Seats: 50. Private dining room 70. Jacket & tie preferred
Smoking: No smoking in dining room
Accommodation: 28 en suite
Credit cards: ▆ ▆ ▆▆ ▆ ▆

Directions: Town centre, junction of A286 and A2721

MIDHURST, Southdowns Hotel ❀❀

Yorkshire pudding might never be the same again – with foie gras and onion gravy it makes a notably successful combination when served at this attractive country hotel and restaurant, nestling in the Sussex countryside. Another cross-cultural dish which has come in for praise is confit of duck with cabbage, onions, bean sprouts and ginger and plum sauce. Details show the kitchen is hardworking and concerned about quality – smoked salmon is served with home-made soda

Trotton
GU31 5JN
Map 4: SU82
Tel: 01730 821521
Fax: 01730 821790
Chef: Peter Broomhead
Owners: Dominic Vedovato, Richard Lion
Cost: *Alc* £20, fixed-price D £25. H/wine £10.95

Southdowns Hotel

Times: 12.30pm-last L 2pm/7pm-last D 9.30pm
Additional: Sunday L; Bar food; No children under 10; 🌢 dishes
Seats: 50. Private dining room 20
Smoking: No-smoking area; air conditioning
Accommodation: 20 en suite
Credit cards: ▨▨ ▨ ▨ ▨ ▨ ▨

Directions: Just off A272 Petersfield Road

bread, chicken liver parfait with home-made piccalilli, for example, and there is the confidence to keep things simple. Roast cod is served on crisp new potatoes with deep-fried anchovies and tartare dressing, chargrilled ribeye of beef with home-cut chips and béarnaise sauce, calves' liver and bacon on horseradish mash potato with balsamic and onion gravy, and all come either with fresh seasonal vegetables or a crisp side salad. As well as British and French cheeses, there are some delicious-sounding desserts such as iced chocolate parfait with lime and pineapple compote and pineapple crisps.

MIDHURST, Spread Eagle Hotel ❀❀

South Street GU29 9NH
Map 4: SU82
Tel: 01730 816911
Fax: 01730 815668
Chef: Ken Jelfs
Owner: Sandy & Anne Goodman
Cost: *Alc* £25, fixed-price L £15.95/D £27. H/wine £10.95
Times: 12.30pm-last L 1.50pm/7.30pm-last D 9.20pm
Additional: Bar food L; Sunday L; Children welcome; 🌢 dishes
Seats: 80. Private dining room 24
Smoking: No smoking in dining room
Accommodation: 39 en suite
Credit cards: ▨▨ ▨ ▨ ▨ ▨ ▨

Overlooking the market square, this former fifteenth-century coaching inn continues to offer consistent standards of service and cooking. Expect individually decorated bedrooms and a beamed restaurant complete with inglenook fireplace. For added comfort, a conservatory and leisure centre were being added as we went to press. Fixed-price menus at lunch and dinner are well balanced and offer ample choice from a repertoire that is classically based but shows a fair degree of improvisation. On our most recent visit dinner commenced with salmon fish cakes, packed with fish, and a lemon butter sauce. Shank of lamb, which literally fell off the bone, was accompanied by a creamy mash potato and fresh vegetables. A chocolate and pear tart with soft vanilla bean ice-cream provided a richly flavoured finale. You are spoilt for choice when it comes to the wine list which is over a dozen pages long. Stick to the house selection for the best value.

Directions: Town centre, corner of South and West Streets.

PULBOROUGH, Chequers Hotel

Church Place RH20 1AD
Map 4: TQ01
Tel: 01798 872486
Fax: 01798 872715
Chefs: Anton Goodwin,
Darren Middle
Owner: John Searancke
Cost: Fixed-price L £7.95/ D £17.95.
☺ H/wine £8.95.
Times: Noon-last L 1.45pm/7.30pm-
last D 8.45pm
Additional: Sunday L; Children
welcome; ✿ dishes
Seats: 24. Private dining room 18
Smoking: No smoking in dining room
Accommodation: 11 (10 en suite)
Credit cards: ▬ ▭ ▭ ▣.

It stands opposite the church overlooking the Arun Valley and for over three decades, John Searancke has presided over this small, intimate hotel that dates from the reign of Queen Anne. High-standards of service and hospitality have a reassuring traditional feel, but new blood in the kitchen has injected modern ideas and enthusiasm into the fixed-price lunch and dinner menus. Duck liver parfait in a baby brioche and topped with crispy leeks, a mélange of seafood served with home-made black noodles, and orange and chocolate mousse with a light coffee sauce, shows a chef with an eye on modern trends. Dinner in early spring saw some skilful cooking, with a casserole of pork braised in cider with honey-roasted apples, and a very light crème brûlée served in a box made of butterscotch toffee surrounded by mango coulis, coming in for particular praise.

Directions: On A29 just N of Pulborough, turn R opposite the church

PULBOROUGH, Stane Street Hollow Restaurant ✿✿

This year the Kaisers celebrate 21 years at Stane Street Hollow, a charming stone building that dates back almost half a millennium. They are rightly proud of their long-running success and play the hosts with enthusiasm; Ann's quiet hospitality front of house never flags and René slaves over the hot stove producing the dishes of his native Switzerland. The menu changes monthly and often includes herbs and vegetables from their own garden. A typical inspection meal began with a freshly baked tartlet with a light goat's cheese egg custard topped with toasted hazelnuts. The centrepiece was a suprême de faisan Rossini, with a good chicken liver parfait filling. Then came assiette René, which provided the opportunity to sample four desserts: orange parfait, vanilla cream tartlet, a 'Kaiser schwan' (a swan-shaped meringue filled with banana bavarois), and a blackberry mousse gâteau. The wine list, too, is worth a mention for offering decent wines at friendly prices.

Codmore Hill RH20 1BG
Map 4: TQ01
Tel: 01798 872819
Chef: René Kaiser
Owners: René & Ann Kaiser
Cost: Alc £25, fixed-price L £15.50.
☺ H/wine £12.
Times: 12.30pm-last L 1.15pm/7pm-
last D 9.15pm. Closed D Sun, Mon,
Tue, 2 wks late May, 2 wks late Oct
Additional: Sunday lunch;
Children welcome; ✿ dishes
Seats: 30. Private dining room 20/14
Smoking: No smoking in dining room
Credit cards: ▬ ▭ ▰ ▣

Directions: N of Pulborough on A29 at Codmore Hill

STORRINGTON,

Manleys Restaurant ❀❀❀

There are some restaurants where, immediately upon entering, one can relax thoroughly in the knowledge that everything will run smoothly. Manleys is one such admirable establishment, and the many regular customers are a tribute to the enduring professionalism of Margaret and Karl Löderer. Margaret still puts in an appearance front of house, whilst Karl remains in charge of the consistently good kitchen, mostly classical French in style, but with a little mid-European accent added as well. The latter is typified by dishes such as crispy duck with red cabbage and rösti potatoes, local venison fillets with a sweet and sour sauce, wild cherries and potato croquette, and Salzburger nockerln (for two). Dishes depend on faultless technique, even a canapé of deep-fried Dover sole revealed accurate, careful timing, as did boned quail, roasted and served with purée of foie gras on a potato galette, and veal roulade roasted with grain mustard sauce and stuffed with a fine veal forcemeat. Vegetables, such as mushroom purée wrapped in courgette slices, 'quenelles' of puréed carrot, fried parsnip slices and broccoli with a first-rate hollandaise, match the fairly elaborate style of the main courses. Profiteroles with hot chocolate sauce and crème brûlée with Grand Marnier may not be cutting edge desserts but they are just the thing to finish with here. The beamed restaurant is light and airy, there are monogrammed plates and lovely flowers on the tables. Not surprisingly the German section is very strong on the wine list, and is an opportunity to put some quality wines, mostly under £18, to the test. Wehlen-Sonnenuhr, Spätlese is worth trying at £23.50 The Burgundy and Bordeaux section are full of the classics (costed accordingly), but the Rhônes offer some well-priced options. Some interesting halves in most sections, and several available in magnum. House wines start at £14.80.

Signature dishes: Aylesbury duck, oriental-style; Salzburger nockerln

Directions: On the main A283, off the A24, just E of Storrington.

Manleys Hill RH20 4BT
Map 4: TQ01
Tel: 01903 742331
Fax: 01903 740649
Chef/Owner: Karl Löderer
Cost: *Alc* £39, fixed-price L £19.60/D £31.50. H/wine £14.80
Times: 12.15-last L 1.45pm/7.15pm-last D 9pm (9.30pm Sat). Closed Mon, 1st 10 days Jan
Additional: Sunday L; Children welcome; ♦ dishes
Seats: 48. Private dining room 22. Jacket and tie preferred
Smoking: No pipes or cigars
Accommodation: 1 en suite
Credit cards: ▉ ▦ ▤ ✈ ⓒ

STORRINGTON, **Old Forge** ❀❀

6 Church Street RH20 4LA
Map 4: TQ01
Tel: 01903 743402
Fax: 01903 742540
Chef: Clive Roberts
Owners: Clive & Cathy Roberts
Cost: *Alc* £25, fixed-price L £15/D £21.50 (3 courses). ☺ H/wine £9.75
Times: 12.15pm-last L 1.30pm/7.15pm-last D 9pm. Closed Mon, Tue L, Sat L, Sun D, 3 wks spring, 2wks autumn
Additional: Sunday lunch; Children welcome; ♦ dishes
Seats: 36. Private dining room 12
Smoking: No pipes or cigars
Credit cards: ▉ ▦ ▤ ✈ ⓓ ⓒ

The name says it all: a modest country restaurant in a converted 500-year-old forge complete with low beams, rough white walls and several eating areas, including one with a table in the inglenook. Cathy Roberts runs front of house, Clive cooks. His monthly menus offer reliable dishes with touches of invention but nothing too wayward. Meals begin with intriguing home-baked breads and the repertoire is typified by dishes such as scallop and prawn mousseline, loin of lamb stuffed with wild mushrooms and sweetbreads wrapped in puff pastry, and medallions of pork on a pile of flageolet beans and salami. Raw materials are spot-on, home-grown vegetables are used to good effect. A trio of iced parfaits was well received at inspection, otherwise desserts range from warm pancakes filled with a praline of toasted hazelnuts and walnuts to home-made ices. The keenly priced wine list majors in the New World and comes with personal tasting notes.

Directions: On a side street in the village centre

TURNERS HILL,
Alexander House ❀❀

East Street RH10 4QD
Map 4: TQ33
Tel: 01342 714914
Fax: 01342 717328
Chef: Sacha Ferrier
Owner: International Hotel Group
Cost: *Alc* £40, fixed-price L £18.75/D £28.50. H/wine £15.50
Times: 12.30pm-last L 2pm/7pm-last D 9.30pm.
Additional: Bar food; Sunday L; No children under 7; ❧ dishes
Seats: 55. Private dining room 16. Jacket & tie preferred
Smoking: No smoking in dining room
Accommodation: 15 en suite
Credit cards: ■ ■ ■ ■ ■

This splendid seventeenth-century country mansion is set in 135 acres of parkland and well-tended gardens – perfect for afternoon tea in summer. As we went to press the kitchen was being refurbished and a new chef was being sought, but the cooking style seems likely to remain much the same. Dishes such as sautéed foie gras and sweetbreads with potato, rocket and shallots, poached breast of maize-fed chicken with corn galette, asparagus and truffle, and pan-fried sea bass with fennel and potato rösti plus a mussel and clam bouillabaisse, show the range. Desserts range from Thai-inspired sticky rice with coconut milk and mango to apple charlotte with pear parfait and sugared sable. Some heavyweight clarets and Burgundies show up strongly on the lengthy wine list.

Directions: 1.5 mile east of Turners Hill on the B2110

WASHINGTON,
The Chardonnay ❀❀

Old London Road RH20 3BN
Map 4: TQ11
Tel: 01903 892271/892575
Chef: Carl Illes
Owners: Carl & Julie Illes
Cost: *Alc* £23.25, fixed-price L £20.50/D £21.50 (3 courses). ☺ H/wine £9.15.
Times: Noon-last L 2pm/7pm-last D 9.30pm. Closed Sun, Mon
Additional: Children welcome; ❧ dishes
Seats: 60
Smoking: No-smoking area in dining room
Credit cards: ■ ■ ■ ■

The former smithy, full of old beams and green plants, provides bread board and knife in order to slice your own loaves at table. After that, it's a lengthy choice of tried and tested dishes such as half a fanned avocado with fresh prawns and a Maryrose sauce, pan-fried Orkney scallops with lemon butter sauce and half a crisp roast Norfolk duck with sage and onion stuffing and apple sauce. More complicated choices such as baked filo baskets filled with mussels and smoked bacon in a cheese sauce, and open lasagne served with a nage butter sauce, tiger prawns, fresh asparagus and oyster mushrooms, also put in an appearance. The eponymous grape stars in a main course of half a guinea fowl served with button mushrooms, baby onions and lardons of bacon with a Chardonnay jus. Desserts have not always matched up to the rest of the meal, but chocolate truffles in a glass goblet overflowing with dry-ice mist, at least ensure a memorable end.

Directions: Telephone for directions

WEST CHILTINGTON,
Roundabout Hotel ❀

Mock-Tudor hotel tucked away in deepest rural Sussex. The intimate Chiltern restaurant overlooking the garden makes a pleasing setting for dishes based largely on local ingredients. The carte promises things like goose rillettes scented with lavender, tempura of monkfish with orange sauce, and gooseberry and apple crumble.

Directions: 1.75 miles S of West Chiltington via A293

Pulborough RH20 2PF
Map 4: SZ11
Tel: 01798 813838
Fax: 01798 812962
Chef: David Isles
Owner: Richard Begley
Cost: *Alc* £21.95, fixed-price L £9.50/D £18.50. ☺ H/wine £9.95.
Times: Last L 1.45pm/last D 9pm
Additional: Bar meals; Sunday L; No children under 3; ❹ dishes
Smoking: No smoking in dining room
Accommodation: 23 en suite
Credit cards:

WORTHING, **Ardington Hotel** ❀ NEW

Well established family-run hotel offering good service and competently cooked food. An interesting set menu lists a tempting selection of modern dishes; the carte is more traditional. Roasted plum tomato soup, seared sea bream with lemon grass and ginger beurre blanc, and poached pear with a warm sabayon impressed our inspector.

Additional: Bar meals L; Children welcome; ❹ dishes
Smoking: No pipes; air conditioning
Accommodation: 48 en suite
Credit cards:

Directions: Central Worthing

Steyne Gardens BN11 3DZ
Map 4: TQ10
Tel: 01903 230451
Fax: 01903 526526
Chef: Richard Catling
Owner: Margaroli family
Cost: *Alc* £28, fixed-price D £17.75.
☺ H/wine £10.
Times: 7pm-last D 8.30pm.
Closed 24 Dec-6 Jan

TYNE & WEAR

BOLDON, Forsters Restaurant

The discreet frontage of this smart modern restaurant is easy to miss if you are driving through the village, so keep your eyes peeled. David Forster's cooking yo-yos convincingly between tradition and invention, taking in Swiss cheese soufflé, grilled salmon fillet with warm smoked salmon and béarnaise sauce, and crisp roast duck breast with French black pudding and Calvados sauce along the way. The highlight of a recent inspection, however, was one of the daily specials – a 'delightfully' fresh piece of monkfish topped with bacon, mushrooms and lentils in a red wine sauce. Puddings are an equally diverse bunch ranging from vanilla crème brûlée and sticky toffee pudding to home-made Ovaltine ice cream. Service ensures that the mood remains friendly and relaxed. The wine list puts the emphasis on value for-money and dependable drinking.

2 St Bedes Station Road NE36 0LE
Map 12: NZ36
Tel: 0191 5190929
Chef: Barry Forster
Owners: Barry & Sue Forster
Cost: *Alc* £24, fixed-price D £17. ☺
H/wine £8.50.
Times: D only, 7pm-9.30pm.
Closed Sun, Mon, 2 wks June,
1 wk Sept, Xmas, New Year, Bhs
Additional: No children under 7
Seats: 30
Smoking: No pipes and cigars
Credit cards: ▆▆ ▆▆ ▆▆ ▣

Directions: In village of East Boldon, off A184 Newcastle/ Sunderland rd

GATESHEAD, Eslington Villa Hotel

Friendly and relaxed Edwardian villa overlooking the Team Valley. Home-cooked dishes such as grilled breast of duck with onion marmalade, warm salad of black pudding and bacon, and iced peach parfait with peach purée are served in generous portions.

Smoking: No smoking in dining room
Accommodation: 12 en suite
Credit cards: ▆▆ ▆▆ ▆▆ ▆▆ ▣

Directions: Off A1(M) along Teme Valley, turn R at Eastern Avenue, then L into Station Road

8 Station Road NE9 6DR
Map 12: NZ26
Tel: 0191 4876017
Fax: 0191 4200667
Chef: Ian Lowrey
Owners: Nick & Melanie Tulip
Cost: *Alc* £30, fixed-price L&D £19.95. ☺ H/wine £8.95.
Times: Last L 1.45pm/D 10pm.
Closed L Sat, D Sun, 25-28 Dec
Additional: Sunday L; Children welcome; ❹ dishes

NEWCASTLE-UPON-TYNE,
Blackgate Restaurant NEW

Spacious restaurant in a former shipping building. The short, modern menu might include a salad of peppered lamb fillet with fine beans and minted apple chutney, charred medallion of salmon with creamed leeks and Cumberland mustard dressing, and spicy apple strudel with walnut ice-cream. Good selection of regional cheeses.

Additional: Children welcome; ❹ dishes
Smoking: No-smoking area. **Credit cards:** ▆▆ ▆▆

Directions: 2 mins walk from Newcastle Central Station. Situated behind St Nicholas Cathedral, opposite Castle Keep

The Side NE1 3JE
Map 7: SJ84
Tel: 0191 2617356
Chef: Douglas Jordan
Owners: Douglas Jordan, Susan Drysdale
Cost: Fixed-price L&D £11.25. ☺ H/wine £11.95
Times: Last L 2pm/last D 10pm.
Closed L Sat, Sun, D Mon, Bhs

NEWCASTLE-UPON-TYNE, Cafe 21

Lively, modern French-style bistro serving good-value, no-nonsense food, from Terry Laybourne (see 21 Queen Street). The spartan decor contrasts with the menu's colourful Mediterranean-influenced

35 The Broadway Darras Hall
Ponteland NE20 9PW
Map 7: SJ84
Tel/Fax: 01661 820357
Chef: Andrew Moore

dishes; expect the likes of grilled aubergine with coriander pesto and rocket salad, and polenta with artichokes and fried mushrooms.

Additional: Children welcome; ⓓ dishes
Smoking: No pipes and cigars
Credit cards: 🔲 💳 💳 🔲 🔲 🔲

Directions: From the A696, follow signs for Darras Hall and turn L at the mini-roundabout, 200yds to restaurant

Owners: Terence & Susan Laybourne
Cost: Alc £23, fixed price L £14.50.
☺ H/wine £9.50.
Times: Noon-last L 2.30pm/6pm-last
D 10.30pm. Closed Sun, Mon, Bhs

NEWCASTLE-UPON-TYNE,
The Copthorne ✦

The Close Quayside NE1 3RT
Map 12: NZ26
Tel: 0191 2220333
Fax: 0191 2301111
Chef: A Afia
Cost: Alc £30. H/wine £10.75
Times: D only, 7.30pm-10.15pm.
Closed Sun
Additional: Children welcome;
ⓓ dishes
Seats: 24
Smoking: Air conditioning
Accommodation: 156 en suite
Credit cards: 🔲 💳 💳 🔲 🔲 🔲

Smart hotel of contemporary design, situated on the banks of the River Tyne in the heart of the city. The formal Le Rivage offers sound cooking along the lines of parfait of hare with goose liver and summer truffles, symphony of seafood Thermidor, and a caramelised crème Catalan.

Directions: From S cross Redheugh Bridge, turn L at B1600 for Quayside, hotel on R

NEWCASTLE-UPON-TYNE,
Courtneys

Apart from its other attributes, Courtneys is certainly in the running for prettiest menu of the year, a soft-focused painting of fruit and flowers – not just aesthetically pleasing, but suggestive of good things to come. The cooking is mostly modern international in concept and uncluttered in execution. Starters are perhaps more spirited than main courses – tempura-fried king prawns with marinated vegetables and saffron oil and Maryland-style crab cake with avocado and basil salsa pave the way for grilled suprême of salmon with braised chicory and red wine gravy and roast loin of lamb with Dijon mustard and garlic breadcrumbs. A short selection of desserts might include caramelised lemon tart with coconut ice cream. Some rarely spotted classic dishes, such as brandade of cod with provençale vegetables, escalopes of veal with a wild mushroom cream sauce and floating islands with praline, are dotted throughout the repertoire.

Directions: Bottom of Dean St on R before roundabout at Quayside.

5-7 The Side NE1 3JE
Map 12: NZ26
Tel: 0191 2325537
Chef: Michael Carr
Owners: Michael & Kerensa Carr
Cost: Alc £24, fixed-price L £15. ☺
H/wine £10.
Times: Noon-last L 2pm/7pm-last D
10.30pm. Closed L Sat, Sun,
2 wks May, 1wk Xmas, Bhs
Additional: ⓓ dishes
Seats: 30
Smoking: No pipes and cigars in
dining room; air-conditioning
Credit cards: 🔲 💳 💳 🔲

NEWCASTLE-UPON-TYNE,
Fisherman's Lodge ❀❀

Jesmond Dene Jesmond NE7 7BQ
Map 12: NZ26
Tel: 0191 2813281
Fax: 0191 2816410
Chef: Steven Jobson
Owners: Franco & Pamela Cetoloni
Cost: *Alc* £35, fixed-price L £17.80/D
£28.50. H/wine £11.50
Times: Noon-last L 2pm/7pm-last D
11pm. Closed L Sat, Sun, Bhs
Additional: No children under 9 at D;
❹ dishes
Seats: 65. Private dining rooms 14-43
Smoking: No smoking in dining room
Credit cards: ▆ ▆ ▆ ▆ ▆ ▆

The former town residence of Lord Armstrong is in the leafy, green setting of Jesmond Dene Park, one of the most delightful spots within the city of Newcastle. Although there is plenty of Northumbrian lamb, duck, prime beef and game to be had, seafood is what the Fisherman's Lodge does best. Lobster is served either grilled with garlic butter or choron sauce, or cold in a salad, or tempura of shellfish and fish with a Chinese soy sauce, and seared peppered salmon with a spicy cucumber pickle. As well as freshly grilled Dover sole and halibut, more elaborate presentations might include lemon sole Walewska or suprême of turbot with mussels provençale and bouillabaisse sauce. Surf and turf, prime beef fillet grilled together with a half lobster and flavoured with garlic, offers the best of both worlds. Home-made ice creams and sorbets feature in most of the desserts, and include some unusual flavours such as white chocolate, Bourbon and marmalade.

Directions: 2.5 miles from City centre, off A1058 (Tynemouth) road at Benton Bank, middle of Jesmond Dene Park

NEWCASTLE-UPON-TYNE,
Fishermans Wharf ❀

With a sound reputation for seafood, a visit to Fishermans Wharf won't disappoint. The menu features game as well as fresh local fish, and might include 'Balantine of guinea fowl with plum and hazelnut salad', fillet of turbot with wild mushrooms, and sautéed asparagus with monkfish.

Additional: No children under 10; ❹ dishes
Smoking: No pipes; air-conditioning
Credit cards: ▆ ▆ ▆ ▆

15 The Side NE1 3JE
Map 12: NZ26
Tel: 0191 2321057
Fax: 0191 2320496
Chef: Simon Tennet
Owner: Alan Taylor
Cost: *Alc* £25, fixed-price L £10 (2 courses). ☺
Times: Last L 2pm/D 11pm
Closed Sat L, Sun, Bhs

Directions: From N side of Tyne bridge, turn L into Mosley Street, L into Dean Street and L again into The Side

NEWCASTLE-UPON-TYNE, The Magpie Room Restaurant

St James Park NE1 4ST
Map 12: NZ26
Tel: 0191 2018439
Fax: 0191 2018611
Chef: John Blackmore
Owners: Newcastle United Football Club
Cost: A/c £22, fixed-price L&D £15.
☺ H/wine £7.95.
Times: Noon-last L 2pm/7.30pm-last D 10pm. Closed L Sat, D Sun, Mon, match days
Additional: Sunday L; Children welcome; 🅐 dishes
Seats: 149. Private dining room 12
Smoking: Air conditioning
Credit cards: ▆ ▆ ▆ ▆ ▆ ▆

What started out as a glitzy sixth floor corporate entertaining dining room for shareholders and privileged fans of Newcastle United Football Club, is now a restaurant in its own right, and open to the public except on match days/nights. But make no mistake, this is no function room for punters. John Blackmore cooks and, with more scope and better resources than previously (he had his own place Blackmore's, at Alnwick), has grown in confidence. From a *carte* that offers the likes of a tart of shallots with layers of calves' liver, Bayonne ham, black pudding, with a reduction of leeks, cream and herbs, and roulade of maize-fed guinea fowl with an asparagus Redesdale cheese mousse served on a light marjoram-scented sauce, our inspector chose roast collops of monkfish with smoked bacon, red peppers, served in a filo tulip with dill-scented vinaigrette. Watercress soup with poached quails' eggs and creamed wild mushrooms followed, then loin of venison in a pastry case with braised chestnuts and a Burgundy sauce, and baked rum and raisin cheesecake with home-made prune ice cream to finish. Good house wines.

Directions: From the South, follow Gateshead A1 signs, then A692 over Redheugh Bridge, Blenheim St & then L on Bath Lane

NEWCASTLE-UPON-TYNE, Swallow Gosforth Park Hotel

Large, modern hotel set in 12 acres of parkland near Newcastle airport. In The Brandling, the elegant dining room, guests enjoy a view of rambling woods while savouring modern cooking in dishes such as vine leaves stuffed with asparagus and mushroom risotto, and oven-baked chicken with braised chicory and smoked haddock.

Additional: Sunday L; Bar meals; Children welcome; 🅐 dishes
Smoking: One no-smoking dining room; air-conditioning
Accommodation: 178 en suite
Credit cards: ▆ ▆ ▆ ▆ ▆ ▆

Directions: 2 mins from A1

High Gosforth Park NE3 5HN
Map 12: NZ26
Tel: 0191 2364111
Fax: 0191 2368192
Chef: Simon Devine
Owners: Swallow Hotels Ltd
Cost: Fixed-price L £18.50/D £24.50.
☺ H/wine £13.
Times: Last L 2.30pm/D 11pm

NEWCASTLE-UPON-TYNE,

21 Queen Street ❀❀❀

The cooking of Terence Laybourne is as direct, honest and
intelligent as the man himself, and meals at this city centre
restaurant near the Quayside have an inner integrity and
construction that are hard to fault. The interior design is
modern and minimalist – stripped light wood floors, light wood
chairs, water-colours of Tyneside scenes and floral displays like
Japanese ikebana. Pre-prandial nibbles are restricted to
marinated olives, simply and sensibly whetting the appetite for
a first-course such as Shanghai shellfish risotto with
langoustine, mussels and lobster and a hint of five spice and
deep-fried ginger. The oriental theme might continue with
peppered tuna, bok choy and ginger vinaigrette, but the
eclectic *carte* is equally likely to offer classic sequences such as
ravioli of salmon with champagne sauerkraut and caviar
cream, and medallions of Kielder venison with grapes, walnuts,
brandied cherries and fresh pasta with sauce Grand Veneur, or
the traditional bistro combination of vinaigrette of young leeks
followed by grilled calves' liver with caramelised apples, onions
and bacon. Laybourne also has the confidence to offer timeless
dishes such as poached salmon with fresh asparagus, new
season Jersey Royals and hollandaise sauce, as well as making
use of local ingredients in unexpected ways, as in roast fillet of
beef stuffed with oxtail with vegetable confit and Newcastle
Brown ale sauce. Assiette of duck cooked five ways is a
particularly tricky dish to carry off perfectly, and our inspector
did praise the slices of breast on rösti, the spicy sausage with
crispy fried onions and the braised lentils with seared foie gras.
Rhubarb strudel with strawberry sorbet and tarte Tatin of
mango and caramel soufflé with orange sorbet and salad of
oranges were reluctantly passed over in favour of the warm,
liquid centred chocolate cake with spot-on coconut sorbet,
followed by a shot of excellent espresso coffee. There are
plenty of good French producers on the wine list, white in
particular offers some excellent examples from Loire and
Burgundy. Reds are similarly well selected producer wise, but
vintages and maturity need careful attention. It is worth
considering some crackers from the New World, notably the
exuberant Clos de Gilroy Grenache at £18.50.
Signature dishes: Noisettes of Northumbrian spring lamb
with provençale vegetables and herbs; thin tomato tart with
pistou and a friture of herbs; roast fillet of beef stuffed with
oxtail, vegetable confit and Newcastle Brown ale sauce; terrine
of ham knuckle and foie gras served with pease pudding.

Directions: Queen Street runs parallel to and just behind
Newcastle Quay – almost under the Tyne Bridge on N side of
the river

21 Queen Street Quayside NE1 3UG
Map 12: NZ26
Tel: 0191 2220755
Fax: 0191 2210761
Chef: Terence Laybourne
Owners: Terence & Susan Laybourne
Cost: *Alc* £31.30, fixed-price L
£14.50-£17.50 (2-3 courses).
H/wine £12
Times: Noon-last L 2pm/7pm-last D
10.30pm. Closed L Sat, Sun, Mon,
Bhs
Additional: Children welcome;
❸ dishes
Seats: 70
Smoking: No pipes
Credit cards: 🔲 🔲 🔲 🔲 🔲 🔲

NEWCASTLE-UPON-TYNE,

Vermont Hotel ❀❀❀

Things have changed down at the old County Hall building,
since it was converted into a luxury hotel a few years ago.
There is a choice of bars and restaurants. The Brasserie, for
instance, serves meals throughout the day, but the Blue Room
(where a pianist plays in the evenings) is the setting for some
impressive cooking. In the kitchen, John Connell, ex head chef

Castle Garth
NE1 1RQ
Map 12: NZ26
Tel: 0191 2331010
Fax: 0191 2331234
Chef: John Connell
Owner: Taz Group Ltd
Cost: *Alc* £20. H/wine £10.50.

Vermont Hotel

Times: D only, 7pm-last D 10.30pm.
Closed Sat, Sun, 2 wks Aug, 2 wks Jan
Additional: Bar meals; Sunday L;
Children welcome; ⏺ Dishes.
Seats: 90. Private dining room 140.
Jacket and tie preferred
Smoking: No-smoking area; air-
conditioning
Accommodation: 101 en suite.
Credit cards: ▬ ▬ ▬ ▬ ⛿ 〔

at 21 Queen Street (see entry), is now at the helm. He has brought a more focused menu and style of cooking than previously seen here. The evening *carte* is packed with interest, whilst lunch brings a simpler selection from a short fixed-price menu. Striking visual appeal and artistry are some of Connel's signatures but it's not over-the-top, and every ingredient has its place. A summer dinner opened with canapés and a selection of flavoured breads. A mosaic of pork knuckle and foie gras, haricot beans and a truffle dressing followed, an eye-catching terrine with a sheen given by a lacing of the pork cooking liquor – a good balance of textures. Pot au feu of salmon confit proved to be a fillet poached in duck fat and chicken stock 'giving a marinade flavour', and surrounded by a 'moat of vegetables' – peas, baby broad beans, leek, baby carrots – and the whole topped by a pancetta with a light touch of chilli. Lime and basil parfait to finish had perfect texture, the lime especially was crisp and clean. Restaurant manager, Bruno, cossets his guests and ensures that his full brigade does the same.

Directions: City centre, by the Castle and swing bridge

SUNDERLAND, **Swallow Hotel** ⊛ NEW

A sea-front hotel, overlooking the Sunderland coast, boasts 'fabulous' sea views. The stylish Promenade Restaurant features a unique Victorian 'bandstand' where a pianist plays at dinner. Modern British cooking is on the menu here, perhaps roast loin of pork with pesto risotto, or poached turbot fillet with buttered fettucini and white wine sauce.

Smoking: No-smoking area; air-conditioning
Accommodation: 65 en suite
Credit cards: ▬ ▬ ▬ ▬ ⛿ 〔

Directions: On A184 (Boldon): at roundabout after Boldon turn L, then 1st R to Seaburn. L at next roundabout, follow road to coast. Turn R; hotel is 100m on R

Queen's Parade Seaburn SR6 8DB
Map 12: NZ35
Tel: 0191 529 2041
Fax: 0191 529 4227
Chef: Ken Thompson
Owners: Swallow Hotels
Cost: Alc £28, fixed-price L £18.50/D £24. ☺ H/wine £12.
Times: Last L 2pm/D 9.45pm
Additional: Sunday L; Bar meals L;
Children welcome; ⏺ dishes

WARWICKSHIRE

ABBOT'S SALFORD,
Salford Hall Hotel ✿✿

The Hall is a sympathetically restored, Grade I listed Tudor manor that now functions as a smart hotel with numerous leisure facilities. At its heart is the stylish Stanford restaurant, which makes a suitable setting for some very creditable interpretations of modern British cooking, all backed up by chatty but professional service. Pan-seared Cornish scallops served on home-made saffron noodles with roasted cherry tomatoes in basil oil is a typically lively starter, otherwise you might opt for a parfait of duck confit, foie gras and woodland mushrooms accompanied by sweet wine jelly and home-made walnut brioche. Main courses range from medallions of monkfish sautéed in orange butter with spring onions, mange-touts and julienne of carrot, to noisettes of lamb with onion soubise and red wine sauce, while desserts are creations like passionfruit delice. Several reasonably priced popular wines augment the heavyweight classic list.

Directions: On the A439 8 miles W of Stratford-upon-Avon

Evesham WR11 5UT
Map 4: SP04
Tel: 01386 871300
Fax: 01386 871301
Chef: Robert Bean
Cost: Fixed-price L £14.95/D £25. H/wine £11.25
Times: 12.30pm-last L 2pm/7pm-last D 9.30pm. Closed L Sat, Xmas
Additional: Bar food L; Sunday L; Children welcome at L only; 🍴 dishes
Seats: 60. Private dining room 50
Smoking: No smoking in dining room
Accommodation: 33 en suite
Credit cards: 〓 〓 〓 〓 🔟 🄲

ALDERMINSTER,
Ettington Park Hotel ✿

Reputedly the most haunted hotel in Britain, this atmospheric neo-gothic building has a restaurant with panelling dating from 1740, plus a rococo ceiling. Typical dishes from the chef's daily menu are roast rump of lamb, and seared monkfish fillet with a white wine velouté and chive risotto.

Accommodation: 48 en suite
Credit cards: 〓 〓 〓 〓 🔟 🄲

Directions: 5 miles S of Stratford

Stratford-upon-Avon CV37 8BU
Map 4: SP25
Tel: 01789 450123
Fax: 01789 450472
Chef: Chris Hudson
Cost: Alc £40, fixed-price L £10.50/ D £29.50. H/wine £15
Times: Last L 2.30pm/D 9.30pm
Additional: Bar Food ; Sunday L; Children welcome; 🍴 dishes
Smoking: No smoking in dining room

ATHERSTONE,
Chapel House Hotel ✿✿

Friar's Gate CV9 1EY
Map 4: SP39
Tel: 01827 718949
Fax: 01827 717702
Chefs: Gary Thompson, Adam Bennett
Owners: Chapel House (Atherstone) Ltd
Cost: Alc £24. H/wine £9.65. ☺
Times: 7pm-last D 9.30pm. Closed D Sun, 25-26 Dec
Additional: Sunday lunch (noon-2.30pm); No children under 10; 🍴 dishes
Seats: 50. Private dining room 26
Smoking: No pipes and cigars
Accommodation: 13 en suite

Hard by the church and partly enclosed by a high red brick wall, this early eighteenth-century former Dower house is a refuge of charm, good hospitality and sound cooking. The kitchen brigade work to a monthly changing *carte* which they supplement with daily specials. Dishes are satisfying, generous and presented with care. Indeed, at an autumn inspection, a smoked chicken broth, dense with vegetables and bacon ravioli, was almost a meal in itself. This was followed by a rich, boned chicken with a truffle stuffing set on a split pea and wild mushroom base and served with a Madeira sauce, the whole noted for true flavours and good combination of textures. A well-made Poire William tarte Tatin was a gratifying dessert. Canapés, petits fours and bread are all made on the premises.

Directions: Town centre

Chapel House Hotel

Credit cards: ▨ ▨ ▨ ▨ ▨ ▨

CLAVERDON, Ardencote Hotel ✿

Lye Green Road CV35 8LS
Map 4: SP16
Tel: 01926 843111
Fax: 01926 842646
Chef: Jonathan Stallard
Cost: Fixed-price L £14.95/D £21.95.
☺ H/wine £9.95.
Times: Last L 2pm/D 9.30pm
Additional: Bar meals; Sunday L;
Children welcome; ♨ dishes
Smoking: No smoking in dining room;
air-conditioning
Accommodation: 18 en suite
Credit cards: ▨ ▨ ▨ ▨ ▨ ▨

Elegant gentleman's residence sympathetically converted into a hotel and country club. Choose between the Palms conservatory dining room or the more formal panelled Oak Room. Expect classically inclined dishes such as broccoli and Stilton soup, grilled halibut steak with parsley butter, and mini-rack of lamb with rosemary and garlic.

Directions: Follow Claverdon signs from Henley-in-Arden, 1 mile on village green on road to Shrewley

HENLEY-IN-ARDEN,
Le Filbert Cottage

Authentic French cooking within a beamed, sixteenth-century cottage on Henley's main street. Varied menus offer simply cooked dishes such as Cornish crab soup, beef fillet with red wine and shallot sauce, and brill with a light mustard and herb sauce. Round off with chocolate mousse or crème caramel.

Additional: No children under 6
Smoking: No-smoking area in dining room
Credit cards: ▨ ▨ ▨ ▨

Directions: Town centre, A3400 at junction of High Street and Station Road

64 High Street B95 5BX
Map 4: SP27
Tel: 01564 792700
Chef: Maurice-Jean Gaudens Ricaud
Owners: Mr & Mrs MJ Ricaud
Cost: *Alc* £30/£35. Fixed-price D
£25. ☺ H/wine £9.
Times: Last L 1.30pm/D 9.30pm.
Closed Sun, Mon

KENILWORTH,
Restaurant Bosquet ❀❀

For more than fifteen years the Ligniers have ploughed a reliable furrow of bourgeois French cooking in their intimate, elegantly furnished town house. They have no truck with modish fashion; instead, their repertoire is built on a solid foundation of the classics. Menu are hand-written in French with (helpful) English translations. Warm terrine of lobster is floated on a light, tangy seaweed butter sauce, while saddle of hare is presented with a rich jus and integrated vegetables. Other options might include pan-fried scallops on fennel and saffron purée with a saffron and ink sauce, thyme-crusted lamb with a light sherry sauce, and stuffed fillet of pork wrapped in filo pastry with Madeira sauce. Desserts such as crème brûlée tend to follow the same path. Mrs Lignier runs the front of house in friendly fashion, with the aid of local helpers. The wine list is as patriotically French as the cooking.

97A Warwick Road CV8 1HP
Map 4: SP27
Tel: 01926 852463
Chef: Bernard Lignier
Owner: B & J Lignier
Cost: Fixed-price L & D £22.
H/wine £11.50
Times: Noon-last L 1.15pm/7pm-last D 9.30pm. Closed Sat, Sun, Mon, 3 wks Aug, 1 wk Xmas
Seats: 26
Smoking: No pipes & cigars
Credit cards: ▆ ▆ ▆ ▆ ▆

Directions: In main street of Kenilworth.

KENILWORTH, Simpson's ❀❀

Menus from some of Andreas Antona's previous ventures decorate the walls of this informal restaurant, with its stripped hardwood floors, green and white basketwork chairs and white linen cloths. His current repertoire is in the modern British idiom, which means that ideas are garnered from far and wide. Sweet tomato risotto with Parmesan chips and steamed cod with olive crust, fennel and basil strike a Mediterranean note, while the Far East has its say with pan-fried salmon with pak choi and oriental sauce, then it's back home for a re-invented British dish such as confit of belly pork with black pudding and cider sauce. Puddings follow a similar path: apple fritters with apricot parfait, pecan pie with crème fraîche, pineapple tarte Tatin with rum and raisin ice cream. The list of around 100 wines is arranged by colour and is as eclectic as the menu.

101-103 Warwick Road CV8 1HL
Map 4: SP27
Tel: 01926 864567
Fax: 01926 864510
Chefs: Andrew Waters, Andreas Antona
Owners: Andreas & Alison Antona
Cost: Alc £23.50, fixed-price L £15/D £23.50. ☺ H/wine £9.95.
Times: 12.30pm-last L 2pm/7pm-last D 10pm. Closed L Sat, Sun, 24 Dec-3 Jan
Additional: Children welcome; ❹ dishes
Seats: 70
Smoking: No-smoking area
Credit cards: ▆ ▆ ▆ ▆ ▆ ▆

Directions: In main street of Kenilworth

ROYAL LEAMINGTON SPA,
Lansdowne Hotel ❀

David and Gillian Allen have been in residence at this Regency hotel for almost two decades and continue to please locals and tourists alike. A refreshingly honest approach typifies the cooking, and fixed-price menus offer sound dishes such as green pea and pesto soup, fillet of hake with prawns and capers, and syrup sponge with creamy egg custard.

87 Clarendon Street CV32 4PF
Map 4: SP36
Tel: 01926 450505
Fax: 01926 421313
Chef: Lucinda Robinson
Owners: David & Gillian Allen
Cost: Fixed-price D £17.95. ☺ H/wine £8.95.
Times: D only, 6.30pm- 9.30pm. Closed Xmas

Additional: No children under 5; ❹ dishes
Smoking: No smoking in dining room
Accommodation: 14 en suite
Credit cards: ▆ ▆ ▆

Directions: Town centre, crossroads of Willes Road and Clarendon Street

ROYAL LEAMINGTON SPA,
Leamington Hotel ✿

Formerly The Inchfield Hotel, but substantially upgraded under its new regime. One bistro-style menu is served in both the bar and restaurant, a mix of traditional English and classic French with a few twists. Confit of duck, slow-braised lamb shank with olive mash, and bread-and-butter pudding made with croissants have been enjoyed.

Accommodation: 22 en suite. **Credit cards:** ▬ ▓ ▓

Directions: Along Newbold Terrace, turn L at lights. Hotel on right-hand corner of Willes Road & Upper Holly Walk

NEW

64 Upper Holly Walk CV32 4JL
Map 4: SP36
Tel: 01926 883777
Fax: 01926 330467
Chef: Robert Rouse
Owner: Frank Nixey
Cost: Alc £15. H/wine £8.75. ☺
Times: Last L 1.45pm/last D 9.30pm.
Closed L Sat, D Sun
Additional: Bar meals L; Sunday L;
Children welcome; Vegetarian dishes

ROYAL LEAMINGTON SPA,
Mallory Court Hotel ✿✿✿

It is not hard to understand why Mallory Court ranks high in many a list of favourite hotels. The tranquil, Lutyens-style manor is set in ten acres of perfectly landscaped grounds and formal gardens; staff are welcoming and discreet and attention to detail is meticulous. Dinner is served in the oak-panelled dining room, and is usually a pleasure worth anticipating. Steven Shore cooks with a light touch, using first-class ingredients, fresh vegetables and herbs from the garden. The *carte* shows lots of inventive ideas, embroidering on classic combinations without straying into the realms of fantasy; pan-fried fillets of red mullet served in its own soup, sautéed breast of duck with a confit of the leg served with a Seville orange sauce, guinea fowl *en cocotte* with garden peas, wild mushrooms and foie gras cream sauce were all on the menu of an early spring visit. Foie gras was also used in a terrine with duck confit and Madeira jelly, plus a fondness for fungi is demonstrated in dishes such as turbot with crispy potato and cep purée, and veal cutlet with girolles and a potato galette. Grand Marnier soufflé, rhubarb compote with iced tangerine mousse, and lemon tart with Cassis sauce are amongst desserts worth leaving a space for. The fixed price menu offers a choice at each course – baked tartlet of Cornish crab with tomato vinaigrette, pan-fried skate wing with shallots and capers, and banana cheesecake, for example, and with coffee and delicate, home-made petits fours, is very fairly priced at £30, especially as service is neither charged nor expected. Lunches are also very good value, when the menu includes more brasserie style items such as Caesar salad, smoked haddock fish cakes with parsley sauce, rabbit in Dijon mustard sauce and devilled lambs' kidneys with saffron rice.

Harbury Lane Bishop's Tachbrook
CV33 9QB
Map 4: SP36
Tel: 01926 330214
Fax: 01926 451714
Chef: Allan Holland
Owners: Allan Holland, Jeremy Mort
Cost: £45, fixed-price L £26/D £30.
H/wine £16
Times: 12.30pm-last L 1.45pm/7pm-last D 9.45pm. Closed 1-8 Jan
Additional: Sunday L;
No children under 9; ✿ dishes
Seats: 50. Private dining room 26
Smoking: No smoking in dining room
Accommodation: 10 en suite
Credit cards: ▬ ▓ ▓ ▓ ▓ ▓

Directions: 2 miles S of Leamington off the B4087 towards Harbury

ROYAL LEAMINGTON SPA,
Regent Hotel ✿

This was the largest hotel in the world when it opened in 1819. The family-run Regent is renowned for exceptional hospitality and service which extends to the Vaults Restaurant where preparation of traditional dishes shows good levels of technical skill and sound knowledge of classical technique.

Directions: In the town centre near Royal Priors Shopping Centre

77 The Parade CV32 4AX
Map 4: SP36
Tel: 01926 427231
Fax: 01926 450728
Telephone for details

STRATFORD-UPON-AVON,

Alveston Manor

*Warm brick and timber façade, gable ends, and well-tended grounds
add up to a striking building that dates from the sixteenth century.
The kitchen is keen and up-to-date with its ideas, delivering the likes
of chicken liver parfait with kumquat jelly, baked 'Canon of Lamb'
encased in a walnut crust, and fresh lime cheesecake for dessert.*

Clopton Bridge CV37 7HP
Map 4: SP25
Tel: 01789 204581
Fax: 01789 414095
Chef: Carl Withers
Owners: Forte
Cost: *Alc* £20. H/wine £11.50. ☺
Times: Last L 2.30pm/D 9.30pm
Additional: Bar food L; Sunday L;
Children welcome; ❹ dishes
Smoking: No pipes and cigars in
dining room
Accommodation: 106 en suite
Credit cards: ▅ ▅ ▅ ▅ ▅ ▅

Directions: Take A46 towards
Stratford, then A439 to town centre;
hotel is on S side of river

STRATFORD-UPON-AVON,

The Arden Thistle

*Bard's Restaurant overlooks the two theatres on Waterside, and in
fine weather there is open-air dining with views of the River Avon.
At inspection, a filo case of fresh crab with sorrel sauce made a light
starter, followed by steamed sea bass with a confit of spring onion
and langoustine sauce.*

Waterside CV37 6BA
Map 4: SP25
Tel: 01789 294949
Fax: 01789 415874
Chef: Michael Bibby
Owner: Thistle Hotels
Cost: Fixed-price L £12.50/D
£24.75. ☺ H/wine £10.60.
Times: Last L 2pm/5.45pm-last D
9.30pm
Additional: Sunday L; Bar meals;
❹ dishes
Smoking: No smoking in dining room
Accommodation: 62 en suite
Credit cards: ▅ ▅ ▅ ▅ ▅ ▅

Directions: On Waterside, opposite
Royal Shakespeare and Swan theatres

STRATFORD-UPON-AVON,

Billesley Manor Hotel

The original site was listed in Domesday book, although the
present manor has only been around for some four centuries.
It stands – just a short drive from the tourist bustle of Stratford
– in 11 acres of grounds complete with an immaculately-
snipped topiary garden, tennis courts and a croquet lawn. The
interior oozes history, whether you are sitting in one of the
lounges or the splendid oak-panelled restaurant. There have

Alcester
B49 6NF
Map 4: SP25
Tel: 01789 279955
Fax: 01789 764145
Chef: Christopher Short
Owners: Queens Moat Houses
Cost: *Alc* £40, fixed-price L £19.50/D
£30 (4 courses). H/wine £12.50

been changes in the kitchen since the last edition of the Guide, but menus continue to take a broadly based European view of things culinary, occasionally veering off east or west for an embellishment or two. Appetisers might range from marinade of red snapper with lime and smoked oysters to chicken terrine with a core of sushi-rolled pork fillet served with sweet onion chutney, while centrepiece dishes could include open ravioli of sea scallops with pink ginger and freshwater crayfish to fillet of Scotch beef with roasted baby vegetables and thyme Burgundy essence.

Times: Noon-last L 2.15pm/7.30pm-last D 9.30pm
Additional: Bar food L; Sunday L; Children welcome; ◑ dishes
Seats: 70. Private dining room 18
Smoking: No smoking in dining room
Accommodation: 41 en suite
Credit cards: ▬ ▣ ▦ ▧ ▨ ▢

Directions: On the A46, 3 miles west of Stratford-upon-Avon

STRATFORD-UPON-AVON,

The Boathouse ❀❀

Swan's Nest Lane
CV37 7LS
Map 4: SP25
Tel/Fax: 01789 297733
Chef: Patrick Robiquet
Owners: W Meredith Owen, M Brebner
Cost: *Alc* £22, fixed-price L £7.50 (2 courses)/D £19.75. ☺ H/wine £9.60.
Times: Noon-last L 1.50pm/5.30pm-last D 10.30pm. Closed D Sun
Additional: Bar food L; Children welcome; ◑ dishes
Seats: 90
Smoking: No-smoking area
Credit cards: ▬ ▣ ▦ ▧ ▢

'The only riverside venue in town', claims the brochure. As the name suggests, this is a working boathouse: guests can hire punts and rowing boats to mess about on the Avon and there's even a gondola ferry service to and from the theatre. The dining room is on the first floor, with fine views of the nautical junketings, especially from the open balcony. Some great timbers, wayward murals and classy stencilling on painted surfaces define the decor and the atmosphere has plenty of fizz. Big, earthy flavours typify the food and dishes are full-blooded in a *terroir* kind of way. Roast fillet of monkfish is served on a bed of creamed cauliflower as a starter, while main courses move into the realms of pan-fried calves' liver and pancetta with bubble and squeak, venison steak on a leek clafoutis with apple and blackberry sauce, and tempura of cod on a sun-dried tomato pistou with a crispy galette. The wine list is a carefully constructed selection of around 40 good-value bins.

Directions: From town centre, cross river by Clopton Bridge toward Oxford and Banbury, then double back around roundabout 50 yards on, then 1st L.

STRATFORD-UPON-AVON,

Lambs of Sheep Street

NEW

A fun place to eat with a determinedly eclectic menu, offering modern British, Oriental and Mediterranean-influenced dishes and

12 Sheep Street CV37 6EF
Map 4: SP25
Tel/Fax: 01789 292554
Chef: Paul Desport

serving everything from a snack, through pastas and salads to a full three-course meal. The building is a tourist's delight, dating from 1547 with oak beams and roaring log fires.

Smoking: No-smoking area. **Credit cards:** ▆ ▆ ▆ ▆ ▆ ▆

Directions: From Stratford town centre, head towards 'Waterside' and 'Royal Shakespeare Theatre'. Sheep Street is 1st R on Waterside

Owner: Bobby Browns Ltd
Cost: *Alc* £18, fixed-price L £5.95 (1 course). ☺ H/wine £7.95.
Times: 12-last L 2.30pm/5.30pm-last D 11pm. Closed 25-26 Dec & 1 Jan
Additional: Sunday L; Children welcome; ⚫ dishes

STRATFORD-UPON-AVON,
Shakespeare Hotel ⚜

No mistaking this Elizabethan-timbered landmark hotel in the centre of the town. Crispy duck with garlic oil and endive salad, calves' liver with red cabbage and herb mash, and fried sea bass with ginger and fennel on a parsnip purée are typical of the modern British style of cooking.

Chapel Street CV37 6ER
Map 4: SP25
Tel: 01789 294771
Fax: 01789 415411
Chef: Richard Walton
Owners: Forte
Cost: *Alc* £24. H/wine £12.45. ☺
Times: D only, 6pm-10pm
Additional: Bar Food; Sunday L (12.30pm-2.30pm); Children welcome; ⚫ dishes
Smoking: No smoking in dining room
Accommodation: 63 en suite
Credit cards: ▆ ▆ ▆ ▆ ▆ ▆

Directions: Follow signs to town centre. Go round one-way system up Bridge Street. At roundabout turn L. Hotel is 200yds on L-hand side

STRATFORD-UPON-AVON,
Stratford House Hotel ⚜

Perfectly placed for anyone planning a trip to the theatre. Quality home cooking is served in the Shepherd's Conservatory Restaurant, and an ever-so-English tea shop is open throughout the day. Refurbishment was under way and staff changes were planned as we went to press.

18 Sheep Street CV37 6EF
Map 4: SP25
Tel: 01789 268288
Fax: 01789 295580
Owner: Sylvia Adcock
Telephone for details

Directions: Town centre, 100 yds from Royal Shakespeare Theatre

STRATFORD-UPON-AVON,
Welcombe Hotel ⚜⚜

The house, built in Jacobean style in 1869, was the home of the historian Sir George Trevelyan. It is set in 800 acres of attractively landscaped parkland, part of which was once owned by Shakespeare. Drinks and cocktails are served in the oak-panelled Trevelyan Bar, with its comfortable leather sofas and chairs. The restaurant is light, airy and spacious, adorned with antique mirrors and Italian crystal chandeliers. Tall bay windows look out over the formal Italian garden, fountain and

Warwick Road CV37 0NR
Map 4: SP25
Tel: 01789 295252
Fax: 01789 414666
Chef: Mark Naylor
Owner: Yamada UK
Cost: *Alc* £35, fixed-price L £19.50/D £32.50 (4 courses). H/wine £14.50
Times: Noon-last L 1.45pm/6pm-last D 9.30pm

Welcombe Hotel

Additional: Bar food; Sunday L;
Children welcome; 🍴 dishes
Seats: 70. Private dining room 100.
Jacket and tie preferred
Smoking: No smoking in dining room
Accommodation: 67 en suite
Credit cards: 🔲 🔲 🔲 🔲 🔲 🔲

magnificent waterfall. Accomplished cooking skills were
clearly evident at a spring meal, the highlight being a foie gras
and chicken liver parfait with fruity apricot chutney and 'melt-
in-the-mouth' brioche. Next, breast of Deben duck came sliced
on a cinnamon sauce with glazed pears, and to finish a warm
pear tart was accompanied by a smooth pear sorbet with the
most delightful flavour.

Directions: On A439 1 mile from town centre

WISHAW, The Belfry

Sutton Coldfield B76 9PR
Map 7: SP19
Tel: 01675 470301
Fax: 01675 470178
Chef: Eric Bruce
Owner: De Vere Hotels
Cost: *Alc* £35, fixed-price L £16.95/D
£28. H/wine £13.50
Times: 12.30pm-last L 2pm/6.30pm-
last D 10pm
Additional: Bar food; Sunday L;
Children welcome; 🍴 dishes
Seats: 200. Private dining room 20
Smoking: No-smoking area; no pipes
and cigars
Accommodation: 267 en suite
Credit cards: 🔲 🔲 🔲 🔲 🔲 🔲

Part of the De Vere group of golfing hotels, The Belfry, thrice
venue for the Ryder Cup, is set amidst 300 acres of countryside
and includes two challenging courses. The French Restaurant
overlooks the Brabazon Course and putting green, with hot
and cold canapés served in the cocktail bar. As well as the
carte, there is a special weekly changing set dinner menu plus a
'chef's gastronomique suggested menu'. This latter gives a
good idea of the kitchen's well-polished skills and includes
gâteau of Galia melon with Bavarian ham and nut dressing,
pan-fried scallops with fresh tagliatelle, champagne and peach
schnapps water ice, chargrilled chicken breast with Anna
potato, roasted beetroot and glazed carrots, finishing with rich
chocolate tart and orange and chocolate ice cream. The *carte*,
however, includes classic dishes such as suprême of Scotch
salmon poached or grilled with hollandaise sauce, and steak
with béarnaise sauce.

Directions: At junction of A446 & A4091, 1 mile NW of M42/J9

WEST MIDLANDS

BALSALL COMMON, Haigs Hotel ❀❀

Kenilworth Road CV7 7EL
Map 7: SP27
Tel: 01676 533004
Fax: 01676 535132
Chef: Paul Hartup
Owners: Alan & Hester Harris
Cost: *Alc* £25, fixed-price L £13.50/D
£17.95. ☺ H/wine £9.75.
Times: D only, 7.30pm-last D
9.30pm. Closed D Sun, Dec 25 –
4 Jan, 25 July – 9 Aug
Additional: Sunday L (12.30pm-2pm);
Children welcome; ❹ dishes
Seats: 60. Private dining room 28
Smoking: No smoking in dining room
Accommodation: 15 en suite
Credit cards: ▬ ▬ ▬ ◻

A small, welcoming hotel that continues to improve. The kitchen offers a varied selection of Anglo/French dishes, including an excellent vegetarian section. An assured hand in saucing is notable in dishes such as pan-fried venison with cranberry and port sauce, and whole lobster flamed with brandy and served in its shell with a mushroom cream sauce. At a meal in September, our inspector enjoyed an 'almost smoky' Mediterranean fish soup, served with garlic bread and saffron mayonnaise. Grilled pork fillet with a mushroom and port sauce followed, and the meal concluded with an iced vanilla parfait with blackcurrant sauce. Other desserts include strawberry charlotte with vanilla sauce, sticky toffee pudding with custard, and pears poached in champagne with passion fruit sauce. The wine list remains below the £20 mark, and includes bottles from the New World, as well as several from the regions of Europe.

Directions: On A452, 4 miles N of NEC/Airport, on L before village centre

BALSALL COMMON, Nailcote Hall ❀❀

Nailcote Lane Berkswell CV7 7DE
Map 7: SP27
Tel: 01203 466174
Fax: 01203 470720
Chef: Mark Shelton

Elizabethan manors were not originally built as country house hotels; as a result, the lounge bar of this lovely, atmospheric

timbered and panelled house gets a little cramped at times. The staff, however, are cheerful and alert and, once ensconced, The Oak Room is a civilised setting for a dinner that mixes classical and modern styles of cooking. The menu offers a good choice, and includes some bold ideas such as sauté of lambs kidneys and pancetta on a bed of colcannon with a piquant sauce, and medallions of monkfish and crayfish tails braised in an américaine butter sauce. Less adventurous souls will be satisfied with chicken liver parfait flavoured with brandy and thyme with tomato chutney, and strips of veal liver flash-fried with crispy shallots and bacon. A crème brûlée flavoured with Calvados and apples was a neat twist on a classic dessert.

Directions: On B4101 (Balsall/Coventry), 10 mins from NEC/Birmingham Airport

Owner: Richard Cressman
Cost: Alc £32, fixed-price L £18.50/D £25.50. H/wine £12.95
Times: 12.30pm-last L 2pm/7.30pm-last D 10pm. Closed L Sat, D Sun
Additional: Bar food; Sunday L; Children welcome; ✿ dishes
Seats: 45. Private dining room 10-120. Jacket and tie preferred
Smoking: No pipes or cigars
Accommodation: 38 en suite
Credit cards: ■ ■ ■ ■ ■ ■

BIRMINGHAM, **Burlington Hotel** ❀

Within walking distance of New Street station, this totally refurbished Victorian hotel offers carefully prepared food in the Berlioz Restaurant. Fresh produce is used in crafting such dishes as lamb's liver and bacon with red onion marmalade, coffee-roasted duck and whisky bread-and-butter pudding with banana ice cream.

Additional: Bar meals; Children welcome; ✿ dishes
Smoking: No-smoking area; air conditioning
Accommodation: 112 en suite
Credit cards: ■ ■ ■ ■ ■ ■

Directions: Adjacent to New Street Railway Station.

6 Burlington Arcade
126 New Street B2 4JH
Map 7: SP08
Tel: 0121 643 9191
Fax: 0121 643 5075
Chef: Charles Anderson
Owner: Hortelux Ltd
Cost: Alc £19.50; fixed-price L&D £17.95. ☺ H/wine £9.
Times: Noon-last L 2.30pm/6.30pm-last D 10pm. Closed L Sat, L Sun

BIRMINGHAM, **Chung Ying Garden** ❀

Modern restaurant with loyal Chinese following – an indication of authentic Cantonese cooking in the heart of China Town. There's a good selection of dim sum as well as dishes such as steamed duck with mange-touts, shredded beef in black bean sauce, and sizzling lamb with ginger and spring onions.

Additional: Children welcome; ✿ dishes
Smoking: Air-conditioning
Credit cards: ■ ■ ■ ■ ■ ■

Directions: City centre, off Hurst Street, nr Hippodrome Theatre

17 Thorp Street B5 4AT
Map 7: SP08
Tel: 0121 6666622/6221668
Fax: 0121 6225860
Chef/Owner: S C Wong
Cost: Alc £12. H/wine £10.50. ☺
Times: Noon-midnight Mon-Sat (Sun noon-11pm).

BIRMINGHAM, **The Copthorne** ❀

Stylish modern hotel set in the heart of the city. A recent meal in the smart Goldsmith's Restaurant highlighted an accurately cooked fish sausage with white wine and chive sauce. Other dishes may include pot-roast duck with blueberry and honey sauce, and white chocolate parfait.

Additional: Bar food; Children welcome; ✿ dishes
Smoking: No-smoking area; air-conditioning
Accommodation: 212 en suite
Credit cards: ■ ■ ■ ■ ■ ■

Directions: City centre

Paradise Circus B3 3HJ
Map 7: SP08
Tel: 0121 2002727
Fax: 0121 2001197
Chef: Terry Malyon
Owners: Millennium & Copthorne Hotels
Cost: Fixed-price D £21.95. ☺ H/wine £9.95.
Times: D only, 7pm-10pm. Closed Sun, Bh Mon

BIRMINGHAM, Jonathans' Hotel

16-24 Wolverhampton Road
Oldbury B68 0LH
Map 7: SP08
Tel: 0121 4293757
Fax: 0121 4343107
Chef: Graham Bradley
Owners: J Baker, J Bedford
Cost: Alc £25. Fixed-price L £12.90/D
£28.50 (6 courses). ☺ H/wine
£12.90.
Times: Last L 2pm/D 10pm
Additional: Bar meals; Sunday L;
Children welcome; ◗ dishes
Smoking: No-smoking area in dining
room; air-conditioning
Accommodation: 44 en suite
Credit cards: 🔲 📖 🔲 ⚡ 🔲 🔲

*An extraordinary evocation of the Victorian era, a real maze of a
place, crammed with bric-à-brac yet behind a modern brick exterior.
The Victorian menu includes soup served in a stoneware jar,
Newcastle fillet with their patent spice mix and Mrs Beeton's Carrack
sauce, and a traditional syllabub.*

Directions: From M5/J2 take A4123 (Birmingham), 1.5 miles on L

BIRMINGHAM, Lombard Room

180 Lifford Lane
Kings Norton B30 3NT
Map 7: SP08
Tel: 0121 4595800
Fax: 0121 4598553
Chef: Anthony Morgan
Owner: Morgan Davis Hotels Ltd
Cost: Fixed-price L £12.50/D £21.50.
☺ H/wine £13.50
Times: 12.30pm-last L 2pm/7.30pm-
last D 9.30pm. Closed L Sat, D Sun,
L Mon, 1st 2 wks Jan
Additional: Bar food L; Sunday L;
Children welcome; ◗ dishes
Seats: 55. Private dining room 12
Smoking: No smoking in dining room;
air-conditioning
Accommodation: 9 en suite
Credit cards: 🔲 📖 🔲 ⚡ 🔲

Set in quiet landscaped grounds away from the conurbation,
this converted Victorian paper mill now houses the stylish
Lombard Room, which is decorated in pastel colour schemes
with bronze chandeliers and wall lights. Up-to-the-minute
ideas and ingredients dominate the fixed-price menu: warm
Thai fish terrine comes with mango and coriander, ravioli of
Cornish crab is served with saffron, spaghetti cucumber and
Parmesan, char-grilled Welsh ostrich steak is given an East-
West twist with stir-fried shiitake mushrooms, bean sprouts,
spinach and black cherries in Kirsch. Desserts keep up the
momentum with the likes of poached pear with pear and fig
mousse and deep-fried noodles. Light lunches are served in the
spacious conservatory, where the menu promises deep-fried
haddock cheeks with chips, bangers and mash, and steamed
salmon salad with minted potatoes and pesto vinaigrette, plus
sandwiches and jacket potatoes.

Directions: From city centre take A441 (Pershore road) until
Stirchley. Turn L at Breadon Bar, hotel is 1 mile on R

BIRMINGHAM, Shimla Pinks

Familiar dishes, tikkas and tandooris especially, using fresh herbs and spices, and the popular, evening help-yourself buffet attract the crowds to this unusual Indian restaurant housed in a converted car showroom. Striking minimalist paintings, designer furniture and stunning floral displays create the stylish interior.

Smoking: Air-conditioning. **Credit cards:** 💳 💳 💳 💳 💳 💳

Directions: In city centre, opposite Novotel and near the ICC

214 Broad Street B15 1AY
Map 7: SP08
Tel/Fax: 0121 633 0366
Chef: Ganesh Shreftha
Owner: Kal Dhaliwal
Cost: Alc £17, fixed-price L £6.95/D £12.95. ☺ H/wine £8.95.
Times: Last L 2pm/last D 11pm.
Closed L Sat, L Sun, Xmas, 1st Jan
Additional: Children welcome; 🍴 dishes

BIRMINGHAM, Swallow Hotel ⚜⚜⚜

12 Hagley Road Five Ways B16 8SJ
Map 7: SP08
Tel: 0121 4521144
Fax: 0121 4563442
Chef: Jonathon Harison
Cost: Alc £35, fixed-price L £21.50/D £32 (4 courses). H/wine £15
Times: 12.30pm-last L 2.30pm/7.30pm-last D10.30pm.
Closed L Sat
Additional: Sunday L; Children welcome; 🍴 dishes
Seats: 60. Private dining rooms 20
Smoking: No-smoking area in dining room; Air-conditioning
Accommodation: 98 en suite
Credit cards: 💳 💳 💳 💳 💳

This smart, well-run hotel has become something of a city landmark and meeting-place; the drawing room is a popular place for afternoon tea and the two restaurants, Langtry's and the Sir Edward Elgar, offer a genuine contrast of cooking styles. The former specialises in traditional English food: cock a leekie broth, poached Finnan haddock in a smoked salmon and dill sauce, breast of chicken with bubble and squeak, sticky toffee pudding with vanilla ice-cream and the like. Regular guests are greeted like old friends and strangers warmly welcomed in the exec-orientated Sir Edward Elgar room, where a pianist plays in the background, and there is a touch of the performing arts about soup served from a tureen by a waiter sporting white gloves, especially when this turns out to be an unexpected star – celeriac and white bean soup with superb flavour and texture, magically enhanced by a drizzle of truffle oil. Main course was a fillet of cod topped with smoked salmon served with tiny saffron pancakes and a vegetable nage. Most dishes on the carte are described with a welcome degree of simplicity: warm quail salad with fried potatoes and pancetta, fillet of beef with winter vegetables and truffles, roasted honey-glazed Barbury duckling with apples and mint (for two people, carved in the restaurant). An orange bavarois with dark chocolate mousse proved an excellent choice of dessert, light and full of sweet but not sickly flavour, but the choice might also include iced honey parfait with a raspberry sauce and a traditional tarte Tatin with crème fraîche. An enthusiastic, first-class sommelier proffers down-to-earth advice and looks like a man who enjoys his job.

Signature dishes: Roasted fillet of salmon with smoked bacon and cabbage; warm crabcake with a lemon and chive mayonnaise; cannelloni of ricotta and spinach with forest mushrooms; pot-roasted rabbit with winter vegetables

Directions: City end of the A546, at the Five Ways roundabout.

COVENTRY,

Brooklands Grange Hotel

Behind the Jacobean façade of Brooklands Grange lies a thoroughly modern, comfortable business hotel. Rich colours and soft furnishing set the tone in the Victorian restaurant, flooded with natural light from the conservatory extension by day, candlelit at night. The modern, fashionable *carte* offers a good choice , and there's a fixed-price menu of roughly three choices at each course. A meal in June yielded roasted scallops on a nest of baby leeks with a garlic and parsley sauce, braised shank of lamb with tomato pesto, and warm chocolate mousse 'a real chocoholics delight', served with a smooth caramel ice cream. Service is professional but friendly.

Directions: On A4144; on right at Allesley roundabout

Holyhead Road CV5 8HX
Map 4: SP38
Tel: 01203 601601
Fax: 01203 601277
Chef: Richard Mellor
Owners: Brooklands Grange
Hotel & Restaurant Ltd
Cost: *Alc* £23.25, fixed-price L/D
£14.95/£17.95. ☺ H/wine £10.95.
Times: Last L 2pm/D 10pm (Sun last
D 8.30pm), closed L Sat, 26 Dec
Additional: Sunday L; Bar meals;
Children welcome; 🍴 dishes
Smoking: No pipes or cigars
Accommodation: 30 en suite
Credit cards: 🔲🔲🔲🔲🔲🔲

HOCKLEY HEATH,

Nuthurst Grange

Nuthurst Grange Lane
Solihull B94 5NL
Map 7: SP17
Tel: 01564 783972
Fax: 01564 783919
Chef/Owner: David Randolph
Cost: *Alc* L £19, fixed-price D from
£26.90. H/wine £10.90
Times: Noon-last L 2pm/7pm-last D
9.30pm. Closed L Sat
Additional: Sunday L;
Children welcome; 🍴 dishes
Seats: 50. Private dining room 45
Smoking: No smoking in dining room
Accommodation: 15 en suite
Credit cards: 🔲🔲🔲🔲🔲🔲

The restaurant is the focal point of Nuthurst Grange, itself in the middle of seven acres of landscaped gardens, in the very heart of England. This sense of being at the centre of things, obviously communicates itself to the young staff who have an eagerness and enthusiasm lacking in many other similar establishments. Chef/Proprietor David Randolph has a great eye for detail, seems ever-present and ensures nobody slacks, nothing is slip-shod. A choice of fixed-priced menus changes seasonally and includes some varied and interesting dishes; before dinner, there may be tempting appetisers such as mini fishcakes served in saffron, chive and garlic sauce. The kitchen's experience shows in the balance required to match the flavours of chicken, leek and foie gras in a terrine. As well as starters such as breast of pigeon with mixed beans, saffron, honey and sesame seed dressing, there is an optional first course, such as steamed mussels with garlic or baked tuna with quails' eggs. Main course fish dishes might include chargrilled monkfish with salsa verde or grilled Dover sole, either on the bone with butter, or off with champagne and dill sauce. Meat courses have a fairly hearty air to them – breast of guinea fowl is served with sauerkraut, olive and basil sauce, saddle of venison with bubble and squeak and gin and juniper berry sauce, for example. Desserts range from a rather racy sounding coconut timbale with Malibu sauce, to a suave white and dark chocolate mousse with marinated figs, or a very grown-up version of prunes and custard – hot prune pudding with creamy Armagnac custard. Coffee is strong and fresh, and petits fours are home-made.

Signature dishes: Fillet of Scotch beef, Stilton and herb mousse, Dijon mustard and tarragon sauce; chargrilled sea bass with salsa verde and Med-style vegetables; casserole of rabbit with dried tomatoes and olives; knuckle of lamb with port wine and sage.

Directions: Off A 34000, half mile S of Hockley Heath, turning at notice board into Nuthurst Grange Lane.

MERIDEN, **Manor Hotel**

Greatly extended Georgian manor house, built in 1745, and now under the same ownership as The Motorcycle Museum. Meals served in the open-plan Regency Restaurant include inviting dishes such as fish terrine with yogurt and herb mayonnaise, pan-fried calves' liver with caramelised red onions and a good version of summer pudding.

Additional: Sunday L; Bar meals; Children welcome; ❹ dishes
Smoking: No smoking in dining room
Accommodation: 74 en suite.
Credit cards: ■■ ▤▤ ▤▤ ▚▚ ▣ ⌐

Directions: In centre of village

Main Road CV7 7NH
Map 4: SP28
Tel: 01676 522735
Fax: 01676 522186
Chef: Peter Griffiths
Owners: Roy Richards, Bracebridge Holdings
Cost: *Alc* £25, fixed-price L £16.95/D £17.95. ☺ H/wine £10.95.
Times: Noon-last L 1.45pm/7pm-last D 9.45pm. Closed L Sat, 26-30 Dec

MERIDEN,
Marriott Forest of Arden

Impressive modern hotel and country club within easy reach of both the M6 and M42. Apart from extensive sporting and leisure activities, there's enjoyable modern cooking in the split-level restaurant. A recent inspection meal chosen from a lively carte yielded a good cheese soufflé and accurately cooked lamb.

Directions: From M42/J6, take A45 (Coventry) after Stonebridge island, then L (Shepherds Lane), 1.5 miles on L

Maxstoke Lane CV7 7HR
Map 4: SP28
Tel: 01676 522335
Fax: 01676 523711
Telephone for details

SOLIHULL, **Solihull Moat House**

State of the art conference facilities and a leisure club are just two of the attributes of this spacious modern hotel not far from the NEC and attractions such as Cadbury World. Stained glass windows with peacock motifs adorn the entrance and there are views of an ornamental lake and fountain from the windows in Brookes Restaurant. Crêpes, pasta, salads and grills share the billing on the menu with more ambitious modern dishes along the lines of timbale of couscous, avocado and noisettes of lamb on a 'collage' of spinach and tomatoes with a light curry sauce. Desserts such as chilled nougat parfait with butterscotch sauce, and pastry cream tartlet with seasonal fruit tread a similar path.

Directions: Follow signs to Town Centre and Conference Centre, 3rd turn at roundabout (Homer Road)

61 Homer Road B91 3QD
Map 7: SP17
Tel: 0121 6239988
Fax: 0121 7112696
Chef: Eddie Stephens
Cost: Fixed-price L £14.50/D £18.75 (3 courses). ☺ H/wine £11.75.
Times: 12.30pm-last L 2pm/7pm-last D 10pm
Additional: Bar food; Sunday lunch; Children welcome; ❹ dishes
Seats: 70. Private dining room 130
Smoking: No-smoking area; air-conditioning
Accommodation: 115 en suite
Credit cards: ■■ ▤▤ ▤▤ ▚▚ ▣ ⌐

SUTTON COLDFIELD, New Hall

Walmeley Road B76 1QX
Map 7: SP19
Tel: 0121 3782442
Fax: 0121 3784637
Chef: David Lake
Owner: Thistle Country House
Cost: Fixed-price L £19.50/D £35.50
Times: 12.30pm-last L 2pm/7pm-last
D 9pm. D Sun residents only
Additional: Sunday L; Children
welcome; ✪ dishes
Seats: 60. Private dining room 45
Smoking: No smoking in dining room
Accommodation: 62 en suite
Credit cards: 🟥 🟥 🟥 🟥 🟥 🟥

New Hall is said to be the oldest-surviving moated manor
house in England and mullioned windows, beams and oak
panelling all add to the atmosphere of this country house
hotel. Add 26 acres of well-tended grounds, and the setting is
complete. David Lake had not been in charge of the kitchen
long when our inspectors called, but his pedigree background
(Dorchester Grill, Hollington House at Newbury and
Horstead Place at Uckfield), is already paying dividends.
Menus are nicely to the point: three meat main course, three
fish, supplemented by daily specials. A terrine of wild salmon
was a meaty mix of cured and fresh salmon, its counterpart,
large juicy scallops, were nicely charred and served on a bed
of mixed leaves with tarragon dressing. The centrepiece of
the meal was a pink breast of Hereford duck, just slightly
salty but lovely and crisp, which came with an excellent confit
of the leg and wilted spinach, all surrounded by a slightly
sharp balsamic jus and good caramelised baby onions.
Puddings took in a first-class lemon tart served with a fresh
berry sorbet and sauce anglaise, and a summer pudding with
clotted cream.

On the wine list, 12 house wines cover Europe and all come
in at under £15. There's some good drinking at under £25 –
Glen Ellen Proprietors Reserve Chardonnay 94 (£17.50); Ch
Haut-Canteloup, cru Bourgeois 93 (£19.95).

Directions: On B4148 E of Sutton
Coldfield, close to M6/M42

WALSALL,
The Fairlawns at Aldridge ✪

178 Little Aston Road
Aldridge WS9 0NU
Map 7 : SP09
Tel: 01922 55122
Fax: 01922 743210
Chef: Todd Hubble
Owners: John and Tammy Pette
Cost: Alc £25, fixed-price L £15/D
£22.50 (5 courses). ☺
H/wine £10.95.
Times: Last L 2pm/D10.30pm
Closed L Sat, D Sun
Additional: Bar Food L; Sunday L;
Children welcome; ✪ dishes
Accommodation: 35 en suite
Credit cards: 🟥 🟥 🟥 🟥 🟥 🟥

Fresh fish from Birmingham market and other suppliers dominates the blackboard in this tastefully refurbished Victorian building. Expect grilled scallops with bacon, monkfish au poivre and fillet of Scottish cod on mash alongside pot roast Deben duck leg with spiced plums and roast pork with apple fritters and Calvados sauce.

Directions: Outskirts of Aldridge, 400 yards from crossroads of A452 (Chester Road) & A454 (Little Aston Road)

WIGHT, ISLE OF

GODSHILL, Cask & Taverners

Owned by Burt's, a local brewery, this is a serious restaurant set within a themed Victorian interior (although parts date from the seventeenth century). Sound cooking of the likes of terrine of venison and wild mushroom with tomato chutney, Mediterranean fish soup, roast loin of lamb with dauphinoise potatoes and rosemary flavoured sauce, and crème brûlée with rice pudding and sauce anglaise.

Smoking: No-smoking area. **Credit cards:**

Directions: From Shanklin take A3020 3 miles into Godshill

High Street PO38 3HZ
Map 4: SZ58
Tel: 01983 840707
Fax: 01983 840861
Chef: Stephen Chiverton
Owner: Burts Taverns Ltd
Cost: *Alc* £18.75, fixed-price L £9.25/D £15.75. ☺ H/wine £7.30.
Times: Last L 2pm/D 9pm
Additional: Sunday L; Bar meals; Children welcome; ❹ dishes

SEAVIEW, Seaview Hotel ❀❀

High Street PO34 5EX
Map 4: SZ69
Tel: 01983 612711
Fax: 01983 613729
Chef: Charles Bartlett
Owners: Nicholas & Nicola Hayward
Cost: *Alc* £20. H/wine £8.20. ☺
Times: Noon-last L 1.30pm/7.30pm-last D 9.15pm. Closed D Sun (ex Bhs)
Additional: Bar food; Sunday L; Children welcome; ❹ dishes
Seats: 80. Private dining room 50
Smoking: One dining room no smoking; no pipes; air-conditioning (one dining room)
Accommodation: 16 en suite
Credit cards:

'The dignified atmosphere and sailing rules of its Yacht Club set the standard for life in the village', runs the brochure advertising this popular seaside hotel. The Haywards have been in residence since 1980 and have made the Seaview one of the most popular venues on the island. In summer, when the breezes blow, the ensigns flutter and boats bob on the water, most people head for the terrace. Inside, there are two bars decked out with nautical memorabilia, but serious eating takes place in the two separate dining rooms – one modern and clean-cut, the other more traditional. Local produce defines the menu: Arreton valley asparagus, garlic, herbs from the hotel garden all find their way into the kitchen, but seafood is the star turn. Hot crab ramekin is a speciality, although our inspector opted for monkfish in balsamic vinaigrette with sorrel, fine beans and new potatoes. Other dishes on the regularly changing menu might include mushroom and horseradish soup, lobster Thermidor and roast best end of lamb with beetroot and potato rösti. Passionfruit mousse with blackcurrant sorbet makes a good sweet.

Directions: In High Street, near seafront, 3 miles E of Ryde

VENTNOR, The Royal ❀❀

The Royal is believed to have been frequented by Queen Victoria herself. The restaurant, decorated with a 'Grand Tour' theme, has walls adorned with oil paintings and etchings punctuated with marble friezes and busts creating a sumptuous yet intimate effect, enhanced by a harpist on alternate evenings. Traditional service, professional but friendly, entirely accords with the surroundings. The fixed-price menu offers an eclectic choice of modern dishes, but without gimmickry. Timbale of wild mushrooms with gingered vegetables and hoi sin sauce was an enjoyable dish, as was a well executed brill ravioli on seaweed with a lobster scented sauce. The favoured dessert of the evening was a light treacle sponge set on an Amaretto sauce. Warm appetisers, home-made bread and petits fours completed the picture.

Directions: On main A3055 coastal road

Belgrave Road
PO38 1JJ
Map 4: SZ69
Tel: 01983 852186
Fax: 01983 855395
Chef: Ashley Carkeet
Owner: William Bailey
Cost: Fixed-price D £17.95. ☺
H/wine £8.75.
Times: 7pm-last D 8.45pm. L Sat
only, 12.30pm-2pm.
Additional: Bar food L; Sunday L;
Children welcome; ➍ dishes
Seats: 120. Private dining room 40.
Jacket & tie preferred
Smoking: No smoking in dining room
Accommodation: 55 en suite
Credit cards: ▨ ▨ ▨ ▨ ▨ ▨

YARMOUTH, George Hotel ❀❀❀

As you approach by ferry, you can spot the colour-washed hotel in this small, picturesque fishing town between the pier and the castle. The former townhouse has been stylishly transformed into a welcoming hotel, with a sophisticated restaurant where Kevin Mangeolles consistently hits the high notes. This is focused, accurate cooking based on a solid French idiom, but opened up with imagination. An appetiser of juicy chunks of rabbit, sun-dried tomato and the crispest of Parmesan croûtons, whets the appetite for a clear, pungent langoustine consommé with soft shellfish and a well-balanced infusion of coriander and chilli. Fechoulette of lamb, a Pierre Koffmann inspired dish, is one for serious meat-eaters: shoulder of lamb stuffed with parsley and trompettes, lamb's tongue, sweetbread, liver and kidney, served with potato purée and salsify. The robust flavours of a cassoulet of seabass, however, rather overwhelmed the fish, served alongside a lobster mousseline, lobster ravioli and lobster sauce. A dessert of fascinating flair and complexity proved to be tabouleh of fresh fruit – a ring of couscous spiced with mint and ginger, speckled with diced melon, oranges and plums, served with raspberries and a sharp, smooth red fruit sorbet. Mangeolles also runs the Brasserie, overlooking the sea, which has a lighter, more Mediterranean slant to the menu, plus decor to match. Pink, well seasoned, succulent tuna is served on a niçoise salad, confit of duck on a bed of Puy lentils and chorizo, and if they're available, try the excellent escabeche of black bream with a sweet, chilled jellied sauce with carrots or the scallops with yellow pepper and spinach, topped with an inspired apple, lime and ginger purée.

A user-friendly wine list details ten good-value house wines at £11.50 with short, but easily read annotation. The rest of the list is cataloged in price order, and offers a good range of champagne, about 12 halves, and an impressive list of old clarets with some outstanding vintages. Ch Caronne-Ste-Gemme, Cru Bourgeoise 90 offers excellent drinking at £21.50
Signature dishes: Quail foie gras mille-feuille; roast lobster with squid ink ravioli and lobster and sesame oil dressing; braised pork shins flavoured with chilli and lemon grass; roast wood pigeon with creamed celeriac.

Directions: Ferry from Lymington. Hotel visible from ferry between castle and pier

Quay Street
Yarmouth
PO41 0PE
Map 4: SZ69
Tel: 01983 760331
Fax: 01983 760425
Chef: Kevin Mangeolles
Owners: J Illsley, J Willcock,
A Willcock
Cost: *Alc* £22.50, fixed-price D
£34.50. ☺ (in Brasserie). H/wine
£11.50.
Times: D only, 7pm-last D 10pm.
Closed D Sun & Mon,
2 wks from 16 Feb
Additional: Brasserie (noon-3pm/7pm-
10pm); No children under 8
(restaurant); ➍ dishes
Seats: 25. Private dining room 20
Smoking: Air-conditioning
Accommodation: 16 en suite
Credit cards: ▨ ▨ ▨ ▨ ▨

WILTSHIRE

ALDBOURNE, Raffles

The society anti-hero Raffles is the chosen hero of this smart little restaurant in a listed Victorian/Edwardian building on the village green. It is run by a dedicated husband and wife team with Mary Hannan front of house and James slaving over a hot stove. He trained at The Ritz and evidence of a classic background and tradition comes through. Starters might include sautéed Cornish scallops with crispy bacon, basil and tomato vinaigrette, or a simply presented but well flavoured chicken and broccoli terrine with toast fingers. Pork with a mustard sauce proved an enjoyable main course, with alternatives such as roast monkfish with Ricard and samphire. Favourite desserts are syrup tart and bread-and-butter pudding, with the option of Cheddar cheese and biscuits. In addition to the *carte*, there is a Sunday lunch and a Friday night bistro menu.

Directions: On B4192 between M4/J14 & 15

The Green SN8 2BW
Map 4: SU27
Tel: 01672 540700
Fax: 01672 540038
Chef: James Hannan
Owners: J & M Hannan
Cost: *Alc* £18. H/wine £8.70. ☺
Times: 12.30pm-last L 2.15pm/7pm-last D 10 pm. Closed L Sat, D Sun, Mon, 25 Aug-6 Sept
Additional: Sunday L; Children welcome
Seats: 36
Smoking: No pipes or cigars in dining room; air-conditioning
Credit cards:

BRADFORD-ON-AVON,
Nettles and Neeps NEW

An innovative menu and a lively atmosphere attract a good local clientele to this well run restaurant in the heart of town. Sound cooking displays interesting touches. Expect pheasant pâté with tomato and aubergine chutney, fishcakes with Thai-style sauce and chocolate meringues.

Directions: Town centre, off Silver Street, S of River Avon

The Georgian Lodge
25 Bridge Street BA15 1BY
Map 3: ST86
Tel: 01225 862268
Fax: 01225 862218
Telephone for details

BRADFORD-ON-AVON,
Woolley Grange

Woolley Green BA15 1TX
Map 3: ST86
Tel: 01225 864705
Fax: 01225 864059
Chef: Peter Stott
Owners: Nigel & Heather Chapman
Cost: Fixed-price L £15/D £29. H/wine £11

Set in beautiful Wiltshire countryside, this atmospheric Cotswold manor house is the perfect place for a restful break. Children are made particularly welcome, with a trained nanny on hand to look after under-eights in the nursery. Peter Stott's well-balanced menus continue to gain praise, especially for imaginative dishes such as ragout of monkfish and mussels with tarragon, tomatoes and white wine, seared escalope of salmon with spring onions, chilli and ginger, and best end of lamb with celeriac dauphinoise and mint jus. Puddings are equally inventive, ginger brûlée decorated with thinly sliced strawberries, and hot raspberry soufflé with raspberry sauce and sorbet, for example. As well as the more formal dinner menu, visitors can opt for lighter meals on the terrace, and for breakfast a farmhouse menu – featuring smoked haddock and kippers – is offered. The wine list is well put together, with a strong selection of reasonably-priced house wines, and an intriguing selection of rare bin ends chosen by a local wine merchant.

Times: 12.30pm-last L 1.45pm/7.30pm-last D 9.30pm
Additional: Sunday L; Terrace menu L&D; Children welcome; ◑ dishes
Seats: 50. Private dining room 22
Smoking: No smoking in dining room
Accommodation: 22 en suite
Credit cards: ▬ ▦ ▰ 🔳 🄲

Directions: On B105 at Woolley Green, 1 mile NE of Bradford, 20 mins from M4/J17

CALNE, Hayle Farm Hotel ❀

Old farmhouse retaining much of its original character, situated at the foot of the Marlborough Downs overlooking the famous White Horse at Cherhill. Careful cooking on a monthly changing menu (with daily specials) offers warm onion and herb tart, breast of duck with a sauce of baby onions, lentils and bacon, and chocolate marquise.

Accommodation: 6 en suite. **Credit cards:** ▬ ▦ ▰ 🄲

Directions: Restaurant at junction of A4 and Compton Bassett roads three miles E of Calne.

Quemerford Calne
Wiltshire SN11 8UJ
Map 3: ST97
Tel/Fax: 01249 813275
Chef: Darren McGrath
Owners: Stephen & Veronica Harding
Cost: *Alc* £19.75. H/wine £7.99. ☺
Times: D only, 7pm-9pm
Additional: Children welcome;
◑ dishes.
Smoking: No smoking in dining room

CASTLE COMBE, Castle Inn ❀

Chippenham SN14 7HN
Map 3: ST87
Tel: 01249 783030
Fax: 01249 782315
Chef: Jamie Gemmell
Owner: Hatton Hotels
Cost: D £15 (3 courses). ☺
H/wine £9.95.
Times: Last L 1.45pm/D 9.15pm
Additional: Bar meals L; Sunday L; Children welcome; ◑ dishes
Smoking: No smoking in dining room
Accommodation: 10 en suite
Credit cards: ▬ ▬ ▦ ▰ 🅿 🄲

Directions: In village centre, M4/J17

A renowned twelfth-century hostelry, set in the market place of historic Castle Combe. Dishes include salmon and dill fishcake on a white wine sauce, and lamb and rosemary hotpot. Puddings range from a light St Clement's mousse to spotted dick with lashings of custard.

CASTLE COMBE,
Manor House Hotel ❀❀❀

Surrounded by 26 acres of gardens and parkland that take in romantic Italianate gardens, their own golf course, and the

Chippenham SN14 7HR
Map 3: ST87
Tel: 01249 782206
Fax: 01249 782159

Manor House Hotel

Chef: Mark Taylor
Cost: Alc £45, fixed-price L £16.95-
£18.95 (2-3 courses)/D £35 (4
courses). H/wine £15.95
Times: Noon-last L 2pm/7pm-last D
10pm
Additional: Bar food; Sunday L;
Children welcome; ● dishes
Seats: 95. Private dining rooms 12 x 3
Smoking: No smoking in dining room
Accommodation: 45 en suite
Credit cards: ▪▪ ▦ ▦ 🖭 ℭ

River Bybrook, the Manor has a lot going for it. Within the
imposing stone-built house there is a choice of several lounges.
Recent reports have indicated that the kitchen is currently on
top form, showing both flair and imagination. The seasonal
selection offers choice, and there's a short *carte* as well as a
range of classic dishes. The style is true and simple: seared
scallops sitting on a smooth purée of parsnip topped with
parsnip crisps, a drizzle of butter sauce and a few green
peppercorns; lemon and basil sorbet that 'really' cleansed the
palate; pan-fried salmon on fine Kenyan beans, a potato cake
and orange butter sauce with a few langoustines and chopped
chives – 'a lovely dish'; and a brûlée of sour cherries with dark
chocolate sorbet. Another meal began with an excellent wild
mushroom ravioli (one plump specimen, served in a huge
bowl), and some simple young asparagus with a butter sauce.
The centrepiece of the meal, this being Sunday lunch, was a
benchmark roast sirloin of beef, served from the trolley, with
good Yorkshire pudding and well-made gravy. Accompanying
vegetables took in puréed swede, cauliflower with a
hollandaise sauce, French beans tied in tiny bundles, and a
superior leek tart. Also chosen was a good salmon and crab
risotto. Desserts included a light lemon mousse with a lime
sauce, and a very moreish pecan tart with clotted cream ice
cream. Attention to small detail is laudable – both home-made
bread and petits fours are of a high standard. The mainly
European wine list includes a smattering of New World wines.

Directions: Off B4039 near centre of village, R immediately
after the bridge

CHIPPENHAM,
Stanton Manor Hotel ❀

*Nineteenth-century country hotel built on the site of a 900-year-old
manor (the original dovecote still stands in the grounds). The
kitchen draws on local and home-grown produce for a daily
repertoire that embraces, say, a duo of game terrines, pan-fried grey
mullet with lemon butter and caramelised rice pudding.*

Smoking: No smoking in dining room.
Accommodation: 10 en suite
Credit cards: ▪▪ ▦ ▦ 🖭

Directions: M4/J17, then A429 Cirencester. Next to village
church.

Stanton St Quintin SN14 6DQ
Map 3: ST97
Tel: 01666 837552
Fax: 01666 837022
Chef: Nicola O'Brien
Owners: Philip and Elizabeth Bullock
Cost: Fixed-price L/D £22. H/wine
£9.50. ☺
Times: Last L 1.30pm/D 9.30pm.
Closed L Sun. New Year
Additional: Bar food L; ● dishes

COLERNE, **Lucknam Park** ❀❀❀

Chippenham SN14 8AZ
Map 3: ST87
Tel: 01225 742777
Fax: 01225 743536

Chef: Alexander Venables

Owner: Lucknam Park Hotels
Cost: Alc £44.50, fixed-price L
£22.50/D £44.50.
Times: 7.30pm-last D 9.30pm
Additional: Bar food; Sunday L;
Children welcome; ❀ dishes
Seats: 75. Private dining room 75.
Jacket & tie preferred at D
Smoking: No smoking in dining room
Accommodation: 42 en suite
Credit cards: ■ ■ ▨ ➰ ▣ ▢

The mile long tree-lined driveway makes a suitably grand first impression for guests approaching this magnificent Palladian mansion. It stands majestically in 500 acres of parkland, yet is only six miles from the Georgian splendours of Bath. The hotel plays heavily on grandiose country house elegance, although it has been extended to include a health spa, gymnasium and a notable equestrian centre. Meals are served in what was the ballroom – a sumptuous setting complete with a fabulous hand-painted ceiling, crystal chandeliers and fine views across the park. Alexander Venables continues to deliver high quality cooking based on class ingredients (organically produced where possible), and he puts great store by visual artistry. An appetiser of carpaccio of scallops with crisp raw asparagus and salad leaves dressed with diced tomato set the tone for a notable inspection dinner. To start, there might be a perfect cep risotto with a subtle fungal flavour made with 'grade one' Arborio rice, as well as tian of crab with caviar and pink grapefruit, and sautéed foie gras with peach and Sauternes. The main course of slices of prime monkfish dusted with vanilla served on a bed of garlicky Savoy cabbage was chosen from stiff competition by alternatives such as fillet of sea bass seared in Chinese five-spices with a confit of peppers, or rump of Wiltshire lamb with oven-roasted shallots and provençale vegetables spiked with rosemary and mint. As a finale, a crisp, light puff pastry tart filled with mirabelles in crème pâtissière with a few plums on the side plus a tuile filled with cinnamon ice cream showed finesse in abundance. Smaller details such as canapés (including excellent mini-pizzas), home-baked rolls and dazzling petits fours suggest that the kitchen may be capable of even higher things. Service benefits from mature professional supervision, with a formal sommelier on hand to advise on drinking from the suitably grand wine list.

Signature dishes: ravioli of langoustines and courgette with a chilli vinaigrette; terrine of smoked ham knuckles with foie gras; Dover sole with fresh mushy peas; game consommé with slices of truffle and a pastry lid.

Directions: Turn off A4 2 miles from Bath for Batheaston and L for Colerne, L again at crossroad, entrance 0.25 mile on L

CRUDWELL,
Mayfield House Hotel

Former family home of TV journalist Julian Pettifer, now a lovely little hotel complete with a two-acre walled garden. Creditable fixed-price dinners run along the lines of pigeon breast with leeks in puff pastry, grilled salmon with basil butter sauce and lemon tart with lime sauce.

Accommodation: 20 en suite.
Credit cards: ▨▨ ▨▨ ▨▨ ▨▨ ▨▨ C

Directions: 10 minutes from M4/J17. On A429 in village centre between Malmesbury and Cirencester

Malmesbury SN16 9EW
Map 3: ST99
Tel: 01666 577409
Fax: 01666 577977
Chef: Mark Bullows
Owners: Max Strelling & Chris Marston
Cost: Fixed-price D £15.95. ☺ H/wine £8.25.
Times: Last L 1.45pm/last D 8.45pm
Additional: Bar food; Sunday L; Children welcome; ❹ dishes
Smoking: No smoking in dining room

FORD, White Hart Inn

Popular sixteenth-century stone inn hard by the Bybrook River, offering a welcoming atmosphere and consistently good food. At inspection, the weekly changing menu, backed up by specials, highlighted home-made minestrone soup, a smooth chicken liver parfait and a chicken with pearl barley risotto.

Chippenham
SN14 8RP
Map 3: ST87
Tel: 01249 782213
Fax: 01249 783075
Chef: Anthony Farmer
Owners: Mr & Mrs C J Phillips
Cost: Alc £20. H/wine £10. ☺
Times: Last L 2pm/D 10pm
Additional: Sunday L; Bar meals L; Children welcome; ❹ dishes
Smoking: No pipes or cigars
Accommodation: 11 en suite
Credit cards: ▨▨ ▨▨ ▨▨ ▨▨ ▨▨ C

Directions: M4/J17 or 18, 10 minutes drive on A420 Colerne road

HINDON, Lamb at Hindon

Once a coaching inn on the road from London to the West Country, the Lamb is now an up-market free house/hotel. 'Sophisticated' bar snacks are alternatives to the restaurant menu, which offers the likes of warm pigeon breast salad, steamed salmon with white wine and chive sauce and roast rack of lamb.

Salisbury SP3 6DP
Map 3: ST93
Tel: 01747 820573
Fax: 01747 820605
Chef: David Salmons
Owner: The Lamb at Hindon
Cost: Alc £18.95. Fixed-price L £15/D £18.95. ☺ H/wine £7.25
Times: Last L 2pm/D 9.30pm
Additional: Bar Food; Sunday L; Children welcome; ❹ dishes
Smoking: No smoking in dining room
Accommodation: 14 en suite
Credit cards: ▨▨ ▨▨ ▨▨ ▨▨ C

Directions: In village centre, 1 mile off A303 & A350

INGLESHAM, **Inglesham Forge**

Manuel Gomez runs things very much his own way in this converted fifteenth-century forge decorated with tools of the trade. Customers come here for the kind of old-school classic continental dishes that most chefs don't seem to prepare any more. Thinly sliced bread and butter is offered with the meal, creamy sauces abound. Simple honesty is what counts. Asparagus with hollandaise is an entire bunch of plump spears cooked to a T, scampi sizzles in garlic butter, fillet steak gets a béarnaise sauce, while pink duck breast arrives with a brandy and green peppercorn sauce. Vegetables – including superb sautéed potatoes with onions – are piled onto the plate separately. Desserts are totally in keeping with the rest of the menu: raspberry cheesecake is the real thing full of fruity flavour, for example. The wine list does the trick and complements the food admirably.

Directions: In hamlet just off A361 midway between Highworth and Lechlade

Lechlade Swindon SN6 7QY
Map 4: SU29
Tel: 01367 252298
Chef: Manuel Gomez
Owners: Manuel & Jacqueline Gomez
Cost: Alc £23. H/wine £9.95. ☺
Times: Noon-last L 1.30pm/7pm-last
D 9.30pm. Closed L Sat, Sun, L Mon
Additional: Children welcome;
🍴 dishes
Seats: 30
Smoking: No pipes or cigars in dining room
Credit cards: ▮ ▨ ▧

MALMESBURY,
The Horse & Groom NEW

Delightful 300-year-old coaching inn, with exposed Cotswold stonework, flagstones and heavy beams. The colourful blackboards shout out a range of imaginative dishes, such as tartlet of wild mushrooms with Gruyère cheese, roast rack of lamb glazed with pork and redcurrant sauce, and beef, Guinness and Stilton pie.

Accommodation: 3 en suite. **Credit cards:** ▮ ▨ ▧ ▢

Directions: M4/J17, take 2nd roundabout exit, B4040 (Cricklade). 2 miles to Charlton, pub on L

The Street Charlton SN16 9DL
Map 4: ST98
Tel: 01666 823904
Fax: 01666 823390
Chef: Philip Gilder
Owners: Nichola King & Philip Gilder
Cost: Alc £20. H/wine £7.15. ☺
Times: Last L 2pm/D 10pm
Additional: Sunday L; Bar meals;
Children welcome; 🍴 dishes

MALMESBURY, **Knoll House**

Swindon Road SN16 9LU
Map 3: ST98
Tel: 01666 823114
Fax: 01666 823897
Chef: Alan Johnson
Owner: Simon Haggarty
Cost: Alc £24. H/wine £9.50. ☺
Times: Last L 1.45pm/last D 9.30pm.
Closed 27-29 Dec
Additional: Bar food; Sunday L;
Chilren welcome; 🍴 dishes
Smoking: No smoking in dining room
Accommodation: 22 en suite
Credit cards: ▮ ▨ ▧ ▧ ▢

Situated on the outskirts of England's oldest borough, this former Victorian family home offers an imaginative fixed-price menu in the elegant Cedar Room Restaurant. Modern, well-presented dishes may include saddle of rabbit on thyme rösti with red wine and cacao sauce and roast peppered monkfish with tapenade. Interesting wine list.

Directions: From M4/J17 take A429 (Cirencester); turn onto B4042 (Swindon); hotel is 500 yards on L

MALMESBURY,
Old Bell Hotel ⚜⚜

Abbey Row SN16 0AG
Map 3: ST98
Tel: 01666 822344
Fax: 01666 825145
Chef: David Richards
Owners: Nicholas Dickinson,
Nigel Chapman
Cost: *Alc* £26, fixed-price L £15/D
£18.50. ☺ H/wine £11.75.
Times: Noon-last L 2pm/7.30pm-last
D 9.30pm.
Additional: Bar food; Sunday L;
Children welcome; 🍴 dishes
Seats: 60. Private dining rooms, 16 &
24
Smoking: No pipes and cigars in
dining room
Accommodation: 31 en suite
Credit cards: ▇ ▇ ▇ ▇ ▇ ▇

Founded by the Abbot of Malmesbury in 1220 as a guest house
for visitors to the abbey, the Old Bell lays claim to being the
oldest hotel in England. It certainly looks the part with its
carved stone window surrounds on the rear walls, and the
canopied fireplace in what was once the Great Hall. Cream
teas and brasserie-style snacks are available for those who
require them, but the centre of the gastronomic action is the
plush Edwardian restaurant with its blue velvet curtains and
pottery flower vases. A new chef was still settling in when we
inspected, but much is promised. The short set menu offers
such commendable dishes as 'beautiful-looking' twice-baked
goat's cheese soufflé coloured with well-dressed greens and
tomato, roast breast of honey-glazed duck served on polenta
('to die for') and wild mushrooms, and pan-roasted monkfish
with lardons, spring onions and cocotte potatoes. The real star
however was an extraordinary vanilla and tarragon ice cream
served with strawberries in tarragon custard. Home-made
breads are first rate and the substantial wine list offers plenty
by the glass.

Directions: In centre of town

MALMESBURY,
Whatley Manor ⚜   NEW

*Impressive, well run, mellow stone-built manor house with good
leisure facilities, large grounds and sound cooking. Asparagus and
apple soup, veal with peppercorns, mushrooms, whisky, chive and
cream sauce, good rösti, and orange and lime mousse are very well
presented. Excellent light lunches and extensive vegetarian menu.*

Additional: Bar food; Sunday lunch; Children welcome;
🍴 dishes
Seats: 60. Private dining room 40
Smoking: No pipes or cigars in dining room
Accommodation: 29 en suite
Credit cards: ▇ ▇ ▇ ▇

Easton Grey
SN16 0RB
Map 3: ST98
Tel: 01666 822888
Fax: 01666 826120
Chef: Pete Halliday
Owner: Whatley Manor Hotel
Cost: Fixed-price L £16/D £29.
H/wine £13.50
Times: Last L 1.30pm/D 9pm

Directions: 3 miles W of Malmesbury on B4040. 15 mins from
M4/J 17 or 18.

MARLBOROUGH, **Ivy House Hotel** ✿

High Street SN8 1HJ
Map 4: SU16
Tel: 01672 515333
Fax: 01672 515097
Chefs: David Ball, Phil Clark
Owners: David Ball, Josephine Scott
Cost: Alc £20, fixed-price L 9.50/D
£19. ☺ H/wine £8.50.
Times: Last L 2pm/last D 9.30pm
Additional: Sunday L; Bar meals;
Children welcome; ◑ dishes
Smoking: No-smoking area
Accommodation: 28 en suite
Credit cards: ▆▆ ▆ ▆▆

This attractive, ivy-clad Georgian residence started life in 1707 as the Marlborough Academy for boys. It is now a comfortable, personally run hotel with a reputation for good cooking. An autumn inspection dinner produced chicken liver pâté, lamb cutlets, cooked nicely pink, with red wine and shallot sauce, and sticky toffee pudding.

Directions: Town centre in main street

MELKSHAM, **Beechfield House** ✿

Impressive stone-built Victorian hotel set in eight acres of pretty gardens and grounds. A relaxed, friendly country house atmosphere, with the fixed price menu offered at both lunch and dinner utilising fruit and vegetables from the garden. Good salmon with baby leeks on a fennel velouté and passion fruit mousse.

Accommodation: 21 en suite
Credit cards: ▆▆ ▆▆ ▆▆ ▣ ▢

Directions: In the village, on the A350 Melksham/Chippenham road

Beanacre SN12 7PU
Map 3: ST96
Tel: 01225 703700
Fax: 01225 790118
Chef: Geoffrey Bell
Owner: Mr C Scott-Moody
Cost: Alc £19.95, fixed-price L
£10.95/D £19.95. ☺ H/wine £9.
Times: Last L 1.45pm/D 9pm
Additional: Sunday L; Bar meals;
No children under 10; ◑ dishes
Smoking: No smoking in dining room

MELKSHAM, **Shaw Country Hotel** ✿

Small, friendly hotel which dates from the sixteenth century and is close to Bath, the M4 and M5. The kitchen tries hard with the likes of avocado, prawn and scallop in a light, crisp pastry case, roast breast of duck, timbale of duck leg and crispy duck skin with ginger. Extensive wine list.

Additional: Bar Food; Sunday L; Children welcome; ◑ dishes
Smoking: No smoking in dining room
Accommodation: 13 en suite
Credit cards: ▆▆ ▆▆ ▆▆ ▆▆ ▣ ▢

Directions: 1 mile NW of Melksham on A365, from M4/J17 or 18

Bath Road Shaw SN12 8EF
Map 3 : ST96
Tel: 01225 702836/790321
Fax: 01225 790275
Chefs Nick & Paul Lewis
Owners: J T & G M Lewis
Cost: Alc £19, fixed-price L&D £12.
☺ H/wine £7.50.
Times: Last L 2pm/D 9pm
Closed D Sun, 26-28 Dec

MELKSHAM, **Toxique** ✿✿

Expect the unexpected, in terms of the decor at least, at this otherwise conventional-looking stone farmhouse. The exotic midnight blue and purple interior is filled with original

187 Woodrow Road SN12 7AY
Map 3: ST96
Tel/Fax: 01225 702129
Chefs: Helen Bartlett, Phil Rimmer
Owners: Helen Barlett, Peter Jewkes

Toxique

Cost: Fixed-price L £18.50/D £28.
H/wine £9.75
Times: D only, 7pm-10pm.
Closed D Sun, Mon, Tue,
Additional: Sunday L (12.30pm-2pm);
Children welcome; ✪ dishes
Seats: 40.
Private dining rooms 24 + 16
Smoking: No smoking in dining room
Accommodation: 5 en suite
Credit cards: ■ ▦ ▦ ▰ ▣ ▢

artwork, chunky candles in flower pots and huge fir cones lining the tops of the walls. The cooking, thankfully, is less outré. Dinner might start with fish bourride, aïoli and rouille, or garden-herb soup with sour cream and chives, and continue with pan-fried calves' liver with caramelised garlic and rosemary mash. An interest in spicing shows itself in dishes such as cod with Puy lentils, coriander, cumin and crispy leek, and boneless lamb with salted lemons, couscous and bab ghanoush. Game and poultry appear regularly – terrine of wood pigeon is served with orange and red onion marmalade, and roasted guinea fowl is given the Italian treatment with Marsala, wild mushrooms, sage and sautéed polenta. As well as a selection of British cheeses, there might be rhubarb and pear strudel, cassata with almond macaroons, or chocolate truffle torte. A branch of Toxique has opened in Bath, Somerset, specialising in seafood.

Directions: Take Calne road from Melksham centre, 0.3 mile turn into Forest Road. Restaurant is on L after 0.75 mile

NOMANSLAND, Les Mirabelles ❀❀

This little wooden shack, adjacent to a pub, is well worth a detour for those in search of good French cooking. As well as the already extensive menu, there are blackboard specials featuring, in winter at least, warm and comforting fodder such as oxtail 'Anglais' and kidneys in Cognac. At times, service can be a little aloof, with regular customers cosseted to the exclusion of unknowns, but no matter. It is worth it for first courses such as a tarte fine of scallops and crab with chives, risotto with langoustines and trompette de mort mushrooms, fish soup, home-made pork liver pâté and a salad of lentils and lambs' tongues. Main courses rely heavily on seasonal game – wild duck, pheasant and partridge. Fish gets a good showing with the noble turbot and Dover sole sharing the billing with more workaday species. Desserts might include fondant chocolate, a tarte aux pommes, crème brûlée, home-made ice creams and sorbets, and a good cheese board. Wines are also well-chosen.

Forest Edge Road
SP5 2BN
Map 4: SU22
Tel/Fax: 01794 390205
Chef: Eric Max Nicolas
Owners: Eric Max Nicolas &
Claude Laage
Cost: Alc £18.50. H/wine £9.50. ☺
Times: Noon-last L 2pm/7pm-last D
9.30pm. Closed Sun D, Mon,
1st 2-3 wks Jan
Additional: Bar food L; Sunday L;
Children welcome; ✪ dishes
Seats: 50
Smoking: No pipes or cigars
Credit cards: ■ ▦ ▰ ▢

Directions: A36 (Salisbury-Southampton); turn R into New Road (signposted Nomansland); straight ahead at crossroads and over cattle grid. Within a mile restaurant on R by church

PEWSEY,

London House Restaurant

Market Place SN9 5AB
Tel: 01672 564775
Fax: 01672 564785
Telephone for details

Within weeks of opening its doors, the London House had already established a reputation as an up-and-coming restaurant. Thoroughly professional service and high quality cooking ensures the place overflows with diners every night, with many chefs apparently trying the place out to assess the competition. Our inspector enjoyed two 'fantastic' starters, a ravioli of chicken, morel mushrooms and tarragon with a Madeira and pancetta jus (well-balanced with all ingredients in harmony), and chargrilled scallops on a risotto of basil, garlic, Parmesan and pine nuts (great attention to detail, and lovely, subtle flavours). Main courses range from loin of lamb with Dijon mustard and a light rosemary jus, to baked salmon on a crab and horseradish tart, with a watercress beurre blanc. The wine list, prepared by a sommelier from the Rhône Valley, is comprehensive and not overly expensive.

PURTON,

The Pear Tree at Purton

Church End SN5 9ED
Map 4: SU08
Tel: 01793 772100
Fax: 01793 772369
Chef: Catherine Berry
Owners: Francis & Anne Young
Cost: Fixed-price L £17.50/D £27.50
(4 courses). H/wine £11.
Times: Noon-last L 2pm/7pm-last D
9.30pm. Closed L Sat, 26-30 Dec
Additional: Sunday L;
Children welcome; ❸ dishes
Seats: 60. Private dining room 50
Smoking: No pipes or cigars in dining room
Accommodation: 18 en suite
Credit cards: ▆ ▆ ▆ ▆ ▆

Originally the local vicarage, this traditional Cotswold-stone house has been impressively transformed into a sophisticated and elegant country retreat by Francis and Anne Young. The focus of attention is the prettily decorated conservatory restaurant overlooking the Victorian gardens. Home-grown herbs and local produce are used to telling effect for a creative menu of modern dishes along the lines of warm Cerney Ash goat's cheese with pistachio nuts and champagne sauce, lamb fillet with rosemary, redcurrants and Purton honey on a Beaujolais sauce, and roast monkfish with basil and saffron sauce. Our inspector was particularly impressed by a timbale of sole with a well-executed chive mayonnaise, as well as succulent fillet of beef served on horseradish-flavoured mash with a red wine sauce and caramelised onions. Desserts such as rich chocolate truffle tart with chilled vanilla cream and pineapple salad are handled with the same dexterity. The wine list comprises a carefully chosen selection of bottles from around the world.

Directions: From M4/J16 follow signs to Purton. Turn right at Spa shop, hotel 0.25 mile on right

REDLYNCH,

Langley Wood Restaurant

Mind the stag's head in the entrance hall of this small, seventeenth-century country house restaurant. Roast guinea fowl with orange butter and spiced pear in red wine, marinated salmon steak with radish and ginger, and chicken in a rich red Indian sauce are amongst the seasonal choices on a short but interesting menu.

Salisbury SP5 2PB
Map 4: SU22
Tel: 01794 390348
Chef: Sylvia Rosen
Owners: David & Sylvia Rosen
Cost: *Alc* £23. H/wine £8.50. ☺
Times: Last L 2pm/D 10.30pm.
Closed D Sun, Mon, Tue, L Sat
Additional: Sunday L;
Children welcome; ❹ dishes
Smoking: No smoking in dining room
Accommodation: 3 rooms
Credit cards: ▬ ▬ ▬ ▬ ▬

Directions: In village, between
Downton (on A338 Salisbury to
Bournemouth) & Landford (A36
Salisbury)

ROWDE, # George & Dragon

The exterior may suggest inauspicious village pub but, despite the wood-panelling, huge stone fireplace festooned with dried flowers and hand pumps dispensing Wadworth's real ales, there's a different story to tell. The location is landlocked Wiltshire, but daily supplies of fresh fish from Cornwall are what drives the kitchen. Tim Withers is a passionate cook who learned all about fresh seafood at The Carved Angel, Dartmouth (see entry) and it shows in his list of blackboard specials, salmon comes with rhubarb and ginger, for example. Alongside this is an eclectic hand-written menu that promises everything from provençale fish soup, to wild rabbit risotto, and pan-fried fillet of beef with tomatoes and balsamic vinegar. Our inspector, however, went for the daily fixed-price menu that provided unbeatable value for tagliatelle with ham and mushrooms, chicken Savoyard (with a great sauce) and rhubarb crumble with Jersey cream. A good number of wines by the glass stand out on the affordable list.

Directions: On A342 Devizes-Chippenham road

High Street SN10 2PN
Map 3: ST96
Tel: 01380 723053
Fax: 01380 724738
Chefs: Tim Withers, Hannah Seal,
Kate Phillips
Owners: Tim & Helen Withers
Cost: *Alc* £25, fixed-price L £10. ☺
H/wine £9.75.
Times: Noon-last L 2pm/7pm-last D
10pm.. Closed Sun, Mon, 2 wks
Xmas-New Year
Additional: Children welcome;
❹ dishes
Seats: 30
Smoking: No smoking in dining room
Credit cards: ▬ ▬ ▬ ▬

SALISBURY,

The Coach and Horses NEW

Intimate restaurant attached to The Coach & Horses, Salisbury's oldest inn. Fixed-price menus offer wholesome home cooking in the shape of summer vegetable soup, stuffed mushrooms in pastry, grilled salmon with hollandaise and chocolate brandy cake. A few interesting wines form the back up.

Smoking: No smoking in dining room
Accommodation: 2 en suite. **Credit cards:** ▬ ▬ ▬ ▬ ▬ ▬

Directions: Past Guildhall Square on L

39 Winchester Street SP1 1HG
Map 4: SU12
Tel: 01722 336254
Fax: 01722 414319
Chefs/Owners: Martin & Angie
Cooper
Cost: Fixed-price D £15. ☺
H/wine £6.50.
Times: 10am-last D 10pm.
Closed Sun, Dec 25
Additional: Bar meals;
Children welcome; ❹ dishes

SALISBURY,

Howard's House Hotel ❀❀❀

Teffont Evias SP3 5RJ
Map 3: ST93
Tel: 01722 716392/716821
Fax: 01722 716820
Chef/Owner: Paul Firmin
Cost: Fixed-price L £18.50/D £25 (3 courses). ☺ H/wine £9.95
Times: L by prior arrangement/7.30pm-last D 9.30pm
Additional: Sunday L 12.30pm-2pm; Children welcome
Seats: 30.
Smoking: No smoking in dining room
Accommodation: 9 en suite
Credit cards: ▆ 🔳 🔳 🔀 💳 💳

Paul Firmin has gained a loyal local following for his imaginative modern cooking. The setting may be a seventeenth-century dower house, surrounded by two acres of flower-filled gardens in Teffont Evias, one of Wiltshire's prettiest villages, but much of the *carte* sings of sunnier climes. For example, sun-dried tomato polenta comes with fillet of English veal, saffron risotto and shrimp bisque is served with rock salmon, while rosemary and pomegranate arrive with lamb shank, but the menu also reveals a more traditional, deluxe strata. Foie gras, ox tongue and truffle pie, more pastry-encased terrine than the name implies, was served cold with Cumberland sauce, and despite the paucity of truffle, was firm, well-seasoned and most enjoyable. Black bream with mousseline of scallops and fresh tomato and orange sauces had a particularly bright flavour, and saddle of rabbit with a casserole of aubergine, roast garlic and Madeira jus came as three little roundels encased in spinach, with a savoury filling on top of a well-constructed sauce. Other interesting dishes might include white bean, ceps and red pepper soup, or 'bourride' of guinea fowl with a saffron corn muffin. A dessert of steamed chocolate and orange pudding with Grand Marnier ice cream and hot chocolate sauce proved perfectly irresistible, and not nearly as heavy on the digestion as it sounds. The well balanced wine list offers a range of well-priced house wines all under £15, plus a good selection of halves. Some classy Burgundies feature but the best value is to be had from the Cru Bourgeois Bordeaux, for example Ch Senilhac at £22.50. Good, well written descriptions throughout offer help for the layman.

Signature dishes: Seared scallops with a julienne of leeks and an orange vinaigrette; timbale of rabbit with a Madeira sabayon, wild mushrooms and walnuts; fillet of lamb with a mint mousseline wrapped in spinach, with hot-pot potatoes; passionfruit crème caramel with vanilla syrup and tropical fruits.

Directions: A36/A30 from Salisbury, turn onto B3089, 5 miles W of Wilton, 9 miles W of Salisbury

SALISBURY, **Milford Hall Hotel**

206 Castle Street SP1 3TE
Map 3: SU12
Tel: 01722 417411
Fax: 01722 419444
Chef: Alfred Kristan
Owners: Graham Fitch, Pam Brudford
Cost: Alc £21.50, fixed-price L
£8.95/D £15.50. ☺ H/wine £8.95.
Times: Last L 2pm/D 9.30pm
Additional: Bar Food L; Sunday L;
Children welcome; ♨ dishes
Smoking: No smoking in dining room
Accommodation: 35 en suite
Credit cards: ▄▄ ▉▉ ▇▇ ▃▃ ▟

Splendid Georgian mansion within easy walking distance of the city centre. The kitchen combines modern ideas with a classical French base, all served in a smart setting. At a meal in January, tender venison with cranberry and wild mushroom sauce was much enjoyed, as was a top-notch crème brûlée.

Directions: At junction of Castle Street, A30 ring rd & A345 (Amesbury), less than 0.5 mile from Market Square

SALISBURY, **The Old Mill** NEW

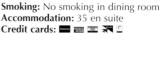

Town Path
West Harnham SP2 8EU
Map 4: SU12
Tel: 01722 327517
Fax: 01722 333367
Chef: Roy Thwaites
Owners: Roy & Lois Thwaites
Cost: Alc £18. H/wine £9.60. ☺
Times: Last L 2.30pm/last D 10pm
Additional: Bar meals; Sunday L;
Children welcome; ♨ dishes

Historic former paper mill, complete with cascading mill race, which dates from 1135 and is beautifully situated on the River Nadder. The stylish dining room sports heraldic decor and offers careful cooking of the likes of leek and potato soup, chicken liver parfait, salmon koulibiac and bread-and-butter pudding.

Smoking: No pipes & cigars. **Accommodation:** 10 en suite
Credit cards: ▄▄ ▉▉ ▇▇ ▃▃

Directions: On the A3094 S of Salisbury, head towards Wilton. Turn L into Lower St

SALISBURY, **White Hart Hotel**

St John Street SP1 2SD
Map 4: SU12
Tel: 01722 327476
Fax: 01722 412761
Chef: Morris McNeill
Cost: Alc £23, fixed-price L £13.50.
H/wine £12.50. ☺
Times: Last L 2.30pm/D 9.30pm.
Closed L Sat
Additional: Bar food; Sunday L;
Children welcome; ♨ dishes

Part of Salisbury's social life for more than 400 years. The refurbished building stands hard by the cathedral precinct and the restaurant overlooks a pretty inner courtyard. Avocado and crab gâteau, honey-roast duck with orange and game jus, and rack of lamb with garlic and herb potatoes are typical dishes.

Smoking: No smoking in dining room; air-conditioning
Accommodation: 68 en suite
Credit cards: ▄▄ ▉▉ ▇▇ ▃▃ ▟ ▟

Directions: Opposite the Law Courts

SWINDON,

Blunsdon House Hotel

Blunsdon SN2 4AD
Map 4 : SU18
Tel: 01793 721701
Fax: 01793 721056

Family-run hotel-cum-leisure club set in 30 acres of grounds in the Vale of Cricklade. Eat informally in Carrie's Carverie or sample

something grander in the Ridge Restaurant. Lobster bisque, Barbary duckling with kumquat and honey sauce and Dover sole with champagne sauce are typical offerings.

Accommodation: 87 en suite
Credit cards: 💳 💳 💳 💳 💳 💳

Directions: 3 miles N of town centre. From A419 take turning signposted Broad Blunsdon, then first L

Chef: E Haines
Owners: Mr & Mrs P Clifford
Cost: Alc £30, fixed-price L £14.50/D £20. ☺ H/wine £10.
Times: Last L 2pm/D 10pm
Additional: Bar Food; Sunday L; Children welcome; 🍴 dishes
Smoking: No-smoking area, air-conditioning

SWINDON,

Chiseldon House Hotel 🏵🏵

A former manor house set in its own lawned gardens, Chiseldon House is convenient both for the M4 and the centre of Swindon. The daily changing menu, served in the airy Orangery Restaurant, offers a choice of four courses and might include pot roast partridge with ginger-scented baby leeks, or grilled monkfish with a basil and hazelnut pesto. Our inspection lunch in March started with pigeon breast layered in tiny circles of pastry 'like a mille-feuille', with red onion marmalade and cranberry jus, went on to home-made orange sorbet, then fillet of pork with goat's cheese and black olive crumble served on a bed of chargrilled peppers and pesto, and finished with crème brûlée, strawberries and a lime sabayon.

Directions: Easily accessible from M4/J15 & 16, on B4006. Short distance from Swindon town centre

New Road Chiseldon SN4 0NE
Map 4: SU18
Tel: 01793 741010
Fax: 01793 741059
Chef: John Farrow
Owners: SKC Group
Cost: Fixed-price L £14.95/D £24.95 (4 courses). H/wine £10.25
Times: Last L 2.30pm/last D 9.30pm
Additional: Sunday L; Children welcome; 🍴 dishes
Smoking: No-smoking area
Accommodation: 21 en suite
Credit cards: 💳 💳 💳 💳 💳 💳

WARMINSTER,

Bishopstrow House 🏵🏵

Bishopstrow House is an ivy-clad classical Georgian property standing in 27 acres of lovely Wiltshire countryside with the River Wylye running by. The cooking is sound, generous and loyal to tradition, though an eye is kept on modern fashions. Thus a meal in winter witnessed a memorable duck confit, the moist meat falling off the bone beneath a crisp skin; this was served in a large white bowl with good home-made bread rolls. Pork tenderloin and wild mushroom risotto followed, with some crisp, bright mange-touts. An individual treacle tart, with lots of zesty orange flavour, and accompanied by vanilla ice cream, completed the meal. There is an appealing wine list with lots of lesser known producers among the big names.

Directions: From Warminster take B3414 (Salisbury). Hotel is signposted

BA12 9HH
Map 3: ST84
Tel: 01985 212312
Fax: 01985 216769
Chef: Chris Suter
Owners: Howard Malin, Simon Lowe, Andrew Leeman
Cost: Alc £29.50, fixed-price L £14-£16 (2-3 courses)/D £29.50 (3 courses). H/wine £13.50
Times: 12.30pm-last L 2pm/7.30pm-last D 9pm
Additional: Bar food; Sunday L; Children welcome; 🍴 dishes
Seats: 65. Private dining room 22
Smoking: No smoking in dining room
Accommodation: 31 en suite
Credit cards: 💳 💳 💳 💳 💳

WARMINSTER, Les Parisiens 🏵🏵

A stylish burgundy and cream Parisian-style bistro, with French prints and jolly Gallic music. Samantha and Nigel Snook ably split duties between them, he cooks, she runs front of house. This is good, no-fuss French food whether you are here for a snack lunch of croque monsieur, or for a three-course dinner. Although the day-time menu is flexible, allowing for a lot of choice, in addition to snacks there is a

28 High Street
BA12 9AF
Map 3: ST94
Tel: 01985 217373
Chef: Nigel Snook
Owners: Nigel & Samantha Snook
Cost: Alc £23, fixed-price L £8.75/D £15.50 (£25 Fri & Sat). ☺ H/wine £9.75.

proper *carte* offering a range of classic French dishes with a modern twist, perhaps fillet of pork with roast peppers and crème fraîche, or sirloin of beef with a blue cheese and garlic glaze. Our inspection lunch opened with mushroom and Gruyère tart, went on to a medley of fish that included some very fresh tuna, in addition to salmon and haddock, and came with a lime, coriander and chilli butter sauce, and finished with an orange and Grand Marnier crêpe.

Directions: In town centre

Times: Last L 2pm/D £9.30pm.
Closed Sun, Mon, 2 wks Jan,
2 wks Aug
Additional: Bar snacks L;
Children welcome; ♨ dishes
Smoking: No-smoking area; no pipes
Credit cards: ▆▆ ▆▆ ▆▆ ⛝

WORCESTERSHIRE

ABBERLEY, The Elms

This fine Queen Anne mansion makes much of its past. Built in 1710 by Gilbert White, a pupil of Sir Christopher Wren, the interior boasts original plasterwork, fine antiques, and a stunning setting surrounded by mature lawns and formal gardens. The cooking aspires to the setting. Typical of the style is the smooth, creamy foie gras terrine complimented by the crunchy texture of crushed pistachios, loin of lamb wrapped in a mousseline of spinach with garlic sauce, and the crème brûlée that formed the components of one early spring meal. More foie gras appeared at another meal, this time in the guise of an amuse-bouche of pan-fried foie gras with caramelised orange. This was followed by a warm, pungent goat's cheese terrine with basil and plum tomatoes, stuffed breast of corn-fed chicken with wild mushrooms and an intensely reduced sauce, and a 'witty, delicately moulded' chocolate cup with home-made coffee ice cream, in the style of Raymond Blanc.

Directions: 15 minutes from M5/J5. 10 miles from Worcester

WR6 6AT
Map 3: SO76
Tel: 01299 896666
Fax: 01299 896804
Chef: Andy Palmer
Owners: Mr & Mrs M Frichot
Cost: Fixed-price L £10/D £25. ☺
H/wine £12.
Times: 12.30pm-last L 2pm/7.30pm-last D 9.30pm
Additional: Bar meals L; Sunday L;
Children welcome; ♨ dishes
Seats: 80. Private dining room 10-80.
Jacket and tie preferred
Smoking: No smoking in dining room
Accommodation: 16 en suite
Credit cards: ▆▆ ▆▆ ▆▆ ▆▆ ▆▆ ⛝

BROADWAY, Collin House Hotel

Sixteenth-century Cotswold stone house complete with oak beams and mullioned windows looking out onto manicured gardens. Choose between bar meals, Cotswold suppers or full dinners along the lines of home-cured gravlax, local duckling with plum and brandy sauce, and home-made elderflower sorbet with stewed fruits.

Accommodation: 7 en suite. **Credit cards:** ▆▆ ▆▆

Directions: NW on A44 for 1 mile from Broadway, turn R at Collin Lane. Restaurant 300 yds on R

Collin Lane WR12 7PB
Map 4: SP03
Tel: 01386 858354
Chef: Anthony Ike
Owner: John Mills
Cost: Fixed-price L & D £16. ☺
H/wine £9.85.
Times: Last L-1.30pm/D-9pm.
Closed 24-28 Dec
Additional: Bar food; Sunday L;
No children under 7; ♨ dishes
Smoking: No smoking in dining room

BROADWAY,
Dormy House Hotel

Built as a farmhouse in the seventeenth century, Dormy House stands proud above Broadway in well-tended grounds. The restaurant is located in the original part of the building, although there is also an adjoining conservatory-style dining room. Tapestries, oak beams and rafters define the decor. The kitchen seeks out raw materials diligently and presentation is a delight to the eye. Timbale of turbot and Cornish scallops is

Willersley Hill
WR12 7LF
Map 4: SP03
Tel: 01386 852711
Fax: 01386 858636
Chef: Alan Cutler
Owner: J Philip-Sorensen
Cost: Alc £38, fixed-price D £28.50.
H/wine £11.50

Dormy House Hotel

Times: 12.30pm-last L 2pm/7pm-last
D 9.30pm. Closed L Sat, 24-27 Dec
Additional: Bar food; Sunday L;
Children welcome; ❸ dishes
Seats: 70. Private dining room 40.
Jacket and tie preferred
Smoking: No-smoking area
Accommodation: 49 en suite
Credit cards: ▅▅ ▅▅ ▅▅ ▅▅ ▅ ◖

served with a coriander and green lentil sauce, poached
suprême of sea bass is paired with spring cabbage, baby
vegetables and a dry vermouth sauce based on stock.
Alternatively there are meaty offerings in the shape of warm
salad of pigeon and smoked bacon with toasted pine kernels or
loin of Welsh venison with poached pear on a port and grape
sauce. To finish a crème brûlée 'of lovely thickness'. The
heavyweight wine list features plenty of well chosen house
wines, a big French contingent and a good deal of quality
drinking from elsewhere.

Directions: Take Saintbury turn off A44, after 1 mile bear left at
staggered crossroads

BROADWAY, The Lygon Arms ❀❀❀

The stunning Great Hall with its arched ceiling, minstrel's
gallery, open fire, chandeliers and coat of arms ensigns on the
walls, is the jewel in the crown of this famous sixteenth-century
coaching inn, whose façade belies the extensive leisure and
conference facilities within. Now the dining room, the Great
Hall is saved from oppressive formality by the easy hospitality
of the staff, and by cooking that offers flashes of the traditional
combined with contemporary style – rabbit and cider cream
soup with Welsh rarebit, loin of wild boar marinated with
honey and cloves and grilled with Bramley apple and black
pudding. Chef Roger Narbett makes excellent use of well-
sourced, fresh produce, and dishes sampled, such as warm
charlotte of English goat's cheese and red onion with grilled
niçoise vegetables, and Indian spiced Cornish crab with
coriander and grilled plump scallops, all had true, clear
flavours and interesting textural balance. Escalope of Cornish
sea bass with wild mushroom and basil ravioli, Dublin Bay
prawns and a carrot and Sauternes sauce was described as
'outstanding'. Although dishes have several elements, nothing
is superflous, as suprême of corn-fed chicken with sweetcorn
and asparagus risotto, spiced chicken liver and green herb
sabayon demonstrated. The "Wait and See" dessert was a
lovingly prepared selection of minature desserts – dark
chocolate parfait parcel-wrapped in white chocolate 'wrapped'
in chocolate ribbon, nutty pecan ice cream, fragrant
mousseline of woodland berries, and a tiny rum baba served
with peaches. Another dessert, Pupton apple tart with liquorice
ice cream and Granny Smith sauce was equally impressive.

Directions: In the centre of the High Street

WR12 7DU
Map 4: SP03
Tel: 01386 852255
Fax: 01386 858611
Chef: Roger Narbett
Owner: The Savoy Group of Hotels &
Restaurants
Cost: *Alc* £40, fixed-price L £24/D
£40. H/wine £15
Times: 12.30-last L 2pm/7.30pm-last
D 9.15.pm
Additional: Bar meals L; Sunday L;
Children welcome; ❸ dishes
Seats: 90. Private dining room 80
Smoking: No smoking in dining room
Accommodation: 63 en suite
Credit cards: ▅▅ ▅▅ ▅▅ ▅▅ ▅ ◖

BROMSGROVE, Grafton Manor ⊛⊛

Shades of the Raj at this fine, family run, Elizabethan manor. The unexpected juxtaposition is a result of Simon Morris's fascination with India and Indian food; every year he visits the sub-continent and does a stage at a major hotel restaurant. This enthusiasm for the subtlety and range of Indian cooking is manifested in dishes such as prawn and banana pakora, Gujarati chicken with apricots and straw potatoes, Bombay fish curry, and smoked Goan pork. Cross-over dishes produce English ham marinated in a tandoori paste with mushy peas and parsley raita, and Lancashire hotpot infused with cardamom and cinnamon and cooked in coconut milk. A parallel, modern British menu might commence with a well-constructed chicken and herb terrine, or gravad lax with a mild mustard and dill sauce, followed by boned leg of Worcestershire lamb cooked on a skillet and served on a bed of flageolet beans with a paprika and mint jus, or fillet of halibut encased in batter, deep-fried and served on a bed of mushy peas with a chervil and parsley sauce. One appropriately manorial desert is the Lord of Grafton's whisky steamed pudding served with whisky cream.

Directions: Off the B4091, 1.5 miles S of Bromsgrove

Grafton Lane B61 7HA
Map 7: SO97
Tel: 01527 579007
Fax: 01527 575221
Chef: Simon Morris
Owners: The Morris family
Cost: Fixed-price L £20.50/D £25.95-£31.50 (3-4 courses). H/wine £10.95
Times: 12.30pm-last L 1.30pm/7pm-last D 9.30pm. Closed Sat L
Additional: Sunday L; Children welcome; ⊕ dishes
Seats: 60. Private dining room 50
Smoking: No smoking in dining room
Accommodation: 9 en suite
Credit cards: ■ ■ ■ ■ ■ ■

BROMSGROVE, Pine Lodge Hotel ⊛⊛

Kidderminster Road B61 9AB
Map 7: SO97
Tel: 01527 576600
Fax: 01527 878981
Chef: Mark Higgins
Owner: Andrew Weir Hotels
Cost: Alc £25, fixed-price D £17.25. ☺ H/wine £9.75.
Times: Noon-last L-2pm/7pm-last D-10pm. Closed L Sat
Additional: Bar food; Sunday L; Children welcome; ⊕ dishes
Seats: 105. Private dining room 25
Accommodation: 114 en suite
Credit cards: ■ ■ ■ ■ ■ ■

The hotel is modern Mediterranean in style, the restaurant – the Parador – is distinctly Spanish. Under its beamed ceiling visitors can wander the world gastronomically. The *carte* also takes in plain grills, vegetarian options (perhaps home-made ravioli filled with vegetable pesto, poached in white wine and finished with Pecorino cheese and basil), and flambé dishes cooked at the table – anything from devilled chicken to crêpes suzette. Terrine of shellfish set in a Sauternes and tarragon jelly made a good starter at inspection. This was followed by rack of English lamb with orange and pine nut stuffing, carved onto a rich port and rosehip reduction. To finish, creamy apricot and rice pudding was served with shortbread biscuits.

Directions: On A448 Kidderminster road 1 mile W of Bromsgrove centre

CHADDESLEY CORBETT,
Brockencote Hall ⊛⊛

Kidderminster DY10 4PY
Map 7: SO87
Tel: 01562 777876
Fax: 01562 777872
Chef: Didier Philipot
Owners: Alison & Joseph Petitjean
Cost: Fixed-price L £19.50/D £24.50.
☺ H/wine £11.40.
Times: Noon-last L 1.30pm/7pm-last
D 9.30pm. Closed L Sat
Additional: Sunday L;
Children welcome; ♨ dishes
Seats: 50. Private dining room 25
Smoking: No smoking in dining room
Accommodation: 17 en suite
Credit cards: 🔲 🔲 🔲 🔲 🔲 🔲

A traditional English country house dating from the seventeenth century, and standing in 70 acres of landscaped grounds beside a tranquil lake. The elegant restaurant and pine-panelled library (the original Edwardian dining room) and a terrace all take in superb views of the glorious surrounding countryside. At a dinner in May our inspector started with canapés of Parmesan crisps, guacamole with chorizo, and plump green olives in oil. Lightly pan-fried lamb sweetbreads followed, served with onion compote, button mushrooms and Hereford snails. The main course featured fillet of sea bass with creamed potatoes and slivers of oven-dried tomatoes. For dessert, a poached pear, cooked in vanilla liquor, was accompanied by excellent pistachio ice cream in a light Amaretto sabayon. The well-stocked wine cellar includes a number of excellent house wines as well as many bottles of famous French vintages.

Directions: On A448, just outside village, btw Kidderminster & Bromsgrove (M5/J5, M42/J1)

CLIFTON UPON TEME,
The Lion Inn ⊛

NEW

1 The Village WR6 6DH
Map 3: SO76
Tel: 01886 812617
Telephone for details

Ancient village inn with character bars full of exposed timbers and beams. Blackboard menus cover a range of pub food and some specials. Try smoked goose breast with orange and apple salad and Cumberland sauce, fillets of brill with lemon butter, and with a rich apple and toffee pudding with some good old-fashioned custard.

CORSE LAWN,
Corse Lawn House Hotel ⊛⊛

GL19 4LZ
Map 3: SO83
Tel: 01452 780771
Fax: 01452 780840
Chefs: Baba Hine, Tim Earley
Owners: The Hine Family
Cost: *Alc* £32.50, fixed-price L
£16.95/D £24.50. H/wine £9.95
Times: Noon-last L 2pm/7pm-last D
10pm

The Hine family (of Cognac fame) have been custodians of this listed Queen Anne property for almost two decades and over the years it has slowly evolved and developed. Outside is an impressive ornamental pond, all around are acres of grounds and the interior impresses with its tasteful furnishings and style. Fixed-price menus and a *carte* offer what the Hines call 'mid-Channel', which means galantine of duckling with apple and walnuts, fillets of plaice with queen scallops and wild garlic, and lean fillet of Scotch beef served on a rösti with a pleasant salsa verde, which our inspector enjoyed as a main course. Desserts could range from creamy lemon tart with home-made lemon ice cream to hot orange sponge pudding, otherwise there are unpasteurised British cheeses from Neals Yard. Less formal meals are also served in the Simply Corse Lawn Bistro where the menu runs from sandwiches and omelettes to dishes like ragout of three fish with basil and tomato.

Directions: Village centre, on B4211 5 miles south-west of Tewkesbury

EVESHAM, The Evesham Hotel

Impressive converted farmhouse dating from 1540 but renovated in Georgian times. Meals are served in the Regency-style restaurant overlooking an ancient Cedar of Lebanon, and the weekly menu offers such things as curried smoked haddock soup, and wild boar cutlets with creamy apple sauce. Enthusiastic wine list.

Accommodation: 40 en suite
Credit cards: ▬ ▬ ▬ ▬ ▣ ©

Directions: Coopers Lane is off road alongside River Avon

Additional: Bar food; Sunday L; Children welcome; ◐ dishes
Seats: 50. Private dining rooms 16-40
Smoking: No smoking in dining room
Accommodation: 19 en suite
Credit cards: ▬ ▬ ▬ ▬ ▣ ©

Coopers Lane WR11 6DA
Map 4: SP04
Tel: 01386 765566
Fax: 01386 765443
Chef: Ian Mann
Owners: The Jenkinson family
Cost: Alc £19. H/wine £9.60. ☺
Times: Last L 2pm/D 9.30pm
Closed 25-26 Dec
Additional: Children welcome; ◐ dishes
Smoking: No smoking in the dining room

EVESHAM,
The Mill At Harvington ❀❀

Eight acres of woodland and 600 feet of river frontage provide the setting for this beguiling little hotel by the banks of the Avon. The place combines a fine old Georgian house and a red-brick malting mill used for hop-drying, brewing and baking. There are pleasant views of the garden from the windows of the elegant dining room, where sound country cooking, with a few Gallic flourishes, is the order of the day. A test meal of salmon and sole mousse with a sauce of wine and spinach, followed by splendid crisp-skinned duckling with orange and ginger sauce, and a fruity Pavlova was well reported. The kitchen also draws on decent ingredients for crab pancakes, medallions of venison with damsons, guinea fowl with cider and sage, and the like. Service is provided courteously by a dedicated, friendly team who are a pleasure to meet. Wines are grouped according to style as well as price and the accompanying notes are well considered.

Anchor Lane WR11 5NR
Map 4: SP04
Tel/Fax: 01386 870688
Chef: Jane Greenhalgh
Owners: Mr & Mrs Greenhalgh
Cost: Alc £23, fixed-price L £13.95/D £23. ☺ H/wine £10.25.
Times: 11.45am-last L 1.45pm/7pm-last D 8.45pm. Closed 23-28 Dec
Additional: Bar food L; Sunday lunch; Children welcome; ◐ dishes
Seats: 40. Private dining room 14
Smoking: No smoking in dining room
Accommodation: 15 en suite
Credit cards: ▬ ▬ ▬ ▬ ▣ ©

Directions: Turn S off B439, opposite Harvington village, down Anchor Lane

EVESHAM, Riverside Hotel ❀❀

Offenham Road
WR11 5JP
Map 4: SP04
Tel: 01386 446200
Fax: 01386 40021
Chef: Rosemary Willmott
Owners: Vincent &
Rosemary Willmott
Cost: Fixed-price L £16.95 (3
courses)/D £24.95 (4 courses).
H/wine £11.50
Times: 12.30pm-last L 1.45pm/
7.30pm-last D 9pm. Closed D Sun,
Mon, 25 Dec
Seats: 45
Smoking: No smoking in dining room
Accommodation: 7 en suite
Credit cards: 💳 💳 💳 💳

An enticing waterside setting – with three acres of grounds running down to the banks of the Avon – is a great crowd-pleaser at Vincent and Rosemary Willmott's restaurant-with-rooms. Fishing, moorings and boats for hire are a bonus. The gastronomic side of things centres around dinner in the elegant restaurant, which has fine views of the waterscape. Meals begin with a wicker basket of crudités plus a bowl of creamy garlic mayonnaise. Starters range from spicy Thai fishcakes with tomato salsa to lamb's sweetbreads with mushroom and tarragon sauce, while main courses could encompass anything from baked Scotch salmon with crème fraîche, lime and chives to the haunch of venison which was enjoyed by our inspector. Passionfruit mousse with shortbread hearts is something of a signature dessert, although oven-baked bananas with rum and brown sugar has been heartily endorsed. Around 60 well chosen wines are drawn from decent sources around the globe.

Directions: 2 miles from town centre on B4510 (Offenham). At end of narrow lane marked 'The Parks'

EVESHAM,
Wood Norton Hall ❀❀

NEW

Wood Norton
WR11 4YB
Map 4: SP04
Tel: 01386 420007
Fax: 01386 420190
Chef: John James Campbell
Owners: BBC

Originally used as a hunting lodge by the Duc d'Orleans, this impressive Victorian hall was acquired by the BBC at the start of World War II and became the largest broadcasting centre in Europe. Set in 170 acres of countryside, it now functions as a training centre/hotel with excellent business facilities. The Duc's Restaurant, with its grand fireplaces and carved oak-panelling, makes an impressive setting for cooking that shows plenty of promise. An inspection meal taken from the fixed-price menu kicked off favourably with warm black pudding served on mash with spinach leaves and parsley sauce. Next came a little portion of beetroot risotto before baked sea bass (fresh from Cornwall) with tomato and red wine dressing. A taster of peach melba with strawberry sabayon heralded a first-rate pear soufflé served with its own sorbet. The wine list is a detailed collection of over 250 bins from around the world.

Directions: 2 miles NW of Evesham on the A4538. Hotel is 0.5 mile on R

Cost: *Alc* £32.50, fixed-price L £19.50 (3 courses)/D £47.50 (7 courses). H/wine £11.75
Times: 12.30pm-last L 2pm/7pm-last D 10pm. Closed L Sat, between Xmas/New Year
Additional: Bar food L; Sunday lunch; Children welcome; ✤ dishes
Seats: 64. Private dining room 20
Smoking: No-smoking area in dining room
Accommodation: 45 en suite
Credit cards: 🟦 🟦 🟦 🟦 🟦 🟦

MALVERN, Colwall Park Hotel ✿✿

Colwall Malvern WR13 6QG
Map 3: SO74
Tel: 01684 540206
Fax: 01684 540847
Chef: Terry Herbert
Owners: Mr & Mrs CJ Sturman
Cost: Fixed-price D £22.50. ☺ H/wine £10.50.
Times: Noon-last L 2pm/7.30pm-last D 9pm
Additional: Bar food; Sunday L; Children welcome; ✤ dishes
Seats: 36. Private dining room 20
Smoking: No smoking in dining room
Accommodation: 23 en suite
Credit cards: 🟦 🟦 🟦 🟦 🟦 🟦

Standing in extensive gardens, Colwall Park was actually purpose-built as a hotel at the turn of the century, to serve the local railway station and travellers to and from London. A new chef has revitalised the quality of the food, and there is now a seasonal *carte*, daily table d'hôte, a good children's and vegetarian selection. Of the dishes sampled Cornish lobster tortelloni with a light and creamy chervil sauce, and thin, tender medallions of Scottish beef fillet on red onion marmalade with roasted shallots and roasted turned potatoes had fine flavour. Other typical dishes might include prime cuts of venison sautéed with juniper berries, or lobster Thermidor with pilaff rice, and rabbit and chicken terrine with plum chutney. Details, such as home-made breads (a choice of six), good freshly brewed coffee, home-made chocolates and appetisers are all good – and the sous chef gets credit for bread-and-butter pudding served with fresh cream.

Directions: On B4218 btw Ledbury and Malvern

MALVERN,
The Cottage in the Wood ✿✿

Holywell Road
Malvern Wells
WR14 4LG
Map 3: SO74
Tel: 01684 575859
Fax: 01684 560662
Chefs: Kathryn Young, Dominic Pattin

The Cottage in the Wood, once the home of Sir Edward Elgar, makes much of its seductive setting on the slopes of the Malvern Hills – the views are stunning, and within, real fires, deep-cushioned sofas and plenty of fresh flowers add to the contentment of the place. The dining room is delightful, nicely

The Cottage in the Wood

Owners: John & Sue Pattin
Cost: Alc £26, fixed-price L £11.95 (3 courses). H/wine £12.
Times: 12.30pm-last L 2pm/7pm-last D 9pm
Additional: Sunday L; Children welcome; ✪ dishes
Seats: 44.
Smoking: No smoking in dining room; air-conditioning
Accommodation: 20 en suite
Credit cards: 🔲 🔲 🔲 🔲 🔲

appointed, good linen, flowers, views, the cooking accomplished. Good, light, home-made lemon and thyme bread kicked off an inspection dinner that took in spinach risotto tart topped with Stilton rarebit and served on a port wine sauce, and roast saddle of venison with goat's cheese gnocchi, red cabbage and a red wine sauce. The meat was cooked to perfection, gnocchi well-executed, the cabbage providing a sharpness of flavour and good contrast of texture. Pudding was a properly made rich, creamy Armagnac parfait served with prunes and an Earl Grey syrup. The wine list is extraordinarily catholic in range, reasonably priced and encompasses some fine makers such as Hochar from the Lebanon and Guigal from the Rhône. There is a good showing of halves.

Directions: Signed turning 3 miles S of Great Malvern off A449

MALVERN,

Croque-en-Bouche ❀❀❀

NEW

221 Wells Road WR14 4HF
Map 3: SO74
Tel/Fax: 01684 565612
Chef: Marion Jones
Owners: Marion & Robin Jones
Cost: Fixed-price D £35.50 (4 courses). H/wine £9
Times: D only, 7.30pm-last D 9pm
Seats: 22. Private dining room 6
Smoking: No smoking in dining room
Credit cards: 🔲 🔲 🔲

The five-storied former Victorian bakery, on the side of the Malvern Hills overlooking the Severn Valley, is run by the husband and wife team of Marion and Robin Jones. The pace of eating is measured, and there is time to appreciate thoroughly Marion's considerable gifts in the kitchen. The emphasis throughout the meal is on the quality of the ingredients, cooked mostly in a modern European style but with oriental influences. The set menu begins with soup brought in a terrine to the table, perhaps a very fresh tasting, split green pea, leek, wild garlic and sorrel, flavoured with some of the wonderful herbs and saladings from the garden. Fish dishes might include halibut fillet, provençale style, baked with tapenade and served with wild rocket and pepperonata, or stunningly simple skate with seakale shoots, walnut oil dressing and green herb pickled lemon relish. Barbary duck or free-range corn-fed chicken is cooked with sesame, ginger and a hoisin glaze, served with oriental greens and a spicy orange and coriander sauce, whilst small escalopes of Bobbington wild boar are grilled and served with Mediterranean vegetables, balsamic vinegar, extra-virgin olive oil and salsa verde. Perfect potato gratin is served with the main courses, followed by a salad with hazelnut oil and seasonal additions such as purple basil or purslane. A long-term favourite, frozen ginger meringue, is always available, otherwise one of the best ways to sample the intriguing desserts is via The Grand Dessert plate, perhaps terrific lemon mascarpone tart, a delicate flourless chocolate cake iced with a dark, fine chocolate mousse, elderberry sorbet, and toffee rice pudding.

Directions: 2 miles S of Gt Malvern on A449

MALVERN, Holdfast Cottage

Little Malvern WR13 6NA
Map 3: SO74
Tel: 01684 310288
Fax: 01684 311117
Chef: Jane Knowles
Owners: Stephen & Jane Knowles
Cost: Fixed-price D £18 (4 courses).
☺ H/wine £9.75.
Times: D only, 7.30pm-9pm.
Closed D Sun, 3 wks Jan
Additional: Children welcome;
dishes
Seats: 20. Private dining room 14
Smoking: No smoking in dining room
Accommodation: 8 en suite
Credit cards: ▬ ▬ ▬ ▬

An ancient wisteria runs along the terrace and hangs over the windows of the pretty blue-and-white dining room of this charming cottage, within sight of the Malvern Hills. The innovative cooking is based on good seasonal produce and herbs from the Victorian herb garden. The set dinner menu changes daily, but always begins with home-made canapés and bread rolls. A butternut squash and roast sweet pepper soup with crème fraîche proved an adventurous, distinctive-tasting starter, and the Welsh lamb cutlets with herb crust which followed were nice and pink and had a fine flavour, set off well by a tasty apple and rosemary jelly. An imaginative selection of vegetables comprised delicious new pink fir apple potatoes, fine beans with a hint of lime, and carrot and turnip mashed with butter, ginger and mustard seeds. Lemon tart with a raspberry and sloe gin coulis was delicious and really made the taste buds tingle. A pot of good coffee comes with home-made choccies.

Directions: On A4104 midway between Welland and Little Malvern

SEVERN STOKE,
Old Schoolhouse Hotel

WR8 9JA
Map 3: SO85
Tel: 01905 371368
Fax: 01905 371591
Chef: Christopher Stephens
Owners: Ken Harris, Veronica Meneaugh
Cost: *Alc* £23.50, fixed-price D £16.50.☺ H/wine £9.25.
Times: Noon-last L 2pm/7pm-last D 9pm. Closed L Sat
Additional: Bar food L; Sunday L; Children welcome; dishes
Seats: 50. Private dining room 25-100

In the seventeenth century, this timbered building overlooking the Severn Vale was a farmhouse then, in Victorian times, it became a seat of learning. Today it functions as a charming country restaurant/hotel. A feature of the dining room is an old well dating back several centuries and the atmosphere is suitably warm and cosy. The kitchen isn't afraid to wear its eclectic heart on its sleeve – lacing smoked salmon and dill soup with star anise, glazing linguine with Indonesian soy sauce, or serving stuffed chicken breast on a bed of couscous flavoured with coriander, mint and chilli. In more full-blooded vein, one inspector praised slowly braised lamb shank on a bed of Savoy cabbage with a rich, garlicky sauce, as well as a refreshing, beautifully presented baked vanilla cheesecake. Another meal noted that flavours were to the point and unhindered by flowery embellishment; dishes also came in 'agricultural size portions'. This meal took in ravioli of mushrooms set on top of an earthy stew of provençale vegetables, venison with juniper on an imaginative chestnut and sweet potato rösti with caramelised red onions and a poivrade sauce, and a well executed tarte Tatin of pears with cinnamon ice cream. Cheery staff dispense organised but informal service. The wine list promises decent drinking at prices that won't threaten the school fees.

Smoking: No smoking in dining room
Accommodation: 14 en suite
Credit cards: 💳 💳 💳 💳

Directions: From the M5/J7, head for Malvern. When ring road crosses the A38, turn L (Tewkesbury). Continue along A38 through Kempsey. Restaurant on R

WORCESTER,
Brown's Restaurant ❀❀

A great riverside location by the banks of the Severn is one of the main scoring points at this converted corn mill. Long-serving owners, the Tansleys point out that the building, with its spacious, high-ceilinged interior, has won architectural and conservation awards for its conversion. Menus are fixed price, dish descriptions are straight to the point and the cooking is zestily contemporary without resorting to fashionable overkill. Daily fish dishes share the billing with, say, warm salad of smoked chicken with orange dressing, spatchcock of boned quails with buttered barley, cassoulet and roast carré of lamb with pease pudding. Desserts are similarly inclined: caramel soufflé, pavé of chocolate with raspberry sauce, grilled pineapple with coconut ice cream, for example. Half-bottles are given a good airing on the wine list, which has a noticeable bias towards France and other European countries.

The Old Cornmill
South Quay WR1 2JJ
Map 3: SO85
Tel: 01905 26263
Fax: 01905 25768
Chef: WR Tansley
Owners: WR & PM Tansley
Cost: Fixed-price L £18.50 (4 courses)/D £33.50 (5 courses). H/wine £11.50
Times: 12.30pm-last L 1.45pm/7.30pm-last D 9.45pm. Closed Mon, L Sat, D Sun, 1 week Xmas Eve -New Year's Eve
Additional: Sunday L; No children under 8; 🍴 dishes
Seats: 90

Smoking: No-smoking area; no pipes in dining room
Credit cards: 💳 💳 💳 💳 💳

Directions: City centre, along riverbank, car park opposite

WORCESTER, Fownes Hotel ❀

Built in 1777 and originally a glove-making factory, this is now an attractively furnished modern hotel. Menus in The Kings restaurant feature such dishes as chicken and mushroom terrine with pear chutney, fillet of salmon roasted with rock salt and rosemary, and braised pheasant with mushrooms and Madeira sauce, plus various steaks.

City Walls Road
WR1 2AP
Map 3: SO85
Tel: 01905 613151
Fax: 01905 23742
Chef: Peter Botterill
Cost: Alc £20, fixed-price L £8.95/D £15.95. H/wine £10.50
Times: Last L 2 pm/D 9.45pm

Additional: Bar food; Sunday L; Children welcome; 🍴 dishes
Smoking: No smoking in dining room
Accommodation: 61 en suite
Credit cards: 💳 💳 💳 💳 💳 💳

Directions: From M5/J7 take signs to city centre – hotel is beside A38 inner ring road, 100 yards from the cathedral

YORKSHIRE
EAST RIDING

BEVERLEY,
The Manor House ❀❀

Northlands Walkington
HU17 8RT
Map 8: TA03
Tel: 01482 881645
Fax: 01482 866501
Chef: Derek Baugh
Owners: Derek & Lee Baugh
Cost: Alc £28.50, fixed-price D
£16.50 (3 courses). ☺ H/wine £8.95.
Times: D only, 7pm-last D 9.15pm.
Closed Sun, Bhs
Additional: No children under 12;
❸ dishes
Seats: 55. Private dining room 24
Smoking: No pipes and cigars in
dining room
Accommodation: 7 en suite
Credit cards: 💳 💳 💳 💳

Standing in three acres of tree-lined grounds overlooking parkland, this tranquil nineteenth-century retreat makes the most of its setting. Some of the best views are from the conservatory, otherwise you can eat in the more formal atmosphere of the blue dining room. Fixed price menus and a *carte* are based around supplies of top-notch local ingredients and the kitchen is capable in its work. Typical dishes might range from salad of warm quail with strawberry dressing, smoked haddock fishcakes with Meaux mustard sabayon, braised oxtail with baby vegetables and a fumet of Amontillado, to chargrilled fillet of cod with samphire and a saffron and ginger glaze. Desserts are recited at the table, otherwise diners are invited to take 'a tour of the cheeseboard'. Caring owners are ably supported by a team of friendly attentive staff. The well-spread wine list includes a big contingent of serious clarets and Burgundies.

Directions: 4 miles SW off the B1230

BEVERLEY,
Tickton Grange Hotel ❀ NEW

Elegant, efficiently run Georgian house standing in four acres of well-tended gardens. An inspection dinner in the smart restaurant highlighted a light tart filled with langoustine tails and scallops and good tomato hollandaise, beef fillet stuffed with a rich pigeon pâté, and iced lemon soufflé.

Additional: Sunday L; Bar meals L; Children welcome; ❸ dishes
Smoking: No-smoking area. No pipes or cigars.
Accommodation: 17 en suite
Credit cards: 💳 💳 💳 💳 💳 💳

Tickton HU17 9SH
Map 8: TA03
Tel: 01964 543666
Fax: 01964 542556
Chef: David Nowell
Owners: The Whymant family
Cost: Alc £25.80, set L £19.80/D
£19.50. ☺ H/wine £9.75.
Times: Last L 2pm/D 9.30pm.

Directions: 3m NE on A1035

HULL, Cerutti's ❀

The restaurant is on the first floor, above the bar, overlooking the Humber estuary. The menu is emphatically seafood, with a couple of alternative starters and the odd steak. Expect crab fishcakes with tangy lemon butter, followed by pan-fried salmon with watercress and tarragon sauce.

Additional: No children under 7; ⚫ dishes
Smoking: No-smoking area; no pipes or cigars in dining room
Credit cards: ▬ ▬ ▬ ▣

Directions: Follow signs for Fruit Market and Corporation Pier

10 Nelson Street
HU1 1XE
Map 8: TA02
Tel: 01482 328501
Fax: 01482 587597
Chef: Tim Bell
Owners: The Cerutti family
Cost: *Alc* £24, fixed-price L/D
£13.50. ☺ H/wine £11.25.
Times: Last L 2pm/D 9.30pm.
Closed Sun, L Sat, 1 wk Xmas

WILLERBY, Willerby Manor Hotel ❀

Commendable modern English cooking at this traditional restaurant in an elegant Victorian house. Expect guinea fowl, leek and Parma ham terrine to start, followed by spiced lamb pudding with rosemary sauce or tournedos of beef with red wine sauce.

Additional: Bar food; Sunday L; Children welcome; ⚫ dishes
Accommodation: 51 en suite. **Credit cards:** ▬ ▬ ▬ ▬ ▣

Directions: Off the A1105 W of Hull, just off main street of Willerby

Well Lane HU10 6ER
Map 8: TA03
Tel: 01482 652616
Fax: 01482 653901
Chef: Tony Papa
Owner: Alexandra Townend
Cost: *Alc* £24, fixed-price L £12/D
£14.50. ☺ H/wine £8.95.
Times: Last-L 2pm/D 9.30pm.
Closed D Sun, 25 Dec

YORKSHIRE NORTH

APPLETON-LE-MOORS,
Appleton Hall Hotel ❀

Gracious Victorian mansion set peacefully in two acres of award-winning gardens. Five-course dinners offer straightforward, freshly prepared dishes along the lines of mushrooms in Wensleydale cheese sauce, rabbit pie with shortcrust pastry, and raspberry Pavlova.

Smoking: No smoking in dining room
Accommodation: 9 en suite. **Credit cards:** ▬ ▬ ▬ ▬ ▣

Directions: 1.5 miles off A170, 2 miles E of Kirkbymoorside

York YO6 6TF
Map 8: SE78
Tel: 01751 417227
Fax: 01751 417540
Chef: Norma Davies
Owners: Graham & Norma Davies
Cost: Fixed-price D £19.50(5
courses). ☺ H/wine £8.50.
Times: D only 6.30pm-8.30pm
Additional: ⚫ dishes

ARNCLIFFE,
Amerdale House Hotel ❀❀

This quite delightful hotel is always a pleasure to visit, standing as it does in lovely countryside on the edge of a small village near Skipton. The short dinner menu provides just enough choice, and is cooked to a consistently high standard. Our inspection started with cream cheese, herb and prawn pâté with home-made toasted brioche, followed by a novel entrée version of 'bangers and mash' – full-flavoured chicken boudin on the lightest of light potato mash. Roast Barbary duck breast, tender and full of flavour, was served on excellent Cumberland sauce

Littondale Skipton BD23 5QE
Map 7: SD97
Tel/Fax: 01756 770250
Chef: Nigel Crapper
Owners: Paula & Nigel Crapper
Cost: Fixed-price D £27 (4 courses).
H/wine £10.95
Times: D only, 7pm-8.30pm.
Closed mid-Nov to mid-March
Additional: Children welcome;
⚫ dishes

with fresh orange, and chocolate tart finished the meal with a bravura flourish. Another night, the menu might include Waldorf salad with smoked chicken, casserole of seafood in a saffron sauce, roast leg of Dales' lamb studded with rosemary and garlic, and gooseberry and apple crumble or local cheeses.

Directions: On edge of village

ASENBY, Crab & Lobster

There's a bohemian uniqueness about this place that works a special kind of magic. From the outside it looks like a dyed-in-the-wool North Yorkshire thatched pub, but inside the decor is an extravagantly shambolic clutter of wicker baskets, fishing rods, old fairground slot machines, jockey caps and crab and lobster pots dangling from the ceiling. The atmosphere fizzes. Fresh fish is the thing to eat here, although the repertoire is a real bonanza of dishes spooned out of the global melting pot. Delve into the bar menu for Thai fish cakes with oriental coleslaw, crab risotto with mustard and coriander, or roast monkfish with fennel and garlic. Alternatively, plunge headlong into the even more ambitious restaurant *carte*. Here you might be tempted by ballotine of salmon with chive fromage frais or calves' liver with champ, cured bacon and sauce diable. Puddings are equally eclectic, with tiramisu sitting alongside sticky toffee pudding. One hundred wines span the world and there is ample drinking by the glass.

Directions: Leave A1 for A19 at Dishforth, 3 miles turn L for Asenby

Dishforth Road YO7 3QL
Map 8: SE37
Tel: 01845 577286
Fax: 01845 577109
Chef: Michael Pickard
Owners: David & Jackie Barnard
Cost: Alc £25, fixed-price L £11.50 (2 courses). ☺ H/wine £9.50.
Times: 11.30am-last L 2.30pm/6.30pm-last D 10pm. Closed D Sun
Additional: Bar food; Sunday L; Children welcome; ♿ dishes
Seats: 120. Private dining room 60
Smoking: No smoking in dining room
Accommodation: 5 en suite
Credit cards: ▄▄ ▄▄ ▄▄ ▄▄ ⓒ

Seats: 24
Smoking: No smoking in dining room
Accommodation: 11 en suite
Credit cards: ▄▄ ▄▄ ⓒ

ASKRIGG, King's Arms Hotel

Market Place
Leyburn DL8 3HQ
Map 7: SD99
Tel: 01969 650258
Fax: 01969 650635
Chef: John Barber
Owners: Liz & Ray Hopwood
Cost: Alc £15, fixed-price L £12.50 (3 courses)/D £25 (4 courses). ☺ H/wine £9.25.
Times: Noon-last L 2pm/6.30pm-last D 9pm
Additional: Bar food; Sunday L; Children welcome; ♿ dishes
Seats: 30. Private dining room 10

Well-known for its appearance as the Drovers' Arms in the TV series *All Creatures Great and Small*, the King's Arms is a charming stone inn located in the centre of the village. The Clubroom Restaurant offers a stylish setting for some fine Anglo-French cooking. The regularly changing menu features, perhaps, smoked duck suprême with citrus fruits and garlic, or a simple plate of oak-smoked Scottish salmon served with lemon and brown bread and butter. Recommended main courses include Charolais beef fillet, crowned with a light mushroom soufflé, and baked canon of local Dales lamb with a rich Madeira and rosemary jus. Local Yorkshire dishes are favoured in the Drover's Bar, a more relaxed and informal

setting. Look out for 'peat bog pie' – shepherd's pie with black pudding and oatmeal – and steamed suprême of chicken, flavoured with leeks in a white wine cream sauce. The 'Director's Choice' wine list features wines from both the famous and little-known wine making regions of France.

Smoking: No smoking in dining room
Accommodation: 11 en suite
Credit cards:

Directions: M6/J37 & A684; in centre of village

BOLTON ABBEY, **Devonshire Arms** ✿✿

Skipton BD23 6AJ
Map 7: SE05
Tel: 01756 710441
Fax: 01756 710564
Chef: Andrew Nicholson
Owners: Duke & Duchess of Devonshire
Cost: Fixed-price L £ 18.95/ D £37. H/wine £12
Times: Noon-last L 2.30pm/7pm-last D 10pm
Additional: Bar food L; Sunday L; No children under 12; ✪ dishes
Seats: 80. Private dining room 120
Smoking: No smoking in dining room
Accommodation: 41 en suite
Credit cards:

For two hundred years Bolton Abbey, which nestles in the Wharfe Valley, has been owned by the Dukes of Devonshire. In its current guise as a country house hotel, it provides guests with elegant surroundings and offers the first rate Burlington restaurant. The menu makes pleasant reading and on our last visit the cooking – somewhat classical with modern overtones – lived up to expectations. Where possible, the fixed-price menus feature local produce, some of it grown in the hotel's kitchen garden. Tortellini of scallops was a 'sensational' starter, its coral butter sauce and diced fennel and tomato really working well. A main course of pan-fried veal fillet with caramelised onions, potato rösti and a velvety soubise sauce, was certainly enjoyable although the meat didn't quite melt in the mouth. A delicate apricot soufflé with a tangy orange and peach sorbet in a tuille basket however provided the perfect ending to dinner. An updated wine list offers a good New World selection.

Directions: On the B6160 to Bolton Abbey, 250 yards north of A59 roundabout junction

BOROUGHBRIDGE,
The Crown Inn ✿

Food is taken seriously at this charming village inn that has been in the same family for three generations. There is a hand-written carte plus substantial bar meals and daily specials on the blackboard. Dishes include fresh lobster, steak and ale pie, cassoulet, and char-grilled tuna in roast pepper sauce.

Smoking: No pipes or cigars in dining room
Accommodation: 14 en suite. **Credit cards:**

Directions: From A1 follow Boroughbridge, turn L for Roecliffe at zebra crossing. Inn at end of village green

Roecliffe YO5 9LY
Map 8: SE36
Tel: 01423 322578
Fax: 01423 324060
Chef: Carlos Richerd
Owners: Philip Barker, Mary Barker
Cost: Alc £14, fixed-price L £9. ☺ H/wine £8.95.
Times: 11.30am-last L 2.30pm/6.30pm-last D 10pm
Additional: Sunday L; Bar meals; Children welcome; ✪ dishes

BUCKDEN, **Buck Inn**

Wool auctions were once held in this atmospheric old village inn. Nowadays, a serious but unstuffy approach to food is evident in dishes such as chargrilled pork loin medallions with black pudding risotto and grain mustard sauce, warm home-made tart of Whitby crab with aïoli dressing, and a trio of Swiss chocolate terrines.

Additional: Bar food; Sunday L; Children welcome; ❹ dishes
Smoking: No smoking in dining room
Accommodation: 14 en suite. **Credit cards:** ▆ ▆ ▆ C

Directions: In centre of village

Near Skipton BD23 5JA
Map 7: SD97
Tel: 01756 760228
Fax: 01756 760227
Chef: Mark Antony Cording
Owners: Roy, Marjorie & Nigel Hayton
Cost: Fixed-price D £20.95. ☺ H/wine £12.75.
Times: Last L 2pm/D 9pm (9.30pm Fri, Sat)

BURNSALL, **Red Lion**

Burnsall BD23 6BU
Map 7: SE05
Tel: 01756 720204
Fax: 01756 720292
Chef: James Rowley
Owner: Elizabeth Grayshon
Cost: Fixed-price L £12.95/D £21.50. ☺ H/wine £9.50.
Times: D only 7-9.30pm
Additional: Bar food; Sunday L (noon-2.45pm); Children welcome; ❹ dishes
Smoking: No smoking in dining room
Accommodation: 11 rooms en suite
Credit cards: ▆ ▆ ▆ ▆ C

There are fine views of the River Wharfe and Burnsall Fell from this beamed, 400-year-old ferryman's inn. Fixed-priced dinners in the restaurant feature classically inclined dishes such as mousseline of lemon sole with lemon beurre blanc, grilled fillet of beef with roasted garlic sauce, and crème brûlée.

Directions: On B6160 between Bolton Abbey (A59) & Grassington

CRATHORNE, **Crathorne Hall**

Spectacular views down the Leven Valley towards the distant Cleveland Hills are one of the outstanding features of this grand Edwardian stately home set in 15 acres of immaculate grounds. Inside, there's a magnificent high-ceilinged dining room dominated by an impressive carved stone fireplace; here you can sample food that is an intriguing blend of classic and contemporary ideas. The highpoints of a springtime inspection were wood pigeon with a rich blackcurrant jus with black pudding crumbled into it, and gloriously fresh sea bass served on olive oil mash with a light tomato sauce. Other dishes might range from, say, medallions of venison on a blueberry and thyme Scotch pancake to honey-roast pork fillet with apple. To finish, expect desserts like Grand Marnier oranges with mascarpone and raspberry mille-feuille with a caramel and pistachio sauce. Service is polished.

Directions: From A19, take junction signposted Crathorne and follow the signs. Hotel entrance is to the L on way into village.

Yarm TS15 0AR
Map 8: NZ40
Tel: 01642 700398
Fax: 01642 700814

Chef: Phillip Pomfret

Owners: Virgin
Cost: Alc £20, fixed-price L £14.50/D £23.50. ☺ H/wine £14.50.
Times: Noon-last L 2pm/7pm-last D 10pm
Additional: Bar food; Sunday L; Children welcome ; ❹ dishes
Seats: 60. Private dining room 120
Smoking: No smoking in dining room
Accommodation: 37 en suite
Credit cards: ▆ ▆ ▆ ▆ ▆ C

EASINGTON, Grinkle Park ❀

Saltburn-by-the-Sea
TS13 4UB
Map 8: NZ71
Tel: 01287 640515
Fax: 01287 641278
Chef: Timothy Backhouse
Owner: Bass plc
Cost: *Alc* £25.40, fixed-price L
£12.75/D £18. ☺ H/wine £9.25.
Times: Last L 2pm/D 9pm

Elegant Victorian house, an intimate setting for dinner by candlelight. From a soundly cooked range of Anglo/French dishes try sautéed chicken with leeks and pasta, followed perhaps by roast rack of lamb with redcurrant and port sauce. Puddings are selected from 'Mrs Atkinson's Dessert Trolley'.

Additional: Bar food; Sunday L; Children welcome; ❹ dishes
Smoking: No cigars and pipes
Accommodation: 20 en suite. **Credit cards:** ▇ ▨ ▨ ▨ ▨

Directions: Nine miles from Guisborough, signed L off main A171 Guisborough-Whitby road

ESCRICK, The Parsonage Hotel ❀

Main Street YO4 6LE
Map 8: SE54
Tel: 01904 728111
Fax: 01904 728151
Chef: Martin Griffiths
Owners: Paul & Karen Ridley
Cost: *Alc* £27, fixed-price L £3.50/D
£14.50. ☺ H/wine £8.95.
Times: Last L 2pm/D 9.30pm
Additional: Sunday L; Bar meals L;
Children welcome; ❹ dishes

An early nineteenth-century parsonage with a long and varied history. Now a delightful country house restaurant, serving soundly prepared Anglo-French dishes. Look out for pork with chestnut and bacon seasoning, and pumpkin paloma filled with wild mushrooms and smoked cheese.

Smoking: No smoking in dining room
Accommodation: 16 en suite. **Credit cards:** ▇ ▨ ▨ ▨ ▨ ▨

Directions: From York head S on A19, Parsonage on R 4 miles out of town in Escrick village

GOATHLAND,
Mallyan Spout Hotel ❀

Whitby YO22 5AN
Map 8: NZ80
Tel: 01947 896486
Fax: 01947 896327
Chefs: David Fletcher, Martin Skelton
Owners: Judith & Peter Heslop
Cost: *Alc* £19.50.
Times: D only, 7pm-last D 8.30pm
Additional: Bar meals; Sunday lunch
(noon-2pm); Children welcome;
❹ dishes

Mallyan Spout takes its name from a nearby moorland waterfall, and is a striking ivy-clad Victorian stone building. Food is well-prepared, and dishes could include mushroom Stroganoff with basmati rice, and grilled sirloin steak with green peppercorn cream sauce. Don't miss the traditional steak and kidney casserole with Yorkshire pudding.

Accommodation: 24 en suite. **Credit cards:** ▇ ▨ ▨ ▨ ▨

Directions: Off A169 (Pickering-Whitby) in village, opposite church

GRASSINGTON,
Grassington House ❀

5 The Square BD23 5AQ
Map 7: SE06
Tel: 01756 752406
Fax: 01756 752135
Chef: Joseph Lodge
Owner: Gordon Elsworth
Cost: *Alc* £18.50. H/wine £7.95 ☺
Times: Last L 2pm/D 9pm

A delightful eighteenth-century house overlooking Grassington's cobbled square. Skilfully prepared meals (served in the Rose Room), include grilled chicken suprême drizzled with honey, orange and chilli jus, roast loin of lamb with a rich fennel and rosemary sauce, and fillet of pork with limes, mango and coconut.

Additional: Sunday L; Bar meals; Children welcome; ❹ dishes
Smoking: No smoking in dining room
Accommodation: 10 en suite. **Credit cards:** ▇ ▨ ▨ ▨

Directions: From Skipton bypass take B6265 to Grassington

HARROGATE, **Balmoral Hotel**

Franklin Mount HG1 5EJ
Map 8: SE35
Tel: 01423 508208
Fax: 01423 530652
Telephone for details

The peaceful country-house atmosphere belies the fact that this hotel is situated close to the town and conference centre. Imaginative public rooms include an Oriental Bar, where dim-sum appetisers are offered, and the traditionally furnished Henry's Restaurant, which is the ideal setting for soundly cooked food backed up by an interesting wine list. A winter dinner yielded fish soup served with a smooth garlic and oil rouille, crisp croûtons and Gruyère cheese, followed by slices of duck on top of slightly salted polenta and young winter root vegetables with a good Calvados sauce. Dessert was crème brûlée with caramelised oranges and Grand Marnier. Coffee comes with a chocolate fondue whereby diners dip strawberries, choux pastry balls and shortbread into a chocolate sauce.

Directions: Town centre, near Exhibition Centre

HARROGATE, **La Bergerie**

11 Mount Parade HG1 1BX
Map 8: SE35
Tel: 01423 500089
Chef: Jacques Giron
Owner: Jacques & Juliet Giron
Cost: *Alc* £20.25, fixed-price L £20.25/£17.75 (4 courses). ☺
H/wine £8.50.
Times: L by prior arrangement/7pm-last D 10.30pm
Additional: Children welcome; ✪ dishes
Seats: 35. Private dining room 15
Smoking: No-smoking area
Credit cards: 💳 💳 💳 💳

Chef/patron Jacques Giron hails from the South-West of France, and his cooking is suffused with the flavours of his native soil. The setting is the ground floor of a terraced house bedecked with photographs and prints of French life and the menu follows suit. Specialities set the tone: cassoulet toulousaine, served in its own pot, also tioro (a Basque fish stew which, in theory, should contain as many pounds of onions as there are seafood). Alongside these authentic offerings is an unlikely interloper in the shape of half-a-dozen oysters topped with a warm Guinness gratinée. Elsewhere the kitchen stays true to its home country with duck and Armagnac terrine with truffle sauce, lamb chops with a boozy provençale sauce, and breast of duck with a sauce of cognac, honey, lime and sage. Desserts focus on the classics – tarte au citron, tarte aux pommes, crème brûlée and so forth. It should come as no surprise that the wine list never strays over the French border; look for the vins du pays.

Directions: From one-way system 1st L onto Chetenham Mount and 1st R into Mount Parade

HARROGATE, **The Bistro**   NEW

1 Montpellier Mews HG1 2TG
Map 8: SE35
Tel: 01423 530708
Fax: 01423 567000
Telephone for details

Situated in an elegant mews complex, this small, cleanly designed restaurant attracts both well-heeled lunchtime shoppers and business suits from the nearby conference and exhibition centre. Within, polished wooded flooring, blue-stained chairs with pale raffia seating and yellow tablecloths help create a warm Mediterranean feel. This extends to the modern menus, but is combined with a reworking of traditional British influences and good use of Far Eastern flavourings. Our inspector enjoyed tartare of 'fresh' red mullet on a 'lovely, almost sweet' pepper purée garnished with deep-fried squid, thinly-sliced calves' liver topped with pancetta and buttered spinach and served with an intense Madeira sauce and colcannon. The meal rounded off with a sound crème brûlée.

Directions: Town centre, near Exhibition Centre

HARROGATE, Boar's Head Hotel

Ripley HG3 3AY
Map 8: SE35
Tel: 01423 771888
Fax: 01423 771509
Chef: Steven Chesnutt
Owner: Sir Thomas Ingilby
Cost: Fixed-price L £17.50 (3 courses)/D £27.50 (3 courses). H/wine £9.95
Times: Noon-last L 2pm/7pm-last D 9.30pm
Additional: Bar food; Sunday L; No children under 10; ◐ dishes
Seats: 45
Smoking: No-smoking area
Accommodation: 25 en suite
Credit cards: 🔲 🔳 🔳 🔳 🔳 ◐

Members of the Ingilby dynasty have been incumbents at Ripley for centuries and they still own the nearby castle, as well as this rather patrician country house hotel. Antiques and portraits reinforce the family connection (pride of place goes to a likeness of Sir William Amcotts Ingilby, who rebuilt Ripley in the 1830s in the style of a model estate village in Alsace-Lorraine). Chef Steven Chesnutt and his young brigade are starting to cook up a storm here, and their fixed-price menus are full of invention and vivid modern ideas. An array of home-baked speciality breads and classy amuse-gueules set the scene. Seared salmon on a gribiche potato cake with a liquor of olive oil and parsley started an inspection dinner in fine style. After that, braised Yorkshire lamb shank with bags of flavour was served on mustard creamed potatoes with port and rosemary sauce. As a finale, there was a layered dark chocolate terrine with a butterscotch sauce, although the presence of a tiny 'after eight mint' in the centre seemed rather bemusing. Sir Thomas Ingilby's personal passion for wine shows up in his realistically priced 200-strong list.

Directions: On A61, 3 miles N of Harrogate

HARROGATE, Dusty Miller

Low-Laithe Summerbridge HG3 4BU
Map 8: SE35
Tel: 01423 780837
Fax: 01423 780065
Chef: Brian Dennison
Owners: Brian & Elizabeth Dennison
Cost: Alc £31, fixed-price D £24. H/wine £9.90
Times: D only, 7pm-last D 11pm. Closed Sun, Mon, 25-26 Dec, 1 Jan, 2 wks Aug
Additional: No children under 9; ◐ dishes
Seats: 32. Private dining room 14
Credit cards: 🔲 🔳 🔳

Brian Dennison trained in the classical style, yet has adapted the light modern interpretation to suit his skills. He has been chef/patron here for about fourteen years and is well settled into this former nineteenth-century ale house with its series of cosy, intimate rooms. The 'Proprietors' Menu' offers a simple choice of two at each course and could include Whitby lobster mayonnaise, coq-au-vin, and passionfruit bavarois, whilst the 'Dinner Menu' takes in the likes of shellfish bisque, king scallops au gratin, and sauté lamb's kidneys with Madeira sauce, or English fillet of beef with béarnaise sauce. A January dinner kicked off with smoked Whitby cod with Cheddar cheese and spinach ('a very hearty portion'). The main course proved even heartier. A trio of game – a seared noisette of venison, a very gamey breast of pheasant, and a breast of duck – with spicy cabbage and a wine sauce came with simple, well-prepared mange-touts, red cabbage with raisins, and boiled potatoes in their skins. Tarte Tatin with home-made vanilla ice cream finished the meal. The wine list is well put together.

Directions: Situated on B6165, 10 miles from Harrogate

HARROGATE, Grundy's Restaurant

*Decor is rich in shades of pink, music is piped classical, and there is
a nice, intimate atmosphere. Chris Grundy waits, Val cooks an
ambitious modern menu, and all is done alone. Praise for puff
pastry parcels of tuna, chilli and water chestnut, guinea fowl braised
in Madeira with walnuts and grapes, and summer pudding with
crème fraîche.*

Additional: Children welcome; ☘ dishes
Smoking: No pipes & cigars. **Credit cards:** ▆ ▆ ▆ ▆ ▆

Directions: From Leeds (A61) turn R at traffic lights in town
centre, next lights R; 50 yds on R

21 Cheltenham Crescent HG1 1DH
Map 8: SE35
Tel: 01423 502610
Fax: 01423 502617
Chef: Val Grundy
Owners: Val & Chris Grundy
Cost: *Alc* £20. Fixed-price D £13.50.
☺ H/wine £8.95.
Times: D only, 6.30pm-10pm.
Closed Sun, 2wks Jan- Feb, 2 wks Jul-
Aug, Bh Mon

HARROGATE,
Harrogate Brasserie Hotel

*Centrally situated close to the shops and conference centre, this
lively, modern bar and hotel serves value-for-money dishes in the
brasserie-style restaurant. The varied blackboard menu may list
Caesar salad, pork fillet en croûte with apple and Calvados sauce,
and white chocolate torte for pudding.*

Smoking: No pipes & cigars
Accommodation: 13 en suite. **Credit cards:** ▆ ▆ ▆ ▆ ▆

Directions: In town centre, 500m from railway station, behind
theatre

28-30 Cheltenham Parade HG1 1DB
Map 8: SE35
Tel: 01423 505041
Fax: 01423 530920
Chef: Brian Dale
Owners: Richard & Amanda Finney
Cost: *Alc* £18, fixed-price L&D
£11.50. ☺ H/wine £8.75.
Times: Last L 2pm/last D 10pm.
Closed L Sun, 26 Dec
Additional: Bar meals L;
Children welcome; ☘ dishes

HARROGATE, Old Swan Hotel ✿

*Agatha Christie chose to 'disappear' here in 1926, and this long-
established hotel is proud of its famous connections. Meals are
served in the ornate Wedgwood Room or the more intimate Library
Restaurant. Dishes sampled have included terrine of pheasant and
guinea fowl, fillet of beef topped with tomato, capsicum and
coriander duxelle, and blackberry and pear flan.*

Smoking: No-smoking area in dining room
Accommodation: 136 en suite. **Credit cards:** ▆ ▆ ▆ ▆ ▆ ▆

Directions: Town centre near junction of Swan Road and York
Road

Swan Road HG1 2SR
Map 8: SE35
Tel: 01423 500055
Fax: 01423 501154
Chef: Trevor Whitehead
Owner: MacDonald Hotels
Cost: *Alc* £25, fixed-price D £19. ☺
H/wine £11.50.
Times: Last L 2pm/D 10pm
Additional: Bar food; Sunday L;
Children welcome; ☘ dishes

HARROGATE,
Rudding Park House

*Part of a conference-orientated complex, with the modern brasserie-
style restaurant serving modern dishes such as griddled sea scallops
with angel hair pasta and spicy red pepper sauce, and baked lamb
rump with garlic, rosemary and roasted vegetables.*

Smoking: No-smoking area; No pipes & cigars; air conditioning
Accommodation: 50 en suite. **Credit cards:** ▆ ▆ ▆ ▆ ▆

Directions: 3 miles S of Harrogate, just off the A658 linking the
A61 from Leeds to the A59 York road

Follifoot HG3 1JH
Map 8: SE35
Tel: 01423 871350
Fax: 01423 872286
Chef: David Parker
Owner: Simon Mackaness
Cost: *Alc* £15, fixed-price L £16/D
£20. ☺
Times: Last L 2pm/last D 10.30pm
Additional: Bar meals L; Sunday L;
Children welcome; ☘ dishes

HARROGATE, Studley Hotel ❀

Swan Road HG1 2SE
Map 8: SE35
Tel: 01423 560425
Fax: 01423 530967
Chef: Michel Boulineau
Owner: Guy Dilasser
Cost: Fixed-price D £16.50. ☺
H/wine £9.95.
Times: Last L 1.45pm/D 10pm
Additional: Bar meals L; Sunday L;
Children welcome; ❹ dishes
Smoking: No pipes & cigars in dining
room; air-conditioning
Accommodation: 36 en suite
Credit cards: 💳 💳 💳 💳 💳 💳

*Hospitable, well-run hotel conveniently placed for Valley Gardens
and the town centre. Sound cooking in Le Breton Restaurant. Value-
for-money menus list chargrilled dishes such as duck breast with
green peppercorn and port sauce, and more classical mustard-glazed
beef fillet with red wine jus.*

Directions: Close to Conference Centre, near the entrance to
Valley Gardens

HARROGATE, The White House ❀❀

10 Park Parade HG1 5AH
Map 8: SE35
Tel: 01423 501388
Fax: 01423 527973
Chef/Owner: Jennie Foster
Cost: Alc £27.50, fixed-price L
£14.50. H/wine £10.95
Times: 12.30pm-last L 2pm/7.30pm-
last D 9pm. Closed Sun.
Additional: Sun L by arrangement
only; Children welcome;
❹ dishes
Seats: 32. Private dining room 12
Smoking: No smoking in dining room
Accommodation: 10 en suite
Credit cards: 💳 💳 💳 💳 💳

A graceful hotel overlooking splendid gardens, The White
House was built in 1836 by the mayor of Harrogate in the style
of a Venetian villa. Now a restaurant-with-rooms, it is also the
home of chef-owner Jennie Forster, who works tirelessly to
produce excellent dishes from the imaginative *carte* and set
menus. Typical starters include Cumbrian air-dried ham, with
grilled polenta and Parmesan, or spinach roulade filled with
wild mushrooms, and baby haggis served with neeps and a
whisky cream sauce. Main courses could include breast of duck
with a cream sauce of sherry, lime and ginger, suprême of
chicken stuffed with mascarpone and scented with rosemary,
and for the more adventurous, pan-fried ostrich with orange
and cranberry sauce. Desserts are deeply indulgent; look out
for 'rich and wicked' chocolate torte, with a duo of chocolate
sauce, and warm Yorkshire parkin with butterscotch sauce.

Directions: Opposite Christchurch, parallel with A59 close to
Wetherby/Skipton junction

HELMSLEY, Black Swan

Traditional standards and old-fashioned courtesy are the hallmarks of this long-established hotel. A good choice of modern dishes is available in the dining room. Typical starters include potted shrimps with lemon dressing, chilled orange and yogurt soup, and duck and pistachio nut terrine. Service is professional.

Additional: Sunday L; Bar meals L; Children welcome; ❹ dishes
Smoking: No smoking in dining room
Accommodation: 44 en suite
Credit cards:

Market Place YO6 5BJ
Map 8: SE68
Tel: 01439 770466
Fax: 01439 770174
Chef: Nigel Wright
Owner: Forte Heritage (Granada plc)
Cost: Alc £35, fixed-price L £15/D £26.50. ☺ H/wine £14.
Times: Last L 2pm/D 9pm

Directions: Take A170 from Scarborough or Thirsk; Black Swan is in centre of village, at top end of Market Place

HELMSLEY,
Feversham Arms Hotel ❀

Old coaching inn with a menu of popular favourites. Egg and prawn cocktail, pâté and toast, grilled lemon sole with cream and herbs, and rack of lamb with mint gravy, are amongst a choice that will suit most tastes.

Additional: Bar snacks; Sunday L (12.15pm-1.30pm); No children under 8; ❹ dishes
Smoking: No smoking in dining room
Accommodation: 18 en suite
Credit cards:

1 High Street YO6 5AG
Map 8: SE68
Tel: 01439 770766
Fax: 01439 770346
Chefs: Linda Barker, Richard Simms
Owner: Rowan de Aragues
Cost: Fixed-price D £20. ☺ H/wine £10.
Times: D only, 7pm-8.45pm
Closed Jan

Directions: 200 yds N of Market Place

HELMSLEY, Star Inn ❀❀

NEW

A fourteenth-century thatched pub that was once used as a resting place for monks on their way to York Minster and other abbeys in north Yorkshire. These days the Star is home to some up-to-the-minute cooking from Andrew Pern who is strong on modern British dishes such as breast of chicken stuffed with goats cheese and served with creamed leeks and smoked bacon, venison casserole flavoured with juniper berries and ginger wine, and grilled queen scallops and smoked salmon with toasted pine nuts. A meal in March included provençale fish soup with aïoli and croutons, pan-fried medallions of beef with braised oxtail, mange-touts and red cabbage, and to finish, a firm but moist bread-and-butter pudding, topped with caramelised bananas. There is a fine wine list, not very long but packed with good house wines, and several by the glass or half-bottle.

Harome YO6 5JE
Map 8: SE68
Tel: 01439 770397
Chef: Andrew Pern
Owners: Andrew & Jacquie Pern
Cost: Alc £19.50. H/wine £10. ☺
Times: 11.30-last L 2.45pm/6.30pm-last D 10.45pm (Sun noon-6pm). Closed D Mon, 2 wks in Jan
Additional: Sunday L; Bar meals; Children welcome; ❹ dishes
Seats: 30
Smoking: No smoking in dining room
Credit cards:

Directions: 3 miles SE of A170, first building in village

HETTON, Angel Inn ❀❀

This North Yorkshire phenomenon is held fast in a centuries-old drovers' pub seemingly off the beaten track – although the crowds who descend from far and wide clearly know exactly where it is. Much interest centres on the bar-cum-brasserie where there's real ale and the pub's magnificent wine list (with

Skipton BD23 6LT
Map 7: SO95
Tel: 01756 730263
Fax: 01756 730363
Chef: John Topham
Owners: Denis Watkins, Julie Watkins, John Topham

Angel Inn

Cost: Fixed-price L £18.50/D £26.50. ☺ H/wine £9.45.
Times: Noon-last L 2 pm/7pm-last D 9.30pm.
Additional: Bar food; Sunday L; Children welcome; dishes
Seats: 54
Smoking: No-smoking area in dining room
Credit cards:

no fewer than two dozen by the glass). The blackboard menu is straight out of the cosmopolitan world of '90s cuisine: rustic fish soup, 'little moneybags' of seafood in filo pastry, and terrine of Tuscan vegetables. Elsewhere you are likely to encounter terrine of ham shank and foie gras, plentiful pasta and more substantial offerings like confit of duck on Normandy red cabbage with orange and thyme sauce. To finish, try Jaffa cake pudding which, needless to say, is a world away from the famous commercial biscuit. There's a more formal evening restaurant.

Directions: In village centre, B6265 (Rylestone) from Skipton bypass

HOVINGHAM,

Worsley Arms Hotel

York YO6 4LA
Map 8: SE67
Tel: 01653 628234
Fax: 01653 628130
Chef: Andrew Jones
Owners: Euan & Debbi Rodger
Cost: *Alc* £27.50, fixed-price L £15 (3courses)/D £23 (4 courses). ☺ H/wine £11.
Times: Noon-last L 2pm/7pm-last D 9.30pm
Additional: Bar food; Sunday L; Children welcome; dishes
Seats: 50. Private dining room 30. Jacket and tie preferred

This civilised, 150-year-old country hotel takes its name from the Duchess of Kent's family, who own the Hovingham Estate. The kitchen has undoubted technical and presentation skills, note a marinated haunch of venison with celeriac, fresh horseradish and beetroot chips that certainly looks the business. The dining room *carte* offers a good choice, from cream of snow pea and fresh coriander soup with roast langoustines, to breast of Gressingham duck with leeks, wild mushrooms and local honey, and pan-fried crispy cod with fresh mussels and clams. The high standard of cooking also extends to the less formal Cricketers Bar and Bistro, decorated with old sporting photos. Our inspector had a particularly good innings with a lunch of pressed terrine of Yorkshire smoked salmon with fresh spinach flavoured with nutmeg and duck confit, followed by super cod, steamed mussels and saffron mash.

Directions: On B1257 midway between Malton and Helmsley

Smoking: No smoking in dining room
Accommodation: 18 en suite
Credit cards: ▬ ▧ ▨ ▧ ▨ ▨

KNARESBOROUGH, Carriages

Good, honest cooking in this beamed, rustic brasserie/wine bar. Choose excellent Thai fishcakes and chicken satay with crunchy peanut sauce for a touch of the Pacific Rim, or stay in modern British mode with twice cooked goat's cheese soufflé with pesto and Mediterranean vegetables, and pan-fried duck breast marinated in orange and mulberry vinegar.

Smoking: No-smoking area; no cigars or pipes
Credit cards: ▬ ▧ ▨ ▧ ▨ ▨

Directions: On the A59 York to Harrogate Road, in the town centre

89 High Street HG5 0HL
Map 8: SE35
Tel: 01423 867041
Chef: Bruce Gray
Owners: Bruce Gray, Jon Holder
Cost: Alc £15. H/wine £7.25. ☺
Times: Last L 2.30pm/last D 9.30pm. Closed Sun, Mon, early Jan
Additional: Bar food L; Sunday L (summer only); Children welcome; ✪ dishes

KNARESBOROUGH,
Dower House Hotel

Fine hospitality and quality British cooking make this Jacobean hotel a great place to stay. A typical winter meal might start with fresh baked brioche with north coast fish braised in tarragon cream, and continue with roast loin of pork with apple and blackberry stew and Calvados gravy.

Smoking: No smoking in dining room
Accommodation: 32 en suite
Credit cards: ▬ ▧ ▨ ▨ ▨

Directions: At Harrogate end of Knaresborough High Street

Bond End HG5 9AL
Map 8: SE35
Tel: 01423 863302
Fax: 01423 867665
Chef: Howard Cansfield
Cost: Fixed-price D £19.50. ☺ H/wine £8.50.
Times: D only, 7pm-9.15pm
Additional: Sunday L (noon-3pm); Bar meals L; Children welcome; ✪ dishes

KNARESBOROUGH,
General Tarleton Inn   NEW

Denis Watkins and John Topham from the Angel Inn, Hetton (see entry) took over and set about developing this eighteenth-century coaching inn. The philosophy is much the same in both places: one brasserie-style menu is served throughout, orders are taken at the bar, staff are casual but courteous. Chef James O'Conner learned his trade at Hetton and there are familiar echoes across the repertoire. The kitchen, however, is prepared to go its own way. Our inspector drooled over a 'wonderful' fish soup with rouille and Gruyère ('as close to a bouillabaisse as I have seen here'). Also impressive were breast of chicken stuffed with garlic wrapped in smoked ham and served on vibrant green spinach with a colourful oven-baked tomato with fried basil, and a clever warm chocolate mousse with mango sorbet to finish. A dozen or so wines by the glass are chalked on a board, and the printed list reads well.

Directions: A1M/Boroughbridge Junction. Follow A6065 (Knaresborough) for 3 miles to Ferrensby

Boroughbridge Road
Ferrensby HG5 0QB
Map 8: SE35
Tel: 01423 340284
Fax: 01423 340288
Chef: James O'Conner
Owners: Mr Watkins, Mr Topham
Cost: Alc £18. H/wine £9.45
Times: Noon-last L 2pm/6pm-last D 9.30pm
Additional: Bar meals; Sunday L; ✪ dishes
Seats: 34. Private dining room 34
Smoking: No smoking in dining room
Accommodation: 15 en suite
Credit cards: ▬ ▧ ▨

LEYBURN, Foresters Arms ❀

Ambitious pub food is the order of the day in this re-vamped seventeenth-century Dales inn. The beams and stone floors are old, but the menu promises modern ideas such as leek and blue cheese strudel with local black pudding, grilled grey mullet with sautéed scallops and tarragon, and banana parfait with chocolate sorbet.

Smoking: No smoking in dining room
Accommodation: 3 en suite. **Credit cards:** ▨ ▨ ▨ ▨

Directions: Off the A684, 5 miles S of Leyburn

Carlton-in-Coverdale DL8 4BB
Map 7: SE19
Tel/Fax: 01969 640272
Chef/Owner: B K Higginbotham
Cost: *Alc* £25. H/wine £8.95. ☺
Times: Last L 2pm/D 9pm.
Closed D Sun, Mon, 2 weeks Jan
Additional: Sunday L; Bar meals;
Children welcome; ❹ dishes

MALTON,
Burythorpe House Hotel ❀

Family-run Georgian country residence set in its own grounds. Meals are served in the elegantly panelled dining room where Mrs Austin's cooking is noted for its consistency. Expect dishes such as duck liver en brioche with Vermouth sauce, grilled fillet of sea bass with tomato, Pernod and cream sauce, and escalope of veal Cordon Bleu.

Additional: No children under 5; ❹ dishes
Smoking: No pipes & cigars; air conditioning
Accommodation: 11 en suite. **Credit cards:** ▨ ▨ ▨ ▨

Directions: Edge of Burythorpe village, 4 miles S of Malton

Burythorpe YO1 9LB
Map 8: SE77
Tel: 01653 658200
Fax: 01653 658204
Chef/Owners: Mr & Mrs T Austin
Cost: *Alc* £18, fixed price L £11/D
£16. ☺ H/wine £9.
Times: L by prior arrangement/7pm-
9.30pm

MALTON, Newstead Grange ❀

A traditional country house hotel run quietly by owners who made hotel-keeping their second profession, having retired from teaching. Pat Williams offers a four-course, no-choice Cordon Bleu-style dinner: tomato and basil soup, fillets of pork with a white wine sauce and banana flambé with orange and a side dish of Greek-style yogurt.

Additional: No children under 11;
❹ dishes
Smoking: No smoking in dining room
Accommodation: 8 en suite. **Credit cards:** ▨ ▨

Directions: On the Beverley Road

Norton YO17 9PJ
Map 8: SE77
Tel: 01653 692502
Fax: 01653 696951
Chef: Pat Williams
Owners: Paul & Pat Williams
Cost: Fixed-price D £16.50. ☺
H/wine £8.25.
Times: D only 7.30- 7.45pm.
Closed mid Nov-mid Feb

MARKINGTON, Hob Green Hotel ❀

A charming country house set in 800 acres of woodland and fields in the rolling Dales. Cooking is modern English with an occasional French accent. Typical dishes from the daily-changing menu include the traditional roast turkey with chestnut stuffing, bread sauce and chipolata, and poached halibut steak bonne femme.

Additional: Sunday L (noon-1.45pm); Bar meals L;
Children welcome; ❹ dishes
Smoking: No cigars or pipes
Accommodation: 12 en suite. **Credit cards:** ▨ ▨ ▨ ▨ ▨

Directions: One mile W of village off A61

Harrogate HG3 3PJ
Map 8: SE26
Tel: 01423 770031
Fax: 01423 771589
Chefs: Andrew Brown, Chris Taylor
Owner: Michael Hutchinson
Cost: *Alc* £21. H/wine £9.85. ☺
Times: D only 7pm-9.30pm

MIDDLEHAM,
Millers House Hotel ⚜

A *finely restored hotel just off the cobbled market square with a restaurant overlooking a pretty walled garden and noted for stylish, imaginative cooking. A meal in November produced excellent pan-fried fillets of fallow deer in a silky Madeira sauce, as well as a good starter of pheasant and pickled walnut terrine.*

Additional: No children under 10; 🍴 dishes
Smoking: No smoking in dining room
Accommodation: 7 en suite
Credit cards: ▬ ▭ ▰ 🗓

Directions: A1 & A684 (Bedale & Leyburn). At Leyburn turn L to Middleham

DL8 4NR
Map 7: SE18
Tel: 01969 622630
Fax: 01969 623570
Chefs: Chris Seal, Judith Sunderland
Owners: Crossley & Judith Sunderland
Cost: Fixed-price D £19.50. ☺
H/wine £5.15
Times: D only, 7pm-8.30pm.

MIDDLEHAM,
Waterford House ⚜⚜

Kirkgate DL8 4PG
Map 7: SE18
Tel: 01969 622090
Fax: 01969 624020
Chef: Everyl M Madell
Owners: Everyl & Brian Madell
Cost: Alc £25, fixed-price L £17.50/D £19.50. ☺ H/wine £9-£11.
Times: 12.30pm-last L 2.30pm/7.30pm-last D 9.30pm
Additional: Sunday L; Children welcome; 🍴 dishes
Seats: 20
Smoking: No smoking in dining room
Accommodation: 5 en suite
Credit cards: ▬ ▭ ▰ 🗓

This is a very special restaurant-with-rooms: a period house close to the market square, filled to the rafters with antiques and treasures of all sorts, some seriously good food, a superb collection of wines, and friendly house-guest atmosphere. The menu changes daily. Starters range from moules marinière to salad niçoise with fresh tuna, and there's an unusual York ham and banana gratin in a Mornay sauce. Our inspector claimed never to have had a more tender fillet of beef, Yorkshire of course, pan-fried with wild mushrooms and red wine sauce, but other typical dishes might include roast duckling (for two) with spiced apricot, plum and Cointreau sauce, roast partridge with smoked bacon, Muscat grape and Barsac sauce, and roast quail with black cherry and Pineau des Charentes sauce. Meat, poultry and game dominate the main courses, but there is always one fish dish such as salmon and halibut fillet with beurre blanc sauce served with tagliatelle. As well as French and English cheeses, desserts include home-made lemon and lime tart, tiramisu, and Madeira trifle.

Directions: Just off Market Square

MIDDLESBROUGH,
The Purple Onion

80 Corporation Road TS1 2RF
Map 8: NZ41
Tel: 01642 222250
Fax: 01642 248088
Chefs: Graeme Benn, Massimo
Gecero, Tony Chapman
Owners: John McCoy, Bruno McCoy
Cost: Alc £25. H/wine £10.95. ☺
Times: Noon-3pm/D from 6.30pm.
Closed D Sun, 25-25 Dec, 1 Jan
Additional: Sunday L;
Children welcome; ♨ dishes
Seats: 96
Smoking: no-smoking area;
air conditioning
Credit cards: ▉ ▨ ▧ ▨

Anyone who grew up in the north east during the 60s will recall the original Purple Onion, the hottest place around and a spawning ground for wannabe rock stars. Its reincarnation is housed in a restored Victorian warehouse. Father and son, John and Bruno McCoy, have imbued the place with fantastic atmosphere. The fact that they are related to the McCoys of Staddlebridge (see entry) may explain their fondness for quirky decor: a glorious mish-mash of 'fin de siècle' mirrors, lamps and antiques, but there's nothing frivolous about what goes on in the open kitchen. The menu strikes exactly the right contemporary note with spicy San Francisco fish soup, or grilled duck breast with a zesty sauce of ginger, sweet peppers and orange. A test meal yielded palpably fresh seafood risotto with an intense saffron sauce, before seared loin of lamb with roasted aubergine, a gâteau of puréed parsnip plus a sauce with baby tomatoes and thyme. To finish, chocolate tart with coffee bean sauce and vanilla ice cream.

Directions: Exit A66 at Hospitality Inn near Riverside Football Stadium. Restaurant centrally located nr Law Courts/Odeon Cinema

---

MOULTON, **Black Bull Inn**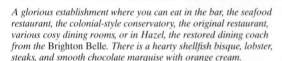

DL10 6QJ
Map 8: NZ20
Tel: 01325 377289
Fax: 01325 377422
Chef: Paul Grundy
Owners: GH, AMC & SC Pagendam
Cost: Alc £25, fixed-price L £14.95.
H/wine £8.50
Times: Last L 2pm/D 10.15pm
Closed Sun, 24 Dec-26 Dec

A glorious establishment where you can eat in the bar, the seafood restaurant, the colonial-style conservatory, the original restaurant, various cosy dining rooms, or in Hazel, the restored dining coach from the Brighton Belle. There is a hearty shellfish bisque, lobster, steaks, and smooth chocolate marquise with orange cream.

Additional: Bar food L; No children under 7; ♨ dishes
Smoking: Air-conditioning
Credit cards: ▉ ▨ ▧ ▨ ▨

Directions: Off A1M, 1 mile S of Scotch Corner

NORTHALLERTON,
Solberge Hall Hotel

Newsby Wiske DL7 9ER
Map 8: SE39
Tel: 01609 779191
Fax: 01609 780472
Chef: Peter Wood
Owners: John & Michael Hollins
Cost: Alc £30, fixed-price L £7.25/D
£21. ☺ H/wine £9.95.
Times: Last L 1.30pm/D 9.15pm
Additional: Sunday L; Bar meals L;
Children welcome; ♨ dishes
Smoking: No smoking in dining room

An attractive Victorian hotel surrounded by glorious countryside. The Garden Room restaurant serves a good range of modern English dishes. Try breast of wood pigeon with avocado slices and port dressing, sautéed mussels with white wine and butterfly prawns, or roulade of pork and spinach with damson and chestnut cream sauce.

Accommodation: 25 en suite. **Credit cards:** ▉ ▨ ▧ ▨ ▨

Directions: 2 miles S of Northallerton, turning R off A167

NUNNINGTON,
Ryedale Lodge Restaurant

YO6 5XB
Map 8: SE67
Tel: 01439 748246
Fax: 01439 748346

Tastefully renovated former railway station, set in open countryside, that's mow a personally-run small country house hotel. Mainly

English cooking with contemporary touches. A typical four-course dinner may include smoked trout terrine, then courgette soup followed by duck with cranberry and onion confit, and tiramisu for dessert.

Smoking: No smoking in dining room
Accommodation: 7 en suite. **Credit cards:** ■ ■

Directions: 1 mile due W of Nunnington village

Chef: Janet Laird
Owners: Jon & Janet Laird
Cost: Fixed-price D £27.75. ☺
H/wine £9.95.
Times: D only, 7.30pm-9pm
Additional: Children welcome;
④ dishes

PATELEY BRIDGE,
Sportsman's Arms

A long-established restaurant offering bold Anglo-French dishes, with the emphasis on fresh fish. Our inspector particularly enjoyed a salmon and bacon tagliatelle with a good white wine sauce, and fried Pateley chicken with garlic mushrooms. The dining room is elegant and comfortable.

Smoking: No smoking in dining room
Accommodation: 7 en suite
Credit cards: ■ ■ ▣

Directions: A1, A59, B6451, B6265. Restaurant is 2 miles N of Pateley Bridge

Wath-in-Nidderdale HG3 5PP
Map 7: SE16
Tel: 01423 711306
Fax: 01423 712524
Chef: Ray Carter
Owners: Ray & Jane Carter
Cost: Alc £25, fixed-price D £21. ☺
H/wine £10.
Times: Last L 2.30pm/D 9.30pm.
Closed 25 Dec
Additional: Sunday L; Bar meals;
Children welcome; ④ dishes

PICKERING, Fox and Hounds

Attractive, stone-built eighteenth-century inn. Expect black pudding with tomato, chive and grain mustard sauce, roast halibut with celeriac and a lemon and ginger sauce, or magret of duck breast with black cherry and rosemary sauce, and rum and fruit pudding parfait with maple syrup for dessert.

Smoking: No smoking in dining room
Accommodation: 10 en suite
Credit cards: ■ ■ ▣

Directions: In centre of Sinnington, 300 yards off A170 between Pickering and Helmsley

Sinnington YO6 6SQ
Map 8: SE78
Tel: 01751 431577
Fax: 01751 432791
Chef: Duncan Lowe
Owners: Mr & Mrs A Stephens
Cost: Alc £20, fixed-price L&D £19.
☺ H/wine £9.
Times: Last L 2pm/last D 9pm
Additional: Bar food; Sunday L;
Children welcome; ④ dishes

RAMSGILL, Yorke Arms NEW

Frances and Gerald Atkins certainly have that roving instinct: after nestling in the Chilterns, they trekked off to Aberfeldy in Scotland, then back to London – where they made a name for themselves at Shaw's in Old Brompton Road. Now they have moved north again, to this converted pub in a wild part of the Dales. In a traditional setting of beams and candlelight, Frances offers a range of accomplished dishes in the modern style. An inspection began well with a warm salad of shredded duck on rocket leaves with a perfect lemon and grapefruit dressing before tender, 'sticky' lamb shank with bags of flavour sitting on a light pesto mash and fresh leeks. The clear simple presentation carried through to the dessert – in this case a home-made cheesecake served with a compote of cherries and plums.

Directions: Take B6265 from Ripon. Turn R in Pateley Bridge for Ramsgill

Pateley Bridge HG3 5RL
Map 7: SE17
Tel: 01423 755243
Fax: 01423 755330
Telephone for details

ROSEDALE ABBEY,
Milburn Arms Hotel

Pickering YO18 8RA
Map 8: SE78
Tel/Fax: 01751 417312
Chef: Richard Guitton
Owners: Terry & Joan Bentley
Cost: *Alc* £24. H/wine £9.50. ☺
Times: 7pm-last D 9.30pm.
Closed 25 Dec
Additional: Bar food;
Sunday lunch (noon-2.15pm)
Seats: 64.
Smoking: No smoking in dining room;
air-conditioning
Accommodation: 11 en suite
Credit cards: 🃏

The Milburn Arms dates from the fifteenth century, has the
warm atmosphere of an inn, the comforts of a country hotel,
and a sound reputation for food. A feeling of well-being
pervades the place, guests appear reluctant to leave. An
autumn inspection dinner in the split-level Priory Restaurant,
revealed a kitchen that could turn out a good spinach and
bacon soup, queenie scallops in the shell topped with a light
tomato and onion sauce, and baked monkfish tails on a bed of
tagliatelle with a light, creamy lemon and chive sauce. Crème
brûlée made a strong finish. Bread comes from the local bakery,
basil, nut or sun-dried tomato, vegetables are full of flavour,
presented plainly and simply, and service is willing to please.
The spacious, beamed bar is full of 'old world charm' and offers
a further choice of food in a more informal atmosphere.

Directions: In village centre, 3 miles W of A170 at Pickering

SCARBOROUGH, **Wrea Head**

Scalby YO13 0PB
Map 8: TA08
Tel: 01723 378211
Fax: 01723 371780
Chef: John Halton
Owner: Four Seasons
Cost: *Alc* £25, fixed-price L £12.50/D
£22.50. H/wine £11.95.
Times: Last L 1.45pm/D 9.15pm
Additional: Bar food L; Sunday L;
Children welcome; ◑ dishes
Smoking: No smoking in dining room
Accommodation: 21 en suite
Credit cards: 🃏

*Charming Victorian country house standing in 14 acres of well-
tended grounds. The elegant dining room is the perfect setting for
carefully prepared food. At inspection a delightfully light avocado
and cheese tart was followed by fresh roast cod served on a leek and
bacon champ with grain mustard sauce.*

Directions: Take A171 N from Scarborough, past Scalby village
until hotel is signposted

SKIPTON,

Hanover International Hotel

An impressive stone-built hotel on the edge of town. The Waterside Restaurant makes the most of a delightful position next to the canal and the rolling hills in the background. A well reported meal took in a light salmon parfait, pork with a good morel sauce, and an interesting Turkish crème caramel.

Times: Last L 2pm/last D 10pm. Closed L Sat
Additional: Sunday L; Bar meals; Children welcome; dishes
Smoking: No smoking in dining room
Accommodation: 75 en suite
Credit cards: ■ ▓ ▓ ▓ ⚊ ⚊

Keighley Road Snaygill
BD23 2TA
Map 7: SD49
Tel: 01756 700100
Fax: 01756 700107
Chef: Gavin Horton
Owner: Hanover International Hotels
Cost: Alc £20, fixed-price L £10/D £15. ☺ H/wine £9.50.

Directions: From M62/J26 onto M606, follow signs for A650 (Keighley), then A629 (Skipton). Hotel 1 mile S of town centre

STADDLEBRIDGE,

McCoys (Tontine Inn) ✿✿

This idiosyncratic feature of the north-country scene is a set-up of two halves. Downstairs in the stone-floored, low-ceilinged bistro, above is the more traditional restaurant. The latter is only open Thursday, Friday and Saturday, but virtually identical menus are served in both. Reading what is on offer you might think you were in London rather than Yorkshire: crispy magret of duck with a salad of chicory, charred celery, fennel and red pepper with spicy hot plum sauce, or herb-roasted rump of lamb with Dijon mustard, braised Savoy cabbage, puréed pulses and tarragon sauce, for example. The same cosmopolitan approach is applied to fish – as in turbot with Chinese leaves and deep-fried ginger or cod on a bed of spinach with a quenelle of brandade, balsamic vinegar and tomato dressing. This is vibrant contemporary stuff. Our inspector found plenty to impress in a meal that included succulent king scallops with smoked bacon, herb crust and garlic vinaigrette as well as roast squab on a rösti with puréed swede and foie gras sauce – a dish of accurate and distinctive flavours. To finish there might be raspberry charlotte with raspberry purée or crêpe San Lorenzo dusted with Amaretti and spiked with a dose of Grand Marnier that is likely to 'hit you in the face'. The wine list keeps pace, with its serious contingent of quality bins at keen prices.

Northallerton DL6 3JB
Map 8: SE49
Tel: 01609 882671
Fax: 01609 882660
Chef: Tom McCoy
Owners: McCoy Brothers
Cost: £35. H/wine £12.95. ☺
Times: Noon-last L 2pm (Bistro).7pm-last D 10pm. (Restaurant D Thu, Fri, Sat only). Closed 25-26 Dec, 1 Jan
Additional: Bar food; Sunday L; Children welcome; ⚫ dishes
Seats: 60. Private dining room 30
Smoking: Air-conditioning
Accommodation: 6 en suite
Credit cards: ■ ▓ ▓ ▓ ⚊ ⚊

Directions: At the junction of the A19 & A172

Our inspectors never book in the name of the AA. They disclose their identity only after the bill has been paid.

THIRSK, Sheppard's Hotel

Front Street YO7 1JF
Map 8: SE48
Tel: 01845 523655
Fax: 01845 524720
Chef: William C Murray
Owners: Roy and Olga Sheppard
Cost: *Alc* £26 (Bistro £16.75). ☺
H/wine £10.50
Times: Last L 2pm/last D 10pm.
Restaurant closed Sun, Mon, 1st wk
Jan
Additional: Bar food L; Sunday L;
Children welcome; ⑤ dishes
Smoking: No pipes and cigars in
restaurant
Accommodation: 8 en suite
Credit cards: ■ ☶ ☴ ▣

*Former farmhouse, now a friendly, family-run hotel, that has been
carefully extended to provide comfortable accommodation, a cheery
bistro and a more formal galleried restaurant. Typical dishes range
from seafood hotpot to herb-crusted lamb with minted hollandaise,
and lobster thermidor.*

Directions: 0.5 mile S of Thirsk market place, off A61
Thirsk/Ripon road towards Sowerby

WHITBY, Larpool Hall Hotel ❀ NEW

*Classical French cooking in an intimate and civilised Georgian
house overlooking the Esk Valley. Meals in the Dales restaurant
might feature smoked salmon mousse, baked halibut with dry
Martini sauce and local game with a pink peppercorn and
mushroom jus followed by, say, dark chocolate terrine.*

Times: Noon- last L 1.45pm/7pm-last D 9pm. Closed L Sun
Additional: Children welcome; ⑤ dishes
Smoking: No smoking in dining room
Accommodation: 20 en suite
Credit cards: ■ ☶ ☷ ☴ ▣ ▢

Larpool Drive Larpool Lane
YO22 4ND
Map 8: NZ81
Tel: 01947 602737
Fax: 01947 820204
Chef: Tony Campbell
Owners: Keith and Electra Robinson
Cost: *Alc* £19.95, fixed-price D
£19.95 (3 courses). ☺ H/wine £8.95.

Directions: Off A171 (Scarborough). Hotel is on R over River
Esk

YARM, Judges Hotel ❀ NEW

*Beautifully restored country mansion set in 22 acres of parkland.
The stylish restaurant, with conservatory extension, overlooks the
gardens and features good modern cooking. A typical meal may
include Whitby fish soup, followed by chicken with spinach mousse
and saffron sauce, and tarte Tatin to finish.*

Additional: Sunday L; Bar meals L; Children welcome; ⑤ dishes
Smoking: No smoking in dining room
Accommodation: 21 en suite
Credit cards: ■ ☶ ☷ ☴ ▣ ▢

Kirklevington TS15 9LW
Map 8: NZ41
Tel: 01642 789000
Fax: 01642 782878
Chef: Jason Moore
Owner: Michael Downs
Cost: *Alc* £29.65, fixed-price L
£12.95/D £22.50 (5 courses). ☺
H/wine £10.95.
Times: Last L 2pm/D 9.45pm.
Closed L Sat

Directions: From A69 take A67 towards Kirklevington, hotel
1.5m on left.

YORK, Ambassador

Popular, elegantly furnished Georgian town house, convenient for the city centre and racecourse, offering a relaxed atmosphere and sound British cooking. Well executed dishes may include watercress roulade, fresh hake topped with Welsh rarebit, and chocolate, rum and raisin cheesecake.

Smoking: No pipes & cigars
Accommodation: 25 en suite. **Credit cards:** 🔲 🔲 🔲 🔲 🔲 🔲

Directions: 5 minutes walk from city centre, near junction of A1036 and A59

125 The Mount YO2 2DA
Map 8: SE65
Tel: 01904 641316
Fax: 01904 640259
Chef: Alexandra Trenholme
Cost: Alc £25, fixed-price £19.50. ☺
H/wine £11.50.
Times: Noon-1.30pm/6.30pm-last D 9.30pm. Closed L Sun
Additional: Bar meals L; Children welcome; 🍴 dishes

YORK, Dean Court Hotel

Duncombe Place YO1 2EF
Map 8: SE65
Tel: 01904 625082
Fax: 01904 620305
Chef: Peter Brown
Cost: Fixed-price L from £11/ D £21.50. ☺ H/wine £9.95.
Times: Last L 2pm/last D 9.30pm
Additional: Bar food; Sunday L; No children under 5 at D; 🍴 dishes
Smoking: No-smoking area
Accommodation: 40 en suite
Credit cards: 🔲 🔲 🔲 🔲 🔲

Directions: City centre, directly opposite York Minster

Hospitable, well-run hotel in an enviable position directly opposite York Minster. Ambitious modern cooking takes in chilled salad of red mullet with rosemary scented queen scallops, pan-fried breast of wood pigeon with beetroot, apple and port jus or medallions of pork with green pea fritters and black pepper cream sauce.

YORK, The Grange Hotel

1 Clifton YO3 6AA
Map 8: SE65
Tel: 01904 644744
Fax: 01904 612453
Chef: Michael Whiteley
Owner: Jeremy Cassel
Cost: Alc £25. Fixed-price L £12.50. D £23. ☺ H/wine £10.
Times: Last L 2pm/last D 10pm. Closed L Sat, D Sun
Additional: Bar food; Sunday L; children welcome; 🍴 dishes
Accommodation: 30 en suite
Credit cards: 🔲 🔲 🔲 🔲 🔲

Delightful period town house, just a few minutes walk from the town centre. The Ivy Restaurant serves modern British cooking, while fans of seafood can eat in the smart 'Dom Ruinart' seafood bar, where a short carte features dishes such as pan-fried sea bass with lime and tomato casserole, and smoked haddock with poached egg.

Directions: 400 yds to N of city walls on A19

YORK, Kilima Hotel

Originally a Victorian rectory, now a comfortable hotel within easy reach of the city centre. The restaurant occupies the cellar, the menu changes weekly. Expect grilled black pudding topped with poached egg, poached fillets of plaice with hollandaise and lamb cutlets in breadcrumbs with sauce provençale .

Smoking: No smoking in dining room
Accommodation: 15 en suite
Credit cards: ▬ ▬ ▬ ▬ ▬ ▬

Directions: On the W side on A59 (Harrogate) road

129 Holgate Street YO2 4DE
Map 8: SE65
Tel: 01904 625787
Fax: 01904 612083
Chef: Christopher Betteridge
Owner: Richard Stables
Cost: Fixed-price L&D £18.95. ☺ H/wine £8.50.
Times: Last L 1.30pm/last D 9.30pm
Additional: Children welcome; ⬤ dishes

YORK, Knavesmire Manor Hotel NEW

Modern British cooking, prepared where possible from local produce, is offered at this hotel restaurant – a late Georgian property overlooking York Racecourse. The new brasserie-style menu includes a well made mushroom soup, pork steak with a light port wine sauce, and summer pudding on a mango coulis.

Smoking: No smoking in dining room
Accommodation: 21 en suite
Credit cards: ▬ ▬ ▬ ▬ ▬ ▬

Directions: A64 to York, then A1036 York-Bishopthorpe leads on to Tadcaster Rd. Hotel on left overlooking racecourse

302 Tadcaster Road YO2 2HE
Map 8: SE65
Tel: 01904 702941
Fax: 01904 709274
Chef: Kenny Noble
Owners: Ian & Margaret Senior
Cost: Alc £18, fixed-price D £12.50. ☺ H/wine £8.
Times: D only 6.30pm-last D 9pm.
Additional: Sunday L (noon-2.30pm); Children welcome; ⬤ dishes

YORK, Melton's Restaurant ⬤⬤

7 Scarcroft Road YO2 1ND
Map 8: SE65
Tel: 01904 634341
Fax: 01904 635115
Chefs: Michael Hjort & T J Drew
Owners: Michael & Lucy Hjort
Cost: Alc £21, fixed-price L £15/D £19.50. ☺ H/wine £10.50
Times: Noon-last L 2pm/5.30pm-last D 10pm. Closed L Mon, D Sun, 24 Dec-14 Jan, 24-31Aug
Additional: Sunday L; Children welcome; ⬤ dishes
Seats: 40. Private dining room 16
Smoking: No-smoking area

The Hjort's converted shop puts on a bright cheery face, with its pastel colour schemes and paintings for sale. It also makes a virtue of value for money with plenty of flexible deals (including an early evening offer of £5 off the set menu for anyone prepared to leave by 7.45pm). The monthly *carte* pays more than lip service to the needs of vegetarians: lightly flashed goat's cheese gnocchi with pesto and tomato makes a fine starter, while mains might include stuffed Mediterranean vegetables with warm couscous salad. The highlight of a recent inspection, however, was a perfect dish of marinated roast monkfish with a duo of sauces – one saffron, the other tomato. Meaty alternatives come in the shape of confit of duck with bitter leaves and a salad of warm Roseval potatoes. To finish, rhubarb baked Alaska surrounded by rhubarb wine syrup is an intriguing idea.

Credit cards: ▆ ▆ ▆ ▆

Directions: From centre head south across Skeldergate Bridge, restaurant opposite Bishopthorpe Road car park

YORK, Middlethorpe Hall ❀❀❀

Bishopthorpe Road YO2 1QB
Map 8: SE65
Tel: 01904 641241
Fax: 01904 620176
Chef: Andrew Wood
Cost: *Alc* £36.95, fixed-price L £12.50/D £26.95. H/wine £12.50
Times: 12.30pm-last L 1.45pm/7pm-last D 9.45pm
Additional: Sunday L; No children under 8; ❹ dishes
Seats: 60. Private dining room 50. Jacket & tie preferred
Smoking: No smoking in dining room
Accommodation: 30 en suite
Credit cards: ▆ ▆ ▆ ▆

It would be hard to imagine a grander or more auspicious setting than this. Middlethorpe is a stupendously restored William III country mansion next to the racecourse and little more than a mile from the centre of York. Outside are beautifully tended grounds complete with ha-has, a walled garden and a little lake, inside you will find antiques, portraits and fine furnishings at every turn. Food is served in either the panelled Oak or Marble dining rooms and there's also a Grill Room for those who want something less formal. Ingredients are seasonal and of the highest quality, and when luxuries are at hand, Andrew Wood employs them judiciously, without diving overboard into oceans of oysters and caviar. A meal taken in February began with good breads and stylish canapés – including smoked duck with red cabbage, deep-fried black pudding and a crisp fishcake. Following that, was a generous slice of foie gras terrine sitting on toasted brioche and surrounded by a ring of corn salad leaves perfumed with truffle essence. The main course consisted of pan-fried fillets of John Dory with a tapenade crust served simply on wilted spinach leaves with sauté potatoes. To finish, a tangy lemon tart with deeply flavoured Pontefract cake ice cream was a novel, if slightly curious combination. A seriously good wine list benefits from worthwhile descriptions that genuinely aid selection and prices throughout are fair. White Burgundy, in particular, offers a broad and representative range. Half-bottles are plentiful.

Signature dishes: Steamed seafood with chillies, lemon and garlic, crispy cabbage and red pepper sauce; boudin of scallops and salmon with saffron risotto and roast courgettes; fillet of Yorkshire lamb, grilled potatoes and tomato jus.

Directions: 1.5 miles S of York, next to the racecourse

YORK, **Mount Royale Hotel** ❀

Run by the Oxtoby family for more than 30 years. The atmosphere is 'country house' and the kitchen is able to produce very proficient dishes. Recent successes from the daily-changing menu have included salted duck breast with orange vinaigrette, followed by seared salmon fillet on a tartare potato cake, then lemon cheesecake.

Seats: 90. Private dining room 16
Smoking: No smoking in dining room
Accommodation: 23 en suite
Credit cards: ▬ ▒ ▒ ▅ 🄳 🄲

The Mount YO2 2DA
Map 8: SE65
Tel: 01904 628856
Fax: 01904 611171
Chef: Karen Brotherton
Owners: The Oxtoby family
Cost: *Alc* £29. H/wine £10.95. ☺
Times: D only, 7pm-last D 9.30pm
Additional: Children welcome;
🍴 dishes

Directions: On The Mount (A1036) leading SW out of the city

YORK, **York Pavilion Hotel** ❀

45 Main Street Fulford YO1 4PJ
Map 8: SE65
Tel: 01904 622099
Fax: 01904 626939
Chef: David Spencer
Owners: Andrew & Irene Cossins
Cost: H/wine £9.95. ☺
Times: Last L 2pm/D 9.30pm
Additional: Sunday L;
Children welcome; 🍴 dishes
Smoking: No-smoking area
Accommodation: 34 en suite
Credit cards: ▬ ▒ ▒ ▅ 🄳 🄲

An attractive Georgian house with well tended gardens. Modern British cooking with a strong Mediterranean slant are offered in the unpretentious dining room. Look out for roast monkfish with red onion and watercress salsa, breast of chicken with Parmesan and roasted red peppers, and chargrilled rump beef with spinach and grilled mushrooms.

Directions: From York city centre head S on A19 (Selby), hotel 2 miles on L

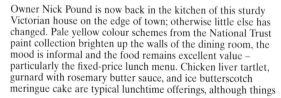

YORKSHIRE SOUTH

BARNSLEY, **Armstrongs** ❀❀

Owner Nick Pound is now back in the kitchen of this sturdy Victorian house on the edge of town; otherwise little else has changed. Pale yellow colour schemes from the National Trust paint collection brighten up the walls of the dining room, the mood is informal and the food remains excellent value – particularly the fixed-price lunch menu. Chicken liver tartlet, gurnard with rosemary butter sauce, and ice butterscotch meringue cake are typical lunchtime offerings, although things

102 Dodworth Road S70 6HL
Map 8: SE30
Tel: 01226 240113
Chef: Nick Pound
Owners: Nick Pound, Deborah Swift
Cost: *Alc* £21, fixed-price L £7.50,
£12.50 (2 courses)/D £14.50 (not Sat).
☺ H/wine £9.95.
Times: Noon-last L 1.30pm/7pm-last
D 9.30pm. Closed L Sat, Sun, Mon

move up a few gears in the evening. Go for dinner and you might find, say, sweet and sour aubergine salad with minted yogurt and fried courgettes, fillet of red mullet with Thai noodles, and duck breast with wilted greens, soy and ginger, followed by honey and lavender ice cream profiteroles, and chocolate truffle cake with coffee crème anglaise. Debbie Swift looks after the front of house charmingly. Eleven house selections head the lively, keenly priced wine list.

Directions: One mile from M1/37. Take A625 towards Barnsley, on right

---

CHAPELTOWN,
Greenhead House Hotel ❀❀

Family loyalties mean a great deal to Neil and Anne Allen, and walking into their stone-built residence on the outskirts of Sheffield is like entering a private home – and that's exactly what Greenhead House is. The Allens deliberately limit opening to four nights a week, so that they can spend time with their young children, although they have started to offer light lunches on Thursday and Friday with a menu reckoned to be on a par with a burger and chips 'price wise', although the quality is in a different league, according to an inspector who visited this delightful set-up in April. He sampled some nourishing home-made bread with an exceedingly moreish soup of mushroom, Cheddar and spinach before moving on to tender veal on a potato rösti with cep sauce, and concluding his commendable meal with crème brûlée studded with pistachio nuts. The monthly dinner menu features serious, deeply flavoured dishes along the lines of soft-cooked polenta with Gorgonzola, roast poussin with chanterelles, sweetbreads and Madeira sauce, and sautéed scallops with a leek and caviar sauce. The short wine list does its job effectively.

84 Buncross Road Sheffield S30 4SF
Map 8: SK39
Tel: 0114 2469004
Chef: Neil Allen
Owners: Mr & Mrs N Allen
Cost: Fixed-price D £29.50 (4 courses). H/wine £10.50
Times: Noon-last L 1.30pm (Thu & Fri)/7pm-last D 9pm (Wed-Sat). Closed Sun, Mon, Tues, 2 wks Easter, 2 wks Aug, 1 wk Xmas
Additional: Bar food L; No children under 8
Seats: 32
Smoking: No-smoking area in dining room
Credit cards: ▭ ▭ ▭ ▭ ▭

Directions: M1/J35 follow signs to Chapeltown, straight across 2 roundabouts onto Buncross Rd. Restaurant is on R, 200m

---

ROTHERHAM, **Swallow Hotel** ❀

Large modern hotel well placed for the town centre and just two minutes from M1/J33. Good standard of cooking in Holly's restaurant takes in home-made broccoli soup, fillet of plaice with prawns and chive butter sauce, or medallions of pork with shallots and peppercorns in a brandy cream, and orange and grapefruit bavarois.

Additional: Bar food; Sunday L; Children welcome; ❂ dishes
Smoking: No-smoking area; air-conditioning
Accommodation: 100 en suite
Credit cards: ▭ ▭ ▭ ▭ ▭ ▭

West Bawtry Road S60 4NA
Map 8: SK49
Tel: 01709 830630
Fax: 01709 830549
Chef: Gary McHugh
Owner: Swallow Hotels
Cost: Fixed-price L £12.95/D £17.75 (5 courses). ☺ H/wine £12
Times: Last L 2pm/last D 9.45pm. Closed L Sat

Directions: From the M1/J37; the hotel stands on the A630, 2 miles from Rotherham centre

---

SHEFFIELD, **Charnwood Hotel** ❀

Within walking distance of the city centre, the Charnwood dates from 1780, when it was the home of a master cutler. Leo's Brasserie

10 Sharrow Lane S11 8AA
Map 8: SK38
Tel: 0114 2589411
Fax: 0114 2555107

is a popular place offering the likes of Caesar salad, steaks, and confit of duck, whilst the more intimate Henfrey's restaurant takes in celeriac and roast chestnut soup, and duo of French duck with sweet cabbage.

Smoking: No-smoking area
Accommodation: 22 en suite. **Credit cards:** ▆ ▆ ▆ ▆ ▆ ▆

Directions: M1/J33 & A621. 1.5 miles SW of city centre, off London Road

Chef: Craig Noble
Owner: C J King
Cost: Alc £17, fixed-priced D £12. ☺
H/wine £8.95.
Times: D only, 6.30pm-10.30pm.
Closed Sun, 25-31 Dec
Additional: Children welcome;
♨ dishes

SHEFFIELD, Harley Hotel ❀

With an elegant combination of silk fabrics, blonde American oak-panelling and marble, this hotel offers a stylish setting for some sound modern cooking. Typical dishes are Stilton mousse with candied pear, roast wood pigeon laid on a croûton heart with game sauce, and a comforting jam roly poly with custard.

Smoking: No pipes; air-conditioning
Accommodation: 23 en suite. **Credit cards:** ▆ ▆ ▆ ▆ ▆ ▆

Directions: In University and Teaching Hospitals campus, 0.5 miles from centre on junction of West Street (A57) and Hanover Street (Inner City Ring Road)

334 Glossop Road S10 2HW
Map 8: SK38
Tel: 01142 752288
Fax: 01142 722383
Chef: Ray Hills
Owner: Turret Hotels Ltd
Cost: Alc £20, fixed-price L £11.50/D £16. ☺ H/wine £11.
Times: Last L 1.45pm/last D 9.30pm.
Closed Sun, L Sat, 25-26 Dec
Additional: Bar food;
No children under 12; ♨ dishes

SHEFFIELD,
Mosborough Hall Hotel ❀

Historic manor house set in its own gardens within easy reach of the M1. Varied menus highlight ambitious cooking. A typical meal might begin with chicken mille-feuille with mushroom and thyme confit, followed by pan-fried pigeon with Madeira jus, and Cassis parfait to finish.

Smoking: No pipes & cigars
Accommodation: 24 en suite. **Credit cards:** ▆ ▆ ▆ ▆

Directions: Hotel on A616, 5 miles from M1/J30

High Street S19 5AE
Map 8: SK38
Tel 0114 2484353
Fax: 0114 2477042
Chef: Ian Torpey
Owner: Brian Nicholas
Cost: Alc £25, fixed-price L £9.95/D £17.50.
Times: Last L 1.45pm/D 9.15pm.
Closed L Sat, D Sun
Additional: Sunday L; Children welcome; ♨ dishes

SHEFFIELD,
Smith's of Sheffield ❀❀❀

The popularity of this modern, relaxed restaurant, with its unusual tented ceiling, is well deserved, and there are now plans in the pipeline to extend next door. All choices within each course cost the same, so total spend is easy to reckon at a glance, especially as prices are exceptionally fair for Richard Smith's bright, new-look Euro cooking. Typical starters may include seared carpaccio of rare tuna with spicy marinated carrots, crispy noodles and an orange, soy and sesame dressing, as well as terrine of pork rillettes, ham hock and chorizo with salami salad, home-made chutney, salsa verde and garlic toast. Fish is given a vibrant, if unorthodox pairing by matching chargrilled monkfish with couscous and herb beurre blanc and sautéed salmon with avocado compote, garlic king prawns and red-pepper dressing. Rare breast of Gressingham duck is served East-West style with five spice greens, shredded duck

34 Sandygate Road S10 5RY
Map 8: SK38
Tel: 01142 666096
Chef: Richard Smith
Owners: Richard & Victoria Smith, John & Sallie Tetchner
Cost: Alc £22.50. H/wine £9. ☺
Times: D only, 6.30pm-10pm.
Closed Sun, Mon, last 2wks Aug
Additional: Children welcome;
♨ dishes
Seats: 45
Credit cards: ▆ ▆ ▆ ▆

Smith's of Sheffield

leg confit and an oriental duck gravy, but there are also simpler, more traditional choices such as pan-roasted chicken breast with braised celery and sauce 'bois boudran', New England cod chowder, and Bramley apple baked with spiced dried fruit and served with vanilla ice cream and butterscotch sauce. Regional pride is well served with a compote of Yorkshire rhubarb presented alongside a crème brûlée. A good selection of British farmhouse cheeses comes with a Granny Smith apple and cheese biscuits.

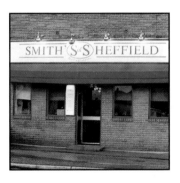

Not a lengthy list but some interesting bins at reasonable prices, divided simply into red and white with ten halves. All but seven of the still wines come in at under £20, and the house Champagne is £20.95. Try the Quincy, Dom Mardon a good, but lesser known Loire white at £18.95; Dom Pelisson's Côtes Du Ventoux is a good example of a well made organic wine and is well priced at £15.85.

Signature dishes: Roast rack of Spring lamb with celeriac mash, braised celery and truffle jus; strawberry beignets with rosewater ice cream and a red fruit coulis; Thai king prawn cake with deep-fried sweet potato, spicy peanut pesto and coriander oil; hare stew with papperdale thyme and shallots.

Directions: From Sheffield centre take A57; at Crosspool turn R onto Sandygate Road. 100 yds on R

SHEFFIELD,
Staindrop Lodge Hotel ❀

Lane End S30 4UH
Map 8: SK39
Tel: 0114 284 6727
Fax: 0114 284 6783
Chef: John Olerenshaw
Owners: Mark & Sue Bailey
Cost: *Alc* £25, fixed-price L £12.50
/D £19.50. ☺
Times: Noon-last L 1.45pm/ 7pm-9.15pm. Closed D Sun, L Mon and Sat, Bhs
Additional: Sunday L; Children welcome; ❸ dishes
Smoking: No smoking in dining room
Accommodation: 13 en suite
Credit cards: ▨ ▨ ▨ ▨ ▨

Ivy-clad country house hotel, just a mile from M1/J35, standing in magnificent gardens. The restaurant has a deserved reputation for its

cooking. A typical dinner could include warm scallop mousse, a salad of watercress and bacon, pan-fried medallions of beef fillet with foie gras and Madeira sauce, and white chocolate truffle cake.

Directions: From M1/J35 follow signs to Chapeltown and Huddersfield; go over first roundabout, turn R at second and hotel is 0.5 mile on R

YORKSHIRE WEST

BRADFORD,

Restaurant Nineteen

19 North Park Road BD9 4NT
Map 7: SE13
Tel: 01274 492559
Fax: 01274 483827
Chef: Stephen Smith
Owners: Robert Barbour, Stephen Smith
Cost: Fixed-price D £28.
H/wine £13.50
Times: D only, 7pm-last D 9.30pm.
Closed Sun, Mon, 1 wk May, Sept, 2 wks Jan
Additional: No children under 10
Seats: 36
Smoking: No pipes or cigars
Accommodation: 4 en suite
Credit cards: ▆ ▆ ▆ ▆

Since 1984, Robert Barbour and Stephen Smith have ensured that their intimate restaurant-with-rooms in an attractive Victorian building sets the standard for European cooking in this multi-cultural quarter of West Yorkshire. Inside, it speaks of understated elegance, with warm colour schemes, ornate Victorian wall lights and tables well-spaced to allow for plenty of elbow room and whispered privacy. Stephen Smith cooks to a fixed-price dinner menu with around five choices at each stage: technical exactness and assurance are his trademarks. Dishes may not be trailblazers for 90s cuisine, but inspectors find little to criticise. A recent meal began with assorted warm rolls, baked on the premises and served with 'a huge wedge' of fresh creamy butter. Fillet of salmon, seared to give it a crisp crust, was arranged as a tower with crispy noodles and pickled ginger on a coriander butter sauce, next came a generous piece of top quality fillet of beef overlaid with a light cheese soufflé and presented with young spinach leaves, neatly trimmed baby vegetables and a well-reduced red wine sauce. To finish, there was variation on the theme of Christmas mince pie served with luscious vanilla ice cream in a tuile. Elsewhere, the menu might promise quail roasted with sage and garlic on a risotto of spring greens, fillet of turbot with lobster sauce and prawn tempura, and Amaretti cheesecake with warm compote of rhubarb. Decent filter coffee comes with decidedly rich chocolate truffles. The wine list gets off to a flying start with the very first bin being the 1990 Côtes de Castillon from the excellent Château Pitray. At £16.50 this is an opportunity to sample a little gem from a great Bordeaux vintage. Prices are fair and sources equally good throughout the list.

Signature dishes: Grilled cod with gremolata potato cake and pea purée; fillet of marinated lamb with cracked wheat and caponata salad; pheasant sausage wrapped in pancetta with cranberries and chestnuts; roast venison with beetroot risotto.

Directions: Take A650 (Manningham Lane) from Bradford. L at Manningham Park gates, then 1st R onto North Park Road

BRADFORD, Victoria Hotel

Enjoying a prime position in the city centre, this elegantly restored former station hotel has a lively bar, plus Vic and Bert's, a stylish brasserie specialising in grills cooked over wood. Modern cooking includes such dishes as wood pigeon and wild mushroom tart and lamb shank cassoulet with minted pesto.

Accommodation: 60 en suite. **Credit cards:** 🔲 🔲 🔲 🔲 🔲 🔲

Directions: From M606 take 3rd turn at roundabout (A6177). Next roundabout R (A641). End of dual carriageway R at roundabout (Hallings). R at next traffic lights; hotel on L

Bridge Street BD1 1JX
Map 7: SE13
Tel: 01274 390321
Fax: 01274 736358
Chef: Chris Heeson
Owner: Jonathan Wix
Cost: *Alc* £18.95, fixed-price L £8/D £14.95. ☺ H/wine £8.95.
Times: Last L 2.30pm/D 10.30pm. Closed L Sat, Sun
Additional: Bar food; Children welcome; ♿ dishes
Smoking: No pipes & cigars

DEWSBURY, Healds Hall Hotel

Leeds Road WF15 6JA
Map 8: SE22
Tel: 01924 409112
Fax: 01924 401895
Chef: Philip McVeagh
Owners: Mr & Mrs TJ Harrington
Cost: *Alc* £22, fixed-price L £9.75/D £16.95. ☺ H/wine £8.25.
Times: Last L 2pm/D 9.30pm; Closed L Sat, D Sun, 26 Dec, 1 Jan
Additional: Bar food L; Sunday L; Children welcome; ♿ dishes
Smoking: No smoking in dining room
Accommodation: 25 en suite
Credit cards: 🔲 🔲 🔲 🔲 🔲

Originally famous because of its links with the Brontës, this eighteenth-century stone house is now a popular hotel with a modern 'peachy hued' restaurant. The kitchen deals in creditable dishes such as rillettes of smoked haddock, medallions of venison with choucroute and sloe gin sauce, and iced rhubarb and cardamom parfait with orange compote.

Directions: On A62 Leeds/Huddersfield road near M1/J40 and M62/J26-27 (turn right at Swan pub)

HALIFAX, The Design House

The converted mill, surrounded by offices and a short walk from the city centre, offers a simple approach to decor and food: white walls show off modern art, orange curtains match orange benches that are teamed with Formica topped tables, the floor is stone-flagged, whilst crisp, clear flavours define the lively modern cooking. The repertoire happily marries a traditional boiled salted silverside of beef, creamed potatoes, mustard and

Dean Clough
HX3 5AX
Map 7: SE02
Tel: 01422 383242
Fax: 01422 322732
Chef: David Watson
Owner: John Leach
Cost: *Alc* £18.50, fixed-price L £12.95. ☺ H/wine £8.95.

parsley, with tempura of sea bream and squid, capers, lemon and garlic mayonnaise. One well reported meal took in roast duck leg on a bed of celeriac and mustard salad, followed by roast salmon perfectly matched by light pasta, pistou and broad bean sauce, and chocolate, prune and Armagnac mousse. Staff are friendly and helpful. A good range of bottled beers from around the world back up the very reasonable wine list.

Directions: From M62 follow signs to Halifax, Dean Clough is signposted (approx 0.5 miles from town centre).

Times: Noon-last L 2pm/6.30-last D 10pm. Closed L Sat, Sun, 25-26 Dec, 1 Jan
Additional: Bar food L; Children welcome; ❹ dishes
Seats: 45
Smoking: No smoking in dining room
Credit cards:

HALIFAX,
Holdsworth House Hotel ❀❀

Holmfield HX2 9TG
Map 7: SE02
Tel: 01422 240024
Fax: 01422 245174
Chef: Eric Claveau
Owner: Cavalier Country Club Ltd
Cost: Alc £24, fixed-price L £14.50. ☺ H/wine £9.75.
Times: Noon-last L 2.30pm/7pm-last D 9.30pm. Closed L Sat
Additional: Bar food D, Sunday L; Children welcome; ❹ dishes
Seats: 70. Private dining rooms 130
Smoking: No-smoking area; no pipes or cigars
Accommodation: 40 en suite
Credit cards:

The original part of the house dates from 1633 and is steeped in history. It takes in two cosy dining rooms and an adjoining lounge, all of which overlook the gardens. The *carte* offers four courses, the middle course being a choice of two soups and a warm salad. Here are essentially British dishes given the contemporary treatment. At a late spring dinner a terrine of Mediterranean vegetables and artichoke with roquette pesto was everything it should be, with the pesto giving the right amount of buzz, whilst confit of oxtail and shallots topped with glazed potatoes – both mash and sautéed potatoes – came with simple but effective sautéed sugar snap peas, and creamed turnip with chives, then, to finish, a sound rhubarb crumble with ginger ice cream. An interesting wine list is arranged by grape variety, and there is a good selection of halves.

Directions: From Halifax take A629 (Keighley), 2 miles turn R at garage to Holmfield, hotel 1.5 miles on R

HALIFAX, The Imperial Crown ❀

Impressive hotel set in the heart of town close to the railway station. The elegant Wallis Simpson restaurant is a delightful setting in which to sample some sound cooking. A recent inspection meal yielded fresh whiting, followed by a delicious confit of duck and a tangy lemon brûlée.

Smoking: No-smoking area; no pipes & cigars
Accommodation: 56 en suite. **Credit cards:**

Directions: Hotel is opposite railway station

42-46 Horton Street HX1 1BR
Map 7: SE02
Tel: 01422 342342
Fax: 01422 349866
Chef: Chris Randle-Bissel
Owner: Regal Hotel Group plc
Cost: Fixed-price D £15.50. ☺ H/wine £10.95.
Times: D only, 7pm-last D 9.45pm
Additional: Bar meals; Children welcome; ❹ dishes

HAWORTH, **Weavers Restaurant**

As the name suggests this likeable restaurant near the Brontë Parsonage was originally a cluster of weavers' cottages. The bar contains a fascinating clutter of items relating to the trade as well as photographs, books and magazines, while the restaurant feels rather like a Victorian drawing room. True to the style of the place, the cooking is a mix of honest, homespun Northern food and dishes that are in tune with today's gastronomic mood. Smoked haddock soup makes a hearty starter, otherwise you might opt for a skewer of spiced lamb with lentil salad. Main courses could be as earthy as roast fillet and belly of pork with 'cracklin', and slow-cooked shoulder of lamb with onion mash, or as vibrant as crispy Gressingham duck with rhubarb sauce and a side dish of Chinese greens. Old school puds such as ginger sponge with custard round things off. There's a refreshing lack of pretension about the whole set-up, helped along by genuine personal service.

15 West Lane Keighley
BD22 8DU
Map 7: SE03
Tel: 01535 643822
Fax: 01535 644832
Chefs/Owners: Colin & Jane Rushworth
Cost: *Alc* £21.50, fixed-price D £10.95. ☺ H/wine £8.95.
Times: D only 6.45pm-9.15pm. Closed Sun & Mon, 2 wks Xmas, 2 wks June
Additional: Children welcome; ♨ dishes
Smoking: No smoking in dining room; air-conditioning
Accommodation: 4 en suite
Credit cards: ▮▮ ▦ ▧ ▧ ▣ ▯

Directions: Haworth centre, by Brontë Museum car park

HUDDERSFIELD, **Bagden Hall**

Elegant Victorian house close to the village of Scisset, offering extensive grounds and a nine hole golf course. The Anglo-French cooking ranges from roulade of smoked salmon and horseradish mousse, and terrine of pheasant and duckling, to roast fillet of monkfish with a rich red wine jus, and warm savarin of black cherries.

Smoking: No-smoking area; air-conditioning
Accommodation: 17 en suite. **Credit cards:** ▮▮ ▦ ▧ ▧ ▣ ▯

Wakefield Road HD8 9LE
Map 7: SE11
Tel: 01484 865330
Fax: 01484 861001
Chef: Jeremy Hanson
Owners: Robert & Mandie Braithwaite
Cost: *Alc* £25, fixed-price L £11.95/D £16.95. ☺ H/wine £8.95.
Times: Last L 2pm/last D 9.30pm. Closed D Sun
Additional: Bar food; Sunday L; Children welcome; ♨ dishes

Directions: Leave M1/J39; hotel is on A636 Denby Dale road after 8 miles

HUDDERSFIELD, **The Lodge Hotel** ⊛

A little piece of the country in a leafy part of the city. Art Nouveau decor and creative modern cooking go together well and the menu offers the likes of mille-feuille of caramelised apple, black pudding and celeriac with Thermidor sauce, saltimbocca of red mullet with meunière butter, and liquorice and sloe gin mousse with prunes and Earl Grey syrup.

Smoking: No smoking in dining room
Accommodation: 11 en suite. **Credit cards:** ▮▮ ▦ ▧ ▧

48 Birkby Lodge Road
Birkby HD2 2BG
Map 7: SE11
Tel: 01484 431001
Fax: 01484 421590
Chefs: Richard G Hanson, Garry & Kevin Birley
Owners: Garry & Kevin Birley
Cost: Fixed-price L £13.95/D £23.95. ☺ H/wine £10.95
Times: Last L 1.45pm/D 9.30pm, Closed L Sat, D Sun
Additional: Sunday L; No children under 5; ♨ dishes

Directions: M62/J24 (Huddersfield), L at 1st lights (Birkby Road), R after Nuffield Hospital (Birkby Lodge Road), 100 yds on L

HUDDERSFIELD,
Weaver's Shed Restaurant

The Weaver's shed is, as the name implies, a former eighteenth-century woollen mill. It stands in a village on the foothills of the Pennines and still retains much of its original decor and structure, with flag floors, beamed ceiling and items of weaving interest adding to the look. Against this striking backdrop the kitchen revels in producing food with a strong

Knowl Road Golcar HD7 4AN
Map 7: SE11
Tel/Fax: 01484 654284
Chefs: Ian McGunnigle, Robert Jones, Stephen Jackson
Owner: Stephen Jackson
Cost: *Alc* £30, fixed-price L £12.95. ☺ H/wine £10.95

modern touch, and ideas are plucked at will from a global hat. Home-cured salmon, creamed cauliflower, keta and lemon oil, and honey/spice roast breast of duck, duck confit's cottage pie and duck jus with honey are typical of the style. A late spring lunch produced a 'super' Lunesdale duckling dumpling with a spicy Chinese sauce, 'sweet' baked cod served on light creamed potatoes, and mint mousse with fresh berries. Service is charming, and caring; one waitress is now in her 23rd year with the restaurant.

Directions: M62/24 & 23 (no exit westbound) take A640, turning L to Golcar. follow rd into village. 3 miles W of Huddersfield.

Times: Noon-last L 2pm/ 7pm-last D 10pm. Closed L Sat, Sun, Mon, 2 wks Jan, 2wks July-Aug
Additional: Children welcome; ⓓ dishes
Seats: 40. Private dining room 25
Smoking: No pipes and cigars
Credit cards: ▬ ▥ ▤ ▧ ▢

ILKLEY, **Box Tree Restaurant** ✿✿✿

35-37 Church Street LS29 9DR
Map 7: SE14
Tel: 01943 608484
Fax: 01943 607186
Chef: Thierry Le Prêtre-Granet
Owner: The Box Tree (Ilkley) Ltd
Cost: *Alc* £38, fixed-price L £22.50/D £29.50.
Times: Noon-last L 2pm/7pm-last D 9.30pm. Closed D Sun, Mon, between Xmas & New Year, 15-30 Jan
Additional: Sunday L;
No children under 5; ⓓ dishes
Seats: 50. Private dining room 16
Smoking: No smoking in dining room
Credit cards: ▬ ▥ ▤

Built as a farmhouse around 1720 and opened as a restaurant in 1962, the Box Tree lays claim to being one of the most enduring fixtures of the Yorkshire scene. Thirty five years can seem like a long time in the business, but the present regime, with Madame Avis at the helm and Thierry Le Prêtre-Granet in the kitchen, is sailing on. The place is famous for its idiosyncratic decor – a haphazard hotch-potch of objects d'art, fine art and collectibles – which, as one inspector observed, is showing signs of 'studied neglect'. The menu goes straight to the heart of luxurious French cooking, calling into play terrine of duck foie gras with globe artichoke salad, ravioli of calves' sweetbreads with truffle oil sauce, sautéed turbot with spices, herb risotto and red wine sauce, and the like. Technique is impeccable. A starter of roast quail is jointed (with the breast boned out) and served on a fragrant, shimmering Muscat sauce dotted with halved green grapes. Main courses are equally fine tuned: steamed sea bass served on strips of chicory with a sweetish sauce liberally sprinkled with fresh tarragon was greatly appreciated in December, but the repertoire also embraces noisettes of venison with grilled potato cake and juniper berry sauce as well as roast rump of veal with spinach and girolle mushrooms and veal jus. As for desserts, there might be spiced bread parfait with a perfectly poached pear in syrup or a dariole of orange and pink grapefruit with an exotic coulis and raspberry sorbet. The Box Tree is also noted for its excellent choice of coffees, fruit and leaf teas.

Signature dishes: Iranian caviar with potato blinis, sour cream and chive sauce; fillet of Aberdeen Angus beef with parsnip purée, Madeira and truffle sauce; hot blackberry soufflé with blackberry coulis.

Directions: On A65, on the Skipton side of Ilkley near the Church

ILKLEY, Rombalds Hotel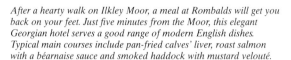

After a hearty walk on Ilkley Moor, a meal at Rombalds will get you back on your feet. Just five minutes from the Moor, this elegant Georgian hotel serves a good range of modern English dishes. Typical main courses include pan-fried calves' liver, roast salmon with a béarnaise sauce and smoked haddock with mustard velouté.

Smoking: No smoking in dining room
Accommodation: 15 en suite
Credit cards: ▬ ▬ ▬ ▬ ▨ ▯

Directions: From A65 lights in town, turn up Brook Street, cross The Grove to Wells Road and hotel is 600 yds on L

11 West View Wells Road LS29 9JG
Map 7: SE14
Tel: 01943 603201
Fax: 01943 816586
Chef: Jason Shaw
Owners: Colin & Jo Clarkson
Cost: Alc £20.35, fixed-price D £12.95. H/wine £9.25. ☺
Times: Last L 2pm/D 9.30pm.
Closed 27-30 Dec
Additional: Sunday L; Bar meals; Children welcome; ♨ dishes

LEEDS, Brasserie Forty Four

42-44 The Calls LS2 7EW
Map 8: SE23
Tel: 0113 2343232
Fax: 0113 2343332
Chef: Jeff Baker
Owner: Michael Gill
Cost: Alc £21.40, fixed-price L&D £11.95. ☺ H/wine £9.90.
Times: Noon-last L 2pm/6.30pm-to last D 10.30pm.
Closed Sun, L Sat, Bhs
Additional: Children welcome; ♨ dishes
Seats: 110. Private dining room 55
Smoking: No pipes and cigars; air-conditioning
Credit cards: ▬ ▬ ▬ ▬ ▨ ▯

Minimalist decor in the shape of bare brick walls, wooden floors and ultra-modern artwork defines the mood in this converted grain store down by the riverside. It is the casual face of a complex that also includes 42 The Calls and Pool Court at 42 (see entry). The menu, which is the same for lunch and dinner, runs on flexibility and cosmopolitan style: this is the world of deep-fried pancakes with crispy duck and plum sauce, roast Whitby cod on split pea purée and apple frangipane tart – all of which were praised by our inspector. Other options might include Turkish spiced aubergines, casseroled rabbit with black olives and rosemary and chocolate fondue with marshmallows. Side orders of fries cooked in the skins and served with dips are great fun. Light lunches for a fiver are unbeatable value, as are 'early bird' and 'night owl' menus (Friday and Saturday). Around 60 wines form a zesty modern slate and good value abounds.

Directions: From Crown Point Bridge, L past Church, L into High Court Road. On the riverside

LEEDS, Haley's Hotel

It may be two miles from Leeds city centre, but this expansive Victorian house (named after a local stonemason) feels unmistakably like a country hotel thanks to its location in a quiet, leafy conservation area. Dinner revolves around a monthly changing *carte* with a modern accent and plenty of high-flown flourishes. This is a kitchen that likes wrapping

Shire Oak Road
Headingley LS6 2DE
Map 8: SE23
Tel: 0113 2784446
Fax: 0113 2753342
Chef: Jon Vennell
Owner: John J Appleyard
Cost: Alc £25. H/wine £10.15. ☺

Haley's Hotel

Times: D only, 7.15pm-last D 9.45 pm. Closed D Sun, 26-30 Dec
Additional: Sunday L (12.15pm-last L 2pm); Children welcome; ❸ dishes
Seats: 52. Private dining room 25
Smoking: No smoking in dining room; air-conditioning
Accommodation: 22 en suite
Credit cards: ▨ ▨ ▨ ▨ ▨ ▨

things in parcels: warm salmon mousse in Savoy cabbage, served with sautéed scallops, button onions and chive cream sauce; baked monkfish tails in smoked salmon and puff pastry with lentils and red pepper coulis; baked fillet of pork in leeks. In a different vein, roast fillet of beef baked with a wild mushroom purée and foie gras, served in a Yorkshire pudding with a rich truffle sauce turns tradition on its head. As for desserts, expect things like iced white chocolate and gingerbread parfait with strawberry coulis, and peppered pineapple with rum and raisin ice cream. A representative from the Leventhorpe Vineyard near Leeds appears on the carefully chosen, global wine list.

Directions: On A660 (Leeds/Otley) in Headingley between Lloyds and Midland banks

LEEDS, Leeds Marriott ❀❀ NEW

Dyson's at the Marriott is an interesting split-level restaurant styled with a profusion of gleaming mahogany, stained glass, clocks, antiques and an abundance of object d'art, originally the home of one of renowned jewellers. Surroundings are relaxed but with a noticeable degree of sophistication, which is reflected in the lively and up-beat modern British cooking. Dishes such as roasted lamb with smoked bacon and basil mousse, baked fillet of salmon with roasted asparagus and risotto of ceps, croustade of goat's cheese with spinach and wild mushrooms, and chargrilled vegetables with feta cheese and balsamic, dressing show the range. Highly recommended are confit of duck set off by slivers of sweet and sour Bramley apple, pan-fried sea bass on a confit of Thai vermicelli and given piquancy by a drizzle of coriander and chilli dressing, and hot, tangy lemon tart with clotted cream and raspberry coulis.

LS1 6ET
Map 8: SE23
Tel: 0113 2366444
Fax: 0113 2366367
Chef: Peter McMahon
Owner: Leeds Marriott Hotel
Cost: *Alc* £15.95, fixed-price L/D £15.95. ☺ H/wine £8.75.
Times: Last L 2.30pm/last D 10.30pm. Closed D Sun, L Sat
Additional: Sunday L; Children welcome; ❸ dishes
Smoking: No-smoking area
Accommodation: 244 en suite
Credit cards: ▨ ▨ ▨ ▨ ▨ ▨

Directions: From M1 or M62 follow signs to City Centre, turn into Sovereign St, L at lights, R into NCP car park adjacent to hotel

LEEDS, Leodis Brasserie ❀❀

The converted waterside warehouse has retained open brick walls, vaulted ceilings and cast iron columns, with modern etched glass partitions giving some feel of privacy without compromising the atmosphere, which is pacy yet relaxed.

Sovereign Street
LS1 4BJ
Map 8: SE23
Tel: 0113 2421010
Fax: 0113 2430432
Chef: Steven Kendell

Leodis Brasserie

Owners: Martin Spalding &
Steven Kendell
Cost: Alc £17.50, fixed-price L & D
£12.95 (3 courses). ☺
H/wine £10.75.
Times: Noon-last L 2pm/6pm-last D
10pm (Fri/Sat 11pm). Closed L Sat,
Sun, 25-26 Dec, L Bhs
Additional: Children welcome;
☺ dishes
Seats: 180
Smoking: Air-conditioning
Credit cards: ■ ▓ ▒ ▒ ▓ ⌂

Inspectors continue to sing the kitchen's praises. Steve Kendell can cook traditional stalwarts such as steamed pudding of beef steak and mushrooms, bangers, mashed potato and onion gravy, and sticky toffee pudding, as well as embarking on more up-to-the-minute ideas (breast of pigeon with red cabbage purée and a Madeira glaze, roast salmon with deep-fried anchovies and red wine glaze, goat's cheese and aubergine pavé with parsley pesto). A February lunch opened with a potage of seafood stuffed with large, fresh pieces of fish and scallops. Confit of duck followed, well made with the sauce rich and dark. Then a cappuccino chocolate cup: a large cup moulded from chocolate, filled with a light cappuccino mousse, set on a saucer made from biscuit. It looked a little odd but the flavours were good. The wine list has much to recommend it, the choice is global and prices are restrained.

Directions: Follow the M/way sign from City square, turn L by the Hilton Hotel onto Sovereign Street, 100 yards on L.

LEEDS, Merrion Thistle ❀   **NEW**

Merrion Centre LS2 8NH
Map: 8 SE23
Tel: 0113 243 9191
Fax: 0113 242 3527
Telephone for details

Smart city centre hotel attracting business and leisure guests. Decorated in Art Deco style, Starlets Restaurant offers a good choice. Expect cream of onion soup, medallions of pork marinated in sage and thyme, served with spiced apple confit and excellent vegetables, and lemon tart

Directions: Town centre

LEEDS, Olive Tree Restaurant ❀

55 Rodley Lane LS13 1NG
Map 8: SE23
Tel: 0113 2569283
Chefs: George Psarias, Andreas
Iacovou
Owners: George & Vasoulla Psarias
Cost: Alc £20, fixed-price L £5/D
£11.95. ☺ H/wine £8.95.

George and Vasoulla Psarias' lively Greek restaurant is seldom less than packed. Live Greek music and dancing on Tuesdays and Fridays draw in the crowds, in addition to the extensive menu. Typical starters include light dips, dolmades and meat and seafood mezes; main courses range from chicken riganati to vegetarian moussaka.

Times: Last L 2.30pm/D 11pm. Closed 25-26 Dec, 1 Jan
Additional: Sunday L; Bar meals; Children welcome; ☺ dishes
Credit cards: ■ ▓ ▒

Directions: By Rodley roundabout on Leeds outer ring road (A6120) NW of city

LEEDS, Oulton Hall Hotel ❀

Rothwell Lane Oulton LS26 8HN
Map 8: SE23
Tel: 0113 2821000
Fax: 0113 2828066
Chef: Stephen Collinson
Owner: Oulton Hall Hotel
Cost: Alc £30, fixed-price L £13.50/D
£21.50. ☺ H/wine £12.95.
Times: Last L 2pm/D 9.30pm
Closed L Sat
Additional: Sunday L; Bar meals;
Children welcome; ❹ dishes
Smoking: No smoking in dining room.
Air-conditioning
Accommodation: 152 en suite
Credit cards: 🔳 🔳 🔳 🔳 🔳

*Impressively restored, Grade II listed mansion set in grounds
comprising a golf course, formal gardens, even a church. The oak-
panelled Brontë Restaurant makes a suitable setting for classically
based dishes such as plaice and salmon mousse terrine, and rack of
lamb with bubble and squeak and Madeira sauce. Passionfruit delice
is a typical dessert.*

Directions: M62/J30, follow signs to Rothwell

LEEDS, Pool Court at 42 ❀❀❀

44 The Calls LS2 7EW
Map 8: SE23
Tel: 0113 2444242
Fax: 0113 2343332
Chef: Jeff Baker
Owner: Michael Gill
Cost: Fixed-price L £12.50
(2courses)/D £ 29.50 (3 courses).
H/wine £12.95
Times: Noon-last L 2pm/7pm-last D
10pm. Closed L Sat, Sun, Bhs.
Additional: No children under 2;
❹ dishes.
Seats: 38
Smoking: No pipes or cigars in dining
room; air-conditioning
Credit cards: 🔳 🔳 🔳 🔳 🔳

The hotel and restaurant development embracing Pool Court,
42 The Calls and Brasserie Forty Four (see entry) is a Leeds
showpiece and a great symbol of the city's rejuvenation as a
serious contender in the food stakes. The setting is a converted
grain mill by the quayside with swish 'Milan-chic' decor,
gleaming chrome and pale blonde surfaces. The effect is at
once mould-breaking, cosmopolitan and cool. Jeff Baker's
cooking suits the place to a T, providing a bedrock of classy,
French inspired food with just enough experimentation to keep
customers on their toes. A choice of menus, ranging from set
lunches to a six-course 'Classics' extravaganza, bristle with
ideas, flair and an instinct for marrying flavours. The breadth of
the repertoire showed up well in a meal that began with a
twice-baked Parmesan soufflé of matchless quality that was set
off by a brilliant roast pepper vinaigrette spiced with cumin.
The main course took a slightly different route to excellence:
crisp skinned Lincolnshire duckling was accompanied by a
crescent-shaped feuilleté containing minced leg and liver,

served with crunchy creamed cabbage, a deeply flavoured port sauce, plus a side dish of exceptional potato purée with chives. Other options might include a grilled boudin of fresh and smoked salmon with aromatic Puy lentils, 'truite bourguignonne' done the old way, and pot roast veal sweetbreads with ceps, rosemary and mousseline potatoes. Desserts conclude proceedings on a resoundingly high note – steamed date pudding with butterscotch sauce and triple cream produced ecstatic drools – 'Heaven', proclaimed the recipient. Around 60 wines, plus a substantial number of halves, are clearly an enthusiast's choice and are well worth exploring.

Signature dishes: Noisettes of local lamb sautéed pink and served with two kinds of celery and a thyme infusion; cassoulet of native lobster with broad beans, tomato and tarragon; steamed chocolate sponge with griottine cherries and triple cream; tarte Tatin of caramelised onions and roast foie gras with an aged balsamic dressing.

Directions: From M1 follow A61 (Harrogate) into city centre, cross River Aire via Crown Point Bridge. 2nd L at roundabout onto Maude St and you arrive at The Calls

LEEDS, Rascasse ✿✿✿

Canal Wharf
Water Lane LS11 5BB
Map 8: SE33
Tel: 0113 2446611
Fax: 0113 2440736
Chef: Simon Gueller
Owners: Simon Gueller, Nigel Jolliffe
Cost: *Alc* £26, fixed-price L £13.50-£17 (2-3 courses). ☺ H/wine from £11.50
Times: Noon-last L 2pm/6.30pm-last D 10pm (10.30pm Fri/Sat). Closed L Sat, Sun. 1 wk after Xmas
Additional: Bar food L; Children welcome; ♨ dishes
Seats: 100 + 30 outside
Smoking: No pipes and cigars; air-conditioning
Credit cards: ▬ ▦ ▭ ▬ ▣ ℂ

On a grim, blustery February lunchtime, a visit here really perked up the senses. Located in a rejuvenated part of the city, next to the canal, the decor is upbeat and cosmopolitan, with polished wood flooring, colourful china and lots of chrome and glass. The upstairs bar is reached by a sweeping staircase, and the trendily attired staff are attentive and alert. Simon Gueller's cooking is fresh and lively. Minimal interference with excellent raw ingredients plus exemplary, uncomplicated execution equals a succession of excellent dishes which can be sampled either via the carte or a 'Fastrack' lunch menu. Abundance of choice is the single most frustrating factor. The genre is Anglo-French with strong Mediterranean influences. A risotto of white truffle oil and button mushrooms made a fine start to our inspection dinner, creamy but still with bite, topped with slices of truffle and encircled by a cordon of olive oil and chives. Other typical choices might have been ravioli of goat's cheese, confit tomatoes and sauce pesto, or gâteau of crab with ginger, avocado and pink grapefruit. A regular conceit is to present soup, cream of celery or vichyssoise perhaps, with a softly poached egg. Francophiles will be pleased to note toast Poilane with the parfait of chicken livers and foie gras. A varied choice of fish dishes might include grilled tuna with

aubergine caviar and sauce vierge, sesame-roast turbot with stir-fried vegetables and soy vinaigrette, or perfectly cooked roast codling with cabbage, pancetta and a cream sauce accented with citrus zest. Meat dishes work equally well – a superbly tender squab pigeon was cooked with decadently rich foie gras, wild mushrooms and truffles wrapped in a parcel of Savoy cabbage leaves. Sauces draw on the classical repertoire but are light and well-balanced; sauce Bercy with escalope of calves' liver, grilled bacon, pomme purée, and pak choi, for example, or sauce Choron with ribeye of beef, haricot verts and pommes gaufrettes. Desserts also look across *La Manche* with Grand Marnier iced soufflé and orange tuiles, vanilla bavarois with fresh strawberry sauce and pomme seche amongst the choices. The genuinely lively selection of wines is drawn from around the globe and deserves applause for both the large number available by the glass and the large selection of sub £15 bins.

Signature dishes: Mediterranean fish soup, rouille and croûtons; risotto of white truffle oil and button mushrooms; supremes of squab pigeon, papillote of foie gras, garlic confit, thyme jus; warm chocolate fondant, coconut ice-cream.

Directions: 0.5 mile from M1/J47 & M621; off road signposted City Centre. On Canal Basin

LEEDS, Shear's Yard

The Calls LS2 7EY
Map 8: SE23
Tel: 0113 2444144
Fax: 0113 2448102
Chef: Danny Janes
Owners: Rob Noble, Peter Conolly
Cost: *Alc* £20, fixed-price D £10.95.
☺ H/wine £9.75.

A former shearing yard and rope/sailmakers, converted into a busy, informal wine bar and restaurant that's stylishly up-to-date with exposed brick walls and wood and slate flooring. Good food. Chicken liver parfait in brioche with a bold mushroom gravy is recommended, as is the excellent salmon served on a lobster flavoured mash.

Times: Last L 2.30pm/last D 10.30pm. Closed Sun, Bh Mon
Additional: Bar meals; Children welcome; ◔ dishes
Smoking: Air-conditioning
Credit cards: 🔳 🔳 🔳 🔳 🔳

Directions: From M1 follow signs for Crown Point Bridge. Cross bridge and turn left at roundabout on to Kirkgate, restaurant 200yds on right

RIPPONDEN,

Over The Bridge Restaurant

Millfold HX6 4DJ
Map 8: SE23
Tel: 01422 823722
Fax: 01422 824810
Chef: Sue Tyer
Owner: Ian Beaumont
Cost: *Alc* £23.50. H/wine £11.20. ☺

Set beside a hump-backed bridge and fast-flowing stream, this long-established restaurant continues to please. The kitchen tries hard and succeeds with dishes such as seared salmon fillet with caper sauce and poached chicken breast with a prawn and tarragon mousse. The delightfully light cheese and spinach soufflé has also been well reported.

Times: D only 7.30-9.30pm. Closed L, Sun D, Bhs
Additional: Children over 10 welcome; ◔ dishes
Credit cards: 🔳 🔳 🔳 🔳

Directions: M62/J22(E)/J24(W), A58 from Halifax, in village centre by church

WENTBRIDGE,
Wentbridge House Hotel ❀

Built in 1700, and famed for its antiques and Thompson of Kilburn furniture. The mirrored Fleur de Lys restaurant makes a stylish setting for creditable dishes such as roast quail with mushroom duxelle and Madeira sauce, rack of lamb with port sauce and apple and Calvados sponge. Polished service, excellent wine list with plenty of depth.

Accommodation: 18 en suite
Credit cards: ▰ ▰ ▰ ▰

Directions: 0.5 mile off the A1, 4 miles S of M62/A1 interchange

WF8 3JJ
Map 8: SE41
Tel: 01977 620444
Fax: 01977 620148
Chef: Richard Deguil
Owners: Page Holdings
Cost: Fixed-price L £12.50/fixed-price D £21. ☺ H/wine £10.20.
Times: Last L 2.15pm/D 9.30pm.
Closed D 25 Dec
Additional: Sunday L;
Children welcome; dishes

WETHERBY, # Wood Hall Hotel ❀

Magnificent Georgian mansion set in parkland overlooking the River Wharfe. Imaginative and accurately cooked dishes are served in the elegant, wood-panelled dining room. A typical meal could be chicken liver and truffle parfait with apple and plum chutney, beef fillet with mustard and whisky sauce, and prune and armagnac tart.

Directions: In town, take turning opposite Windmill pub signed Wood Hall and Linton

Trip Lane Linton LS22 4JA
Map 8: SE44
Tel: 01937 587271
Fax: 01937 585353
Owner: Arcadian Hotels
Telephone for details

CHANNEL ISLANDS
ALDERNEY

ALDERNEY, Inchalla Hotel ❀❀

Inchalla has enjoyed the personal touch of Valerie Willis for seventeen years. The hotel, just a couple of hundred yards from the main street of town, may be modern but the service is based on old-fashioned values. New thinking in the kitchen has ably maintained standards. An autumn dinner opened with avocado with quenelle of salmon – it worked well with pieces of fish as well as the moist mousse and good mustard and dill dressing. Pork fillet came with apple and orange segments and well-balanced Calvados and thyme sauce and notably good vegetables, especially Savoy cabbage with onion and almonds. From the homely desserts (banoffee pie, bread-and-butter pudding, some six or seven in all, recited at table) came a superb apple and local blackberry crumble. Although the bread is no longer home-made, the excellent granary bread from the local baker compensated.

Directions: On the outskirts of St Anne, 3-4 minutes' walk from town centre

St Anne GY9 3UL
Map: 16
Tel: 01481 823220
Fax: 01481 824045
Chef: Anne Marie Burbidge
Owner: Valerie Willis
Cost: *Alc* £20, fixed-price L £11.60 (4 courses). ☺ H/wine £8.
Times: Noon-last L 2 pm/7pm-last D 8.45pm. Closed Mon, Xmas
Additional: Bar food (L only); Sunday lunch; Children welcome; ❸ dishes
Seats: 30
Smoking: No-smoking area in dining room
Accommodation: 9 en suite
Credit cards: ▆▆▆ ▆▆ ▆▆ ▆▆ ▆

GUERNSEY

L'ANCRESSE,
Symphony House Hotel ❀❀

Set in landscaped gardens, a few minutes from the Bays of L'Ancresse and Cobo, this smart little hotel is making quite a name for itself. As might be expected, Symphony's restaurant has a musical theme with its ebony black, ivory and terracotta colour schemes and menus that are dotted with 'Fanfares', 'Intermezzos' and 'Virtuosos'. The stars of a recent inspection were an incomparable lemon sole with langoustines, prawns and a delicate beurre blanc and shellfish butter sauce, and a chocolate pudding with chocolate sauce and home-made Tia Maria ice cream. Or you might find duck and chicken liver parfait with grape chutney, seared fillet steak on a 'cannelloni cake' of spinach and minced veal, and breast of duck served with seasonal greens, smoked bacon, Ratte potatoes and duck sausages with a sherry vinegar and honey jus. Efficient, bubbly staff provide suitably professional service.

Directions: Telephone for directions

Hacse Lane GY3 5DS
Map: 16
Tel: 01481 45418
Fax: 01481 43581
Chef: Phil Ashman
Owners: Keith & Dorothy Martel
Cost: *Alc* £21, fixed-price L £9.95/D £13.50. ☺ H/wine £8.50
Times: D only, 7pm-last D 9.30pm
Additional: Sunday L (noon-2pm); No children under 5; ❸ dishes
Seats: 68
Smoking: No-smoking area; no pipes & cigars
Accommodation: 15 en suite
Credit cards: ▆▆▆ ▆▆ ▆▆ ▆

CATEL, Cobo Bay Hotel ❀❀

The views out to sea are magnificent, and so is the location; the family-run hotel overlooks the golden sands of Cobo Bay on Guernsey's west coast. The quality of the food here continues to impress, the kitchen working from a repertoire that is mainstream but still lively. A meal that took in satay chicken

Cobo GY5 7HB
Map: 16
Tel: 01481 57102
Fax: 01481 54542
Chef: Hylton Wardale
Owner: David Nussbaumer

on a bed of pesto-flavoured couscous, fillet of chargrilled brill with a beurre blanc flavoured with lobster and champagne and served on top of a medley of root vegetables, finishing with a steamed lemon sponge with toffee cream and crème anglaise, was a treat for one inspector. Top marks too, for both the wholemeal and the Parmesan bread, imaginative vegetable selection, and the espresso coffee. Global wine list has much to offer under £10.

Directions: First turn L from hotel, approximately 3 miles to St Peter Port

Cost: Alc £24, fixed-price D £17.50 (4 courses). ☺ H/wine £6.95.
Times: 7.00pm- last D 9.45pm. Closed L (except Sun), Jan/Feb
Additional: Sunday lunch; Children welcome; ✪ dishes
Seats: 120
Smoking: No pipes & cigars in dining room; air-conditioning
Accommodation: 36 en suite
Credit cards: ▨ ▨ ▨ ▨ ▨

CATEL,
La Grande Mare Hotel ✿✿

La Grand Mare is hotel, golf and country club all rolled into one, with the option of self-contained apartments in addition to standard in-house accommodation. The fact that it stands a stone's throw from the sea is a bonus. Dishes such as Lancashire sausages with mash and onion gravy appear on the lunch menu, while fish dominates the evening *carte*. Meals begin with an intriguing selection of breads (chive or curry-flavoured, for example) before chicken and leek terrine with a fresh herb and olive sauce, sautéed scallops with shallots, bacon and saffron butter, fillet of locally caught brill baked in foil with julienne of fennel or lamb cutlets 'cooked to perfection', and served with orange and mint sauce. Chilled rice pudding makes a pleasing dessert, otherwise expect various flambéed crêpes. Service is attentive and the wine list contains plenty of interesting stuff.

Directions: Telephone for directions

The Coast Road
Vazon Bay GY5 7LL
Map: 16
Tel: 01481 56576
Fax: 01481 56532
Chef: Fergus Mackay
Owner: S Vermeulen
Cost: Alc £16, fixed-price L £10.95/D £16. ☺ H/wine £7.45.
Times: Noon-last L 2pm/7pm-last D 9.30pm
Additional: Bar meals L; Sunday L; Children welcome; ✪ dishes
Seats: 100. Private dining room 30
Smoking: No-smoking area; no pipes & cigars; air-conditioning
Accommodation: 26 en suite
Credit cards: ▨ ▨ ▨ ▨ ▨ ▨

PERELLE, L'Atlantique Hotel ✿✿

St Saviours GY7 9NA
Map: 16
Tel: 01481 64056
Fax: 01481 63800
Chef: Tony Leck
Owner: Michael Lindley
Cost: Alc £20, fixed-price D £15.50 (5 courses). ☺ H/wine £7.95.
Times: 6.30pm-D 9.30pm. Closed L except Sun
Additional: Bar food; Sunday L; Children welcome; ✪ dishes

Perelle Bay – famed for its spectacular sunsets – forms a suitably dramatic backdrop for this comfortable modern hotel. There are wonderful views from the large windows of the restaurant with its classy design and menus that major in local seafood. An inspection dinner commenced with a terrine of sole with spiced prawns, followed by a successful consommé; as a main course there was succulent breast of chargrilled chicken served on a bed of mash with a tarragon scented jus and an assortment of interesting vegetables, while proceedings concluded with iced chocolate and orange parfait with a mint sauce. An extensive choice of well-chosen wines provides a suitable accompaniment to the food.

Directions: On west coast road overlooking Perelle Bay

Smoking: No-smoking area; no pipes and cigars in dining room
Accommodation: 21 en suite
Credit cards:

ST MARTIN, La Barbarie

Saints Bay GY4 6ES
Map: 16
Tel: 01481 35217
Fax: 01481 35208
Chefs: Jerry Allen, Anthony Lawson
Cost: *A/c* £18.50, fixed-price D £14.25. H/wine £7.95. ☺
Times: Last L 2pm/D 9.30pm
Additional: Sunday L; Bar meals L; Children welcome; dishes

A seventeenth-century granite priory, La Barbarie is now a charming hotel easily reached from the island's capital St Peter Port. A typical meal in the beamed restaurant might include chicken liver pâté with toasted brioche and cranberry jelly, and grilled Guernsey mackerel on a bed of mixed leaves, red onions and tomato.

Smoking: No-smoking area
Accommodation: 23 en suite
Credit cards:

Directions: At traffic lights in St Martin take road to Saints Bay – hotel is on R at end of Saints Road

ST MARTIN, Bella Luce Hotel

La Fosse GY4 6EB
Map: 16
Tel: 01481 38764
Fax: 01481 39561
Chef: James Scowen
Owner: Richard E Cann
Cost: *A/c* £17, fixed-price D £14.90. H/wine £6.50
Times: D only, 6.30pm-9.30pm
Additional: Bar food; Sunday L; Children welcome; dishes
Smoking: No-smoking area; no pipes or cigars in dining room; air-conditioning
Accommodation: 31 en suite
Credit cards:

Extended twelfth-century former manor house where first-class local seafood takes top billing on the extensive carte and fixed-price menus. Typical dishes may include roast monkfish wrapped in bacon with Burgundy sauce, fresh lobster, and honey-glazed duck with orange and lemon sauce.

Directions: From harbour take road S to St Martins and after approximately 2.5 miles go straight on at traffic lights

ST MARTIN, Idlerocks Hotel

Jerbourg Point GY4 6BJ
Map: 16
Tel: 01481 37711
Fax: 01481 35592
Chef: Kevin Buckley
Owners: Paul & Jan Hamill
Cost: *A/c* £20, fixed-price L £10.50/D £14.50. ☺ H/wine £9.90.
Times: Last L 2pm/D 9pm
Additional: Sunday L; Bar meals; Children welcome; dishes

Attractive family-run hotel in a spectacular cliff-top location. The Admirals Restaurant enjoys stunning views across the bay, with the other Channel Islands in the distance. Fresh fish is a strong point. Expect pan-fried turbot steak, roasted monkfish tails wrapped in Parma ham, and seafood roulade with mustard and Cognac sauce.

Smoking: No-smoking area; no cigars or pipes.
Accommodation: 28 en suite
Credit cards:

Directions: 5 mins drive from St Peter Port on main road

ST MARTIN,

St Margaret's Lodge

A well-run hotel, convenient for the airport, offering a varied menu that makes good use of local seafood. A recent meal featured 'beautifully fresh' brill with grapes and almonds, topped with plump, seared scallops. Also look out for the daily flambé specials, medallions of beef with brandy shallots, for example.

Accommodation: 47 en suite
Credit cards: ▬ ▒ ▒ ▒ ▣ ▢

Directions: Out of airport, turn L. Follow road for 1.5 miles. Hotel on L

Forest Road GY4 6UE
Map: 16
Tel: 01481 35757
Fax: 01481 37594
Chef/Owner: Adrian Davison
Cost: Alc £15.95, fixed-price D £15.95. ☺ H/wine £7.60.
Times: Last L 1.45pm/D 9.30pm
Additional: Sunday L; Bar meals; Children welcome; ➌ dishes
Smoking: No smoking in dining room

ST PETER PORT, **The Absolute End**

A seafood restaurant in a converted fisherman's cottage overlooking the sea. The decor is clean and fresh, with picture windows as the main feature. The long menu offers plenty of choice, including meat and vegetarian options, all with a French or Italian treatment.

Directions: Less than 1 mile from town centre, going N on seafront road to St Sampson

Longstore GY1 2BG
Map: 16
Tel: 01481 723822
Fax: 01481 729129
Chef: Antonio Folmi
Owner: Gastone Toffanello
Cost: Alc £24, fixed-price L £11. ☺ H/wine £7.
Times: Last L 2pm/last D 10pm. Closed Sun, Jan
Additional: Children welcome; ➌ dishes
Smoking: No pipes and cigars in dining room
Credit cards: ▬ ▒ ▒ ▒ ▢

ST PETER PORT, **Café du Moulin**

The setting is a joy. This popular restaurant occupies the ground floor of a granite-built granary down a tiny lane in a wooded valley. The mood inside is relaxed and congenial and the cooking takes a more global view of things compared with some other, French-inspired establishments on the island. Flavours are forthright and fish is a strong suit. An inspection meal proved that kitchen can keep pace with current trends as well as delivering sound versions of the classics. Ravioli of wild mushrooms came with a piquant walnut oil and grain mustard vinaigrette, while stuffed fillets of sole were served with a thermidor sauce. There's also a fondness for things past, as in venison sausage prepared to a Victorian recipe, and the splendid traditional trifle that forms part of the highly praised assiette of desserts. France is the strongest contender on the serviceable, well-chosen wine list.

Directions: Take the Forest rd from St Peter Port, L in St Peters – signed Torteval, take 3rd R; restaurant 0.25 miles

Rue du Quanteraine
St Pierre du Bois GY7 9BP
Map: 16
Tel: 01481 65944
Fax: 01481 65708
Chef: David Mann
Owners: David & Gina Mann
Cost: Alc £26, fixed-price D £17.95. ☺ H/wine £9.
Times: 12.15pm-last L 1.15pm/7.15pm-last D 9.15pm. Closed D Sun, Mon
Additional: Bar food L; Sunday L; No children under 7 at D; ➌ dishes
Seats: 50
Smoking: No smoking in dining room
Credit cards: ▬ ▒ ▢

ST PETER PORT, La Frégate Hotel

Captivating views of the harbour and castle are big pluses at this eighteenth-century manor house high on a hillside above the town. Seafood is local, some vegetables are grown in the hotel garden and the menu takes in everything from oysters, lobster and stir-fried scallops to beef tartare and roast rack of lamb.

Accommodation: 13 en suite
Credit cards: ■ ■ ■ ■ ■ ■

Directions: Town centre, above St Julian's Avenue

Les Cotils GY1 1UT
Map: 16
Tel: 01481 724624
Fax: 01481 720443
Chef: Günter Botzenhardt
Cost: Alc £25, fixed-price L £12.50/D £20. ☺ H/wine £8.50.
Times: Last L 1.30pm/D 9.30pm
Additional: Sunday L;
No children under 8; ● dishes
Smoking: Air-conditioned

ST PETER PORT, Le Nautique

Converted seventeenth-century seafront warehouse with a distinct nautical theme – fishing paraphernalia adorns the oak beams and whitewashed walls. Seafood is the speciality and the cooking is traditional in style, with a strong French influence.

Smoking: No pipes and cigars
Credit cards: ■ ■ ■ ■ ■ ■

Directions: Sea front opposite Harbour and Victoria Marina

Quay Steps GY1 2LE
Map: 16
Tel: 01481 721714
Fax: 01481 721786
Chef: Vito Garau
Owner: Carlo Graziani
Cost: Alc £22. H/wine £8. ☺
Times: Last L 2pm/D 10pm
Closed Sun, 2 wks Jan
Additional: No children under 5;
● dishes

ST PETER PORT,
St Pierre Park Hotel

Rohais GY1 1FD
Map: 16
Tel: 01481 728282
Fax: 01481 712041
Chef: John Hitchen
Cost: Alc £25, fixed-price L £11.95/D £19.95 (4 courses). ☺ H/wine £9.50
Times: Noon-last L 2.30pm/7pm-last D 10.30pm
Additional: Bar meals; Sunday L; Children welcome; ● dishes
Seats: 80. Private dining rooms 50
Smoking: No-smoking area; air-conditioning
Accommodation: 135 en suite
Credit cards: ■ ■ ■ ■ ■ ■

'Forty five acres of unrivalled luxury' is how the owners describe this hotel developed from the an early Victorian college. Today, the place boasts a lake and a nine-hole golf course, while on the food front, the main focus of attention is the elegant Victor Hugo restaurant, where fish tends to be the star of the show on the seasonally changing, up-to-the-minute menus. Lobsters feature strongly, perhaps home-smoked then paired with smoked scallops and brandied foie gras, otherwise braised with asparagus tips and a light veal jus, or sea bream is spiced Chinese-style and served in a warm salad with bacon, aubergine and a chilli infusion. Meaty alternatives appear in the shape of carpaccio of venison or pan-fried duck breast with blackcurrants. Desserts could feature chocolate sponge pudding with a sharp cherry compote.

Directions: 1 mile from town centre on route to west coast

VALE,
Pembroke Bay Hotel

Family run hotel close to an excellent bathing beach, with its own outdoor pool and tennis court. Local fish is the star of the show in the split-level Melting Pot, where the menu features, say, a creamy soup of roasted Guernsey tomatoes and grilled brill with chive butter.

Directions: Northern tip of island, next to Royal Guernsey Golf Club

Pembroke Bay GY3 5BY
Map: 16
Tel: 01481 47573
Accommodation: 12 en suite
Telephone for further details

VAZON BAY,
Les Embruns House Hotel

Set in an acre of mature gardens within striking distance of Vazon Bay, this modest family-run hotel is an asset to the island. Daily-changing menus offer an interesting selection of freshly prepared dishes backed up by a varied wine list.

Directions: On west coast. At Richmond end of Vazon Bay

Route de la Margion GY5 7LG
Map: 16
Tel: 01481 64834
Telephone for details

HERM

HERM, White House Hotel

GY1 3HR
Map: 16
Tel: 01481 722159
Fax: 01481 710066
Chef: Chris Walder
Owners: Pennie & Adrian Heyworth
Cost: Fixed-price L £12/D £17.20. ☺ H/wine £8.
Times: Last L 1.30pm/last D 9pm.
Additional: Bar food L; Sunday L; No children under 9; ♨ dishes
Smoking: No smoking in dining room
Accommodation: 38 en suite
Credit cards: ▆▆ ▆▆ ▆▆ ▆▆ ▆

A unique hotel in a harbour setting with an island as its garden. The daily menu offers an interesting selection of dishes such as fresh picked crab and shrimp platter with lemon and dill dressing, and local brill with leeks and Herm mussels in a delicately curried white wine sauce.

Directions: Only hotel on island; 20 mins by ferry from St Peter Port

JERSEY

GOREY,

Jersey Pottery Restaurant ✿✿✿

It is remarkable that the Jones family set up this renowned pottery more than half-a-century ago. The idea was that visitors should be able to watch every aspect of the manufacturing process, as well as enjoying the landscaped gardens and taking time for something to eat. Snacks and light meals are served throughout the day, but the main focus of attention is the Garden Restaurant. This is an expansive, verdant area with vines covering the roof and plants everywhere; you might imagine you were dining in a greenhouse. Splendid displays of fruit, pâtisserie, and seafood, dominate the scene. Not surprisingly, the 'plateau de fruits de mer' holds pride of place on the menu, but there is much more besides. Mussels are cooked in Jersey cider, roast sea bass comes with braised fennel and thyme, lobster might be served as a salad or grilled with pesto, garlic butter or hollandaise. Presentation is neat and colourful. Wild mushroom ravioli are arranged around a mound of leaf spinach with tomato sauce, herb-crusted baked cod is set on a tomato and sweet chilli relish with a vivid butter sauce laced with fresh green coriander. There are also a few alternatives for meat lovers in the shape of carpaccio of smoked venison with walnut oil dressing, roast duck breast with Armagnac and black pepper sauce, and grilled breast of corn-fed chicken with leeks, bacon and a lemon and herb dressing. The atmosphere is pleasurably informal, although service is brisk and smart.

Signature dishes: Poached chicory, grilled with garlic and Parmesan; pan-fried Jersey scallops with a herb salad; crab cakes from local Chancres with a sweet chilli sauce; pan-fried fillet of beef with pearl barley risotto and white truffle oil broth.

Gorey Village JE3 9EP
Map: 16
Tel: 01534 851119
Fax: 01534 856403
Chef: Tony Dorris
Owner: Colin Jones
Cost: *Alc* £22. H/wine £11.55
Times: L only, noon-last L 4pm.
Closed Sun, 10 days Xmas
Additional: Children welcome;
✇ dishes
Seats: 250
Smoking: No-smoking area in dining room
Credit cards: ▓ ▓ ▓ ▓ ▣ ▢

Directions: In Gorey village, well signposted from main coast road.

GOREY, The Village Bistro ✿✿

It's a spacious restaurant, housed in a converted church, and decorated with hanging suns, moons and stars. A mixed crowd hang out here – locals, tourists and business suits – for cooking that is both modern British in concept (with plenty of adventurous flourishes), and offers value-for-money. Typical starters include fresh mussel and red pepper soup, goat's

Gorey Village
Map: 16
Tel: 01534 853429
Chef: David Cameron
Owners: David Cameron, Sandra Dalziel
Cost: *Alc* £22.50, fixed-price L £12.50 (3 courses). ☺ H/wine £6.
Times: Noon-last L 2pm/7pm-last D 10pm. Closed Mon (except Bhs), 2 wks Feb, last 2 wks Nov
Additional: Sunday L;
Children welcome; ✇ dishes
Seats: 40
Smoking: No pipes and cigars in dining room
Credit cards: ▓ ▓ ▢

Directions: Village centre

cheese with cranberry chutney, and mousseline of guinea fowl and woodland mushrooms. A meal in September kicked off with confit of duck, watercress salad, pine nuts and a lemon and garlic dressing, and was followed by the dish of the day – panaché of salmon, sea bass, king prawns and scallops in a chive butter, served in a large bowl with lightly buttered Jersey potatoes, broccoli and red cabbage. For dessert, crème brûlée topped with crispy caramel and surrounded by sliced strawberries. The restaurant has a large open-air terrace for summer meals, and is handily close to the beach.

L'ETACQ, Lobster Pot, Kevin John Broome

'The arrival of Kevin Broome must have been a shock for the regulars', noted one inspector. Gone are the prawn cocktails and battered fish of yesteryear, now you might find roast foie gras with fried egg and balsamic jus or baked salmon with warm French bean and aubergine pickle and lime butter. Light daytime meals are served in the Coach House, but four nights a weeks this is transformed in 'Sex the Restaurant' where Kevin cooks up a storm for a maximum of 20 people. Otherwise, there is the bistro/brasserie which is open right through the week. Majoring in seafood – including, of course, lobsters every which way – there's no lack of invention or sophistication. Roast sea scallops with a salad of new potatoes and crème fraîche topped with a medley of herbs makes a fine starter, while for main course there could be sea bass on an onion and fennel confit with a creamy herb sauce. Desserts are exceedingly rich.

St Ouen's JE3 2FB
Map: 16
Tel: 01534 482888
Fax: 01534 481574
Chef: Kevin John Broome
Owners: Mr & Mrs K J Broome
Cost: *Alc* £25, fixed-price L/D £15.50. ☺ H/wine £12.95.
Times: Noon-last L 2.30pm/6.30pm-last D 10pm (Restaurant closed Sun-Tue). Closed 3 wks Jan
Additional: Bar food L; Sunday L; Children welcome; ♦ dishes
Seats: 85. Private dining room 25
Smoking: No cigars or pipes; air-conditioning
Accommodation: 12 en suite
Credit cards: 🟥 🟥 🟥 🟥 🟥 🟥

Directions: From St Ouen's Parish Hall on A12 take B64, turn R on B35 at L'Etacq Road. Hotel is at the end on R

ROZEL BAY, Château La Chaire

JE3 6AJ
Map: 16
Tel: 01534 863354
Fax: 01534 865137
Chef: Simon Walker
Owners: Hatton Hotels Ltd
Cost: *Alc* £28, fixed-price L £15.50/D £21.50 (5 courses). ☺ H/wine £9.80.
Times: Noon-last L 2pm/7pm-last D 10pm

A nineteenth-century country house set in five acres of terraced gardens which lead down to Rozel Bay. The well-appointed oak-panelled dining room overlooks a wooded hillside. Imaginative menus (gourmand, fixed-price and *carte*), are modish without resorting to gimmickry, and the cooking is modern English, but with classical French undertones. This translates into starters such as warm salad of chicken livers, pancetta and roast leeks dressed with mixed leaves and balsamic vinaigrette, half a dozen lightly poached oysters served on a bed of spinach, and rillettes of salmon wrapped in oak-smoked salmon with toasted brioche and lemon and dill crème fraîche. Our inspector enjoyed seared scallops served with aubergine 'crisps', black olives and rocket, then pot-roast leg of lamb with sweet-potato cake, and finished with strawberry and cream meringue. A number of good vintages from big-name Châteaux appear on the mainly European wine list.

Additional: Sunday L; Bar meals L; No children under 7; ◑ dishes
Seats: 65. Private dining room 20
Smoking: No-smoking area; no cigars or pipes
Accommodation: 14 en suite
Credit cards: 🃏 🃏 🃏 🃏 🃏 🃏

Directions: From St Helier head N/E towards Five Oaks, Maufant, then St Martin's Church & Rozel; 1st L in village, hotel 100m

ST BRELADE, **The Atlantic Hotel** ❀❀

JE3 8HE
Map: 16
Tel: 01534 44101
Fax: 01534 44102
Chef: Tom Sleigh
Cost: Alc £32.50, fixed-price L £15/D £22.50 (4 course). ☺ H/wine £9.50.
Times: 12.45pm-last L 2.15pm/7.30pm-last D 9.30pm. Closed Jan-Feb
Additional: Sunday L; Children welcome; ◑ dishes
Seats: 80. Private dining room 24
Smoking: No pipes or cigars
Accommodation: 50 en suite
Credit cards: 🃏 🃏 🃏 🃏 🃏 🃏

Privately owned by Patrick Burke since 1970, this stylishly refurbished hotel boasts one of the finest settings on the island: La Moye championship golf course is next door and there are breathtaking views over St Ouen's Bay. A pair of antique terracotta urns mark the entrance to the restaurant, which is done out with dark plum coloured carpets and potted palms. Lunch features dishes such as Caesar salad, beef Stroganoff and pot-roast lamb shank with mash, while dinner moves up a notch or two. You might begin with lobster ravioli with scallops and basil cream or confit of duck with beetroot and five spice jus, before grilled local sea bass with a two caviar sauce or braised chicken breast with kaffir lime, sweet chilli and egg noodles. Then dessert, perhaps pistachio and hazelnut soufflé with chocolate sauce or iced banana crumble.

Directions: From St Brelade take the road to Petit Port, turn into Rue de Sergente and R again, signed to hotel

ST BRELADE, **Hotel la Place** ❀

Created around a seventeenth-century farmhouse, the hotel enjoys a peaceful rural location. The Knights Restaurant is richly decorated in medieval style and has a conservatory extension. The cooking is rather more up to date, with dishes such as shellfish bisque, saddle of rabbit, and sticky toffee pudding.

Accommodation: 43 en suite. **Credit cards:** 🃏 🃏 🃏 🃏 🃏 🃏

Directions: Before St Aubin turn up La Haule Hill by La Haule Manor Hotel, then L at sign towards red houses, hotel 400yds on R

Route Du Coin La Haule JE3 8BT
Map: 16
Tel: 01534 44261
Fax: 01534 45164
Chef: Thomas Illing
Owners: T L S Hotels Ltd
Cost: Alc £30, fixed-price D £19. ☺ H/wine £10.75.
Times: D only, 7.30pm-9.30pm
Additional: Bar Food L; Sunday L (12.30pm-2.30pm); ◑ dishes
Smoking: No-smoking area. No cigars or pipes

ST BRELADE,
The Grill at Hotel L'Horizon

St Brelade's Bay JE3 8EF
Map: 16
Tel: 01534 490082
Fax: 01534 46269
Chef: Paul Stanton
Cost: *Alc* £28, fixed-price L £15
(4 course). ☺ H/wine £12.50.
Times: 12.30pm-last L
2.15pm/7.30pm-last D 10.15pm
Additional: Sunday L;
No children under 8; ❹ dishes
Seats: 50. Jacket & tie preferred
Smoking: No-smoking area;
No pipes; air-conditioning
Credit cards:

Panoramic south-facing views over the picture-postcard vistas of St Brelade's Bay make this hotel something of an island idyll. A choice of three eating outlets includes the impressively refurbished Grill, decorated in 1930s style with cherry wood furniture, classy upholstery and etched glass partitions. The mood is of an up-market brasserie. The cooking embraces everything from contemporary ideas such as crab and coriander risotto with lobster cream and tapenade toast, Thai tom yum soup, and monkfish with black bean sauce and rice noodles to suprême of mustard-crusted chicken with a scallion and parsnip purée, roast grouse with red wine jus and grills of various sorts. Desserts tend to be things like apple and blueberry tart, crème brûlée or a duo of chocolate mousses. Smart staff provide friendly, attentive service. The wine list covers a lot of territory – there's even a representative from Jersey itself.

Directions: Overlooking St Brelade's Bay

ST HELIER, Bistro Central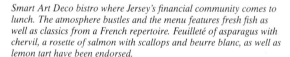

Smart Art Deco bistro where Jersey's financial community comes to lunch. The atmosphere bustles and the menu features fresh fish as well as classics from a French repertoire. Feuilleté of asparagus with chervil, a rosette of salmon with scallops and beurre blanc, as well as lemon tart have been endorsed.

Smoking: No-smoking area; air-conditioning
Credit cards:

Directions: Just off pedestrian precinct

9-11 Don Street
Map: 16
Tel: 01534 876933
Fax: 01534 80423
Chef: Ian Jones
Owner: Michel BS Therault
Cost: *Alc* £24, fixed-price L £11.50/D
£19.75. ☺ H/wine £7.95.
Times: Last L 2.15pm/last D 10.15pm.
Closed Sun
Additional: Children welcome;
❹ dishes

ST HELIER, The Grand Hotel

The Grand is a busy hotel overlooking St Aubin's Bay and Elizabeth Castle. Victoria's, one of the hotel's two restaurants, is decorated in sumptuous Victorian style and offers carefully crafted, fairly elaborate cooking, with the kitchen dealing mainly in Anglo-French dishes with a few detours to other continents for such things as Szechuan peppered pavé of salmon served with Princess eggs placed on a warm toasted

The Esplanade
JE4 8WD
Map: 16
Tel: 01534 22301
Fax: 01534 37815
Chef: Adrian Doolan
Owners: De Vere Hotels Ltd
Cost: *Alc* £25, fixed-price L £15.50/D
£19.50 (3-courses). ☺ H/wine £9.50.

The Grand Hotel

Times: Noon-last L 2.15pm/7pm-last
D 10pm. Closed L Sat, D Sun
Additional: Sunday L;
Children welcome; ⑤ dishes
Seats: 140. Jacket & tie preferred
Smoking: No-smoking area:
air-conditioning
Accommodation: 115 en suite
Credit cards: ■ ▦ ▧ ▩ ⑨

muffin and crowned with crisp arame seaweed and spinach.
The menu is written in French with comprehensive English
translations. There is, of course, a good choice of seafood,
including local lobster, an interesting main course, 'celebration
des viandes', comprising a piccata of beef, a stuffed lamb
cutlet, chicken in filo pastry and a calves' liver rösti, served
with their contrasting sauces, and a range of speciality flambé
dishes, including crêpes suzette.

Directions: On outskirts of town, overlooking Victoria Park

ST HELIER, Pomme d'Or Hotel ❀❀

Liberation Square JE2 3NF
Map: 16
Tel: 01534 88011
Fax: 01534 37781
Chef: Steve Le Corre
Owner: Seymour Hotels
Cost: *Alc* £25, fixed-price L £13.50/D
£16.50. ☺ H/wine £6.50.
Times: 12.30pm-last L 2pm/7pm-last
D 10pm.
Additional: Bar food L; Sunday L;
Children welcome; ⑤ dishes
Seats: 45. Private dining rooms 200
Smoking: Air-conditioning
Accommodation: 147 en suite
Credit cards: ■ ▦ ▧ ⑨ ⑤

Visitors to this town-centre hotel close to the harbour have
plenty to choose from when it comes to seeking solid
sustenance. The informal Coffee Shop and the popular
Harbour Room Carvery are casual options, otherwise go for
the grander style of La Petite Pomme. Monthly changing *table
d'hôte* menus supplement the *carte*, which offers capably
executed mid-Channel dishes along the lines of duck liver
parfait with pickled plum chutney and mushroom bread,
lobster bisque, fillet of pork and celeriac purée with
caramelised apple and peppercorn glaze, plus grills and
flambées. On the list of desserts, expect to find things like
baked lemon cheesecake with hot cherries in port, and
poached pears with white chocolate and poppy seed mousse.
Back-up arrives in the shape of a varied and interesting wine
list.

Directions: Opposite Harbour and Marina

ST SAVIOUR, Longueville Manor ✸✸✸

JE2 7WF
Map: 16
Tel: 01534 25501
Fax: 01534 31613
Chef: Andrew Baird
Owner: Malcom Lewis, Sue Dufty
Cost: *Alc* £38.50, fixed-price L £20/D
£35 (4 courses).
Times: 12.30pm-last L 2pm/7.30pm-
last D 9.30pm
Additional: Bar food; Sunday L;
Children welcome; ✪ dishes
Seats: 65. Private dining room 16-65
Smoking: No-smoking area
Accommodation: 32 en suite
Credit cards: 🔲🔲🔲🔲🔲🔲

Brother and sister, Malcolm Lewis and Sue Dufty represent
the third generation of the family to preside over this
prestigious manor house, parts of which dates from the
thirteenth century. The building stands in 15 acres of grounds,
and a stream trickles down the hillside into the hotel's lake,
which is home to black swans and mandarin ducks. Meals are
served in two sumptuous medieval dining rooms famed for
their carved oak panelling. Andrew Baird's cooking is rated as
some of the finest on the island, and he offers a range of
menus. Despite occasional guest appearances by lemon grass
and pak choy greens, the culinary thrust is broadly French
rather than modern eclectic. Grilled red mullet, sardines and
fennel are served with a tomato sauce, suprême of turbot
comes with fondant shallots and bacon, while on the meat
front you might find hot-pot of lamb with boulangère potatoes,
garlic and rosemary. A recent inspection began well with a
mille-feuille of wafer-thin duck breast interleaved with
shredded confit and roundels of rösti garnished with turned
apple. Next came cream of mushroom soup, before grilled
salmon set on a bed of leaf spinach then topped with a creamy
langoustine risotto. Best of all, however, was an assiette of four
passionfruit 'delicacies' – a small caramelised tartlet, iced
parfait, sponge-layered mousse and a sorbet in a tuile. The
extensive wine list leans heavily towards France but with very
little under £30. There are wines to suit smaller pockets from
elsewhere in Europe and the New World, including some 40
half-bottles.
   Signature dishes: Nage of Jersey lobster with scallops, tomato
and basil; mille-feuille of oven-roasted pheasant, glazed pears
and chicory; roasted assortment of suckling pig, glazed apples
and cider cabbage.

Directions: From St Helier take A3 to
Gorey, hotel 0.75 mile on left

SARK

SARK, Stocks Island ✸

*Tucked away in a little wood, this stone-built former farmhouse
offers a peaceful retreat for weary travellers. In the Cider Press
Restaurant (an intimate rustic affair), visitors enjoy 'franglais' dishes
such as breast of duck stuffed with apricots and almonds, and grilled
fillet of sea bass with a sweet pepper sauce.*

GY9 0SD
Map: 16
Tel: 01481 832001
Fax: 01481 832130
Chef: Kristian Gregg
Owners: The Family
Armorgie

Stocks Island

Cost: Alc £25, fixed-price L £9/D £19. ☺ H/wine £6.
Times: Last L 2pm/D 9pm. Closed Oct-Mar
Additional: Sunday L; Bar meals; Children welcome; ❹ dishes
Smoking: No-smoking area
Accommodation: 24 en suite
Credit cards: 💳💳💳💳💳💳

Directions: Sark – by launch from St Peter Port, Guernsey (40 mins). Hotel – ten minutes easy walk from top of harbour hill

SARK, **La Sablonnerie** ❀❀

GY9 0SD
Map: 16
Tel: 01481 832061
Fax: 01481 832408
Chef: Colin Day
Owner: Miss E Perrée
Cost: Alc £26, Fixed-price L £19.80/D £21.50 (5 courses). ☺ H/wine £7.50.
Times: Noon-last L 2.30pm/7pm-last D 9.30pm. Closed Mid Oct-Easter.
Additional: Bar food. Sunday L. Children welcome. ❹ dishes.
Seats: 39
Smoking: No-smoking area
Accommodation: 22 en suite
Credit cards: 💳 💳 💳

Reached via a narrow isthmus with spectacular views, La Sablonnerie is set in a 400-year-old former farmhouse surrounded by immaculately tended gardens. Despite the rustic architecture, the overall atmosphere is one of understated sophistication. There is a separate beamed bar with log fire for pre-dinner drinks and canapés; dinner is in the dining-room whose ceiling is the exposed joist and boarded floors of the rooms above. Colin Day is a chef who knows how to present well-conceived dishes without any unnecessary flourishes. A guinea fowl and wild mushroom boudin, set on a bed of puréed leeks and a little jus, was a first-rate dish, as was a mussel and saffron soup that was simply bursting with flavour, and a fine piece of turbot, on a bed of asparagus and shredded snow peas with some baby fennel was served with an excellent beurre blanc. Hot chocolate tart with vanilla sauce was described as 'simply the best for a long time'. Much of the fresh butter, cream, meat and vegetables used comes from the hotels' own farm and gardens, and wonderfully fresh fish and shellfish star in dishes such as sea scallops with oriental-spiced ratatouille and chive oil, and fillets of sea bass in a black olive crust, not forgetting the freshly caught Sark lobster grilled with garlic butter.

Directions: On southern part of island

IRELAND
ANTRIM

BALLYMENA, Galgorm Manor

A listed manor house set by the impressive River Maine, and surrounded by an 86-acre estate. The elegant dining room certainly reflects the gracious living of a bygone era. An enjoyable spring meal comprised a tartlet of sweet and sour tomatoes, fillet of salmon in a herb crust, and a vanilla crème brûlée.

Accommodation: 23 en suite
Credit cards:

Directions: One mile outside Ballymena, on the A42 between Galgorm and Cullybackey

BT42 1EA
Map 1: D5
Tel: 01266 881001
Fax: 01266 880080
Chef: Charles O'Neil
Owner: Mr N Hill
Cost: Alc £22.50, fixed-price L £14.95/D £22.50. ☺ H/wine £10.50.
Times: Last L 2.30pm/last D 9.30pm.
Additional: Bar food L; Sunday L; Children welcome; ❸ dishes.

PORTRUSH, Ramore ❀❀

There's always plenty to watch in George McAlpin's vibrant restaurant overlooking Portrush harbour. Customers can view the maritime goings-on from the windows of the first-floor dining room or keep their eyes on the chefs going about their work at the open-plan grill. Fish from the quay is, not surprisingly, the main attraction on the menu and it couldn't be fresher. During a visit in August, our inspector sampled glorious seared scallops set atop little mounds of lobster and pea risotto as well as grilled turbot with Dublin Bay prawns with puff pastry and a creamy garlic sauce. Flavours are honest, presentation is creative. Elsewhere it's invention all the way, with pork fillet in black bean sauce with cabbage, spring onions, chilli, ginger and garlic, or grilled breast of chicken with lobster coleslaw, red onions and coriander pesto. Interesting brûlées such as Thai coconut with exotic fruit or cherry pithiviers with chocolate ice cream figure among the desserts. The wine list is as realistically priced as the food.

Directions: On the harbour

The Harbour BT56 8DF
Map 1: C6
Tel: 01265 824313
Fax: 01265 823194
Chef: George McAlpin
Owners: George & Jane McAlpin
Cost: ☺ H/wine £8.50
Times: D only, 6.30pm-10.30pm. Closed Sun, Mon, 24-26 Dec, 1 Jan
Additional: Children welcome; ❸ dishes
Seats: 75
Smoking: Air-conditioning
Credit cards:

BELFAST

BELFAST, Barnett Restaurant

Set in a 400-year-old parkland estate, this splendid Georgian building houses an elegant, high-ceilinged restaurant. The daily changing set-dinners offer a short choice of imaginative, well-executed dishes. A typical meal may feature cucumber soup with ginger, Cajun chicken with mango salsa, and pistachio tart with rum cream.

Smoking: No smoking in dining room
Credit cards:

Directions: At junction of Malone Road and Shaw's Bridge, close to M1.

Malone House
Malone Road BT19 5PB
Map 1: D5
Tel: 01232 681246
Fax: 01232 682197
Chef: Martin Wilson
Cost: Fixed-price L £12.95/D £22.50. ☺ H/wine £10.50.
Times: Noon-last L 3pm/D on Fri & Sat only, 6.30pm-9pm. Closed Sun, 11-15 Jul, 25 Dec
Additional: Bar snacks L; Children welcome; ❸ dishes

BELFAST, Culloden ❀

Bangor Road BT18 0EX
Map 1: D5
Tel: 01232 425223
Fax: 01232 426777
Chef: Paul McKnight
Owners: Hastings Hotels
Cost: *Alc* £24, fixed-price L £22.50/D
£24. ☺ H/wine £10.
Times: Last L 2.30pm/last D 9.45pm
(8.30pm Sun). Closed L Sat,
24-25 Dec
Additional: Bar food L; Sunday L;
Children welcome; ❹ dishes
Smoking: No-smoking area; air-
conditioning
Accommodation: 80 en suite
Credit cards: 📧 📧 📧 📧

A former bishop's palace, this nineteenth-century baronial mansion stands in 12 acres of gardens overlooking Belfast Lough. A spring meal began with pan-fried scallops, followed by loin of lamb with a wild mushroom crêpe, with a poached white peach in a brandy snap basket with praline cream for dessert.

Directions: From M3 take A3 then A2 (Bangor); hotel is on L just through Holywood

BELFAST, Deanes ❀❀❀

38-40 Howard Street BT1 6PD
Map 1: D5
Tel: 01232 560000
Chef: Michael Deane
Telephone for details

Deanes has come to town, and it's the talk of Belfast. Michael Deane has moved from Deanes on the Square in Helens' Bay and joined forces with restaurateurs Lynda and Brian Smith to open this lively street-level brasserie and more formal first-floor restaurant. The latter is highly contemporary in style, with large mirrors, ochre coloured walls, burgundy drapes, and linen-skirted upholstered chairs in shades varying between neutral to brown. The cooking has a strong oriental, mainly Thai, slant, with an extensive use of oils – coriander, roast curry, chilli, ginger and garlic – as dressings drizzled around the plate. After an appetiser such as lobster bisque served in miniature espresso cups, starters might include spiced carpaccio of salmon served with sticky rice, jazzed up with chilli oil and sweet soya, as well as a generous portion of smoothly-textured brandade of salt cod, presented in the form of an extra-large quenelle with a few tiny drops of black olive tapenade. The earthy tones of risotto of wild mushrooms with roast foie gras and pigeon breast were underlined by the subtle use of truffle oil and jus of star anise. Main courses of beautifully tender beef fillet, built on pale green fennel mash, creamed horseradish and perfect jus with just a waft of rosemary, or delicately cinnamon-spiced quail with cardamom rice and fine green beans, topped with a signature confit wun-tun are stunningly constructed. One of the best dishes sampled was an almost translucent turbot with roasted scallops and miniature carrots. Pre-pudding miniature pear tart with mango coulis kept the spirits high during a rather lengthy wait for a fruit brûlée with an unusual brandy snap flat topping, delicious lemon grass ice cream and vanilla-sweetened syrup.

Directions: Telephone for directions

BELFAST,
Rayanne Country House 🏵🏵

60 Desmesne Road BT18 9EX
Map 1: D5
Tel: 01232 425859
Fax: 01232 423364
Chef: Raymond McClelland
Owners: Raymond & Anne McClelland
Cost: Alc £27. ☺ H/wine £9
Times: D only, 7pm-9pm.
Closed Sun, 1 wk Xmas, 2 wks Jul
Additional: Children welcome;
🍲 dishes
Seats: 30. Private dining room 10.
Jacket & tie preferred
Smoking: No smoking in dining room
Accommodation: 6 en suite
Credit cards: 💳 💳 💳 🄲

The elegant Victorian house is set well back from the road, in an elevated position overlooking its own lawns. Everything here is freshly and carefully cooked and the flavour of good quality ingredients shines through. Past dishes that have met with satisfied approval include confit of duck with orange and passion fruit sauce (perhaps one of the most 'different' dishes), fillet of spring lamb with a crust of garlic crumbs, tarragon jus, fresh tarragon and cucumber, and a good choice of home-made desserts from chocolate soufflé to fruit tarts. Vegetables are plainly cooked but fresh, colourful and well seasoned. Coffee is served with home-made petits fours. Above all the welcome is warm, and the owners work hard, both in and out of the kitchen to ensure each guest is well looked after during their visit.

Directions: From A2 take Belfast Road into Holywood; immediate R into Jacksons Road leading to Desmesne Road

BELFAST Roscoff 🏵🏵🏵

Hot chefs don't come much hotter than Jeanne and Paul Rankin, who have jointly put Belfast on the gastronomic map and built successful TV careers for themselves along the way. Whilst much is made of Paul's eclectic style that draws ideas from the Pacific Rim and the US, it is as well to remember he also spent time at Le Gavroche and is more than capable of producing top-notch classical French food as well. A visit to the airy, modern restaurant, with light wood floorboards, magnolia walls, hard-core modern abstracts and techno spotlights can take in dishes sourced from the Wolfgang Puck school of pizza making (spiced chicken pizza with grilled red onion and aubergine), to Australasian ideas such as a starter of cold oysters with soba, ginger and mirin. Roux Bros-style roast chump of lamb, crusty on the outside with caramelised juices, was meltingly pink and tender within, garnished with crisp ribbons of courgette, turned carrots, broccoli, artichokes, spinach and fondant potatoes and wonderfully sauced with garlic cream infused with rosemary. Our inspector began the meal with an inspired dish of local prawns with inky black spaghetti, confit of tomatoes, basil, chilli and olive oil, choosing from a selection that included carpaccio of salmon with Japanese spices and sticky rice, and warm goat's cheese and potato tart with beetroot vinaigrette. Other main courses might

7 Lesley House
Shaftesbury Square BT2 7DB
Map 1: D5
Tel: 01232 331532
Fax: 01232 312093
Chef/Owners: Paul & Jeanne Rankin
Cost: Fixed-price L £16.95/D £28.95.
H/wine £11-£16
Times: 12.30pm-last L
2.30pm/6.30pm-last D 10.30pm.
Closed L Sat, Sun, 25-26 Dec,
Easter Monday, 12 July
Additional: Children welcome;
🍲 dishes
Seats: 70
Smoking: No-smoking area;
air-conditioning
Credit cards: 💳 💳 💳 💳 💳 🄲

Directions: At top of Belfast's 'Golden Mile', Shaftesbury Square area

include corn-fed pigeon with balsamic lentils and chargrilled mushrooms, and grilled fillet of monkfish with red wine butter and pommes frites. Dessert takes in the likes of oven-roast plums with a little orange cake and almond ice cream, or chocolate pithiviers with poached pear and chocolate sauce. Good espresso and petits fours, and a lively, cosmopolitan buzz in the air.

DOWN

BANGOR,

Clandeboye Lodge Hotel 🏵🏵

10 Estate Road Clandeboye
BT19 1UR
Map 1: D5
Tel: 01247 852500
Fax: 01247 852772
Chef: Jean-Pierre Carré
Owners: Pim Dalm, Peter Woolnough
Cost: Fixed-price D £18.50 (3 courses). ☺ H/wine £9.75.
Times: Noon-last L 2.30pm/6.30pm-last D 10pm. Closed 25-26 Dec
Additional: Bar food (L only); Sunday L; Children welcome; 🍴 dishes.
Seats: 55. Private dining room 10-300
Smoking: No-smoking area
Accommodation: 43 en suite
Credit cards: 🔲🔲🔲🔲🔲🔲

In acres of landscaped and wooded grounds close to Blackwood Golf Course and the deer park belonging to Clandeboye Estate, this Gothic-style country lodge continues to make a good impression with visitors. The complex has its own conference and leisure facilities as well as a country pub offering informal food and drink, although most attention is focused on the main restaurant, where weekly fixed-price menus point to plenty of imagination and flair in the kitchen. The climax of a recent inspection was a dish of superbly light sautéed scallops served with an intriguing sauce based on dry sherry, tarragon and crème fraîche. To start there might be game and foie gras terrine served with a mustard seed compote or wild mushroom mille-feuille, while desserts could range from a 'wicked' duo of dark Belgian chocolates with a delectable praline sauce to a parfait of red berries with Morello cherry coulis.

Directions: Leave A2 at Newtownards sign, 1st junction left, 300 yds.

BANGOR, Shanks 🏵🏵🏵

Despite being tacked on, as it were, to the side of a golf clubhouse, the award-winning, Conran-designed interior is a triumph of style over location. Contemporary, light and airy, a collection of Hockney prints hangs in the restaurant, which also has red leather banquettes and burr walnut backed chairs. The

The Blackwood,
Crawfordsburn Road BT19 1GB
Map 1: D5
Tel: 01247 853313
Fax: 01247 853785
Chef: Robbie Millar
Owner: Robbie & Shirley Millar

kitchen is visible behind a glass screen. Robbie Millar is young and dedicated and battles valiantly against the ubiquitous steak and champ mentality of much of the region. Nonetheless, his impressive level of technical skill is showcased in dishes such as perfectly creamy, textured saffron risotto with langoustines, mussels and julienne of chorizo, exquisitely presented on a plate dotted with pesto. Another first course of Roquefort and walnut tart with quenelles of red onion marmalade effectively matched the tartness of the former with the sweetness of the latter. A modern classic, a main course of confit of duck leg with grilled potato gnocchi, grilled fennel, rosemary scented lentils in balsamic vinegar and spinach, was served in an Ulster trencherman's sized portion. Although at first observation there seemed an excessive number of elements on the plate, all worked together with surprising compatibility. More novel, experimental dishes might include grilled breast of duck with sweet potato fondant, and Thai-style prawn and scallop cakes with braised black beans, tomato salsa and chunky guacamole, the latter saved from terminal culinary mish-mash by the skill of the cooking. Puddings are superb, and mostly include innovative home-made ice cream. A compote of rhubarb topped with pistachio nut powder and gingerbread ice cream, and dark chocolate tart with mandarin sorbet, both impressed with their taste and style. There is also a fine, carefully chosen selection of new Irish cheeses. Shirley Millar runs the cheerful front of house team with a professional flair that matches that of her husband. There are some good bargains to be found on this interesting wine list, a vast range available for under £20. The selection of Italian and New World wines offer the best deals with Cloudy Bay Sauvignon Blanc at £20, Amarone 'Corte Rubini' at £17. Good Burgundy and Alsace sections, and topping the bill Château Margaux 1985 at £225.

Signature dishes: Potato and black truffle gnocchi with grilled asparagus and porcini essence; seared scallops with avocado frittata, charred tomato salsa; foie gras, potato and cep ravioli with Savoy cabbage and Madeira; sautéed calves' liver and crispy onions on wild mushroom brioche, truffle aïoli.

Directions: From A2 (Belfast-Bangor), turn R onto Ballysallagh Road 1 mile before Bangor, 1st L after 0.5 miles (Crawfordburn Road) to Blackwood Golf Centre. Shanks is in the grounds.

Cost: *Alc* D £28.50, fixed-price L £16.95/D £28.50. ☺ H/wine £10.
Times: 12.30pm-last L 2.30pm/7pm-last D 10pm. Closed L Sat, D Sun, Mon, 2wks July
Additional: Sunday L; Children welcome; ♨ dishes
Seats: 85. Private dining room 24
Smoking: No pipes and cigars in dining room; air-conditioning
Credit cards: ▨ ▨ ▨ ▨ ▨

PORTAFERRY, Portaferry Hotel ❀❀

10 The Strand BT22 1PE
Map 1: D5
Tel: 012477 28231
Fax: 012477 28999
Chef: Donal Keane
Owners: John & Marie Herlihy
Cost: Fixed-price L £15/D £22.50. ☺ H/wine £9.95.
Times: Last L 2.30pm/D 9pm. Closed 24-25 Dec
Additional: Bar food L; Sunday L; children welcome; ♨ dishes
Smoking: No smoking in dining room
Accommodation: 14 en suite
Credit cards: ▨ ▨ ▨ ▨ ▨

A welcoming hotel, situated on the shore of Strangford Lough. The dining room offers plenty of window views, especially of the little ferry that runs constantly back and forth. The kitchen no longer offers a *carte*, but has introduced a fixed-price menu, although the choice is good, some eight starters, ten main courses and four puddings. Seafood figures strongly alongside prime Ulster beef, Mourne lamb and local game. Strangford scallops, pan-roasted with bacon and glazed apple on a saffron sauce, baked fillet of hake 'fresh as they come', with tempura vegetables on spiced champ with soya and black bean sauce, and summer berry tartlet with Grand Marnier, made up one well reported meal. The wine list offers adequate choice and is reasonably priced.

Directions: Opposite Strangford Lough ferry terminal

DUBLIN

DUBLIN, The Commons

85-86 St Stephens Green
Map 1: D4
Long established, formal basement restaurant, popular with business   **Tel:** 01 4752608
and corporate diners. Magret of honey-roasted goose on a bed of   **Fax:** 01 4780551
colcannon, with a broad bean cream sauce and light almond gâteau   **Chef:** Sebastian Masi
with compote of red berries are typical of the polished repertoire.   **Owner:** Michael Fitzgerald
Cost: *Alc* £40, fixed-price L £20/D
Times: 12.30pm-2.15pm/7pm-10.15pm. Closed L Sat, Sun,   £35. H/wine £18
2 wks Xmas, Bhs
Additional: 🍴 dishes. **Smoking:** No-smoking area
Credit cards: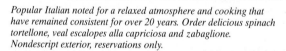

Directions: In the basement of Newman House, close to the city centre

DUBLIN, Kapriol

45 Lower Camden Street
Map 1: D4
Popular Italian noted for a relaxed atmosphere and cooking that   **Tel:** 01 4751235/4985496
have remained consistent for over 20 years. Order delicious spinach   **Chefs:** Maura Hughes, Ronan
tortellone, veal escalopes alla capriciosa and zabaglione.   Flannagan
Nondescript exterior, reservations only.   **Owner:** Ronan Flannagan
Cost: *Alc* £25. ☺ H/wine £13
Times: D only, 7pm-midnight. Closed Sun, Mon, 27 July-12 Aug
Additional: No children under 2; 🍴 dishes
Smoking: No-smoking area
Credit cards:

Directions: Taxi strongly advised as limited parking.

DUBLIN, Restaurant
Patrick Guilbaud 🌸🌸🌸

Hotel Merrion
21 Upper Merrion Street
After the following inspection took place, when three AA   **Map 1:** D4
Rosettes were awarded, Restaurant Patrick Guilbaud moved to   **Tel:** 01 6764192
the Hotel Merrion.   **Chef:** Guillaume Le Brun
One of the key pace-setters in changing the face of Irish   **Owner:** Patrick Guilbaud
cooking, Patrick Guilbaud's modern French Hibernian style is   **Cost:** Fixed-price L £22/D £38.
consistently successful. His team, including chef Guillaume Le   H/wine £18
Brun, are dedicated, accomplished and inventive. The kitchen

uses only produce of the highest quality, with some ingredients specially sourced for them. A smartly clad all-French front-of-house team are impeccably attentive and happy to guide diners through the menus. Pre-dinner drinks are served with canapés such as hot fish mousse; at the table there is an excellent choice of kitchen-fresh breads. Our inspector's early spring dinner began with pan-fried foie gras de canard, perfectly cooked and served with fanned, roasted sweet pears and decorated with dried fruits, enhanced but not overwhelmed by a rich jus. Steamed pavé of turbot with herb mousseline and celery cream was given a clever counterpoint by an acidulated verjus sauce. Vegetables are selected to match individual dishes – with the fish came puréed spinach with cream, mangetout and tiny boiled new potatoes, all freshly cooked and full of flavour. Salads are made from a good selection of mixed leaves and pine nuts, dressed with first-class oil. Just the right amount of alcohol gave a zing to an expertly made chilled lemon and vodka soufflé, which also had a hint of mint, a praline topping and raspberry coulis. The sommelier is extremely knowledgeable about the extensive wine list, which includes twenty house wines, and his skill in decanting is a pleasure to watch!

Times: 12.30pm-2pm/7.30pm-10.15pm. Closed Sun, Mon, 1st wk Jan
Additional: Children welcome; ❸ dishes
Seats: 85. Private dining room 28
Smoking: No-smoking area; no pipes; air-conditioning
Credit cards: ▆ ▆ ▆ ▆

Directions: Town centre

DUBLIN, Roly's Bistro ❀❀

7 Ballsbridge Terrace
Map 1: D4
Tel: 01 6682611
Fax: 01 6608535
Chef: Colin O'Daley
Owner: Roly Saul
Cost: Fixed-price L £10.50. H/wine £8.95
Times: Noon-3pm/6pm-10pm. Closed 2 days Xmas
Additional: Sunday L; No babies; ❸ dishes
Seats: 150
Smoking: No-smoking area
Credit cards: ▆ ▆ ▆ ▆ ▆ ▆

High quality cooking and modest prices draw the crowds. Windows on three sides overlook the general comings and goings of the world outside; inside, the atmosphere positively hums. Tables are closely spaced within partitioned areas, but are smartly laid with Irish linen. The menu is set at lunchtime, a *carte* in the evening. The latter yielded game terrine with caramelised chestnuts and onion chutney, tender medallions of pork fillet layered with rice and onion, served with a broad bean and cream sauce, Roly's mixed salad – a crisp, fresh mixture of leaves, pistachio nuts and tomato dressed with a rich vinaigrette – and Sauternes syllabub in an almond tuile basket with poached seedless grapes and apricot and red fruit coulis. Extras, such as a wide choice of breads and freshly made coffee, are all excellent.

Directions: In the centre of Ballsbridge, at the multiple junction shared with the American Embassy

DUBLIN, La Stampa ❀

35 Dawson Street
Map 1: D4
Tel: 01 6778611/6772119
Fax: 01 6773336
Chef: Michael Benjamin
Owner: Louis Murray
Cost: Alc £26, fixed-price L £12. H/wine £12.50

A popular, attractive restaurant with a strong Italian bias to the menu and moderate prices. Veal, bacon and spinach terrine, baked cod with oyster mushrooms, chorizo and mashed potato, and banana and caramel galette have all been enjoyed.

Times: 12.30pm-2.30pm/6.30pm-11.15pm. Closed L Sat, L Sun, Good Friday, Xmas, 1 Jan, St Steven's Day
Additional: No children under 2; ❸ dishes
Smoking: No-smoking area; no pipes; air-conditioning
Credit cards: ▆ ▆ ▆ ▆ ▆ ▆

Directions: In Dawson St, facing the Mansion House

DUBLIN,

Thornton's Restaurant

This is the place for a wild night out – in the sense that chef/patron Kevin Thornton boasts all his food is wild, not farmed. How valid this claim can be in respect of certain ingredients such as ostrich is uncertain, but there is an emphasis on game dishes and few concessions to 'non-exotic' dining. As such, it attracts a young and fashionable crowd who are sophisticated enough not to feel daunted by the rather elaborate and overworked style of presentation. The dining-room itself is long and narrow, broken by windows on two sides and fine fabric drapes. Padded high-backed chairs are comfortable and tables are well-spaced. Staff are on the ball, and although there are some language difficulties presented by the multi-national team, on the whole everything runs smoothly and efficiently. Dinner in February kicked off with an appetiser of fillet of grey mullet in a delicate mustard sauce, and a variety of very fresh rolls that included fennel, fruit and tomato breads. Ravioli of brill, with linguine of cucumber and confit of lime and ginger made a rich and excellent starter. Although a main course of loin of Sikka deer with roasted salsify and Valhrona sauce had tender, juicy meat, the over-reduced sauce eclipsed rather than enhanced the loin. Perfectly cooked vegetables included cheese and garlic potatoes on a bed of spinach. An exemplary dessert was nougat pyramid with fresh fruits in an orange Cointreau sauce. The 75 bins on the wine list range in price from £21 to £330, and although generally high on price, there is a good selection of well-known names and half-bottles.

Directions: North bank of Grand Canal, halfway between Portobello Bridge, Rathmines and Emmet bridge, Harolds Cross

1 Portobello Road
Map 1: D4
Tel: 01 4549067
Fax: 01 4532947
Chef/Owner: Kevin Thornton
Cost: Alc £35, fixed-price L £18.95.
H/wine £14
Times: 12.30-2pm (Fri only)/7pm-10.30pm. Closed Sun, Mon,
2 wks Xmas
Additional: Children welcome;
dishes
Seats: 45. Private dining room 14
Smoking: No-smoking area; no pipes;
air-conditioning
Credit cards: ▆ ▆ ▆ ▆ ▆ ▆

LONDONDERRY

LIMAVADY, **The Lime Tree**

A simply appointed restaurant serving generous portions of honest, good-value food. Our inspector enjoyed the best, freshest home-made wheaten he'd ever tasted. Fresh fish is a speciality, with dishes such as cod with spinach and cheese sauce alongside rich beef, mushroom and Guinness pie.

Additional: Sunday L; Children welcome; dishes
Smoking: No pipes or cigars
Credit cards: ▆ ▆ ▆ ▆

Directions: Entering Limavady from the Derry side, the restaurant is on the right side on a small slip road

60 Catherine Street BT49 9DB
Map 1: C5
Tel: 015047 64300
Chef: Stanley Matthews
Owners: Stanley & Maria Matthews
Cost: Alc £17. H/wine £7.95. ☺
Times: Last L 2pm/last D 9.30pm.
Closed Mon, Tue

LIMAVADY,

Radisson Roe Park Hotel

Local produce stars at this elegant two-tier courtyard restaurant. There's fresh seafood from Donegal's Atlantic coast, lamb from the

BT49 9LB
Map 1: C5
Tel: 015047 22222
Fax: 015047 22313

hill farms of the Sperrins, and game in season. Plump chicken breast stuffed with pesto on a robust tomato sauce proved an enjoyable main course at our most recent inspection.

Smoking: No-smoking area; no pipes; air-conditioning
Accommodation: 64 en suite
Credit cards: ▬ ▦ ▦ ⋙ ⚇ 𝄢

Directions: From Belfast take M2 (Londonderry) as far as Dungiven, then B68 to Limavady

Chef: Phillipe Maratier
Owner: Roe Park Holdings
Cost: Alc £30, fixed-price L £10.50/D £23.50 (5 courses). ☺ H/wine £12.50.
Times: Last L 3pm/D 10.30pm
Additional: Bar food; Sunday L; Children welcome; ◑ dishes

LONDONDERRY,

The Everglades Hotel ✸

Stylish modern hotel standing beside the River Foyle. A serious approach to classical cooking, with a contemporary twist, is evident. Our inspector enjoyed wild mushroom and langoustine ravioli, turbot on ratatouille with crayfish sauce, and caramelised apple tart.

Smoking: No-smoking area; air-conditioning
Accommodation: 64 en suite
Credit cards: ▬ ▦ ▦ ⋙ ⚇ 𝄢

Directions: 1 mile from city centre on main Dublin road

Prehen Road BT47 2PA
Map 1: C5
Tel: 01504 346722
Fax: 01504 349200
Chef: Adrian McDaid
Cost: Alc £21, fixed-price L £12/D £25.50 (4 courses). ☺ H/wine £9.75
Times: 12.30pm-last L 2.15pm/7pm-last D 9.45pm. Closed L Sat, 25 Dec

MAGHERA,

Ardtara Country House ✸✸

Daylight streams into the wood-panelled restaurant of this delightful former Victorian manor house, from a skylight which overlooks what was originally the billiards room, enhancing the cheery, attentive atmosphere. Carefully prepared local produce features strongly on the fixed-price lunch menu or the evening *carte* – which is changed each month. A starter of a well-flavoured clear fish consommé with Dublin Bay prawns and a brunoise of red peppers and spring onions proved to be the highlight of a recent dinner. That said, a main course of hake on a bed of julienned green peppers, was correctly cooked and extremely moreish. Pudding consisted of a smooth rum and raisin ice-cream with some of the best caramelised bananas we've tasted. What the wine list lacks in variety – only two house wines are offered from a 30-plus strong selection – it more than compensates for with reasonable prices.

Directions: From Belfast follow M2 to A6. After Castledawson, take A29 to Maghera/Coleraine. Follow B75 (Kilrea) until Upperlands.

8 Gorteade Road
Upperlands BT46 5SA
Map 1: C5
Tel: 01648 44490
Fax: 01648 45080
Chef: Patrick McLarnon
Owner: Maebeth Fenton
Cost: Alc £23.50, fixed-price L £12.50. ☺ H/wine £9.50.
Times: 12.30pm-last L 2pm/7pm-last D 9pm. Closed L Sat, D Sun, 25-26 Dec
Additional: Sunday L; No children under 12; ◑ dishes
Seats: 45. Private dining room 12
Smoking: No smoking in dining room
Accommodation: 8 en suite
Credit cards: ▬ ▦ ▦

Entries in this Guide are based on reports filed by our team of professionally trained, full-time inspectors.

SCOTLAND
ABERDEEN CITY

ABERDEEN, Ardoe Hotel

A baronial mansion, overlooking Royal Deeside, with an impressive panelled interior. Game, seafood and prime Aberdeen Angus beef are features of the *carte*, and the quality and freshness of ingredients comes through in the sound cooking that is now paying dividends. Balmoral loaf, very popular on Deeside and provided by a local baker, opened a May dinner. This comprised of tian of marinated scallops and crab with a chilled gazpacho dressing, roast rack of Scottish lamb stuffed with minted apricots, served with fresh crunchy vegetables and good creamy dauphinoise with the garlic coming through, and orange and honey brûlée with Drambuie sabayon and a compote of red berries to finish. The extensive wine list offers an interesting international choice.

Directions: 3 miles from Aberdeen on B9077, on left-hand side

South Deeside Road Blairs
AB1 5YP
Map 15: NJ90
Tel: 01224 867355
Fax: 01224 861283
Chef: Ivor Clark
Owner: Macdonald Hotels
Cost: *Alc* £28.50, fixed-price L £27.50/D £29.95. ☺ H/wine £14.
Times: Last L 2.30pm/D 9.45pm
Additional: Bar food; Sunday L; Children welcome; ◑ dishes
Smoking: No smoking in dining room; air-conditioning
Accommodation: 71 en suite
Credit cards:

ABERDEEN, Maryculter House

Five acres of wooded grounds surround this charming hotel, and there are views over the River Dee. Of the original thirteenth-century Knights Templar priory, only the room that's now a cocktail bar remains. Dishes include smoked salmon wrapped around smoked mackerel mousse, and chargrilled Aberdeen sirloin with Chinese straw mushrooms on a red wine sauce.

Smoking: No smoking in dining room
Accommodation: 23 en suite
Credit cards:

Directions: 8 miles west of Aberdeen off A93 or B9077

South Deeside Road
AB1 6BB
Map 15: NJ90
Tel: 01224 732124
Fax: 01224 733510
Chef: Alfie Murray
Owner: Maryculter House Hotel Ltd
Cost: Fixed-price D £29. ☺ H/wine £12.50.
Times: Last L 2.15pm/D 9.15pm. Closed D Sun, 26 Dec, 1 Jan
Additional: Bar food; Sunday L; Children welcome; ◑ dishes

ABERDEEN, Patio Hotel NEW

New hotel close to the seafront. The kitchen aims high, has a seafood emphasis and delivers honest-flavoured lobster bisque, lobster and monkfish tails on a bed of squid-ink noodles and a delicate creamy citrus sauce, or the likes of Moroccan lamb casserole, and calves' liver and locally smoked bacon. The Atrium offers simpler lunchtime fare.

Additional: Children welcome; ◑ dishes
Smoking: No pipes and cigars; air conditioning
Credit cards: ▆▆▆▆▆▆

Directions: From Union St turn onto King St; at 1st traffic lights turn R onto East North St; at next r/about 2nd exit. Hotel on L

Beach Boulevard AB24 1EF
Map 15: NJ90
Tel: 01224 633339
Fax: 01224 638833
Chef: Ian Green
Owner: Patio Hotel Aberdeen Ltd
Cost: *Alc* £25. H/wine £10.95. ☺
Times: 6.30pm-last D 10.30pm. Closed L, D Sun. 2wks pre/post Xmas

ABERDEEN, Q Brasserie

Wood floors, large ceiling fans and bench seating set a contemporary scene, yet Q Brasserie is on the second floor of a former Church of Scotland training establishment, and the

9 Alfred Place AB1 1YD
Map 15: NJ90
Tel: 01224 595001
Fax: 01224 584425
Chef: Paul Whitecross

Q Brasserie

Owner: Stuart Clarkson
Cost: *Alc* £20. H/wine £10.95. ☺
Times: Noon-last L 2.15pm/7pm-last
D 10.45pm. Closed L Sat, Sun
Additional: Children welcome;
⑤ dishes
Seats: 120. Private dining room 15
Credit cards: ▬ ▬ ▬ ▣

'churchy' ambience is very evident – the bar is in the former altar area. Paul Whitecross's innovative style of cooking continues to impress inspectors, with sound saucing and honest flavour combinations receiving strong endorsement this year. Lunch in January was an enjoyable experience. It opened with four slices of lightly cooked breast of pigeon on a 'nicely' reduced red wine sauce scented with rosemary and accompanied by a light purée of turnip. Main course was pan-fried calves' liver set between puff pastry and placed on a bed of fresh spinach with an intensely flavoured sauce that complemented the liver well. It was topped with 'fluffy' puréed potatoes and spaghetti vegetables, with cabbage decorating the plate. A 'wicked' dark chocolate samosa came with vanilla ice cream in a brandy snap basket decorated with berries.

Directions: Top of Union Street at Holborn Junction

ABERDEENSHIRE

ABOYNE, White Cottage ⊛⊛

'Rather nice little cottage restaurant', observes one inspector who was surprised by the interior: 'central feature is a spiral staircase which goes nowhere – stops at the ceiling. Also a piano.' The original part of the restaurant is white-painted panelling adorned with prints and pictures; otherwise you can relax in a conservatory that overlooks the garden. Laurie Mill works hard in the kitchen. He keeps a firm eye on modern trends, with Scotland's abundant larder providing the likes of Glenberrie beef in Madeira sauce with roast shallots and wild mushrooms, or steamed noisettes of Aberdeenshire lamb with jus of tarragon *en crépinette*. A May inspection lunch produced much to recommend: deep-fried saffron sea-cakes of Norwegian red haddock and smoked mackerel, well contrasted by salad leaves and oven-dried tomatoes in olive oil and basil; flash-fried fresh scallops, served with Pernod and fennel butter sauce; crêpe filled with a tangy rhubarb fool.

Directions: On A93 between Aboyne and Kincardine O'Neil

AB34 5BP
Map 15: NO50
Tel/Fax: 013398 86265
Chef: Laurie A Mill
Owners: Laurie & Josephine Mill
Cost: *Alc* L £16, fixed price D £27.50
(4 courses). ☺ H/wine £11.70.
Times: Noon-last L 2.45pm/6pm-last
D 9pm. Closed Mon
Additional: Bar meals; Sunday L;
Children welcome; ⑤ dishes
Seats: 40
Smoking: No smoking in dining room
Accommodation: 1 en suite
Credit cards: ▬ ▬ ▣

BALLATER,

Balgonie House Hotel ❀❀

Standing in four acres of mature gardens, the welcoming Arts and Crafts-style Edwardian house commands superb views over the golf course towards the hills of Glen Muick. The daily changing *carte* features salmon from the Dee, excellent local game and prime Aberdeen beef, as well as wonderfully fresh seafood from the East coast and Orkney. The choice is not extensive, but is nicely balanced and ingredients are handled with style. For example, croquette of salmon is topped with a quail's egg and glazed hollandaise sauce, breast of guinea fowl is set on a bed of couscous with Mediterranean-style vegetables and finished with a thyme-scented jus. More straightforward dishes include cream of chicken soup garnished with vegetable brunoise, medallions of beef fillet with shallots, wild mushrooms and a red Burgundy jus, and a light lemon mousse served with raspberry coulis. Vegetables such as crispy green beans wrapped in bacon, honey-roast celeriac and broccoli with toasted almonds are imaginatively rescued from conventional neglect.

Braemar Place AB35 5NQ
Map 15: NO39
Tel/Fax: 013397 55482
Chef: Steven Leitch
Owners: John & Priscilla Finnie
Cost: Fixed-price L £17 (3 courses)/D £29 (4 courses). ☺ H/wine £14
Times: 12.30-last L 2pm (by reservation only)/7pm-last D 9pm. Closed 5 Jan-12 Feb
Additional: Sunday L; No children under 10
Seats: 25
Smoking: No smoking in dining room
Accommodation: 9 en suite
Credit cards:

Directions: On outskirts of Ballater, signposted off A93 (Ballater-Perth)

BALLATER,

Darroch Learg Hotel ❀❀❀

Built in 1888 as a fashionable residence in equally fashionable Royal Deeside, Darroch Learg stands proud on a wooded hillside with panoramic views across the Dee Valley towards the Grampian Mountains. You can take in the vistas from the spacious dining room and the light, airy conservatory. David Mutter's dinner menus are fixed-price, short and to-the-point; one changes daily, the other monthly and guests are welcome to dip into either. To begin, there might be open ravioli of crottin cheese with artichokes and crispy leeks or gloriously fresh West Coast scallops that could be lightly seared, presented with a confit of tomatoes and diced avocado and arranged on a pastry base with sauce Nero. Main courses are also guaranteed to dazzle: saddle of Scottish lamb with cabbage, parsnips and a sauce of morels, or superbly tender fillet of Aberdeen Angus beef complemented by some braised oxtail, pomme rösti and a delicate tarragon sauce, for example. Round things off in style with iced vanilla parfait and roasted rhubarb, or a vividly contrasting duo of chocolate desserts set off by tangy lemon sorbet, cool lime custard and warm chocolate sauce. There's little doubting that this is highly accomplished cooking from start to finish. The wine list has much to recommend it. Enthusiastically and irreverently annotated, there is a pleasing emphasis on wines that are within the reach of ordinary mortals. Bordeaux in particular boasts some cracking examples from the end of the last decade, astutely selected from the best of the lesser estates. No-one should begrudge £19.10 for the finesse and depth of a 1990 Ch Liversan or an extra £1.50 for Ch Marbuzet 1988. Similar philanthropy distinguishes the rest of a wide ranging list with a generous selection of half-bottles being the icing on the cake.

Braemar Road AB35 5UX
Map 15: NO39
Tel: 013397 55443
Fax: 013397 55252
Chef: David Mutter
Owners: The Franks family
Cost: Fixed-price D £25. H/wine £12.30
Times: 12.30pm-last L 2pm/7pm-last D 9pm. Closed Xmas & Jan, excluding New Year
Additional: Bar food L; Sunday L; Children welcome; ❹ dishes
Seats: 48
Smoking: No smoking in dining room
Accommodation: 18 en suite
Credit cards: ▆ ▆ ▆ ▆ ▆ ▆

Directions: On A93 at the W/end of village

BALLATER, Green Inn

9 Victoria Road AB35 5QQ
Map 15: NO39
Tel/Fax: 013397 55701
Chef: J J Purves
Owner: Mr & Mrs JJ Purves
Cost: A/c £25, fixed-price D £23.50.
☺ H/wine £9.95.
Times: D only, 7pm-last D 9pm.
Closed late Nov/early Dec.
Additional: Sunday L (12.30pm-
1.45pm). Children welcome.
🍴 dishes.
Seats: 30
Smoking: No smoking in dining room;
air-conditioning
Accommodation: 3 en suite.
Credit cards: 🔳 🔳 🔳 🔳

Formerly a temperance hotel, this two-storey granite building
by the village green is now a thoroughly unpretentious
restaurant-with-rooms run engagingly by Jeff and Carol
Purves. The kitchen puts its faith in local produce and dusts off
a number of old Scottish dishes such as inky pinky (a kind of
beef hash), and whipkull (a variant on zabaglione which Jeff
laces with Tia Maria and serves with frozen mango puree). A
patriotic flavour runs through the fixed-price menu – Ayrshire
bacon and chicken terrine is served on a purée of butter beans
and parsley, a timbale of Parma ham and oak-smoked haddock
is served on Caesar salad – but there are other influences
aplenty as well. Our inspector chose a delicate mousse of
chicken livers and foie gras on a bed of sautéed turnip with a
port jus lie, Sauternes sorbet and orange brioche. Next came
roast fillet of turbot on a thyme potato cake and spinach, but
the real highlight was a 'positively wicked' mandarin mousse
with a rich, dark chocolate sauce. The line-up of local and
regional cheeses is a credit to the place, as is the selection of
home-made liqueurs and cask-strength malt whiskies.

Directions: On A93 in centre of Ballater on the Green

BANCHORY,
Raemoir House Hotel

*Popular fishing hotel that has grand, old fashioned style without
being starchy. The Regency-style restaurant has wonderful antique
chandeliers, huge windows and high ceilings, and the tables are laid
with linen and silver. The best local produce is used in dishes such as
deep-fried haggis, and poached darne of salmon with lime and
cucumber sauce.*

AB31 4ED
Map 15: NO69
Tel: 01330 824884
Fax: 01330 822171
Chef: Derek Ayton Smith
Owners: Mrs Kit Sabin, Ollis family
Cost: A/c £30, fixed-price D £26.95.
H/wine £12
Times: Last L 2pm/D 9pm

Additional: Bar Food L; Sunday L; No children under 10 at D;
🍴 menu
Smoking: No smoking in dining room
Accommodation: 25 en suite
Credit cards: 🔳 🔳 🔳 🔳

Directions: A93 to Banchory then A980, hotel at crossroads in
2.5 miles

BRIDGE OF MARNOCH,
The Old Manse of Marnoch 🏵🏵

By Huntly AB54 7RS
Map 15: NJ55
Tel/Fax: 01466 780873
Chef: Keren Carter
Owner: Patrick & Keren Carter
Cost: Fixed-price D £25 (4 courses).
☺ H/wine £9.50
Times: D only, 7.30pm for 8pm.
Additional: No children under 12
Seats: 16. Private dining room 8.
Jacket & tie preferred
Smoking: No smoking in dining room
Accommodation: 5 en suite
Credit cards: 🔳 ▩ 🔳

Set in four acres of gardens by the banks of the River
Deveron, this converted Georgian manse is now a most
welcoming little country house hotel. At the heart of the place
is the dining room bedecked with paintings and prints of boats
and ships, where guests are offered a four-course dinner menu.
The daily selection may be quite short but there is plenty of
variety and raw materials are first-rate. Natural flavours shine
through across the board, whether it be in a richly coloured
roasted red pepper soup, baby haggis rolled in breadcrumbs, or
chargrilled darne of salmon with a creamy cucumber sauce,
and interesting vegetables such as tomatoes baked in pesto, all
of which were tasted at an inspection meal. On other occasions
you might find cock a leekie (with 'optional prunes'), smoked
Loch Etive trout with horseradish cream, and collops of wild
venison with bitter chocolate sauce. Desserts could range from
honestly flavoured chocolate and orange mousse to lemon
syllabub or toffee sponge pudding. The carefully selected wine
list has plenty of quality bins, and the breakfast menu is one of
the most extensive around.

Directions: On B9117 just off A97
Huntly/Banff road

INVERURIE, Thainstone House 🏵🏵

AB51 5NT
Map 15: NJ72
Tel: 01467 621643
Fax: 01467 625084
Chef: Allan Donald
Owner: Thainstone House
Hotel & Country Club
Cost: Alc £25, fixed-price L
£15.50/£29.95 (4 courses). ☺
H/wine £13.25
Times: Noon-last L 2pm/7pm-last D
9.30pm.
Additional: Bar food; Sunday L;
Children welcome; 🍴 dishes.
Seats: 60. Various private dining
rooms
Smoking: No smoking in dining room
Accommodation: 48 en suite.
Credit cards: 🔳 ▩ 🔳 🔳 🔳

The Jacobites put the original eighteenth-century mansion to
the torch. The present house dates from the nineteenth, and
offers 40 acres of parkland, a heated swimming pool and a gym
for those wishing to drum up an appetite for dinner. The

Directions: 2 miles from Inverurie on
the A96 Aberdeen road

kitchen works hard to produce clean, honest, wholesome flavours, and keeps a firm eye on what is happening elsewhere. Thus smoked haddock risotto, poached egg, hollandaise and crisp Parmesan, roasted lamb loin with dauphinoise, wilted spinach and port wine sauce, and seared ribeye steak with horseradish gnocchi and wild mushroom sauce, are typical offerings. Properly cooked ravioli with spinach and ricotta opened a November dinner. It was followed by a Mediterranean dish of grilled chicken breast with grilled vegetables and couscous, with a warmed chocolate tart to finish, served with an enjoyable chocolate sauce and orange sorbet in a brandy snap basket.

KILDRUMMY, Kildrummy Castle

AB33 8RA
Map 15: NJ41
Tel: 019755 71288
Fax: 019755 71345
Chef: Kenneth Whyte
Owners: Thomas and Mary Hanna
Cost: *Alc* £27, fixed-price L £15/D £28. ☺ H/wine £11.50.
Times: Last L 1.30pm/last D 9pm
Additional: Sunday L;
Children welcome; ❹ dishes
Smoking: No smoking in dining room
Accommodation: 16 en suite
Credit cards: ▨ ▨ ▨ ▨ ⎐

Directions: Off A97 Huntly/Ballater Road 35 miles W of Aberdeen

One of Scotland's finest country houses, this converted Victorian mansion overlooks the original thirteenth-century castle. The sound cooking is based on the best local produce, including game, fish and prime Aberdeen Angus beef, and are complemented by an extensive list of wines from around the world.

NEWBURGH, Udny Arms Hotel

Main Street
Newburgh, Ellon
AB41 0BL
Map 15: NJ92
Tel: 01358 789444
Fax: 01358 789012
Chef: Craig Rennie
Owners: Jennifer and Denis Craig
Cost: *Alc* £20, fixed-price D £14.50. ☺ H/wine £11.95.
Times: Last L 2.15pm/D 9.30pm
Additional: Sunday L; Bar food; Children welcome. ❹ dishes.
Smoking: No cigars or pipes in dining room.
Accommodation: 26 en suite
Credit cards: ▨ ▨ ▨ ▨ ▨ ⎐

A family-run Victorian hotel overlooking the Ythan estuary, the sand dunes and the golf course. The split-level bistro offers a sound choice of dishes prepared from quality ingredients. Expect Shetland salmon, Orkney oysters, chargrilled Grampian chicken breast and Aberdeen Angus steaks.

Directions: Village centre – A92 Aberdeen/Peterhead, turn right to Newburgh.

PETERHEAD, **Waterside Inn**

Welcoming hotel where Ogilvies Restaurant provides an appropriate setting for some carefully prepared Scottish fare. Dishes sampled at inspection were shellfish bisque, fillet of monkfish with saffron and herb beurre blanc, and an impressive bread-and-butter pudding.

Seats: 150. Private dining room 35
Smoking: No smoking in dining room; air-conditioning
Accommodation: 109 en suite. **Credit cards:** 📖 💳 📇 🏧

Directions: Follow A90 (A952) to roundabout on outskirts of Peterhead; turn L for Fraserburgh

Fraserburgh Road AB42 3BN
Map 15: NK14
Tel: 01779 471121
Fax: 01779 470670
Chef: Robert Horne
Owner: Macdonald Hotels
Cost: Alc £26, fixed-price D £21 (4 courses). ☺ H/wine £12.50.
Times: Noon-last L 2pm/7pm-last D 9.45pm
Additional: Bar meals; Sunday L; Children welcome; 🍴 dishes

ANGUS

CARNOUSTIE, **11 Park Avenue**

An unpretentious restaurant tucked away down a side street in the centre of town. In the high-ceilinged dining room, visitors can enjoy the likes of fresh west coast mussels cooked in white wine, and lightly grilled fillet of salmon served with a spring onion and Vermouth sauce.

Smoking: No smoking in dining room. **Credit cards:** 💳 💳 💳

Directions: From Dundee take A92 N (Arbroath). At 10-12 miles turn R to Carnoustie; at crossroads L, then R at mini-roundabout. Restaurant on L

11 Park Avenue DD7 7JA
Map 12: NO53
Tel/Fax: 01241 853336
Chef/Owner: Stephen Collinson
Cost: Alc L £12, fixed-price D £22. ☺ H/wine £9.25
Times: Last L 2pm/D 10pm.
Closed Sun, Mon, 1st wk Jan
Additional: No children under 12; 🍴 dishes

GLAMIS, **Castleton House Hotel**

Distinctive country house hotel set in its own grounds. The kitchen offers a daily changing fixed-price menu supported by an imaginative carte built around Scotland's larder of game, lamb, beef and fish. Expect game terrine with Cumberland sauce, pan-fried suprême of salmon with chive and lemon sauce, and banana brûlée for dessert.

Directions: 3 miles W of Glamis on A94, between Forfar and Coupar

Forfar DD8 1SJ
Map 15: NO34
Tel: 01307 840340
Chef: William Little
Owners: William Little, Maureen Little
Telephone for further details

INVERKEILOR,
Gordon's Restaurant

Traditional menu reflecting classical French influences, backed up by prime Scottish produce, at this cottage-style hotel. Expect dishes such as fishmarket soup – a crab bisque with a multitude of seafood – king scallops with white wine sauce and mushrooms, and suprême of chicken stuffed with haggis and served with Drambuie sauce.

Seats: 30. **Smoking:** No pipes; air-conditioning
Accommodation: 2 en suite. **Credit cards:** 📖 💳 💳

Directions: Just of the A92 from Arbroath to Montrose, at N end of main street.

Homewood House Main Street
Arbroath DD11 5RN
Map 15: NO64
Tel: 01241 830364
Chefs: Gordon Watson, Garry Watson
Owners: Gordon & Maria Watson
Cost: Alc £13.25, fixed-price D £22.
☺ H/wine: £8.
Times: Last L 2pm/D 9pm.
Closed Mon, 1st 2 wks Jan
Additional: Children welcome; 🍴 dishes

ARGYLL & BUTE

ARDBEG,
Ardmory House Hotel

The cooking is fresh and interesting at this most welcoming small hotel. Haggis flavoured with whisky in a filo parcel with plum sauce, cream of broccoli soup, steamed suprême of Loch Fad trout drizzled with citrus herb butter, and Ardmory style mango cheesecake with Cointreau might be a typical four-course dinner, but there's plenty of choice.

Accommodation: 5 en suite
Credit cards: ▆ ▆ ▆ ▆ ▆ ▆

Directions: N from Rothesay on A844. 1m turn L up Ardmory road. 300 metres on left

Ardmony Road
Isle of Bute PA20 0EG
Map 10: NS06
Tel: 01700 502346
Fax: 01700 505596
Chef: Edward McGarvey
Owners: Donald G Cameron,
William P Jeffrey
Cost: Fixed-price D £17.50. ☺
H/wine £8.70.
Times: Last L 2pm/last D 9pm
Additional: Bar meals; Sunday L;
Children welcome; ❺ dishes
Smoking: No smoking in dining room

ARDENTINNY,
Ardentinny Hotel

The hills and lochs surrounding this old droving inn provide the kitchen with its fresh Scottish produce. Expect dishes such as braised local venison with pastry fleurons and wild rice, and grilled west coast scallops with pickled ginger and tarragon beurre blanc. The hotel looks over Loch Long and the Argyllshire hills.

Smoking: No smoking in dining room
Accommodation: 11 en suite. **Credit cards:** ▆ ▆ ▆ ▆

Directions: Telephone for directions

Loch Long Nr Dunoon
PA23 8TR
Map 10: NS28
Tel: 01369 810209
Fax: 01369 810241
Chef: Alex Rennie
Owners: Bob & Anne Rennie
Cost: Fixed-price D £24.50. ☺
H/wine £9.45.
Times: Last L 2.30pm/D 9.30pm
Additional: Bar meals L&D;
Children welcome; ❺ dishes

ARDUAINE, Loch Melfort Hotel

Oban PA34 4XG
Map 10: NM71
Tel: 01852 200233
Fax: 01852 200214
Chef: Philip Lewis
Owners: Philip & Rosalind Lewis
Cost: Fixed-price D £27.50 (5 courses). H/wine £12.50
Times: Last L 2.30pm/D 9pm.
Closed 4 Jan-28 Feb
Additional: Bar food;
Children welcome; ❺ dishes
Smoking: No smoking in dining room;
air-conditioning
Accommodation: 26 en suite
Credit cards: ▆ ▆ ▆ ▆

The hotel is in a superb setting beside Arduaine Gardens with glorious views over Loch Asknish Bay. Not surprisingly the restaurant specialises in seafood, though other tastes are well catered for. Dishes include shellfish bisque, halibut with asparagus sauce, and pears in red wine with vanilla cream terrine.

Directions: From Oban – 20 miles S on the A816; from Lochgilphead – 19 miles N on A816

BUNESSAN, ISLE OF MULL

Assapool House Hotel

Peacefully set beside Loch Assapool, this charming small country house hotel offers a welcoming atmosphere and home-cooked food. Watercress and almond soup, salmon with dill hollandaise, and hay-baked chocolate cheesecake are typical choices on the short set menu.

Accommodation: 6 en suite
Credit cards: ▆▆ ▆▆ ▆▆ ▆

Directions: Turn off A849 just after Bunessan School and follow sign for 1m on minor road

PA67 6DW
Map 10: NM32
Tel: 01681 700258
Fax: 01681 700445
Chef: Mrs O Robertson
Owners: Mr TA Robinson,
Mrs O Robinson
Cost: Fixed-price D £15. ☺
H/wine £8.50.
Times: D at 7.45pm. Closed L
Additional: No children under 10
Smoking: No smoking in dining room

CLACHAN-SEIL, ISLE OF SEIL,

Willowburn Hotel

PA34 4TJ
Map 10: NM71
Tel: 01852 300276
Chef: Maureen Todd
Owners: Archie & Maureen Todd
Cost: *Alc* £23.50. Fixed-price D
£19.50. ☺ H/wine £7.25.
Times: Last L 2pm/D 8pm.
Closed Nov-March
Additional: Bar food;
Children welcome; ❸ dishes
Smoking: No smoking in dining room;
air-conditioning
Accommodation: 7 en suite
Credit cards: ▆▆ ▆▆

The dining room at the Willowburn overlooks the Atlantic Ocean and is more formal than the Waterside Bistro. The 'Taste of Scotland' menus include Willowburn pâté, with chicken liver, smoky bacon, oatmeal and whisky, pan-roasted salmon fillet with orange and Drambuie, and butterscotch tart.

Directions: 11 miles S of Oban via A816 and B844 (Easdale) over Atlantic Bridge

DERVAIG, ISLE OF MULL

Druimard Hotel

Mull Little Theatre (the smallest professional outfit in Britain) stands right next door to this attractively restored Victorian country house and pre-theatre dinners are a highly popular attraction. Caring owners, Wendy and Haydn Hubbard, offer keenly priced fixed-price menus with supplements, and there is plenty of local and Scottish produce on show. Potted wild salmon is served with chive sauce and oatcakes, saddle of wild venison appears on a bed of braised red cabbage with game sauce. Our inspector was impressed by a well-constructed terrine of mixed game, as well as skilfully created gingered sole and crab with spinach in filo pastry. Vegetables are improving all the time and desserts such as rich chocolate torte or trifle laced with Bailey's liqueur are both adventurous and decadent.

PA75 6QW
Map 13: NM45
Tel/Fax: 01688 400345
Additional Tel: 01688 400291
Chef: Wendy Hubbard
Owners: Haydn and
Wendy Hubbard
Cost: *Alc* £21.95, fixed-priced D
£21.95 (5 courses). ☺
H/wine £8.95.
Times: 12.30pm-last L 2pm/6.30pm-
last D 8.30. Closed Sun D (except
residents), Nov-Mar
Additional: Children welcome;
❸ dishes

Several decent Scottish cheeses (including some from Mull itself) are also available. Attractively priced house wines top the list of around 40 bins.

Directions: From the Craignure ferry turn R to Tobermory. Go through Salen, turn L at Aros, signposted Dervaig, hotel on right-hand side before village

Seats: 28
Smoking: No smoking in dining room
Accommodation: 6 en suite
Credit cards:

DUNOON, Beverley's Restaurant ❀

Set in wooded grounds, the Ardfillayne Hotel looks over the Firth of Clyde. A meal in the elegant restaurant could start with Loch Fyne smoked salmon, or chicken liver, garlic and brandy pâté. Main courses include honey-roast duck cooked with cherries and ginger, and haunch of wild boar with a Burgundy and spice sauce.

Accommodation: 7 en suite
Credit cards:

Directions: On the Innellan Road, 1 mile from Dunoon Pier

West Bay PA23 7QJ
Map 10: NS17
Tel: 01369 702267
Fax: 01369 702501
Chef/Owner: Bill McCaffrey
Cost: Fixed-price D £25 (4 courses).
☺ H/wine £10.
Times: D only, 7pm-9.30pm.
Additional: No children under 14;
🍴 dishes
Smoking: No smoking in dining room

DUNOON, Enmore Hotel ❀

A lovely old Georgian house on the banks of the Clyde Estuary. Angela Wilson welcomes guests while husband David slaves over a hot stove preparing imaginative modern dishes such as roast monkfish with saffron and red pepper dressing, and oven-baked trout with a fresh chive and cream sauce.

Directions: From Glasgow M8/A8 (Greenock) & ferry, or via Loch Lomond, A815 to Dunoon. Hotel on promenade btw 2 ferry terminals, 1 mile N of Dunoon

Marine Parade Kirn PA23 8HH
Map 10: NS17
Tel: 01369 702230
Fax: 01369 702148
Chef: David Wilson
Owners: David & Angela Wilson
Cost: Alc £25, fixed-price D £25. ☺ H/wine £10.50.
Times: All day L/7pm – last D 9pm. Closed Xmas wk
Additional: Sunday L; Bar meals; Children welcome; 🍴 dishes
Smoking: No smoking in dining room
Accommodation: 10 en suite
Credit cards:

ERISKA, Isle of Eriska ❀❀❀ NEW

If you don't have a helicopter, then you have to cross a metal bridge to reach this granite and sandstone baronial mansion situated in splendid isolation on its own picturesque island. The grounds are like a private nature reserve, with seals and otters offshore, herons high in the trees and badgers who call in for a midnight snack. Not that anyone's likely to go hungry, after one of Robert McPherson's dinners, which always feature a daily roast such as rib of Scottish beef carved at the table. The focus, otherwise, is on fish and seafood – tian of scallop mousse, enclosed in thinly sliced courgette with a

Ledaig by Oban PA37 1SD
Map 10: NM94
Tel: 01631 720371
Fax: 01631 720531
Chef: Robert McPherson
Owners: The Buchanan-Smith family
Cost: Fixed-price D £35 (7 courses). H/wine £9
Times: D only, 8pm-9pm. Closed Jan
Additional: No children under 5;
🍴 dishes
Seats: 40. Jacket & tie preferred

champagne and chive butter sauce, makes a delicate entrée, followed perhaps by a selection of fish – turbot, seatrout, hake and monkfish with a tartlet of mussels and a carrot butter sauce. Game is also much used – our inspector enjoyed the fine flavour of a galantine of duck and pigeon meat and foie gras, with pistachio and warmed raisins in Armagnac. As well as ornate desserts, such as chunks of honey marinated pear encased in a brandy snap, topped with a smooth crème de cacao sorbet and pistachio cream, it's worth sampling the Eriska savoury, haggis on toast. Details on the set-price, four-course menu are all top quality, from the little glazed quail's egg tartlet appetiser, to the various breads and the good chocolate petits fours served with coffee in the lounge. Service is formal, but still friendly and welcoming.

Signature dishes: Roast saddle of spring lamb with sweetbread timbale and baked new seasons garlic; trilogy of Eriska berries: raspberry gratin, tayberry soufflé, strawberry water ice; braised boneless oxtail filled with a bacon and herb farce on roasted root vegetables.

Smoking: No smoking in dining room
Accommodation: 17 en suite
Credit cards:

Directions: On private island with vehicular access to mainland

---

KILCHRENAN,
Ardanaiseig Hotel ❀❀

Peacefully set amidst spectacular gardens and breathtaking scenery, the wildly romantic Scottish baronial-style Victorian house specialises in local produce, especially seafood. The set dinner menu offers a choice of three dishes at each course. A typical May menu featured leek and potato soup, confit of pheasant legs with mustard vinaigrette and tartare of scallops with marinated aubergine, followed by tournedos of pork with glazed sweet potatoes, pan-fried salmon with fennel and mushroom ragout and lasagne of chargrilled vegetables. All dishes are served with a selection of fresh vegetables, with herbs from the walled garden. Desserts might include banana pie with chocolate sauce or caramelised apple strudel. Various special events are held throughout the year, such as wine weekends and a Chinese gourmet night. Breakfasts are huge, and at tea time the home-made breads, scones and jams come into their own.

By Taynuilt PA35 1HE
Map 10: NN02
Tel: 01866 833333
Fax: 01866 833222
Chef: Scott Dixon
Owner: Mr SB Gray
Cost: Alc £25
Times: Noon-last L 2pm/7.30pm-last D 9pm.
Additional: Bar food L; Sunday L; Children welcome; ❸ dishes
Seats: 30. Jacket & tie preferred
Smoking: No smoking in dining room
Accommodation: 15 en suite
Credit cards: ▆▆ ▆▆ ▆▆

Directions: From A85 take B845 S. At Kilchrenan village, bear left and follow road to hotel

---

KILCHRENAN,
Taychreggan Hotel ❀❀

The most stressful thing about a stay at this idyllic 300-year-old former drovers' inn, on the shores of Loch Awe, is having to choose between roasted loin of hare sliced around braised leeks and toasted pine nuts glazed with a rich red wine sauce, or a timbale of chicken, celery and scallops, bound in crème fraîche laced with herbs and set on a citrus dressing – and that's only the starters. The nightly changing five-course dinner offers a choice at each course (and that's including a fine choice of Scottish cheeses with date and walnut bread), in which local ingredients feature strongly – Loch Etive scallops, Spean Bridge hare, Coulter's black pudding and Grampian pork, for example. The composition of dishes shows a

Taynuilt PA35 1HQ
Map 10: NN02
Tel: 01866 833211/366
Fax: 01866 833244
Chef: Martin Wallace
Owner: Mrs A. Paul
Cost: Alc £14.25. Fixed-price L £15/D £28 (5 courses). H/wine £12.95.
Times: 12.30pm-last L 2pm/7pm-last D 8.45pm.
Additional: Bar food L; Sunday L; Children welcome; ❸ dishes.
Seats: 45. Private dining room 24

Taychreggan Hotel

Smoking: No smoking in dining room; air-conditioning
Accommodation: 20 en suite.
Credit cards:

somewhat startling eclecticism at times, especially in main courses such as seared collops of Atlantic monkfish tail set on a ratatouille and watercress pesto with couscous, and a penchant for elaborate presentation manifests itself in desserts such as apple and Calvados mousse presented under a caramel cage accompanied by fruit coulis.

Directions: One mile before Taynuilt, turn L onto B845 and follow signs to loch side

KILFINAN, Kilfinan Hotel

Tighnabruaich PA21 2EP
Map 10: NR97
Tel: 01700 821201
Fax: 01700 821205
Chef: Rolf Mueller
Owner: Otter Estate
Cost: Fixed-price D £26 (4 courses).
☺ H/wine £10.50.
Times: Noon-last L 2pm/7.30pm-D 9pm. Closed Feb
Additional: Bar food;
No children under 12 in restaurant
Seats: 22. Private dining room 20
Smoking: No smoking in dining room
Accommodation: 11 en suite
Credit cards:

Built as a coaching inn sometime during the seventeenth century and standing amid thousands of acres of unspoilt highland countryside close to the eastern shores of Loch Fyne, Kilfinan is a magnet for lovers of the great outdoors. Light meals are served in the bar, but the serious action takes place in the formal dining room. Chef Rolf Mueller works to a daily fixed-price menu of four courses based around what he can lay his hands on locally. Fish from the loch and nearby waters might show up in the shape of king scallops in hazelnut oil, langoustines with garlic butter or a trio of rainbow trout, salmon and hake in tarragon sauce. Game is from the Otter estate, while Aberdeen Angus steaks might be paired with, say, green peppercorns and Italian mostarda di frutta. Desserts tend to be things like Grand Marnier parfait, crêpe normande and chocolate marquise. The wine list features around 50 fine quality bins.

Directions: On B8000 between Tighnabruaich and Otter ferry

KILLIECHRONAN, ISLE OF MULL

Killiechronan House ⊛⊛

The small highland lodge dating from the 1840s, stands within its own estate at the head of Loch na Keal in one of the Isle of Mull's many quiet corners. A five-course dinner taken in May was notable for fresh, true flavours, and careful technique. It opened with thinly sliced oak-smoked venison and a Waldorf salad, went on to cream of asparagus soup, then a blackberry sorbet with 'loads of flavour', before medallions of pork with wild mushrooms and gnocchi, served with cabbage, aubergine provençale and fondant potatoes, and finished with a first-class chocolate marquise and Grand Marnier sauce. A short wine list has reasonable representation with nothing too pricey. A very popular hotel, booking is advisable.

Directions: Leaving ferry turn R to Tobermory (A849), in Salen (12 miles) turn L to B8035, after 2 miles turn R to Ulva ferry (B8073). Killiechronan on R

PA72 6JU
Map 10: NM53
Tel: 01680 300403
Fax: 01680 300463
Chef: Patrick Freytag
Owner: J L Leroy
Cost: Fixed-price D £23.90 (5 courses). ☺ H/wine £10.
Times: D only, 7pm-8pm.
Closed Nov-Feb
Additional: Sunday L (not Jul/Aug); No children under 12; ◑ dishes
Seats: 14. Private dining room 10.
Jacket & tie preferred
Smoking: No smoking in dining room
Accommodation: 6 en suite
Credit cards: 💳 💳 💳 💳 💳

KILMARTIN, **Cairn Restaurant** ⊛

A converted drapers' shop, The Cairn is a popular restaurant with a tremendous atmosphere. The menu features a mix of new and old ideas – expect dishes such as fillet of pork with apple and prune stuffing, Highland venison with port and redcurrant sauce, and duck breast coated in poppy seeds with gooseberry sauce.

Smoking: Air-conditioning. **Credit cards:** None

Directions: On A816 Lochgilphead-Oban road

Lochgilphead PA31 8RQ
Map 10: NR89
Tel: 01546 510254
Chef: Marion Thomson
Owners: Ian & Marion Thomson
Cost: Alc £20, fixed-price L £12. ☺ H/wine £8.30.
Times: Last L 3pm/D 10pm.
Closed Tue, Jan
Additional: Sunday L; Bar meals; No children under 10 at D; ◑ dishes

---

OBAN, **Dungallan House** ⊛

Fresh local produce, notably fresh seafood, prevails on the daily-changing menu at this delightful Victorian mansion, which overlooks the bay to the Isle of Mull. Choices may include baked sole with lobster sauce or roast Highland beef, with blueberry crème brûlée for pudding.

Smoking: No smoking in the dining room
Accommodation: 13 en suite. **Credit cards:** 💳 💳

Directions: From Argyll Square in Oban follow signs for Gallanach. Approx 0.5 miles from Square

Gallanach Road PA34 4PD
Map 10: NM82
Tel: 01631 563799
Fax: 01631 566711
Chef: Mrs Janice Stewart
Owner: Mr and Mrs GW Stewart
Cost: Fixed-price L £11/D £23.50. ☺ H/wine £7.
Times: Last L 1.45pm/D 8.15pm
Additional: Bar food L; Sunday L; Children welcome; ◑ dishes

OBAN, **Manor House Hotel** ⊛

Former Georgian dower house complete with views (over Oban Bay) and atmosphere. Excellent ingredients and classic ideas are used to good effect. Look out for terrine of west coast scallops, seasonal leaves and truffle-oil dressing, roasted saddle of Isle of Mull lamb with ratatouille in a port and rosemary jus, and whisky and toasted oatmeal parfait.

Smoking: No smoking in dining room
Accommodation: 11 en suite. **Credit cards:** 💳 💳 💳 💳 💳

Directions: 300 metres past Oban ferry terminal

Gallanach Road
PA34 4LS
Map 10: NM82
Tel: 01631 562087
Fax: 01631 563053
Chef: Neil O'Brien
Owner: J L Leroy
Cost: Alc £25. Fixed-price D £23.90. ☺ H/wine £9.50.
Times: Last L 2pm/D 9pm.
Closed D Sun, Mon, L Tue, Nov-Feb
Additional: Bar food L; Sunday L; No children under 12; ◑ dishes

PORT APPIN, Airds Hotel

The simple whitewashed exterior of the former Ferry Inn belies the luxury within, for the place has been transformed by the Allen Family into an elegant hotel with stylish decor. The scenery is stunning: views across Loch Linnhe, scattered with islands, to the Morvern mountains beyond. Graeme Allen runs the kitchen, cooking with an assured skill that show lots of creativity and finesse, yet without losing sight of the principal ingredients. This was evident in a winter dinner that opened with rich, satisfying roast loin of rabbit, served with a neat, central spiral of tagliatelle, a pungent infusion of lovely truffle flavour, and interspersed with several varieties of wild mushrooms. Cream of red pepper and fennel soup followed, then fillet of monkfish with scallops, squat lobster and tarragon butter sauce, the latter a sensation of tarragon that complemented the fish without overwhelming it. Accompanying vegetables (carrots, broccoli, new potatoes) were simple in cooking and presentation. A good apple and cinnamon flan with cinnamon ice cream came with a light sauce anglaise. Attention to detail is sound with both home-made breads and petits fours receiving endorsement. Indeed, one experienced inspector holds the view that Graeme Allen's cooking significantly exceeds the high standards set by his mother, Betty, for many years. The wine list represents Eric Allen's love and understanding of wines.

Thoroughbred Bordeaux, Burgundy and Rhône form the backbone of the superb list. Bins have been selected with care and there is an immense selection of ready to drink winners from the cream of French producers. Italy is also particularly well served, and there is an excellent selection of house wines.

Directions: Leave the A828 at Appin, hotel is 2.5 miles between Ballachulish and Cannel

Appin PA38 4DF
Map 14: NM94
Tel: 01631 730236
Fax: 01631 730535
Chef: Graeme Allen
Owners: The Allen Family
Cost: Fixed-price D £35 (4 courses). H/wine £20
Times: 8pm-last D 8.30pm
Seats: 36
Smoking: No smoking in dining room
Accommodation: 12 en suite
Credit cards: ███ ▩ ▢

SCALASAIG, Colonsay Hotel

Colonsay is a remote Hebridean island with a ferry service every second day. To make the most of fresh produce, the hotel's daily changing, fixed-price menu offers no choice, but features the likes of grilled Colonsay mackerel with gooseberry sauce, smoked Argyll venison, gratin of Colonsay crab, and fillet of salmon with hollandaise sauce. Bar suppers are available too.

Accommodation: 11 (8 en suite)
Credit cards: ███ ▩ ▩ ▢ ▢

Directions: 400 yards west of Colonsay pier

Isle of Colonsay PA61 7YP
Map 10: NR39
Tel: 01951 200316
Fax: 01951 200353
Chef: Christa Byrne
Owner: Kevin & Christa Byrne
Cost: Fixed-price D £22. H/wine £9.10. ☺
Times: Last L 1.30pm/D at 7.30pm.
Additional: Bar meals; Children welcome; ♨ dishes
Smoking: No smoking in dining room

STRACHUR, Creggans Inn NEW

Fresh flowers and candlelit tables create the mood at this attractive split-level restaurant overlooking Loch Fyne. Good use is made of Scottish produce such as game, prime beef and seafood. A typical meal might be seafood and scallop terrine, baked sea bass with red wine butter, followed by a tangy lemon tart.

Accommodation: 19 en suite. **Credit cards:** ███ ▩ ▩ ▩ ▢ ▢

Directions: From Glasgow via Loch Lomondside, Arrochar, the 'Rest & Be Thankful', the A83, or by Gourock, the car ferry across the Clyde to Dunoon, and the A815

PA27 8BX
Map 10: NN00
Tel: 01369 860279
Fax: 01369 860637
Chef: Mark Walker
Owners: Lady Veronica Maclean, Sir Charles Maclean
Cost: Fixed-price dinner £18. ☺
Times: Last L 2.30pm/7pm-last D 8.45pm
Additional: Bar meals (till 8pm); Children welcome; ♨ dishes
Smoking: No smoking in dining room

AYRSHIRE, EAST

DARVEL, Scoretulloch House

A *fifteenth-century stone building, situated on the edge of the grouse moor, restored in period character with half-panelled walls and great roof beams in the restaurant. Our inspector enjoyed 'beef black velvet' braised and marinated in Guinness gravy, and Annie's 'famous bread-and-butter pudding'.*

Additional: No children under 12; ♨ dishes
Smoking: No smoking in dining room
Accommodation: 4 en suite
Credit cards: 💳 💳 💳 💳 💳

Directions: Take M74/J 8 for A71. Hotel is clearly signed 1 mile S of A71 (Strathaven-Kilmarnock), just E of Darvel.

KA17 0LR
Map 11: NS53
Tel: 01560 323331
Fax: 01560 323441
Chef: Annie Smith
Owners: Annie & Donald Smith
Cost: *Alc* £23.50, fixed-price D £23.50. ☺ H/wine £7.90.
Times: Last L 2pm/last D 9pm. Closed L Sat, Sun, D Mon, D Tues, 25 Dec, 1 Jan

STEWARTON, Chapeltoun House

Old-world style hotel set in extensive wooded and landscaped grounds close to Annick Water. The views across rolling countryside towards the coast are magnificent. The kitchen is currently back on form. This year's inspector was particularly impressed with a meal that opened with canapés of stir-fry of vegetables in filo pastry and a smoked salmon roulade, went on to smoked haddock encased in smoked salmon with a vermouth and chive sauce, then neatly grilled tuna with a Japanese sea vegetable cake ('a sort of deep-fried seaweed mixed with finely diced vegetables'), plus some juicy mussels in their shells. Dessert was a creative idea: Belgian milk chocolate mousse sandwiched between sesame wafers. the wine list offers good variety.

Directions: Take B778 at Stewarton Cross then B769 (Irvine) for 2 miles; hotel is off to R

KA3 3ED
Map 10: NS44
Tel: 01560 482696
Fax: 01560 485100
Chef: Tom O'Donnell
Owners: The Dobson family
Cost: Fixed-price L £15.95 (3-courses)/D £24.80 (3-courses). ☺ H/wine £10.50.
Times: Noon-last L 2.30pm/7pm-last D 9.30pm
Additional: Bar food L only; Sunday lunch; Children welcome; ♨ dishes
Seats: 50. Private dining room 20
Smoking: No smoking in dining room
Accommodation: 8 en suite
Credit cards: 💳 💳 💳 💳 💳

AYRSHIRE, NORTH

BRODICK, Auchrannie Hotel

As the name implies, The Garden Restaurant leads into a conservatory extension that overlooks the six acres of wooded and landscaped grounds surrounding the renovated and much expanded Victorian mansion. The fixed-price menu changes daily, and the overall style of cooking puts a French accent on traditional country ingredients. Note wild rabbit saddle stuffed with Agen prunes in a puff pastry net served with a beetroot and hawthorn salad and lovage dressing. The soup of the day might be brown lentil and vegetable (lighter and more refreshing than it sounds), followed by crisp breast of Gressingham duck paired with a rillette, black pudding and apple stack, and moistened with a morel jus. Other interesting combinations are whole sea bass roasted on fennel fronds with stuffed baby artichokes, and baked loin of roe deer with a bread and marjoram timbale, puréed parsnips and sloe gin and

KA27 8BZ
Map 10: NS03
Tel: 01770 302234
Fax: 01770 302812
Chef: Robert Macpherson
Owners: Iain and Linda Johnston
Cost: Fixed-price D £23 (4-courses). ☺ H/wine £11.25.
Times: D only, 6.30pm-9.30pm
Additional: Bistro for L&D; Sunday L; Children welcome; ♨ dishes
Seats: Garden Restaurant 60, Bistro 60
Smoking: No smoking in Garden Restaurant
Accommodation: 28 en suite
Credit cards: 💳 💳 💳 💳 💳

Auchrannie Hotel

juniper jus. A warm apple charlotte made with brioche was well worth the 15 minute wait; alternatively there is a separate, largely Scottish, artisan cheese menu.

Directions: From ferry terminal turn R and follow coast road through Brodick village, then take second L past golf club

BRODICK, Kilmichael Country House Hotel 🏵🏵

Dating from the sixteenth century and built on the site of an early Christian missionary cell, Kilmichael is reckoned to be the oldest house on Arran and, as a hotel, it is a credit to the island. Ex-teachers Geoffrey Botteril and Antony Butterworth have made the place feel like home, with its antique furniture, oriental porcelain and objects d'art accumulated from jaunts around the world. The cooking here might be described as modern European with a slight bias towards the Mediterranean. Guests can choose between the *carte* and a fixed-price deal billed as 'chef's special selection'. To begin there are often unexpected ravioli, beetroot filled with four cheeses or hare and rosemary packed into rich chocolate pasta, for example, as well as, say, sautéed lamb's kidneys on a croûton with Arran mustard sauce. Main courses could range from seared king scallops with a rich orange and wasabi beurre blanc to honey-roast duck with kumquats and a whisky, ginger and rowan berry sauce. To finish, a feuillantine with berries and a Chartreuse sabayon was thought to be 'creative and quite fragile'. The wine list has a popular selection at reasonable prices.

Glen Cloy Isle of Arran KA27 8BY
Map 10: NS03
Tel: 01770 302219
Fax: 01770 302068
Chef: Antony Butterworth
Owners: A Butterworth, G Botterill
Cost: *Alc* £20, fixed-price D £28.50 (5 courses). ☺ H/wine £9.95.
Times: Noon-last L 1.45pm/7.30pm-last D 8.30pm. Closed L Mon-Thurs, Xmas
Additional: No children under 12; ᓰ dishes
Seats: 24. Jacket & tie preferred
Smoking: No smoking in dining room
Accommodation: 9 en suite
Credit cards: 🃏 🃏

Directions: Follow Shore Road to golf course, turn L inland at sharp bend. Past church to road end

DALRY, Braidwoods 🏵🏵

Keep your eyes peeled for the sign; Keith and Nicola Braidwood's converted miller's cottage is down a path in the middle of a field. Within, is a seven-table dining room where booking is essential. It may sound almost domestic, but this is a sharply organised set-up frequented by a smart clientele. Fixed-price menus change regularly, although some signature dishes such as roast loin of red deer with caramelised shallots are fixtures. Keith Braidwood is a chef who knows what he is doing and his dexterity shows in, say, a neatly presented terrine

Drumastle Mill Cottage KA24 4LN
Map 10: NS34
Tel: 01294 833544
Chef: Keith Braidwood
Owners: Keith & Nicola Braidwood
Cost: Fixed-price L £14-£16 (2-3 courses)/D £25-£28 (3-4 courses). H/wine £11.95
Times: Noon-last L 1.45pm/7pm-last D 9pm. Closed D Sun, Mon, L Tue, 1st 3 wks Jan, last wk Sep, 1st wk Oct

of fresh and potted salmon with a cucumber vinaigrette, or breast of Gressingham duck with a brilliant crisp-skinned confit of the leg on a 'lip-smacking' green and pink peppercorn sauce. Vegetables are individually tailored to each dish and they look good – a tower of creamy leaf spinach, a tube of thinly sliced courgette containing carrot and a purée of parsnip, for example. Puddings are real dazzlers – witness a brilliantly innovative dark chocolate soufflé pudding containing melted chocolate sauce and served with Grand Marnier ice cream. The well chosen wine list offers plenty of interesting drinking to suit all pockets.

Additional: Sunday L;
No children under 12
Seats: 24
Smoking: No smoking establishment
Credit cards: 💳 💳 💳 💳 💳

Directions: 1 mile from Dalry on the Saltcoats Road

KILWINNING, Montgreenan Mansion House Hotel

Montgreenan Estate
KA13 7QZ
Map 10: NS34
Tel: 01294 557733
Fax: 01294 850397
Chef: Alan McColl
Owners: The Dobson family
Cost: Alc £25, fixed-price L £13.75/D £25.80. ☺ H/wine £11.20.
Times: Last L 2.30pm/D-9.30pm
Additional: Bar food L; Sunday L; Children welcome; 🍴 dishes
Smoking: No smoking in dining room
Accommodation: 21 en suite
Credit cards: 💳 💳 💳 💳 💳 💳

Directions: 4 miles N of Irvine, & 19 miles S of Glasgow on A736

West coast seafood hors d'oeuvre, seared Tay salmon with a prawn and mussel broth and cannon of Ayrshire lamb with a duo of mint and rosemary sauce, are amongst local ingredients given an upmarket treatment at this nineteenth-century mansion set in 50 acres of grounds.

LARGS, Brisbane House 🏵

14 Greenock Road KA30 8NF
Map 10: NS25
Tel: 01475 687200
Fax: 01475 676295
Chef: Steven Peddie
Owners: Brisbane House Hotel
Cost: Alc £28, fixed-price D £19.50 (4-courses). ☺ H/wine £11.
Times: Last L 2.15pm/D 9.15pm
Additional: Children welcome; 🍴 dishes
Smoking: No pipes and cigars
Accommodation: 23 en suite
Credit cards: 💳 💳 💳 💳 💳

Directions: On main road, 200 yds from the Pier

Attractive Georgian house by the promenade and close to the centre of this popular resort. Good choice of menus, especially seafood, with the kitchen adopting a traditional/classical style. A typical meal could be chef's home-made pâté, Dover sole served with a lobster sauce with prawns, and a milk chocolate torte.

AYRSHIRE, SOUTH

AYR, Fairfield House Hotel

A Victorian mansion house with classic interior design by Lady Henrietta Spencer-Churchill. The kitchen has settled down of late, and now offers an imaginative fixed-price menu in the Fleur de Lys restaurant, and a *carte* with popular, but no less creative dishes in the informal Conservatory – it is the former that is the more stylish operation. Here, an April dinner opened with slivers of salmon and scallops marinated in a mango vinaigrette and served with a crab salad – rather different and refreshing with all the flavours clearly defined. Roast tomato soup contrasted well with a smoked cheese croûton, then came the centrepiece, fillet of lamb with a ragout of garlic and shallots with a hint of rosemary and a well judged red wine sauce. Dessert was a good pear Normandy with a sauce anglaise and honey ice cream.

Directions: Town centre, down Miller Rd to T junction with traffic lights, filter L, immediately R into Fairfield Rd

12 Fairfield Road
KA7 2AR
Map 10: NS32
Tel: 01292 267461
Fax: 01292 261456
Chef: James Thomson
Owners: Mr & Mrs Martin
Cost: Fixed-price L £14.50/D £24. ☺
H/wine £13.95.
Times: Last L 2pm/D 9.30pm
Additional: Sunday L; Bar meals;
Children welcome; ✪ dishes
Smoking: No smoking in dining room
Accommodation: 33 en suite
Credit cards: 🏧

AYR, Fouters Bistro

Steep stone steps lead down into the former vaults of the old British Linen Bank, built in 1725. The flagstone floor and white walls allow both the food and customers to shine (the owner describes his customers as 'colourful'). Certainly, there's plenty of character in dishes such as roast saddle of Carrick venison with gin and juniper sauce, purée of sweet potatoes and soused red cabbage, or breast of guinea fowl with a plum and chicken stuffing served with a fruity wine and stock sauce. Locally landed hake fillet may be pan-seared and served with parsley flavoured mash and roast red pepper coulis, and a large bowl of steamed Loch Fyne mussels arrives aromatic with wine, garlic, parsley and lemon. Chargrilled steaks come from locally certified herds. A mid-week set menu offers 'A Taste of Burns Country' with whisky marinated salmon, cullen skink soup and pot roast Ayrshire pigeon amongst the attractions. Pavlova meringue and bread-and-butter pudding are amongst a fairly conventional choice of puddings.

Directions: Town centre, opposite Town Hall, down Cobblestone Lane

2A Academy Street KA7 1HS
Map 10: NS32
Tel: 01292 261391
Fax: 01292 619323
Chef: Laurie Black
Owner: Laurie & Fran Black
Cost: Fixed-price D £21.50. ☺
H/wine £12.50.
Times: Noon-last L 2pm/6.30pm-last
D 10.30pm. Closed Sun, Mon, 4 days
Xmas, 4 days New Year
Additional: Children welcome;
✪ dishes
Seats: 38
Smoking: No-smoking area, no pipes,
air-conditioning
Credit cards: 🏧

GIRVAN, Wildings

There's a marvellous atmosphere at this family-run restaurant, lots of good banter with the regulars and a general air of enthusiasm in both the welcome and the cooking. No wonder it is always busy (booking is essential – note they don't take credit cards), with the fish specialities being the popular choice. Both fresh prawns in garlic butter and butterfly prawns with spicy sauce were good, uncomplicated choices, as was a perfectly cooked Cajun salmon with sliced new potatoes and salad. Another main course of sea bream, hake and salmon, in which the fish was lightly cooked, seared and served on top of noodles with lobster vinaigrette, demonstrated both the kitchen's creativity and skill. Meat dishes include peppered

Montgomerie Street
KA26 9HE
Map 10: NX29
Tel: 01465 713481
Chef: Brian Sage
Owners: Mr & Mrs BJ Sage
Cost: H/wine £10.25. ☺
Times: Noon-last L 2pm/6.30pm-last
D 9.30pm. Closed D Sun, Mon, Tue,
4 wks Sept/Oct, 3 wks Xmas/New
Year
Additional: Children welcome;
✪ dishes
Seats: 45

steak and rack of lamb with potato pancake and cabbage, and there are good French fries. Crêpes filled with caramelised pears with toffee ice cream, and iced caramel soufflé with a raspberry and a mango coulis feature amongst the desserts.

Directions: Just off A77 at the north end of village

TROON, Highgrove House

Booking is essential at this popular hotel overlooking the Firth of Forth – there are spectacular views on a clear day. Good value lunches might begin with country pâté with Cumberland sauce and crusty herb and garlic bread, followed by breast of chicken with creamy curried sauce and rice with raisins, plus two sorts of potato, courgettes, and cauliflower with cheese. After the bread-and-butter pudding, save a little space for the light shortbread served with good filter coffee. Dinners are equally carefully cooked and creatively presented, although there is a tendency to go in for some very intricate garnishing. Wines have been thoughtfully chosen, the house selection changes regularly and the list has informative tasting notes.

Directions: A77 from Ayr (Glasgow), L at Prestwick Airport, first R to Irvine. First L to Loans, R at mini roundabout to Highgrove

Old Loans Road KA10 7HL
Map 10: NS33
Tel: 01292 312511
Fax: 01292 318228
Chefs: James Alison, Bill Costley
Owner: Bill Costley
Cost: Alc £22.50, fixed-price L £12/D £22.50. ☺ H/wine £9.95.
Times: Noon-last L 2.30pm/6pm-last D 9.30pm
Additional: Children welcome; 🍴 dishes
Seats: 80. Private dining room 16
Smoking: No pipes & cigars; air-conditioning
Accommodation: 9 en suite
Credit cards: 🖪 🖪 🖪 🖪 🖪

TROON, Lochgreen House

A popular, traditional country house hotel with the four dining rooms, characterised by wood panelling, open log fires and fine floral displays, looking out over extensive gardens. There is plenty of variety in all departments, from the nibbles in the bar, starters such as terrine of venison, guinea fowl and wild mushrooms, with a port wine and orange preserve and a prettily presented mousseline of fish with white wine sauce and mussels to main courses such as slices of duck breast with onion marmalade, served with a side bowl of vegetables. Other options could be a vegetarian tagliatelle, or escalope of salmon with pesto pasta, langoustines and seared peppers. The wide choice continues at the dessert stage, ranging from lemon posset with petticoat tails and vanilla parfait, to rich chocolate torte with Cointreau sauce.

Directions: Off A77 (Prestwick Airport) onto B749, S/E of Troon

Monktonhill Road
Southwood KA10 7EN
Map 10: NS33
Tel: 01292 313343
Fax: 01292 318661
Chef: Ian Ferguson
Owner: Mr & Mrs W Costley
Cost: Fixed-price L £17.95 (4 courses)/D £28.50 (5 courses). H/wine £12.50.
Times: Noon-last L 2pm/7pm-last D 9pm
Additional: Sunday L
Seats: 80
Smoking: No smoking in dining room
Accommodation: 15 en suite
Credit cards: 🖪 🖪 🖪 🖪 🖪

TROON, Marine Highland Hotel 🏵

There's a choice of restaurants at this hotel, which overlooks the 18th fairway of the Royal Troon Golf Course. Rizzios, which offers a full Italian menu, and Fairways with views of the course. In the latter, typical dishes include lobster and sole terrine, Scotch lamb, and steamed toffee pudding.

Additional: Sunday L; Children welcome; 🍴 dishes
Smoking: No smoking in dining room
Accommodation: 72 en suite
Credit cards: 🖪 🖪 🖪 🖪 🖪

Directions: Take A77 from Glasgow (following signs for Prestwick Airport) and turn onto B789 – hotel overlooks 18th fairway of Royal Troon Golf Course

KA10 6HE
Map 10: NS33
Tel: 01292 314444
Fax: 01292 316922
Chef: Richard Sturgeon
Owners: Scottish Highland
Cost: Alc £19.95, fixed-price L £14.50/D £19.95. ☺ H/wine £9.95.
Times: Last L 2pm/last D 9.30pm. Closed L Mon, L Tue

TROON, Piersland House Hotel

Craigend Road KA10 6HD
Map 10: NS33
Tel: 01292 314747
Fax: 01292 315613
Chef: John Rae
Owners: Piersland House Hotel
Cost: Fixed-price L £11.95/D £19.95.
☺ H/wine £9.25.
Times: Last L 2.30pm/D 9.30pm
Additional: Sunday L; Bar meals;
Children welcome; ✿ dishes
Smoking: No smoking in dining room
Accommodation: 26 en suite
Credit cards: 🔲🔲🔲🔲🔲🔲

*A mock Tudor hotel in handsome grounds close to the
championship golf course. The four-course menu might include
succulent prawns with salmon in a seafood mayonnaise followed by
a soup or sorbet. Chicken Piersland flambé is a house speciality
with, perhaps, bread and butter pudding to finish.*

Directions: Opposite Royal Troon Golf Club

TURNBERRY, Malin Court

KA26 9PB
Map 10: NS20
Tel: 01655 331457
Fax: 01655 331072
Chef: Andrea Brach
Owners: Malin Court Ltd
Cost: Fixed-price L £10.95/D £21.95.
H/wine £10.95. ☺
Times: Last L 2.15pm/last D 9pm
Additional: Bar food L; Sunday L;
Children welcome; ✿ dishes
Smoking: Air-conditioning
Accommodation: 17 en suite
Credit cards: 🔲🔲🔲🔲🔲

*Lots of light and pastel shades characterise this hotel restaurant,
which offers views over the Firth of Clyde and surrounding
countryside. Smoked mackerel pâté with horseradish dressing might
be followed by Ayrshire lamb rolled in a garlic crust on ratatouille.
And to finish, perhaps lemon tart with basil ice cream.*

Directions: On A719 one mile from A77 on N side of village

TURNBERRY, Turnberry Hotel

The window seats at the flagship Turnberry restaurant are as
hotly contested as any of the championship matches at this
great golfing hotel. The traditional Edwardian-style setting –
all polished silver and meat carved from the trolley – matches
a *carte* full of madly luxurious ingredients with prices to match:
lobster Thermidor, foie gras terrine with black truffle, and
Loch Fyne oysters. But, if money is no object, then enjoy to
the full dishes such as a melt-in-the-mouth carpaccio of
Aberdeen Angus beef, veal cutlet sautéed with morel

KA26 9LT
Map 10: NS20
Tel: 01655 331000
Fax: 01655 331706
Chef: Stewart Cameron
Cost: *Alc* £55; fixed-price D £43.50
(4 courses). ☺ H/wine £19.50
Times: D only, 7.30pm-last D 10pm
Additional: Bar food; Sunday L (1pm-
2.30pm); Children welcome; ✿ dishes
Seats: 180. Private dining room 12

Turnberry Hotel

Smoking: No pipes in dining room
Accommodation: 132 en suite
Credit cards: ▆ ▆ ▆ ▆ ▆

mushrooms and Marsala essence, and seared confit of magret duck with mandarins and rosemary scented haricot beans. Alternatively, the Bay at Turnberry offers modern Scottish cooking in a light and airy setting.

Directions: On the main A77. Turn right at Turnberry village, hotel is half a mile on right opposite golf courses

CLACKMANNANSHIRE

ALLOA, Gean House

Built in 1912 as a family wedding present and set in a vast estate, this beautiful Edwardian house has been enthusiastically restored by Sandra Frost. Everywhere are ornate ceilings and inglenook fireplaces, while the dining room is sumptuously done out in African black-walnut panelling. It makes a suitably civilised setting for food that is creating a good deal of interest – especially with city-dwellers from Glasgow and Edinburgh. An inspection lunch showed what the kitchen is capable of: pan-fried button mushrooms with tarragon and a Drambuie cream sauce, fillet of cod with asparagus and cheese, plus firm vegetables in a pastry tartlet, followed by bread-and-butter pudding. More ambitious dinners bring into play oysters wrapped in bacon with lemon dressing, warm pigeon salad, breast of guinea fowl with herb-scented rice and rosemary jus, and poached salmon with lemon and dill. The short wine list offers a carefully chosen, well balanced selection.

Directions: A907 (Stirling-Alloa), L (Tullibody) B9096, hotel signed 250yds past Jaegar of Alloa

Tullibody Road FK10 2HS
Map 11: NS89
Tel: 01259 219275
Fax: 01259 213827
Chef: William Finnerty
Owner: Mrs Sandra Frost
Cost: *Alc* £15, fixed-price L £16 (3 courses)/D £26.50 (3 courses). ☺
H/wine £11.
Times: Noon-last L 2.30pm/7pm-last D 9.30pm
Additional: Sunday L; Children welcome; ✦ dishes
Seats: 40. Private dining room 20
Smoking: No smoking in dining room
Accommodation: 7 en suite
Credit cards: ▆ ▆ ▆ ▆ ▆ ▆

DUMFRIES & GALLOWAY

KIRKCUDBRIGHT, Selkirk Arms

Recently converted from a barn, the bright and attractive restaurant signals its ambitions with dishes such as savoury smoked salmon and trout cheesecake, pan-fried saddle of venison with green lentils, celeriac purée and beetroot and red wine jus, and crème brûlée with compote of summer berries and vanilla sauce.

Accommodation: 16 en suite
Credit cards: ▨ ▨ ▨ ▨ ▨ ▨

Directions: In centre of Kirkcudbright, 5 miles S of A75 junction with A711

Old High Street DG6 4JG
Map 11: NX65
Tel: 01557 330402
Fax: 01557 331639
Chef: Adam McKissock
Owners: EJ & SJ Morris
Cost: Fixed-price D £21.75. ☺
H/wine £6.50.
Times: Last L 2pm/last D 9.30pm
Additional: Bar meals; Sunday L;
Children welcome; ᕯ dishes
Seats: 70. Private dining room 20
Smoking: No smoking in dining room

LOCKERBIE,
Dryfesdale Hotel

Personally run eighteenth-century former manse offering imaginative cooking in the attractive restaurant complete with sun terrace and sweeping views. Highly recommended are double-baked cheese soufflé, sole and prawn raviolis with deep-fried vegetables and whisky sauce, and profiteroles with chocolate sauce.

Additional: Bar meals; Sunday L; Children welcome; ᕯ dishes
Smoking: No smoking in dining room
Accommodation: 15 en suite. **Credit cards:** ▨ ▨ ▨ ▨

Directions: Lockerbie M74/J17

DG11 2SF
Map 11: NY18
Tel: 01576 202427
Fax: 01576 204187
Chef: Michael Dunbobbin
Owners: Mr & Mrs R &
Mr & Mrs M Dunbobbin
Cost: £20, fixed-price L £10.95/D
£18.95 (4 courses). ☺ H/wine £8.95.
Times: Last L 2pm/last D 9pm

MOFFAT, Beechwood
Country House Hotel ❀

Harthorpe Place DG10 9RS
Map 11: NT00
Tel: 01683 220210
Fax: 01683 220889
Chef: Carl S Shaw
Owners: Mr & Mrs J P Rogers
Cost: Fixed-price L £14 (4-courses)
Times: Last L 2pm/D 8.45pm.
Closed L Mon, L Tue, L Wed,
Jan – 20 Feb
Additional: Sunday L;
Children welcome; ᕯ dishes
Seats: 20. Private dining room 12
Smoking: No smoking in dining room
Accommodation: 7 en suite
Credit cards: ▨ ▨ ▨

Once a school for young ladies, this charming Victorian property is set high up overlooking the valley. Traditional country house style epitomises the dining room, and the short menu might offer smoked eel pâté, roast duck with a plum tartlet, and hot chocolate muffins with chocolate sauce.

Directions: At N end of High Street turn R into Harthorpe Place (hotel signed)

MOFFAT, **Well View Hotel** 🏵🏵

'Small is beautiful' aptly sums up John and Janet Schuckardt's converted Victorian house set in gardens overlooking the town. John tends to guests in a dignified and professional manner, while Janet works industriously at the stove. Dinner is a leisurely occasion, and the menu runs to six courses with canapés and palate-refreshing sorbet. The style is contemporary, with the emphasis on flavours rather than fussy gestures. Highlights from a recent test meal included a beautifully light chicken mousseline with fine herbs and a zesty cream sauce, roasted cod with wilted greens, mustard dressing and grilled prosciutto and first-class medallions of local venison with a glossy red wine and wild cherry sauce. Bringing up the rear are British cheeses with home-made oatcakes, followed by desserts such as lemon mousse with raspberry and claret sauce and treacle and orange steamed pudding. The sound wine list is keenly priced and organised region by region.

Directions: From Moffat take A708 (Selkirk); turn left after fire station in Ballplay Road 300 yds to hotel.

Ballplay Road
DG10 9JU
Map 11: NT00
Tel: 01683 220184
Fax: 01683 220088
Chef: Janet Schuckardt
Owners: Janet & John Schuckardt
Cost: Fixed-price L £13 (3 courses)/D £27 (6 courses). H/wine £10
Times: 12.30pm-last L 1.15pm/7pm-last D 8.30pm. Closed L Sat, 2 weeks Jan/Feb, 2 weeks Oct
Additional: Sunday lunch; No children under 5
Seats: 24. Private dining room 6. Jacket & tie preferred
Smoking: No smoking in dining room
Accommodation: 6 en suite
Credit cards: 🟦 🟦 🟦 🟦

NEWTON STEWART,
Kirroughtree House 🏵🏵🏵

Stately as a galleon, the eighteenth-century mansion stands in an elevated position, surrounded by landscaped gardens and rolling forestry. There is an air of opulence throughout, and the service is discreetly professional. The cooking is precise and

Minnigaff
DG8 6AN
Map 10: NX46
Tel: 01671 402141
Fax: 01671 402425
Chef: Ian Bennett
Owners: McMillan Hotels Ltd
Cost: A/c L £18, fixed-price L £12/D £27.50 (4 courses). H/wine £12.
Times: Noon-last L 1.30pm/7pm-last D 9pm. Closed 3 Jan-mid Feb
Additional: Sunday L; No children under 10; 🍴 dishes
Seats: 50. Jacket & tie preferred
Smoking: No smoking in dining room
Accommodation: 17 en suite
Credit cards 🟦 🟦 🟦 🟦

tightly disciplined, and generally impresses with its accuracy and keen ideas. Canapés and appetisers set the pace – crab tartlet, cream cheese puff pastry, soused herrings on wholemeal blinis with lemon crème fraîche, chargrilled red pimento with buffalo mozzarella cheese. A terrine of Ayrshire bacon and chicken, with a strong tomato chutney and a slice of brioche and a smoked salmon bavarois with truffles, salmon caviar and a red pepper sauce opened an inspection meal. Main courses described as 'superb', included a rump of (their own) venison with braised red cabbage, glazed shallots, spiced pear and a grand veneur sauce (actually more of a bordelaise), which had meat of a quality and tenderness rarely encountered, and a moist fillet of sea bass on a bed of spinach with a vegetable cannelloni was delicate and well-flavoured. Care is taken with accompanying vegetables – dauphinois potatoes, baby corn beignets, creamed leeks with bacon and a rather retro, but much-enjoyed, broccoli Mornay. Raspberry soufflé, with warm coulis poured inside, arrived with an unusual matching water ice – unorthodox, but, as our inspector commented, a surprisingly good contrast. An excellent selection of hand-crafted Scottish cheeses are well worth serious consideration. Coffee is served with freshly-made petits fours that include lemon curd mini-tarts, vanilla tuilles and dark chocolate truffles.

Directions: From A75 turn left into A712 (New Galloway), hotel entrance 300yds on left

PORTPATRICK,

Knockinaam Lodge ❀❀❀

Stranraer
DG9 9AD
Map 10: NX16
Tel: 01776 810471
Fax: 01776 810435
Chef: Tony Pierce
Owners: Michael Bricker,
Pauline Ashworth
Cost: Fixed-price D £35 (5 courses).
H/wine £12
Times: Noon-last L 2.30pm/7.30pm-
last D 9.30pm
Additional: Bar food L; Sunday L;
No children under 12; ❺ dishes
Seats: 32
Smoking: No smoking in dining room
Accommodation: 10 en suite
Credit cards: ▨ ▨ ▨ ▨ ▨ ▨

The former Victorian hunting lodge stands in a secluded, romantic location on the edge of the Irish Sea. At the end of a three mile drive, it is bordered on three sides by cliffs, while the lawns to the front lead down to the bay. Guests are greeted with a warmth almost as great as that produced by the roaring winter fires, and the cosy bar has a wide range of rare malt whiskies whilst the dining room overlooks the sea. The four-course set dinner menu changes nightly, and chef Tony Pierce does full justice to the wealth of fine produce in the area. Fillet of West Coast turbot is poached with tagliatelle of carrot and a saffron emulsion, loin of Galloway lamb roasted with vegetable couscous, broccoli with hollandaise sauce and a rosemary and port wine jus. The fish course uses native species – halibut, for example, is pan-fried with beetroot beurre noisette. Starters are likely to feature either ravioli of smoked

salmon with a tomato butter sauce, a risotto such as one made with carrot, roast loin of rabbit and thyme sauce, or a sausage, maybe of chicken mousse with roasted sweetbreads, French beans and a Madeira froth. There is also the confidence to keep things simple – pan-fried breast of corn-fed chicken comes with mashed potatoes and a Madeira jus, cream of celeriac and potato soup garnished with a softly poached egg. Bitter chocolate pudding tart with caramel sauce, pear crème brûlée with apple sorbet and tarte Tatin are amongst the dessert repertoire.

Signature dishes: Terrine of duck foie gras with ice wine jelly, sultana brioche and a salad of mango; seared West Coast scallop with a potato crust and a beetroot beurre noisette; hot sticky toffee pudding soufflé with butterscotch ice cream.

Directions: A77 or A75 follow Portpatrick. 2 miles W of Lochans watch for Colfin Smokehouse & hotel signs and follow.

DUNBARTONSHIRE, WEST

BALLOCH,

Cameron House Hotel ✿✿✿

Alexandria
G83 8QZ
Map 10: NS38
Tel: 01389 755565
Fax: 01389 759522
Chef: Peter Fleming
Owner: De Vere Cameron House
Cost: *Alc* £40, fixed-price L £18.50 (3 courses)/D £37.50 (4 courses). H/wine £12.50
Times: Noon-last L 1.45pm/7pm-last D 9.45pm. Closed L Sat & Sun
Additional: Bar food L; Sunday L in brasserie; Children welcome in brasserie; ✿ dishes
Seats: 45. Private dining room 40. Jacket & tie preferred
Smoking: No smoking in dining room; air-conditioning
Accommodation: 98 en suite
Credit cards: ▬ ▦ ▨ ▨ ▨

There's been a house on this glorious strip of land jutting into Loch Lomond since 1400. Only the cellar of the original dwelling remains, but the new hotel makes the most of its magnificent setting; acres of lawns, gardens and woodlands sweep along the shoreline, Ben Lomond looms as a majestic backdrop. Luxuries abound and the place calls into play a whole gamut of leisure and sporting facilities. The kitchen is clearly capable of responding to such surroundings and the cooking is shot through with technical thoroughness and complex elaboration. Local and seasonal supplies are put to good use for a range of menus that brim over with imagination and finesse: pan-fried foie gras is served with crisp rounds of celeriac and oniony spinach all set off by a delicate and shiny Madeira sauce, while terrine of artichokes and potatoes receives an Arran mustard sauce. Main courses lift the creativity a notch or two higher. An inspection dish of seared turbot was presented on a cake of potato and fennel interleaved with a layer of tomato purée and spectacularly garnished with browned scallops and a couple of crispy deep-fried oysters. The pairing of ingredients is a trademark: fillet of

Aberdeen Angus beef with an oxtail galette and braised vegetables; whole roast veal kidneys with an aubergine gâteau, veal fillet and a polenta sauce, for example. To conclude, there might be walnut and apple tart topped with cinnamon ice cream, or prunes cooked in red wine with malt whisky parfait. A less formal approach defines the Brasserie, where dishes such as duck cakes with shallot sauce, and salmon lasagne with leeks and mushrooms are on offer. Interesting wines of the month support the high-class main list.

Signature dishes: Home-cured salmon and parsley sauce; casserole of Scottish lobster, spinach noodles and fennel sauce; asparagus cream soup with Parmentier potatoes served with a chicken and truffle dumpling; braised oxtail.

Directions: M8/A82 to Dumbarton: take road to Luss, hotel signed 1 mile past Balloch on R

CLYDEBANK, **Beardmore Hotel**

Impressive hotel on the banks of the River Clyde. Bright ideas feature in the plush Symphony Room restaurant. Dinner on a wild February night took in a risotto of queen scallops with spaghetti of leeks, then vichyssoise of oak-smoked haddock, followed by collops of guinea fowl breast, fine beans and 'black' – home-made black pudding, lightly battered – all set on top of a thick 'pancake' of fondant potato and crisp French beans and a 'lovely, sweet' demi-glace based wine sauce. Dessert was a taste of apples – individual apple strudel, apple tart with a caramelised top, an apple parfait with a smooth apple purée topping, all offering different degrees of sweetness and texture. Other typical dishes from the short menu may include venison with wild mushrooms and Madeira, fillet of Angus beef with parsley crust, and baked German cheesecake.

Beardmore Street
G81 4SA
Map 11: NS56
Tel: 0141 9516000
Fax: 0141 9516018
Chef: James Murphy
Cost: *Alc* £15, fixed-price L&D from £10.50. ☺ H/wine £11.50.
Times: Last L 2pm/D 10pm. Closed L Sat
Additional: Bar food; Sunday L; Children welcome; ❸ dishes
Accommodation: 168 en suite
Credit cards: ▬ ▦ ▦ ▦ ▣ ▢

Directions: M8/J19, follow signs for Clydeside Expressway to Glasgow Rd, then Dumbarton Rd (A814), then signs for Clydebank Business Park. Hotel on L within HCI International Medical Centre complex

DUNDEE CITY

DUNDEE, **Stakis Dundee**

Great location on the old quay overlooking the Tay estuary. The open-plan restaurant of this modern hotel features fresh local produce in dishes such as Highland game terrine and Finnan haddock with spinach, Orkney smoked cheddar cheese sauce, poached egg and deep-fried leeks.

Additional: Bar food L; Sunday L; Children welcome; ❸ dishes
Smoking: No cigars or pipes; air conditioning
Accommodation: 131 en suite
Credit cards: ▬ ▦ ▦ ▦ ▣ ▢

Earl Grey Place
DD1 4DE
Map 11: NO43
Tel: 01382 229271
Fax: 01382 200072
Chef: Edward Sharkey
Owner: Stakis plc
Cost: *Alc* £25, fixed-price L £9.95/D £16.50. ☺ H/wine £10.50.
Times: Last L 2pm/D 10pm

Directions: Follow signs to Tay Road Bridge. At roundabout outside railway station, take last turning to Olympia Leisure Centre. Hotel is at end of cul-de-sac

EDINBURGH, CITY OF

EDINBURGH, Atrium ❀❀❀

Cambridge Street
EH1 2ED
Map 11: NT27
Tel: 0131 2288882
Fax: 0131 2288808
Chefs: Andrew Radford, Glyn Steven
Owners: Andrew & Lisa Radford
Cost: *A/c* L £18/D £25. ☺
Times: Noon-last L 2.30pm/6pm-last
D 10.30pm. Closed L Sat, Sun,
1 wk Xmas/New Year
Additional: Snack meals L;
Children welcome; ✪ dishes
Smoking: Air-conditioning
Credit cards: ▬ ▬ ▬ ◖

Directions: From Princes Street, turn
into Lothian Road, 2nd L and 1st R,
by the Traverse Theatre.

This is the bullish '90s face of cooking in Edinburgh. The decor
takes no prisoners with its sharp features, acute lighting and
chairs draped in canvas, and the kitchen follows suit. There is
an immediacy about this place that tingles the senses: as one
inspector noted 'you can hear the action and you can smell the
food'. The menu is presented to customers in an A4 sheet of
copper with slits and the calligraphy is seriously sinuous. Never
mind the writing, relish the litany of ingredients: pesto, Paris
Brown mushrooms, ramsons (wild garlic), samphire, and mash
everywhere. Dishes are described in that staccato style that
loves commas: wood pigeon, ham champ, wild mushrooms,
lentil gravy; Feta, asparagus, cherry tomato, courgette frittata;
langoustine and monkfish samosa, shellfish risotto and so forth.
An inspector who dropped in for lunch – which also offers the
option of snacks such as a pastry of goat's cheese with spinach
and pine nuts – was dazzled by the freshness and honesty of
pan-fried monkfish on buttered vegetables with a sun-dried
tomato butter sauce zinged with lemon, as well as succulent
steak and kidney in a rich refined sauce with perfectly
seasoned creamed potato that was given an extra dimension
with chopped spring onion. The dessert on this occasion was a
banana franzipan with soak sun-dried bananas and marinated
fresh banana: three ingredients, one accomplished whole. In
the evening, Andrew Radford's kitchen takes flight with ideas
such as fillet of sea bass with piperade, fine herb salad and
vanilla oil or loin of venison with cabbage, onions, bacon and
mustard jus. Service is perfectly in tune – which means that the
approach is casual, cosmopolitan, well punctuated and friendly.
A well balanced wine list offers over 20 wines by the glass
and an unusually impressive range of old and rare Sherries.
A quick selection page offers wines grouped according to style,
with most offering good value at under £20 – try the Morgon,
Ch de Raousset at £19.50. The USA offers some interesting
drinking with Berlin Semillon from Joseph Swan at £23.50, and
Niebaum Coppola Chardonnay 92 at £36.75.
Signature dishes: Grilled spring lamb with rosemary buttered
greens; roast fillet of sea bass with tomato confit and pressed
new potatoes; wood pigeon with root purée and parsley gravy;
pan-fried venison liver with roasted shallots and lentils.

EDINBURGH,
L'Auberge Restaurant ❀❀

True to its name, L'Auberge creates the mood of a modest eating place somewhere in France. The decor might be described as '80s bistro with its soft peach and grey colour schemes and the food is true partisan stuff. A choice of menus provides a wide range of dishes with some interesting ideas and unexpected touches. A test lunch yielded cream of vegetable soup of superb consistency, a delightful mousseline of aubergine and smoked trout, and a precisely crafted suprême of poached salmon on a compote of cumin-tinged onions and a sauce of beer, butter and fish stock. The highlight, however, was a memorable fondant of Belgian chocolate offset by cinnamon cream. Other dishes with greater ambition show up on the full *carte*: saddle of hare wrapped in a crepinette served with parsnip purée and a juniper-flavoured jus, for example. Daniel Wencker is a true host and Gallic staff continue with their winning ways. The wine list meanders at length through the French regions with promising results notably in Bordeaux.

Directions: City centre, in old town, off the Royal Mile

56 St Mary's Street EH1 1SX
Map 11: NT27
Tel: 0131 5565888
Fax: 0131 5562588
Chef: Michel Bouyer
Owner: Daniel Wencker
Cost: *Alc* £35, fixed-price L £13.75/D £24.50. H/wine £12.50.
Times: Noon-last L 2pm/6pm-last D 10pm. Closed 26 Dec/1-2 Jan
Additional: Sunday L; No children under 6; ❹ dishes
Seats: 60. Private dining room 25
Smoking: No pipes or cigars in dining room; air-conditioning
Credit cards: 🔲 🔲 🔲 🔲 🔲

EDINBURGH, # Balmoral Hotel, No 1 The Restaurant

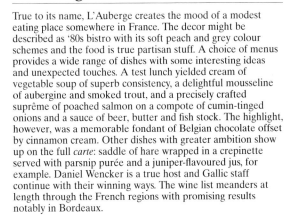

1 Princes Street EH2 2EQ
Map 11: NT27
Tel: 0131 5562414
Fax: 0131 5573747
Chef: Jeff Bland
Owners: Meridien Hotels
Cost: *Alc* £35, fixed-price L £19.95/D £29.50. H/wine £14.50.
Times: Noon-last L 2.15pm/7pm-last D 10.15pm. Closed L Sat, L Sun, 1st wk Jan
Additional: Bar food L; Sunday L in Brasserie; Children welcome; ❹ dishes

As we went to press we were informed that the AA three rosetted chef Jeff Bland (ex Cameron House, Balloch, see entry) was to move to No 1 The Restaurant, thus no rosette award this year. The magnificent room, modelled on the Grill Room at the Mandarin, Hong Kong, with deep-red Chinese-lacquered walls, sumptuously comfortable cushioned chairs and subdued lighting, will remain the same. As will the service, old-school professional to a fault – right down to removing the cover from the butter with a pair of tweezers.

Seats: 50. Private dining room up to 250
Smoking: Air-conditioning
Accommodation: 187 en suite
Credit cards: 🔲 🔲 🔲 🔲 🔲

Directions: Hotel at east end of Princes Street; hotel is next to Waverley Station

EDINBURGH, Caledonian Hotel ❀❀

Princes Street EH1 2AB
Map 11: NT27
Tel: 0131 4599988
Fax: 0131 2256632
Chef: Tony Binks
Owner: Queens Moat House
Cost: Alc £35
Times: D only, 7pm-last D 10.15pm.
Closed Sun, Mon
Additional: ❸ dishes.
Seats: 60. Jacket & tie preferred
Smoking: No-smoking area
Accommodation: 246 en suite
Credit cards: 🟦 📇 📇 📇 💳 💳

The 'Cally' is an Edinburgh institution, and dinner in the magnificent Pompadour dining-room smacks of the special occasion. A pianist plays in background, the experienced staff are professional and discreet and there are fine views of the Castle. The classically-based French cooking brings a first course of caramelised squab pigeon with spiced pear tartlet and ginger scented sauce (which worked well), and loin of Welsh lamb accompanied by a cassoulet of smoked bacon and boudin noir. Saucing is in the modern mode – a light watercress sauce moistens sautéed medallions of monkfish and jasmine scented rice, and Bresse chicken breast is served with it's own juice, sautéed griolles and truffle potatoes. Desserts are selected from the trolley.

Directions: At western end of Princes Street

EDINBURGH,
Carlton Highland Hotel ❀

Quills restaurant, with its library theme, oak panelling and wooden beams, provides elegant surroundings for some serious eating at the Carlton Highland. Dishes include crayfish bisque, Balbeggie farm duck with a honey and cinnamon glaze on a gooseberry compote, and crêpes suzette. Other flambé options and vegetarian dishes are offered.

North Bridge EH1 1SD
Map 11: NT27
Tel: 0131 556 7277
Fax: 0131 556 2691
Chef: Martin Buttrick
Owner: Scottish Highland Hotels

Cost: Alc £21.50, fixed-price L £14.50/D £21.50. ☺
H/wine £10.95.
Times: Last L 2.30pm/D 9.30pm. Closed L Sat, Sun
Additional: Bar food; Children welcome; ❸ dishes
Smoking: No-smoking area; air-conditioning
Accommodation: 197 en suite
Credit cards: 🟦 📇 📇 💳 💳

Directions: Turn R onto North Bridge at E/end of Princes St

EDINBURGH, Channings ❀

Five Edwardian town houses make up this smart city centre hotel. Channings Brasserie offers the likes of Parmesan tart topped with roasted plum tomatoes, basil and 'Paris browns', and glazed peppered duck with pak choy and crispy polenta cake.

South Learmonth Gardens
EH4 1EZ
Map 11: NT27
Tel: 0131 3152226
Fax: 0131 3329631
Chef: Richard Glennie

Owner: Peter Taylor
Cost: Fixed-price D £21. ☺
H/wine £10.75.
Times: Last L 2.30pm/last D 9.30pm
(10pm Fri-Sat)
Additional: Bar food L; ◢ dishes
Seats: 70. Private dining room 18
Smoking: No smoking in dining room
Accommodation: 48 en suite
Credit cards: ▄▄ ▄▄ ▄▄ ▄▄

Directions: From Princes St follow signs to Forth Bridge (A90),
cross Dean Bridge and take 4th R into South Learmonth Ave.
Follow road to R at bottom of hill

EDINBURGH,

Duck's at Le Marché Noir ⚜⚜

An unpretentious, loyally patronised, little French restaurant
in the New Town, where candles, fresh flowers and decorative
rows of corks from used wine bottles set the scene for honest
French country cooking. The simplicity of a first course of
smoked and gravlax salmon, with a crisp lettuce leaf topped
with crème fraîche, allowed the flavours to shine through.
Lightly roasted fillets of monkfish were served on the bone
with ratatouille and a delicate herb butter sauce; other choices
might be escalopes of veal with Arran mustard sauce or breast
of guinea fowl with onion confit and baby corn and honey
sauce. Even haggis gets the French provincial treatment in a
baked filo parcel on a bed of sweet potato purée with a thyme
scented sauce. Lemon tart, strawberry bavarois and crème
brûlée are amongst a reliable choice of desserts.

Directions: Follow the 'Mound' across Princes Street, George
Street, Queen Street to bottom of Dundas Street

2/4 Eyre Place EH3 5EP
Map 11: NT27
Tel: 0131 5581608
Fax: 0131 4677230
Chef: David Connell
Owner: Malcolm K Duck
Cost: Fixed-price L £15.50/D £26.50.
☺ H/wine £9.50.
Times: Noon-last L 2.30pm/6.30pm-
last D 10.30pm. Closed L Sat, L Sun,
25-26 Dec
Additional: Children welcome;
◢ dishes
Seats: 50. Private dining room 30.
Jacket & tie preferred
Smoking: One room – no smoking
Credit cards: ▄▄ ▄▄ ▄▄ ▄▄ ▣ ◖

EDINBURGH,

George Inter-Continental

19-21 George Street EH2 2PB
Map 11: NT27
Tel: 0131 225 1251
Fax: 0131 226 5644
Chef: Klaus Knust
Owners: George Intercontinental
Cost: *Alc* £25, fixed-price L/D
£17.95. ☺ H/wine £14.75.
Times: Last L 2.30pm/D 10pm
Additional: Sunday L; Bar meals;
Children welcome; ✪ dishes
Smoking: Non-smoking area
Accommodation: 195 en suite
Credit cards: ■ ■ ■ ■ ■ ■

A long-established hotel in the heart of the city, boasting a magnificent classical façade and marble-floored foyer. Le Chambertin restaurant sports high-moulded ceilings, huge chandeliers, and has comfortable, intimate atmosphere. The highlight of a meal in March was roast monkfish tarte Tatin, served on a compote of red onion.

Directions: At E end of George St, nr St Andrew's Square

EDINBURGH, **Iggs**

Ignacio Campos (Igg for short) has stamped his Latin personality on this popular addition to the Edinburgh scene and his menus offer an intriguing blend of Spanish and Scottish dishes based around regional produce. Lunchtime brings in the crowds for a lively selection of tapas including West Coast scallops with ginger and chicory, braised oxtail with Rioja and Serrano ham, Loch Fyne oysters, tortillas and potatoes cooked with garlic and paprika sauce. Full menus offer a touch more elaboration in the shape of artichoke mousseline with a blue cheese and coriander sauce, roast guinea fowl with smoked bacon, judion beans, spring cabbage and crème fraîche tinged with star anise, or even grilled salmon served on a bed of spinach with a nicely constructed beurre blanc. Lime and pistachio parfait with passion fruit syrup is a typically accomplished dessert. The wine list is dominated by bottles from Spain's Crianzas, Reservas and Gran Reservas.

15 Jeffrey Street EH1 1DR
Map 11: NT27
Tel: 0131 557 8184
Fax: 0131 441 7111
Chef: Coleman Maquire
Owner: Ignacio Campos
Cost: *Alc* £22, fixed-price L £7.50
(1 course)/D £19.50 (4 courses). ☺
H/wine £11.
Times: Noon-last L 2.30pm/6pm-last
D 10.30pm. Closed Sun, 1-3 Jan
Additional: Children welcome;
✪ dishes
Seats: 40
Smoking: No-smoking area; air-
conditioning
Credit cards: ■ ■ ■ ■ ■ ■

Directions: At the heart of Edinburgh's Old Town, just off the Royal Mile

EDINBURGH, **Jacksons**

NEW

Occupying a 300-year-old listed building on the historic Royal Mile, this popular, stone-walled cellar restaurant offers a relaxed atmosphere and sound, modern Scottish cooking. Dishes enjoyed at inspection included haggis with a creamy whisky sauce, chargrilled sea bass and mascarpone and raspberry crème brûlée.

Additional: Sunday L, No children under 10; ✪ dishes
Smoking: No pipes and cigars. **Credit cards:** ■ ■ ■ ■ ■

209 High Street EH1 1PZ
Map 11: NT27
Tel: 0131 225 1793
Fax: 0131 220 0620
Chef: Andrew Smith
Owner: Lyn Mackinnon
Cost: *Alc* £26, fixed-price L £6.25/D
£21.95. ☺ H/wine £11.75.
Times: Last L 2pm/D 10.30pm.
Closed 25-26 Dec

Directions: On Royal Mile, near St Giles Cathedral

EDINBURGH, Kelly's ❀❀

46 West Richmond Street EH8
Map 11: NT27
Tel: 0131 6683847
Chef: Stephen Frost
Owners: Stephen & Ann Frost
Telephone for details

A minimalist decor of creams and beiges and tasteful artwork sum up this modern Edinburgh restaurant. Stephen Frost offers a menu that is a mix of classical and modern dishes with a good value fixed-price dinner, and choices from a *carte* at lunch. The menu actually delivers more excitement than it promises, mainly because at first glance it is as understated as the decor. But inspection revealed the likes of seared garavad lax cut into thick slices and set on a bed of oriental leaves with a subtle grain mustard and honey sauce, and an excellent chicken liver parfait with Cumberland sauce. Main courses took in rack of lamb with roast ratatouille on polenta, and chargrilled steak with superb rösti. White chocolate mousse for dessert was outstanding. Service by Ann Frost is charming and knowledgeable.

Directions: Telephone for directions

EDINBURGH, Malmaison

1 Tower Place Leith EH6 7DB
Map 11: NT 27
Tel: 0131 5556868
Fax: 0131 5556999
Chef: Keith Shearer
Owner: Ken McCulloch
Cost: *Alc* £20, fixed-price L&D from £9.50. ☺ H/wine £11.95.
Times: Last L 2.30pm/D 10.30pm
Additional: Bar Food; Sunday brunch; Children welcome; ♨ dishes

Set in the historic docklands revival area of Leith, there's a good choice of simple Med-style food at this modishly designed brasserie and hotel that was once a seaman's mission. Fettucine with tomatoes, basil and roast garlic and huge bowls of moules marinière were both thoroughly enjoyed on our visit.

Accommodation: 60 en suite
Credit cards 🟥 📰 📰 🔀 💲 ⬜

Directions: From the city centre follow Leith Docklands, through 3 sets of lights and L into Tower Street

EDINBURGH,
Marriott Dalmahoy ❀❀

Kirknewton
EH27 8EB
Map 11: NT27
Tel: 0131 3331845
Fax: 0131 3331433
Chef: Wayne Asson
Cost: *Alc* £25, fixed-price L £14.50. ☺ H/wine £11.75.
Times: Noon-last L 2pm/7pm-last D 10pm. Closed L Sat

The famous golf courses are one of the big attractions of this fine hotel, set in extensive parkland with commanding views of the Pentland hills and Edinburgh Castle beyond. The smart, split-level restaurant overlooks the lake, but at the time of our visit (just before going to press), a newly arrived chef was about to bring in a new-look *carte*. Nonetheless an inherited menu – wild mushroom terrine wrapped in leeks served with a watercress dressing, poached halibut with a light port wine jus and parsnip purée, and lime bread-and-butter pudding with malt whisky chocolate sorbet – was cooked with enough accomplishment for the future to bode well.

Directions: On A71, 3 miles from Calder roundabout, opposite Ratho turn off

Additional: Bar food; Sunday L; Children welcome; ❹ dishes
Seats: 112. Private dining room 22
Smoking: No smoking in dining room
Accommodation: 151 en suite
Credit cards: ▬ ▦ ▆ ▣ ▢

EDINBURGH,

Martin's Restaurant ❀❀❀

The location is a fairly uninspiring back alley off the main drag, and the main feature of the dining room is the collection of contemporary artwork by Scottish artists covering the pale walls. What matters here is the food. For the last 14 years, Martin and Gay Irons have championed the cause of organic produce and wild foods, and Martin's father still grows herbs for the kitchen in his own garden; the quality of the raw materials is beyond reproach. Menus change daily and the formula is a well-tried one: fish dominates, closely followed by game and lamb, while beef is generally noticeable by its absence. Some new young blood in the kitchen has give the cooking a lift, as our inspector discovered. A meal taken one evening in April began emphatically with superb blackened monkfish combined with glistening green samphire and an oriental sauce before lightly seared fresh sea trout on a bed of red cabbage with a delicate tomato and tarragon sauce. To finish, a strawberry mille-feuille with sauce of feathered apricot and strawberry was produced with real artistry. Other choices from the meaty side of things might include roast breast of mallard with beetroot pavé, leeks and a star anise jus, and loin of mutton and Dijon mustard 'pot au feu'. The owners look after the front of house personally with the help of friendly assistants. A carefully assembled wine list put the emphasis on the better French regions, although the New World is not neglected.

Directions: North Lane is off Rose Street which runs parallel to and behind Princess Street

70 Rose Street
North Lane EH2 3DX
Map 11: NT27
Tel: 0131 2253106
Chefs: Forbes Stott, Peter Banks
Owners: Martin & Gay Irons
Cost: *Alc* £34, fixed-price L £12.95.
H/wine £9.95
Times: Noon-last L 2pm/7pm-last D 9.45pm. Closed L Sat, Sun, Mon, 1 wk May/Jun, 1 wk Sep/Oct, 24 Dec-21 Jan
Additional: No children under 8;
❹ dishes
Seats: 48. Private dining rooms 8-12
Smoking: No smoking in dining room
Credit cards: ▬ ▦ ▆ ▚ ▣ ▢

EDINBURGH, **Norton House** ❀❀

Set in 50 acres of parkland to the west of the city, this extended Victorian mansion still retains many of its original features, but offers up-to-the-minute comforts for all-comers. Formal meals are served in the Conservatory restaurant overlooking the nearby countryside, where the high point of a recent test meal was venison with celeriac purée served on a sloe berry sauce tinged with vanilla. Elsewhere the kitchen delivers accurately crafted modern dishes along the lines of seared loin of Border lamb with broccoli mousse and rosemary juice, marinated Scotch salmon with spring greens and champagne sauce, and saddle of rabbit with leeks and lardons in a cracked pepper and sorrel sauce, in addition to grills. Savouries such as pear and Stilton tart are alternatives to, say, date and banana filo parcels with butterscotch sauce, or lemon and lime iced soufflé. The unusual wine cellar at the back of the restaurant has plenty of decent stuff worth exploring.

Directions: M8/J2, off the A8, 0.5 mile past Edinburgh Airport

Ingliston EH28 8LX
Map 11: NT27
Tel: 0131 3331275
Fax: 0131 3335305
Chef: John Newton
Owners: Virgin Hotels
Cost: *Alc* £32. Fixed-price D £25 (4 courses) ☺ H/wine £11.50.
Times: Noon-last L 2.30pm/7pm-last D 10pm. Closed L Sat
Additional: Bar meals; Sunday L; Children welcome; ❹ dishes.
Seats: 85. Private dining up to 170
Smoking: No-smoking area
Accommodation: 47 en suite
Credit cards: ▬ ▦ ▆ ▣ ▢

EDINBURGH,

Sheraton Grand Hotel ❀❀❀

1 Festival Square
EH3 9SR
Map 11: NT27
Tel: 0131 2299131
Fax: 0131 2296254
Chef: Nicholas Laurent,
Philippe Wagenfuhrer
Cost: *Alc* £35, fixed-price L £19.50/D
£25. H/wine £14
Times: Noon-last L 2.30pm/7pm-last
D 10.30pm. Closed L Sat, Sun
Additional: Bar food; Sunday L
(Terrace restaurant);
Children welcome; ❸ dishes
Seats: 62. Private dining room 20
Smoking: No-smoking area; no pipes
in dining room; air-conditioning
Accommodation: 261 en suite
Credit cards: ■ ■ ■ ▣ ℂ

Directions: Off Lothian Road

The hotel's own tartan adorns the Grill Room of this imposing, purpose-built hotel; in terms of cooking, however, the influence is classical French, and the execution skilled enough to make us feel this is a kitchen on a fast-rising curve. Home-made bread is served warm and well seasoned, a good prelude to a nigh perfect tortellini of morels with langoustine salsa and truffle oil, and a full-flavoured consommé with smoked duck liver ravioli. Our inspector chose as a main course a confit of beautifully tender pork belly with a honey and spice sauce, with a fine sweet-sour effect, and followed with a warm chocolate gingerbread pudding with fromage frais ice cream. Specialities such as mosaic of pot-au-feu with crudités, and fillet of Dover sole with fondant potatoes and braised fennel, can be sampled in a set menu, and there is also a menu gourmet and a menu dégustation featuring dishes such as pan-fried smoked salmon with sauerkraut and bacon sauce, poached Poularde breast with truffle rice and cream sauce, and sea bass pan-fried with fresh thyme and served with niçoise vegetables. The wine list is deep, well balanced and expensive.

EDINBURGH, 36 at The Howard ❀❀

36 Great King Street
EH3 6QH
Map 11: NT27
Tel: 0131 5563636
Fax: 0131 5563663
Chef: Malcolm Warham
Owner: Peter Taylor

The Howard is a splendid, centrally located Georgian town house hotel. The stylish decor of its restaurant, 36, is backed up by an equally stylish modern menu that appears to revolve around a repeating repertoire. Excellent, very rare seared tuna served with salad niçoise, and a terrine of duck confit with plum chutney opened one inspection meal taken this year. Then 'super' monkfish, although it lacked evidence of promised saffron, was served on Savoy cabbage, and 'tip-top' lamb came wrapped in cabbage stuffed with a ginger pesto. Dessert was a mixed bag: surprisingly light rhubarb mousse but poor chocolate tart served with a watery Amaretto ice cream. Coffee and home-made bread have both been well reported.

Directions: Turn off Princes St into Frederick St for 0.5 mile and turn R into Great King St. Past traffic lights, hotel on L

Cost: *Alc* £25. H/wine £11.50. ☺
Times: Noon-2.30pm (Sun 2pm)/7pm-8pm
Additional: Sunday L;
Children welcome; 🍴 dishes
Seats: 70
Smoking: No smoking in dining room; air-conditioning
Accommodation: 15 en suite
Credit cards: 🔳 🔳 🔳 🔳 🔳 🔳

EDINBURGH, The Vintners Room ✿✿

Atmosphere counts for a great deal in this lively restaurant/wine bar set above the 800-year-old vaults where Augustinian friars once stored wine for Holyrood Palace. Visitors can choose between the bustling informality of the bar or the more sedate atmosphere of the dining room. Consistency is the kitchen's hallmark and an inspection lunch of pan-fried scallops with risotto nero and squid ink sauce followed by chargrilled halibut with a duo of contrasting sauces (one sweet red pepper, the other flavoured with anise) was favourably received. A French provincial thrust is also evident in dishes such as boudin noir with cranberry and apple sauces, herb-crusted loin of lamb and rare roast sirloin with sauce marchand de vin. Desserts range from a positively wicked 'chocolate silk' with crème chantilly to apricot, almond and Amaretto tart. The wine list is worth serious consideration, with its hefty contingent of Bordeaux and Burgundies, and quality stuff from the New World.

Directions: At end of Leith Walk; L into Great Junction Street, R into Henderson Street. Restaurant is in old warehouse on R

87 Giles Street, Leith
EH6 6BZ
Map 11: NT27
Tel: 0131 5546767
Fax: 0131 4677130
Chef: AT Cumming
Owners: AT & SC Cumming
Cost: *Alc* £25, fixed-price L £13 (3 courses). H/wine £10
Times: Noon-last L 2pm/6pm-last D 10.30pm. Closed Sun, 2 wks Xmas
Additional: Bar food L;
Children welcome; 🍴 dishes
Seats: 36
Smoking: No smoking in dining room
Credit cards: 🔳 🔳 🔳 🔳

EDINBURGH,
The Witchery by the Castle ✿✿

The Witchery is two rooms, each with its own individual look. The Secret Garden, by day light and airy, by night lit completely by candles, is opulently decorated with stone walls hung with tapestries, lots of hanging plants, and an ornate painted timber ceiling. Upstairs is dark, austere, atmospheric; it too is candlelit at night. The same menu is offered in both rooms, an amalgamation of all that is currently fashionable: tartare of tuna with cucumber spaghetti, tomato and avocado salsa; escalope of salmon cooked in goose fat with roast chicory and celeriac purée; roast loin of lamb with aubergine mousse and deep-fried spinach. A winter dinner took in an intensely flavoured shellfish bisque, with a basil mousse and fresh prawns, and a fillet of turbot with lime and green ginger, served on a bed of noodles with a delicate soya sauce. The doorstopper of a wine list is an astonishing achievement. Almost 600 bins of consistent quality, all accompanied by worthwhile descriptions and informative introductions to each region. For those without the inclination to delve deeper, a dozen house selections can all be relied upon and the availability of all twelve by the glass is icing on the cake.

Directions: At the entrance to Edinburgh Castle at the very top of the Royal Mile

Castle Hill EH2 1NE
Map 11: NT27
Tel: 0131 2255613
Fax: 0131 2204392
Chef: Douglas Roberts
Owner: James Thomson
Additional: No children under 6;
🍴 dishes
Times: Noon-last L 4pm/5.30pm-last D 11.30pm. Closed 25-26 Dec
Seats: 120 (2 dining rooms).
Private dining room 60
Smoking: No-smoking area
Accommodation: 1 en suite
Credit cards: 🔳 🔳 🔳 🔳 🔳

FALKIRK

GRANGEMOUTH,
Grange Manor Hotel

Glensburgh Road
FK3 8XJ
Map 11: NS98
Tel: 01324 474836
Fax: 01324 665861
Chef: Don McGovern
Owners: Bill & Jane Wallace
Cost: Alc £24, fixed-price L £9.50/D £19.85. ☺ H/wine £9.60.
Times: Last L 2pm/D 9pm
Additional: Bar Food; Sunday L; Children welcome; ◑ dishes
Smoking: Air-conditioning
Accommodation: 7 en suite
Credit cards: 🖮 🖮 🖮 🖮 🖮 🖮

Popular business hotel and venue for local functions. Visitors to the smart restaurant enjoy the good Scottish produce that forms the base of the kitchen's modern cooking. Pan-fried breast of chicken with noodles and pesto cream sauce, or medallion of venison loin with apricot and apple chutney, show the range.

Directions: M9 exit 6 200m on right, M9 exit 5/A905 2 miles

FIFE

ANSTRUTHER,
Cellar Restaurant ❀❀❀

'A restaurant of character and completely devoid of pretentiousness', was how one inspector summed up The Cellar. Orders are taken at the bar, where you are likely to be offered a neat little canapé – perhaps a dainty pastry case filled with creamy smoked haddock and topped with bacon. Dinner is served in the beamed dining room, where the walls are exposed stone, the floor is brick and the tables are fashioned from Singer sewing machines. Seafood is the main theme, but what is offered is totally dependent on the catch from the boats; Peter Jukes is not one to compromise just to flesh out the menu. After an appetiser of marinated herring with lettuce and lemon dressing, there might be delicate pan-seared scallops served simply with chopped mushrooms and pan jus. Next, a 'delightful' crayfish bisque that is almost a light chunky stew glazed on top with Gruyère and cream. The main course could be grilled fillet of local halibut presented on a mound of chopped green beans, shredded cabbage, pine kernels and smoked bacon; alongside this is likely to be a little pot of hollandaise and the dish needs only some boiled potatoes to set it off. As for desserts, spiced apple crêpe with cinnamon ice cream hits the button. In an attempt to encourage regulars out-of-season, an excellent-value supper menu has been introduced.

24 East Green KY10 3AA
Map 12: NO50
Tel: 01333 310378
Chef/Owner: Peter Jukes
Cost: Alc £16, fixed-price D £28.50. H/wine £13.50
Times: 12.30pm-last L 1.30pm/7pm-last D 9.30pm. Closed D Sun, Mon (low season), 4 days Xmas
Additional: Sunday L; No children under 8
Seats: 30
Smoking: No smoking in dining room
Credit cards: 🖮 🖮 🖮 🖮 🖮

Signature dishes: Roasted monkfish and scallops with herb and garlic spiced butter with courgette and pepper stew; roast wild salmon with pesto served on warm English asparagus and snow pea salad; smoked Finnan haddock omelette.

Directions: Behind the Scottish Fisheries Museum

CUPAR, Eden House Hotel

Victorian country house with a candlelit conservatory restaurant boasting splendid views of the River Eden. The kitchen makes good use of local ingredients producing honest dishes such as salmon terrine with dill mayonnaise, and grilled fillet of halibut with tangy citrus butter, followed perhaps by spicy apple strudel.

Smoking: No-smoking area
Accommodation: 11 en suite. **Credit cards:** 💳 💳 💳

Directions: Turn R after railway bridge in Cupar. Hotel is 100 yds to R

2 Pitscottie Road KY15 4HF
Map 11: NO31
Tel: 01334 652510
Fax: 01334 652277
Chef: Alan Lunn
Owners: Laurence & Mary Vizan
Cost: Alc £20, fixed-price D £18 (3 courses). ☺ H/wine £8.95.
Times: Noon- last L 2pm/6.30pm-last D 9pm. Closed L Sun, 25 Dec, 1 Jan
Additional: Bar meals;
Children welcome; 🍴 dishes

CUPAR,
Ostlers Close Restaurant

Bonnygate KY15 4BU
Map 11: NO31
Tel: 01334 655574
Fax: 01334 654036
Chef: James Graham
Owners: James & Amanda Graham
Cost: Alc £27. H/wine £9. ☺
Times: 12.15pm-last L 2pm/7pm-last D 9.30pm. Closed Sun, Mon, 25-26 Dec, 1 Jan
Additional: Children welcome; 🍴 dishes
Seats: 26
Smoking: Smoking at end of evening only
Credit cards: 💳 💳 💳 💳 💳

Directions: In small lane off main street (A91) of Cupar.

Over the years, Jimmy and Amanda Graham have build up a well-deserved, loyal, local following who appreciate Scottish cooking that is modern without being 'trendy'. Quality ingredients are paramount, and Jimmy goes to painstaking lengths to ensure everything meets his own exacting standards. A winter lunch started with soft, fresh home-baked bread rolls and a fine-flavoured fish soup, full of salmon, monkfish and scallops, at the centre of which was a delicious cannelloni stuffed with a salmon and prawn mousse. The main course was equally good; lightly pan-fried cod and scallops on a bed of sea kale accompanied by a delicate shellfish sauce. Organic vegetables, served on the side, were particularly special, innovative, colour-contrasting but not too fussy – lightly baked thin scalloped potato, a delightful mound of sweet potato, stir-fried cabbage, superbly flavoured yellow beetroot, and a small but perfectly formed spinach and ricotta tartlet. A wicked, sticky toffee pudding with a full-bodied toffee sauce was both unpretentious and totally satisfying. Mushrooms have always been a speciality – in season, there may be pot-roast breasts of pigeon with wild mushrooms and pan juices, or roast rib of

Scottish beef with roasted shallots in a cep sauce. Game is also a favourite choice, frequently served with red wine sauce; whilst leg of free-range duck is made into a confit with mixed salad in a balsamic vinaigrette, or the breast roast with apples on Calvados sauce (and served along with the confit leg). Desserts include a luscious-sounding home-made honey, Drambuie and oatmeal ice-cream, and a harmonious trio of meringue desserts – strawberry Pavlova, iced meringue cake and hazelnut meringue. Cheese are Scottish, of course. Look out for the popular, special gourmet nights.

Signature dishes: New season's lamb saddle with caramelised shallots and coriander; seared scallops on a bed of samphire; baked East Neuk crab Thermidor; gamekeeper's bag – roast selection of local game with skirlie and red wine sauce.

DUNFERMLINE,

Keavil House Hotel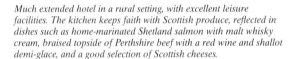

Much extended hotel in a rural setting, with excellent leisure facilities. The kitchen keeps faith with Scottish produce, reflected in dishes such as home-marinated Shetland salmon with malt whisky cream, braised topside of Perthshire beef with a red wine and shallot demi-glace, and a good selection of Scottish cheeses.

Smoking: No smoking in dining room
Accommodation: 33 en suite
Credit cards:

Directions: M90/J3, 7 miles from Forth Road Bridge, take A985, turning R after bridge. From Dunfermline, 2 miles W on A994

Crossford KY12 8QW
Map 11: NT19
Tel: 01383 736258
Fax: 01383 621600
Chef: Volker Steinemann
Cost: Alc £20, fixed-price L £8.50/D £18.50. ☺ H/wine £9.25.
Times: Last L 2pm/last D 10pm
Additional: Bar food L; Sunday L; Children welcome; ❸ dishes

ELIE,

Bouquet Garni Restaurant ❀❀❀

51 High Street
KY9 1BZ
Map 12: NO40
Tel/Fax: 01333 330374
Chef/Owner: Andrew Keracher
Cost: Alc £25. H/wine £9.50
Times: Noon-last L 1.30pm/7pm-last D 9.15pm. Closed Sun, last wk Nov, 2nd-3rd wk Jan
Additional: No children under 12 at D; ❸ dishes
Seats: 50.

As we went to press Andrew Keracher informed us that Bouquet Garni was up for sale and that he was in the process of opening a new restaurant in Perth, above Keracher's, the family's wet fish shop. It will be a 70 seater restaurant specialising purely in seafood – 'everything on sale in the shop we will cook upstairs', plus Scottish game. In the meantime, Bouquet Garni will continue to trade under the guidance of Andrew Keracher and his team. This is how we found the cooking on our last visit:

'What I liked about this place is the fact that, where appropriate, they keep things simple, but can demonstrate sound technical ability in the more complicated dishes; above all else, natural flavours shine through and the quality of produce is beyond reproach; it is all refreshingly unpretentious.' It was a cold February day and our inspector had been impressed by a meal that opened with a langoustine and tomato bisque of lovely rich colour and flavour, then turbot and scallops, sealed in the pan and finished off in the oven, and served on a bed of thinly sliced carrot and leeks with a creamy peppercorn sauce – 'all very light with just a hint of peppers'; accompanying vegetables included 'lovely flavoured' carrots, broccoli, red cabbage and new potatoes. To finish, a 'wicked' dark chocolate pot filled with a light, white chocolate mousse and topped with a variety of fruit including strawberry, kiwi and red berries.

Smoking: No smoking in dining room; no pipes and cigars
Credit cards: ▬ ▬ ▬ ▬

Directions: 12 miles from St Andrews. Village centre: from A915 (St Andrews) take A917 to Elie

GLENROTHES, Rescobie Hotel ❁

Food is a priority at this country house hotel, where good use is made of quality ingredients. At inspection, crab bisque with white wine rather than brandy proved an interesting variation, and a main course of monkfish wrapped in bacon also worked well. The chocolate pot selected for pudding was 'simply wicked.'

Valley Drive Leslie KY6 3BQ
Map 11: NO20
Tel: 01592 742143
Fax: 01592 620231
Chef: Stuart Aitken
Owners: Tony & Judith Hughes-Lewis
Cost: Fixed-price D £17.50. ☺ H/wine £8.50.
Times: Last L 2pm/D 9pm. Closed 24-27 Dec
Additional: Sunday L; Children welcome; ⚘ menu
Accommodation: 10 en suite
Credit cards: ▬ ▬ ▬ ▬

Directions: At west end of Leslie village, turn S off A911

KINCARDINE-ON-FORTH,
Unicorn Inn

The name suggests a pub, but the interior of this fascinating local venue is rustic bistro with open fires, hops hung around the place and Spanish music adding to the atmosphere. Menus are chalked on blackboards which are taken to the tables as and when needed, and the kitchen deals in eclectic dishes with a forthright Mediterranean bias. Starters might range from a salad of thin strips of smoked salmon with avocado and a chive-based dressing, to whole roasted vine tomatoes with samphire. Main dishes are equally enticing, taking in, say, chargrilled Oban scallops on skewers with teriyaki sauce, sesame pork fillet with Chinese noodles, and roasted duck with melted onions and Marsala. Light and airy lime mousse topped with fresh strawberries makes a good finale, otherwise expect anything from iced zabaglione cream with ratafia biscuits to meringue gâteau with toffee and pecan sauce.

Directions: From S, cross Kincardine Bridge, take 1st L, L again, 1st R

15 Excise Street FK10 4LN
Map 11: NS98
Tel: 01259 730704
Fax: 01259 731567
Chef: Brian Ainslie
Owner: Lesley Mitch
Cost: Alc £25; fixed-price L £7.50 (2 courses). ☺ H/wine £10.25
Times: Noon-last L 1.45pm/6.30pm-last D 8.45pm. Closed Sun, Mon, 25-26 Dec, 1-3 Jan, 2 wks July
Additional: No children after 7pm; ⚘ dishes
Seats: 50. Private dining room 20
Smoking: No-smoking area; no pipes or cigars
Accommodation: 4 rooms
Credit cards: ▬ ▬ ▬ ▬ ▬

LETHAM, Fernie Castle Hotel

Cupar KY7 7RU
Map 11: NO31
Tel: 01337 810381
Fax: 01337 810422
Chef: Craig Millar
Owner: Marshall Stevens
Cost: Alc £19.50. H/wine £9.95. ☺
Times: Noon-last L 2.30pm/6.30pm-9.30pm
Additional: Bar meals; Sunday L; Children welcome; ◑ dishes
Seats: 30. Private dining room 120
Smoking: No-smoking area
Accommodation: 15 en suite
Credit cards: ■ ▩ ▭ ▣

Historic castle setting for up-to-date dishes along the lines of salad of seared red mullet with ratatouille and cherry tomato coulis, and honey roasted duck breast with sweet potato rösti and wild cherry sauce. As well as the formal dining-room, there is a good bar menu – look out for the special steak and kidney pie.

Directions: On A914 signposted Forth Bridge (West). Through Cupar to 1st roundabout (Melville Lodges). N on A914, 1.2 miles; hotel on R

LUNDIN LINKS,
Old Manor Hotel

Leven Road KY8 6AJ
Map 12: NO40
Tel: 01333 320368
Fax: 01333 320911
Chef: Alan Brunt
Owners: Alistair Clark & Family
Cost: Alc £27.50, fixed-price L £12.75/D £28 (4 courses). ☺ H/wine £10.75
Times: Noon-last L 2pm/7pm-last D 10pm. Closed Sun, 1-2 Jan
Additional: Bar food; Sunday L; Children welcome; ◑ dishes
Seats: 36.
Private dining rooms 14 & 20
Smoking: No smoking in dining room
Accommodation: 25 en suite
Credit cards: ■ ▩ ▭ ▰ ▣

The spectacular views over Lundin Golf Course, Largo Bay and the Forth Estuary may be all-absorbing, but there is also plenty to contemplate on the subject of matters gastronomic. The *carte* is sub-divided into various categories: starters include roast breast of pigeon with woodland mushrooms and truffle oil, under 'Soups, Chowders and Bisques' there is west coast mussel chowder with garlic and herb croûtons, and the fish section includes the house speciality, 'Symphony of Seafood', a combination of local fish and shellfish lightly steamed on a saffron sauce. Main courses feature roasted loin of smoked lamb with a rosemary galette on redcurrant jus, and the grilled Aberdeen Angus steaks warrant a whole page to themselves. Desserts, such as fresh raspberry cheesecake made on an oatmeal base, typify the modern Scottish style. Service is black-tie formal, and the wine list is a serious distraction from the view.

Directions: On A915 Leven-St Andrews road in the village

MARKINCH, **Balbirnie House**

Balbirnie Park KY7 6NE
Map 11: NO20
Tel: 01592 610066
Fax: 01592 610529
Chef: David Kinnes
Owners: The Russell family
Cost: Fixed-price D £28.50
(4 courses). H/wine £12.50
Times: Noon-last L 2.15pm/7pm-last
D 9.30pm
Additional: Bar food L; Sunday L;
Children welcome; ❹ dishes
Seats: 50. Private dining room 10-120
Smoking: No smoking in dining room
Accommodation: 30 en suite
Credit cards:

Despite the formality of the elegant, candlelit dining room overlooking the gardens, specimen trees and magnificent rhododendrons, the welcome at this family-run Georgian mansion is refreshingly natural and unpretentious. There is ample choice from the fixed-price menu and much use is made of traditional Scottish produce. Starters might include Glen Moray smoked salmon or a well-flavoured smoked chicken mousseline with tarragon sabayon, followed by a soup or entrée course such as game consommé or smoked haddock gratin. Main courses put a global spin on classics, such as roast rack of lamb with pesto crust and rosemary and mint stuffing, or seared halibut with saffron sauerkraut, red pepper and lychee butter. Traditionalists will stick with the prime Scottish steaks, chargrilled and served either plain or with a choice of rather rich sauces. If you're lucky, desserts might include the perfectly delicious butterscotch pecan pie with banana ice cream and maple syrup. An excellent wine list includes some fine clarets and there is a good choice of half-bottles.

Directions: M90/J3, follow signs to Glenrothes & Tay Bridge, turn R onto B9130 to Markinch & Balbirnie Park

PEAT INN, **The Peat Inn**

Cupar KY15 5LH
Map 12: NO40
Tel: 01334 840206
Fax: 01334 840530
Chef: David Wilson
Owners: David & Patricia Wilson

Expectations are always high when dining at The Peat Inn – rarely are there disappointments and the experience remains as thoroughly enjoyable as ever. Over the years the dedicated owners, David and Patricia Wilson, have built up an enviable

reputation for the excellence of their kitchen at this charming small restaurant in rural Fife. Consistency is the hallmark, ingredients are of irreproachable quality and David's cooking is accomplished and well-judged. A typical dinner might start with pan-fried venison liver and kidney with rhubarb in a rich red wine sauce, followed perhaps by delicious whole lobster poached in a wonderful vegetable and herb broth, or fillet of beef in Madeira sauce with roast shallots and potato cake, and finish with caramelised banana with white chocolate mousse, orange and chocolate sauce. A 'Tasting Menu' (for a complete table only) allows the sampling of various specialities (served in slightly smaller portions), and might include warm scallops and langoustine with herb salad, roast halibut on roast vegetables with a beef juice, julienne of pigeon breast on a confit of spiced pork, and roast venison saddle, mushroom and truffle crust in a red wine sauce. A four-course 'Menu of the Day' might start with fricassée of prawns and wild mushrooms and continue with crispy braised duck leg with spiced lentils, roast loin of spring lamb with a herb crust and thyme-flavoured sauce, and end with caramelised apple pastry and caramel sauce or a selection of cheeses from the trolley. The well-motivated staff are friendly and unobtrusively attentive. 'A return visit here would not be a hardship', concluded our inspector. The wine list, whilst bursting with quality, is happily free from pomposity, a down to earth approach that is carried through to the pricing. Burgundy, both white and red, continues to be a mainstay, from well-made and affordable Mâconnais through to *premier cru* Côtes de Beaune. Pol Roger champagnes are a well represented enthusiasm and there is plenty of depth in the half-bottles.

Signature dishes: Herb salad with scallops and prawns with spiced mayonnaise; lobster in a vegetable and herb broth; roast young grouse; braised shoulder of lamb with potato and onion.

Directions: At junction of B940/B941, 6 miles SW of St Andrews

Cost: Fixed-price D £28 (4 courses). H/wine £14
Times: L at 1pm/7pm-last D 9.30pm. Closed Sun, Mon, 25 Dec, 1 Jan
Additional: Children welcome; ✪ dishes
Seats: 48. Private dining room 24/12
Smoking: No smoking in dining room
Accommodation: 8 en suite
Credit cards: ▬ ▩ ▦ 💷 ℂ

ST ANDREWS,

The Old Course Hotel ❀❀

Golfers will need no introduction to this hotel, which takes its name from the course over which it presides. Although purpose-built in the late 60s, it has been well upgraded, and the roof-top Road Hole Grill provides an eagle's nest view of the course, clubhouse and the town. The name comes from the famous 17th Road Hole, and the 'grill' harks back to the days when grill rooms were in vogue. The open-plan restaurant does not marry all that easily with the elegant decor and formal service, but the food is good and in summer there is a 'menu gastronomique' alongside the *carte* and fixed price ones. The first two are modern international – seared loin of venison with arugula, egg plant and balsamic oil was visually stunning, wok-fried scallops were superb, inventively matched with caramelised corn, tomato risotto and red wine sauce. More classic combinations include braised veal shin with mustard sauce, carrots and garlic potatoes and seared halibut with grilled fennel and provençale vinaigrette. On our visit, a warm chocolate mousse with vanilla pod ice-cream scored above a rhubarb Tatin.

Directions: Situated close to the A91 on the outskirts of the city

KY16 9SP
Map 12: NO51
Tel: 01334 474371
Fax: 01334 477668
Chef: Mark Barker
Cost: Alc £36.50, fixed-price L £15.50/D £36.50. H/wine £16.50
Times: 12.30pm-last L 2pm/7pm-last D 10pm. Closed Xmas
Additional: Bar food L; Sunday L; Children welcome; ✪ dishes
Seats: 70. Private dining room 90
Smoking: No pipes and cigars; air-conditioning
Accommodation: 125 en suite
Credit cards: ▬ ▩ ▦ 💷

ST ANDREWS, Parkland Hotel

Castle-style mansion, a popular port of call for golfers (to play the wealth of local courses). Food is a plus too, with sound skills evident in dishes such as breast of pheasant with wild mushrooms and rich game sauce, collops of Angus fillet steak with a mustard grain and whisky cream sauce, and crème caramel with summer berries.

Times: Last L 2pm/D 8.30pm Closed D Sun, Mon
Additional: Sunday L; No children under 12 at D
Smoking: No smoking in dining room
Accommodation: 15 en suite
Credit cards: ▆ ▆ ▆ ▆

Directions: West of town centre, opposite Kinburn Park

Kinburn Castle
Double Dykes Road
KY16 9DS
Map 12: NO51
Tel/Fax: 01334 473620
Chef: Brian J MacLennan
Owners: Mr & Mrs B. J. MacLennan
Cost: Fixed-price L £5.95/D £18.50.
☺ H/wine £8.50.

ST ANDREWS, Rufflets

Strathkinness Low Road KY16 9TX
Map 12: NO51
Tel: 01334 472594
Fax: 01334 478703
Chef: Robert Grindle
Owner: Ann Russell
Cost: Fixed-price L £16.50/D £28.
H/wine £12.
Times: 12.30pm-last L 2pm (Sat & Sun only)/7pm-last D 9pm. Closed 1st wk Jan
Additional: Bar food L; Sunday L; Children welcome; ❹ dishes
Seats: 80. Private dining room 24
Smoking: No smoking in restaurant
Accommodation: 26 en suite
Credit cards: ▆ ▆ ▆ ▆

Award-winning gardens, a well-stocked bar, relaxing lounges and the proximity of St Andrews all add to the pleasure of a meal in the civilised setting of The Garden Restaurant. This year, the kitchen has been on form, the cooking showing a new-found maturity in the daily fixed-price three-course menu or set tasting menu. The latter might include a warm salad of king scallops seared with ginger, spring onion and lime juice, a light pastry galette layered with caramelised apple and black pudding in a white wine, shallot and chive cream sauce, fillet of lamb baked with minted pine kernel crust on a Madeira jus with fresh spinach, and iced cranachan parfait with a compote of local berries. Other interesting dishes are cold kiln-roasted smoked Shetland salmon with boiled new potatoes and orange and pine kernel salad, pan-fried breast of Perthshire pheasant with a beetroot and orange sauce, and hot clouti dumpling with coddled cream.

Directions: On B939 1.5 miles before St Andrews

ST ANDREWS,
St Andrews Golf Hotel

Popular golfing hotel, fashioned from two solidly built Victorian houses, with views over the links and St Andrews Bay. The kitchen tries hard, delivering an ambitious menu of lasagne of Tay salmon

40 The Scores
St Andrews
KY16 9AS
Map 12: NO51
Tel: 01334 472611

and asparagus, breast of Kildrummy pheasant, the thigh boned and filled with smoked ham forcemeat, and baked chocolate tart.

Additional: Bar food; Sunday L; Children welcome; ❸ dishes
Smoking: No smoking in dining room
Accommodation: 22 en suite
Credit cards: 💳 💳 💳 💳 💳

Directions: Enter town on A91, cross both mini-roundabouts, turn left at Golf Place and first right into The Scores. Hotel 200 yards on right

Fax: 01334 472188
Chef: Colin Masson
Owners: Brian & Maureen Hughes
Cost: Alc £27, fixed-price L £14.95/D £27.50. ☺ H/wine £11.
Times: Last L 2.30pm/D 9.30pm. Closed L (restaurant) Mon-Fri Nov-Mar

GLASGOW, CITY OF

GLASGOW, Buttery Restaurant ❀❀

Sumptuously rich Victorian decor is a feature of this popular venue sandwiched between a modern housing estate and Kingston Bridge. All around are red velvet banquettes, sofas and leather armchairs, with plants, stained glass and pictures providing distraction. Lunch is excellent value for, say, curried egg on a warm croissant, lamb's liver and onions with grain mustard sauce, and warm banana crêpe with chocolate sauce. Evening brings a more catholic selection of dishes ranging from patriotically Scottish ideas such as mignons of Highland venison layered with redcurrants and apple chutney, or fillet of beef with skirlie and a dark malted sauce, to grilled fillet of red snapper on sautéed leeks with a chilled yellow pepper coulis, or steamed suprême of chicken filled with Brie in a Calvados cream. Bringing up the rear are creditable Scottish cheeses plus desserts such as spring rhubarb crème brûlée and butter shortbread. In addition, there's a full menu for vegetarians. The Loire and other French regions are well represented on the wide ranging wine list.

Directions: City centre

652 Argyle Street G3 8UF
Map 11: NS56
Tel: 0141 2218188
Fax: 0141 2044639

Chef: Stephen Johnson

Owners: Alloa Pubs & Restaurants Ltd
Cost: Alc £28, fixed-price L £14.85. H/wine £10.95
Times: Noon-last L 2.30pm/7pm-last D 10.30pm. Closed L Sat, Sun, 25-26 Dec, 1-2 Jan
Additional: Bar food L; ❸ dishes
Seats: 30. Private dining room 10
Smoking: Air-conditioning
Credit cards: 💳 💳 💳 💳 💳 💳

GLASGOW, Devonshire Hotel ❀

Something of a gem and one of the most glamorous hotels of its kind in the city. Imaginative Scottish dishes are served in the intimate four-table restaurant, where the menu might include loin of Border lamb with redcurrant and basil glaze and braised fillet of sea bass on a 'tricolour of vegetables'.

Additional: Bar Food L; Children welcome; ❸ dishes
Smoking: No smoking in dining room
Accommodation: 14 en suite
Credit cards: 💳 💳 💳 💳

Directions: On Great Western Road turn L at lights towards Hyndland, 200 yards turn R and R again

5 Devonshire Gardens G12 0UX
Map 11: NS56
Tel 0141 339 7878
Fax: 0141 339 3980
Chef: Peter Lindsay
Owner: Devonshire Hotel
Cost: Alc £30. H/wine £10.95 ☺
Times: Last L 2.15pm/D 10pm

GLASGOW, Glasgow Hilton ❀❀

1 William Street G3 8HT
Map 11: NS56
Tel: 0141 2045555
Fax: 0141 2045004
Chef: Michael Mizzen
Owner: Hilton International
Cost: *Alc* £30, fixed-price L £19.50/D
£38 (7 courses). ☺ H/wine £16.95
Times: Noon-2pm/7pm-10pm.
Closed L Sat, Sun, Bhs
Additional: No children under 5;
🍴 dishes
Seats: 45. Private dining room 14.
Jacket & tie preferred
Smoking: No-smoking area;
air-conditioning
Accommodation: 319 en suite
Credit cards: ▨ ▨ ▨ 🅭 🅲

This magnificent polished granite and mirrored glass building
has become something of a landmark in the city centre. The
upper floors have the most superb views. The smart Camerons
Restaurant offers a menu that reads well, is concise, and offers
a good balance of dishes with many of the ingredients sourced
from Scotland's larder: east coast smoked salmon, salmon
cured in Glayva and whisky, Loch Fyne oysters, Oban scallops,
Ayrshire pork, Black Angus beef. Confit of Barbary duck on
bitter leaves with a Puy lentil dressing, pan-fried turbot with a
confit of new potatoes and baby tomatoes served with a sauce
vierge, and a chocolate cup of Ovaltine ice cream and pecan
cookies served with a mango and vanilla sauce, formed the
components of one well-reported meal. Good home-made
bread comes in interesting flavours, notably orange ('a dried,
almost candied flavour'), which works well. Service is
professional, attentive and helpful.

Directions: Charing Cross exit from M8, turn R at 1st traffic
lights, R again & follow signs for hotel

GLASGOW,

Glasgow Moat House ❀❀

The ultra modern building is one of the tallest in Scotland, and
is instantly recognisable by its mirrored glass exterior. The
Mariner Restaurant is part of the open-plan public areas which
overlook the river Clyde, and is smartly furnished with dark
tartan carpet and comfortable, high-backed carver chairs. The
cooking is classically upmarket – sausage of brill is flanked by
quenelles of pike, saffron and chive cream, potatoes and
champagne sauce, and a tartlet of foie gras, beetroot and red
wine vinaigrette accompanies breast of duck. Game is
frequently on the menu, as in terrine of rabbit and smoked
bacon with redcurrant dressing, and venison and pigeon on a
bed of braised Savoy cabbage, Puy lentil and tomato jus.
Sunnier notes are struck with a salad of gratinated goat's
cheese with plum tomatoes and pesto dressing, and marinated
suprême of chicken on a polenta cake with chargrilled
Mediterranean vegetables.

Congress Road
G3 8QT
Map 11: NS56
Tel: 0141 3069988
Fax: 0141 2212022
Chef: Tom Brown
Cost: *Alc* £28, fixed-price L £16.50.
☺ H/wine £12.50.
Times: 12.30pm-last L 2.30pm/7pm-
last D 10.30pm. Closed L Sat, Sun,
26 Dec, 1-2 Jan
Additional: No children under 2;
🍴 dishes.
Seats: 50. Private dining rooms
Smoking: No-smoking area;
air-conditioning
Accommodation: 283 en suite.
Credit cards: ▨ ▨ ▨ ▨ 🅭 🅲

Directions: Adjacent to Scottish Exhibition & Conference
Centre, follow signs

GLASGOW,
Holiday Inn Garden Court

An attractive modern hotel featuring La Bonne Auberge, an informal French-style brasserie. The menu is French inspired, and includes dishes such as pan-fried duck suprême with salsa verde, warm spinach and cheese quiche with a herb sauce, and roasted breast of chicken with Chardonnay and mushroom cream.

Additional: Bar food; Children welcome; 🍴 dishes
Smoking: No-smoking area. **Accommodation:** 112 en suite
Credit cards: �▬ ▦ ▨ ◥◤ ▣ ℂ

Directions: Next to Royal Concert Hall (M8/J16)

161 West Nile Street G1 2RL
Map 11: NS66
Tel: 0141 332 0110
Fax: 0141 332 7447
Chef: Gerrey Sharkey
Owner: Chardon Leisure Ltd
Cost: Alc £15.95, fixed-price L
£4.95/D £7.95. ☺ H/wine £8.25.
Times: Last L 2.30pm/D 10.15pm.
Closed L Sun, Dec 25-26

GLASGOW, **Killermont Polo Club**

Ultra-smart Indian modelled on the theme of a 1930s polo club with faded echoes of the Raj. Lamb korma and rogan josh sit alongside more innovative dishes such as hariali (chicken cooked with three types of spinach); garlic nan and gulab jamun have also been recommended. Lunch is particularly good value.

Additional: Bar meals; Sunday L; Children welcome; 🍴 dishes
Seats: 90. Private dining room 24
Credit cards: ▬b ▦ ▨ ◥◤

Directions: Telephone for directions

2002 Maryhill Road
Maryhill Park G20 0AB
Map 11: NS56
Tel: 0141 946 5412
Chefs: Jas Sagoo, Amrik Uppal,
Balbir Farwana
Owner: Killermont Polo Club
Cost: Alc £15, fixed-price L £6.95. ☺
H/wine £8.95.
Times: Last L 1.45pm/D 10.30pm.
Closed Dec 25, 1 Jan

GLASGOW, **Malmaison Hotel**

A former church transformed into one of the city's most stylish hotels. The restaurant, in the old crypt with the original vaulted ceiling, is modelled on a French-style brasserie. The cooking is good, and the highlight of a recent meal was the salmon fishcakes served with parsley sauce.

Smoking: Air-conditioning
Accommodation: 73 en suite
Credit cards: ▬b ▦ ▨ ▣ ℂ

Directions: From George Square take Vincent Street to Pitt Street – hotel is on corner of this and West George Street

278 West George Street G2 4LL
Map 11: NS56
Tel: 0141 2216400
Fax: 0141 2216411
Chef: Roy Brett
Owner: Ken McCulloch
Times: Last L 2.30pm/D 11pm
Additional: Bar food L; Sunday L;
Children welcome; 🍴 dishes

GLASGOW,
One Devonshire Gardens

This unique and very individual hotel is a pleasure from the outside where three adjoining (but not interconnecting) classical Victorian town houses, complete with Ionic porticoes, all bear the discreet number 1. Within, all three houses are striking, with magnificent use of dark, dramatic colours set against period features. The restaurant occupies the first house and is equally stunning, with the luxurious dark colour scheme contrasting with the crisp white linen and sparkling glassware. Andrew Fairlie cooks bright, lively modern food noted for painstaking attention to detail and backed up by sound technique. This came over well in a dinner taken in early

1 Devonshire Gardens G12 0UX
Map 11: NS56
Tel: 0141 3392001
Fax: 0141 3371663
Chef: Andrew Fairlie
Owner: Ken McCulloch
Cost: Fixed-price L £25/D £40 (4 courses). H/wine £18
Times: Noon-last L 2pm/7.15pm-last D 10pm. Closed L Sat
Additional: Sunday L;
Children welcome; 🍴 dishes
Seats: 45. Private dining rooms 10+16

One Devonshire Gardens

Smoking: No smoking in dining room
Accommodation: 27 en suite
Credit cards: ▭ ▭ ▭ ▭ ▭

December. It opened with a glazed onion tart with bacon, walnuts, Roquefort and creamed onion sauce 'a good mélange of flavours and textures with the Roquefort bursting through spasmodically', was followed by an exact mushroom consommé bolstered by tarragon and chervil, then seared fillet of salmon on a bed of buttered spinach with root vegetables in a herb broth. Lemon mousse with pink grapefruit sorbet and spiced port wine sauce showed an ability to achieve perfect balance with textural contrasts. Carefully sourced produce ensures seasonality; a May menu offered seared spiced scallops with basil couscous, soy and citrus vinaigrette, cream of fresh pea and mint soup, roast wood pigeon with celeriac purée and honey-glazed root vegetables, and hot beignet of prunes with pear coulis and Armagnac ice cream for dessert. Service is unobtrusive but very attentive.

Signature dishes: Roast stuffed saddle of spring lamb with aubergine and garlic purée and grilled Mediterranean vegetables; home-smoked lobster with warm herb butter sauce; braised stuffed oxtail with wild mushrooms; warm salad of roasted teal with ceps.

Directions: On Great Western Road turn L at lights towards Hyndland, 200 yards turn R and R again

GLASGOW,

Papingo Restaurant   NEW

104 Bath Street G2 2EN
Map 11: NS56
Tel: 0141 3326678
Fax: 0141 3326549
Chef: Derek Marshall
Owner: Alan Tomkins
Cost: Fixed-price D £17.95. ☺
H/wine £9.95.
Times: Last L 3pm/D 10.30pm.
Closed L Sun, 1-12 Jan
Smoking: No-smoking area;
no pipes & cigars
Credit cards: ▭ ▭ ▭ ▭ ▭ ▭

Directions: 200yds from Glasgow Central Station

Centrally located café-bar-restaurant, underneath Taylor Ferguson hairdressing salon. Smart looks with lots of light yellowish colours and upmarket clientele, attracted by the excellent value. Modern menu takes in the likes of a fresh tasting mussel, leek and crab soup, aromatic breast of duck with port and orange, and ratatouille tartlet with Parmesan cream.

GLASGOW, La Parmigiana ❀❀

Angelo and Sandro Giovanazzi's long-serving Glasgow trattoria has been providing a great service for more than 15 years and is loyally supported by a local clientele, most of whom the proprietors seem to know by name. Yellow colours, crisp white cloths and personalised crockery define the mood, and a congenial atmosphere prevails. Fixed-price lunches woo the business crowd with tuna with borlotti beans, earthy rabbit alla cacciatore, and crostata di frutta. The *carte* features fresh pasta in plenty of guises, plus crespelle, carpaccio and stalwarts like pollo alla diavola, fillet of beef served on a croûton with stewed artichoke hearts and, of course, escalope of veal alla Parmigiana. Fish specials vary with the market. Home-made ice creams, zabaglione and cantuccini (almond biscuits for dunking into vin santo) are typical finales. The wine list features a goodly fistful of decent vintages from reputable Italian regional producers.

447 Great Western Road
G12 8HH
Map 11: NS56
Tel: 0141 3340686
Fax: 0141 3323533
Chef: Sandro Giovanazzi
Owners: Angelo & Sandro Giovanazzi
Cost: *Alc* £12, fixed-price L £7.50 (3 courses). ☺ H/wine £9.60.
Times: Nppn-last L 2.30pm/6pm-last D 11pm. Closed Sun & Bhs
Additional: Children welcome; ❹ dishes
Seats: 60
Smoking: Air-conditioning
Credit cards: 🔳 🏧 🔳 🔳 🔳 🔳

Directions: Close to Kelvinbridge underground station

GLASGOW, Rogano ❀❀

11 Exchange Place G1 3AN
Map 11: NS56
Tel: 0141 2484055
Fax: 0141 2482608
Chef: Andrew Cummings
Owner: Alloa Pubs & Restaurants
Cost: *Alc* £16.50. Fixed-price L £16 (3 courses)
Times: Noon-last L 2.30pm/6.30pm-last D 10.30pm
Additional: Bar food; Sunday L; Children welcome; ❹ dishes
Seats: 60. Private dining room 16
Smoking: Air-conditioning
Credit cards: 🔳 🏧 🔳 🔳 🔳 🔳

Rogano is the oldest surviving restaurant in the city. Opened in 1935, with an interior in the Art Deco style of the Queen Mary, it has outlasted the yards where the great Cunard liner was built. Fish and seafood have always been the thing here, and the *carte* offers a wide choice from poached mussels marinière, and their famous fish soup, to grilled halibut with cracked peppercorns and Cognac cream, and steamed scallops with Mornay sauce on spinach. Lobster comes either with lemon mayonnaise, grilled or thermidor, and there are chilled oysters on the half shell. Modern influences seem a little out of place amidst the classics but, as a change from lemon sole meunière, there is roast monkfish tail with chilled orange salsa, and grilled sardines with sun-dried tomato butter. There are also a couple of meat and vegetarian choices. The basement Café Rogano offers a cheaper, faster alternative and there is also an excellent choice of bar food.

Directions: City centre between Buchanan Street & Royal Exchange Square

GLASGOW, **Stravaigin**

30 Gibson Street G12
Map 11: NS56
Tel: 0141 3342665
Fax: 0141 3344099
Chef/Owner: Colin Clydesdale
Cost: Alc £15.50, fixed-price L £6.95.
☺ H/wine £9.65.
Times: Noon-11pm. Closed L Sun,
25 Dec, 1-2 Jan
Additional: Bar meals;
Children welcome; ◑ dishes
Seats: 70
Smoking: No pipes & cigars;
air conditioning
Credit cards: 🟦 🟦 🟦 🟦 🟦 🟦

When the chef/patron describes one of his dishes as akin to 'a
fly cemetery', then you realise there's no standing on ceremony
at this vibrantly coloured subterranean restaurant, hung with
bunches of dried chillies, herbs and garlic. No cause for
concern, though, as the aforementioned creation is really more
of a spiced raisiny, curranty compote, that makes a fine savoury
match to roast breast of Galloway pheasant, onion tatties and
Muscatel gravy. Global influences abound – Hanoi duck soup,
for example, almost a meal in itself, is an aromatic broth of
marinated roast duck, shiitake mushrooms, egg noodles and
fresh herbs, and curanto is a traditional Chilean dish made
with mixed shellfish, roasted meats, and potatoes. Estofado de
lengua is described as Mexican-style home-cooked tongue with
a rich tomato and cinnamon sauce, pimento, olives and
Stravaigin pickled chilli – and as the menu cheerily adds 'don't
be put off by the contents, this dish is delicious!'

Directions: Next to Glasgow University. 200 yds from
Kelvinbridge underground.

GLASGOW, **Ubiquitous Chip** ✿

*Simple city suburb diner with stone floors, lots of greenery and a
lively, informal atmosphere. Popular with lunchtime shoppers and
business suits, it offers a short, appealing bistro menu. A test meal
highlighted meaty pan-fried scallops and tender wood pigeon with
wild mushroom sauce. Good selection of Scottish cheeses.*

12 Ashton Lane G12 8SJ
Map 11: NS56
Tel: 0141 334 5007
Fax: 0141 337 1302
Telephone for details

Directions: Telephone for directions

GLASGOW, **Yes** ✿✿

Yes, yes, yes! This sophisticated city-centre restaurant hums
like a fairground at lunch times, packed with members of the
local business community, who clearly know a good thing when
they see it. Rich purple and red colours, comfortable booths
and prints and paintings by Glasgow artists, set the striking but
non-intimidating tone. The cooking is equally eclectic and
original, enthusiastically drawing on influences from near and
far. Local pride is satisfied with a cream of Finnan haddock
soup with lentils and crisp bacon, gâteau of haggis, neeps and
tatties with a whisky sauce, and a pastry of west-coast seafood
with saffron, plum tomato and herb cream. More wide-ranging

22 West Nile Street
G1 2PW
Map 11: NS56
Tel: 0141 2218044
Fax: 0141 2489159
Chefs: Iain McMaster,
Ferrier Richardson
Owner: Ferrier Richardson
Cost: Alc £26.45, fixed-price L
£15.95/D £24.50. H/wine £10.95
Times: Noon-last L 2.30pm/7pm-last
D 11pm. Closed Sun, Bhs, 25-26
Dec, 1 Jan

Yes

Additional: Bar food;
Children welcome; ④ dishes
Seats: 100. Private dining room 20
Smoking: Air-conditioning
Credit cards: ▬ ▬ ▬ ▬ ▣ ⊆

is best end of lamb with ratatouille and minted couscous, and roast chicken breast with buttered spinach and gratin of macaroni, Parmesan and Parma ham. Two well-reported innovative dishes have been hot-smoked Otter Ferry salmon and Mull of Kintyre cheddar soufflé with hollandaise sauce, and breast of Perthshire pheasant with an oatmeal, Savoy cabbage and potato cake in a red wine and tarragon sauce. The Brasserie also serves a good choice of dishes, from pizzas and pastas at lunchtime to grilled rib-eye steak with pommes frites in the evening.

Directions: City centre. M8 exit for George Sq. Turn L at 2nd lights into Port Dundas Rd, which joins West Nile St

HIGHLAND

ARDVASAR, Ardvasar Hotel ❀

Isle of Skye IV45 8RS
Map 13: NG60
Tel: 01471 844223
Chef: Bill Fowler
Owners: Bill and Gretta Fowler
Cost: Alc £23. Fixed-price L £12. ☺
Times: Last L 2pm/D 8.30pm.
Closed Nov
Additional: Bar food;
Children welcome; ④ dishes
Smoking: No smoking in dining room
Accommodation: 10 en suite
Credit cards: ▬ ▬ ▬ ⊆

Refreshingly honest little hotel (a former coaching inn), not far from the Armadale ferry terminal. Quality island produce is used to good effect in dishes such as fresh Skye salmon mousse, potted crab, roast chicken leg with Skye honey-mustard glaze, and braised local lamb chops with rosemary, tomato and potato crust. Highland game pie and Scottish scampi feature in the bar.

Directions: From Armadale ferry turn L and on through village

ARISAIG, Arisaig House ❀❀❀

Beasdale PH39 4NR
Map 13: NM68
Tel: 01687 450622
Fax: 01687 450626
Chef: Gary Robinson
Owners: Ruth, John &
Andrew Smither
Cost: Fixed-price L from £5/D £35
(4 courses). H/wine £14.50
Times: 12.30pm-last L 2pm/7.30pm-
last D 8.30pm.
Closed Nov-end March
Additional: Bar food L;
No children under 10 at D; ❹ dishes
Seats: 36. Jacket & tie preferred
Smoking: No smoking in dining room
Accommodation: 14 rooms, 13 en
suite
Credit cards: ▬ ▤ ▨ ⒢

Guests can wander down a footpath to the sea, or potter amongst the well-tended formal gardens and terraces full of rhododendrons, azaleas and roses. Polished floors, antiques, deep-cushioned sofas and real fires characterise the splendid rooms. The sense of unobtrusive luxury extends to Gary Robinson's daily changing, set-price, four-course dinner. High quality ingredients are treated with care, but combinations are sensitively restrained – tarte Tatin of scallops with red pepper and chive oils or grilled fillet of hare with rabbit and mushroom steamed pudding, for instance. Dinner starts well with canapés, delicious marinated black olives, and freshly baked bread. A first course of roasted quail with black pudding and Madeira dressing showed off the kitchen's impressive technical skills, as did a slightly frothy velouté soup of artichoke and squat lobster. Our inspector's luck was in with a main course of braised darne and grilled fillet of turbot with sauce Jacqueline, which proved a most interesting dish to sample, as the same fish provided a complete contrast of tastes and textures by being cooked in different ways. Classic saucing also sets off whole grilled Eigg lobster with sauce choron, grilled fillet of halibut with creamed parsley and sauce antiboise, and smooth parfait of chicken livers studded with artichoke with sauce gribiche. This, however, goes hand in hand with a more contemporary use of red wine jus in a dish of fillets of John Dory and black bream with wild mushrooms, or garden herb emulsion with baked salmon gâteau and creamed leeks. Lemon tart with redcurrant sorbet made a tangy, smooth pudding.

Directions: On A830 Fort William to Mallaig road, 3 miles east of Arisaig village

BRORA, Royal Marine Hotel ❀ NEW

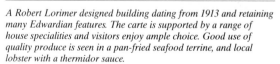

A Robert Lorimer designed building dating from 1913 and retaining many Edwardian features. The carte is supported by a range of house specialities and visitors enjoy ample choice. Good use of quality produce is seen in a pan-fried seafood terrine, and local lobster with a thermidor sauce.

Smoking: No smoking in dining room
Accommodation: 16 en suite. **Credit cards:** ▬ ▤ ▨ ▩ ⒢

Directions: Turn off A9 in village toward beach and golf course

Golf Road KW9 6QS
Map 14: NC90
Tel: 01408 621252
Fax: 01408 621181
Chef: Steve Mackenzie
Owner: Robert Powell
Cost: Alc £20. H/wine £10. ☺
Times: Last L 2pm/last D 9pm.
Closed 25 Dec
Additional: Sunday L; Bar meals;
Children welcome; ❹ dishes

CANNICH, Mullardoch House

Stunningly located at the head of a remote glen amid lovely scenery, this comfortably refurbished former shooting lodge continues to impress. Dinner – a fixed four-course affair – could follow the lines of cauliflower and Stilton soup, sirloin steak with a well-balanced pepper sauce, and a smooth lemon posset.

Additional: Bar food; Children welcome; ❸ dishes
Smoking: No smoking in dining room
Accommodation: 7 en suite
Credit cards: ▆ ▆ ▆

Directions: 8 miles W of Cannich (A831) on unclassified Glen Cannich road to Loch Mullardoch

Glen Cannich
Beauly IV4 7LX
Map 14: NH23
Tel/Fax: 01456 415460
Chef: Helen Johnston
Owners: Andrew & Helen Johnston
Cost: Fixed-price D £24.
H/wine £8.50
Times: Last L 2pm/D at 8pm

COLBOST,
Three Chimneys Restaurant

Dunvegan IV55 8ZT
Map 13: NG24
Tel: 01470 511258
Fax: 01470 511358
Chef: Shirley Spear
Owner: Eddie & Shirley Spear
Cost: *Alc* L £25/D £30. ☺
H/wine £10.95.
Times: 12.30pm-last L 2.30pm/7pm-last D 9pm. Closed Sun, Nov-Easter
Additional: No children under 10 at D; ❸ dishes
Seats: 30. Private dining room 15
Smoking: No smoking establishment
Credit cards: ▆ ▆ ▯

Eddie and Shirley Spear's 100-year-old crofter's cottage is set in a tiny village close to Colbost Museum, a stones throw from the sea. There's a real sense of domesticity about this set-up: sturdy polished tables are laid-out in the two stone-walled dining areas, Celtic music plays, and the owners are forever baking breads and scones. You can eat virtually any time of day, whether you want morning coffee, a light lunch or afternoon tea, although the greatest pleasures are reserved for the evening. Fresh seafood is the star attraction – culminating in a grand platter of piscine delights for two people. Partan bree (a traditional crab soup) is a favourite way to start, otherwise you might kick off with a tartlet of mussels with saffron cream. Following this might be hot lobster and langoustines flamed in brandy with chive and sherry sauce or fillet of halibut with a savoury vanilla custard. Those with a penchant for red meat are not neglected, and vegetarians are well accommodated. A trio of red deer, pigeon and hare is served with a dark game gravy, beetroot and blackcurrants, while white nut loaf with prune and walnut stuffing is paired with spiced pear and port sauce. Desserts could range from hot marmalade pudding with Drambuie custard to white chocolate mousse. The top-class wine list ranges far and wide for quality.

Directions: From Dungevan take B884 to Glendale. Restaurant is at Colbost 4.5 miles from main road turn off

CONTIN, Coul House

Contin By Strathpeffer
IV14 9EY
Map 14: NH45
Tel: 01997 421487
Fax: 01997 421945
Chef: Christopher Bentley
Owners: Martyn & Ann Hill
Cost: Alc £23, fixed-price D £27.50
(6 courses). ☺ H/wine £14.30.
Times: Last L 2pm /D 9pm
Additional: Bar food; Sunday L;
No children under 6; ❹ dishes.
Smoking: No smoking in dining room.
Accommodation: 20 en suite.
Credit cards:

*Welcoming Victorian country house with acreage and atmosphere.
'Taste of Scotland' dishes feature prominently on a something-for-
everyone menu. Roast crown of Highland lamb stuffed with smoked
ham and mushrooms in a red wine sauce is matched by a simply
grilled River Conon salmon with lemon sauce. Look out for
Ecclefechan butter tart for dessert.*

Directions: A9 and A385 to Contin. Half mile up private drive
on right.

DINGWELL, Kinkell House

*A comfortable farmhouse above the Cromarty Firth. Marsha Fraser
produces a well-reported, daily changing set-price menu. Typical
main courses include seared scallops with fettucine, and pan-fried
fillet of venison with sloe gin sauce. Look out for the delicious
Kinkell brioche bread-and-butter pudding.*

Easter Kinkell IV7 8HY
Map 14: NH55
Tel: 01349 861270
Fax: 01349 865902
Chef: Marsha Fraser
Owners: Steve & Marsha Fraser
Cost: Alc £20, fixed-price L £11. ☺
H/wine £9.50.
Times: Last L 1.45pm/D 8.45pm

Additional: Sunday L; Children welcome; ❹ dishes
Smoking: No smoking in dining room
Accommodation: 7 en suite
Credit cards:

Directions: On B9169 10 miles N of Inverness, 1 mile from A9
& A835

DULNAIN BRIDGE,
Muckrach Lodge Hotel

*Enthusiastic new owners have taken over this Victorian shooting
lodge and the signs are encouraging. Daily five-course dinners are
served in the conservatory, and the kitchen delivers dishes such as
Thai fishcakes, carrot and celeriac soup and roast pork fillet, stir-
fried vegetables and soy sauce.*

PH26 3LY
Map 14: NH92
Tel: 01479 851257
Fax: 01479 851325
Chef: Tom Riding
Owners: James & Dawn Macfarlane
Cost: Fixed-price D £23. ☺
H/wine £12.
Times: Last L 2.30pm/last D 9pm

Additional: Bar meals; Sunday L; Children welcome; ❹ dishes
Smoking: No pipes & cigars
Accommodation: 13 en suite
Credit cards:

Directions: On A938, 0.5 mile from Dulnain Bridge

DUNDONNELL,
Dundonnell Hotel

Genuine Highland hospitality, combined with good modern cooking, continues to attract visitors to this comfortable hotel located at the head of Little Loch Broom. An inspection dinner highlighted a delicious parcel of smoked salmon filled with trout mousse, courgette and ginger soup, and medley of seafood served with vermouth and dill sauce.

Accommodation: 28 en suite. **Credit cards:** ▄▄ ▄▄ ▄▄ 🔲

Directions: On A832 Ullapool/Gairloch road, 14 miles from Braemore Junction

IV23 2QS
Map 14: NH08
Tel: 01854 633204
Fax: 01854 633366
Chef: Mrs I Bellshaw
Owners: Mr & Mrs S Florence
Cost: Fixed-price D £23.95. ☺
H/wine £8.25.
Times: Last L 2.15pm/last D 8.15pm
Additional: Bar food; Children welcome; ✦ dishes
Smoking: No smoking in dining room

DUROR, Stewart Hotel

Polished mahogany tables and a Merano chandelier set the scene for a meal at this friendly family-run hotel. The dinner menu changes daily in order to make the best use of local ingredients. To start with there may be sautéed scallops, or chicken livers with a cream and brandy sauce in a pastry box, followed by a soup course, perhaps mussel chowder or cream of mushroom. Imaginative fish dishes include steamed salmon and sole with lime beurre blanc sauce, and a seafood medley of langoustine, plaice, sardine and cod with velouté sauce. Loin of lamb is enlivened with a honey and ginger sauce, pheasant well paired with cranberry and gooseberry sauce. Apple and pear crumble, strawberry palmier and whisky oranges with Atholl brose cream give the final touch.

Directions: Midway between Fort William and Oban on A828

Appin PA38 4BW
Map 14: NM95
Tel: 01631 740268
Fax: 01631 740328
Chef: Michael Lacy
Owner: The Lacy family
Cost: Fixed-price D £25 (4 courses).
☺ H/wine £9.50.
Times: D only, 7pm- last D 9pm.
Closed 15 Oct-1 April
Additional: Bar food;
No children under 6; ✦ dishes
Seats: 35
Smoking: No smoking in dining room
Accommodation: 19 en suite
Credit cards: ▄▄ ▄▄ ▄▄ 🔲

FORT AUGUSTUS, Brae Hotel

Comfortable, personally run small hotel with views over the Caledonian Canal and surrounding hills. Mari Reive's house party-style cooking is based on quality raw ingredients. Expect warm bacon and scallop salad, carrot, apple and cashew soup, and pan-fried fillet steak with malt whisky and cream.

Accommodation: 7 en suite. **Credit cards:** ▄▄ ▄▄ ▄▄ 🔲

Directions: Turn L off A82 just before leaving Fort Augustus heading N to Inverness. Hotel is on L after 300 metres

Fort Augustus PH32 4DG
Map 14: NH30
Tel: 01320 366289
Fax: 01320 366702
Chef: Mari Reive
Owner: Andrew & Mari Reive
Cost: Fixed-price D £23.50. ☺
H/wine £8.
Times: D only, 7pm-8.30pm.
Closed Nov-March.
Additional: No children under 7
Smoking: No smoking in dining room

FORT WILLIAM,
Crannog Restaurant

The building is a converted fishermen's bait shed, with white walls, blue carpet and natural wood furniture. There's a patio section with spectacular views of Loch Linnhe, where you can see the boats off-loading the day's catch. Scottish seafood is the speciality of the house, particularly local langoustine.

Credit cards: ▄▄ ▄▄ ▄▄ 🔲

Directions: On town pier in Fort William; approach from by-pass

Fort William PH33 7NG
Map 14: NN17
Tel: 01397 705589
Fax: 01397 705026
Chef: Anne Mackinnon
Cost: Alc £20. H/wine £9.95
Times: Last L 2.30pm/D 10pm.
Closed 25-26 Dec, 1-2 Jan
Additional: Children welcome;
✦ dishes
Smoking: No-smoking area

FORT WILLIAM,

Inverlochy Castle ❀❀❀

Torlundy
PH33 6SN
Map 14: NN17
Tel: 01397 702177
Fax: 01397 702953
Chef: Simon Haigh
Cost: *Alc* £45, fixed-price L £27.50/D £45. H/wine £15
Times: 12.30pm-last L 1.45pm/7pm-last D 9.30pm.
Additional: Bar meals L; Sunday L; Children welcome; ❧ dishes
Seats: 35. Private dining room 12. Jacket and tie preferred
Smoking: No smoking in dining room
Accommodation: 17 en suite
Credit cards: ▰ ▰ ▰ ▰ ▰

Ben Nevis looms awesomely behind this grand Victorian mansion set in 500 acres of grounds awash with rhododendrons. This is a country house hotel with real style and its strengths are legendary. Simon Haigh's cooking is founded on a bedrock of classical technique and training, although he is quite capable of taking on board current trends: roast scallops with candied onion, tomato and citrus vinaigrette sits alongside guinea fowl and leek terrine with Caesar salad, while grilled fillet of John Dory with tomato coulis and aubergine caviar shares the billing with roast partridge and wild mushrooms. This is a kitchen with an intuitive feel for the seasons and for local ingredients. A June inspection began with a fine selection of appetisers, before a well-wrought duck galantine studded with pistachios and dressed with pieces of apple. Soups also impress, whether an intense chick pea or roast tomato with basil. On this occasion, the main course was a succulent, browned tranche of halibut accompanied by an orange sauce plus a soft timbale of spinach and a mélange of sea kale, asparagus and beans. To finish, there was a delicate filo basket filled with pieces of pineapple and banana topped with ice cream on swirls of caramel sauce and crème anglaise. The big wine list has an extraordinary layout – not that easy to read. Some top quality wines in a range of vintages but at a price; look to the the youngsters – Frank Phélan (St Estèphe) 93 (£20), and a number of Cru Bourgeois under £25. Burgundies are mostly of the higher, pricier echelon but the Fixin les Chenevrières is good value at £25. Some very good halves. Italy and the New World are easiest on the pocket.

Directions: 3 miles N of Fort William on A82, just past the Golf Club

FORT WILLIAM, **Moorings Hotel** ❀❀

Banavie PH33 7LY
Map 14: NN17
Tel: 01397 772797
Fax: 01397 772441
Chef: Karen Melville
Owner: Mr N Sinclair
Cost: *Alc* £26, fixed-price D £27. H/wine £13.75
Times: L by prior arrangement/7pm-last D 9.30pm. Closed Xmas
Additional: Bar food; No children under 6; ❧ dishes
Seats: 76. Private dining room 20

Peacefully situated beside Neptune's Staircase on the banks of the Caledonian Canal, the Moorings plays up its nautical connections. Serious eating takes place in the Jacobean Restaurant, where a choice of menus is built solidly around supplies of Scottish produce. This shows up most strongly on the 'Taste of Scotland' *carte*, where you might find Highland venison sausage, soused Mallaig herrings, fillets of West Coast sole with saffron cream sauce, and saddle of Mamore lamb served with a compote of shallots, garlic and pine kernels and a rosemary glaze. Our inspector opted for flavoursome chicken liver parfait with apple and tarragon jelly and Orkney oatcakes before poached local salmon garnished with smoked salmon and served with a lime beurre blanc. Crème brûlée with raspberries is the signature dessert, but the range extends to warm date pudding with sticky toffee sauce and home-made strawberry ice cream with langue-de-chat biscuits. The carefully chosen wine list has an excellent selection from 'developing countries'.

Smoking: No smoking in dining room
Accommodation: 21 en suite
Credit cards:

Directions: From A82 take A830 W 1 mile. 1st R over Caledonian Canal on B8004

GARVE, Inchbae Lodge Hotel ❀

A short, fixed-price menu features freshly prepared, good local produce such as pot-roasted whole wood pigeon braised with red wine, mushrooms, bacon and celery. Other dishes might include chicken liver, garlic and herb pâté, mint, pea and lettuce soup and sticky toffee pudding. Booking for non-residents is essential.

Smoking: No smoking in dining room
Accommodation: 12 en suite
Credit cards: ▬ ▬ ▬

Inchbae IV23 2PH
Map 14: NH36
Tel: 01997 455269
Fax: 01997 455207
Chef: Patrick Price
Owners: Patrick & Judy Price
Cost: Fixed-price D £23 (5 courses).
☺ H/wine £8.50.
Times: Last L 2pm/last D 8pm
Additional: Bar meals;
Children welcome; ♨ dishes

Directions: Hotel is on A835, 6 miles on Ullapool side of Garve

GRANTOWN-ON-SPEY, Garth Hotel ❀

Friendly holiday/sporting hotel, set in acres of landscaped gardens. The daily-changing set-price menu offers simple dishes based on prime Scottish produce and cooked with a French accent. Typical main courses include pan-fried Buchan steak with whisky sauce, and poached fillet of Spey salmon with a white wine sauce.

Smoking: No smoking in dining room
Accommodation: 16 en suite
Credit cards: ▬ ▬ ▬ ▬ ▬ ▬

Castle Road PH26 3HN
Map 14: NJ02
Tel: 01479 872836
Fax: 01479 872116
Chef: Mr R Toward
Owners: Mr G McLaughlan
Cost: Alc £23, fixed-price D £24. ☺
H/wine £9.
Times: Last L 1.30pm/D 8.30pm.
Closed end Nov
Additional: Sunday L; Bar meals;
Children welcome; ♨ dishes

Directions: A9 to Aviemore, then A95 to Grantown-on-Spey. Hotel overlooks town square

HARLOSH, Harlosh House ❀❀❀

Built around 1750 as a tackman's house and turned into an enchanting little hotel in the 1970s, Harlosh stands on a small peninsula jutting out into Loch Bracadale with views of the Cuillin Hills beyond. Peter Elford produces impressive four-course dinners built around supplies of local produce – shellfish from the loch, fish from Lallaig, locally grown vegetables, wild herbs and so on. In an effort to ensure that returning guests always taste something new, he keeps a record of every dish and meal eaten. Home-made bread rolls show that he knows what baking is about and the man is a skilled pastry cook too: witness a first-rate tartlet filled with juicy marinated red peppers, tomato and basil topped with crumbly smoked goat's cheese. At inspection, this was presented with a pretty bouquet of herbs and edible flowers drizzled with olive oil. The sheer quality of fish has also impressed mightily; for example tip-top monkfish, sliced and then arranged with each piece arranged atop a construction of 'great' spinach and onion marmalade with a perfectly acidulated rosemary beurre blanc

Dunvegan Isle of Skye
IV55 8ZG
Map 13: NG24
Tel/Fax: 01470 521367
Chef: Peter Elford
Owners: Peter & Lindsey Elford
Cost: Fixed-price D £26 (4 courses).
H/wine £10.50
Times: D only, 7pm-last D 8.30pm.
Closed D Wed, Nov to Easter
Additional: Children welcome.
Seats: 18
Smoking: No smoking in dining room
Accommodation: 6 en suite
Credit cards: ▬ ▬ ▬

spooned around the plate or, again, Loch Bracadale crab with a salad of chargrilled local asparagus (yes, they can grow it on Skye!) and neatly dressed leaves. Other possibilities from the sea might be seared scallops flavoured with spring onion and pickled ginger and a tranche of cod with a brioche crust on a plum tomato salsa. Desserts tend to be competent, rather than inspirational: hazelnut and praline parfait with a fruit coulis or date pudding with crème anglaise and caramel sauce, and so forth. It would be sinful to miss out on the cheeseboard, which features the cream of the crop from Scotland's farmhouse producers – Bonchester, Strathkinness, Drumleish, Galloway Diamond, to name but four. The owners offer the best in hospitality and staff are relaxed.

Directions: 4 miles S of Dunvegan, turn R off A863, signed Harlosh

---

INVERNESS,

Bunchrew House Hotel

A sixteenth-century baronial mansion, set in 20 acres of wooded grounds, with stunning views over the Beauly Firth. The evening carte features local produce in dishes such as aromatic salmon with beetroot and crème fraîche, haunch of venison with braised chestnuts, and a caramelised lemon tart.

Accommodation: 15 en suite
Credit cards: ▆▆ ▆▆ ▆▆ ▆

Directions: 2.5 miles from Inverness on A862 towards Beauly Bunchrew IV3 6TA

IV3 6TA
Map 14: NH64
Tel: 01463 234917
Fax: 01463 710620
Chef: Walter Walker
Owners: Stewart & Lesley Dykes
Cost: Alc L £22, fixed-price L £17. ☺ H/wine £11.50.
Times: Last L 1.45pm/D 8.45pm
Additional: Children welcome; ❹ dishes
Smoking: No smoking in dining room

INVERNESS, **Café 1**   **NEW**

Trendy venue for modern Scottish cooking. A winter meal kicked off with smooth chicken liver parfait and Cumberland sauce. Then came West Coast salmon fillet, roasted with pine kernels and basil, and served with sliced leeks. To finish, a rich, tangy lemon torte.

Additional: Children welcome; ❹ dishes
Credit cards: ▆▆ ▆▆ ▆▆ ▆

Directions: Opposite Jnverness Castle on Castle Street

75 Castle Street IV2 3EA
Map 14: NH64
Tel: 01463 226200
Fax: 01463 716363
Chef: Charles Lockley
Owners: John Ewart
Cost: Alc £17.50, fixed-price L £8.95. ☺ H/wine £8.
Times: Last L 2.30pm/D 10pm. Closed Sun (Oct-Jun), 25-26 Dec, 1-2 Jan

---

INVERNESS,

Culloden House Hotel

Handsome Palladian country house enjoying romantic associations with Bonnie Prince Charlie. An imaginative fixed-price menu, served in the elegant Adam dining room, reflects use of quality ingredients in such dishes as quail filled with orange and pork mousse with a wild mushroom and red wine sauce. Comprehensive wine list.

Accommodation: 28 en suite. **Credit cards:** ▆▆ ▆▆ ▆▆ ▆ ▆

Directions: From Inverness take A96 (Airport road), R at sign "Culloden". After 1.2 miles L at dovecote after 2 sets of traffic lights

Culloden IV1 2NZ
Map 14: NH64
Tel: 01463 790461
Fax: 01463 792181
Chef: Michael Simpson
Cost: Alc L £18, fixed-price D £25-35. H/wine £11
Times: Last L 2pm/D 9pm
Additional: Sunday L; No children under 10; ❹ dishes
Smoking: No smoking in dining room

INVERNESS, **Dunain Park Hotel**

IV3 6JN
Map 14: NH64
Tel: 01463 230512
Fax: 01463 224532
Chef: Ann Nicholl
Owners: Edward & Ann Nicholl
Cost: Alc £25. H/wine £14.50. ☺
Times: L by prior arrangement/7pm-last D 9pm.
Additional: Children welcome; ✪ dishes
Smoking: No smoking in dining room
Accommodation: 12 en suite
Credit cards: 🔲 🔲 🔲 🔲 🔲 🔲

The restaurant at this Georgian country house hotel is divided into three smaller areas, allowing guests to enjoy a more intimate atmosphere. Beef Wellington contrasted well with a mille-feuille of asparagus at a May meal, and there's a good wine list plus over 200 malt whiskies on offer.

Directions: One mile from town boundary on A82 to Fort William

INVERNESS, **Inverness Thistle**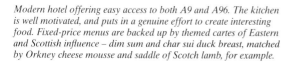

Modern hotel offering easy access to both A9 and A96. The kitchen is well motivated, and puts in a genuine effort to create interesting food. Fixed-price menus are backed up by themed cartes of Eastern and Scottish influence – dim sum and char sui duck breast, matched by Orkney cheese mousse and saddle of Scotch lamb, for example.

Additional: Bar food L; Sunday L; Children welcome; ✪ dishes
Accommodation: 118 en suite
Credit cards: 🔲 🔲 🔲 🔲 🔲 🔲

Millburn Road IV2 3TR
Map 14: NH74
Tel: 01463 239666
Fax: 01463 711145
Chef: Alec Summers
Owners: Thistle Hotels
Cost: Alc £20, fixed-price D £16.95. ☺ H/wine £10.50.
Times: Last L 2pm/D 9.30pm

Directions: Just off A9 at Raigmoll interchange, 1 mile from town centre

INVERNESS, **Kingsmills Hotel** NEW

Long-established tourist and business hotel where the serious eating is done in the comfort of the refurbished Inglis restaurant. Dishes such as scallops with fennel and lightly roasted best end of lamb with rosemary sauce are typical of the care with which fine Scottish produce is handled.

Additional: Bar meals L; Sunday L; Children welcome; ✪ dishes
Smoking: No smoking in dining room; air-conditioning
Accommodation: 80 en suite
Credit cards: 🔲 🔲 🔲 🔲 🔲

Culcabock Road IV2 3LP
Map 14: NH64
Tel: 01463 237166
Fax: 01463 225208
Chef: Patrick Dobbin
Cost: Alc £25, fixed-price L £13/D £22. ☺ H/wine £12.
Times: Last L 2pm/last D 9.30pm

Directions: From A9 S take slip road for Culduthel/Kingsmills; follow Kingsmills signs; hotel at junction of Kingsmills Rd/Culcabock Rd

ISLE ORNSAY,
Hotel Eilean Iarmain ❀

Isle of Skye IV43 8QR
Map 13: NG71
Tel: 01471 833332
Fax: 01471 833275
Chefs: Rodger Brown,
Morag MacInnes
Owners: Sir Iain & Lady Noble
Cost: Fixed-price L £16.50/D £28.
H/wine £12.50
Times: Last L 1.45pm/last D 8.45pm
Additional: Bar food; Sunday L;
Children welcome; ❹ dishes
Smoking: No smoking in dining room
Accommodation: 12 en suite
Credit cards: ▬ ▬ ▬

What a waterside position! This nineteenth-century island inn has its
own quay and landing stage and looks out over a sheltered bay. The
kitchen is ambitious and offers innovative cooking of local seafood
and game. A typical meal could take in pheasant soup, gently
steamed scallops with a saffron sauce, and hot chocolate and
almond pudding.

Directions: Overlooking harbour – cross bridge at Kyle of
Lochalsh then take A850 and A851 down to harbour front

ISLE ORNSAY, **Kinloch Lodge** ❀❀

Isle of Skye IV43 8QY
Map 13: NG61
Tel: 01471 833214
Fax: 01471 833277
Chefs: Lady Macdonald & Peter
Macpherson
Owners: Lord & Lady Macdonald
Cost: Fixed-price D £35 (5 courses).
H/wine £5.50
Times: D only from 8pm. Closed Jan
Seats: 30
Smoking: No smoking in dining room
Accommodation: 10 en suite
Credit cards: ▬ ▬ ▬

There are great views of Loch Na Dal from Lord and Lady
Macdonald's converted 300-year-old lodge and the mood
inside is one of a family home with warming log fires,
comfortable settees, and personal photographs and portraits
dotted all around. Lady Macdonald still oversees the kitchen in
between her popular cookery courses and writing duties.
Dinner is a fixed-price affair running to four courses and dishes
are based resolutely on what the local region can provide. Our
inspector began with a full flavoured scallop terrine served
with a suitably sharp cucumber and fennel relish, before
sampling a clear mushroom soup tinged with fresh mint. As a
main course, he chose roast breast and leg of duck
accompanied by Calvados and apple purée and a green
peppercorn sauce plus a decent assortment of vegetables,
including the ubiquitous 'riced' potatoes. Dessert was dark

chocolate nemesis (a real 'killer', and as fine a chocolate pudding as the recipient had tasted). Coffee and superb fudge are served in the drawing room. The wine list runs to about four dozen bins from most major producing countries.

Directions: 1 mile off main road, 6 miles S of Broadford on A851, 10 miles N of Armadale

KINGUSSIE, The Cross

Ruth and Tony Hadley run this converted tweed mill as a homely restaurant-with-rooms. A mood of modest domesticity prevails in the lounges and the spacious beamed dining room – which has doors opening onto the patio just a stone's throw from the bubbling Gynack burn. Ruth's five-course dinners kick off with a tantalising amuse-gueule such as salmon tartare with quail's egg before, say, a delicate scallop mousse with a piece of intact bivalve suspended in the middle alongside a prawn and basil sauce. Next comes soup – perhaps piquant onion, apple and cider or celeriac perfumed with truffle oil. After that there is generally fish, a hot-smoked salmon (cured in-house) with avocado salsa, perhaps. Main courses home in on local ingredients – new season's lamb, Ayrshire guinea fowl (occasionally scented with lemon grass), or wild red deer (fresh off the hill) which might be lightly sautéed with redcurrants and port. To finish, expect a choice of three desserts: for example, aniseed parfait laced with Pernod, baked lime cheesecake with rhubarb compote or a layered marquise-like cake of chocolate and raspberries with an intense raspberry coulis dribbled around. Tony Hadley's enthusiasm is the driving force behind the compilation of the fulsome wine list. There's no apology for the lack of description, the list is very much a personal effort and every assistance is offered with selection. Half-bottles are clearly a priority, occupying the first ten pages. Less esteemed areas of the globe (Austria, Canada) receive vigorous support and there's quality and value from South Africa.

Signature dishes: Fillet of Highland lamb with Madeira and tarragon; boudin of scallops with asparagus; oriental marinated quail;

Directions: Town centre, 300m uphill from lights along Ardroilach Road & turn left onto Tweed Mill Brae

Tweed Mill Brae
Ardbroilach Road
PH21 1TC

Map 14: NH70
Tel: 01540 661166
Fax: 01540 661080
Chef: Ruth Hadley
Owners: Tony & Ruth Hadley
Cost: Fixed-price D £35 (5 courses). H/wine from £10
Times: D only, 7pm-9pm. Closed Tues, 1-26 Dec, 6 Jan-28 Feb
Additional: No children under 12; 🍴 dishes
Seats: 28
Smoking: No smoking in dining room
Accommodation: 9 en suite
Credit cards: ▬ ▒ ▚ ▢

KINGUSSIE, Osprey Hotel

Charming, family-run hotel in the heart of the Spey Valley. Aileen Burrow mixes the best of Scotland's larder with up-to-date ideas in dishes such as pan-fried chicken fillet with fennel and tarragon, and guinea fowl with lime and ginger sauce. For dessert don't resist the temptation of raspberry shortcake with whisky custard.

Additional: No children under 10
Smoking: No smoking in dining room
Accommodation: 8 en suite
Credit cards: ▬ ▒ ▒ ▢

Directions: South end of High Street off A9

Ruthven Road
PH21 1EN
Map 14: NH70
Tel/Fax: 01540 661510
Chef: Aileen Burrow
Owners: Aileen & Robert Burrow
Cost: Fixed-price D £21. ☺ H/wine £8.
Times: D only, 7.30pm-8.30pm

KINGUSSIE, The Scot House Hotel

A charming family-run hotel where the cooking features the best of local produce. Main courses include roast noisettes of local lamb with heather honey and ginger sauce, and pan-fried escalope of pork in a whisky and mustard sauce. Desserts include fruity Ecclefechan tart and traditional clootie dumplings.

Additional: Bar food; Children welcome; ♨ dishes
Smoking: No smoking in dining room
Accommodation: 9 en suite. **Credit cards:** ▧ ▧ ▧ ▧

Directions: South end of main village street

Newtonmore Road PH21 1HE
Map 14: NH70
Tel: 01540 661351
Fax: 01540 661111
Chef: Andrew Woods
Owners: Mr & Mrs W Gilbert,
Mr & Mrs N McConachie
Cost: *Alc* £25, fixed-price D £18. ☺
H/wine £9.
Times: D only, 7pm-last D 9pm.
Closed Jan

KYLESKU, Kylesku Hotel

Occupying a waterside position by the old ferry slip, this small hotel has a good reputation for the seafood that guests can often see landed minutes before it appears on their dinner table. Expect local salmon with lobster sauce, pan-fried haddock, and grilled jumbo langoustine with garlic mayonnaise.

Smoking: No smoking in dining room
Accommodation: 8 rooms, 6 en suite. **Credit cards:** ▧ ▧ ▧ ▧

Directions: 30 miles north of Ullapool

Lairg IV27 4HW
Map 14: NC23
Tel: 01971 502231
Fax: 01971 502313
Chef/Owner: Marcel Rene Klein
Cost: *Alc* £15, fixed-price L £15/D £18. ☺ H/wine £8.50.
Times: Last L 2.15pm/5.30pm-last D 9.30pm. Closed 25 Oct-1 Mar
Additional: Bar meals;
Children welcome; ♨ dishes

LOCHINVER, Lochinver Larder

This bay-windowed restaurant-cum-coffee shop overlooks the Inner River and Lochinver Bay, and serves a home-cooked mix of local seafood, prime sirloin steaks and other dishes such as chicken in white wine, roghan josh lamb curry, venison Stroganoff and nut roast. Children's meals also available.

Smoking: No smoking in dining room. **Credit cards:** ▧ ▧ ▧ ▧

Directions: On A837, second property on R coming from Inverness/Ullapool

Main Street IV27 4JY
Map 14: NC02
Tel: 01571 844356
Fax: 01571 844688
Chefs: IN & DA Stewart,
Mrs W Isbister
Owners: Ian & Debra Stewart
Cost: *Alc* £15.25. H/wine £8. ☺
Times: Last L 4.45pm/last D 9pm.
Closed Nov-30 Mar
Additional: Children welcome;
♨ dishes

MUIR OF ORD, The Dower House

More of a private house than a hotel, the cottage orné style of this secluded, seventeenth-century, one-storey hotel proves that small is beautiful. The dining-room has antique mahogany tables, Persian rugs, oil paintings and a white marble fireplace. Masses of fresh flowers fill the room. The no-choice menu (apart from dessert) changes daily, but is thoughtfully balanced. Our inspection meal began with spinach tagliatelle with sliced scallops and cockles, perked up with a touch of chilli. Excellent roasted pepper soup was full of flavour, and fillet of beef was served with rösti, shallot marmalade, diced vegetables and garden herbs. Orange crème brûlée, decorated with caramelised orange peel, finished the meal. Details such as crusty brown bread, good coffee and home-made truffles are all up to par, and service is quiet and careful. The wine includes some good growers.

Directions: From Muir of Ord take A862 (Dingwall) 1 mile, L at double bend

Highfield IV6 7XN
Map 14: NH55
Tel/Fax: 01463 870090
Chef: Robyn Aitchison
Owners: Robyn & Mena Aitchison
Cost: Fixed-price D £30 (4 courses).
☺ H/wine £13.
Times: L by arrangement/7pm-last D 9pm. Closed Xmas
Additional: Children welcome;
♨ dishes
Seats: 26
Smoking: No smoking in dining room
Accommodation: 5 en suite
Credit cards: ▧ ▧

NAIRN, **Newton Hotel**

Imposing Baronial mansion set in 27 acres overlooking the Moray Firth. The short set-dinner menu offers an interesting choice of well-prepared, modern Scottish dishes at realistic prices. Expect pigeon with black pudding fritter and onion marmalade, Cajun-style beef with red wine and balsamic vinegar essence, and crème caramel.

Additional: Sunday L; Bar meals; Children welcome; 🍴 dishes
Smoking: No smoking in dining room
Accommodation: 43 en suite
Credit cards: ■■ ■■ ■■ ■■ 🄲

Directions: West of the town centre

Inverness Road IV12 4RX
Map 14: NH85
Tel: 01667 453144
Fax: 01667 454026
Chef: Martyn Woodward
Cost: Fixed-price D £21.50. ☺
H/wine £9.75.
Times: D only, 7pm-9.15pm

ONICH,
Allt-Nan-Ros Hotel 👑👑

PH33 6RY
Map 14: NN06
Tel: 01855 821210
Fax: 01855 821462
Chef: Gavin Hughes
Owners: James, Fiona and
Lachlan MacLeod
Cost: Fixed-price D £25.
H/wine £9.75
Times: 12.30pm-last L 2pm/7pm-last
D 8.30pm
Additional: Sunday L;
Children welcome; 🍴 dishes
Seats: 50
Smoking: No smoking in dining room
Accommodation: 20 en suite
Credit cards: ■■ ■■ ■■ 🄽 🄳 🄲

The name is Gaelic for 'Burn of the Roses' – and refers to the cascading stream which passes through the hotel's gardens and on down to Loch Linnhe. The restaurant, which enjoys superb views across the loch to the Morvern Hills beyond, offers an imaginative set-price menu of French- based dishes with a strong modern west Highland accent. Typical starters might include smooth parfait of chicken livers served with toasted brioche and Cumberland sauce, twice-baked goat's cheese and garlic soufflé, and roast quail stuffed with tarragon and pink peppercorn mousse. A meal in May featured lightly roasted scallops with pesto, mushroom soup with chopped chives, roast breast of guinea fowl with grain mustard, mange-touts and new potatoes, and brandied date pudding with hot caramel sauce. The wine list offers a good range of French wines, together with the usual selection of bottles from the New World.

Directions: On the shores of Loch Linnhe, 10 miles S of Fort William on A82

PLOCKTON, **Haven Hotel**

Delightful small hotel, a former merchant's house, in a village setting. The kitchen combines up-to-date thinking with the best quality ingredients to produce dishes such as Plockton prawns with lime and coriander dip, honey-roasted gammon with a plum and

IV52 8TW
Map 14: NG83
Tel: 01599 544223
Fax: 01599 544467
Chef: Ian James
Owners: Annan and Jill Dryburgh

sherry sauce, and west coast scallops with carrot and lime purée and julienne of crystallised ginger.

Additional: No children under 7; ✦ dishes
Smoking: No smoking in dining room
Accommodation: 15 rooms
Credit cards: ▬ ▓ ▓ ▢

Directions: On main road to Plockton, on left hand side just before lochside

Cost: Fixed-price D £23 (5-courses).
☺ H/wine £7.
Times: Last L 2pm/last D 8.30pm.
Closed 20 Dec-1 Feb

PORTREE, Bosville Hotel ✿

Bosville Terrace Isle of Skye
IV51 9DG
Map 13: NG44
Tel: 01478 612846
Fax: 01478 613434
Chef: Craig Rodger
Owner: Donald W Macleod
Cost: *Alc* £22, fixed-price L £9. ☺
H/wine £9.
Times: 11.30am-10pm

Well established family hotel providing a good range of menus in two differently styled restaurants. One offers an all day menu, while Chandlery's (evenings only) specialises in seafood dishes. Here you can expect seafood and avocado baked with Pernod cream, panaché of seafood with dill and lemon butter, and white and dark chocolate terrine.

Additional: Bar meals; Sunday L; Children welcome; ✦ dishes
Smoking: No smoking in dining room; air-conditioning
Accommodation: 15 en suite
Credit cards: ▬ ▓ ▓ ▢

Directions: In centre of Portree

PORTREE,
Cuillin Hills Hotel ✿

Isle of Skye IV51 9LU
Map 13: NG44
Tel: 01478 612003
Fax: 01478 613092
Chef: Jeff Johnston
Owner: Kevin Wickman
Cost: Fixed-price D £24. ☺
H/wine £9.95.
Times: D only 6.30pm-9pm.
Additional: Bar Food; Sunday L (noon-2pm); Children welcome; ✦ dishes
Smoking: No smoking in dining room
Accommodation: 25 en suite
Credit cards: ▬ ▓ ▓ ▢

Former hunting lodge enjoying superb views over Portree Bay to the Cuillin Hills. Expect a friendly welcome and a successful modern style of cooking highlighting quality local ingredients. Specialities may include venison steak with juniper berry, gin and garlic jus, and oven-roasted pheasant with green peppercorn whisky sauce.

Directions: Signed to right 0.25 miles from Portree on A855 north

PORTREE, Rosedale Hotel ✿

Isle of Skye IV51 9DB
Map 13: NG44
Tel: 01478 613131
Fax: 01478 612531
Chef: Tony Parkyn

Originally three nineteenth-century fishermen's cottages, this welcoming quayside hotel boasts splendid sea views from its attractive upstairs restaurant. Innovative modern cooking using

Rosedale Hotel

Owner: HM & MB Andrew
Cost: Fixed-price D £26.56. ☺
H/wine £9.
Times: D only, 7pm-8.30pm.
Closed Oct-Apr
Additional: ❸ dishes
Smoking: No smoking in dining room
Accommodation: 23 en suite
Credit cards: ▬ ▭ ➹ ⬜

prime local ingredients produces dishes such as lentil and apricot soup, pot roast beef with prunes and Guinness, and rhubarb tarte Tatin.

Directions: Centrally located on waterfront in Portree

SHIELDAIG, Tigh an Eilean Hotel ✿

Strathcarron IV54 8XN
Map 14: NG85
Tel: 01520 755251
Fax: 01520 755321
Chef/Owner: Callum F Stewart
Cost: Fixed-price D £21.50. ☺
H/wine £8.40.
Times: D only, 7pm-8.30pm.
Seasonal opening, phone for details
Additional: Bar meals;
Children welcome

The 'house of the island' is set on the seashore amid white-washed crofts and fishermen's cottages, sheltered by pine trees. The short menu of popular dishes, which includes local fish, beef and lamb, is sympathetically cooked to retain full flavours.

Smoking: No smoking in dining room
Accommodation: 11 en suite
Credit cards: ▬ ▭ ➹ ⬜

Directions: In centre of Shieldaig, at water's edge

SPEAN BRIDGE, Old Station Restaurant ✿

Station Road
PH34 4EP
Map 14: NN28
Tel: 01397 712535
Chef/Owners: Richard and Helen
Bunney
Cost: Alc £21, fixed-price D (Sat only)
£21.50. ☺ H/wine £9.75.
Times: D only, 6.30pm-D 9pm.
Closed Mon, 24-26 Dec

Trainspotting is one of the extra attractions at this popular little restaurant carved out of the ticket office of a still working station. Richard Bunney's short menu offers honest cooking and excellent value. Try baked goat's cheese, grilled duck breast with apricot and lemon sauce, and white chocolate cheesecake.

Smoking: No-smoking area
Credit cards: ▬ ▭ ➹ ⬜

Directions: Approximately 10 miles N of Fort William, in centre of village (follow signs for BR station)

STRONTIAN, Kilcamb Lodge ✿✿

Acharacle PH36 4HY
Map 14: NM86
Tel: 01967 402257
Fax: 01967 402041
Chef: Neil Mellis
Owners: Peter & Anne Blakeway
Cost: Fixed-price D £25 (4 courses).
H/wine £9.50
Times: Noon-last L 1.30pm/D at
7.30pm.

Built in 1745 as a barracks, and later used as a private residence, this restored Highland hunting lodge now functions as a family-run country hotel with a very special 'get away from it all' feel. Outside are 28 acres of natural lawns and grounds, with half a mile of shoreline to Loch Sunart and the Strontian river. The views, particularly from the dining room, are splendid. Home-grown organic vegetables and local produce figure strongly on the daily-changing four-course menu. A typical day's selection might begin with pot-roast quail with apricot stuffing and truffle jus, or open ravioli of squat lobsters before a soup, such as cream of mussel and turnip. Main courses might include fillets of lemon sole with couscous and pimento fondue, or roast Argyll venison with aubergine compote and a chocolate and game sauce. Bringing up the rear are Scottish cheeses, and desserts such as sticky toffee pudding and Swiss meringue roulade with orange and strawberries.

Directions: Over the Corran ferry off A82. Follow A861 to Strontian. First L over bridge in centre of village

Additional: Light lunches; Children welcome
Seats: 26
Smoking: No smoking in dining room
Accommodation: 11 en suite
Credit cards: ▬ ▬ ▬ ▅ *C*

TONGUE, **Ben Loyal Hotel** ✤

Comfortable, family-run Highland hotel enjoying a splendid outlook, especially from the attractive dining room, over Kyle of Tongue and the ruins of Varrich Castle. A short, well balanced menu features quality Scottish produce. Expect leek and potato soup, Scrabster cod with Orkney cheese sauce, and Atholl brose for pudding.

IV27 4XE
Map 14: NG95
Tel: 01847 611216
Fax: 01847 611212
Chef: Mel Cook
Owners: Mel & Pauline Cook
Cost: Fixed-price D £18.50. ☺
H/wine £10.75.
Times: D only, 7pm-8.30pm.
Closed 1 Nov-28 Feb
Additional: Bar food noon-2pm; 🌢 dishes
Smoking: No smoking in dining room
Accommodation: 18 rooms
Credit cards: ▬ ▬ ▬ ▅ *C*

Directions: The hotel stands in the centre of this village at the A836/A838 intersection

TORRIDON, **Loch Torridon** ✤✤

A beautifully refurbished Victorian shooting lodge overlooking Loch Torridon. The house is set against a backdrop of wooded, granite hills, while Highland cattle graze in the grounds. The wood-panelled dining room provides a formal setting for the creative cooking of chef Ged Boylan. The short dinner menu changes daily to ensure the freshest local ingredients are

Achnasheen IV22 2EY
Map 14: NG95
Tel: 01445 791242
Fax: 01445 791296
Chef: Ged Boylan
Owners: David & Geraldine Gregory
Cost: Fixed-price D £35. H/wine £10
Times: D only, 7.15pm – last D 8.30pm
Additional: Bar meals; 🌢 dishes
Seats: 40. Private dining room 14. Jacket and tie preferred
Smoking: No smoking in dining room
Accommodation: 20 en suite
Credit cards: ▬ ▬ ▬ ▅ ▅ *C*

Directions: From Inverness, follow signs to Ullapool (A835). At Garve take A832 to Kinlochewe; take A896 to Torridon. Don't turn off to Torridon village – hotel is one mile on L

always used. Expect dishes such as blue cheese soufflé with walnut salad, roasted monkfish with tomato, garlic and saffron stew, and ballotine of chicken with a bacon and spinach stuffing. A meal in May began with langoustine, scallop and potato terrine, was followed by halibut with a mushroom crust and tomato, basil and black olive compote and a tapenade sauce. For dessert, a lemon tart was accompanied by a bitter sweet chocolate sorbet and raspberry coulis. The wine list has a fair spread of countries and styles and the bar boasts over 250 malt whiskies.

ULLAPOOL,
Altnaharrie Inn ❀❀❀❀❀❀

IV26 2SS
Map 14: NH19
Tel: 01854 633230
Chef: Gunn Eriksen
Owners: Fred Brown, Gunn Eriksen
Cost: Fixed-price D £70 (5 courses). H/wine £9.50
Times: D at 8pm. Closed Nov-Easter
Additional: No children under 8; ❀ dishes by arrangement
Seats: 16
Smoking: No smoking establishment
Accommodation: 8 en suite.
Credit cards: ▬▬ ▬▬ ▬▬ ▬

Directions: Telephone from Ullapool for directions to ferry

'Wow! This is a truly magical place. Gunn Eriksen's cooking is simply outstanding – words can hardly describe it. The setting is wonderful – booking is surprisingly not easy – rooms are full from week to week but it is worth every minute of the wait', wrote one inspector in a report strewn with superlatives, emphasising the many reasons why this is one of the best restaurants in Britain. It's rather an adventure waiting for the hotel boat to collect you from the quay in Ullapool (you phone when you arrive). Guests never eat the same dish twice – Gunn keeps meticulous records. On our visit, canapés were whole prawns, split and served warm with a wonderful parsley and garlic dressing, and a small light pastry case filled with creamed salmon and prawn roe topped with caviar. Dinner opened with the lightest of seafood mousses, covered by thin buttery pastry and served with both a slightly sweet meat jus and a sharper champagne sauce that worked perfectly together. Next came lobster soup, light and frothy, served with mayonnaise and crème fraîche crammed with the freshest lobster, topped with truffle and finished with a perfectly cooked lobster claw removed from the shell. Main course was a squab pigeon, full of flavour, and served with chanterelle mushrooms and a sweet rowan jelly to offset the richness of two 'superbly decadent' slices of foie gras; potatoes cooked in stock and baby asparagus accompanied the dish. Then cheese, individually detailed by Fred Brown, a wide selection of Scottish, French, English and Irish, all perfectly presented. Pineapple pudding was 'the best pudding I have ever tasted'. It proved to be a warm tart of sweet, tender pineapple, a slightly sharper pineapple sauce and a small amount of caramel to add a further depth of sweetness, and pineapple ice cream. Other puddings 'you don't get away with just one', were crème caramel,

caramel ice cream with a caramel sauce and warm slices of caramelised pear with superb spun sugar. A laudable selection of imaginative, pocket sensitive, house wines range from the balanced and elegant Côtes de Castillon of Château Pitray to the no nonsense antipodean punch of St Hallett's Cabernet Sauvignon. Well chosen Bordeaux and Burgundy offer both maturity for the heavyweights and youthful exuberance for the lighter, early drinkers. A fine range of halves are a fitting finale.

WHITEBRIDGE,

Knockie Lodge Hotel 🏵🏵

Set on the south side of Loch Ness, in a peaceful yet dramatic setting, stands this former shooting lodge, built over 200-years-ago by the chief of Clan Fraser. Nowadays, it is run house-party style by Nicholas Bean and Louise Dawson; the spacious, comfortable lounge with its log fire, honesty bar and masses of periodicals acts as a focal point for guests. 'Very fine' set dinners are served at 8pm, with no choice except for pudding. At a dinner in May this proved to be an amuse-gueule of oyster in the shell with scrambled egg and chopped chives, ravioli of foie gras with truffle sauce, rosette of Loch Fyne scallops with a creamy sauce made of the coral and served on a bed of puréed leeks, a 'hearty portion' of fillet of Aberdeen Angus beef with a morel butter sauce – accompanying vegetables included an artichoke bottom filled with baby corn – and chocolate mousse in a dark chocolate shell with a vanilla ice cream and a kirsch sauce.

Directions: On the B862 8 miles north of Fort Augustus

IV1 2UP
Map 14: NH41
Tel: 01456 486276
Fax: 01456 486389
Chef: Mark Dexter
Owners: Nicholas Bean, Louise Dawson
Cost: Fixed-price D £27.50 (5 courses). H/wine £9.50
Times: L residents only/D at 8pm. Closed 25 Oct- 4May
Additional: No children under 10; dishes
Seats: 25
Smoking: No smoking in dining room
Accommodation: 10 en suite
Credit cards: ▆ ▆ ▆ ▆ ▆ ▆

LANARKSHIRE, NORTH

CUMBERNAULD,

Westerwood Hotel 🏵

The Tipsy Laird is the restaurant of this hotel, golf and country club. The kitchen adopts a modern approach, using the best quality

1 St Andrews Drive
Westerwood G68 0EW
Map 11: NS77
Tel: 01236 457171
Fax: 01236 738478
Chef: Anthony Leck
Cost: *Alc* £20, fixed-price L £9.95/D £15. ☺ H/wine £10.95.
Times: Last L 1.45pm/last D 9.45pm. Closed L Sat
Additional: Bar food; Sunday L; Children welcome; ⬥ dishes
Smoking: No-smoking area; air-conditioning
Accommodation: 49 en suite
Credit cards: ▆ ▆ ▆ ▆ ▆ ▆

ingredients. Game terrine with poacher's chutney and winter salad, for instance, might be followed by baked fillet of Atlantic cod with seasoned cabbage, crisp pancetta and red wine jus.

Directions: Take exit from A80 signposted Ward Park. At mini roundabout take 1st L, at 2nd roundabout turn R, leads into St Andrew's Drive

LANARKSHIRE, SOUTH

BIGGAR, Shieldhill Hotel

Evocatively named Shieldhill was built as a fortified mansion in 1199 and was home to the Chancellor family for more than seven centuries before becoming a country hotel. The daily changing dinner menu draws much of its inspiration from the Scottish larder and the kitchen is clearly capable of cooking with real imagination and dexterity. Two starters sampled recently were out of the top drawer: a confiture of Gressingham duck leg resting on stewed Puy lentils with Agen prunes and loganberry jus was reckoned to be a 'super dish', while cream of snow pea soup was given a lift with slivers of ginger deep-fried in duck oil. Main dishes might include saddle of local venison carved onto black pudding with red onion compote and a bittersweet port sauce, or steamed pavé of salmon in a light lobster and chive fish fumet. Meals finish strongly with desserts such as crème vanilla with autumn berries and raspberry coulis topped with a hat of spun sugar or warm lemon tart with orange and Cointreau sauce.

Directions: Off B7016 (Carnwath), turn L 2 miles from centre of Biggar

Quothquan ML12 6NA
Map 11: NT03
Tel: 01899 220035
Fax: 01899 221092
Chef: Eric Avenier
Owners: Bob & Christina Lamb
Cost: Fixed-price D £27. ☺
H/wine £9.95.
Times: Noon-2pm/7pm-9pm
Additional: Bar meals; Sunday L; Children welcome; ❹ dishes
Seats: 40
Smoking: No smoking in dining room
Accommodation: 12 en suite
Credit cards: 🔲 🔲 🔲 🔲

STRATHAVEN, Strathaven Hotel

Designed by Robert Adam, this enthusiastically run mansion offers comfortable accommodation and sound modern cooking. Interesting blends of flavours feature in such carefully prepared dishes as venison, duck and rabbit pâté with berry compote and noisettes of lamb with roasted vegetables and redcurrant and rosemary essence.

Additional: Sunday L; Bar meals; Children welcome; ❹ dishes
Smoking: No smoking in dining room
Accommodation: 10 en suite
Credit cards: 🔲 🔲 🔲 🔲 🔲 🔲

Directions: Off the A723 Hamilton road on the edge of town

Hamilton Road ML10 6SZ
Map 11: NS74
Tel: 01357 521778
Fax: 01357 520789
Chef: Paul Dunn
Owners: MacIntyre family
Cost: *Alc* £19, set L £10.50/D £17.95.
☺ H/wine £8.
Times: Last L 2.30pm/D 9.30pm.
Closed 1 Jan

LOTHIAN, EAST

DIRLETON, Open Arms Hotel

No doubt the obvious quip wears a bit thin, but the personally run country hotel really does have an inviting, welcoming air. At the time of writing, plans were in hand for a major refurbishment of the restaurant and the addition of a new bistro-style eating area, but there should be no change to the quality of the good classic Scottish cooking. Dinner is chosen from an extensive fixed-price menu that changes about every three weeks. A typical meal of roulade of smoked salmon and cream cheese on a bed of seasonal leaves with a cucumber and watercress dressing, soup or sorbet, collops of Aberdeen Angus fillet beef on a fried dumpling with a whisky and bramble sauce, and bread and butter pudding flavoured with peaches, nutmeg and sultanas with fresh cream, followed by coffee with petits fours, show good reason why the hotel was one of the founder members of the 'Taste of Scotland' scheme.

Directions: From A1 (S) take A198 to North Berwick, the follw for Dirleton – 2 miles W. From Edinburgh take A6137 leading to A198.

Dirleton EH39 5EG
Map 12: NT58
Tel: 01620 850241
Fax: 01620 850570
Chef: Steven Renton
Owner: Tom & Emma Hill
Cost: Fixed-price D £25 (4 courses). H/wine £9.95
Times: Noon-last L 2.15pm/7pm-last D 9.15pm.
Additional: Bar food L. Sunday L. Children welcome. ❸ dishes.
Seats: 55. Private dining room 35
Smoking: No pipes & cigars in dining room; air-conditioning
Accommodation: 10 en suite
Credit cards: ▬ ▬ ▬ ▮

GIFFORD, Bonars Restaurant   **NEW**

The tea-room turned cosy country restaurant is immediately identified by the old fashioned delivery boy's bike parked outside. Inside, there is a motley but engaging selection of tables, chairs and church pews, taken upmarket with crisp white linen and cut glass. The modern Scottish *carte* is excellent value and although dishes sound a little fussy, each ingredient has its place. Starters might include timbale of trout mousseline with steamed mussels, smoked salmon strips and a mussel and saffron reduction, or chicken and foie gras terrine studded with pistachio nuts served with a warm compote of orange and English pears. Main courses are based on restaurant staples but are given an up-to-date look: breast of chicken comes stuffed with three cheeses, is wrapped in baby leeks and set on a peppercorn reduction, and an individual salmon coulibiac comes with a duet of langoustine and spinach creams. Desserts are well worth leaving space for – a brandied date pudding with hot caramel sauce and home-made vanilla ice cream pulled off the hat-trick of being simultaneously delicious, rich and light.

Directions: From A1 follow Haddington; from there signs to Gifford. As you enter Gifford turn R. Restaurant is immediately on R

Main Street EH41 4QH
Map 12: NT56
Tel: 01620 810264
Chef: Douglas Bonar
Owners: Annabel & Douglas Bonar
Cost: Fixed-price L £12.80 (3 courses)/D £22.95 (5 courses). ☺ H/wine £10.95.
Times: Noon-last L 2.30pm/6pm-last D 9.30pm. Closed D Sun
Additional: Sunday L; ❸ dishes
Seats: 28. Private dining room 20
Credit cards: ▬ ▬ ▬ ▮

GULLANE, Greywalls Hotel

Set overlooking the Firth of Forth, this impressive Lutyens house rates highly among Scotland's country houses. Within, the attractive restaurant is civilised without being stuffy, and enjoys sweeping views across Muirfield golf course. Paul Baron rules in the kitchen, preparing modern British dishes which take full advantage of Scotland's larder. A typical spring meal might start with lightly pan-fried scallops in white wine sauce

Muirfield
EH31 2EG
Map 12: NT48
Tel: 01620 842144
Fax: 01620 842241
Chef: Paul Baron
Owners: Giles & Ros Weaver
Cost: Fixed-price L £12.50/D £35 (5 courses). H/wine £12

spiked with a hint of lime, and continue with pan-fried mignons of beef with a red wine sauce, accompanied by a pastry basket filled with roasted baby onions. To finish, perhaps a light vanilla soufflé with a strong blackcurrant sauce, or maybe a rich bitter chocolate and hazelnut mousse. Before dinner, guests can relax with an aperitif in the comfort of the 'clubby' bar and study the extensive wine list that includes many strong vintages, as well as a good range from the New World.

Directions: From Edinburgh take A1 to North Berwick slip road, then follow A198 along coast to far end of Gullane – Greywalls is up last road on L

Times: 12.30pm-last L 1.45pm/7.30pm-last D9.15pm.
Closed Nov-Mar
Additional: Sunday L; Bar meals L; Children welcome
Seats: 40. Private dining room 20. Jacket and tie preferred
Smoking: No smoking in dining room
Accommodation: 22 en suite
Credit cards:

GULLANE, La Potinière ❀❀❀

Dining at this intimate restaurant is more akin to being at a dinner party. Everyone sits down together (lunch and dinner are served at 1pm and 8pm respectively), and all the guests are served a no-choice menu. That said, The Browns' 22 years' experience of creative cooking means you are unlikely to miss choosing your own selection. This is a consistent, well run, successful operation. Hilary has a tried and tested repertoire at the stove. Her cooking is straight to the point – all the component flavours and textures of each dish serve a carefully considered purpose. Take the pea, lettuce and mint soup which kicked off a quite memorable dinner, the flavours were beautifully balanced and it was simply finished with a dash of fresh cream. We could have eaten the next course twice it was so delicious: a warm mousse of Arbroath smokie was accompanied by a drizzle of virgin olive oil with a hint of basil and finely chopped tomato. Finely sliced extremely moist maize-fed chicken on a bed of shredded cabbage came with a competent aigre-doux sauce. Then came a bowl of the freshest salad made with nuts, seeds and apple slices, before concluding an outstanding meal with a rich flavoured, light textured chocolate sponge served with a sorbet – an interesting combination. Service is relaxed and unhurried under David's watchful eye. As he serves each course, he frequently advises guests about the ingredients. After a superlative dinner we could not resist throwing a coin into the wishing well outside and keeping our fingers crossed we would eat here again.

Main Street EH31 2AA
Map 12: NT48
Tel/Fax: 01620 843214
Chef: Hilary Brown
Owners: David & Hilary Brown
Cost: Fixed-price L £20 (4 courses)/D £30 (5 courses). H/wine £11.50.
Times: L at 1pm/D at 8pm.
Closed 1 week early June, all Oct.
Additional: Sunday L.
Children welcome.
Seats: 30
Smoking: No smoking in dining room
Credit cards: None

Directions: Village centre

NORTH BERWICK, The Grange ❀❀

The substantial Victorian house is readily identified by its green painted facade and colourful flowering window boxes. The candlelit dining-room is full of antiques and decorated in warm, rich shades. Inventive fish dishes are a particular strength – lightly seared salmon fillet is accompanied by sliced avocado and a delicate tarragon dressing, for example. An intriguing main course is breast of chicken filled with a herb mousseline, steamed on a bed of seaweed, the juices enhanced by saffron. Simpler starters might include onion soup or local asparagus served warm with hollandaise sauce. Our visit was rounded off with a deliciously sweet poached pear served with a sabayon of dark chocolate and decorated with sliced strawberries. The restaurant has a loyal following, but even on busy nights service is always attentive and friendly.

35 The High Street EH39 4HH
Map 12: NT58
Tel/Fax: 01620 895894
Chef: René Gaté
Owners: P Laird, S Mattison
Cost: Fixed-price L £5/D £12 (2 courses). ☺ H/wine £10.50.
Times: Last L 2.30pm/last D 10.30pm.
Closed 1st 3 wks Jan
Additional: Children welcome; ⑨ dishes
Credit cards:

Directions: In the centre of town

LOTHIAN, WEST

LINLITHGOW,

Champany Inn ❀❀❀

Thick ceiling beams clearly betray the history of this old mill house which dates from the time of Mary, Queen of Scots. Nowadays, it is a restaurant that one inspector described as 'plush, homely, decadent', with a rather stately teak bar, the lounge sporting comfortable Chesterfields and smart tub chairs, and the circular restaurant with each polished-wood table sporting a candelabra and a good fruit display. Clive Davidson's cooking is centred on specially hung Aberdeen Angus beef, chargrilled and served with a selection of accompaniments such as french fries and garlic bread; fillet steaks come with a variety of sauces. Amongst the starters there are creditable dishes of interest, including chicken liver parfait with red onion marmalade, prawns peri-peri, their own smoked salmon and cullen skink, other main courses take in baked chicken filled with smoked bacon and tarragon mousse with a mushroom sauce, and fish comes in the guise of lobster – the tank is visibly on display – grilled langoustine, and supreme of cod marinated in oil and saffron with crisp celeriac. A winter meal opened with good, chargrilled North Sea prawns with home-made pasta and a light butter sauce, was followed by roast breast of Gressingham duckling with a honey and spiced sauce, with bread-and-butter pudding, vanilla ice cream and crème anglaise to finish.

A vast tome covers the major wine producing regions of the world in detail. France gets the greatest depth with big names being offered in a wide range of vintages (La Tache from Romanée-Conti 76 tops the list at £1,200). South Africa offers some of the best bargains – a large number at under £27. Extensive Spanish section offers rarer classics in several old vintages. Seven house wines at under £14.

Signature dishes: Hot smoked salmon; asparagus hollandaise; Scottish spring lamb; Aberdean Angus steak with local wild mushrooms; local raspberries with home-made vanilla ice cream.

EH49 7LU
Map 11: NS97
Tel: 01506 834532
Fax: 01506 834302
Chef: Clive Davidson
Owner: Clive & Anne Davidson
Cost: *Alc* £50. Fixed-price L £15.75 (2 courses). H/wine £12.50
Times: 12.30pm-last L 2pm/7pm-last D 10pm. Closed Sun (restaurant), 24-26 Dec, 31 Dec-1 Jan
Additional: Chop Ale House for Bar food & Sunday L.
Smoking: No-smoking area
Seats: 50. Private dining room 20. Jacket and tie preferred
Accommodation: 16 en suite
Credit cards: 💳 💳 💳 💳 💳 💳

Direction: 2 miles N/E of Linlithgow at junction of A904 & A803

LINLITHGOW,
Livingston's Restaurant

Tucked away down a courtyard, this former stable dates from the days of the 'pony express', and provides an intimate old world atmosphere. An enjoyable lunch began with celery soup, followed by sea bass encased in a crêpe, but the highlight was a delicious crème brûlée with roast banana.

Smoking: No-smoking area; no pipes in dining room
Credit cards: ■ ▥ ▚ ▢

Directions: Opposite Post Office on Linlithgow High St

52 High Street EH49 7AE
Map 11: NS97
Tel: 01506 846565
Chef: David Williams
Owners: Ronald & Christine Livingston
Cost: Alc £9.99, set L £9.99/D £25. ☺ H/wine £8.90.
Times: Last L 2.30pm/last D 9pm. Closed Sun-Mon, 1st 2wks Jan
Additional: No children under 8; ⬤ dishes

UPHALL,
Houston House Hotel

The three panelled dining rooms are in the original seventeenth-century part of this sympathetically extended house, built by Sir John Sharp, advocate to Mary Queen of Scots. The atmosphere is sophisticated 'Scottish laird', with polished tables, fine silver, antiques and paintings, plus a vaulted bar where, in front of the log fire, one can steadily work through the list of 100 malt whiskies. The *carte* is unfortunately peppered with redundant descriptions, 'breast of duck with a pillow of gingered spaghetti vegetables lined with a herb and soya sauce' is typical, but, once past the extra words, the cooking is accurate and the food enjoyable. Boudin of west coast fish with a pillow lemon and vegetable broth, and an individual venison and black pudding Wellington with a rosemary scented Puy lentil casserole both had well balanced flavours and texture. All beef used comes from the renowned Donald Russell of Inverurie, so prime quality is assured.

Directions: At junction between A89 and A899

Broxburn EH52 6JS
Map 11: NT17
Tel: 01506 853831
Fax: 01506 854220
Chef: David Murray
Owners: MacDonald Hotels
Cost: Alc £27.50, fixed-price L £16.50/D £30. ☺ H/wine £11.95
Times: Noon-last L 2.30pm/7pm-last D 9.30pm. Closed L Sat
Additional: Sunday L; Bar meals L; Children welcome; ⬤ dishes
Seats: 80. Private dining room 20. Jacket & tie preferred D Sat
Smoking: No-smoking area; no pipes & cigars
Accommodation: 72 en suite
Credit cards: ■ ▥ ▤ ▣ ▢

MORAY

ARCHIESTOWN,
Archiestown Hotel

Anglers wanting to try their luck on the River Spey make up much of the custom in Judith and Michael Bulger's delightful little hotel – along with golfers and touring holidaymakers. Food now centres on the informal bistro and Michael's good humoured presence out front adds to the relaxed atmosphere of the place. All around are artefacts and bric-a-brac – mostly relating to fishing or the local distilleries, and menus are chalked on a blackboard. The repertoire changes daily, but fish is a strong suit, closely followed by robust casseroles and roasts. There's no flim-flam, just honest natural flavours in abundance. Poached halibut comes with a delicate white butter sauce, baked salmon is served with samphire, cod with parsley sauce and if you want something meaty, there's steak and chips, rack of lamb or chicken curry. Start with 'super' devilled

Aberlour
AB38 7QX
Map 15: NJ24
Tel: 01340 810218
Fax: 01340 810239
Chef: Judith Bulger
Owners: Judith & Michael Bulger
Cost: Alc £17.50. H/wine £10
Times: 12.30pm-last L 2 pm/6.30pm-last D 8.30pm. Closed Oct-Jan
Additional: Bar food; Sunday L; Children welcome; ⬤ dishes
Seats: 30. Private dining room 18
Accommodation: 9 (6 en suite)
Credit cards: ▥

kidneys or smoked sprats, and finish with treacle sponge pudding or chocolate mousse. Clarets are a major strength on the carefully selected wine list.

Directions: Turn off A95 onto B9102 at Craigellachie

CRAIGELLACHIE,
Craigellachie Hotel ❀❀

Set in the heart of Speyside overlooking the river, this popular Victorian country house has seen plenty of changes and improvements of late. The main Rib Room restaurant now occupies the ground floor, and it provides an elegant setting in which to enjoy some very capable cooking. The dinner menu changes daily and local produce is given a good airing in, say, open ravioli of Spey salmon with spinach and a sauce of chanterelles or peppered Banffshire venison with sweet red cabbage and a decent celeriac purée. Other options might be langoustine bisque with garlic and parsley crostini, pan-fried calves' liver with creamed leeks and lime jus, and Aberdeen Angus steaks with hand-cut chips. Scottish cheeses are alternatives to desserts such as chocolate pavé or sticky toffee pudding. Lunch is a simpler affair. Over 240 malts are stacked up in the bar and the wine list is a serviceable slate of more than 100 bins.

Craigellachie
AB38 9SR
Map 15: NJ24
Tel: 01340 881204
Fax: 01340 881253
Chef: David Tilbury
Owner: Mermaid Hotels Ltd
Cost: *Alc* £25. H/wine £9.95. ☺
Times: 12.30pm-last L 2.15pm /6pm-last D 9.30pm
Additional: Bar food L; Sunday L; Children welcome; ❹ dishes
Seats: 60. Private dining room up to 50
Smoking: No pipes and cigars
Accommodation: 30 en suite
Credit cards: ▩ ▩ ▩ ▣ ▣

Directions: In the village centre.

DRYBRIDGE, **The Old Monastery Restaurant** ❀❀

Buckie AB56 2JB
Map 15: NJ46
Tel/Fax: 01542 832660
Chef: Douglas Gray
Owners: Maureen & Douglas Gray
Cost: *Alc* £27.50. H/wine £10.50
Times: Noon-last L 1.30pm/7pm-last D 9.30pm. Closed Sun, Mon, 2 wks Nov, 3 wks Jan
Additional: No children under 8
Seats: 48. Jacket and tie preferred
Smoking: No smoking in dining room
Credit cards: ▩ ▩ ▩ ▣

As the name suggests the core of this loyally supported restaurant was originally a monastery, and it boasts superb views over the Moray Firth to the hills of Sutherland. The sunsets hereabouts can be quite spectacular. Douglas and Maureen Gray have been in residence for more than a decade, and consistency is the hallmark of their cooking. Lunch is taken in the informal Cloisters Bar, dinner in the slightly more formal, but intimate restaurant. An inspector who opted for the former, was more than satisfied with a meal of French onion soup and an assemblage of local seafood in a light herby sauce, followed by chilled Monastery Mist (a dessert of crushed meringues, flaked chocolate and nuts laced with a touch of Benedictine). Other more ambitious ideas might include scallops en papillote, noisettes of Banffshire lamb with red onion and rosemary marmalade, and passionfruit tart with crème fraîche. Around 80 wines provide plenty of sound drinking.

Directions: Leave A98 at Buckie junction onto Drybridge Road for 2.5 miles; don't turn into Drybridge village

DUFFTOWN, A Taste of Speyside

Excellent value-for-money menus featuring quality local ingredients, especially game, are served at this simple, pine furnished restaurant, conveniently situated in the middle of the 'Whisky Trail'. Traditional Scottish dishes may include cullen skink, Lossiemouth scampi with birch wine and cream, and hot fruit dumpling with Drambuie cream. Good range of malt whiskies.

Additional: Bar food L; Sunday L; Children welcome; dishes
Smoking: No-smoking area; no pipes or cigars in dining room
Credit cards:

10 Balvenie Street AB5 4AB
Map 15: NJ34
Tel/Fax: 01340 820860
Chef: Joseph Thompson
Owners: J Thompson, R McLean, P Thompson
Cost: Alc £16, fixed-price D £12.50. ☺ H/wine £7.90.
Times: Last L 5.30pm/6pm-last D 9pm. Closed 8 Nov-28 Feb

Directions: Take A941 from Elgin and turn L at Craigellachie; restaurant is on R just before the town square

ELGIN, Mansefield House Hotel

Converted Georgian manse – the restaurant is housed within the former stable block. Fish ranges from grilled fillets of lemon sole with parsley butter to seafood provençale and lobster, chicken is every-which-way including haggis en croûte with a light demi-glace, and the sweet trolley is loaded with banoffee pie and several creamy gâteaux.

Additional: Sunday L; Children welcome; dishes
Smoking: No smoking in dining room
Accommodation: 21 en suite
Credit cards:

Mayne Road IV30 1NY
Map 15: NJ34
Tel: 01343 540883
Fax: 01343 552491
Chef: Scott Hood
Owners: Mr and Mrs T R Murray
Cost: Alc £20-£25. ☺ H/wine £10.95.
Times: Last L 2pm/D 9.30pm

Directions: From A96 to town centre, R at first roundabout, R at mini roundabout, first L

ELGIN, Mansion House Hotel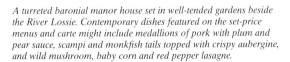

A turreted baronial manor house set in well-tended gardens beside the River Lossie. Contemporary dishes featured on the set-price menus and carte might include medallions of pork with plum and pear sauce, scampi and monkfish tails topped with crispy aubergine, and wild mushroom, baby corn and red pepper lasagne.

Additional: Bar Food; Sunday L; Children welcome; dishes
Smoking: No smoking in dining room
Accommodation: 23 en suite
Credit cards:

The Haugh
IV30 1AW
Map 15: NJ26
Tel: 01343 548811
Fax: 01343 547916
Chef: John Alexander
Owners: James & Joan Stirrat
Cost: Alc £20, fixed-price L £12.95/D £24 (4 courses). ☺ H/wine £10.
Times: Last L 1.45pm/D 9pm

Directions: In Elgin turn off the A96 into Haugh Road; hotel is at the end of the road by the river

FORRES, Knockomie Hotel

Grantown Road IV36 0SG
Map 14: NJ05
Tel: 01309 673146
Fax: 01309 673290
Chef: Ian White
Owner: Gavin Ellis
Cost: *Alc* £25, fixed-price L £15.20/D £26. ☺ H/wine £11.50.
Times: Noon-last L 2pm/7pm-last D 9pm. Closed 25-26 Dec
Additional: Bar meals (bistro) Sunday L; Children welcome; ◑ dishes
Seats: 30. Private dining room 12
Smoking: No smoking in dining room
Accommodation: 14 en suite
Credit cards: ▆ ▆ ▆ ▆ ▆ ▆

Overlooking the Royal Burgh of Forres, guests can return here from a day touring distilleries to an evening sampling the fine collection of malts. The elegant Scottish villa combines genuine hospitality with good food, and there is a choice of small dining rooms, so that on a quiet night the diner does not feel conspicuous. Fine Scottish produce is the springboard for a well-judged menu that's as civilised as the setting. Oak-smoked salmon canapés, might precede a soufflé made with smoked haddock and a hint of fennel, and Angus beef steaks, not surprisingly, are a regular fixture, but other choices might be civet of roe deer braised in red wine and juniper berries topped with pigeon breast, or chicken and prawn fricassée finished with a light coriander meat jus. Desserts are particularly good – Drambuie and oatcake parfait served with strawberry coulis, and prune and walnut sponge pudding with sauce anglaise, are rounded off nicely with Colombian coffee and Highland truffles.

Directions: On A940 1 mile S of Forres

FORRES, Ramnee Hotel ✿

Edwardian residence, now a charming, personally-run hotel. Honest cooking, with a four-course dinner taking in lattice of haddock and salmon on a chive cream sauce, peach sorbet, breast of roast chicken with rosemary and onion, with a tomato and provençale sauce, and strawberry cheesecake to finish.

Additional: Bar food; Sunday L; Children welcome; ◑ dishes
Smoking: No smoking in dining room
Accommodation: 20 en suite
Credit cards: ▆ ▆ ▆ ▆ ▆ ▆

Victoria Road IV36 0BN
Map 14: NJ05
Tel: 01309 672410
Fax: 01309 673392
Chef: Craig Wilson
Owners: The Dinnes family
Cost: *Alc* £20, fixed-price L £11/D £22.50. ☺ H/wine £9.
Times: Last L 2pm/D 9pm.
Closed Xmas, New Year's Day

Directions: Turn off A96 into eastern side of Forres, hotel is 200 yds on R

ROTHES,
The Rothes Glen Hotel ✿✿

Turreted baronial mansion in ten acres of grounds (complete with a burn and 'lochan'), boasting brilliant views over the Spey Valley. A chandelier sparkles in the ornate drawing room,

AB38 7AQ
Map 15: NJ26
Tel: 01340 831254
Fax: 01340 831566
Chef: Colin Campbell

while candle-lamps reflect in the huge Rococo mirror of the stately drawing room. The formula is simple – a daily changing menu offering the likes of gravlax, and noisettes of lamb with leek purée and roast garlic, with good skills in evidence. Macallan smoked salmon parcels opened a May dinner that went on to medallions of venison with a red cabbage marmalade and a piquant sauce, and finished with warm coconut tart with coconut ice cream. Daily fixed-price menus might offer, and warm coconut tart. Service is elegant, friendly and efficient.

Accommodation: 16 en suite
Credit cards: ▬ ▦ ▆

Directions: Six miles S of Elgin on A941

Owners: Michael MacKenzie, Frederic Symonds
Cost: Fixed-price L £14.50 (3 courses)/D £27.50 (4 courses). ☺
H/wine £12.95
Times: L 12.30pm-1.45pm/D 7.30pm-9pm
Additional: Sunday L;
No children under 7; ❹ dishes
Seats: 30. Private dining room 30.
Jacket and tie preferred
Smoking: No smoking in restaurant

ORKNEY

ST MARGARET'S HOPE,
Creel Restaurant ❀

Set in the centre of the village right beside the bay, Creel Restaurant has a sound reputation with visitors and islanders alike. The focus is on fresh Orkney produce. Specialities include seafood, prime Scottish beef and 'bere bannocks' – a traditional Orkney scone. Advance booking is advisable.

Additional: Children welcome
Smoking: No smoking in dining room
Accommodation: 3 en suite
Credit cards: ▬ ▆

Directions: 13 miles S of Kirkwall on the A961, crossing the 4 Churchill barriers.

Front Road
KW17 2SL
Map 16: ND49
Tel: 01856 831311
Chef: Alan Craigie
Owners: Alan and Joyce Craigie
Cost: Alc £25.
Times: D only, 7pm-9pm.
Closed Jan, Feb

PERTH & KINROSS

ABERFELDY, La Meridiana ❀   NEW

Located just off the main square, this small, simply decorated Italian offers an informal atmosphere and plenty of pizzas and pasta meals on the good value lunchtime menu. The more extensive carte may list tagliatelle carbonara, followed by rack of lamb with a mint and berry sauce, and dark chocolate mousse.

Additional: Children welcome; ❹ dishes
Credit cards: ▬ ▦ ▆ ▚ ▣ ▢

Directions: In the town square

The Square PH15 2DD
Map 14: NN84
Tel: 01887 829000
Fax: 01796 473256
Chefs: John Keogh, Claudio Pisciotta
Owners: John Keogh, Joel Lautradou
Cost: Alc £24. ☺ H/wine £12.50
Times: Last L 2.30pm/last D 10pm.
closed L Mon

ABERFELDY,

Guinach House Hotel ❀❀

'By the Birks' Urlar Road
PH15 2ET
Map 14: NN84
Tel: 01887 820251
Fax: 01887 829607
Chef: Albert Mackay
Owners: The Mackay family
Cost: Fixed-price D £25 (4 courses).
H/wine £9.95
Times: D only. 7pm-9.30pm.
Closed Xmas
Additional: Children welcome;
❀ dishes
Seats: 22
Smoking: No smoking in dining room
Accommodation: 7 en suite
Credit cards: 💳 💳

Close by the Birks 'o Aberfeldy and surrounded by secluded gardens, this modest country house hotel owes much to the unassuming hospitality of the Mackay family. The place has a really genuine home-from-home atmosphere. Bert Mackay is an industrious chef who bakes bread, makes preserves and scours the region for local produce. His daily, fixed-price dinner menus run to four courses, with everything from Loch Fyne smoked salmon to Bonchester cheese. In between you might find West Coast mussels cooked in white wine with onions and saffron, Isle of Barra queen scallops with Noilly Prat, chopped leeks and a butter sauce, and breast of Tombuie smoked guinea fowl served on a sweet sherry and bramble jus. Desserts could range from strawberry mille-feuille to warm apple and almond pie with crème fraîche. Three dozen wines are realistically priced.

Directions: From Aberfeldy: A826 (Crieff) hotel is on R

ALYTH, **Drumnacree House** ❀❀

St Ninians Road PH11 8AP
Map 15: NO24
Tel/Fax: 01828 632194
Chef: Allan Cull
Owners: Allan & Eleanor Cull
Cost: Alc £21, fixed-price D £19.50.
☺ H/wine £12
Times: D only, 7pm-last D 9pm.
Closed Sun, Mon, 15 Dec-30 March
Additional: Children welcome;
❀ dishes
Seats: 25. Private dining room 12
Smoking: No smoking in dining room
Accommodation: 6 en suite
Credit cards: 💳 💳 💳

Situated at the foot of Glenisla with raspberry fields in the background, this tastefully converted Victorian house is now a family-run country hotel with an elegant dining room – complete with a grand piano. It is evident that Allan and Eleanor Cull are a much travelled couple. Two menus are offered, one promising the likes of French black pudding with caramelised apples, spiced suprême of pigeon on a bed of couscous with a sauce of chanterelles, and pan-fried Barbary duck with raspberry sauce, the other devoted to Cajun specialities. Here you will find the fiery delights of prawn and okra gumbo, and 'blackened' dishes served authentically with so-called 'dirty' rice. Our inspector took the more conventional route with a smooth Arbroath smokie mousse served on a delicate tomato and basil sauce, before medallions of monkfish topped with peppers and spiked with chilli salsa. To finish, a soft, sweet pear poached in red wine and served with cinnamon ice cream was perfectly acceptable. The wine list is sensible and realistically priced.

Directions: From Blairgowrie take A926 to Alyth and turn L after Clydesdale Bank. Hotel is 300yds on R

AUCHTERARDER,
Auchterarder House

PH3 1DZ
Map 11: NN91
Tel: 01764 663646
Fax: 01764 662939
Chef: Kiernan Darnell
Telephone for details

The epitome of a fine Scottish country house: Victorian features include lovely oak panelling, ornate ceilings and beautiful fireplaces, fresh flowers are everywhere, and the grounds are magnificent. The kitchen builds its menus around the best Scottish produce working to a simple formula of a no-choice daily changing menu and a more adventurous table d'hôte with the option of three or four courses. Terrine of wild mushroom and pigeon with crunchy baby vegetables and oil scented with bay leaf and juniper opened a summer dinner. Lightly grilled fillet of fresh halibut followed, with a soft crust of olives and spinach, saffron fennel and roasted cherry tomatoes and lifted by a bold mussel-based sauce flavoured with cider and a little cream. To finish, a dark chocolate soufflé with a light, white chocolate sauce and fresh strawberries. The wine list is especially strong on clarets, but there's a good range of New World wines.

Directions: 1.5 miles N of Auchterarder on B8062

AUCHTERARDER, **Cairn Lodge**

Attractive turreted house on the edge of the village. The elegant Capercaille restaurant is the setting for some serious cooking from an innovative menu based on Scotland's rich larder. Expect roast pheasant stuffed with pork and apricots, or corn-fed chicken filled with smoked Tay salmon mousse.

Additional: Bar food; Sunday L; Children welcome; ⏺ dishes
Smoking: No smoking in dining room
Accommodation: 7 en suite
Credit cards: ▦ ▦ ⬜

Directions: From A9 take A824 (Auchterader). Hotel at S end of town, on road to Gleneagles

Orchil Road PH3 1LX
Map 11: NN91
Tel: 01764 662634
Fax: 01764 664866
Chef: Mark Riva
Owners: Michelle & Alex McDonald
Cost: *Alc* £27, fixed-price L
£14/D£18. ☺ H/wine £10.50
Times: Last L 2pm/D 9.30pm

AUCHTERARDER,
Duchally House Hotel ⬡

Hospitable hotel offering a set gourmet menu as well as a 'Taste of Scotland' carte. A typical meal could take in cornets of oak-smoked

PH3 1PN
Map 11: NN91
Tel: 01764 663071
Fax: 01764 662464

salmon filled with a mousse of Arbroath smokie, roast cutlets of Perthshire lamb with black olives and couscous, and apple fritter in beer batter.

Additional: Bar Food; Sunday L; Children welcome; 🍴 dishes
Smoking: No-smoking area in dining room
Accommodation: 13 en suite
Credit cards: ▆▆ ▆▆ ▆▆ 🄳

Directions: From A9 take A823 (Crieff/Dunfermline), after 1 mile turn left at sign for Duchally. Hotel in 0.25 mile

Chef: Richard Hudson
Owner: Arne Raeder
Cost: *Alc* £24, fixed-price L £12.50/D £26 (5 courses). ☺ H/wine £8.50.
Times: Last L 2pm/D 9.30pm

AUCHTERARDER,

The Gleneagles Hotel 🏵🏵🏵

This world-wide mecca for golfers is centred around an imposing Edwardian building, with a fine staircase and wide corridors that seem to stretch forever. A pianist plays nightly in the elegant Strathearn Restaurant, little changed since Gleneagles opened in the 1920s, and service is extremely attentive, friendly but still impeccably formal. The cooking has moved from the ultra-classical style, and the tip-top Scottish ingredients are now subject to a more modern interpretation; the traditional roast of the day carved from the trolley, however, is still a popular fixture – 'tonight was beef Wellington with white wine sauce'. The formula is simply a *carte* with a fixed-price menu that changes three times a week. Ravioli of lobster and saffron bisque came bursting with flavour and aroma – our inspector's only criticism was there wasn't enough! Roast breast of duck was served with tomato, 'nice, young' broad beans, tender barley amidst a good, light orange flower sauce, and a panaché of organic vegetables that showed commendable commitment to sourcing. A visually stunning toffee cheesecake with banana and candied tuille wafer, plus Caribbean flavours from passion fruits, oranges and apricots made 'a lovely summer dessert in spring'. The wine list has a global appeal, but classic French growths are represented, albeit mostly 1990 vintages. Good range of half-bottles. The sommelier is well worth consulting.

Directions: Just off the A9, well signposted

PH3 1NF
Map 11: NN91
Tel: 01764 662231
Fax: 01764 662134
Chef: Mike Picken
Cost: *Alc* £45, fixed-price D £39.50. H/wine £16.50
Times: D only, 7pm-last D 10.30pm
Additional: Bar food L; Sunday L (12.30pm-2.30pm); Children welcome; 🍴 dishes
Seats: 180.
Private dining room 12-200
Smoking: No-smoking area; no pipes and cigars in dining room
Accommodation: 234 en suite
Credit cards: ▆▆ ▆▆ ▆▆ 🄽 🄳 🄲

BLAIRGOWRIE,

Kinloch House Hotel 🏵🏵🏵

Last year, the original nineteenth-century walled garden was completely restored and now produces masses of good Scottish fruit and vegetables that taste the way things ought to taste. The garden also provides an abundance of fresh flowers for the charming country house hotel set in 25 acres of woods and parkland grazed by Highland cattle. Chef Bill McNicholl cooks with a particularly light touch – so all the hard work in the hotel's new health and fitness centre is not completely undone at one go. The *carte* is imaginative and extensive, matched by an equally wide-ranging, carefully chosen wine list. Ingredients are of a high standard and precisely handled so that textures and flavours come through clearly. Dinner starts in the conservatory with a choice of canapés – perhaps Scotch eggs, duck pâté or a tartlet of marinated scallops. Moving through

PH10 6SG
Map 15: NO14
Tel: 01250 884237
Fax: 01250 884333
Chef: Bill McNicoll
Owners: David & Sarah Shentall
Cost: Fixed-price D £29.90 (4 courses). H/wine £12.20
Times: 12.30pm-last L 2pm/7pm-last D 9.30pm. Closed 20-30 Dec
Additional: Bar food L; Sunday L; No children under 7 at D; 🍴 dishes
Seats: 55. Private dining room 25. Jacket and tie preferred
Smoking: No smoking in dining room
Accommodation: 21 en suite

Kinloch House Hotel

Credit cards: ■ ▦ ☰ ◣ ▣ 🗓

into the elegant pink and green, candlelit restaurant, there might be Mallard duck liver pâté, crab cake with braised sea kale, red pepper sauce and crispy fried leeks and braised oxtail with red wine sauce and finely diced vegetables from the set four-course carte. A number of dishes, such as Kyle of Lochalsh scallops on spinach with orange butter sauce, are available at a supplement. A special 'Scottish' menu includes old-fashioned potted hough (boiled shin of beef, shredded and set in its own jelly – albeit with a modern touch), and a fine-sounding traditional fillet of hare marinated in port, sautéed in garlic butter, set on savoury red cabbage and served with a port and redcurrant sauce. Desserts might include delicious marmalade and whisky soufflé with cream and butterscotch sauce on the side. Salmon fishcakes at breakfast also deserve honourable mention.

Directions: Three miles W of Blairgowrie on A923.

CLEISH,

Nivingston House Hotel ✿

Cleish Hills KY13 7LS
Map 11: NT09
Tel: 01577 850216
Fax: 01577 850238
Chef: Michael Thompson
Owners: Allan Deeson
Cost: *Alc* £25, fixed-price L £15.50/D £25. ☺ H/wine £11.95.
Times: Last L 2pm/D 9pm
Additional: Bar food L; Sunday L; Children welcome; ◑ dishes
Smoking: No smoking in dining room
Accommodation: 17 en suite
Credit cards: ■ ▦ ☰ ◣ 🗓

Extended eighteenth-century former farmhouse in a peaceful setting yet within easy reach of the M90. A carefully chosen wine list complements the interesting menus that combines Scottish produce with more exotic fare. Lookout for medallions of pork with prune, apple and Calvados sauce, and Scotch salmon with hollandaise.

Directions: M90 exit 5 & B9097 (Crook of Devon) and 2 miles to Cleish.

COUPAR ANGUS,
Moorfield House

There is a refreshingly unpretentious air to this family-run, highly convivial hotel. Dinners are taken in the traditionally-styled dining room hung with co-ordinated swags and drapes. The cooking, despite describing itself as 'rustic' is actually more sophisticated in concept. The four-course menu starts with a choice of dishes such as a warm salad, a fish soufflé or fresh fruit-based platter. Then it might feature carrot and orange soup or a warm tartlet of seafood with a Cheddar 'liaison'. Main courses usually include one steak dish, perhaps topped with a ragout of creamed mushrooms and bacon, one fish dish such as nuggets of fresh salmon and monkfish served with a spaghetti of vegetables in a lemon butter sauce, and one chicken dish – either pan-fried supreme with roasted parsnips, wild garlic and a light cream sauce or with fresh porcini and truffle pasta with a light chicken velouté. Desserts range from tarte Tatin of apple and caramel to an ambitious chocolate brioche filled with macerated oranges and coated with a dark chocolate fudge sauce.

By Blairgowrie PH13 9HS
Map 11: NO24
Tel: 01828 627303
Fax: 01828 627339
Chef: Paul Bjormark
Owners: Paul & Jayne Bjormark
Cost: Fixed-price L £14/D £24.50 (4 courses). ☺ H/wine £9.50.
Times: Noon-last L 2pm/6pm-last D 9.45pm. Closed 2-5 Jan
Additional: Bar food; Sunday L; Children welcome; ♨ dishes
Seats: 34
Smoking: No-smoking area; no pipes & cigars
Accommodation: 12 en suite
Credit cards: ▆ ▆ ▆ ▆

Directions: on the A923 halfway between Coupar Angus and Blairgowrie

DUNKELD, **Atholl Arms**

Bridgehead
PH8 0AQ
Map 11: NO04
Tel/Fax: 01350 727219
Chef: Annie Darbishire, Sue O'Neill
Owners: Callum & Annie Darbishire
Cost: Alc £15. H/wine £8. ☺
Times: Last L 1.45pm/D 8.45pm
Additional: Bar Food; No children under 8 after 6pm; ♨ dishes
Smoking: No smoking in dining room
Accommodation: 16 (9 en suite)
Credit cards: ▆ ▆ ▆ ▆ ▆

Directions: A9 & A923 (Blairgowrie) to Dunkeld, 1st building on R

Centrally located former Georgian coaching inn overlooking the River Tay. The comfortably traditional dining room boasts polished wood and open fires, and a menu built around local produce. Expect dishes such as cullen skink, chicken suprême with haggis, and steamed ginger pudding.

DUNKELD, **Kinnaird**

Unashamedly luxurious, this private country house hotel is set in the midst of a 9,000 acre estate overlooking the Tay Valley. One of the two jacket-and-tie dining rooms features exquisite painted-panelled figures and landscapes, the other a lovely ornate marble fireplace and chandelier. Both are appropriate settings for the assured and imaginative cooking of John Webber whose hallmark is consistency matched with sound technical skills and superb raw ingredients. He also manages to side-step the pitfall of over elaboration – shellfish minestrone, based mostly on a mussel stock, with prawns, scallops, mussels

Kinnaird
PH8 0LB
Map 11: NO04
Tel: 01796 482440
Fax: 01796 482289
Chef: John Webber
Owner: Mrs CC Ward
Cost: Fixed-price L £19.50-£24 (2-3 courses)/D £39.50 (4 courses). H/wine £18

Kinnaird

Times: Noon-last L 1.45pm/7.15pm-last D 9.30pm. Closed Mon, Tue, Wed in Jan & Feb
Additional: No children under 12; ✦ dishes
Seats: 35. Private dining room 25. Jacket & tie preferred
Accommodation: 9 en suite
Credit cards: ▬ ▬ ▬ ◖

Directions: From A9 north take B898 Dalguise/Kinnaird/ Balnaguard road for approx 4.5 miles. Hotel main gates on R

and mixed vegetables, had the intensity of flavour and colour gained from focusing on the essence of a dish. Grilled fillet of moist, tender halibut was served simply, with spinach, grilled vegetables, saffron flavoured mash and a delicate pesto and soy jus. Breast of pigeon, with lentils, tomato and smoked bacon, and noisettes of lamb topped with a parsley and mint salsa, may be amongst the other main courses. Dinner, on our visit, finished with a wonderfully wicked dark chocolate marquise. Details are all as good as might be expected in such a top-notch operation – canapés, offered in the lounge before dinner, might include a wonderful mini-croissant, a mini-onion quiche and a delicious slice of pastry with anchovy paste. Appetisers such as red snapper presented on a thyme risotto accompanied by a vinaigrette dressing are suitably mouth-watering, and although the cost of dinner is £39.50, this also includes coffee, petits fours and mineral water. And after that, all that remains is to retire upstairs to a king-sized bed, surrounded by antique furnishings, and sleep soundly until kippers the next morning.

A pomposity-free wine list offers brief descriptions of each region and a selection of typical wines from each area at the front of the list. Bordeaux is in particularly good order with some smart selections from good vintages at reasonable prices. The list of half-bottles offers an exemplary range.

Signature dishes: Brochette of king scallops with Parma ham and braised lentils; a filo flan of courgette and tomato seasoned with feta cheese and basil; risotto of white truffle and cep served with a salad of smoked duck breast; loin of venison wrapped in a mousse of herbs and puff pastry served with a sauce of port and pickled walnuts.

KILLIECRANKIE,

Killiecrankie Hotel ❀❀

A super little hotel, run by enthusiastic owners, whose major strength lies in a very personal way of running things; they create a terrific atmosphere. The fixed-price menu, whilst not extensive, offers a decent choice. Starters of game soup, terrine of Arbroath smokie mousse wrapped in smoked salmon and served with Scottish oatcakes, or baked Isle of Gigha goat's cheese served in a warm focaccia bun with sweet pepper and tomato compote, show a strong loyalty to regional produce, whilst pan-fried fillet of rock turbot in Malaysian red curry, aubergine sauce and steamed rice, or roast breast of corn-fed guinea fowl served on a cassoulet of smoked leg and chestnuts, are the marks of a kitchen well aware of modern trends. The

Pitlochry PH16 5LG
Map 14: NN96
Tel: 01796 473220
Fax: 01796 472451
Chef: John Ramsay
Owners: Colin & Carole Anderson
Cost: Fixed-price dinner £28 (4 courses). H/wine £11.40
Times: 12.30pm-last L 2pm/6.30pm-last D 9.25pm.
Closed 1 wk early Dec, Jan-Feb
Additional: Bar food;
Children welcome; ✦ dishes
Seats: 34

white chocolate mousse cake for dessert is highly recommended. The wine list is quite comprehensive and well chosen, and has a good range of half-bottles.

Directions: From A9 take B8079 for Killiecrankie, hotel on right just past village signpost

Smoking: No smoking in dining room
Accommodation: 10 en suite
Credit cards: ▨ ▨ ▨ 🄯

KINCLAVEN,
Ballathie House Hotel ❀❀

Stanley PH1 4QN
Map 11: NO13
Tel: 01250 883268
Fax: 01250 883396
Chef: Kevin MacGillivray
Owner: Chris Longden
Cost: *Alc* £15, fixed-price D £29
(4 courses). H/wine £9.50.
Times: Last L 2pm/7pm-last D 9pm
Additional: Bar food L; Sunday L;
Children welcome; 🄯 dishes
Seats: 80. Private dining room 30.
Jacket and tie preferred
Smoking: No smoking in dining room
Accommodation: 28 en suite
Credit cards: ▨ ▨ ▨ ▨ ▨ 🄯

The prospect of serious fishing and hunting brings hordes of devotees to this baronial turreted mansion in a 1,500 acre sporting estate on the banks of the Tay. Salmon from the river might find its way onto the dinner menu (perhaps chargrilled and served on basil and pesto mash), while the kitchen also makes use of king scallops from Skye and Aberdeen Angus beef. A warm salad of chicken livers with orange segments and a piquant dressing began a test meal on a high note. Our inspector also praised the French onion soup, and a main course of lemon sole rolled and filled with crab, ginger and pimento accompanied by braised leeks in a delicate saffron sauce. To finish, there are desserts ranging from chilled citrus fruit tart with lemon sorbet and passionfruit coulis to steamed marmalade pudding. Around a dozen house wines by the glass head the wide ranging list.

Directions: Off A93 at Beech Hedges, follow signs for Kinclaven, approx 2 miles

KINNESSWOOD,
Lomond Country Inn ❀

Popular village inn with lovely views across Loch Leven. Cullen skink, Pittenweem haddock, deep-fried haggis with a whisky vinaigrette, wild salmon wrapped in filo pastry with a white wine cream sauce, and roast pheasant in bramble and rosemary sauce show a kitchen with a strong Scottish flavour and sound modern ideas.

Accommodation: 12 en suite
Credit cards: ▨ ▨ ▨ ▨ ▨ 🄯

Directions: On A911, 10 mins from M90/J5 (Glenrothes) or J7 (Milnathort)

KY13 7HN
Map 11: NO10
Tel: 01592 840253
Fax: 01592 840693
Chef: Mark Cooper
Owner: David Adams
Cost: *Alc* £15, fixed-price L/D £12.50
(3 courses). ☺ H/wine £8.50
Times: Last L 2.30pm/D 9pm
Additional: Bar food; Sunday lunch;
Children welcome; 🄯 dishes
Smoking: No smoking in dining room

KINROSS, Croft Bank

Bill and Diane Kerr have held sway in this stylish Victorian villa for more than a decade and it remains a loyally supported venue for both food and accommodation. Two dining rooms – one ornately plastered, the other more light and flowery – provide the setting, and the kitchen works capably with produce from Scotland's larder. Game terrine comes with a bramble and port sauce, casseroled rabbit comes with a tomato and garlic sauce, while poached Shetland salmon is served on sautéed leeks with a tangy lemon and chive sauce. Daily specials such as warm chicken salad with balsamic dressing and medallions of Scotch beef with red wine sauce and porcini mushrooms broaden the repertoire, while desserts range from a skilfully executed raspberry crème brûlée to banana Pavlova with warm chocolate sauce. Set lunches are popular with the business community, otherwise there are bar meals. The wine list provides plenty of decent drinking at fair prices.

Directions: Just off M90/J6 towards Kinross

KY13 7TG
Map 11: NO10
Tel: 01577 863819
Chef: Bill Kerr
Owners: Bill & Diane Kerr
Cost: Alc £21,fixed-price L £ 13.95.
☺ H/wine £10.50.
Times: Noon-last L 1.45pm/6.30pm-last D 9pm. Closed D Sun, Mon, 1-2 Jan, 1 wk Feb
Additional: Bar food L/supper menu; Sunday L; No children under 4; ❹ dishes
Seats: 45. Private dining rooms 20-50
Smoking: No smoking in dining room
Accommodation: 5 en suite
Credit cards: ▬ ▨

PERTH, Huntingtower Hotel

A Taste of Scotland is assured at this country house hotel, where food is served in both the conservatory and the elegant dining room. Dishes are built around local ingredients and can include Highland game terrine flavoured with malt whisky, and fillet of cod roasted with sesame seeds and garlic.

Directions: 5 mins from Perth, on A85 Creiff/Crianlarich Road. Just off A9

Crieff Road Almondbank PH1 3JT
Map 11: NO12
Tel: 01738 583771
Fax: 01738 583777
Chef: Bob Goodwin
Cost: Fixed-price L £11.95/D £19.75.
☺ H/wine £9.65.
Times: Last L 2.30pm/D 9.30pm
Additional: Bar food; Sunday L; Children welcome; ❹ dishes
Smoking: No cigars or pipes
Accommodation: 27 en suite
Credit cards: ▬ ▨ ▨ ▨ ▨ ▨

PERTH, Kinfauns Castle ❀❀ ⓃⒺⓌ

This fine, sympathetically restored house-cum-castle is the works: ornate ceilings, marble fireplaces, inviting lounges, a dragon-boat bar, the owners' extensive collection of Eastern artefacts, magnificent panelled restaurant. The kitchen shows a serious approach to food, and builds its menus around excellent raw ingredients. Although the menu is not extensive, the dishes reflect imagination and sound technical skills. A game terrine proved a successful starter, was followed by 'pottage grisons' (a Swiss-style Scotch broth), then medallions of Ceannacroc Blackface lamb, lightly coated with a soft herb crust and, to finish, a beautifully light and soft dark chocolate mousse, although the advertised Glenfarclus whisky failed to

Kinfauns PH2 7JZ
Map 11: NO12
Tel: 01738 620777
Fax: 01738 620778
Chef: Jeremy Waine
Owners: Mr & Mrs Smith
Cost: Fixed-price L £15.50/D £32 (5 courses). H/wine £12.50
Times: 12.30pm-last L 2pm/7pm-last D 9pm
Additional: Sunday L; No children under 8 at D; ❹ dishes
Seats: 36. Private dining room 12
Smoking: No smoking at D

come through. Delicious petits fours with coffee – ice cream encased in solid dark chocolate on cocktail sticks. Booking is essential.

Accommodation: 16 en suite
Credit cards: ▉ ▨ ▨ ▨

Directions: Two miles beyond Perth on A90 Dundee road; turn L at sign for Kinfauns Castle

PERTH, Let's Eat ❀❀

77/79 Kinnoull Street
Map 11: NO12
Tel: 01738 643377
Fax: 01738 621464
Chef: Tony Heath
Owners: Tony Heath, Shona Drysdale
Cost: *Alc* £17
Times: Noon-last L 2.15pm/6.30pm-last D 9.45pm. Closed Sun, Mon, 2 wks July
Additional: Children welcome; ❸ dishes
Seats: 60
Smoking: No smoking in dining room
Credit cards: ▉ ▨ ▨ ▨ ▨ ▨

Tony Heath's return to his own 'fair city' has proved to be a roaring success and faithful locals continue to support him to the hilt. His restaurant is housed in what was the original Theatre Royal and more recently an antique shop. Customers define the mood of the place: it can be 'casual bistro' or more formal, depending on requirements. Eclectic lunch and dinner menus brim over with ideas and ingredients of the moment – tapenade, pancetta, truffle oil, lemon grass – while salsas and confits provide the zest and spice. In more traditional vein there might also be perfectly smooth chicken liver terrine with toasted brioche, a mélange of seared halibut, salmon and squat lobsters on a bed of crunchy mange-tout with langoustine sauce, and chargrilled ribeye steak with fries. Desserts are capably fashioned offerings like crème brûlée, chocolate truffle cake, and poached pear with orange caramel sauce. The short wine list hits the button reliably.

Directions: On corner of Kinnoull Street and Atholl Street, close to North Inch

PERTH, Murrayshall Country House Hotel ❀❀

New Scone PH2 7PH
Map 11: NO12
Tel: 01738 551171
Fax: 01738 552595
Chef: Brenden Monk
Owner: Old Scone Ltd
Cost: *Alc* £20.50, fixed-price D £18.95. ☺ H/wine £12.50
Times: Noon-2.30pm/7pm-9.30pm. Closed 26 Dec
Additional: Bar meals L; Sunday L; Children welcome; ❸ dishes
Seats: 55. Private dining room 30
Smoking: No-smoking area; no pipes & cigars
Accommodation: 26 en suite
Credit cards: ▉ ▨ ▨ ▨ ▨

The Old Masters Restaurant manages to be refined without being stuffy, and sympathetic extension has resulted in better views over the golf course. The kitchen strives hard to provide consistently good food at affordable prices; warm mousseline of Arbroath smokies layered with creamed leeks and glazed with a grated horseradish and chive hollandaise impressed as a starter from the Taste of Tayside menu, as did a main course of grilled halibut steak served with sweet potato rösti and a warm coriander flavoured tomato coulis. Local ingredients feature strongly in dishes such as roasted loin of woodland roe deer served with pickled red cabbage and a port and fresh Highland thyme reduction, and herb-baked entrecôte of Tay salmon in lattice pastry with a subtle Vermouth and dill cream sauce. Steamed orange sponge pudding with sauce anglaise and fresh whipped cream went down well.

Directions: From Perth A94 (Coupar Angus) turn R signed Murrayshall before New Scone

PERTH, Newmiln Country Estate ❀❀❀

By Scone Palace PH2 6AE
Map 11: NO12
Tel: 01738 552364
Fax: 01738 553505
Chef: John Paul Burns
Owners: James & Elaine McFarlane

Standing cheek-by-jowl with historic Scone Palace, this glorious 300-year-old country mansion holds dominion over a 700-acre sporting estate; guests have exclusive shooting rights. Inspectors have been impressed by Paul Burns's technical prowess, a feel for honest flavours and commitment to local produce. Game is from the estate, fish from Scottish waters, lamb from Perthshire, ham from Ayr, while apples and plums for a superb crumble are procured from the hotel's walled garden. The set-up is currently as follows: from Monday to Wednesday a limited set menu is available only to residents; the rest of the week non-residents are welcome when the repertoire is extended and booking is essential. Dinner of a mousseline of scallops with dill, grapefruit and mussel sauce or a 'cameo' of lemon sole served delightfully with a spaghetti of vegetables and a light creamy reduction tinged with vermouth precedes medallions of Highland venison served with a compote of onions and toasted pine kernels, plus a port and redcurrant sauce, or a superb breast of guinea fowl centred with a tarragon mousseline and set off admirably with a mushroom and truffle sauce buoyed-up with lentils. Desserts might feature iced Drambuie parfait with seasonal fruits. The brief wine list nevertheless manages a broad sweep across the regions. Prices are startlingly fair for a restaurant of this merit with some shining example for under £15. Mâcon Uchizy from Domaine Talmard being a zippy, citrus example at £13.

Signature dishes: New season's Perthshire lamb on spinach and tomato finished with truffle and thyme jus; estate-shot pigeon oven-roasted with shallots served on brown lentils and wild mushroom ragout enriched with Madeira juices.

Directions: Take A93 (Blairgowrie Road) out of Perth, following signs for Scone Palace. Newmiln is signposted 3 miles beyond Scone on L

Cost: *Alc* £29.50, fixed-price L £16/D £29.50 (4 courses). H/wine £10
Times: 12.30pm-last L 2pm/7pm-last D 9pm
Additional: Sunday L; No children under 12
Seats: 40
Smoking: No smoking in dining room
Accommodation: 7 (not all ensuite)
Credit cards: ▬ ▬ ▬

PERTH, Number Thirty Three Seafood Restaurant ❀

City-centre location for this family-run café bar-cum-restaurant. Cooking is sound, majors in fresh fish, and allows flavours to shine through. Crab terrine with prawns, halibut with yogurt and orange sauce, and sticky toffee pudding, made up one well-reported meal. Lighter meals are served in the Oyster Bar.

Additional: Bar meals; No children under 5; ❹ dishes
Smoking: No pipes & cigars
Credit cards: ▬ ▬ ▬

Directions: In the city, just off the High Street, near the river

33 George Street PH1 5LA
Map 11: NO12
Tel: 01738 633771
Chef: Mary Billinghurst
Owners: Gavin & Mary Billinghurst
Cost: *Alc* £25. H/wine £10.60. ☺
Times: Last L 2.30pm/last D 9.30pm. Closed Sun, Mon, 3 wks Jan/beginning of Feb.

PERTH, Parklands Hotel ❀

Pleasant hotel, just a few minutes walk from the city centre, with an attractive conservatory restaurant. Cooking is sound. Look out for medallions of monkfish, pan-fried Aberdeen Angus sirloin steak, and pot-roast breast of pheasant. Service is very friendly and attentive.

Additional: Bar food; Sunday L; Children welcome; ❹ dishes
Smoking: No smoking in dining room
Accommodation: 14 en suite
Credit cards: ▬ ▬ ▬ ▬ ▬ ▬

Directions: Overlooking South Inch Park, round the corner from train and bus stations

St Leonards Bank PH2 8EB
Map 11: NO12
Tel: 01738 622451
Fax: 01738 622046
Chef: Michael Singer
Owner: Allan Deeson
Cost: *Alc* £25, fixed-price L £9.95/D £24.95. ☺ H/wine £11.95.
Times: Last L 2pm/D 9pm. Closed 24 Dec-8 Jan

PITLOCHRY,
Knockendarroch House Hotel

There are new owners at this Victorian mansion, which stands in its own grounds surrounded by mature trees. For the benefit of theatre-goers, dinner is available from 6pm, and choices from the short menu might include baked Tay salmon with mild grain mustard sauce, and roast haunch of venison.

Additional: No children under 12; ❹ dishes
Smoking: No smoking establishment
Accommodation: 12 en suite
Credit cards: 🔲 🔲 🔲 🔲 🔲

Directions: On entering town from Perth 1st R (East Moulin Road) after railway bridge, then 2nd L, last hotel on L

Higher Oakfield PH16 5HT
Map 14: NN95
Tel: 01796 473473
Fax: 01796 474068
Chef: Jane Ross
Owners: Mr & Mrs AD Ross
Cost: Fixed-price D £22.50. ☺
H/wine £7.50.
Times: D only, 6pm-last D 8pm.
Closed Dec/Jan

PITLOCHRY, Pine Trees Hotel

Elegant mansion in a beautiful setting. Consistent results from a daily changing menu that embraces the likes of pigeon and duck terrine with Cumberland sauce and onion marmalade, cream of parsnip and apple soup, paupiettes of sole filled with trout mousseline and a creamy herb sauce, and poached pear in red wine with Atholl brose.

Additional: Sunday L; Bar food; Children welcome; ❹ dishes
Smoking: No smoking in dining room
Accommodation: 20 (19 en suite)
Credit cards: 🔲 🔲 🔲 🔲

Directions: Signed at north end of town

Strathview Terrace PH16 5QR
Map 14: NN95
Tel: 01796 472121
Fax: 01796 472460
Chef: Richard Axford
Owners: Mr & Mrs J T MacLellan
Cost: Fixed-price D £25 (4 courses).
☺ H/wine £12.
Times: Last L 2pm/D 8.30pm

POWMILL,
Whinsmuir Country Inn

By Dollar
FK14 7NW
Map 11: NT00
Tel: 01577 840595
Fax: 01577 840779
Chef/Owner: Paul Mathieson Brown
Cost: Alc £15, fixed-price L £11.50/D
£15. ☺ H/wine £9.50.
Times: Last L 5.30pm/D 9.30pm
Additional: Bar Food; Sunday L;
Children welcome; ❹ dishes
Smoking: No-smoking area; no pipes
or cigars
Accommodation: 13 en suite
Credit cards: 🔲 🔲 🔲 🔲

Country inn overlooking the Gairney and Ochil Hills, with a bistro-style restaurant serving 'Taste of Scotland' dishes. These include west coast prawns, prime beef, and roast salmon on a bed of spinach with a rich tomato coulis. Frosted Turkish delight soufflé is among the imaginative puddings.

Directions: Village centre

SPITTAL OF GLENSHEE,
Dalmunzie House

A striking turreted mansion, peacefully set in its own private glen, offering sound hospitality and uncomplicated Scottish fare. Quality local ingredients are used in such successful dishes as smoked trout mousse with dill cream, baked halibut with a herb crust and red caviar cream, and sherry trifle. Well chosen wine list.

Additional: Bar meals L; Children welcome; 🍴 dishes
Smoking: No smoking in dining room
Accommodation: 17 en suite.
Credit cards: ▄▄ ▄▄

Directions: Turn off A93 at Spittal of Glenshee, hotel 200yds on L

Blairgowrie PH10 7QG
Map15: NO17
Tel: 01250 885224
Fax: 01250 885225
Chef: Ronnie McDonald
Owners: Simon & Alexandra Winton
Cost: Fixed-price D £22. ☺
H/wine £9.50.
Times: Last L 1.50pm/last D 8.30pm.
Closed Dec

ST FILLANS,
The Four Seasons Hotel ❀❀

Beautifully located on Loch Earn, there are glorious views all round as the seasons change throughout the year. Family owned, and with friendly but unobtrusive service, the cooking caters for both those with traditional tastes and guests who enjoy something a touch more adventurous. The dinner menu changes nightly and offers a good choice based on fresh local produce. Saddle of venison is cooked with juniper and whisky flavourings, fillet of lamb with rosemary and shallots, Aran mustard and leeks set off a fillet of halibut, whilst a pastry case focuses attention on its filling of West Coast queen scallops, mussels, bacon, garlic and tomato. Cream of mushroom soup, terrine of chicken, basil and tomato, and roast monkfish with cracked black pepper and fresh pasta are amongst the starters. Desserts keep it nice and easy with warm lemon tart, apple and sultana crumble, and iced blackcurrant parfait.

Directions: On A85 overlooking Loch Earn

Crieff
PH6 2NF
Map 11: NN62
Tel/Fax: 01764 685333
Chefs: Andrew Scott
Owners: Scott family
Cost: Fixed-price D £13.95/£22.75.
☺ H/wine £9.75.
Times: D only, 7.15pm-last D 9.30pm. Closed Dec-Feb
Additional: Bar food; Sunday L (12.15pm-2pm); Children welcome; 🍴 dishes
Seats: 60. Private dining room 6-30
Smoking: No smoking in dining room
Accommodation: 12 en suite
Credit cards: ▄▄ ▄▄ ▄▄ ▄▄ ▄▄ ▄▄

STANLEY, The Tayside Hotel 🌸

A welcoming hotel that retains its Edwardian character, notably in the restaurant where tartan wall coverings, distinctive lampshades and traditional sideboard make a strong impression. Robust country cooking, based on good quality local ingredients, may include Royal Perth haggis, prime Scottish steak, and venison MacDuff.

Mill Street
Perth PH1 4NL
Map 11: NO13
Tel: 01738 828249
Fax: 01738 827216
Chefs: Peter Graham & Liz Robertson
Cost: A/c £20.50, fixed-price D £17.50. ☺ H/wine £7.75.
Times: Last L 1.45pm/D 8.30pm
Additional: Bar food; Children welcome; 🍴 dishes
Accommodation: 16 rooms
Credit cards: ▄▄ ▄▄ ▄▄ ▄▄

Directions: Five miles north of Perth on B9099. Turn right at village green, then left to hotel at top of hill

RENFREWSHIRE

LANGBANK,
Gleddoch House Hotel ֎֎

Set in a 360-acre estate high above the River Clyde with spectacular views across to Ben Lomond, this historic house was once the residence of shipping magnate Sir William Lithgow. These days it keeps up appearances with excellent facilities for sporting and business types. On the food front there's an ambitious modern *carte* offering the likes of roast saddle of Perthshire venison on a brioche croûton, glazed and marbled with a light Drambuie and walnut cream, although our inspector chose from the four-course fixed-price dinner menu. To begin, there was an oven-baked gâteau of aubergine layered with ratatouille and fresh basil served with a piquant tomato sauce. Next came a neat-looking seafood risotto with Parmesan 'scrolls', before pot-roast guinea fowl stuffed with apricot and pine kernels. Proceedings concluded with a tangy orange and passionfruit tart served with a quenelle of lemon sorbet and feathered with lime and Cointreau syrup. The wine list is strong on vintage clarets and Burgundies.

PA14 6YE
Map 10: NS37
Tel: 01475 540711
Fax: 01475 540201
Chef: Brian Graham
Cost: *Alc* £18, fixed-price L £17.50/D £29.50 (4 courses). ☺ H/wine £10.50.
Times: Noon-last L 3pm/7pm-last D 9.30pm
Additional: Bar food; Sunday L; Children welcome; ֎ dishes
Seats: 120. Private dining rooms 30. Jacket and tie preferred
Accommodation: 38 en suite
Credit cards:

Directions: From Glasgow take M8 (Greenock) then B789 Houston/ Langbank exit. Follow signs to hotel

SCOTTISH BORDERS

CHIRNSIDE, Chirnside Hall ֎֎

The restaurant at Chirnside Hall has panoramic country views and its restaurant provides an intimate, candlelit setting for dinner. Fresh local produce inspires interesting combinations, note a superb courgette soup with blue Dunsyre cheese served with home-made soda bread. Our inspector had nothing but praise for a meal that kicked off with poached monkfish served with a light tartlet of langoustine and salmon with a sharp but well matched butter sauce, went on to the aforementioned soup, then took in crisp-edged duckling with a honey and soy sauce. Vegetables were fresh and plainly cooked, and nougatine parfait for dessert came with a nicely judged, sharp berry sauce. Service is pleasantly relaxed.

TD11 3LD
Map 12: NT85
Tel: 01890 818219
Fax: 01890 818231
Chef: Tom Rowe
Owners: Alan and Karla White
Cost: *Alc* £22, fixed-price D £19.50. ☺ H/wine £9.50.
Times: Last L 2pm/last D 9pm
Additional: Sunday L; Children welcome; ֎ dishes
Smoking: No smoking in dining room
Accommodation: 10 en suite
Credit cards:

Directions: Turn off A1 onto A6105 (Berwick-upon-Tweed) and pass Foulden village – hotel is on right-hand side before Chirnside village.

KELSO, Sunlaws House Hotel ֎֎

An elaborate mansion (owned by the Duke of Roxburghe), with an equally intriguing history going back over five centuries. One rumour has it that Bonnie Prince Charlie spent a night at the house in 1745, and while he was there planted a white rose bush somewhere in the grounds. Another links the property to the Jacobite cause. Of one thing guests can be certain, the cooking at Sunlaws is well worth a detour. Using

Heiton TD5 8JZ
Map 12: NT73
Tel: 01573 450331
Fax: 01573 450611
Chef: David Bates
Owners: Duke & Duchess of Roxburghe
Cost: Fixed-price L £12.50/D £27. ☺ H/wine £12/14.

Sunlaws House Hotel

Times: 12.30pm-last L 2pm/7.30pm-last D 9.30pm
Additional: Sunday L; Bar meals L; Children welcome; ⓢ dishes
Seats: 35. Private dining room 18
Smoking: No smoking in dining room
Accommodation: 22 en suite
Credit cards: ▀ ▀ ▀ ▀ ▀ ▀

the best local ingredients, the kitchen produces sound modern Scottish dishes such as Loch Fyne oysters with shallot dressing, roast rack of Borders lamb with mint-scented red wine jus, and prime Scotch sirloin steak au poivre. Highlights of a recent meal were potted salmon terrine with yoghurt and dill sauce, and a banana parfait served with caramelised bananas and deliciously light honey wafers.

Directions: On A698, 3 miles S of Kelso in Heiton village

MELROSE, Burts Hotel

The Square TD6 9PN
Map 12: NT53
Tel: 01896 822285
Fax: 01896 822870
Chef: Gary Moore
Owners: Graham, Anne & Nick Henderson
Cost: Alc £28, fixed-price L £17.50/D £25. ☺ H/wine £11.50.
Times: Noon-last L 1.45pm/7pm-last D 9pm. Closed 26 Dec
Additional: Bar food; Sunday L; Children welcome; ⓢ dishes
Seats: 50. Private dining room 24
Smoking: No smoking in dining room
Accommodation: 20 en suite
Credit cards: ▀ ▀ ▀ ▀ ▀ ▀

Built as a coaching inn in 1722, and now a listed building, this long-serving family-run hotel is still very much the hub of the town. Formal meals are served in the elegantly decorated restaurant which takes fishing and shooting as its theme, with old rods, flies and prints dotted around the room. The kitchen handles Scottish ingredients effectively for a modern menu that pulls together many strands and influences. Chicken and haggis sausage is sliced around quenelles of clapshot with a whisky jus, lasagne of salmon and halibut is served with ratatouille in a sesame oil, while a trio of local feathered game is garnished with horseradish dumplings and presented on a bed of Puy lentils. Scottish cheeses line up alongside puddings and double-cream ice creams. Decent lunches and suppers are also available in the lounge bar. Ten house wines head the serviceable global list.

Directions: Centre of Melrose

PEEBLES, **Cringletie House** ❀

A turreted baronial mansion set in 28 acres of gardens and woodland. The impressive first-floor dining room offers a short fixed-price menu, with dishes such as smoked salmon, sautéed suprême of guinea fowl with Drambuie cream, and Jamaican banana torte with coffee and rum.

Smoking: No smoking in dining room
Accommodation: 13 en suite
Credit cards: ▄▄ ▒▒ ▒▒ ◻

Directions: 2.5 miles N of Peebles on A703

EH45 8PL
Map 11: NT24
Tel: 01721 730233
Fax: 01721 730244
Chefs: Sheila McKellar, Paul Maguire
Owners: Stanley & Aileen Maguire
Cost: Alc L £16.50, fixed-price D £26. H/wine £12.50
Times: Last L 1.45pm/last D 7.30pm. Closed Jan-mid March
Additional: Sunday L; Children welcome; 🌢 dishes

SWINTON, **Wheatsheaf Hotel** ❀

Friendly, informal country inn overlooking the village green. It has a well-deserved reputation for food, served in either the cosy lounge or conservatory dining room, with seasonal produce taking centre stage. Smoked haddock and Mull cheddar soup, and roast beef fillet with malt whisky and wild mushroom sauce, show the range.

Accommodation: 5 rooms, 4 en suite
Credit cards: ▄▄ ▒▒

Directions: B6461 – half way between Kelso and Berwick upon Tweed; A6112 – half way between Duns and Coldstream.

Main Street TD11 3JJ
Map12: NT84
Tel/Fax: 01890 860257
Chefs: Alan Reid, John Keir
Owners: Alan & Julie Reid
Cost: Alc £20. H/wine £9.45. ☺
Times: Last L 2pm/D 9.30pm. Closed Mon, last 2 wks Feb, last wk Oct
Additional: Bar food; Sunday L; Children welcome; 🌢 dishes
Smoking: No smoking in dining room

STIRLING

ABERFOYLE, **Braeval** ❀❀❀

Chef/patron Nick Nairn is currently enjoying a high profile through his TV series. This has put him very much to the fore on the Scottish culinary map and clearly this is good for business; Braeval is now one of the best known restaurants in Scotland and advance booking is essential. The restaurant is a sympathetic conversion of an old mill, it is all very civilised with natural stone walls, flagstoned floor, attractive pictures, a central stone fireplace with log burning stove, and a discreet blue colour scheme. The format is simple – dinner and Sunday lunch are a four course affair with no choice until dessert, (weekday lunches are three courses). On booking one is asked for dislikes and vegetarians are willingly catered for. A former merchant seaman, Nairn's self-taught style is best described as modern Scottish. This translates, at a dinner taken in April, as a delightful, very lightly seared, fully flavoured fillet of fresh salmon on a bed of delicate saffron risotto and finished with a green-coloured herb oil. Then a main course of confit of duck 'lightly cooked and not the least fatty', with a crisp skin and honest flavoured meat, served with a stir-fry of Savoy cabbage and a 'lovely' lentil and wild garlic jus – 'all very nicely balanced and refreshingly uncomplicated, the natural flavours spoke for themselves'. An accompanying dauphinoise potato was creamy with a good balance of garlic. Crème brûlée had a 'wonderful, light filling'. Front of house staff are friendly and attentive and the pace is leisurely which suits the clientele. A lively selection of 16 house wines, all under £20, benefit from

Braeval FK8 3UY
Map 11: NN50
Tel: 01877 382711
Fax: 01877 382400
Chefs: Nick Nairn, Jeremy Wares
Owners: Nick & Fiona Nairn
Cost: Fixed-price 3 course L (Wed-Sat) £18.50/D £30 (4 courses). H/wine £15
Times: Last L 1.30pm (Thu-Sun)/last D 9.30pm (Wed-Sat). Closed Mon, Tue, Feb, Jun, Nov
Additional: Sunday L; No children under 10
Seats: 36
Smoking: Smoking restricted
Credit cards: ▄▄ ▒▒ ▚▚ ◻

brief, but helpful descriptions on the wine list. There is quality drinking throughout, with an abundance of sub £25 options and plenty of half-bottles.

Directions: On A81 Callander road 1 mile from Aberfoyle

BALQUHIDDER,

Monachyle Mhor ❀❀

Lochearnhead FK19 8PQ
Map 11: NN52
Tel: 01877 384622
Fax: 01877 384305
Chef/Owners : Jean & Tom Lewis
Cost: Fixed-price L £16 (3 courses)/D £21 (3 courses). ☺ H/wine £10
Times: Noon-last L 2pm/7pm-last D 9pm. Closed last 2 wks Jan
Additional: Bar food L; Sunday L; No children under 10; ⍟ dishes
Seats: 38. Private dining room 14
Smoking: No smoking in dining room
Accommodation: 10 en suite
Credit cards: ▆ ▆ ▇

This is a super little family-run hotel and restaurant with an unpretentious, individual style all its own. The cooking is honest and refreshingly uncomplicated but still has flair, and quality raw ingredients are treated with due respect in the two daily-changing fixed-price cartes. A starter of West Coast prawn tails served in the shell come poached to perfection, enlivened by a light garlic butter – simple, yes, but also simply delicious. Another excellent starter is oven-roasted sweetbreads with a pot of spiced gooseberries. Main courses might feature fresh halibut with a spinach and Parmesan crust or sirloin of Perthshire steak with wild mushrooms. Local game stars in mouthwatering dishes such as pan-fried breasts of saltwater mallard and widgeon with Puy lentils and bramble reduction. Desserts can also reinvent the wheel – a superbly flavoured bread-and-butter soufflé was exactly that. Lovely brown bread is baked fresh daily.

Directions: On A84, 11 miles N of Callander turn R at Kingshouse Hotel. Monachyle Mhor 6 miles.

CALLANDER, Lubnaig Hotel ❀

Sue Low cooks while husband Crawford tends to the needs of guests in their immaculate little hotel. There are views of the garden from the restaurant, where dinner might consist of honest, straightforward dishes like pea pod soup, roast duck with Morello cherry sauce, and casseroled pork with apples and red wine.

Smoking: No smoking in dining room
Accommodation: 10 en suite
Credit cards: ▆ ▆ ▇ ▇

Directions: Follow A84 and signs to Callander then main street to western outskirts; turn R into Leny Feus 35 yds from Poppies Hotel

Leny Feus FK17 8AS
Map 11: NN60
Tel/Fax: 01877 330376
Chef: Susan Low
Owners: Crawford and Susan Low
Cost: Fixed-price D £18.00. H/wine £10.50
Times: D only, 7pm-8.00pm. Closed Nov-March
Additional: No children under 7; ⍟ dishes

CALLANDER,

Roman Camp Hotel ❀❀

FK17 8BG
Map 11: NN60
Tel: 01877 330003
Fax: 01877 331533
Chef: Ian McNaught
Owners: Eric & Marion Brown
Cost: *Alc* £45, fixed price L £18.50/D £34 (4 courses). H/wine £14.50.
Times: Noon-2pm/7pm-last D 8.30pm
Additional: Sunday L;
No children under 4; ◑ dishes
Seats: 45. Private dining room 45.
Jacket & tie preferred
Smoking: No smoking in dining room
Accommodation: 14 en suite
Credit cards: 🔲 🔲 🔲 🔲 🔲 🔲

Directions: Turn L into driveway at east end of Callander main street

Built as a hunting lodge for the Dukes of Perth in 1625, this country hotel takes its name from the earth works to the east of the walled gardens which were believed to be the site of a Roman fort. The house is perched on the north bank of the River Teith and private fishing can be arranged for guests. Tapestries of English cathedrals hang on the walls of the candlelit restaurant, which also boasts an eye-catching painted ceiling replicating Scottish designs from the sixteenth century. A five-course 'taster' menu offers residents a chance to sample some of the chef's specialities such as parsnip consommé with a curried dumpling and tournedos of Aberdeen Angus beef with a thyme rösti and caramelised onions. Otherwise, there is a seasonal *carte* featuring accomplished dishes along the lines of terrine of rabbit and foie gras with cabbage and lentils, grilled fillet of salmon with langoustine lasagne, and chocolate marquise with dried apricots. The wine list includes a decent range of vintages.

DUNBLANE,

Cromlix House Hotel ❀❀

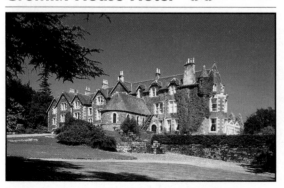

Kinbuck By Dunblane
FK15 9JT
Map 11: NN70
Tel: 01786 822125
Fax: 01786 825450
Chef: Craig Wilson
Owner: David & Ailsa Assenti

'Style without stuffiness' is how many guests affectionately describe Cromlix House. This awesome Edwardian edifice – which boasts its own private chapel – sits spectacularly at the heart of a 3,000 acre estate, a couple of minutes from the

tranquillity of House Loch. Inside is a 'glorious mélange' of architectural styles culminating in the twin dining rooms, one done out in elegant country house style, the other 'Scots Victorian' with panelled walls and rich fabrics. The carefully composed dinner menu runs to five courses and the kitchen deals appropriately with well-sourced raw materials. A recent inspection began with terrine of chicken liver and foie gras with Cumberland sauce and crisp apple salad, before a cauliflower, Cheddar cheese and Arran mustard soup that displayed plenty of finesse. The main course was marinated saddle of venison carved over carrot rösti with woodland mushrooms and sherry jus, and proceedings concluded with hot caramelised lemon tart with Cassis coulis, plus a selection of Scottish cheeses. The wine list is a diverse collection that ranges far and wide, although France is the major contributor; prices suit all pockets.

Cost: Fixed-price L from £18/D £36.50 (5 courses). H/wine £12
Times: 12.30pm-last L 1.30pm/7pm-last D 8.30pm. Closed Jan
Additional: Sunday L
Seats: 40. Private dining rooms 6-42. Jacket & tie preferred
Smoking: No smoking in dining room
Accommodation: 14 rooms, 8 en suite.
Credit cards:

Directions: From A9 take B8033 (Kinbuck), through village, 2nd L after small bridge

KILLEARN, Black Bull 🏵🏵 🆕

Extensive alterations have given this long-established village inn an attractive new look. A two or three course, nightly changing fixed-price dinner is served in The Conservatory Restaurant, with a choice of four dishes at each course. Fresh local produce is handled with care – seared scallops need no more than a simple tomato dressing, and pan-fried grey mullet is given a Mediterranean treatment with fresh pasta, dried tomatoes and olive dressing. Dishes such as carpaccio with Parmesan and red onions, and chargrilled fillet steak, rösti, fresh vegetables and horseradish gravy allow good ingredients to speak for themselves. Combinations are classically simple but tempting – guinea fowl and chestnut terrine with apple salad, breast of Barbary duck with sour cherry sauce and oriental leaf salad, warm almond tart with prune and Armagnac ice cream. There's a New Mexico look to the Brasserie, where you can enjoy such user-friendly dishes as cod fishcakes and parsley sauce, grilled Cumberland sausages, mash and onion gravy, and warm pecan and treacle tart with vanilla ice cream.

The Square G63 9WG
Map 11: NS58
Tel: 01360 550215
Fax: 01360 550143
Chef: Simon Hagan
Owner: J Wilson
Cost: Alc £16.50, fixed-price D £25. ☺ H/wine £8.95.
Times: L from noon/6.30pm-9.30pm
Additional: Bar meals; Sunday L; Children welcome; ♨ dishes
Seats: 40. Private dining room 60
Smoking: No-smoking area
Accommodation: 11 en suite
Credit cards:

Directions: Take A81 N from Glasgow towards Aberfoyle. Turn off on A875 to Killearn, just past distillery.

PORT OF MENTEITH, Lake Hotel 🏵🏵

Stirling FK8 3RA
Map 11: NN50
Tel: 01877 385258
Fax: 01877 385671
Chef: Micheal Clayton
Owner: JL Leroy

There are always flowers in bloom at the Art Deco-style Conservatory Restaurant which has splendid views across the Lake of Menteith to the Island of Inchmahome and the Trossachs. The short, well-priced menu changes daily and

includes dishes such as fish sausage on a bed of couscous with chive butter sauce, perhaps followed by fennel and potato soup, roast loin of lamb with red cabbage, puréed potatoes, red wine and mint jus, and fresh fruit terrine with orange jelly and blackcurrant coulis. Another night the choice might include warm duck liver salad with raspberry vinaigrette and garlic croutons, tomato and pepper soup, breast of guinea fowl with oyster mushrooms and a port and redcurrant sauce, and caramelised pineapple with coconut ice cream. Coffee comes with home-made tablet and shortbread. Service is courteous and attentive.

Cost: Fixed-price L £12 (2 courses)/D £23 (4 courses). ☺ H/wine £10.
Times: Noon-last L 2pm/7pm-last D 8.30pm
Additional: Sunday L; No children under 12; 🌢 dishes
Seats: 35. Jacket and tie preferred
Smoking: No smoking in dining room
Accommodation: 16 en suite
Credit cards: ■■ ▦ ⊞ ⧗ ⊠

Directions: On the A873 in Port of Monteith

STIRLING,

Stirling Highland Hotel ❀

Only 500 yards from the famous castle, this listed building is a clever conversion of a former high school. Vaulted ceilings and wood panelling are features. There's a 'Scottish Larder' menu and a 'Chef's Signature' selection, both offering the best of Scottish seafood, meat and game.

Smoking: No smoking in dining room; air-conditioning
Accommodation: 76 en suite
Credit cards: ■■ ▦ ⊞ ⧗ ⊡ ⊠

Spittal Street FK8 1DU
Map 11: NS79
Tel: 01786 475444
Fax: 01786 462929
Chef: Kieran Grant
Owners: Scottish Highland Hotels plc
Cost: Alc £28.95 Fixed-price L £10.95/ D £18.95. ☺ H/wine £10.95.
Times: Last L 2.30pm D 9.30pm.
Closed L Sat, D Sun
Additional: Sunday L;
Children welcome; 🌢 dishes

Directions: In the road leading to Stirling Castle – follow Castle signs

STRATHYRE, Creagan House ❀

Meals are taken in the baronial-style dining room of this former farmhouse, where polished wood tables set off the exclusively designed Isle-of-Skye pottery. The cooking is innovative, with dishes such as 'Smokie in a Pokie' and 'Fig 'n' Lamb with roast aubergine and vodka peppered sauce'.

Smoking: No smoking in dining room
Accommodation: 5 en suite
Credit cards: ■■ ▦ ⊞

Directions: Lies 0.25 miles N of village off A84

Callander FK18 8ND
Map 11: NN51
Tel: 01877 384638
Fax: 01877 384319
Chef: Gordon A Gunn
Owners: Gordon & Cherry Gunn
Cost: Alc £22.50, fixed-price D £17.50. ☺ H/wine £9.
Times: 7.30pm-last D 8.30pm.
Closed L except Sun, Feb & 1 wk Oct
Additional: Sunday L;
No children under 10

WALES
ANGLESEY, ISLE OF

BEAUMARIS,
Ye Olde Bulls Head Inn 🏵🏵

Built in 1472 and improved in 1617, this venerable old inn near the castle is justly proud of its past. It boasts the largest single-hinged gate in Britain and the whole place is crammed with antiques and curiosities – including the town's original ducking stool and a brass water clock. Downstairs is still emphatically a pub, upstairs – in the converted hay loft – is the oak beamed dining room. Welsh lamb, local fish including sea bass, Lleyn Rose beef and Conwy samphire all find their way onto the menu, along with Welsh farmhouse cheeses. Typical offerings might include home-cured bresaola with pickled walnuts, black olives and shaved Parmesan, monkfish tails roasted in Carmarthen ham on warm saffron sweet potato, and roast saddle of rabbit with celeriac mash and local chanterelles. Puddings could be anything from pistachio and hazelnut praline parfait to bara brith butter pudding with Can y Delyn ice cream. The wine list is serious and well considered with quality across the range and realistic prices to boot.

Castle Street LL58 8AP
Map 6: SH67
Tel: 01248 810329
Fax: 01248 811294
Chefs: Soames Wittingham, Keith Rothwell
Owners: Rothwell & Robertson Ltd
Cost: *Alc* £25, fixed-price D £20.95. ☺ H/wine £13.50.
Times: Noon-2.30pm/7.30pm-9.30pm. Closed 25-26 Dec, 1 Jan
Additional: Bar food L (not Sun); Sunday L; No children under 7 at D; 🍴 dishes
Seats: 60
Smoking: No smoking in dining room
Accommodation: 15 en suite
Credit cards: ▨ ▨ ▨ ▨ ▨

Directions: Town centre, main street

LLANGEFNI, Tre-Ysgawen Hall 🏵🏵

Built in 1882, this lovely stone-built mansion has a great deal to offer: wooded grounds, stunning views, excellent hospitality. The kitchen puts some imagination and thought into the short menu, and has a firm eye on modern trends, producing such dishes as tortellini of pheasant on a bed of sauerkraut with a Chartreuse sauce, and a smoked Finnan haddock soup with cottage cheese and herb dumplings. Main courses could be smoked lamb noisettes on a bed of purée, new potatoes and olive oil, with black pudding and an apple and sage sauce, or saddle of venison braised with apple and beetroot served in a rich balsamic game sauce. Desserts such as a coconut and banana chocolate chip ice cream served in a biscuit cup with a pineapple compote scented with mint are equally imaginative.

Directions: Take B5111 from Llangefni for Amlach, through Rhosmeich, turn R to Capel Coch.

Capel Coch LL77 7UR
Map 6: SH47
Tel: 01248 750750
Fax: 01248 750035
Chef: Gary Pennington
Cost: *Alc* £29, fixed-price L £14/D £19.95. ☺ H/wine £9.95.
Times: Noon-last L 2pm/7pm-last D 9.30pm
Additional: Sunday L; Children welcome; 🍴 dishes
Seats: 20-60-120. Private dining rooms
Smoking: No smoking in dining room
Accommodation: 19 en suite
Credit cards: ▨ ▨ ▨ ▨ ▨

TREARDDUR BAY,

Trearddur Bay Hotel ❀

A fine modern hotel overlooking the beach, with a smart restaurant serving fairly formal meals. Local produce features in the up-to-date cooking, with dishes such as roast Anglesey scallops glazed with honey, noisettes of Welsh lamb with port and rosemary, and breast of local chicken encasing a mango mousse showing the range.

Additional: Bar food; Children welcome; ◐ dishes
Smoking: No smoking in dining room; air-conditioning
Accommodation: 32 en suite
Credit cards: ▬ ▦ ▧ ▣ ▨

Directions: Take A5 from Bangor to Valley crossroads, continue onto B4545 then turn L after 3 miles

Holyhead LL65 2UN
Map 6: SH27
Tel: 01407 860301
Fax: 01407 861181
Chef: John Holt
Cost: Alc £18.50, fixed-price D £18.50. ☺ H/wine £9.95.
Times: Last L 2pm/last D 9.30pm

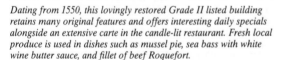

BRIDGEND

BRIDGEND, Coed-y-Mwstwr ❀

The domed ceiling adds extra character to the Victorian panelled dining-room, where modern Welsh cuisine comes in the form of medallions of wild venison on a turnip and celeriac rösti with a rich cranberry, thyme and cinnamon sauce. There are also classic grills and crêpes suzette for the unreconstructed traditionalist.

Additional: Bar food; Sunday L; Children welcome; ◐ dishes
Seats: 45. Private dining room 24
Accommodation: 23 en suite
Credit cards: ▬ ▦ ▧ ▅ ▣ ▨

Directions: M4 exit 35, A473 (Bridgend) into Coychurch, R at petrol station and up hill for 1 mile

Coychurch CF35 6AF
Map 3: SS97
Tel: 01656 860621
Fax: 01656 863122
Chefs: Scott Morgan
Owner: Virgin Hotels
Cost: Fixed-price L £12.45/D £24 (4 courses). ☺ H/wine £10.75.
Times: Last L 2pm/D 10pm

BRIDGEND,

The Great House ❀ NEW

Dating from 1550, this lovingly restored Grade II listed building retains many original features and offers interesting daily specials alongside an extensive carte in the candle-lit restaurant. Fresh local produce is used in dishes such as mussel pie, sea bass with white wine butter sauce, and fillet of beef Roquefort.

Additional: Sunday L, Bar meals L, Children welcome, ◐ dishes
Smoking: No smoking in dining room. Air conditioning
Accommodation: 12 en suite
Credit cards: ▬ ▦ ▧ ▅ ▣ ▨

Directions: M4/J35, A473 then A48 signed Porthcawl and Laleston

Laleston CF32 0HP
Map 3: SS97
Tel: 01656 657644
Fax: 01656 668892
Chefs: Neil Hughes, Darran McNulty
Owners: Norma & Stephen Bond
Cost: Alc £28, fixed-price D £15.95/£17.95. ☺ H/wine £9.25.
Times: Last L 2pm/D 9.30pm.
Closed Sat L, Sun D, 25 Dec

CARDIFF

CARDIFF, Cardiff Bay Hotel

Halyard's Restaurant, at this cleverly converted Victorian warehouse in the heart of Cardiff's revitalised waterfront, has a nautical theme appropriate for the setting. The cooking is based on relatively simple, unfussy combinations – grilled fillet of red mullet with a citrus and basil butter sauce, for example, was well timed, delicate and refreshingly straightforward. A main course of ribeye of beef, with brilliant beetroot fritters and a pesto sauce, displayed the fine flavour that can only come from properly hung beef. The fixed-price menu might also include dishes such as roast chicken on boulangère potatoes with lime and redcurrant jus, and confit of duck with stir-fried vegetables, oriental sauce and home-made noodles. The dessert choice is equally as good – steamed treacle sponge with hot custard vies with mille-feuille of strawberries and vanilla cream with strawberry sauce.

Directions: From A48M follow 'Docks & Cardiff E'. L at r/bout, R fork onto flyover. At 3rd r/bout take 2nd exit (Ocean Way – Atlantic Wharf). L at r/bout (Penarth). Over next r/bout, under flyover, L at 1st lights; hotel on R

Schooner Way
Atlantic Wharf CF1 5RT
Map 3: ST17
Tel: 01222 465888
Fax: 01222 481491
Chef: Peter Farrow
Owner: Andrew Weir Hotels
Cost: Fixed-price L £9/D £15.50. ☺
H/wine £8.50.
Times: Noon-last L 1.45pm/7pm-last
D 9.45pm. Closed L Sat
Additional: Bar food; Sunday L;
Children welcome; ❹ dishes
Seats: 80
Smoking: No smoking in dining room
Accommodation: 65 en suite
Credit cards: ▩ ▩ ▩ ▩ ▩ ▩

CARDIFF, Le Cassoulet

You can get an idea of the partisan nature of Gilbert and Claire Viader's bistro from the fact that it is decorated in red and black – the colours of the Toulouse rugby team. Not surprisingly, the menu is entrenched in the Viader's home country, which means that the eponymous cassoulet is a fixture – here crafted the proper way with white haricot beans, neck of pork, confit of duck and Toulouse sausage served in an earthenware dish. Fixed-priced menus (of two or three courses) also feature a trio of regional cheeses on a rocket salad, and roast rump of lamb with a tian of aubergine, garlic, fondant potato and rosemary flavoured tomato jus, as well as crème brûlée with iced honey and walnut parfait. You can set the ball rolling with a home-made cocktail made with 'seven secret ingredients' or orange-flavoured Armagnac and sparkling wine and then proceed to explore the wine list, which is a patriotic celebration of the French regions.

Directions: From M4 follow B4267 Canton, Restaurant is next to Post Office

5 Romilly Crescent
Canton CF1 9NP
Map 3: ST17
Tel/Fax: 01222 221905
Chef: Mark Freeman
Owner: Mr & Mrs G Viader
Cost: Fixed-price L £14.95/D £26. ☺
H/wine £9.95.
Times: Noon-last L 2pm/7pm-last D
10pm. Closed L Sat, Sun, Mon,
2 wks Xmas & Aug
Additional: Children welcome;
❹ dishes
Seats: 45
Credit cards: ▩ ▩ ▩ ▩ ▩ ▩

CARDIFF,
Chikako's Japanese Restaurant

Situated in the ethnic café quarter and decorated in typical minimalist style, this popular Japanese offers authentic cooking. Choose from beef teriyaki, or lightly battered deep-fried king prawns and succulent vegetables, or an aromatic soy bean paste and seafood soup.

Directions: City centre, opposite Marriott Hotel, in 'The Hayes' café quarter

10-11 Mill Lane CF1 1FL
Map 3: ST17
Tel/Fax: 01222 665279
Chef/Owner: Mrs Chikako Cameron
Cost: Alc £20. H/wine £8.60. ☺
Times: L by prior arrangement/6pm-
last D 11pm.
Additional: Children welcome;
❹ dishes. **Smoking:** Air-conditioning
Credit cards: ▩ ▩ ▩

CARDIFF,

Copthorne Cardiff-Caerdydd

Modern hotel conveniently positioned for both city and airport. Visitors may choose between an informal meal in Beauchamps Brasserie, or the more ambitious cooking in Raglans, overlooking the lake. Here meals include ragout of venison with forest mushrooms, and confit of duck with fresh blackberries.

Additional: Sunday L; Bar meals; Children welcome; 🌢 dishes
Accommodation: 135 en suite
Credit cards: ▆▆ ▆▆ ▆▆ ▆▆ ▆▆ ▆

Directions: M4/33 take A4232 (Cardiff West); after 3 miles turn onto A48

Copthorne Way,
Culverhouse Cross
CF5 6XJ
Map 3: ST17
Tel: 01222 599100
Fax: 01222 599080
Chef: Mark Jameson
Cost: Alc £17, fixed-price L/D £17. ☺
H/wine £10.50.
Times: Last L 2pm/D 10pm

CARDIFF, **Manor Parc Hotel**

An attractive country house set in extensive grounds. The classical dining room features an impressive domed lantern ceiling, as well as sound cooking. Market-fresh fish and quality produce appear in such dishes as poached salmon with champagne and cream sauce, and prime fillet steak with brandy and green peppercorns.

Additional: Sunday L; Children welcome; 🌢 dishes
Smoking: No cigars or pipes
Accommodation: 12 en suite
Credit cards: ▆▆ ▆▆ ▆▆ ▆▆ ▆

Directions: N of Cardiff on A469

Thornhill Road CF4 5UA
Map 3: ST17
Tel: 01222 693723
Fax: 01222 614624
Chef: Giovanni Morabito
Owners: Mr Efisio-Cimus & Salvatore
Cost: Alc £30, fixed-price D £17. ☺
H/wine £8.95.
Times: Last L 2pm/D 10pm.
Closed Sun D, 24-26 Dec

CARDIFF,

Metropolis Restaurant NEW

60 Charles Street CF1 4EG
Map 3: ST17
Tel: 01222 344300
Fax: 01222 666602
Chef: Stephane Hervé
Owner: David Williams
Cost: Alc £20, fixed-price L £5.95. ☺
H/wine £7.95.
Times: Last L 3pm/D 11pm.
Closed Sun
Additional: Bar meals L;
Children welcome; 🌢 dishes
Smoking: No-smoking area
Credit cards: ▆▆ ▆▆ ▆▆ ▆▆ ▆▆ ▆

Fashionable city-centre restaurant with striking modern decor and eclectic brasserie-style cooking. Simple combinations and fresh flavours impressed our inspector, who sampled game terrine with piquant red onion relish, juicy monkfish with fennel and onion ragout and saffron sauce, and an iced lemon soufflé.

Directions: In city centre, off Queen Street

CARDIFF, New House Hotel

Thornhill CF4 5UA
Map 3: ST17
Tel: 01222 520280
Fax: 01222 520324
Chef: Ian Black
Owner: Eventdetail Ltd
Cost: Alc £25, fixed-price L £12.50/D £18.50. ☺ H/wine £9.50.
Times: Last L 2pm/last D 9.30pm
Additional: Bar food; Sunday L; Children welcome; ❹ dishes
Smoking: No-smoking area; no pipes and cigars
Accommodation: 35 en suite
Credit cards: ▆ ▆ ▆ ▆

This 'New House' is in fact an impressive-looking, tastefully converted Georgian mansion. Within, the elegant, white clothed dining room looks out over extensive grounds to the Cardiff skyline and bay far beyond. It's a stunning setting for a kitchen that has a relatively simple approach, based on 'as local as possible raw materials'. Sturdy unadorned flavours and textures came through in an April inspection dinner. Hot crab and spinach tart revealed fresh and flaky crab and still crunchy spinach, then came buttery breast of maize-fed chicken, with a 'punchy' chicken broth sauce and 'earthy' braised garden vegetables, and an accurate, well-executed three chocolate mousse. Yeasty, home-baked white and brown bread rolls, and accomplished petits fours, show a team with a consistent approach.

Directions: Take the A469 to the north of city. Entrance on L shortly after crossing the M4 flyover

CARMARTHENSHIRE

BRECHFA,
Tŷ Mawr Country Hotel

The River Marlais meanders through the grounds of this carefully tended old house. Beryl and Dick Tudhope are now considering retirement, and have put the hotel on the market. While they remain, the food will be based around local produce and Beryl's bread should not be missed.

Additional: Children welcome; ❹ dishes
Smoking: No smoking in dining room
Accommodation: 5 rooms (4 en suite)
Credit cards: ▆ ▆ ▆

SA32 7RA
Map 2: SN53
Tel: 01267 202332
Fax: 01267 202437
Chef: Beryl Tudhope
Owners: Beryl & Dick Tudhope
Cost: Fixed-priceD £20. ☺ H/wine £9.25.
Times: L by arrangement/7pm-last D 9.30pm. Closed last 2 wks Nov, Dec 25-26, last 2 wks Jan

Directions: In village centre 6.5 miles from A40/B4310 junction at Nantgaredig

Old Cornmill Restaurant ❀

Cosy, intimate atmosphere and pleasing food in this Welsh-stone former miller's cottage. An autumn lunch took in home-made pork terrine complemented by Cumberland sauce, fillet of pork pruneaux with a creamy purée of cranberries, and crème caramel garnished with fresh fruits and almond biscuit.

Additional: Sunday lunch; Bar food L; Children welcome; ❀ dishes
Smoking: No pipes and cigars
Credit cards: ▅ ▆ ▇

Directions: 0.5 mile from Cynwyl Elfed on A484, 7 miles NW of Carmarthen

Cynwyl Elfed
SA33 6UJ
Map 2: SN42
Tel: 01267 281610
Chef: Adriaan John de Wreede
Owners: Sue & Adriaan de Wreede
Cost: *Alc* £17.50, fixed-price D £11.95. ☺ H/wine £7.40.
Times: Last L 2.30pm/D 9pm.
Closed Sun D, Mon,Tue, Feb

Cors Restaurant ❀❀

Chef/proprietor Nick Priestland is a man of many talents. His vibrant abstract paintings adorn the interior of this converted vicarage and the fruits of his green-fingered labours can be seen in the exceptional gardens. Matching the ebullience of the interior is a menu with a strong Mediterranean slant. Presentation is all primary colours, flavours are undiluted, the overall effect is of bold simplicity. Gazpacho is a 'garrulous' version with no stinting on the olive oil or garlic, while 'piping hot' potato and dill rösti comes with a parcel of smoked salmon and crème fraîche dotted with caviar. An inspector's main course of chargrilled Welsh lamb cutlets was outstanding, complete with barbecue-strength overtones and a Parmesan crust that really gave the whole dish an extra dimension. To finish, rhubarb fool was sharp, fresh and redolent of the kitchen garden. The shortish wine list bubbles with character.

Directions: Telephone for directions

NEW

Newbridge Road
Map 2: SN31
Tel: 01994 427219
Chef/Owner: Nick Priestland
Telephone for details

Cawdor Arms Hotel ❀❀

Llandeilo goes global, at least in the daily-changing menu of the busy market town's central Georgian hotel. Saffron risotto of local brill is served with tempura of fine beans, charred suprême of chicken with Chinese leaves and beansprouts on plum and five spice with crispy seaweed. A filo tartlet of 'pant ys gawn' and dried tomatoes is interestingly paired with pickled oyster mushrooms, and a main course of roast fillet of Welsh beef includes seared calves' livers as well as balsamic jus. Salmon, possibly straight out of the nearby River Tywi, may be steamed on English asparagus with couscous and avocado and horseradish sauce. More homely items include a nice, old-fashioned boiled leg of bacon with pease pudding, thyme potato and mustard sauce, steamed toffee sponge with fudge sauce, and Welsh rarebit served with apple and walnut salad.

Directions: Large Georgian building in town centre

Rhosmaen Street SA19 6EN
Map 3: SN62
Tel: 01558 823500
Fax: 01558 822399
Chef: Rod Peterson
Cost: *Alc* £25, fixed-price L £13.50. ☺ H/wine £9.90.
Times: Noon-last L 2pm/7.30pm-last D 9pm. Closed D Sun
Additional: Sunday L; Children welcome; ❀ dishes
Seats: 70
Smoking: No smoking in dining room
Accommodation: 16 en suite
Credit cards: ▅ ▆ ▇ ▇ ▢

NEWCASTLE EMLYN,

Emlyn Arms Hotel

National pride is stamped all over the menu at this historic eighteenth-century coaching inn. Fresh local produce is used wherever possible – and Welsh influences are apparent in many dishes. An inspection meal in early summer started with a smooth, attractively presented mousse of carrots, served just warm, with a rosemary butter sauce and several shelled mussels. Welsh black beef is always worth ordering – here two medallions are pan-fried with red cabbage and served with wild mushrooms and a mild grain mustard sauce to make the most of the tender, superb flavour of the meat. A rich iced chocolate parfait with passionfruit coulis ended a meal of considerable distinction. The three course set menu has five choices at each course and changes every four or five days; in addition a 'fine dining' six course menu is available at weekends.

Bridge Street
SA38 9DU
Map 2: SN34
Tel: 01239 710317
Fax: 01239 710792
Chef: Mark Freeman
Owner: John Retallick
Cost: Fixed-price L&D £15.50. ☺
H/wine £8.45.
Times: Noon-3pm/7pm to late
Additional: Bar meals; Sunday L;
Children welcome; ◑ dishes
Seats: 45. Private dining room 12
Smoking: No smoking in dining room
Accommodation: 20 en suite
Credit cards: ■■ ▄▄ ▀▄ ▒

Directions: Turn off A484 at Newcastle Emlyn; turn R into town centre – hotel at bottom of main street on L just before river

CEREDIGION

ABERPORTH,

Penbontbren Farm Hotel

Owned by the Humphreys family for more than 120 years, and set in what is still a working farm, the restaurant occupies a converted cow barn with pitch-pine ceilings and walls of local stone. Local produce also features on the menu, which advertises wholesome dishes ranging from laverbread pancakes to haddock with parsley sauce, and fillet steak with Cassis.

Smoking: No smoking in dining room
Accommodation: 10 en suite
Credit cards: ■■ ▒▒ ▄▄ ▀▄ ▣ ▒

Glynarthen Cardigan SA44 6PE
Map 2: SN25
Tel: 01239 810248
Fax: 01239 811129
Chef: Nan Humphreys
Owners: GB & MM Humphreys
Cost: Alc £17. H/wine £8.90. ☺
Times: D only. Last D 8.15pm.
Closed Xmas
Additional: No children under 5;
◑ dishes

Directions: E from Cardigan on A487 to Tanygroes. 1 mile after Tanygroes take 2nd R signposted Penbontbren

ABERYSTWYTH,

Belle Vue Royal Hotel

The Royal Grille Room at this long established hotel enjoys fine views out to sea. Local produce is used wherever possible, including fresh fish and seafood, plus Welsh beef steak, and roast rack of Ystwyth lamb perfumed with fresh rosemary and served with a Burgundy sauce.

Smoking: No cigars or pipes; air-conditioning
Accommodation: 37 en suite
Credit cards: ■■ ▒▒ ▄▄ ▀▄ ▣ ▒

Directions: Overlooking Cardigan Bay

Marine Terrace
SY23 2BA
Map 6: SN58
Tel: 01970 617558
Fax: 01970 612190
Chefs: Michael Stagg, Mark Hughes
Owners: Alan & Marilyn Davies,
David & Thelma Jones
Cost: Fixed-price L £12 /D £19.50. ☺
H/wine £8.
Times: Last L 1.45pm/D 9.15pm
Additional: Bar food L; Sunday L;
Children welcome; ◑ dishes

ABERYSTWYTH, Conrah Hotel ❀❀

Ffosrhydygaled Chancery
SY23 4DF
Tel: 01970 617941
Fax: 01970 624546
Chef: Stephen West
Owner: FJ & P Heading
Cost: Fixed-price L £23.50/D £26.
H/wine £10.50
Times: Noon-last L 2pm/7pm-last D
9pm. Closed Xmas week
Additional: Bar food L; Sunday L;
No children under 5; ❸ dishes
Seats: 50. Private dining room 40
Smoking: No smoking in dining room
Accommodation: 20 en suite
Credit cards: ▨ ▨ ▨ ▨ ▨ ▨

The three-course menu starts in the bar with home-made canapés and also ends there with cafetière coffee and petits fours. In between, guests are served in the elegant dining-room overlooking the Cader Idris mountain range and the Conrah kitchen garden. After a choice of freshly baked rolls, our inspector plumped for a delicious timbale of local crabmeat served on a bed of chopped avocado with a sharp sauce of herb mayonnaise and mustard. The standard was well maintained with a richly flavoured duck breast with plum, ginger and sesame sauce. Pudding was a proper pudding, not a dessert – spotted Dick, with a good old-fashioned custard sauce. The kitchen rightly favours good regional produce and the quality of both ingredients, cooking and presentation skills comes through in dishes such as chargrilled fillet of Welsh black beef with shallots, oranges and Cointreau sauce, and smoked breast of local pheasant on a bed of red cabbage with caramelised apples, wild mushrooms and Calvados sauce.

Directions: On A487, 3 miles S of Aberystwyth

ABERYSTWYTH, Groves Hotel ❀

44-46 North Parade SY23 2NF
Map 6: SN58
Tel: 01970 617623
Fax: 01970 627068
Chef: Steve Albert
Owners: JG, GM & SJ Albert
Cost: Fixed-price D £16. ☺
H/wine £8.
Times: Last L 2pm/D 8.45pm. Closed
D Sun, Xmas

Friendly, family-run hotel, just a short stroll from the seafront. Welsh produce features on the menu, perhaps roast Welsh lamb with 'Miss Vaughan's Pudding', or Welsh organic cheeses. Vegetarians get an imaginative look in with vegetable Wellington with ginger sauce.

Additional: Bar food; Children welcome; ❸ dishes
Smoking: No smoking in dining room
Accommodation: 9 en suite
Credit cards: ▨ ▨ ▨ ▨ ▨ ▨

Directions: Town centre, take road opposite station & 2nd R

EGLWYSFACH,
Ynshir Hall Hotel ❀❀❀

Welcome to Wales, Chris Colmer. After proving his worth at the Greenway, Cheltenham (see entry) this highly talented and innovative chef moved across the border in the autumn of 1996 and claimed his place at Ynshir Hall – a 400-year-old shooting lodge once owned by Queen Victoria. Here is a

Machynlleth
SY20 8TA
Map 6: SN69
Tel: 01654 781209
Fax: 01654 781366
Chef: Chris Colmer
Owners: Rob & Joan Reen

Ynshir Hall Hotel

Cost: Fixed-price D £29.50.
H/wine £15
Times: 12.30pm-last L 1.30pm/7pm-last D 8.30pm. Closed 2 wks Jan.
Additional: Bar food L; Sunday L;
No children under 9; ❹ dishes
Seats: 35. Private dining room 16
Smoking: No smoking in dining room
Accommodation: 8 en suite
Credit cards: 🔲 🔲 🔲 🔲 🔲 🔲

cook with bags of youthful creativity who seems destined for even higher things, judging by a recent inspection meal. He has a real feel for ingredients, scouring the region for what is best and appropriate and, in the kitchen, treating what is offered with respect and affection. Canapés in the bar laid down the ground rules and signalled what was to come: gently fried squid sitting perkily on an oatmeal wafer followed by an extraordinarily effective demi-tasse of parsley and oyster velouté with the said bivalve ' resting like a treasure' at the bottom of the cup. Great stuff, but there was even better in store. Next came a tenderly sweet confit of chicken accompanied by butterbean purée laced with lemon grass and sesame that managed to retain just the right amount of grainy texture and bitterness. Equally dazzling were fat, sweet scallops – just warm in the centre – allowed to open in Gewürztraminer wine, with creamy mash piped around the shell edge and a tagliatelle of leeks to provide colour and contrast; as a final flourish, the whole dish was presented on a harvest of fresh flowering herbs and sea salt. The momentum levelled off slightly when it came to desserts – in this case an apple confit with champagne granite, chilled rhubarb compote and apple chips that was rather one dimensional, but saved by worthy components. Service is smooth, cheery and intelligent.

A dozen house wines under £20, and available by the glass, offer good value. Burgundy and Bordeaux are towards the higher end of the price scale, but there is reasonable drinking from the New World. Southern France offers some 10 wines under £15.

Signature dishes: Velouté of Jerusalem artichoke laced with vanilla; roast cod with an aromatic tomato crust, caponata and a herb aïoli; hot chocolate fondant pudding with Drambuie ice cream; saddle of Welsh venison with swede and carrot dauphinoise.

Directions: On the A487, 6 miles from Machynlleth & 11 miles from Aberystwyth

LAMPETER, Falcondale Mansion

Large Italianate mansion enjoying an idyllic setting at the head of a sheltered forested valley. Personally-run by the Smith family, there are the added bonuses of attractively-appointed bedrooms and good quality food. Varied menus may highlight chicken and port pâté with Cumberland sauce, and salmon and sole Wellington with white wine sauce.

SA48 7RX
Map 2: SN34
Tel: 01570 422910
Fax: 01570 423559
Chef: Michael Green
Owner: Mr Stephen Smith
Cost: *Alc* £17.50, fixed-price D £17.50. H/wine £7.95.

Falcondale Mansion

Times: D, 7pm-9.30pm.
Closed 2nd & 3rd wk Jan
Additional: Bar meals (noon-2pm);
Sunday L; Children welcome;
🍃 dishes
Smoking: No smoking in restaurant
Accommodation: 20 en suite
Credit cards: ▬ ▬ ▬ 🅲

Directions: From High Street turn right up South Drive

CONWY

ABERGELE, Kinmel Arms ❀❀

St George LL22 9BP
Map 6: SH98
Tel/Fax: 01745 832207
Chef: Gary Edwards
Owners: Gary Edwards,
Dermot McGee
Cost: *Alc* £20.50, fixed-price L&D
£13.95. ☺ H/wine £8.25.
Times: Noon-2pm/7pm-9pm.
Closed 25 Dec
Additional: Bar meals; Sunday L;
No children under 10 in restaurant;
🍃 dishes
Seats: 35. Private dining room 20
Smoking: No smoking in dining room
Credit cards: ▬ ▬ ▨ 🅲

The dining-room of this old coaching inn has been decorated
in burgundies and greens, with neo-classical pictures and busts.
A short modern menu seems longer than it actually is, as
dishes that are perfectly self-explanatory are further
deconstructed in sub-headings. For example, tournedos of
peppered beef with glazed mushrooms and a red wine sauce is
then described as 'Welsh black beef fillet served as the classic
au poivre with balsamic glazed mushrooms'; breast of chicken
stuffed with spinach and ricotta and wrapped in Parma ham
has the ricotta explained as an 'Italian curd cheese which with
the spinach and ham gives the dish excellent colour and
flavour'. But our inspector had an excellent meal of chicken
liver parfait with onion chutney, super pan-fried sea bass and
lemon tart with lemon sorbet. And we're still smiling at the
entry under 'best end of Welsh spring lamb with a rosemary
and garlic herb crust and a rich piquant gravy', with the
translation 'pink and succulent Welsh spring lamb'.

Directions: Take A55 towards Conwy; L turn signed 'St George';
L at top of hill and inn on L

BETWS-Y-COED,
Tan-Y-Foel Hotel ❀❀❀

Capel Garmon LL26 0RE
Map 6: SH75
Tel: 01690 710507
Fax: 01690 710681
Chef: Janet Pitman
Owners: Peter & Janet Pitman
Cost: Fixed-price D £24. H/wine £10
Times: D only at 7.45pm. Closed
Xmas (check opening times for Jan).
Additional: No children under 7
Seats: 16
Smoking: No smoking establishment
Accommodation: 7 en suite
Credit cards: ▉ ▧ ▨ ▧ ▧ ▧

The Pitmans are proud hosts, and they have every reason to
be. For six years they have been welcoming guests at their
sixteenth-century manor house high above the Conwy Valley.
What a treat a visit here is! You won't forget the relaxed
ambience of this boldly decorated fine old house, the
breathtaking views from the intimate dining room and tiny
conservatory, nor the skilfully cooked food. Janet Pitman's
cooking remains true to the quality of the first class
ingredients, the majority of which are locally sourced. What
you loose in choice from the short, fixed-price dinner menu,
you gain in quality and taste. For Janet to focus on her classic
style, which has what she describes as 'French touches', a
choice of two dishes are offered at each course. Dinner is
served at 7.45pm prompt. Enjoy canapés in the comfortable
lounges, and put yourself in the good hands of Peter Pitman
who looks after guests with an assured bonhomie and
obviously enjoys playing the perfect host. The textures and
flavours of a starter of superbly cooked lemon sole on a rough
spinach purée, surrounded by pools of creamy aïoli, were a
dream. A startlingly good roasted breast of maize-fed chicken
set on lovage rösti with a morel sauce followed. Again textures
and flavours complimented each other wonderfully. Janet
elevates a traditional dessert of cherry frangipane tart to star
status by her careful judgement and superior technique: the
pastry perfectly delicate; the frangipane filling light and the
fruit intensely flavoured. For those who favour cheese over
pudding, be sure to sample the platter of three Welsh cheeses.
Booking is essential.

Directions: A5 onto A470; 2 miles
N towards Llanrwst, then turning for
Capel Garmon. Hotel on L before
village

COLWYN BAY, # Cafe Niçoise ❀❀

Candlelit tables in a dusky pink dining room provide a
welcoming atmosphere at this recently refurbished restaurant.
Café Niçoise was converted from a Victorian sweetshop and
the curved glass frontage adds to the cottagey feel; it is all very
informal and friendly. A 'menu touristique' offers four or five
dishes at each course, supported by a blackboard selection. A
winter meal began with goats' cheese on crispy fried bread
with salad leaves and a vinaigrette dressing and 'delicious'
strips of lean smoked bacon. The bass and monkfish were
especially good in an assiette of seafood set on a bed of pasta
strips and spinach with a light bouillabaisse sauce. A plate of

124 Abergele Road
LL29 7PS
Map 6: SH87
Tel: 01492 531555
Chef: Carl Swift
Owners: Carl & Lynne Swift
Cost: Alc £22.50, fixed-price L/D
£12.95. ☺ H/wine £8.95.
Times: Noon-last L 2pm/7pm-last D
10pm. Closed Sun, L Mon &Tue,
1 wk Jan, 1 wk Jun
Additional: dishes
Seats: 32

desserts in small portions followed: chocolate terrine with caramel sauce, lemon tart with raspberries, crème brûlée with Tia Maria and poached pears – all rich, wicked and attractively presented.

Directions: From A55 take Old Colwyn exit, L at slip road, R at mini-roundabout, R towards Bay; restaurant is on L

Smoking: No-smoking area
Credit cards: 🟦 ▓ ▒ 📰 💷 🔾

CONWY, Castle Bank Hotel 🏵

Small, friendly hotel, known for sound country cooking that has taken on board some up-to-date ideas. Inspectors have spoken highly of Marilyn Gilligan's poached fillet of salmon with spinach sauce, rib-eye steak with Welsh cheese and herbs, and roast loin of pork with apple and apricot sauce.

Accommodation: 9 en suite
Credit cards: 🟦 ▓ ▒ 📰 💷

Directions: From A55 take Conwy exit. Through Conwy to Bangor Archway then L into Mount Pleasant and R through public car park

Mount Pleasant LL32 8NY
Map 6: SH77
Tel: 01492 593888
Fax: 01492 596466
Chef: Marilyn Gilligan
Owners: Mr & Mrs Gilligan
Cost: Fixed-price L £9/D £13.50. ☺
H/wine £8.50.
Times: Last L 1pm/D 8pm.
Closed Jan – Mid Feb
Additional: Sunday L;
Children welcome; 🍴 dishes
Smoking: No smoking in dining room

CONWY, The Old Rectory 🏵🏵🏵

The Vaughans have run their attractive small hotel with great style for a dozen years. All the cooking is done by self-taught Wendy Vaughan, working seven days a week when necessary. After talking to guests about their likes and dislikes, noting any particular preferences, she writes a set menu, providing a choice only for the savoury and pudding. She makes a point of using Welsh ingredients whenever possible, but quality is the overriding factor. The result is a delight. The style is innovative without being outlandish and is executed with keen attention to detail. A roulade of salmon and monkfish, for example, comes with a saffron risotto and crayfish, whilst chargrilled breast of chicken is served on polenta with mixed greens and ravioli of wild mushrooms. A typical February meal opened with a delicately executed panache of fish – fillets of salmon, bream, red and grey mullet – attractively presented skin side up in a large bowl with carrot and courgette ribbons, surrounded by a deep yellow saffron sauce. The centrepiece was a fillet of local Welsh black beef ('Mrs Vaughan knows the herds and virtually the name of each beast'), cooked pink with a delicious sauce simply made from a reduction of beef stock,

Llanrwst Road
Llansanffraid Glan Conwy
Colwyn Bay
LL28 5LF
Map 6: SH77
Tel: 01492 580611
Fax: 01492 584555
Chef: Wendy Vaughan
Owners: M & W Vaughan
Cost: Fixed-price D £25.
H/wine £13.
Times: D only at 8pm
Additional: No children under 5
Seats: 16. Jacket and tie preferred
Smoking: No smoking in dining room
Accommodation: 6 en suite
Credit cards: 🟦 ▓ ▒ 📰 💷 🔾

Directions: On A470, 0.5 mile S of junction with A55

red wine, balsamic vinegar and, curiously, pork stock to give extra body. Then came grilled goat's cheese on marinated peppers (alternative savouries were a green salad, a choice of Welsh/Celtic cheeses, and an apple and plum sorbet), and a lemon and raspberry crème brûlée, chosen against stiff competition from a chocolate torte with crème anglaise. Distinguished by a commendable collection of half-bottles, the wine list is consistently well sourced. Bordeaux offers plenty from vintages that will be drinking well, and there are some bargains to be had, particularly in the whites of Burgundy and the reds of Italy.

Signature dishes: Platter of salmon; rack of Welsh lamb with a tian of aubergines; chargrilled guinea fowl with butternut squash and spinach.

LLANDUDNO,
Bodysgallen Hall Hotel ❀❀❀

LL30 1RS
Map 6: SH78
Tel: 01492 584466
Fax: 01492 582519
Chef: Mike Penny
Owner: Historic House Hotels
Cost: Alc £36, fixed-price L £14.50/D £27.50. ☺ H/wine £11.75.
Times: 12.30pm-last L 1.45pm/7.30pm-last D 9.30pm
Additional: Bar food L; Sunday L; No children under 8; ✪ dishes
Seats: 60. Private dining room 40, Jacket and tie preferred
Smoking: No smoking in dining room
Accommodation: 35 en suite
Credit cards: ▬ ▦ ▩ ▚ ▣

Two hundred acres of parkland and formal gardens surround this imposing seventeenth-century country mansion. Guests can wander around, explore the rose gardens, or simply gaze at the breathtaking views of Snowdonia and the Conwy Valley. Inside it is all you might expect from a hall in the grand manner – mullioned windows, oak panelling, splendid fireplaces and other trappings. The dining room is a stately affair, with high ceilings, heavy drapes, large oil paintings, chandeliers, plus views over the lawns. Dinner is a choice of two fixed-price menus, and the kitchen makes productive use of local ingredients. Smoked salmon and seafood sausage might be served with laverbread noodles, a terrine of tomato, aubergine and Welsh goat's cheese comes garnished with globe artichoke, while loin of Welsh veal is rolled in mustard and parsley and served on a mead and honey sauce. At a spring dinner a mille-feuille of smoked rabbit and foie gras came with a confit of red cabbage, then blood orange and tarragon sorbet, followed by grilled turbot, spanking fresh, and set on a classic rice pilaff flavoured with fish stock, creamed leeks were set in a filo basket at the top of the plate, around the outside were dotted morels and pesto gnocchi – 'all of which played their own parts divinely'. Dessert was a home-made brandy snap filled with a white chocolate and toffee mouse, plus raspberry and mango purée finished with a hand-piped chocolate florentine. Indeed, desserts show up favourably; another inspection meal finished with cinnamon and hazelnut parfait with a tangy kumquat confit. A goodly assortment of breads

Directions: From A55 take A470 and follow towards Llandudno. Hotel is 1 mile on R

are baked on the premises, and the kitchen also smokes its own meat and poultry. Service was 'swan-like', very refined 'as dishes seemed to levitate to the table'. The international wine list has some useful house selections and a plentiful choice of half-bottles.

LLANDUDNO, **Empire Hotel** ✸

Church Walks LL30 2HE
Map 6: SH78
Tel: 01492 860555
Fax: 01492 860791
Chefs: Michael Waddy,
Andrew Hadfield
Owners: Len & Elizabeth Maddocks
Cost: Fixed-price L £12.50/D £21.50.
☺ H/wine £11.
Times: Last L 2pm/D-9.30pm. Closed
L weekday, 1 wk Xmas
Additional: Poolside restaurant;
Sunday L; Children welcome;
🍴 dishes
Smoking: No-smoking area; no pipes
and cigars; air-conditioning
Accommodation: 58 en suite
Credit cards: ▆ ▆ ▆ ▆ ▆ ▆

Long established and well appointed family-run hotel occupying an impressive position close to the Promenade. Creative dishes using local produce are served in the formal Watkins and Co restaurant. Typical of the extensive set menu is ragout of pheasant, and oven-roasted haddock with tomato, red onion and basil salsa.

Directions: In Llandudno, follow promenade along entire length, turn sharp L into Church Walks. Hotel 150yds on R

LLANDUDNO, **The Imperial Hotel** ✸

The Promenade LL30 1AP
Map 6: SH78
Tel: 01492 877466
Fax: 01492 878043
Chef: Andrew Goode
Cost: Fixed-price D £20. ☺
H/wine £10.
Times: Last L 2pm/D 9.30pm
Additional: Bar food L; Sunday L;
Children welcome; 🍴 dishes

Part of Llandudno's imposing Victorian seafront, this hotel restaurant offers a monthly changing menu supplemented by daily specials. There is a choice of dishes from the chargrill, red mullet perhaps, or fillet steak, plus the likes of roast Welsh lamb, and supreme of chicken stuffed with Llanboidy cheese.

Smoking: No smoking in dining room
Accommodation: 100 en suite. **Credit cards:** ▆ ▆ ▆ ▆ ▆

Directions: On The Promenade

LLANDUDNO,
Number One's Bistro ✸   NEW

1 Old Road LL30 2HA
Map 6: SH78
Tel/Fax: 01492 875424
Chef: Stephen Rawicki
Owners: Stephen & Jacquie Rawicki
Cost: Alc £20, fixed-price D £15.75.
☺ H/wine £8.95.
Times: Last L 1.45pm/last D 9.30pm.
Closed Sun, L Mon

Burgundy walls give a cosy feeling to this informal restaurant, and the benches, tables and bar are made of pitch-pine from the old Welsh chapel in Llanwrst. Recommended dishes include goat's cheese parcels roasted in tapenade and served with salad, followed by fresh cod in basil and tomato sauce.

Additional: Children welcome; 🍴 dishes
Credit cards: ▆ ▆ ▆ ▆

Directions: Old Road is three streets from the Promenade, running between Church Walks and Llewelyn Avenue

LLANDUDNO, St Tudno Hotel ❀❀❀

Promenade LL30 2LP
Map 6: SH78
Tel: 01492 874411
Fax: 01492 860407
Chefs: David Harding, Ian Watson
Owners: Martin & Janette Bland
Cost: Fixed-price L £15.50/D £29.50
(5 courses). H/wine £10.50
Times: 12.30pm-last L 1.45pm/7pm-
last D 9.15pm (9pm Sun).
Additional: Bar food L only;
Sunday lunch; No young children at
D; ❹ dishes.
Seats: 55
Smoking: No smoking in dining room
Accommodation: 20 en suite
Credit cards: ■■■■ ■■■ ■■ ■■ ■ ■

Alice Liddell (of Wonderland fame) stayed at this hotel when she was a girl, but there's nothing fanciful about proceedings at Martin and Jeanette Bland's long-serving venue on the elegant Victorian promenade near the Great Orme headland. Heart-warming hospitality and meticulous attention to detail are the cornerstones of their success. At the core of the place is the aptly named Garden Room restaurant with its trellis wallpaper, Chinoiserie panels and lime-green cane-backed chairs. All around are plants and hanging baskets. The kitchen makes admirable use of Welsh ingredients for lunches and 'gourmet' dinner menus: Conwy mussels appear in a hot-pot with saffron, oranges, leeks and cream, a 'butterfly' of salmon is served with baby cucumbers and a butter sauce, while saddle of lamb comes with garlic potato and a minted butter sauce. Inspectors have raved about the quality of the vegetables – especially new potatoes 'as sweet as yams'. Desserts are also out of the top drawer. Poached pear comes with toffee sauce and immaculate quenelles of clotted cream on the side, there's iced strawberry parfait, plus warm honey and walnut tart with crème fraîche sauce. There's also a fine selection of Welsh farmhouse cheeses, including several organically produced specimens; otherwise try a savoury such as Welsh rarebit. The carefully planned, balanced wine list makes interesting reading. 'Proprietor's Choice' offers some interesting 20 wines under £25. The Austrian Pinot Blanc dry spätlese from Willi Opitz is well-priced at £23, as is the Savigny-lès-Beaune 'Vieille Vignes' from Camus Bruchon at £22.

Signature dishes: Loin of Welsh spring lamb wrapped in spinach and herb crust served with a puree of wild garlic and potato; fricassée of wild Conwy salmon and sea scallops with Gewürztraminer sauce;

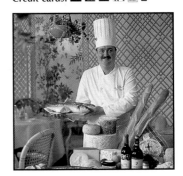

Directions: Town centre, on Promenade opposite the pier entrance

TREFRIW, Chandlers ❀❀   NEW

Chandlers is located in one of the oldest buildings in one of the oldest villages in the Conwy Valley. As the name suggests, this was at one time used as a corn chandlers and for the sale of marine hardware. The present enterprise is run by a family crew, complete with junior members working for their pocket money. The restaurant itself has a floor of local slate, white walls judiciously hung with bright pictures and slender modern

Conwy
LL27 0JH
Map 6: SH76
Tel: 01492 640991
Chef/Owners: Adam & Penny
Rattenbury
Cost: Alc £21, fixed-price L £7.50. ☺
H/wine £8.95.

wooden tables and chairs. Tucked away in a corner, are a couple of sofas, where early birds can take aperitifs in front of an open fire. The cooking is pleasingly economical, leaving space for flavours to be expressed and concentrating on accurate cooking of first-class ingredients. A lightness of touch was exemplified by delicate fritters of crisp fried aubergine, made piquant by a roasted red pepper sauce. An uncompromising approach to the sourcing of produce ensures sea trout is from local rivers, not Scottish farms, and this increasingly rare delicacy is accorded due respect, chargrilled with precision and accompanied by a restrained beurre blanc. Desserts make much of the restaurant's own ice creams, which go very well with the likes of a faithfully prepared Normandy apple tart.

Times: 11.30am-2pm/7pm-9.30pm. Closed L Sat, D Sun, Mon, Tue, D Wed
Additional: Bar meals; Sunday L; Children welcome; ◑ dishes
Seats: 24
Smoking: No smoking in dining room
Credit cards: ▬ ▣ ▣

Directions: On the main B5106, on left if coming from Conwy. Parking at rear

TREFRIW, Princes Arms Hotel ◑

LL27 0JP
Map 6: SH76
Tel: 01492 640592
Fax: 01492 640559
Chef: Ann Gordon
Owners: Ann & Lindsay Gordon
Cost: *Alc* £20, fixed-price D £15.50.
☺ H/wine £8.45.
Times: Last L 2pm/ D 9.15pm
Additional: Bar food; Sunday lunch; Children welcome; ◑ dishes
Smoking: No smoking in dining room
Accommodation: 18 en suite
Credit cards: ▬ ▣

Long-serving tourist hotel with great views overlooking the river and the glorious Conwy valley. Co-owner Ann Gordon offers varied, regularly changing menus along the lines of baked avocado with prawns, lamb's liver with orange and Dubonnet sauce and raisin tart with a spiced crumble topping.

Directions: At far end of village on L

DENBIGHSHIRE

LLANDEGLA, Bodidris Hall

This fine centuries-old ivy-clad manor house is set in mature woodland. From the house, visitors look out over ornamental gardens to a lake where swans glide. Inside, original oak timbers and inglenook fireplaces contribute to the time-worn atmosphere – visitors even use an old duellist's staircase with its uneven steps when retiring to their rooms. The kitchen bases some of the menu around fresh produce from the vegetable garden and a typical dinner might take in smoked salmon and lobster risotto served with pistachio-scented leaves and coriander butter sauce, followed by rack of Welsh lamb, stuffed with spinach and tarragon. For dessert choose from a

Wrexham LL11 3AL
Map 7: SJ25
Tel: 01978 790434
Fax: 01978 790335
Chef: Kevin Steele
Owner: Bill Farnden
Cost: Fixed-price L £16/D £27.50 (6 courses). H/wine from £10.75
Times: Noon-last L 2pm/7pm-last D 9.15pm
Additional: Sunday L; Bar meals; Children welcome; ◑ dishes

good selection prepared on the premises by the French pastry chef – roast hazelnut and chocolate gâteau, or light lime bavarois served with brandy wafer orange zest confit, are both recommended.

Directions: Llandegla is on A525 (Wrexham-Ruthin). In village (from Wrexham direction) turn R onto A5104. Hotel is signed 1 mile on L

Seats: 40. Private dining room 20.
Jacket and tie preferred
Smoking: No smoking in dining room
Accommodation: 9 en suite
Credit cards: ■ ▓ ▒ ▓ ▣ ℂ

LLANDRILLO,

Tyddyn Llan Hotel ❀❀❀

Corwen LL21 0ST
Map 6: SJ03
Tel: 01490 440264
Fax: 01490 440414
Chef: Jason Hornbuckle
Owners: Bridget & Peter Kindred
Cost: Fixed-price L £15/D £25.
H/wine £13
Times: 12.30pm-last L 2pm/7pm-last D 9pm.
Additional: Bar food L; Sunday L; Children welcome; ◔ dishes
Seats: 65. Private dining room 50
Smoking: No smoking in dining room
Accommodation: 10 en suite
Credit cards: ■ ▓ ▒ ▓ ▣ ℂ

Set in landscaped gardens in the ancient Vale of Edeyrnion, this unassuming Georgian house has been turned into an idyllic country retreat by Peter and Bridget Kindred. Things are looking up on the food front now that Jason Hornbuckle is in charge of the kitchen. He worked with Bruno Loubet before moving here and Jason's approach is as thorough as might be expected; he has already stamped his mark on the cooking. This is sharp, modern stuff, with vibrant natural flavours allowed to shine through, and not too much in the way of superfluous complication. Ingredients are local, menus seasonal. A test dinner in April began impressively with warm salt-cod sausage wrapped in the flesh of red peppers with tiger prawns, marinated squid and a light seafood vinaigrette based on a reduction of prawn shells. Next came an assiette of Welsh spring lamb – kidney, crisp liver pink on the inside, a small minty burger and a best end cutlet served with an intensely flavoured jus. To finish there was a mille-feuille of crisp sablé biscuit with poached pears in spiced white wine and a light Cassis mousse surrounded by a properly sharp blackcurrant sauce to cut through the sweetness. Details such as canapés, biscuits and petits fours reinforce the serious intent of the kitchen. Another meal in June found the cooking full of genuine enthusiasm for raw materials, eschewing the flippant and flashy in favour of well judged and carefully considered dishes. This meal took in a meaty, bold salt cod brandade served with a marinated squid salad, an intense, aromatic celeriac and truffle soup, guinea fowl that was built for flavour and bolstered by a peasantish risotto studded with bright and unctuous broad beans, and a white chocolate mousse with a bushy ginger wig of candied orange and a just bitter enough chocolate sauce. It was, in fact, a meal where nothing went astray. A dozen house wines and abundant half-bottles feature on the mainly European list.

Directions: Take B4401 from Corwen to Llandrillo. Restaurant on R leaving village

LLANGOLLEN,
Bryn Howel Hotel ❀❀

LL20 7UW
Map 7: SJ24
Tel: 01978 860331
Fax: 01978 860119
Telephone for details

Don't miss the views of the mountains and the Vale of
Llangollen from the dining room of this substantial Edwardian
house set in well-tended grounds. The kitchen works to a
seasonal menu based around local ingredients; some dishes
change daily, others are fixtures. The high point of a recent
inspection was pan-fried fillet of Usk venison, carved and
fanned on a potato galette and served with Puy lentils, roasted
shallots and Madeira sauce. You might begin with forest
mushrooms infused with roasted garlic accompanied by a
'sausage' of spicy chicken mousse wrapped in air-cured ham,
while terrine of dark chocolate with sharp caramel sauce
makes a creditable finale. An extensive wine list complements
the food admirably.

Directions: Two miles east of Llangollen on A539

RUTHIN, ## Ye Olde Anchor Inn ❀❀

Rhos Street LL15 1DX
Map 6: SJ15
Tel: 01824 702813
Fax: 01824 703050
Chef/Owner: Rod England
Cost: *Alc* £20. H/wine £8.95. ☺
Times: Noon-last L 2pm/7pm- last D
9pm
Additional: Bar food L; Sunday L;
Children welcome; ❸ dishes.
Seats: 40. Private dining room 40.
Jacket and tie preferred
Smoking: No smoking in dining room
Accommodation: 17 en suite
Credit cards: ▇▇ ▇▇ ▇▇ ▇

Originally a drover's inn, now an extended and modernised
hotel. The main menu relies heavily on steaks and chicken,
with a separate list of available fish and one or two other
dishes. Best dish on our most recent meal was a first course of
devilled lamb kidneys, properly trimmed and cooked, spiced
with white pepper, but alas, without the advertised sautéed
onions. Mango, ginger and spring onion sauce accompanied a
salty roast breast of duck, and crème brûlée came dramatically
presented on a black plate. Bar meals are served at lunchtime
only.

Directions: Situated in Ruthin at the junction of A525 & A494

FLINTSHIRE

EWLOE, St David's Park Hotel

St David's Park
CH5 3YB
Map 7: SJ36
Tel: 01244 520800
Fax: 01244 520930
Chefs: Graham Tinsley,
Graham Wilson
Cost: Alc £17.50, fixed-price L
£11.95/D £17.50. ☺ H/wine £10.50.
Times: Last L 2.30pm/D 10pm
Additional: Bar food L; Sunday L;
Children welcome; ⏺ dishes.
Smoking: No smoking in dining room;
air-conditioning.
Accommodation: 145 en suite
Credit cards: ▬ ▨ ▨ ▨

Very modern hotel with excellent conference and leisure facilities. Sound cooking takes in home-made bread, excellent terrines in the shape of Dee salmon and leeks with a balsamic dressing, and imaginative fish dishes such as brill and sea trout with asparagus and chive cream sauce touched with a crayfish essence.

Directions: A494 Queensferry to Mold for 4 miles, then B5127 towards Buckley.

NORTHOP, Soughton Hall Hotel

You are not so much spoilt for choice at this sumptuous, former Bishop's Palace, as practically overwhelmed by it. Eight starters, nine desserts and ten main courses, plus an intermediate soup or sorbet course, make lengthy reading, especially when each hand-written dish is described in loving detail. Warm terrine of locally smoked chicken perfumed with fresh basil and mixed with pheasant, pigeon and black pudding, wrapped in bacon and presented upon a grilled potato and caraway seed salad complemented by a home-made green grape chutney is typical of the style, and also shows the kitchen's interest in good game dishes. Poached roulade of local hare fillet wrapped in its own mousseline and carved upon a red wine and balsamic vinegar sauce accompanied by a home-made apple and tomato chutney and deep-fried slivers of celeriac, is another interesting choice. The enthusiasm, however, is endearing rather than irritating; one of the most popular desserts is Mrs R's now infamous sticky toffee pudding served with a walnut and honey ice-cream and finished with a 'lip-smacking' toffee sauce. Who could resist?

CH7 6AB
Map 7: SJ26
Tel: 01352 840811
Fax: 01352 840382
Chef: Michael Carney
Owners: John & Rosemary
Rodenhurst
Cost: Alc £37.50. H/wine £11.50
Times: Noon-last L 1.45pm/7pm-last
D 9.45pm. Closed Sun, 1st wk Jan
Additional: No children under 12;
⏺ dishes
Seats: 45. Private dining room 20
Smoking: No smoking in dining room
Accommodation: 14 en suite
Credit cards: ▬ ▨ ▨

Directions: Turn off A55 expressway at Northrop, and follow the A5119 towards Mold. After 0.5 mile, the hotel is signposted on L

GWYNEDD

ABERDYFI, **Maybank Hotel** ❀

4 Penhelig Road
Penhelig LL35 0PT
Map 6: SN69
Tel: 01654 767500
Chef: Elizabeth Dinsdale
Owners: Elizabeth Dinsdale & Paul
Massey
Cost: Fixed-price D £20.95. ☺
H/wine £10.95.
Times: D only, 7pm-last D 9pm
during season
Additional: No children under 10;
❸ dishes
Smoking: No smoking in dining room
Accommodation: 6 (5 en suite)
Credit cards:

*There are superb views over the estuary from the pine-decorated
dining room. The cooking is pleasingly straightforward – steak and
kidney pie, rack of Welsh lamb with a rosemary jus, or halibut
grilled with parsley butter, with good puddings such as home-made
treacle tart or rhubarb crumble to finish.*

Directions: On A483 (Machynlleth - Aberdyfi), 500 yards on R from
village sign

ABERDYFI, **Penhelig Arms** ❀

LL35 0LT
Map 6: SN69
Tel: 01654 767215
Fax: 01654 767690
Chef: Jane Howkins
Owners: Robert and Sally Hughes
Cost: Fixed-price D £19. ☺
H/wine £9.
Times: Last L 2.00pm/D 9.30pm.
Closed 25-26 Dec
Additional: Bar food; Sunday L;
Children welcome; ❸ dishes
Smoking: No smoking in dining room
Accommodation: 10 en suite
Credit cards:

*Greatly improved and extended eighteenth-century inn opposite the
harbour where ocean-going schooners were once built. Bar food and
restaurant menus major in local produce: from the latter you might
find duck and game terrine, salad of seared sea bream and scallops
with tomato and chive vinaigrette, and chargrilled leg of lamb steak.
The wine list is a fascinating enthusiast's selection.*

Directions: From Machynlleth take A439 coastal route (9 miles)

ABERDYFI, **Plas Penhelig** ❀   NEW

*Fine Edwardian country house located high above the Dovey
Estuary. A daily set-price menu, featuring Anglo-French dishes, is
served in the airy dining room. Highly recommended are roast*

LL35 0NA
Map 6: SN69
Tel: 01654 767676
Fax: 01654 767783
Chef: Nicole Riot

boned quails, stuffed with Glamorgan sausage and served with
cranberry and port wine sauce. Smart dress is expected.

Additional: Sunday L; Bar meals L; No children under 8;
③ dishes
Smoking: No smoking in dining room
Accommodation: 11 en suite
Credit cards: 🔲 🔲 🔲 🔲

Directions: From Machynlleth take A493 coastal route (9 miles)

Owner: David Richardson
Cost: Fixed-price D £18.50. ☺
H/wine £10.50.
Times: Last L 1.45pm/D 8.45pm.
Closed Jan, Feb

ABERSOCH, Neigwl Hotel ✸

The Neigwl's restaurant enjoys views of the sea and Snowdonia, and
the furnishings and decor are comfortable and relaxing. Fresh fish is
a feature whenever possible, perhaps in 'Fisherman's Catch' a trio of
home-made fishcakes or seafood Thermidor. Other options are
grilled Welsh lamb cutlets or chicken with créole sauce.

Accommodation: 9 en suite.
Additional: Children welcome; ③ dishes
Credit cards: 🔲 🔲 🔲 🔲 🔲 🔲

Directions: 400 yards past village centre on the L

Lon Sarn Bach
Pwllheli LL53 7DY
Map 6: SH32
Tel/Fax: 01758 712363
Chef: Nigel Higginbottom
Owners: Gerry & Pat Heptonstall
Cost: Fixed-price D £20. ☺
H/wine £8.50.
Times: D only, 7-9pm

ABERSOCH, Porth Tocyn Hotel ✸✸

There are gorgeous views through the picture windows across
Cardigan Bay to Snowdonia from the dining-room filled with
antique country furniture. *Toujours la politesse* is still the rule
at this popular family hotel, which caters for children
exceptionally well. The five-course dinner menu changes daily
and offers lots of choice, but there is plenty of flexibility
towards guests requiring lighter or alternative feeding. Still, it
would be a shame to miss out on a meal that might begin with
roast quail stuffed with apricots and rosemary with redcurrant
sauce, then continue with cream of cauliflower and Stilton
soup, grilled local sea bass on a glazed saffron sabayon with
sautéed king prawns, whisky cream pie with blackberry coulis,
and a selection of cheeses and fresh fruit, not forgetting the
coffee with home-made petits fours.

Bwlch Tocyn LL53 7BU
Map 6: SH32
Tel: 01758 713303
Fax: 01758 713538
Chefs: David Carney,
Louise Fletcher-Brewer
Owners: The Fletcher-Brewer family
Cost: Fixed-price D £27.75
(5 courses). H/wine £10.50
Times: 12.30pm-last L 2pm/7.30pm-
last D 9.30pm. Closed mid Nov-wk
before Easter
Additional: Bar food L; Buffet Sunday
L; No children under 7 at D;
③ dishes.
Seats: 50. Jacket and tie preferred
Accommodation: 17 en suite.
Credit cards: 🔲 🔲 🔲

Directions: 2.5 miles beyond village of Abersoch, through
hamlets of Sarn Bach and Bwlch Tocyn. Follow signs marked
'Gwesty/Hotel' and 'Remote Hotel' from Sarn Bach onwards.

ABERSOCH, Tudor Court

Friendly village-centre hotel with attractive accommodation and a welcoming cosy bar. Local fish catches usually appear on the menu, alongside a range of soundly cooked popular dishes.

Smoking: No smoking in dining room
Accommodation: 8 (7 en suite)
Credit cards: ▬ ▭ ◥

Directions: On main road in centre of village

Lon Sarn Bach LL53 7EB
Map 6: SH32
Tel/Fax: 01758 713354
Chef: J Courtney
Owner: Jennifer Jones
Cost: Alc £20, fixed-price L £12.50 (3-courses)
Times: Last L 2pm/last D 9pm
Additional: Sunday L; Children welcome
Seats: 40. Private dining room

ABERSOCH,
The White House Hotel

The hotel has an elegant restaurant with stunning views over Cardigan Bay and Cader Idris. Good use is made of fresh ingredients, with dishes such as fish soup with croûtons, rouille and Parmesan; breast of duck with potato galette and kumquat marmalade, and a dessert of caramelised oranges.

Accommodation: 11 en suite. **Credit cards:** ▬ ▭ ◥ ▣ ▢

Directions: Hotel on A499 Pwllheli/Abersoch Road, on R (from Pwllheli)

Pwllheli LL53 7AG
Map 6: SH32
Tel: 01758 713427
Fax: 01758 713512
Chef: Dafydd E Jones
Owners: David & Jayne Smith
Cost: Alc £22.50, fixed-price D £19.50. ☺ H/wine £9.50.
Times: 6.30pm-last D 8.30pm
Additional: Light lunch; Sunday L; Children welcome; ❹ dishes
Smoking: No smoking in dining room

BALA, Palé Hall

Llanderfel LL23 7PS
Map 6: SH93
Tel: 01678 530285
Fax: 01678 530220
Chef: Wendy Phillips
Owner: Saul Nahed
Cost: Set L £14.95/D £23.95. ☺ H/wine £9.95.
Times: Last L 2pm/D 9pm. Closed Sat D
Additional: Sunday L; Children welcome by arrangement; ❹ dishes
Smoking: No smoking in dining room
Accommodation: 17 en suite
Credit cards: ▬ ▭ ▭ ◥ ▣

Queen Victoria once stayed at this fine Victorian mansion and the room she occupied is now much in demand. The interior is suitably impressive, yet offers a restful atmosphere. The kitchen works to a short but imaginative menu that is built around quality ingredients, offering the likes of breast of duck on a bed of braised red cabbage, and pan-fried wild boar steak with a port and prune sauce. A dinner in early summer opened with roast chicken livers served on a bed of creamed leeks in a crisp pastry tartlet, with red wine jus and leek chiffonade. Then came pork tenderloin with onion marmalade and Calvados and apple sauce, a colourful side dish of crisp vegetables, and, to finish, summer pudding crammed full of fresh fruit. Home-made bread rolls and petits fours show attention to small details.

Directions: Just off B4401, 4 miles from Llandrillo

BANGOR, Menai Court Hotel

Readers of a certain age will be pleased to learn that two former members of the *Black and White Minstrel Show* are alive and well and running this delightful small Victorian hotel looking out towards the Menai Straights and Anglesey. They certainly offer a warm, Welsh welcome, and the hospitality is now matched by a kitchen that has really found its form this year. Fish dishes are particularly good – and Thursday evenings feature speciality fish dinners starring the likes of fillet of sea bass in champagne sauce, grilled Jamaican red snapper and Norwegian haddock provençale amongst other international artistes. Friday is flambé night, with old favourites steak Diane, beef Stroganoff and crêpes suzette. Other nights, the repertoire might include Parma ham and peppercorn mousseline, home-smoked duck breast with red onion, prune and Madeira confit, roast partridge with port wine and shallot sauce, or fillet of pork and king prawn with a Sherry jus. Angus steaks from Inverurie come with official health certification. Don't miss the Bara Brith bread-and-butter pudding.

Directions: Turn L out of railway station, R at top of hill by Bank into College Road, 1st L into Craig y Don Road

Craig y Don Road LL57 2BG
Map 6: SH57
Tel/Fax: 01248 354200
Chef: John Connor
Owners: Mr & Mrs Elwyn Hughes
Cost: Alc £21, fixed-price L £11.95/ D £19.95. ☺ H/wine £9.50.
Times: Noon-last L 2pm/7pm-last D 9.15pm. Closed L Sat, 26 Dec-5 Jan
Additional: No children under 6; dishes
Seats: 40
Smoking: No smoking in dining room
Accommodation: 14 en suite
Credit cards: ■ ▦

BARMOUTH,
Ty'r Graig Castle Hotel

The creation of Birmingham gunsmith W W Greener in 1891, this Gothic-style edifice was built in the shape of a double barrelled shotgun. The stained glass windows and panelled walls are impressive features. The food is of sound quality with dishes such as green-lip mussels in white Stilton sauce, and caramelised pork fillet with sweet apricot sauce.

Additional: Bar Food; Sunday L; Children welcome; ● dishes
Smoking: No smoking in dining room
Accommodation: 12 en suite
Credit cards: ■ ▦ ▦ ▦ ▣

Directions: On coast road 0.75 miles towards Harlech

Llanaber Road LL42 1YN
Map 6: SH61
Tel: 01341 280470
Fax: 01341 281260
Chef: Christopher Wright
Owners: Mike & Bev Holbrooke
Cost: Fixed-price D £18.50. ☺ H/wine £8.75.
Times: Last L 2pm/D 8.30pm Closed Jan

BARMOUTH,
Wavecrest Hotel

Eric and Shelagh Jarman have been at the helm of this pleasant hotel by the beach for more than 17 years, and they continue to please. Shelagh's set dinner menus change daily, but a typical meal might take in Gruyère profiteroles, Welsh lamb with a redcurrant jelly tartlet, then cream cheese tart with strawberries and raspberry purée.

Additional: Children welcome; ● dishes
Smoking: No smoking in dining room
Accommodation: 10 rooms
Credit cards: ■ ▦ ▦

Directions: On seafront, at the centre of the promenade

8 Marine Parade
LL42 1NA
Map 6: SH61
Tel: 01341 280330
Fax: 01341 280350
Chef: Shelagh Jarman
Owners: Eric & Shelagh Jarman
Cost: Alc £15, fixed-price D £15. ☺
Times: D only, 7pm-8pm. Closed Nov-March

BONTDDU,

Bontddu Hall Hotel 🏵🏵

Dolgellau LL40 2SU
Map 6: SH61
Tel: 01341 430661
Fax: 01341 430284
Chef: Didier Bienaime
Owners: Michael & Margaretta Ball
Cost: Fixed-price L £12.75/D £23.50.
☺ H/wine £10.
Times: Noon-last L 2pm/7pm-last D
9.30pm. Closed Nov-March
Additional: Bar food; Sunday L;
No children under 3; 🏵 dishes
Seats: 45. Private dining room 25.
Jacket and tie preferred
Smoking: No smoking in dining room
Accommodation: 20 en suite
Credit cards: ▬ ▬ ▬ ▬ ▯ ▯

Camelias, azaleas and rhododendrons compete for the light
with palms, breadfruit and apricot trees in the luxuriant
gardens of this glorious country house. Built in 1873 as a bolt-
hole for the Lord Mayor of Birmingham it also boasts some of
the finest views in all Wales, with the Mawddach Estuary and
the mountains of Cader Idris beyond. Lunch menus now look
to the world of the brasserie for inspiration, while dinner
remains in the formal mould of the hotel restaurant. To begin,
there might be carrot and coriander soup or a tartlet of pigeon
sautéed with almonds and pineapple, before freshly caught sea
bass with spinach and a yellow pepper coulis or pan-fried
Meirionnydd mountain lamb steak marinated in ginger served
on a rosemary scented jus. Desserts range from iced hazelnut
parfait to orange and brandy caramels, and there's a trio of
Welsh cheeses to finish. The wine list is safe, sound and
affordable.

Directions: From A470 1 mile N Dolgellau take A496 to
Barmouth, then 4 miles to Bontddu. Hotel on R as you enter
village

CAERNARFON,

Seiont Manor Hotel 🏵

*Snowdon looms just a few miles from this tranquilly situated
country house standing in 150 acres of parkland. Paintings by local
artists decorate the blue and yellow dining room, where you can
sample well-executed dishes such as warm salad of pigeon with
hazelnut and lime vinaigrette, chunky cassoulet of seafood and rich
bread and butter pudding.*

Llanrug LL55 2AQ
Map 6: SH56
Tel: 01286 673366
Fax: 01286 672840
Chef: Anthony Murphy
Cost: Alc £27.70, fixed-price L /D
£22.95 (4 courses). ☺
H/wine £10.95.
Times: Last L 2.30pm/D 9.45pm

Additional: Bar food; Sunday L; Children welcome; 🏵 dishes
Smoking: No smoking in dining room
Accommodation: 28 en suite
Credit cards: ▬ ▬ ▬ ▯ ▯

Directions: From Bangor follow signs for Caernarfon. Leave
Caernarfon on A4086. The hotel is 3 miles on L

DOLGELLAU,
Clifton House Hotel

Exposed timbers and slab floors feature in this cellar restaurant that used to be the county gaol. 'Excellent ingredients, winning ideas'. Black pudding with apple, onion and a Dijon mustard sauce, roast rack of Welsh lamb with a white wine, honey, garlic and herb sauce, and coffee, date and walnut pudding show the range.

Smoking: No smoking in dining room
Accommodation: 6 rooms
Credit cards: ▪▪ ▪▪

Directions: On L in town centre one-way system

Smithfield Square
LL40 1ES
Map 6: SH71
Tel: 01341 422554
Chef: Pauline Dix
Owners: Pauline & Rob Dix
Cost: *Alc* £16. ☺ H/wine £8.95.
Times: 7pm-last D 9pm.
Closed Nov-mid March
Additional: Children welcome;
❹ dishes

DOLGELLAU, # Dolmelynllyn Hall

The Victorian-style furnishings of the panelled dining room suit the Gothic look of the house. The cooking, however, has a more up-to-date air with dishes such as seared cutlet of tuna on spicy lentils and lime, coriander butter, or pot-roasted loin of pork with a celeriac and chive rösti. The wine list includes a good choice of organic wines.

Smoking: No smoking establishment
Accommodation: 10 en suite
Credit cards: ▪▪ ▪▪ ▪▪ ▪▪

Directions: Village centre on the A470, 4 miles N of Dolgellau

Ganllwyd LL40 2HP
Map 6: SH71
Tel/Fax: 01341 440273
Chef: Joanna Reddicliffe
Owners: Jonathan Barkwith,
Joanna Reddicliffe
Cost: Fixed-price D £23.50. ☺
H/wine £10.
Times: Last L 2pm/D 9pm
Closed L Sun, Dec, Jan, Feb
Additional: Bar Food L;
No children under 6; ❹ dishes

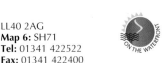

DOLGELLAU, # Dolserau Hall ✿

Fine Victorian country house with grounds sweeping down to the River Wnion. The restaurant, in the former Victorian conservatory, offers farmhouse vegetable soup, traditional roast leg of lamb with mint sauce and the roast gravy, or fresh grilled trout with lemon caper sauce, and chocolate rum and raisin trifle for dessert.

Accommodation: 15 en suite
Credit cards: ▪▪ ▪▪ ▪▪ ▪▪

Directions: Situated 1.5 miles from Dolgellau on lane between A470 to Dinas Mawddwy and A494 to Bala

LL40 2AG
Map 6: SH71
Tel: 01341 422522
Fax: 01341 422400
Chef: Huw Roberts
Owners: Marion and Peter Kaye
Cost: Fixed-price D £18.50. ☺
Times: D only, 7pm-8.30pm.
Additional: No children under 6;
❹ dishes
Smoking: No smoking in dining rom

DOLGELLAU,
Penmaenuchaf Hall Hotel ✿✿

At the foot of Cader Idris, the fine country mansion stands in 21 acres of mature woodland. Originally the summer and sporting residence of a Lancashire cotton magnate, it has several miles of private fishing, plus its own snooker room. The oak-panelled dining room has ample-sized high-backed tapestry chairs, an open fire and a grand piano. Dishes use good quality local and home-grown produce, and there is an emphasis on light, well-flavoured combinations. Caramelised breast of duck is carved onto a pear purée with red cabbage and a five spice scented jus, for example, whilst corn-fed chicken is studded with scallops then braised in lobster oil and served with tender young vegetables. Braised Welsh oxtail is

Penmaenpool LL40 1YB
Map 6: SH71
Tel/Fax: 01341 422129
Chefs: Hugh Cocker, Carl Ellis
Owners: Mark Watson, Lorraine Fielding
Cost: *Alc* £31, fixed-price L £14.95/D £25 (4 courses). H/wine £12
Times: Noon-last L 2pm/7pm-last D 9.30pm. Closed 6-16 Jan
Additional: Sunday L;
No children under 8; ❹ dishes
Seats: 40. Private dining room 16
Smoking: No smoking in dining room

Penmaenuchaf Hall Hotel

Accommodation: 14 en suite
Credit cards: ▦ ▦ ▦ ▦ ▦ ▦

given a more robust treatment with creamy parsnip mash, Madeira and pan-seared foie gras. Follow this with either a hot apple pudding served with rhubarb and vanilla ice cream or a selection of Welsh farmhouse cheeses with home-made soda bread.

Directions: From A470, take A493 (Tywyn/Fairbourne), entrance 1.5 miles on L by sign for Penmaenpool

HARLECH, Castle Cottage ✿✿

The stone sixteenth-century cottage is full of pigs – china pigs, painted pigs, pigs on napkin rings. And, yes, escalopes of pork, breadcrumbed and flavoured with five spice, served with a black bean sauce, also makes an appearance on the set two or three course dinner menu. The choice is not large, but it changes every week and features local produce whenever possible, perhaps rack of lamb or loin of Brecon venison both matched with parsnip purée and port and redcurrant sauce. Fish is always good – seafood thermidor with a mustard and cheese sauce, and salmon en croûte for main courses, or in the form of soup, either Mediterranean fish soup with rouille or New England-style cockle and prawn chowder. An occasional savoury, such as grilled duck liver on toast, sometimes pops up amongst the sponge puddings, crumbles and home-made ice cream; more surprising, perhaps, is the presence of Welsh haggis with neeps and whisky gravy as a first course. Celtic solidarity runs deep.

Directions: Just off High Street (B4573) 100yds from Harlech Castle

Pen Llech LL46 2YL
Map 6: SH53
Tel/Fax: 01766 780479
Chef: Glyn Roberts
Owners: Mr & Mrs GH Roberts
Cost: Fixed-price D £17.95-£19.95 (2-3 courses). ☺ H/wine £9.
Times: 7pm-last D 9pm. Closed 3 wks Feb
Additional: Sunday L only (12.30pm-last L 2pm); Children welcome; ✿ dishes
Seats: 45
Smoking: No smoking in dining room
Credit cards: ▦ ▦ ▦ ▦ ▦ ▦

LLANBERIS, Y Bistro ✿

Welsh folk music, and a Welsh menu (with English subtitles), set the tone at this pleasant, family-run restaurant with several intimate bar areas and a candlelit restaurant. In season there could be cream of nettle soup, slices of Lleyn Rose beef served with a garlic, mushroom and port wine sauce, and bara brith ice cream.

Smoking: No smoking in dining room
Credit cards: ▦ ▦ ▦ ▦

Directions: In the centre of the village at the foot of Mount Snowdon by Lake Padarn

Glandwr
43-45 Stryd Fawr LL55 4EU
Map 6: SH56
Tel/Fax: 01286 871278
Chefs: Nerys Roberts, Sion Llwyd Elis
Owners: Danny & Nerys Roberts
Cost: Fixed-price D £22.50. ☺ H/wine £8.
Times: D only, 7.30pm-10pm. Closed Sun Bh.
Additional: Children welcome; ✿ dishes

LLANDDEINIOLEN,
Ty'n Rhos Country House

Caernarfon LL53 3AE
Map 6: SH56
Tel: 01248 670489
Fax: 01248 670079
Chefs: Carys Davies, Lynda Kettle, Ian Cashen
Owners: Nigel & Lynda Kettle
Cost: Alc £25, fixed-price D £19.50 (4 courses). ☺ H/wine £5.75.
Times: D only, 7pm-9pm.
Closed D Sun, Mon, 23-31 Dec
Additional: Sunday L (Noon-2.30pm); No children under 6; 🍴 dishes
Smoking: No smoking in dining room
Accommodation: 14 en suite
Credit cards: 🔳🔳🔳🔳🔳

The dining room looks out over rolling countryside, garden and two small lakes. Fresh local ingredients are treated with care with say, seafood and herb ravioli with tomato and brandy chowder followed by roast loin of pork with prune and hazelnut seasoning, meringue roulade and Llanboidy cheese.

Directions: In hamlet of Seion between B4366 & B4547

PENRHYNDEUDRAETH,
The Hotel Portmeirion

Portmeirion LL48 6ET
Map 6: SH53
Tel: 01766 770228
Fax: 01766 771331
Chef: Colin Pritchard
Owner: Portmeirion Ltd
Cost: Fixed-price L £13.50/D £26.50. H/wine £9.50
Times: 12.30pm-last L 1.45pm/D 7pm-last 9.30pm.
Additional: Sunday L; Children welcome; 🍴 dishes
Seats: 100. Private dining room 30
Smoking: No smoking in dining room
Accommodation: 37 en suite
Credit cards: 🔳🔳🔳🔳🔳🔳

The famous Italianate village, created by Sir Clough Williams Ellis, is a private fantasy in which we can all share (graphically demonstrated by the summer daytime crowds). Celebrated guests have included George Bernard Shaw, H.G. Wells, Bertrand Russell and Noël Coward, and Patrick McGoohan found it almost impossible to leave. The curvilinear dining room dates back to the 1930s. Facing onto the estuary, it seems at high tide almost to be afloat; there are few more romantic settings in this country. The menu, written in Welsh and English, changes daily, and each dish is individually cooked to order. Warm salad of smoked mackerel with tomatoes in basil dressing and parfait of duck livers with toasted walnut bread were amongst the starters one April night, followed by a choice of dishes such as pot-roasted guinea fowl with apple, apricots and dill cream sauce, or a trio of local fish with buttered

Directions: Off A487 at Minffordd

cabbage and sticks of fennel. Desserts are equally concisely described and sound equally tempting – apricot mousse between chocolate leaves, or mille-feuille of fresh raspberries.

PWLLHELI, **Plas Bodegroes** 🏵🏵🏵

Plas Bodegroes is a peach of a place. The sizeable Georgian manor stands in its own extensive grounds and gardens and has been meticulously refurbished over the years by Christopher and Gunna Chown. It is a testament to their energy and dedication. Period furnishings have been cleverly and tastefully combined with restful colour schemes in the spacious restaurant, where Scandinavian track lighting and illuminated display cabinets create their own special effects. Chown's fixed-price dinner menus provide variety and choice in abundance without indulging in too much pretension along the way. Descriptions get straight to the heart of the matter: griddled monkfish with tomato and pesto, kebab of Welsh lamb with garlic cream, loin of pork with apple, Calvados and marjoram, and so forth. Other dishes, such as seared salmon wrapped in Carmarthen ham with leeks and laverbread are further reminders that the kitchen keeps faith with the produce of the principality. As a test of Chown's prowess, our inspector chose to begin with smoked haddock and scallop fishcake, which was impeccably presented and served with a piquant tartare sauce. Next, a thinly cut rib-eye steak of Welsh beef was chargrilled, placed on a seared cake of mashed potato and served with a fine oxtail sauce, the flavour of which had been lifted by small pieces of oxtail flesh. To finish, bara brith-and-butter pudding was a neat idea; this came topped with first-class ice cream and surrounded by a moat of sharply flavoured apricot sauce. The wine list is top class and ranges wide, although big stuff from France stands out.

Nefyn Road LL53 5TH
Map 6: SH33
Tel: 01758 612363
Fax: 01758 701247
Chef: Christopher Chown
Owners: Christopher & Gunna Chown
Cost: Fixed-price D £29.50. H/wine £12
Times: D only, 7pm-last D 9.30pm (9pm Sun, low season). Closed Mon
Additional: Sunday L (12.30pm-last L 2pm); No children under 10
Seats: 45. Private dining room 16
Smoking: No smoking in dining room
Accommodation: 11 en suite
Credit cards: ■ ■ ■ 🐾 Ⓒ

Directions: On A497, 1 mile W of Pwllheli

TAL-Y-BONT, **Lodge Hotel** 🏵

Set in a peaceful, beautiful part of the Conwy valley, a welcoming log fire burns in the bar whilst visitors study the daily changing menu. Much produce derives from the hotel's own fruit and vegetable gardens. Try chicken and duck liver pâté, pan-fried lamb's liver with Madeira sauce and blackcurrant fool.

Smoking: No smoking in dining room
Accommodation: 10 en suite. **Credit cards:** ■ ■ 🐾 Ⓒ

Directions: From Conwy Castle take B5106 to village of Tal-y-Bont. The Lodge is on R, 100yds into village

Conwy LL32 8YX
Map 6: SH76
Tel: 01492 660534
Fax: 01492 660766
Chef: Simon Baldon
Owners: Simon & Barbara Baldon
Cost: Alc £15, fixed-price L £6.25/D £14.95. ☺ H/wine £9.
Times: Last L 1.30pm/last D 8.30pm. Closed L Mon
Additional: Sunday L; Children welcome; 🍴 dishes

TAL-Y-LLYN, **Minffordd Hotel** 🏵

Nestling beneath Cader Idris amid spectacular countryside, this comfortably upgraded 300-year-old drovers inn produces enjoyable food cooked by owner/chef Mark Warner. A typical meal may feature tomato and rosemary soup, loin of lamb with port and redcurrant sauce, followed by chilled orange and Cointreau soufflé.

Smoking: No smoking in dining room
Accommodation: 6 en suite. **Credit cards:** ■ ■ 🐾

Directions: Take A470 from Dolgellan, and turn R onto A487 – hotel is at the junction of that road with the B4405

Tywyn LL36 9AJ
Map 6: SH70
Tel: 01654 761665
Fax: 01654 761517
Chef: Mark Warner
Owners: Mary McQuillan, Mark Warner
Cost: Fixed-price D £18.95. ☺ H/wine £8.45.
Times: D only at 8pm. Closed Dec-Feb
Additional: No children under 5

TALSARNAU,
Hotel Maes y Neuadd ❀❀❀

Maes y Neuadd started life in the fourteenth-century as a manor house – a granite edifice with walls five feet thick in places, and set in grounds that overlook Snowdonia National Park and the Tremadoc Bay. It is now house and home to the Horsfall and Slatter families who have been running the place in tandem for more than 15 years. When the weather closes in a fire blazes in the gracious Georgian dining room. Chef Peter Jackson makes admirable use of fresh local and Welsh produce and stocks his larder with curly kale, sewin, laverbread, wild fungi and much more besides. This is bolstered by industrious domestic enterprise, which yields everything from home-baked breads (leek and onion, carrot and herb, for example) to fruit and vegetables harvested from the hotel's extensive gardens. Here is a kitchen that is capable of delivering roast sea bass with olive oil, turbot with lobster sauce, breast of goose with fennel sauerkraut, and Welsh lamb's liver with avocado. What matters is the way ingredients are combined and contrasted with one another. A test meal of delicate marinated salmon with sour cream and a garnish of salad leaves, pumpkin soup and pan-fried fillet of lemon sole with capers and brown butter, also featured medallions of Welsh venison with thyme and field mushrooms, served dramatically with a sprig of smouldering rosemary ('lit up like a joss stick so that its perfume filled the dining room'). Meals always end with, quite literally, a 'grand finale' taking in Welsh cheeses such as Llanboidy, Pantysgawn, Llangloffan and others, plus a brace of desserts like dark chocolate terrine and poached pear in filo pastry with a syrup containing chopped walnuts, sultanas and cherries.

Signature dishes: Goetre chicken with asparagus and curly kale; sewin with a rhubarb and rosemary butter sauce; roast sea bass on a bed of Swiss chard, laverbread and wild mushrooms; potted game with marrow chutney.

Directions: 0.75 mile off B4573 between Talsarnau & Harlech (sign on corner of unclassified road)

Harlech LL47 6YA
Map 6: SH63
Tel: 01766 780200
Fax: 01766 780211
Chef: Peter Jackson
Owners: June & Michael Slatter, Olive & Malcolm Horsfall
Cost: Fixed-price L £12.75 (3 courses)/D £30 (5 courses). ☺
H/wine £9.75.
Times: Noon-last L 1.45pm/7pm-last D 9pm.
Additional: Sunday L; No children under 8; ♨ dishes
Seats: 50. Private dining room 12
Smoking: No smoking in dining room
Accommodation: 16 en suite
Credit cards: ▆ ▆ ▆ ▆ ▆ ▆

MONMOUTHSHIRE

ABERGAVENNY, **Llansantffraed**
Court Hotel ❀❀

NEW

This red-brick country house is the works: 20 acres of extensive grounds, lovely views of the Brecon Beacons, an Italianate interior yet with a wealth of history inherited from its fourteenth-century origins, and service that's a rare, successful mix of the informal and the professional. The kitchen is predominantly French influenced, but not of the heavy sauced variety, more classic techniques and combinations executed with skill and delicacy. An amuse-gueule of local salmon marinated in shallot and lime juice ('a shrewd, sharp and exact appetite whetter') opened an inspection dinner that showed much promise. Pressed terrine of confit duck with foie gras and home-made shallot chutney proved to be of real depth of flavour, the coarse terrine set off by the smooth, rich foie gras.

Llanvihangel Gobion
NP7 9BA
Map 3: SO21
Tel: 01873 840678
Fax: 01873 840674
Chef: Richard Quinney
Owners: Mike & Heather Morgan
Cost: Alc £28.50, fixed-price L £14.50/D £19.50. ☺
H/wine £9.95.
Times: Noon-last L 2pm/7.30pm-last D 9.30pm
Additional: Bar meals; Sunday L; No children under 2; ♨ dishes
Seats: 40. Private dining room 25

Llansantffraed Court Hotel

Smoking: No smoking in dining room
Accommodation: 21 en suite
Credit cards: ▨ ▨ ▨ ▨ ▨ ▨

Braised saddle of rabbit stuffed with prunes and spinach and served with button onions and baby carrots was beautifully judged with intense game flavours. Dessert was a 'wonderful' caramelised rice pudding flavoured with white chocolate and poached summer fruits, supremely light, and topped with a leaf of crisp sugar. The enterprising wine list concentrates on fashionable style from outside France.

Directions: From Abergavenny take B4598 signposted Usk towards Raglan. Stay on this road for 3.5 miles. White gates on L are hotel entrance.

ABERGAVENNY,
Llanwenarth Arms

The bright conservatory restaurant overlooking the River Usk serves good local produce cooked in a straightforward way. Salmon with home-made hollandaise was spot-on for accuracy and flavour. Individual puff pastry pies, roast pheasant and deep-fried battered hake fillets also sound bets. Leave room for the cold lemon soufflé.

Smoking: Air-conditioning
Accommodation: 18 en suite
Credit cards: ▨ ▨ ▨ ▨ ▨ ▨

Directions: On A40 midway between Abergavenny and Crickhowell

Brecon Road NP8 1EP
Map 3: SO21
Tel: 01873 810550
Fax: 01873 811880
Chef: D'Arcy McGregor
Owners: The Llanwenarth Arms Ltd
Cost: *Alc* £19. H/wine £8. ☺
Times: Last L 1.45pm/D 9.45pm
Additional: Bar food; Sunday L;
Children welcome; ✦ dishes

CHEPSTOW, Beaufort Hotel

Coquilles St Jacques thermidor, tournedos Rossini and duck breast with port and red wine sauce are amongst the main courses at this former Georgian coaching inn. The cooking is mostly French in style, but the carte also includes more internationally minded dishes such as Japanese king prawns in filo pastry and chicken jalfrezi.

Additional: Bar food; Sunday L; No children under 10 in restaurant; ✦ dishes
Smoking: No pipes
Accommodation: 20 en suite
Credit cards: ▨ ▨ ▨ ▨ ▨ ▨

Beaufort Square
NP6 5EP
Map 3: ST59
Tel: 01291 622497
Fax: 01291 627389
Chef: Justin Sterry
Owner: Michael Collins
Cost: *Alc* £16, fixed-price L £9/D £13.95. ☺ H/wine £7.50.
Times: Last L 2.15pm/D 9.45pm

Directions: Turn L from A48 immediately before St Mary's Church then L again; car park is at top of Nelson Street

CHEPSTOW,
Marriott St Pierre Hotel ❀

Fourteenth-century manor house offering fine views over the scenic golf course from the Orangery Restaurant. Here, dishes include baked lamb loin with herb mousse, and chargrilled tuna fish niçoise. The alternative Long Weekend brasserie-style restaurant overlooks the swimming pool.

St Pierre Park NP6 6YA
Map 3: ST59
Tel: 01291 625261
Fax: 01291 629975
Chef: Mark Linsey
Cost: *Alc* £25, fixed-price D £20. H/wine £11.50
Times: Last L 1.45pm/D 9.45pm
Additional: Bar Food; Sunday L; Children welcome; ❸ dishes
Smoking: No smoking in dining room; air-conditioning
Accommodation: 148 en suite
Credit cards:

Directions: From M4 J21 take M48 towards Chepstow. Exit at J2 for A466. L at 1st roundabout. Hotel in 2 miles.

LLANDEWI SKIRRID,
Walnut Tree Inn ❀❀❀

Elizabeth David once declared that the Walnut Tree was her favourite restaurant in Britain; inspectors – and almost everyone who has ever stepped over the threshold – tend to agree. What is remarkable is that this is no big-city venue, but an inauspicious country pub. Over the last 34 years Franco and Ann Taruschio have quietly revolutionised the idea of eating out, largely because their philosophy is one of unaffected honesty, unfussy style and flexibility. Service is casual, tables are crammed close together, and the place gets packed, but no one seems to mind because the food is joyous. The menu is hand-written, almost scrawled, with crossings-out and some near-illegible wording, but you can almost feel the energy behind the scenes. The repertoire is ever-changing, although some dishes have become trademarks: the home-cured bresaola, the Llanover salt duck with preserves, the home-made Italian sausages with butter beans, the brodetto (mixed fish casserole). Italy may be in Franco's blood, but he is quite prepared to look elsewhere for a buzz of inspiration. Crispy crab pancakes suggest Thailand, venison pie is surely pure England. Fish is a particular strength, as our inspector discovered when he sampled glorious smoked haddock fishcake with a 'benchmark' lobster bisque and brilliant roast cod fillet wrapped in crisp rösti potato with a simple but quite perfect caponata. A full page is devoted to desserts – Sicilian cheesecake, Toulouse chestnut pudding, strawberry Pavlova and a version of tiramisu that is smooth, rich but full of the delicate flavours of coffee, mascarpone, brandy and cream. The well priced wine list offers good drinking from around the world, with some excellent French and New World wines under £25. However, this is a good opportunity to try something from the vast selection of Italian wines – there are lesser known wines offering good value as well as some rare grape varieties.

Abergavenny NP7 8AW
Map 3: SO31
Tel: 01873 852797
Chef: Franco Taruschio
Owners: Ann & Franco Taruschio
Times: Noon-last L 3pm/7pm-last D 10.30pm. Closed Sun, Mon, 5 days Xmas, 2 wks Feb
Additional: Children welcome; ❸ dishes
Seats: 45 (60 Bistro/Bar)
Smoking: Air-conditioning
Credit cards: None taken

Directions: Three miles N/E of Abergavenny on the B4521

LLANGYBI, Cwrt Bleddyn Hotel ❀❀

An old manor on the Welsh Borders is the setting for some sound cooking. The kitchen visibly works hard to please and when it hits the mark, as in a confit of duck leg with a purée of split peas finished with a sherry vinaigrette, the result is most rewarding. A first course of open lasagne with porcini and baby spinach worked well, but the surprise of the evening was the 'Christmas Pudding Extravaganza '- not least because it was the end of May! A combination of Christmas pudding ice cream, soufflé and baked filo parcel of sweetmeats, it was cooked with care and delicacy, and was a serious match for honours with a trio of Chef's chocolate desserts that included both hot and cold chocolate puddings. Form sometimes triumphs over content as in an assiette of Welsh lamb that looked splendid, comprising a roulade of the loin, liver and cassoulet of kidneys, but the dominant flavour of the offal tended to eclipse that of the lamb.

Usk NP5 1PG
Map 3: SO30
Tel: 01633 450521
Fax: 01633 450220
Chef: Nigel Goodwin
Owner: Virgin Hotels Ltd
Cost: *Alc* £26.50, fixed-price L £16.95/D £24.50 (4 courses). ☺ H/wine £10.50.
Times: 12.30pm-last L 2.30pm/7pm-last D 10pm
Additional: Bar menu; Sunday L; Children welcome; ❹ dishes
Seats: 45. Private dining room 20
Smoking: No smoking in dining room
Accommodation: 36 en suite
Credit cards: ▬ ▦ ▦ ▧

Directions: Near Llangybi village on A449 between Caerleon and Usk

TINTERN, Parva Farmhouse Hotel ❀

There are splendid river views from the windows of this beautifully preserved seventeenth-century farmhouse, a stone's throw from the Wye. On the food front, expect capably prepared dishes such as Stilton and cauliflower soup, baked salmon with coriander and dill, and leg of Welsh lamb with honey and rosemary.

Accommodation: 9 en suite
Credit cards: ▬ ▦ ▦ ▧

Directions: North end of Tintern on A466 alongside the Wye, 0.75 mile from the Abbey

Chepstow NP6 6SQ
Map 3: SO50
Tel: 01291 689411
Fax: 01291 689557
Chef: Dereck Roy Stubbs
Owners: Dereck & Vickie Stubbs
Cost: Fixed-price D £17.50 (4 courses). ☺ H/wine £8.50.
Times: 7pm- 8.30pm. Closed L
Additional: Children welcome; ❹ dishes
Smoking: No smoking in dining room

TINTERN, Royal George ❀

Chepstow NP6 6SF
Map 3: SO50
Tel: 01291 689205
Fax: 01291 689448
Chef: David Parkinson
Owners: Tony & Maureen Pearce
Cost: Fixed-price L £11.95/D £18. ☺ H/wine £7.50.
Times: Last L 2pm/last D 9.30pm
Additional: Bar food; Sunday L; Children welcome; ❹ dishes
Smoking: No smoking in dining room
Accommodation: 19 en suite
Credit cards: ▬ ▦ ▦ ▧ ▨ ▩

Try a taste of Wales whilst looking out at the River Angiddy flowing through the gardens of this old coaching inn. Good local produce includes salmon and lamb, or else there may be roast fillet of Welsh black beef served with Madeira and mushroom sauce, or medallions of pork with white wine, garlic and herb sauce.

Directions: On A466 between Chepstow & Monmouth, 10 minutes' drive from M4 exit 22

USK, **Three Salmons Hotel**

This seventeenth-century coaching inn is well-regarded locally for its ambitious modern cooking. Starters might include smoked salmon with olive ciabatta and ragout of pigeon with artichoke and sage butter. Roast rack of lamb with port wine and figs, and magret of duck with sugared kumquats and soft chestnuts are typical main dishes.

Additional: Sunday L; Bar meals; Children welcome; ⚘ dishes
Smoking: No smoking in dining room; air-conditioning
Accommodation: 24 en suite
Credit cards: ▇ ▇ ▇ ▇ ▇ ▇

Bridge Street NP5 1BQ
Map 3: SO40
Tel: 01291 672133
Fax: 01291 673979
Chef: Martyn Williams
Owners: Kevin & Elaine Burke
Cost: Alc £18, fixed-price L £15.50/D £17.50. ☺ H/wine £9.50.
Times: Last L 2pm/D 9.30pm

Directions: M4/J24, A449 N, first L A472 to Usk. Hotel in centre of village

WHITEBROOK,

Crown at Whitebrook

For a moment, you might think you had stumbled upon a French auberge when you arrive at Roger and Sandra Bates' restaurant-with-rooms in the remote Whitebrook Valley. The welcome is genuinely heartfelt, the atmosphere is one of restorative tranquillity. A glance at the fixed-price dinner menu will reinforce the impression of Frenchness – even if the dishes themselves do not have their roots in the home country. Ingredients are from sound Welsh sources and the quality is generally high, although our inspector was not impressed by a piece of less-than-fresh cod on one occasion. There are, however, plenty of good ideas to consider. Among the starters, you might find scallop mousse wrapped in nori seaweed with chive beurre blanc or a sausage of smoked chicken and mushrooms on Calvados sauce. Main courses tend to favour meat and game: roast loin of venison served with a puff pastry case filled with creamed chestnuts and roasted shallots perhaps, or sautéed breast of Gressingham duck with a pithiviers of its livers on a wild mushroom jus. Vegetables are a harvest festival that impress with their flavour and variety. The line-up might include sugar snap peas, green beans, carrots, broccoli, cauliflower, a parsnip bouchée, dauphinoise, new potatoes. Rounding things off are well-crafted desserts along the lines of plum and almond strudel with crisp, dry filo pastry, tarte Tatin, and white chocolate parfait with bitter chocolate sorbet. A really useful wine list benefits from the tireless and informative annotation of Roger Bates. Coverage is extensive and very well chosen with some truly remarkable pricing. Gaston Hochar's intense Chateau Musar 1989 at £17.95 from Lebanon and the rich, opulent Meerlust Rubicon from South Africa at £19.50 are just two notable examples.

Monmouth NP5 4TX
Map 3: SO50
Tel: 01600 860254
Fax: 01600 860607
Chef: Sandra Bates
Owners: Sandra & Roger Bates
Cost: Fixed-price L £16.95/D £27.95. H/wine 9.95
Times: Noon-last L 1.45pm/7pm-last D 9pm. Closed D Sun, L Mon (non residents), 2 wks Jan, 2 wks Aug
Additional: Bar food L; Sunday L; No children under 12 at D; ⚘ dishes
Seats: 24. Private dining room 12
Smoking: No smoking in dining room
Accommodation: 12 en suite
Credit cards: ▇ ▇ ▇ ▇ ▇ ▇

Directions: Turn W off A66 immediately S of Bigsweir Bridge (5 miles from Monmouth), 2 miles up this unclassified road

NEWPORT

NEWPORT, Celtic Manor Hotel

A large golfing and leisure hotel has grown up around the original, beautifully restored nineteenth-century manor. Hedley's Restaurant is one of several in the hotel, but is the most atmospheric, with fine wood panelling, mouldings and stained-glass windows. Dinner starts with an appetiser, such as a small salmon quiche, and home-made breads include a bara brith. A first-course of terrine of smoked chicken, leeks and Carmarthen ham was very decoratively presented and served with a delicately flavoured chilli mayonnaise. This was followed by an equally stylish looking roast fillet of cod on a bed of langoustine mash with shellfish jus and asparagus. A fine rosemary and raspberry crème brûlée rounded off the meal. A separate cheese menu lists an all-Welsh selection, apart from the statutory Stilton. As well as a *carte* and daily menu, at weekends there is a five-course 'Chef's Concept', for that special blow-out occasion.

Directions: On A48 just off M4/J24 towards Newport

Coldra Woods NP6 2YA
Map 3: ST38
Tel: 01633 413000
Fax: 01633 412910
Chef: Trefor Jones
Owner: Mr T Matthews
Cost: Fixed-price L £14-£16/D £27.95-£30.95. ☺ H/wine £10.25.
Times: Noon-last L 2.30pm/7pm-last D 10.30pm. Closed L Sat, Sun, Bhs
Additional: Children welcome; ❹ dishes
Seats: 58
Smoking: No pipes and cigars
Accommodation: 73 en suite
Credit cards: ■■ ▩ ▩ ▨ ▨ ▧

NEWPORT, Junction 28

Former railway station stylishly converted into a smart, informal restaurant serving straightforward food. Long brasserie-style menu (with an emphasis on fresh fish) yielded pan-fried scallops, bacon and mange-touts with balsamic vinaigrette, tender lamb with garlic cream, and iced vanilla parfait.

Additional: Sunday L; Children welcome; ❹ dishes
Smoking: No-smoking area; air-conditioning
Credit cards: ■■ ▩ ▨ ▧

Directions: M4 (junction 28), follow signs Risca, then L in 1/2m signed Caerphilly. Turn R at mini-roundabout, then 1st left beyond St Basil's church.

NEW

Station Approach
Bassaleg NP1 9LD
Map 3: ST 38
Tel: 01633 891891
Chef: Jon West
Owners: Richard Wallace, Jon West
Cost: *Alc* £19.50, fixed-price D £11.95. ☺ H/wine £8.95.
Times: Last L 2pm/D 9.30pm. Closed D Sun

PEMBROKESHIRE

FISHGUARD, Tregynon Country Farmhouse Hotel

A sixteenth-century farmhouse set deep in the beautiful Gwaun Valley. The place enjoys such peaceful isolation that few, other than residents, dine here. It is well worth making the effort to eat here. The set price menu changes daily and continues to offer very good food, made from the best wholefood and organic produce. Typical starters include grilled goat's cheese muffins with four-leaf salad, gently baked pasta shells topped with local Llangloffan cheese, and home-made soup of the day – perhaps cream of Stilton and watercress or

Gwaun Valley SA65 9TU
Map 2: SM93
Tel: 01239 820531
Fax: 01239 820808
Chefs: Jane Heard, Sian Davies, Peter Heard
Owners: Jane & Peter Heard
Cost: *Alc* £19.95, fixed-price D £17.95. ☺ H/wine £9.90.
Times: L by arrangement, 7.30pm-last D 8.30pm (must book)

carrot and lentil. Main courses range from Preseli lamb cutlets with orange and mint sauce, to sweet red peppers oven-baked with a ground almond and red wine stuffing. The hotel has been carefully converted, with log fires burning in the inglenook fireplaces when required. A traditional smokehouse is still used to cure the restaurant's gammon and bacon.

Directions: At intersection of B4313/B4329 take the former towards Fishguard. Take 1st R and 1st R again and follow signs

Additional: No children under 8; dishes
Seats: 28. Private dining room 12
Smoking: No smoking in dining room
Accommodation: 8 en suite
Credit cards:

PEMBROKE, Court Hotel ✿

Lamphey SA71 5NT
Map 2: SM90
Tel: 01646 672273
Fax: 01646 672480
Chef: Michael Lewis
Owner: A W & F T Lain
Cost: H/wine £8.95. ☺
Times: Last L 2pm/D 9.45pm
Additional: Bar food; Sunday L; Children welcome; ◑ dishes
Smoking: No smoking in dining room.
Accommodation: 37 en suite
Credit cards:

Local produce features strongly on the menu at this elegant Georgian hotel. Teifi salmon may be steamed and garnished with asparagus spears, white wine and dill sauce, and chargrilled noisettes of Preseli lamb served with a port-wine glaze flavoured with rosemary and orange. Special dietary requirements are available on request.

Directions: Hotel signed in Lamphey

ST DAVID'S,
Morgan's Brasserie ✿✿ NEW

20 Nun Street SA62 6NT
Map 2: SM72
Tel: 01437 720508
Chef: Ceri Morgan
Owners: Ceri & Elaine Morgan
Cost: Alc £21. H/wine £8.75.
Times: D only, 6pm-9pm, May-Sept. Closed Sun, Jan/Feb (restricted winter opening times).
Additional: Children welcome; ◑ dishes
Seats: 36
Smoking: No smoking in dining room; air-conditioning
Credit cards:

Opened in 1993, this tasteful little brasserie does a good service to the citizens of St David's. Mrs Morgan runs front of house with the help of young staff, while her husband holds the reins in the kitchen. Fresh fish and seasonal Welsh ingredients are a strong suit on the *carte* and the daily specials board: crab and parsley soup makes a distinctly flavoured starter, fleshy fillet of plaice is stuffed with prawn and laverbread mousse, fillet of sewin might be baked with Penclawydd cockles. Alternatives surface in the shape of confit of guinea fowl with orange and lime conserve, chicken saltimbocca and roast loin of Welsh lamb scented with garlic and rosemary. Crème brûlée is a rich, creamy version, otherwise finish with damson sorbet or strawberry mille-feuille. Around three dozen affordable wines are drawn from growers around the world.

Directions: 60yds off Cross Square

ST DAVID'S, St Non's Hotel

Well-presented, freshly cooked food at this cheerful hotel. Expect tempura prawns with honey and oyster sauce, whole boneless chicken stuffed with sweetcorn, garlic and herb stuffing on a red wine sauce, and tuile basket filled with raspberry cranachan with mango coulis amongst the choices.

Smoking: No smoking in dining room
Accommodation: 22 en suite. **Credit cards:** ▬ ▬ ▅ ▢

Directions: Close to Cathedral and St Non's Retreat

Catherine Street SA62 6RJ
Map 2: SM72
Tel: 01437 720239
Fax: 01437 721839
Chef: Karl Westoby
Owner: Peter Trier
Cost: Fixed-price D £19.50. ☺
H/wine £9.
Times: Last L 2pm/last D 8.30pm.
Closed Dec
Additional: Bar meals;
Children welcome; ♨ dishes

ST DAVID'S,
Warpool Court Hotel ❀❀

Inspectors continue to endorse this fine Victorian hotel overlooking St Brides Bay; it was once the cathedral choir school. Much is made of the kitchen's cooking which makes use of local fish, Welsh lamb and game. A fixed-price daily menu offers the likes of grilled duck breast with vinaigrette leeks and salad leaves, or home-smoked salmon glazed with chive sabayon, an interim sorbet, then perhaps seabass with basil, sun-dried tomatoes and olives, or slices of best end of lamb fried with tomato, olives and truffle oil, a sound selection of al dente vegetables, and a rich bread and butter pudding or Welsh cheeses to finish. Canapés and petit fours are made on the premises.

Directions: From Cross Square, left by Midland Bank into Goat St, at fork follow hotel signs.

SA62 6BN
Map 2: SM72
Tel: 01437 720300
Fax: 01437 720676
Chef: John Daniels
Owner: Peter Trier
Cost: Fixed-price L £18.95 (3 courses)/D £32.50 (4 courses). ☺
H/wine £9.50.
Times: Noon-last L 2pm/7pm-last D 9.15pm. Closed Jan
Additional: Bar food; Sunday lunch; Children welcome; ♨ dishes
Seats: 50. Private dining room 24
Smoking: No smoking in dining room
Accommodation: 25 en suite
Credit cards: ▬ ▬ ▬ ▅ ▣ ▢

TENBY, Atlantic Hotel ❀

Family-run hotel situated above South Beach, with views over the sea to Caldey Island. Restaurant menus offer sound cooking in the shape of stir-fried chicken livers in Stilton sauce, grilled Dover sole with dill and white wine, beef Stroganoff and treacle pudding. Light meals are also served in the basement bistro.

Accommodation: 42 en suite. **Credit cards:** ▬ ▬ ▬ ▅ ▢

Directions: Town centre, halfway along Esplanade on R

Esplanade SA70 7DU
Map 2: SN10
Tel: 01834 842881/844176 ext 256
Chef: Julian Rees
Owners: Mr & Mrs W James
Cost: Fixed-price D £18 (4 courses).
☺ H/wine £7.95.
Additional: All day bistro;
Children welcome; ♨ dishes
Smoking: Air-conditioning

TENBY, Penally Abbey ❀❀

Penally Abbey is the works: a Gothic-style, stone built mansion hard by the village green and church, with a ruined chapel, the last surviving link with a monastic past. The interior is stylish, and the magnificent five acres of gardens overlook the sea. The cooking hits a modern mark with dishes such as devilled Pembrokeshire crab, herring fillets in lime and coriander, Welsh lamb with redcurrants, rosemary and red wine, or grilled fillet of cod with coconut cream. Puddings take in the nursery comforts of apple and bramble crumble; as well as the more sophisticated luxury bread-and-butter pudding made with double cream and sherry, and meringues with strawberry coulis.

Directions: From Tenby take A4139 to Penally

Penally SA70 7PY
Map 2: SN10
Tel: 01834 843033
Fax: 01834 844714
Chef: Mrs E Warren
Owners: Mr & Mrs ST Warren
Cost: *Alc* £24.50, fixed-price L £16/D £24.50 (4 courses). ☺ H/wine £10.95.
Times: Noon-last L 1.45pm/7.30pm-last D 9pm
Additional: Sunday L (reservations only); No children under 7; ♨ dishes
Seats: 44. Private dining room 16
Smoking: No smoking in dining room
Accommodation: 12 en suite
Credit cards: ▬ ▬ ▬ ▅ ▢

WOLF'S CASTLE,
Wolfscastle Country Hotel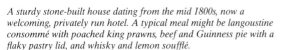

SA62 5LZ
Map 2: SM92
Tel: 01437 741225/741688
Fax: 01437 741383
Chef: Steve Brown
Owner: Mr A Stirling
Cost: H/wine £6.95. ☺
Times: Last L 2pm/D 9pm.
Closed D Sun, 24-27 Dec
Additional: Sunday L; Bar meals;
Children welcome; ⑨ dishes

A sturdy stone-built house dating from the mid 1800s, now a welcoming, privately run hotel. A typical meal might be langoustine consommé with poached king prawns, beef and Guinness pie with a flaky pastry lid, and whisky and lemon soufflé.

Smoking: No smoking in dining room
Accommodation: 20 en suite
Credit cards: ▆ ▆ ▆ ▆ ▆

Directions: On A40, in centre of village

POWYS

BUILTH WELLS,
Caer Beris Manor Hotel

LD2 3NP
Map 3: SO05
Tel: 01982 552601
Fax: 01982 552586
Chef: John Ainsworth
Owners: Peter & Katherine Smith
Cost: Fixed-price D £19.95. ☺
H/wine £8.95.
Times: Last L 2.30pm D 9.30pm
Additional: Sunday L; Bar meals;
Children welcome; ⑨ dishes
Smoking: No smoking in dining room

Rambling country house with Elizabethan charm, set in extensive grounds close to the River Irfon. A sample meal may include rabbit terrine with red onion marmalade, followed perhaps by lamb with grilled polenta and wild mushrooms, and apple and blackberry crumble.

Accommodation: 22 en suite
Credit cards: ▆ ▆ ▆ ▆ ▆ ▆

Directions: Off A483 on W side of town

CRICKHOWELL, **Bear Hotel**

NP8 1BW
Map 3: SO21
Tel: 01873 810408
Fax: 01873 811696
Chef: Daren Bridge
Owners: Mrs JL Hindmarsh,
Mrs S Hindmarsh
Cost: Alc £22. H/wine £7.95. ☺
Times: 11am-last L 2pm/7pm-last D
9.30pm. Closed D Sun, 25 Dec

More than six centuries old and still very much the hub of life in Crickhowell, this venerable coaching inn is justly proud of its modest roots. There are no swathes of landscaped parkland, just a little country garden where guests can relax. Flowers and hanging baskets grace the frontage, while the bars are bedecked with beams, plates and tankards. Local produce is used to telling effect for a bar menu that roams far and wide, taking in baked salmon with a pesto crust, wild rabbit casserole, and chicken curry, as well as Welsh rarebit with dry-cured bacon. Full meals in the two dining rooms move up a gear for roast breast of local goose with Chinese spices, parsley noodles and plum sauce, or chargrilled tuna on a bed of fine beans with tomato and olive oil fondue. Desserts range from apple and whimberry pie to vanilla cream mousse with poached pears. Eight house wines are served by the glass and the list is a good-value slate.

Directions: Town centre off the A40

Additional: Bar food; Sunday L; Children welcome; 🍴 dishes
Seats: 60. Private dining room 30-60
Smoking: No-smoking area; no pipes or cigars in dining room
Accommodation: 36 en suite
Credit cards:

CRICKHOWELL, Dragon Hotel ✿

Christine and Alan Thomas have been in residence at this eighteenth-century inn for almost two decades, and they continue to flourish. The bar is all beams and flagged floors and the cottagey theme continues in the restaurant. Salmon and scallop tagliatelle, Black Welsh sirloin steak and venison with black pudding and red wine are typical of the menu.

Accommodation: 14 en suite. **Credit cards:** ▬ ▬ ▬ ▬ ▭

Directions: Turn L in centre of town by monument. Hotel 100m on L

High Street NP8 1BE
Map 3: SO21
Tel: 01873 810362
Fax: 01873 811868
Chefs: Alan Thomas, Angela Edmunds
Owners: Alan & Christine Thomas
Cost: Alc £16.95. ☺ Fixed-price D £15.95 (3 courses). H/wine £7.95.
Times: Last L 2pm/last D 8.30pm
Additional: Sunday L; Bar meals; 🍴 dishes
Smoking: No smoking in dining room

CRICKHOWELL, Gliffaes Hotel ✿✿

NP8 1RH
Map 3: SO21
Tel: 01874 730371
Fax: 01874 730463
Chef: Mark Coulton
Owner: John, Nick & Peta Brabner
Cost: D £20.95 (4 courses). ☺ H/wine £9.50.
Times: 12.30pm-last L 2pm/7.30pm-last D 9.15pm
Additional: Bar Food L; Sunday L; Children welcome; 🍴 menu
Seats: 70. Private dining room 40. Jacket and tie preferred
Smoking: No smoking in dining room
Accommodation: 22 en suite
Credit cards: ▬ ▬ ▬ ▭

The River Usk runs through the magnificent grounds and gardens that surround this eighteenth-century Italianate house. Trout and salmon fishing is available for those who fancy trying their luck, there are waterside views from the terrace and the Brecon Beacons National Park provides an awesome backdrop. Dinner is a daily fixed-price menu that sounds a contemporary note. Oak-roasted salmon is served on thinly sliced fennel with basil scented tomatoes, while chicken livers and bacon are accompanied by pickled vegetables. Among the main courses you might find seared cod on bubble-and-squeak, home-cured pork braised with fresh herbs, tomato and garlic served with couscous or the dish that our inspector sampled – full flavoured chicken breast with a sauce containing Jerusalem artichokes and wild mushrooms. Desserts range from tiramisu to French apple tart, and the selection of British farmhouse cheeses is a good one. The wine list has been expertly selected by John Harvey & Sons.

Directions: 1 mile off A40, 2.5 miles W of Crickhowell

HAY-ON-WYE, Kilverts Hotel

Lively town centre hotel converted from a Victorian house. Enjoyable cooking uses good quality fresh produce. Look out for daily blackboard specials and robust, simple dishes such as sautéed laverbread with bacon and cockles on toast, and braised shank of lamb with root vegetables; save room for the tarte au citron.

Additional: Bar meals; Sunday L (winter only); Children welcome; ◐ dishes
Accommodation: 11 en suite
Credit cards: ▨ ▨ ▨ ▨ ▨

Directions: Centrally placed in Hay

The Bull Ring HR3 5AG
Map 3: SO24
Tel: 01497 821042
Fax: 01497 821580
Chef/Owner: Colin Thomson
Cost: Alc £17. H/wine £8.50. ☺
Times: Last L 2pm/last D 9.30pm. Closed 25 Dec

HAY-ON-WYE,
Old Black Lion

26 Lion Street HR3 5AD
Map 3: SO24
Tel: 01497 820841
Chefs: John Morgan, Peter Bridges
Owners: John & Joan Collins
Cost: Alc £19. H/wine £7.60. ☺
Times: Noon-last L 2.30pm/7pm-last D 9.30pm
Additional: Bar food; Sunday lunch; No children under 5; ◐ dishes
Seats: 24.
Smoking: No smoking in dining room
Accommodation: 10 en suite
Credit cards: ▨ ▨ ▨

Low ceilings and abundant exposed beams, complete with a 'lovely creaky feel' testify to the fact that the former coaching inn is very old – fourteenth century to be precise – and the character has been carefully retained. Dinner in the candlelit Cromwell Restaurant (named after Oliver Cromwell who occupied the place whilst besieging a nearby castle) reveals a kitchen aware of modern trends, offering the likes of ravioli of crab with ginger and coriander, and ragout of chicken with mussels in an aniseed and basil sauce, but also looks to traditional Welsh cooking for Glamorgan sausages and laverbread with cockles. Fish appears in the guise of fresh lobster plainly grilled or Thermidor, baked wing of Cornish skate, or in more complicated dishes such as parcels of lemon sole filled with a smoked salmon mousse or panache of fish served with a herb butter and puff pastry. There is an extensive range of bar meals and snacks.

Directions: Town centre, 100 yards from junction of Brecon Road & Oxford Road

HAY-ON-WYE,
The Swan-at-Hay Hotel

Fine old house dating from 1821 with views onto pretty gardens from the restaurant. Popular options include moules marinière, local

Church Street HR3 5DQ
Map 3: SO24
Tel: 01497 821188
Fax: 01497 821424

The Swan-at-Hay Hotel

Chef: Nathan Millikin
Owners: Colin & Rosemary Vaughan
Cost: *Alc* £22.50. Fixed-price D
£18.50 (3 courses). ☺ H/wine £8.75.
Times: Last L 2pm/D 9.30pm
Additional: Bar food; Sunday lunch;
Children welcome; ❸ dishes
Seats: 40. Private dining room 20.
Jacket and tie preferred
Smoking: No pipes and cigars in
dining room
Accommodation: 19 en suite
Credit cards: 🔲 🔲 🔲 🔲 🔲 🔲

brown trout with horseradish sauce, Welsh Black fillet steak with
creamy pepper sauce, and tournedos of venison with a red wine and
fresh coriander sauce. Decent wine list.

Directions: From Hereford enter town, follow Brecon sign, hotel
on right

KNIGHTON,
Milebrook House Hotel ✿

Milebrook LD7 1LT
Map 7: SO27
Tel: 01547 528632
Fax: 01547 520509
Chef: Beryl Marsden
Owners: Rodney & Beryl Marsden
Cost: *Alc* £18.80, fixed-price L
£10.95/D £17.50. ☺ H/wine £9.40.
Times: Last L 1.30pm/D 8.30pm.
Closed Sun D, Mon
Additional: Sunday L; Bar meals; No
children under 6; ❸ dishes
Smoking: No smoking in dining room
Accommodation: 10 en suite
Credit cards: 🔲 🔲 🔲 🔲 🔲

Delightful eighteenth-century Dower house whose kitchen garden
supplies much of the restaurant's herbs and vegetables. The
imaginative set-price menus feature sound cooking: casserole of
Welsh lamb with ginger and almonds, prime rump steak with garlic
butter and poached lemon sole with cheese sauce.

Directions: 2 miles E of Knighton on A4113 (Ludlow)

LLANFYLLIN, Seeds

In between courses at this cosy, slate-floored restaurant, guests can
amuse themselves with the puzzles and games on each of the six pine
tables. The good-value set menu includes garlic snails, roast rack of
Welsh lamb with Dijon and herb crust, pan-seared tuna with tomato
and courgette salsa, and treacle tart and cream.

Additional: Bar food L; Sunday L; Children welcome; ❸ dishes
Smoking: No smoking in dining room. **Credit cards:** 🔲 🔲 🔲

Directions: Village centre, on A490 13 miles from Welshpool

5 Penbryn Cottages
High Street SY22 5AP
Map 7: SJ11
Tel: 01691 648604
Chef: Mark Seager
Owners: Felicity & Mark Seager
Cost: Fixed-price D £17.50. ☺
H/wine £8.95.
Times: Last L 2pm/D 9pm(9.30pm
Sat). Closed D Sun (Mon in winter),
3 wks Jan/Feb

LLANGAMMARCH WELLS,

Lake Country House

LD4 4BS
Map 3: SN94
Tel: 01591 620202
Fax: 01591 620457

Chef: Richard Arnold

Owners: Mr & Mrs J P Mifsud
Cost: Fixed-price D £27.50 (5
courses) H/wine £9.75. ☺
Times: 12.30pm-last L
1.45pm/7.30pm-last D 8.45pm
Additional: Bar food L; Sunday L; No
children under 7; ❹ dishes.
Seats: 70. Jacket and tie preferred
Smoking: No smoking in dining room
Accommodation: 19 en suite.
Credit cards: ▨ ▨ ▨ ▨ ▣ ▢

Surrounded by beautiful countryside, with paths leading round
a lake and a well-stocked river running through the grounds,
this hotel is perfect for any lover of the great outdoors. But
every comfort inside the Victorian house ensures that a stay
here is a special experience, even for lounge lizards. The
cooking is sensitive and accomplished, and ingredients are of
an impressively high quality. A fillet of Welsh venison, for
example, was tender and full of flavour, cooked pink and
served with champ, onion confit, crunchy carrots and a rich
Puy lentil ragout. The set dinner menu changes daily and
includes plenty of choice apart from the initial soup course.
Typically, mussel, pepper and rosemary soup might be followed
by cannelloni of their own hot-smoked salmon or pan-fried
breasts of pigeon with a leaf and herb salad. Main courses also
have a lavish air – breast of chicken comes filled with a
mousseline of cheese and herbs with a cream sauce, and an
assiette of sea fish is cooked en papillote with plum tomato
fillets, basil and roasted red onions. Layered chocolate crème
brûlée with oranges and Grand Marnier and deep-fried toffee
ice-cream with hot fudge sauce compete past the finishing post.
An extensive list offers over 300 wines including some serious
first growths.

Directions: A483 from Garth, turn L for Llangammarch Wells &
follow signs to hotel

LLANWYDDYN,

Lake Vyrnwy Hotel ❀❀

The setting is a stunner. Built in the 1800s, around the same
time as the renowned dam nearby, this hotel stands proud on
the slopes of the Berwyn Mountains surrounded by the 26,000
Vyrnwy Estate. No wonder it is a magnet for fishermen,
walkers, and bird watchers. Much produce comes from the
hotel garden, the lake and the estate, and the kitchen goes
about its business with single-minded industry: four kinds of
breads are baked on the premises, salmon is home-smoked and
the larder shelves are stocked with all kinds of home-made
preserves. A test meal began with rich cream of mushroom,
courgette and toasted hazelnut soup, before pot-roast leg of
Welsh lamb served on Savoy cabbage with a timbale of pearl

Lake Vyrnwy SY10 0LY
Map 6: SJ01
Tel: 01691 870692
Fax: 01691 870259
Chef: Andrew Wood
Owner: Market Glen Ltd
Cost: Fixed-price L £15.95/D £25.50.
H/wine £9.95
Times: 12.30pm-last L
1.45pm/7.30pm-last D 9.15pm
Additional: Bar food; Sunday L;
Children welcome; ❹ dishes
Seats: 70. Private dining room 120
Smoking: No smoking in dining room

Lake Vyrnwy Hotel

Accommodation: 35 en suite
Credit cards: ▨ ▨ ▨ ▨ ▨ ▨

barley, mushroom and onion plus a decent red wine sauce. For dessert, there was Welsh whisky and orange sponge pudding topped with a dollop of marmalade.

Directions: Follow Tourist signs on A495/B4393, 200 yards past dam at Lake Vyrnwy

LLANWRTYD WELLS,
Carlton House ❀❀❀

Mary Ann Gilchrist makes a wickedly good chocolate and Tia Maria ice-cream, but her reputation and passion for cooking are based on far more than that. Unfortunately, the word seems not to have spread locally, and most of the diners at this small, family hotel are either residents or visitors. Mary Ann runs the show single-handedly, which she does exceptionally well, and offers a daily-changing set price and 'Epicurean' menu, both based on high quality local produce. The former might consist of seared salmon trout with a chive and horseradish cream, followed by carrot and lentil soup, pan-fried breast of chicken with lime, lemongrass, ginger, coriander and coconut cream accompanied by rice noodles and sugarsnap peas, and either lemon syllabub or Welsh and border cheeses. The 'Epicurean' menu (either three or four courses), as chosen by our inspector, started with a fan of fresh pear with tarragon cream sauce, followed by roast fillet of salmon topped with pesto and served with a mild tomato coulis. Superb cannon of Welsh lamb (from the butchers opposite, and hung for five days) was pink, juicy and simply cooked with a crust of laverbread and oatmeal. The indefatigable Mary Ann also makes her own olive oil ciabatta bread, canapés and chocolate petits fours.
   Signature dishes: Roast cannon of Welsh lamb in a laverbread and oatmeal crust with baby leeks, mashed potatoes and mustard sauce; seared fillet of sewin with an avocado salsa, new potatoes and a salad of mixed leaves; roast partridge on Savoy cabbage with bacon, fondant potato and bramble and red wine sauce; pan-fried fillet of Welsh black beef, potato pancake, spinach and wild mushroom and Madeira sauce.

Directions: In the town centre

Dolycoed Road LD5 4RA
Map 3: SN84
Tel: 01591 610248
Fax: 01591 610242
Chef: Mary Ann Gilchrist
Owners: Alan & Mary Ann Gilchrist
Cost: Fixed-price D £19.50
(4 courses). ☺ H/wine £9.50.
Times: D only, 7pm-8.30pm.
Closed Xmas
Additional: No children under 9
Seats: 14
Smoking: No smoking in dining room
Accommodation: 7 rooms
(5 en suite)
Credit cards: ▨ ▨

LLYSWEN, Griffin Inn ⊛

Local fish and game dominate the menu at this atmospheric fifteenth-century sporting inn near the River Wye. Robust country dishes such as ragout of venison with claret, rabbit pie and hot-smoked salmon with Glanwye sauce line up alongside more up-beat ideas like deep-fried cockles with salsa and laverbread. Decent wines by the glass and real ales.

Accommodation: 7 en suite
Credit cards: ▬ ▦ ▨ ▚ ▣ ₵

Directions: On A470 in village

Brecon LD3 0UR
Map 3: SO13
Tel: 01874 754241
Fax: 01874 754592
Chef/Owner: Richard Stockton
Cost: *Alc* £18.50, fixed-price D £15
(3 courses). ☺ H/wine £8.75.
Times: Last L 2pm/D 9pm.
Closed D Sun, Dec 25-26
Additional: Bar food; Sunday L;
Children welcome; ◑ dishes
Smoking: No smoking in dining room

LLYSWEN, Llangoed Hall ⊛⊛⊛

Some famous names have been associated with this largely Edwardian manor house: the building was refurbished by Clough Williams Ellis (of Portmeirion fame) and the current owner is Sir Bernard Ashley (husband of the late Laura). Not surprisingly his personal preferences and tastes define the decor: a plethora of antiques and all kinds of railway ephemera are bolstered by a collection of original paintings that would warrant a catalogue. The elegant restaurant extends into the Whistler Room which, as the name suggests, is devoted to works by the artist. Imaginative use of local ingredients and a persuasive youthful spirit sum up Ben Davies' cooking and it's not difficult to spot both Mediterranean and provençale influences on his *carte* and four-course *table d'hôte*. Our inspector's taste buds were sharpened up by a perfectly judged little appetiser of marinated salmon with a sprightly lemon and coriander dressing before rose-tinted 'veal-like' fillet of tuna loin on a crab and herb risotto with tomato and chive oil. Main courses range from calves' liver with Parma ham, olive potatoes and sage sauce to tournedos of salmon on a panaché of root vegetables with citrus butter sauce, although 'unusually moist' chicken breast with a foie gras mousse wrapped in crisp potato with a daringly intense chicken and herb sauce passed the test with flying colours. As a finale, a beautifully composed hazelnut soufflé was presented with a nugget of coffee and walnut ice cream fashioned into an autumnal nut set in leaves of golden brown tuile. Service is smartly uniformed, attentive and knowledgeable.

On the wine list the Cellarman's Choice offers 10 wines ranging from £13.50 to £34, with over 20 halves including some good New World wines. New World bottles take in America,

Brecon LD3 0YP
Map 3: SO13
Tel: 01874 754525
Fax: 01874 754545
Chef: Ben Davies
Owner: Sir Bernard Ashley
Cost: *Alc* £38, fixed-price L £17/D
£29.50 (4 courses)
Times: 12.15pm-last L 2pm/7.15pm-
last D 9.30pm
Additional: Sunday L;
No children under 8; ◑ dishes
Seats: 40. Private dining room 16 +
50. Jacket & tie preferred
Smoking: No smoking in dining room
Accommodation: 23 en suite
Credit cards: ▬ ▦ ▨ ▚ ▣ ₵

Directions: On A470, 2 miles from
Llyswen heading towards Builth Wells

Australia, Chile, New Zealand, South Africa, Lebanon and Israel – with two white wines from the Yarden Vineyards at £18. Montagny 1er Cru from Louis Latour is good value at £22.

Signature dishes: Fillet of Wye salmon with a saffron and Parmesan risotto and basil dressing; pan-fried queen scallops with Carmarthen ham, baby onions and balsamic dressing; fillet of Welsh Black beef with confit of grilled potato, chargrilled vegetables and red wine jus.

NANT-DDU,

Nant Ddu Lodge Hotel ❀

Fine Georgian house, formerly a shooting lodge. Modern ideas surface in dishes served in the informal bistro – a bright, vibrant room with a lively atmosphere. The chalkboard menu changes daily, but might include blackened fillet of sea bream, and grilled pork steak with cider and apple sauce.

Accommodation: 16 en suite. **Credit cards:**

Directions: 6 miles N of Merthyr Tydfil, and 12 miles S of Brecon on A470

Cwm Taf Nr Merthyr Tydfil
CF48 2HY
Map 3: SO12
Tel: 01685 379111
Fax: 01685 377088
Chef: John McAveney
Owners: Mr & Mrs D Ronson
Cost: *Alc* £16. H/wine £7.95. ☺
Times: Last L 2.30pm/D 9.30pm. Closed D 25-26 Dec
Additional: Bar food; Sunday L; Children welcome; ♨ dishes

NEW RADNOR, **Red Lion Inn** ❀ NEW

An old whitewashed drovers' inn, the Red Lion has an excellent atmosphere and is always busy. Gareth Johns cooks traditional and modern Welsh dishes, with eclectic influences. Expect main courses such as pork scallops with cream and Hen Sîr cheese, roast rump of Radnor lamb, and braised Powys pigeon.

Accommodation: 3 en suite
Credit cards: ▬ ▬ ◥

Directions: Directly road-side on N side of A44, 7 miles E of Crossgates and 3 miles W of New Radnor

Llanfihangel-nant-Melan LD8 2TN
Map 3: SO26
Tel: 01544 350220
Chef: Gareth Johns
Owners: Keith, Elizabeth & Gareth Johns
Cost: *Alc* £15. H/wine £5-£6. ☺
Times: Last L 2pm/D 9pm.
Closed Tue (Nov-Apr), 1 wk Nov, 1 wk Feb
Additional: Sunday L; Bar meals; Children welcome; ♨ dishes
Smoking: No smoking in dining room

THREE COCKS,

Three Cocks Hotel ❀❀

Overlooking the Brecon Beacons, this converted, creeper-clad inn has been dispensing hospitality since the fifteenth century. The building was constructed around a tree which is still visible today, and it also boasts a cobbled courtyard, crooked doorways and mighty oak beams. A brook runs along the edge of the property. Michael and Marie-Jeanne Winstone offer food that often harks back to their Belgian roots – as in mussel soup, Ardennes ham with honey-pickled onions and roast pheasant brabançonne. Michael's fixed-price menus also make good use of local produce: his Welsh lamb (perhaps cooked with herbes de Provence) is not to be missed and you might also find such things as wood mushrooms with sour cream in puff pastry, and loin of Welsh venison with red wine and elderberry sauce. A prodigious line-up of imported Belgian bottled beers provides an alternative to the mainly French wine list.

Directions: In the village of Three Cocks, 4 miles from Hay-on-Wye, 11 miles from Brecon.

Brecon LD3 0SL
Map 3: SO13
Tel/Fax: 01497 847215
Chef: Michael Winstone
Owners: Michael & Marie-Jeanne Winstone
Cost: *Alc* £29, fixed-price L&D £26 (5 courses). ☺ H/wine £8.50
Times: Lunch by prior arrangement/7pm-last D 9pm.
Closed D Tue, Dec & Jan
Additional: Bar food D; Children welcome; ♨ dishes
Seats: 40.
Accommodation: 7 en suite
Credit cards: ▬ ▬

WELSHPOOL,
Edderton Hall Restaurant

There are great views of Powis Castle from the bow windows of this double-fronted Georgian mansion, which has been home to Warren and Evelyn Hawksley for more than eight years. Evelyn is a self-taught cook and her enthusiasm for the craft remains as sharp and as passionate as ever: if the fire is lit in the dining room, for example, you might find her standing in front of the flames, finishing off a joint of local lamb studded with rosemary and garlic. She regularly delves into the Welsh larder for ingredients and ideas – hence potted wild duck and boar with pickles and chutneys, leek and Caerphilly sausage with walnuts, or Langfords Welshpool ham with roast chicory mousse and green sauce. Desserts look to the countryside for that extra dimension: gooseberry fool with elderflowers and strawberries or apple tart with bramble 'snow' are typically seasonal finales. England and Wales both feature on the highly affordable wine list.

Directions: From Welshpool follow A490 towards Churchside and turn right at sign post

Forden SY21 8RZ
Map 7: SJ20
Tel: 01938 580339
Fax: 01938 580452
Chef: Evelyn Hawksley
Owners: Warren & Evelyn Hawksley
Cost: Fixed-price L £10/D £19.95. ☺
H/wine £8.50.
Times: D only, 7.30pm-10.30pm.
Closed D Sun
Additional: Bar food; Sunday L
(12.30pm-2.30pm);
No children under 10; ✦ dishes
Seats: 22. Private dining room 16
Accommodation: 8 en suite
Credit cards: ▬ ▬

WELSHPOOL, **Golfa Hall Hotel**

Country house hotel (with extensive grounds), noted for good, sound cooking. A summer dinner took in home-made cream of mushroom soup, rack of lamb with rosemary and redcurrant essence, with cauliflower, carrots and new potatoes, and crème brûlée.

Accommodation: 15 en suite
Credit cards: ▬ ▬ ▬ ▬ ▣ ▢

Directions: On A458 (Dolgellau), 1.5 miles W of Welshpool on R

Llanfair Road SY21 9AF
Map 7: SJ20
Tel: 01938 553399
Fax: 01938 554777
Chef: Angus Cameron
Owners: Mr & Mrs David Bowen
Cost: Alc £18.45, fixed-price L £16/D £18.45. ☺ H/wine £6.95.
Times: Last L 2pm/last D 9pm
Additional: Bar food; Sunday L;
Children welcome; ✦ dishes
Smoking: No smoking in dining room

RHONDDA CYNON TAFF

MISKIN, **Miskin Manor Hotel**

Built of mellow grey stone, the old manor house is approached by a long drive through its own grounds. Carew oysters, Camarthen

Pendoylan Road Groes Faen
Pontyclun CF72 8ND
Map 3: ST08
Tel: 01443 224204
Fax: 01443 237606
Chef: Tony Kocker
Owners: Miskin Manor
Cost: Alc £21. Fixed-price L £7.95 D £18.95. ☺ H/wine £9.95.
Times: Last L 2pm/D 9.45pm. Closed L Sat, 25 Dec
Additional: Bar food; Sunday L;
Children welcome; ✦ dishes
Smoking: Air-conditioning
Accommodation: 32 en suite
Credit cards: ▬ ▬ ▬ ▬ ▣

smoked duck breast, salmon, game, and Welsh Black beef are amongst the local ingredients used to good effect in dishes such as nage of seafood and fish, and rack of peppered Welsh lamb with dauphinoise potatoes.

Directions: 8 miles W of Cardiff. M4/J34, follow hotel signs

PONTYPRIDD,

Llechwen Hall Hotel ❀

Llanfabon CF37 4HP
Map 3: ST08
Tel: 01443 742050
Fax: 01443 742189
Chef: Louis Huber
Owners: Louis & Helen Huber
Cost: A/c £27.95. Fixed-price L £10.95/D £17.95. ☺ H/wine £7.99.
Times: Last L 2.30pm/D 9.30pm
Additional: Bar food; Sunday L; children welcome; ❹ dishes
Accommodation: 12 en suite
Credit cards: ▩ ▩ ▩ ▩ ▩ ▩

Directions: 1 mile off the A4054 (Cilfynydd) N/E of Pontypridd

A seventeenth-century long house on a hillside. The intimate beamed restaurant is the setting for some robust cooking, perhaps home-made bouillabaisse followed by roast loin of Welsh lamb, rolled in mustard and herbs and served on sweet red onion confit. Brandy and orange pudding is a highly recommended, intensely flavoured dessert.

SWANSEA

LANGLAND, Langland Court ❀

Langland Court Road SA3 4TD
Map 2: SS68
Tel: 01792 361545
Fax: 01792 362302
Chef: Kevin Strangward
Owner: C R Birt
Cost: Fixed-price L £9.75/D £19.95. ☺ H/wine £8.50.
Times: Last L 2pm/last D 9.30pm
Additional: Bar food; Sunday L; Children welcome; ❹ dishes
Smoking: No smoking in dining room
Accommodation: 19 en suite
Credit cards: ▩ ▩ ▩ ▩ ▩

Directions: Take the A4067 Swansea-Mumbles road then the B4593 (Caswell); turn L at St Peter's Church (hotel signed)

Tudor-style Victorian mansion strong on period features, extensive gardens and views over Langland Bay. Good ingredients combine with an obvious high degree of skill and care to produce well reported dishes such as spring vegetable soup, stir-fried strips of beef fillet in a black bean sauce, and raspberry trifle.

MUMBLES,
Hillcrest House Hotel

Eclectic is the word here, both for decor and for cooking that might take in black bean tart with salsa and sour cream, beef kebab with Thai spiced rice and chilli sauce, haggis-stuffed steamed breast of chicken with herb sauce, and chocolate ripple ice-cream all on the same night.

Smoking: No smoking in dining room
Accommodation: 7 en suite
Credit cards: ▬ ▬ ▬

Directions: From Swansea take coast road to Mumbles. Go through village, 4th turning on L by church. On L at next crossroads.

1 Higher Lane SA3 4NS
Map 3: SS79
Tel: 01792 363700
Fax: 01792 363768
Chef/Owner: Yvonne Scott
Cost: Fixed-price D £17. ☺
H/wine £9.25.
Times: D only, 7pm-9pm.
Closed Sun, 23 Dec – 21 Jan

REYNOLDSTON, Fairyhill

The quality of the food is one of the major strengths of this charming late Victorian house, although the secluded setting in the beautiful Gower peninsula does help as well. Chef Paul Davies cooks with skill and enthusiasm, and is committed to sourcing good regional ingredients. Canapés, served in the comfortable lounge, frequently include deep-fried Penclawdd cockles; the latter may also give a savoury edge to a popular starter of free-range scrambled eggs, cockles and roasted peppers. Laverbread, another local speciality, is served in a tart with confit tomatoes or in a roulade with a gazpacho coulis. A warm salad of local skate and bacon with balsamic and sesame dressing proved a contrast in taste and textures, with delicate strips of melting skate and salty lardons on a bed of bitter leaves. Loin of venison and a venison sausage with an apple and coriander sauce, breast of Pembrokeshire duckling with roast orange sauce, and cod baked in paper with garlic, prawns and lemon, are amongst a well-balanced range of main courses. Desserts include lemon Monmouth soufflé with red berry compote, apple and Llanboidy rarebit, and a cassata Siciliana whose creamy, rich sweetness was tempered by an accompanying pool of blackcurrant coulis.

A clear, quite lengthy wine list that includes an impressive number of well priced classics in a range of vintages, plus two full pages of wines under £16 and a wide choice if the budget stretches to £25. Or why not try the ten local wines: Mewslade from Rhossili on the Gower Peninsula or Glyndwr from Llanblethian in the Vale of Glamorgan.

Signature dishes: Carpaccio of salmon with honey, lime and dill; seared loin of Welsh lamb with cawl vegetables and jus; supreme of pheasant with a dark meat sausage and cider sauce; fillet of beef with a steak and kidney pudding and sauce.

Directions: Just outside Reynoldston, off the A4118 from Swansea

SA3 1BS
Map 2: SS48
Tel: 01792 390139
Fax: 01792 391358
Chef: Paul Davies
Owners: Paul Davies, Andrew Hetherington, Jane & Peter Camm
Cost: Fixed-price L £14.50/D £29.50.
H/wine £12.50
Times: 12.30pm-last L 1.45pm/7.30pm-last D 9.15pm.
Additional: Sunday L;
No children under 8; ♿ dishes
Seats: 40. Private dining room 40
Smoking: No smoking in dining room
Accommodation: 8 en suite
Credit cards: ▬ ▬ ▬ ▬ ▬

SWANSEA, Beaumont Hotel

There's a careful hand at work in the kitchens of this personally run little hotel to the west of the city centre. The short *carte* is well balanced, with imaginative touches such as adding cockle fritters to seared monkfish with chive fish cream,

72 Walter Road SA1 4QA
Map 3: SS69
Tel: 01792 643956
Fax: 01792 643044
Chef: Jon Choolsen
Owner: JW Jones, JK Colenso

Beaumont Hotel

Cost: *Alc* £24.50, fixed-price L
£17.50/D £22.50. ☺ H/wine £10.50.
Times: Noon-last L 1.30pm/7.30pm-
last D 9.30pm. Closed Sun, L Mon
Additional: No children under 8;
❸ dishes
Seats: 40. Jacket & tie preferred
Smoking: No smoking in dining room
Accommodation: 17 en suite
Credit cards: 🔲 🔲 🔲 🔲 🔲 🔲

and combining potato with pumpkin to make a rösti for roast
quail with truffle sauce. The technical capability shows in
dishes such as quenelles of fresh salmon mousse with beetroot
crisps and delicately flavoured minted cucumber sauce, and
open ravioli of fresh fish and shellfish with a light lobster
broth. Lamb may be served in summer with an apricot mousse
and black olive sauce, or on a chill winter's day with garlic
cream sauce. Our inspector singled out the home-made rice
pudding for praise, 'creamy and thoroughly enjoyable'. Coffee
comes with cream-filled meringues. A completely new wine list
gives greater emphasis to New World wines, especially from
South America, and are listed in drinking order.

Directions: N/W of town centre on A4118, opposite St James'
Church in an area called Uplands

SWANSEA,
Windsor Lodge Hotel ❀

Mount Pleasant SA1 6EG
Map 3: SS69
Tel: 01792 642158/652744
Fax: 01792 648996
Chefs: Ron Rumble & Tina Steward
Owners: Mr & Mrs Rumble
Cost: Fixed-price L £12/D £19. ☺
H/wine £6.95.
Times: L by prior
arrangement/7.30pm-last D 9.30pm.
Closed Sun, 25-26 Dec
Additional: Bar food;
Children welcome; ❸ dishes
Smoking: No smoking in dining room
Accommodation: 19 en suite
Credit cards: 🔲 🔲 🔲 🔲 🔲 🔲

US President Jimmy Carter lunched here during the 1995 Swansea
Year of Literature, and no doubt thoroughly appreciated a menu
that included Towy salmon with chive sauce, roast rack of Welsh
lamb with a herb crust and red wine sauce and French lemon tart.
The simple, unfussy cooking is based on fresh seasonal produce.

Directions: Town centre, left at station, right immediately after
2nd set of lights

VALE OF GLAMORGAN

BARRY, **Egerton Grey Hotel**

Porthkerry CF62 3BZ
Map 3: ST16
Tel: 01446 711666
Fax: 01446 711690
Chef: Craig Brookes
Owners: Anthony & Magda Pitkin
Cost: Fixed-price L&D £18-£22
(2-3 courses). ☺ H/wine £10.50.
Times: Noon-last L 2pm/7pm-last D
9.30pm
Additional: Sunday lunch;
Children welcome; ✦ dishes
Seats: 40. Private dining room 14
Smoking: No smoking in dining room
Accommodation: 10 en suite
Credit cards: ■ ■ ■ ▓ ▓ 🔲 ℂ

Built as a rectory and private residence during Victorian times,
Egerton Grey is a gloriously peaceful retreat set in seven acres
of lush gardens at the head of a wooded valley. A short stroll
away is Porthkerry Park and the shingle beach. Lunch and
dinner are served in the splendour of the Billiard Room with
its Cuban-mahogany panelling and original cornices. It makes
an apt backdrop for assured cooking with elaborate overtones.
The complex style is evident in dishes such as fillet of cod with
a lemon and red pepper crust on braised fennel with leek and
crab butter sauce, or tender medallions of beef served on
bubble and squeak with pancetta, shallots and whisky jus.
Simpler offerings, such as rich shellfish bisque, have also
pleased. Desserts include such inviting ideas as sticky toffee
and coconut pudding served on butterscotch sauce. The global
wine list has been put together with help from Averys of
Bristol.

Directions: M4/J33, follow signs for Airport then Porthkerry, & L
at hotel sign by thatched cottage

WREXHAM

MARCHWIEL, **Cross Lanes Hotel**

Cross Lanes
Bangor Road LL13 0TF
Tel: 01978 780555
Fax: 01978 780568
Chef: Ian Chapman
Owner: Michael Kagan
Cost: *Alc* £22, fixed-price L £12.50/
D £19.50. ☺ H/wine £9.45.
Times: Last L 1.50pm/D 9.15pm.
Closed L Sat
Additional: Bar Food; Sunday L;
Children welcome; ✦ dishes
Smoking: No-smoking area;
no pipes & cigars
Accommodation: 16 en suite
Credit cards: ■ ■ ■ ▓ ▓ 🔲 ℂ

*Victorian hotel with some Jacobean oak panelling, lovely grounds,
and a licence for civil marriages. Decent cooking offers the likes of
filed mushrooms stuffed with onions, bacon, Parmesan and tomato,
noisettes of lamb wrapped in bacon on a bed of root vegetables with
juniper and redcurrant sauce, and plum tart with rich custard.*

Directions: 3 miles SE of Wrexham on A525

ROSSETT, Llyndir Hall Hotel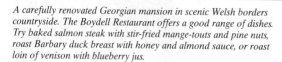

LL12 0AY
Map 7: SJ35
Tel: 01244 571648
Fax: 01244 571258
Chef: Jeremy Stone
Owner: Celebrated Group plc
Cost: *Alc* £25, fixed-price L £14.50/
D £18.95 (4 courses). ☺
H/wine £12.50.
Times: Last L 2pm/D 9.30pm
Closed L Sat
Additional: Bar Food; Sunday L;
Children welcome; ⬩ dishes

*There is no lack of choice at this comfortable, modern hotel on the
English/Welsh border. Amongst the rather ambitious ten starters and
main courses are lobster and crab bisque glazed with a Dijon
mustard sabayon, and honey-glazed duck breast topped with a
spaghetti of root vegetables, apple and potato cake and tangy lemon
grass sauce.*

Smoking: No smoking in dining room; air-conditioning
Accommodation: 38 en suite
Credit cards: ▬ ▥ ▦ ▧ ▨ ▩

Directions: S from Chester on A483 to Wrexham, follow signs
for Pulford/Rossett B5445. Llyndir Hall signed on the R

ROSSETT, Rossett Hall Hotel

Chester Road LL12 0DE
Map 7: SJ35
Tel: 01244 571000
Fax: 01244 571505
Chef: David Hadfield
Cost: *Alc* £20, fixed-price D £18.50.
☺ H/wine £9.25.
Times: Last L 2pm/D 9.30pm.
Closed L Sat
Additional: Sunday L; Bar meals L;
Children welcome; ⬩ dishes

*A carefully renovated Georgian mansion in scenic Welsh borders
countryside. The Boydell Restaurant offers a good range of dishes.
Try baked salmon steak with stir-fried mange-touts and pine nuts,
roast Barbary duck breast with honey and almond sauce, or roast
loin of venison with blueberry jus.*

Smoking: No smoking in dining room
Accommodation: 30 en suite
Credit cards: ▬ ▥ ▦ ▧ ▨ ▩

Directions: M56, take M53 to Wrexham – becomes A55. Take
A483 Chester/Wrexham exit to Rossett (B5445). Hotel in centre
of village

Greater London

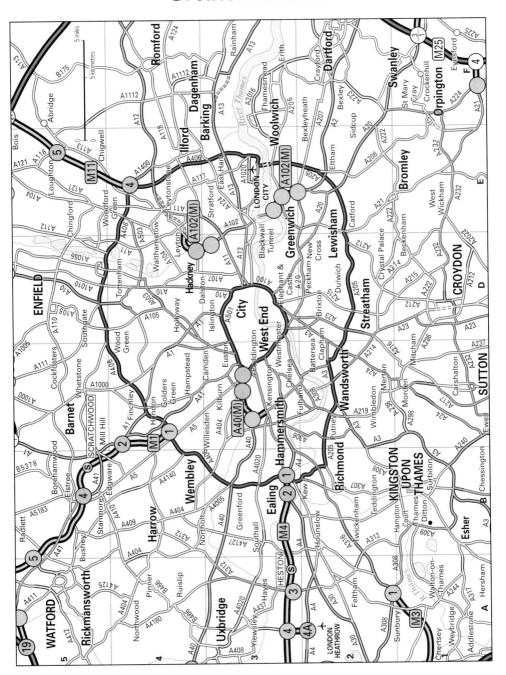

Central London

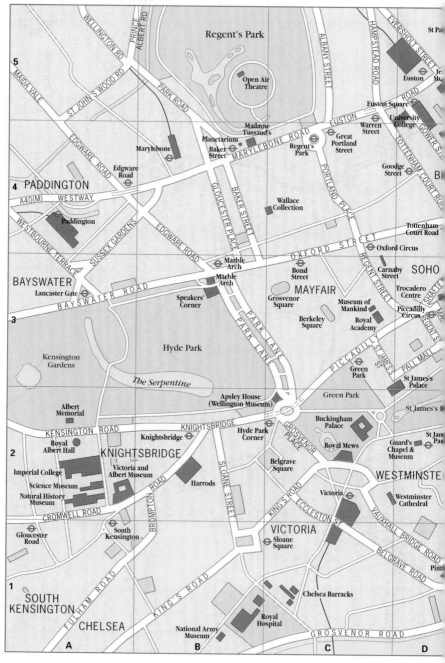

Regent's Park

Open Air Theatre

St Pa

5

WELLINGTON RD
PRINCE ALBERT RD
ALBANY STREET
HAMPSTEAD ROAD
EVERSHOLT STREET

MAIDA VALE

ST JOHN'S WOOD RD

PARK ROAD

Euston
Je
Mu

EUSTON ROAD

Euston Square

University College

EDGWARE ROAD

Madame Tussaud's

Planetarium

Marylebone

Baker Street

MARYLEBONE ROAD

Warren Street

Great Portland Street

Regent's Park

GOWER S.

TOTTENHAM COURT RD

Edgware Road

Goodge Street

B

PORTLAND PLACE

4 PADDINGTON

A40(M)   WESTWAY

Wallace Collection

GLOUCESTER PLACE

BAKER STREET

WESTBOURNE TERRACE

Paddington

SUSSEX GARDENS

EDGWARE ROAD

Tottenham Court Road

OXFORD   STREET

Oxford Circus

REGENT STREET

Marble Arch

Bond Street

Carnaby Street   SOHO

BAYSWATER

Lancaster Gate

BAYSWATER   ROAD

Marble Arch

Speakers' Corner

Grosvenor Square

MAYFAIR

Museum of Mankind

Trocadero Centre

SHAFT

3

Berkeley Square

Royal Academy

Piccadilly Circus

REGENT S

Kensington Gardens

Hyde Park

PARK LANE

The Serpentine

Apsley House (Wellington Museum)

PICCADILLY

Green Park

ST JAMES'S

PALL MALL

St James's Palace

Green Park

St James's

Albert Memorial

KENSINGTON   ROAD

KNIGHTSBRIDGE

Hyde Park Corner

Buckingham Palace

GROSVENOR PLACE

St Jan
Pa

2

Royal Albert Hall

Knightsbridge

Royal Mews

Guard's Chapel & Museum

WESTMINSTE

Imperial College

KNIGHTSBRIDGE

Victoria and Albert Museum

SLOANE STREET

Belgrave Square

Science Museum

Harrods

Victoria

Westminster Cathedral

Natural History Museum

BROMPTON ROAD

CROMWELL ROAD

Gloucester Road

South Kensington

KING'S ROAD

ECCLESTON ST

VICTORIA

VAUXHALL BRIDGE ROAD

Sloane Square

BELGRAVE ROAD

Pim

1

SOUTH KENSINGTON

FULHAM ROAD

CHELSEA

KING'S ROAD

Chelsea Barracks

National Army Museum

Royal Hospital

GROSVENOR   ROAD

A   B   C   D

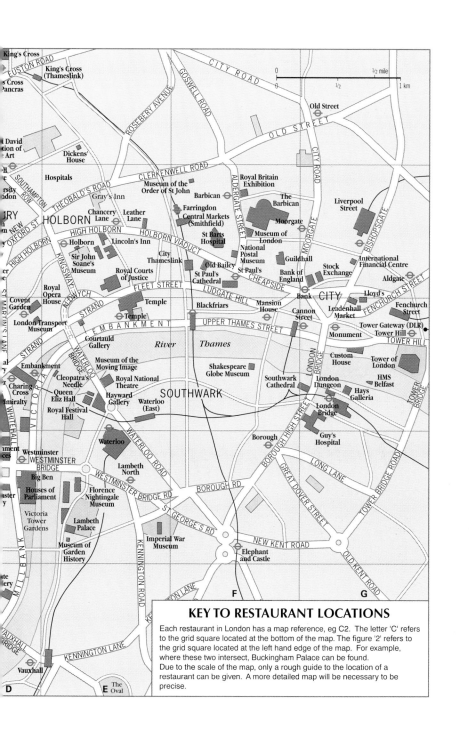

King's Cross
EUSTON ROAD
King's Cross
(Thameslink)
's Cross
Pancras
CITY ROAD
0
½ mile
GOSWELL ROAD
½
1 km
Old Street
ROSEBERY AVENUE
OLD STREET
David
tion of
Art
Dickens'
House
CITY ROAD
H
e
rsity
don
Hospitals
CLERKENWELL ROAD
Royal Britain
Exhibition
SOUTHAMPTON ROW
THEOBALD'S ROAD
Museum of the
Order of St John
ALDERGATE STREET
Gray's Inn
Barbican
The
Barbican
Liverpool
Street
BISHOPSGATE
JRY
HOLBORN
Chancery
Lane
Leather
Lane
Farringdon
Central Markets
(Smithfield)
Moorgate
RY NEW OXFORD ST
HIGH HOLBORN
St Barts
Hospital
Museum of
London
MOORGATE
HOLBORN VIADUCT
HIGH HOLBORN
y OXFORD HOLBORN
Holborn
Lincoln's Inn
National
Postal
Museum
International
Financial Centre
Sir John
Soane's
Museum
City
Thameslink
Old Bailey
Guildhall
Stock
Exchange
er
Royal Courts
of Justice
St Paul's
St Paul's
Cathedral
Bank of
England
Aldgate
CHEAPSIDE
ST MARTIN'S LN
Royal
Opera
House
ALDWYCH
FLEET STREET
LUDGATE HILL
Bank
CITY
Lloyd's
FENCHURCH STREET
Covent
Garden
STRAND
Temple
Blackfriars
Mansion
House
Cannon
Street
Leadenhall
Market
Fenchurch
Street
London Transport
Museum
KINGSWAY
Temple
EMBANKMENT
UPPER THAMES STREET
Monument
Tower Gateway (DLR)
Tower Hill
TOWER HILL
STRAND
WATERLOO BRIDGE
Courtauld
Gallery
River   Thames
LONDON BRIDGE
Custom
House
Tower of
London
al
y
Embankment
VICTORIA
Museum of the
Moving Image
Cleopatra's
Needle
Shakespeare
Globe Museum
Southwark
Cathedral
London
Dungeon
HMS
Belfast
TOWER BRIDGE
Charing
Cross
miralty
WHITEHALL
Queen
Eliz Hall
Royal Festival
Hall
Royal National
Theatre
Hayward
Gallery
Waterloo
(East)
SOUTHWARK
Hays
Galleria
London
Bridge
Waterloo
WATERLOO ROAD
Borough
BOROUGH HIGH STREET
Guy's
Hospital
ment
ces
Westminster
WESTMINSTER
BRIDGE
Lambeth
North
LONG LANE
GREAT DOVER STREET
Big Ben
WESTMINSTER BRIDGE RD
Florence
Nightingale
Museum
BOROUGH RD
TOWER BRIDGE ROAD
aster
y
Houses of
Parliament
ST GEORGE'S RD
Victoria
Tower
Gardens
Lambeth
Palace
MILLBANK
Museum of
Garden
History
Imperial War
Museum
NEW KENT ROAD
Elephant
and Castle
OLD KENT ROAD
te
ery
KENNINGTON ROAD
ON LANE
F
G
VAUXHALL BRIDGE
Vauxhall
KENNINGTON LANE
D
E
The
Oval

KEY TO RESTAURANT LOCATIONS

Each restaurant in London has a map reference, eg C2. The letter 'C' refers
to the grid square located at the bottom of the map. The figure '2' refers to
the grid square located at the left hand edge of the map. For example,
where these two intersect, Buckingham Palace can be found.
Due to the scale of the map, only a rough guide to the location of a
restaurant can be given. A more detailed map will be necessary to be
precise.

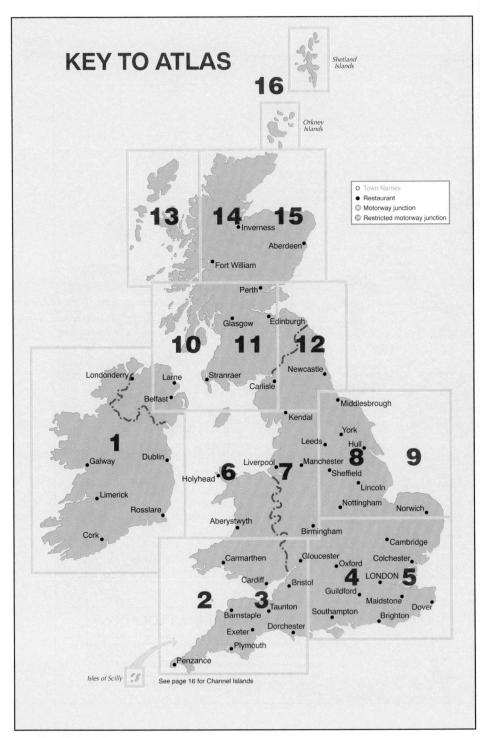

KEY TO ATLAS

Shetland Islands

16

Orkney Islands

O Town Names
● Restaurant
⊕ Motorway junction
⊕ Restricted motorway junction

13   **14** **15**
●Inverness

Aberdeen●

●Fort William

Perth●

Glasgow● Edinburgh●

10   **11**   **12**

Londonderry●   ●Larne   ●Stranraer   Newcastle●
            Belfast●   Carlisle●

                                        ●Kendal   Middlesbrough●

1   York●
                                          Leeds●   Hull●
Galway●   Dublin●   Liverpool● Manchester● **8**   **9**
                    Holyhead● **6**   **7** Sheffield●
●Limerick   ●Lincoln
            Rosslare●   Nottingham●   Norwich●
                   Aberystwyth●
Cork●   Birmingham●   ●Cambridge
                    Carmarthen●   Gloucester●   Colchester●
                      Cardiff● Oxford●
                              ●Bristol   **4** LONDON **5**
2 **3**Taunton   Guildford●
      Barnstaple●   Southampton● Maidstone●   Dover●
       Exeter● Dorchester●   Brighton●
          ●Plymouth
       ●Penzance

Isles of Scilly   See page 16 for Channel Islands

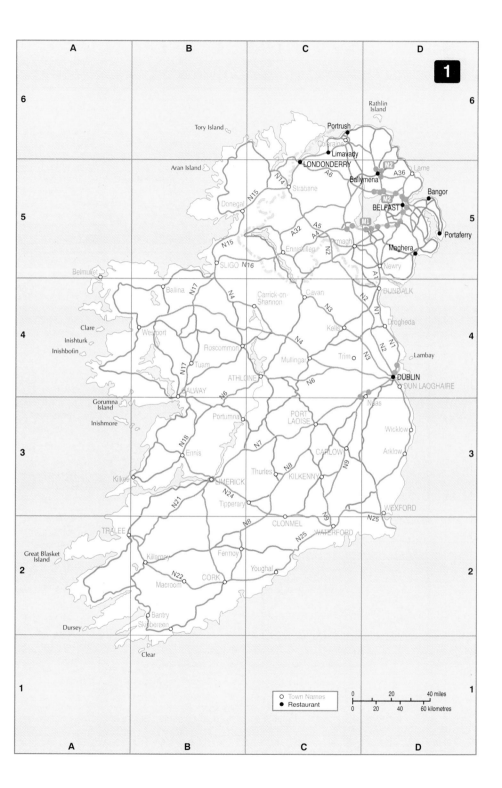

A B C D

6 6

Rathlin
Island

Tory Island

Portrush

Coleraine
Limavady
LONDONDERRY
Aran Island
A6
Ballymena
M2
Larne
A36

Donegal
N14
Strabane
BELFAST
M2
Bangor
Portaferry

5 5

N15

N15
A32
A5
A4
M1
Armagh
N2
Enniskillen
Maghera

Belmullet
SLIGO
N16
Newry
A1

Ballina
N17
Carrick-on-
Shannon
Cavan
DUNDALK

Clare
N4
N3
Drogheda

4 4
Inishturk
Westport
Kells
Inishbofin
Roscommon
N4
Lambay

Tuam
Mullingar
Trim
N3
N1
N2

N17
ATHLONE
N6
DUBLIN
DUN LAOGHAIRE

Gorumna
Island
GALWAY
N6
Naas

Inishmore
Portumna
PORT
LAOISE
Wicklow

3 3
N18
Ennis
N7
CARLOW
Arklow

Kilkee
Thurles
N8
KILKENNY
N9

N24
Tipperary
WEXFORD
N21
N25

TRALEE
N8
CLONMEL
N25
WATERFORD
N9

2 2
Great Blasket
Island
Killarney
Fermoy
Youghal

Macroom
N22
CORK

Dursey
Bantry
Skibbereen

Clear

1 1

○ Town Names
● Restaurant

0   20   40 miles
0   20   40   60 kilometres

A B C D

1

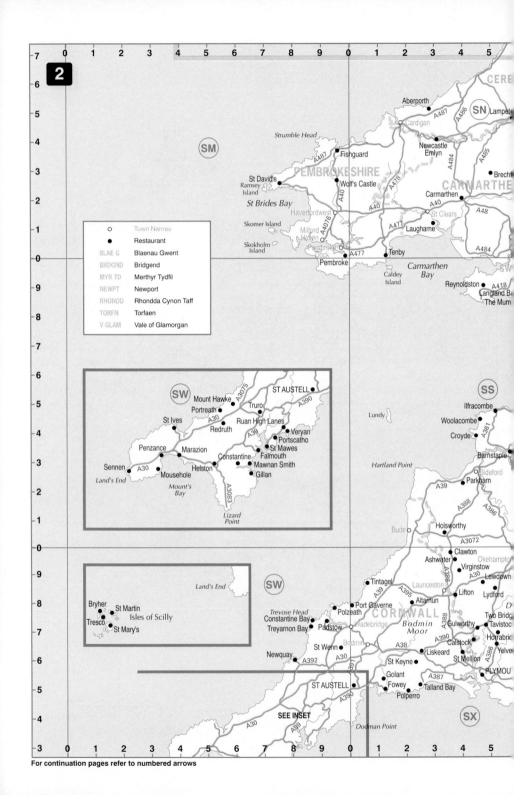

2

CERE

Aberporth

SN Lampet

A487 A486

Strumble Head

SM

Newcastle Emlyn

A484 A485

Fishguard

A487

Brech

St David's

PEMBROKESHIRE

A478

CARMARTHE

Ramsey Island

Wolf's Castle

A40

Carmarthen

St Brides Bay

Haverfordwest

A40

St Clears

A48

A40

Skomer Island

Milford Haven

A4076

A471

Laugharne

A484

Skokholm Island

Pembroke Dock

A477

Tenby

Pembroke

Carmarthen Bay

SW

Caldey Island

Reynoldston

A418

Langland B

The Mum

○	Town Names
●	Restaurant
BLAE G	Blaenau Gwent
BRDGND	Bridgend
MYR TD	Merthyr Tydfil
NEWPT	Newport
RHONDD	Rhondda Cynon Taff
TORFN	Torfaen
V GLAM	Vale of Glamorgan

SW

Mount Hawke

A3075

ST AUSTELL

SS

Portreath

Truro

A390

Ilfracombe

St Ives

Ruan High Lanes

Lundy

Woolacombe

Redruth

A39

Veryan

Croyde

A361

Portscatho

Penzance

Marazion

Constantine

St Mawes

Barnstaple

Falmouth

Sennen

A30

Helston

Mawnan Smith

Hartland Point

Bideford

Mousehole

Gillan

A39

Parkham

Land's End

Mount's Bay

A3083

A388

A386

Lizard Point

Bude

Holsworthy

A3072

Clawton

Ashwater

Okehampto

SW

Virginstow

A30

Lewdown

Land's End

SW

Tintagel

Launceston

A395

Lifton

Lydford

Bryher

St Martin

Isles of Scilly

Trevose Head

Polzeath

Port Gaverne

Altarnun

A39

A388

Two Bridg

Tresco

St Mary's

Constantine Bay

CORNWALL

Gulworthy

Tavistoc

Treyarnon Bay

Padstow

Wadebridge

Bodmin Moor

A390

Hobrabrie

Newquay

St Wenn

Bodmin

A38

Calstock

A386

Yelve

A392

A30

St Keyne

Liskeard

St Mellion

PLYMOU

Golant

A387

ST AUSTELL

Fowey

Talland Bay

A390

Polperro

SX

SEE INSET

A30

A399

Dodman Point

For continuation pages refer to numbered arrows

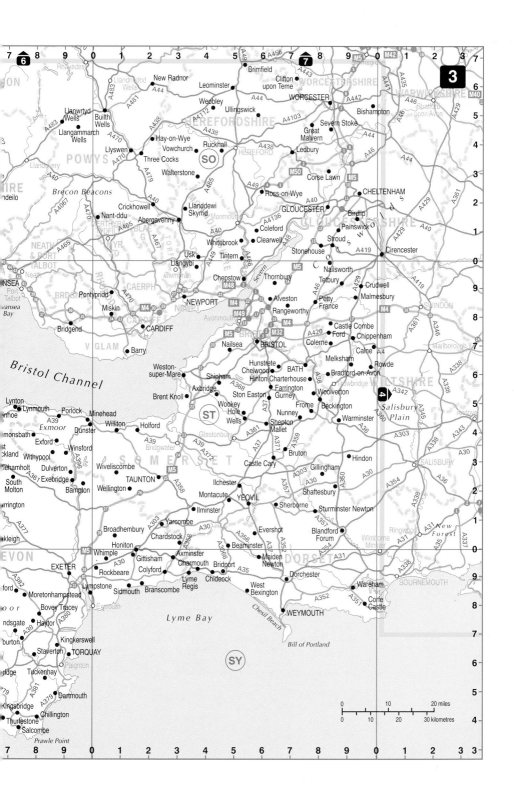

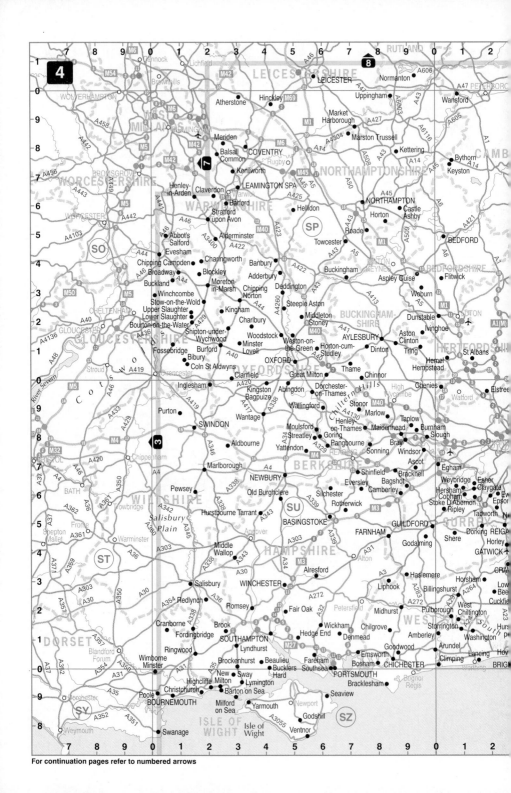

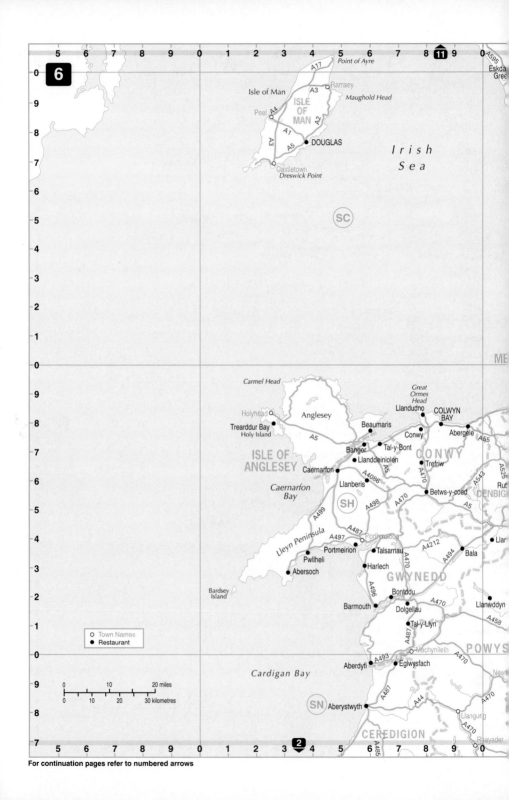

5   6   7   8   9   0   1   2   3   4   5   6   7   8   9   0   A595

6

A17
Point of Ayre
Eskda
Gree

Isle of Man   A3 Ramsey
ISLE   Maughold Head
OF
Peel A4 MAN
A1   A2
A3   A5
DOUGLAS

*I r i s h
S e a*

Castletown
Dreswick Point

SC

ME

Carmel Head
Great
Ormes
Head
Holyhead   Anglesey   Llandudno   COLWYN
BAY
Trearddur Bay   Beaumaris
Holy Island   Conwy   Abergele   A55
A5   Bangor Tal-y-Bont   CONWY
Llanddeiniolen   Trefriw   A525
ISLE OF   Caernarfon   A4086   A470   A543   Rut
ANGLESEY   Llanberis   Betws-y-coed   DENBIG
Caernarfon   SH   A498   A470   A5
Bay   A470
A499   A5
A487   Llar
Lleyn Peninsula   A497 Porthmadog   A4212   A494   Bala
Portmeirion   Talsarnau
Pwllheli   Harlech   GWYNEDD
Abersoch   A496   Bontddu
Bardsey   Barmouth   Dolgellau   Llanwddyn
Island   A470   A458
Tal-y-Llyn
A487

O Town Names   Machynlleth   POWYS
● Restaurant   Aberdyfi   A493 Eglwysfach   A470

0   10   20 miles   *Cardigan Bay*   New
0   10   20   30 kilometres   A487   A44   A470
SN Aberystwyth
Llangurig

CEREDIGION   A470
Rhayader

5   6   7   8   9   0   1   2   3   4   5   6   7   8   9   0
A485

2
For continuation pages refer to numbered arrows

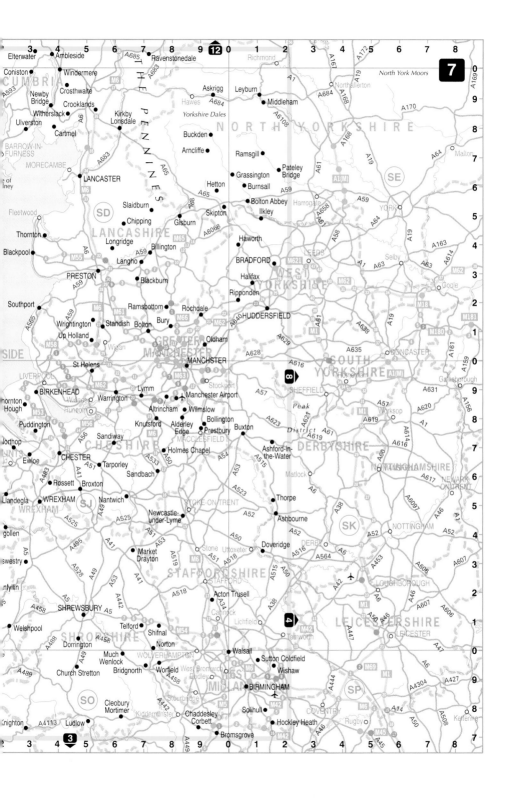

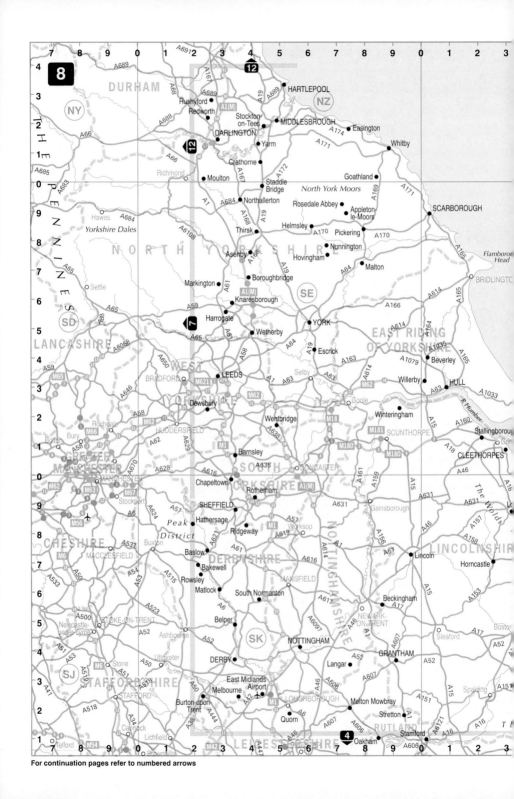

For continuation pages refer to numbered arrows

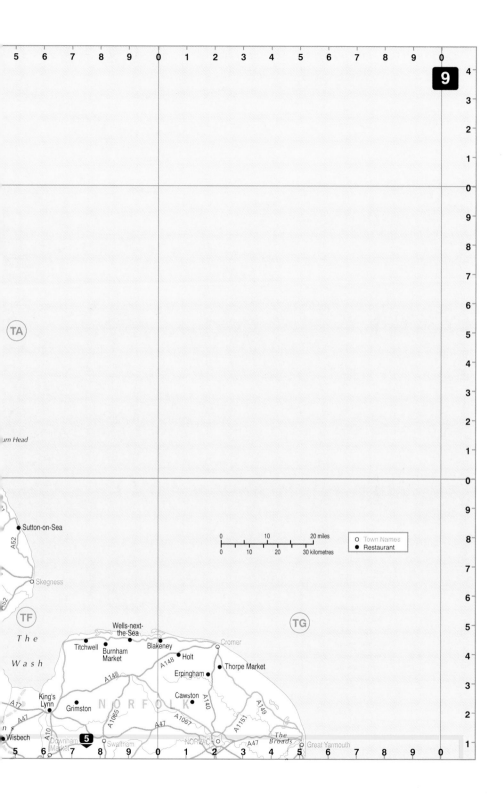

9

5 6 7 8 9 0 1 2 3 4 5 6 7 8 9 0

4
3
2
1
0
9
8
7
6

TA

5
4
3
2
1
0

urn Head

9

• Sutton-on-Sea

8

A52

7

o Skegness

6

TF

Wells-next-
the-Sea

The   Titchwell   Burnham   • Blakeney   o Cromer
•   Market   • Holt
Wash   A148   • Thorpe Market
              A148   Erpingham •
                                Cawston •
King's   A140
Lynn   Grimston   N O R F O L K   A149
                    A1065   A1067
                    A47
• Wisbech   Downham   5   Swaffham   A47   The   o Great Yarmouth
  Market   Market   NORWICH o   Broads

5 6 7 8 9 0 1 2 3 4 5 6 7 8 9 0

	0	10	20 miles
	0	10	20	30 kilometres

o Town Names
• Restaurant

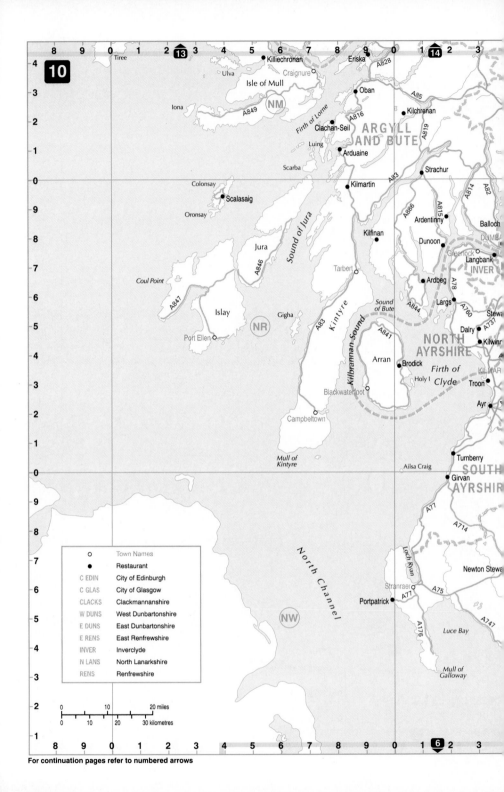

10

Tiree
Killiechronan
Eriska
A828

Ulva
Craignure
Oban
A85

Isle of Mull
Kilchrenan
A819

Iona
A849
NM

Firth of Lorne
A816
Clachan-Seil
ARGYLL
AND BUTE

Luing
Arduaine
Strachur

Scarba
A83

Colonsay
Kilmartin
A814
A82

Scalasaig
A886
A815

Oronsay
Ardentinny
Balloch

Kilfinan
Dunoon
DUMB

Jura
Greenock
Langbank
INVER

A846
Tarbert
Ardbeg
A78

Coul Point
A847
Sound
of Bute
A844
Largs
A760
Stewa

Islay
Gigha
NR
Dalry
A737

Port Ellen
A83
Kilbrannan Sound
A841
NORTH
AYRSHIRE
Kilwinn

Arran
Brodick
Firth of
KILMAR

Blackwaterfoot
Holy I
Clyde
Troon

Campbeltown
Ayr

Mull of
Kintyre
Turnberry

Ailsa Craig
SOUTH
Girvan
AYRSHIR

A71

A714

North Channel

Loch Ryan
Newton Stewa

Stranraer
A77
A75

Portpatrick
A77

NW
A176
Luce Bay
A747

Mull of
Galloway

○	Town Names
●	Restaurant
C EDIN	City of Edinburgh
C GLAS	City of Glasgow
CLACKS	Clackmannanshire
W DUNS	West Dunbartonshire
E DUNS	East Dunbartonshire
E RENS	East Renfrewshire
INVER	Inverclyde
N LANS	North Lanarkshire
RENS	Renfrewshire

0   10   20 miles
0   10   20   30 kilometres

For continuation pages refer to numbered arrows

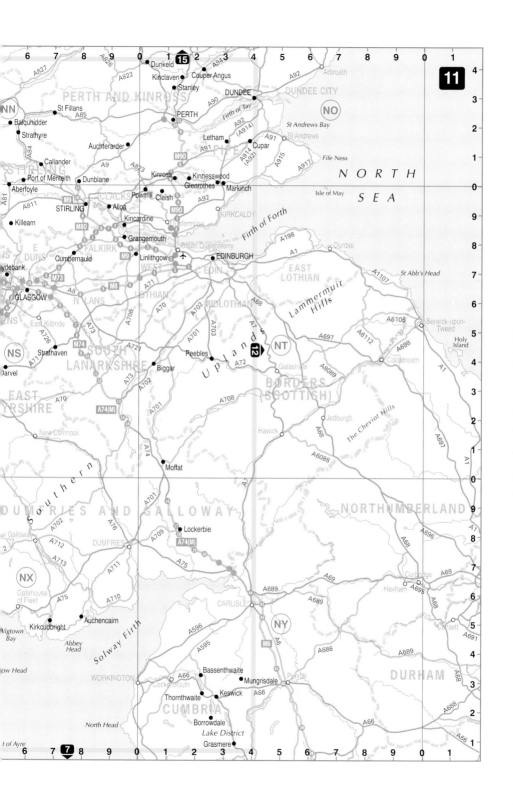

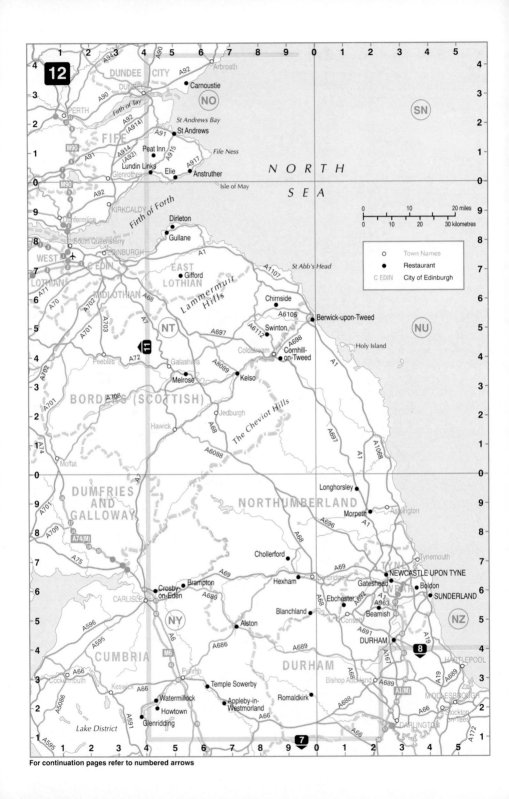

For continuation pages refer to numbered arrows

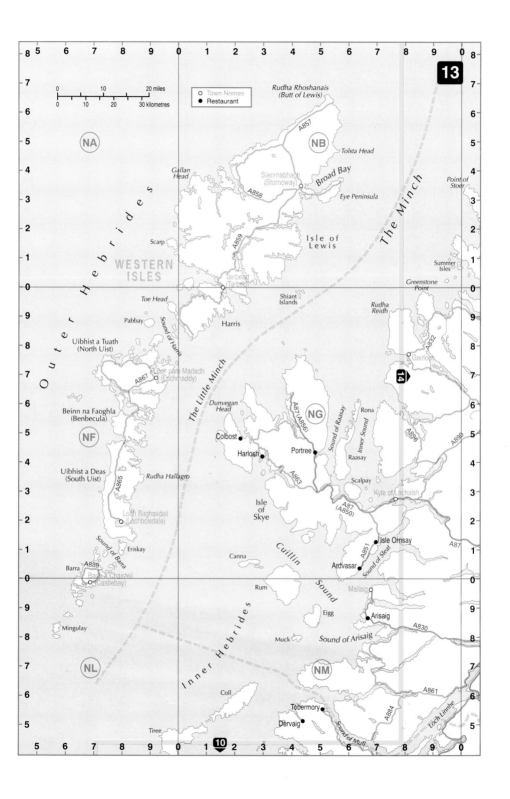

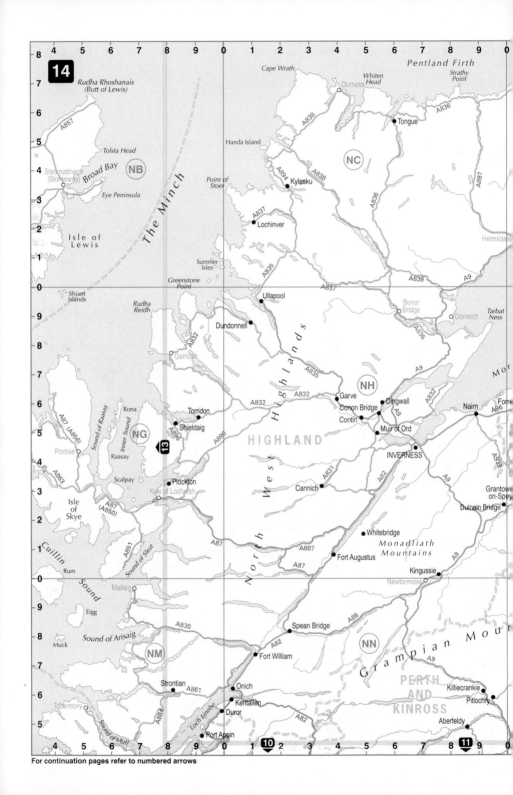

Rudha Rhoshanais
(Butt of Lewis)

Pentland Firth

Cape Wrath
Whiten Head
Strathy Point
Durness

A838

A836

Tongue

Tolsta Head

Broad Bay

NB

Handa Island

NC

A897

Steornabhagh
(Stornoway)

Eye Peninsula

A857

The Minch

Point of Stoer

A694
Kylesku

A838

A836

Helmsdale

Isle of
Lewis

A837

Lochinver

A836

Summer Isles

Shiant Islands

Greenstone Point

Rudha Reidh

A835

A837

Bonar Bridge

Dornoch

Tarbat Ness

Ullapool

A839

A9

Dundonnell

Gairloch

A832

North West Highlands

A835

A9

Mor

Rona

Torridon

Shieldaig

A832

A832

Garve

Dingwall

NH

Nairn

Forr
A96

A87 (A855)

Portree

Sound of Raasay

NG

Inner Sound

A896

A890

13

Conon Bridge
Contin

A9

A832

Raasay

HIGHLAND

Muir of Ord

A832

Scalpay

Plockton

A87
(A850)

Kyle of Lochalsh

INVERNESS

A939

Isle of
Skye

A883

Cuillin
Sound

Rum

A851

Sound of Sleat

A87

Cannich

A831

A82

A9

Grantown-on-Spey

Dulnain Bridge

Whitebridge

A887

Monadliath
Mountains

A9

Mallaig

A87

Fort Augustus

Eigg

Kingussie

Newtonmore

Sound of Arisaig

A830

NM

Muck

Spean Bridge

A86

NN

Grampian Mou

Fort William

A82

Strontian

A861

Onich

Kentallen

Duror

A82

PERTH
AND
KINROSS

Killiecrankie

Pitlochry

Tobermory

A884

Loch Linnhe

Sound of Mull

Port Appin

10

11

Aberfeldy

For continuation pages refer to numbered arrows

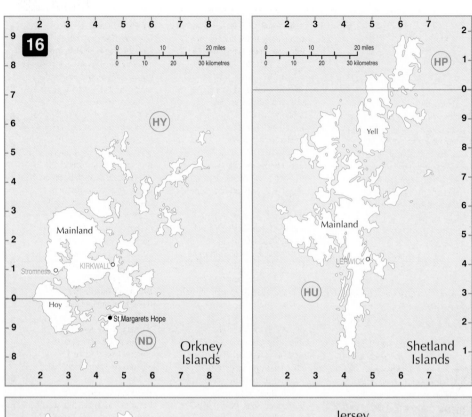

20 miles
30 kilometres

HY

Mainland

Stromness   KIRKWALL

Hoy

St Margarets Hope

ND

Orkney
Islands

20 miles
30 kilometres

HP

Yell

Mainland

LERWICK

HU

Shetland
Islands

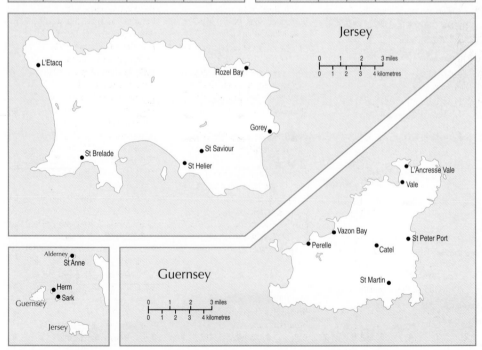

Jersey

L'Etacq

Rozel Bay

Gorey

St Saviour

St Brelade

St Helier

3 miles
4 kilometres

Alderney
St Anne

Herm
Sark

Guernsey

Jersey

Guernsey

L'Ancresse Vale

Vale

Vazon Bay

Perelle

St Peter Port

Catel

St Martin

3 miles
4 kilometres

Index

Reader's Recommendations

If you have recently eaten well at a restaurant that is not included in this guide, we should be interested to hear about it. Please send this form to Head of Guidebooks, Editorial Department, AA Publishing, Fanum House, Basingstoke RG21 4EA.

Recommendations, and/or any adverse comments will be carefully considered, and passed on to our Hotel & Restaurant inspectors, but the AA cannot guarantee to act on them nor to enter into correspondence about them. Complaints are best brought to the attention to the management of the restaurant at the time, so that they can be dealt with promptly and, it is hoped, to the satisfaction of both parties.

Your name and address

....

....

....

....

....

....

Name and address of the restaurant

....

....

....

....

Was the meal lunch or dinner?

....

....

Approximate cost for two £

....

(continued over)

Type of cuisine English/French/Italian/Thai/Indian/Chinese/Other (please specify)

....
....
....
....

Comments

....
....
....
....
....
....
....
....
....
....
....
....
....
....
....
....
....
....
....
....
....
....
....
....

Reader's Recommendations

If you have recently eaten well at a restaurant that is not included in this guide, we should be interested to hear about it. Please send this form to Head of Guidebooks, Editorial Department, AA Publishing, Fanum House, Basingstoke RG21 4EA.

Recommendations, and/or any adverse comments will be carefully considered, and passed on to our Hotel & Restaurant inspectors, but the AA cannot guarantee to act on them nor to enter into correspondence about them. Complaints are best brought to the attention to the management of the restaurant at the time, so that they can be dealt with promptly and, it is hoped, to the satisfaction of both parties.

Your name and address

....
....
....
....
....

Name and address of the restaurant

....
....
....
....

Was the meal lunch or dinner?

....
....

Approximate cost for two £

....

(continued over)

Type of cuisine English/French/Italian/Thai/Indian/Chinese/Other (please specify)

Comments

Reader's Recommendations

If you have recently eaten well at a restaurant that is not included in this guide, we should be interested to hear about it. Please send this form to Head of Guidebooks, Editorial Department, AA Publishing, Fanum House, Basingstoke RG21 4EA.

Recommendations, and/or any adverse comments will be carefully considered, and passed on to our Hotel & Restaurant inspectors, but the AA cannot guarantee to act on them nor to enter into correspondence about them. Complaints are best brought to the attention to the management of the restaurant at the time, so that they can be dealt with promptly and, it is hoped, to the satisfaction of both parties.

Your name and address

....
....
....
....
....
....

Name and address of the restaurant

....
....
....
....
....

Was the meal lunch or dinner?

....
....

Approximate cost for two £

....

(continued over)

Type of cuisine English/French/Italian/Thai/Indian/Chinese/Other (please specify)

....

....

....

....

....

Comments

....

....

....

....

....

....

....

....

....

....

....

....

....

....

....

....

....

....

....

....

....

....